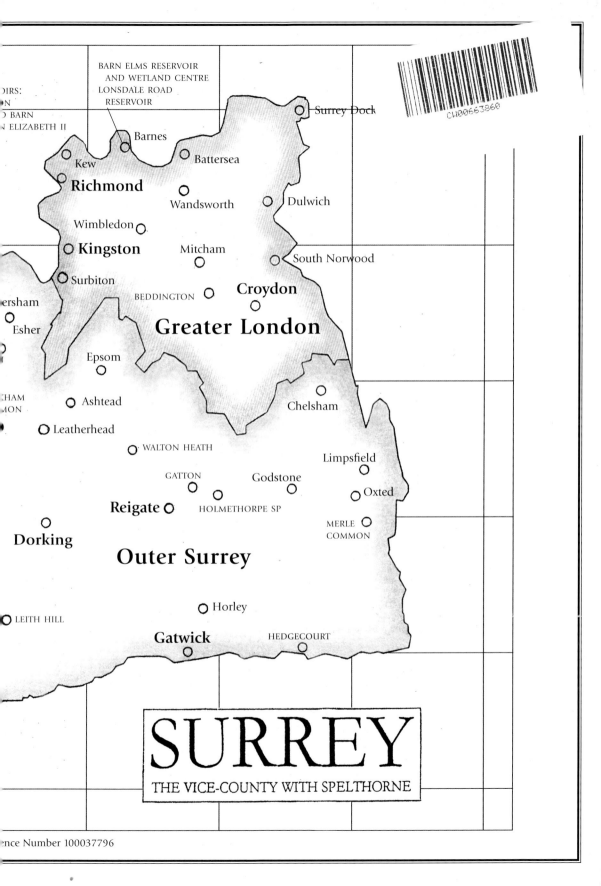

RESERVOIRS:
?N
O BARN
N ELIZABETH II

BARN ELMS RESERVOIR
AND WETLAND CENTRE
LONSDALE ROAD
RESERVOIR

Barnes

Kew

Richmond

Battersea

Wandsworth

Surrey Dock

Dulwich

Wimbledon

Kingston

Mitcham

South Norwood

Surbiton

BEDDINGTON

Croydon

Greater London

ersham

Esher

Epsom

Chelsham

CHAM
MON

Ashtead

Leatherhead

WALTON HEATH

GATTON

Limpsfield

Godstone

Reigate

HOLMETHORPE SP

Oxted

MERLE
COMMON

Dorking

Outer Surrey

Horley

LEITH HILL

Gatwick

HEDGECOURT

SURREY

THE VICE-COUNTY WITH SPELTHORNE

Birds of Surrey

Devil's Punch Bowl. Dartford Warbler numbers have increased as a result of heathland restoration measures. Pied Flycatchers have been seen in recent autumns.

John Davis

Birds of Surrey

Jeffery J. Wheatley

Principal Artist John Davis

Additional drawings by
Paul Carney, Alan Harris, Ernest Leahy, David Nurney,
John Reaney and Jan P. P. Wilczur

Surrey Bird Club

Published in 2007 by the Surrey Bird Club
Aerial photography by Flight Images
Printed by Ian Allan Printing Ltd, Hersham
Surrey KT12 4RG

ISBN 978-0-901963-08-6

British Library Cataloguing-in-Publication data. A catalogue record for this book is available from the British Library.

Contents

Publication of this book was made possible by
generous financial support from:

British Airways Environment Fund
Haslemere Natural History Society
Thames Water plc
and a private donor.

We also thank Penny Hollow for considerable help with fundraising.

Acknowledgements

The staff of the Booth Museum of Natural History at Brighton have been helpful in providing access to Surrey specimens that they hold. The British Trust for Ornithology has supplied excellent Surrey information for the 1981-84 *Winter Atlas*, the Common Birds Census, the Garden Bird Survey, the 1994-2004 Breeding Bird Survey and a summary of bird ringing recoveries. Peter Lack of the BTO and Keith Herber helped in the interpretation of the *Winter Atlas* information. Mike Toms and Mike Raven of the BTO have been similarly helpful with the Garden Birds Survey and the Breeding Birds Survey respectively. Hugh Evans, BTO Representative for Surrey, has been splendid in locating sources and in providing information about Egyptian Geese in Spelthorne.

Cyril Walker was adept in locating information about the earliest Surrey bird fossil, *Gastornis klaasseni*. The Natural History Museum, through Sandra Chapman and Hilary Smith, went to some trouble to provide the *Gastornis* photographs used in this volume.

The Haslemere Museum has been an invaluable source of information, including access to historic Surrey specimens such as a Pratincole, documentation of the egg and skins collections, the records of the Frensham Watchers, an excellent document collection and a fine library, from which the works of Dresser and Walpole Bond have been especially valuable.

The London Biodiversity Audit Team have supplied a great deal of useful information about land use in the London Boroughs of Croydon, Kingston upon Thames, Lambeth, Merton, Richmond upon Thames, Southwark, Sutton and Wandsworth.

Many others have assisted with details of the task. John Birkett carried out research on Cherry Kearton's Kenley property. Jonathan Bowley added the Little Bustard and the Dark-breasted Barn Owl to the Surrey list by finding the only Surrey records of them in a Sussex avifauna and also for finding an account of an Alpine Accentor and for comments on a Red-footed Falcon and a Turnstone. Much time has been saved by the use of bound copies of Surrey Bird Reports (1953-88) obtained from Thelma Chappell, for which many thanks.

M. J. Cowlard, has been very helpful in correcting the accounts of breeding Honey Buzzards and Goshawks. Canada Geese have benefited from research by N. J. Donnithorne. Steve P. Dudley, BOU Administrator clarified the status of Barrow's Goldeneye. S. W. Gale assisted with records at Holmethorpe, David Griffin helped with ringing and Ring-necked Parakeet information. Keith J. Herber helped with the history of the Runnymede Ringing Group. Penny Hollow (neé Kirkpatrick) found a report of breeding Ospreys. Arthur James provided new information about the history of Ring-necked Parakeets. R. H. Kettle provided a valuable critique of the section on sound recording. Dr Alan Knox has been helpful with a problem Nutcracker. Barry A. Marsh helped with the Common Nighthawk and the Richmond Park divers. Henry McGhie of the Manchester Museum provided information on the Slender-billed Nutcracker. Vivienne Oakley was generous with her time in providing access to the Holmesdale Natural History Club's Museum and records. Alan D. Prowse provided information about Bookham Common, John Richardson located the 1841 Alpine Swift in the Booth Museum. John A. Sage has helped with *British Birds* research and provided breeding information for Egyptian Geese. William Salmon provided information about a Cormorant roost at Hedgecourt. Brian Thomas researched records of the Epsom College Natural History Society and other local material. Sir Richard Thornton has been helpful with information about the Long family.

Thanks are due to Jenny Blaker for providing access to the papers of George B. Blaker and to Wesley

Attridge for help with them. John Clark has given very substantial assistance with west Surrey heathland records. Shaun Peters provided information on the Chestnut Mannikin and gave much other help in other ways. David Holloway and Shirley Corke (both of Charterhouse School) have been very helpful in providing access to the Charterhouse Collection and its records. Ian Merling-Blake has provided a useful commentary on its history. John Greig and Mavis Barber have been helpful in matters relating to the Croydon Natural History and Scientific Society. Kenneth Noble and Christopher Welsh have helped in locating old place names,

Information for the Atlas maps includes records which were collected in marginal and overlap areas by members of the Berkshire Atlas Group, the Hants/Surrey Border Bird Report group, the Haslemere Natural History Society, the London Natural History Society, the Surbiton and District Bird Watching Society and the Sussex Ornithological Society. They were made available by collaboration or exchange. The Atlas maps were produced by using Dr Alan Morton's excellent DMap software.

The artwork is a special feature of the book. Particular thanks are due to John Davis, Principal Artist, for his fine paintings of some of the main bird sites in Surrey. There is a way in which paintings and drawings can tell more, by attention to relevant detail, than even the best photographs. This is also well shown by the excellent drawings from Paul Carney, John Davis, Alan Harris, Ernest Leahy, David Nurney, John Reaney and Jan P. P. Wilczur. Photographs have their own place and David Brassington has provided a fine set of landscapes and a dramatic 2006 firescape from Thursley Common. A selection of photographs of interesting and unusual birds and places from M. B. Lancaster, Jeremy Gates, David Griffin, David Harris and Andrew Moon brings avian life and colour to the page.

The final stages of the work could not have been completed without the valuable assistance with proof-reading, corrections and suggestions that were provided by David Brassington, Richard A. Denyer, Hugh Evans, Jeremy Gates, David Griffin, David Harris, David Hollow, Shaun Peters and David Smith and the design and marketing work of David Hollow.

I would like to thank my wife Jean for her help and forbearance. Residual errors are my own.

Drawings and sketches
Paul Carney: Carrion Crow; Carrion Crow x Hooded Crow
John Davis: Barn Owl; Bearded Tits; Bewick's Swans; Blackcap; Coal Tits; Collared Doves; Cormorants; Dartford; Fieldfare; Great Grey Shrike; Green Woodpecker; Grey Partridges; Grey Wagtail; Hobby; Kingfisher; Little Egret; Little Grebe; Milford Plovers; Red Kite; Redstart; Reed Bunting; Rooks; Sand Martins; Stonechat; Tufted Ducks; Turnstone and Wagtail; Unstead Sewage Farm; Woodcock; Woodlark
Alan Harris: Firecrest; House Sparrow; Siskins
Ernest Leahy: Little Ringed Plover; Moorhen and young; Snipe; Water Rail; Whimbrel
David Nurney: Cirl Bunting; Crossbill; Golden Oriole; Lesser Black-backed Gull; Mandarin; Water Pipit
John Reaney: Frensham Little Pond; Gadwall; Greenshank; Little Owl; Moat Pond; Smew; Sparrowhawk
Jan P. P. Wilczur: Bankside Power Station; Nightingale; Staines Reservoirs; The Surrey Docks; The Thames at Battersea

Foreword

The first Surrey avifauna, by John Bucknill, was published over a century ago. This pioneering volume was not followed by a similar work until Donald Parr's Birds of Surrey 1900-70 appeared in 1972.

The London Natural History Society, *British Birds* and *The Zoologist* as well as the *South-Eastern Bird Report* have all provided partial and patchy coverage of the birdlife of the county of Surrey. The *Surrey Bird Report* started with the year 1953 (actually before the formation of the Surrey Bird Club) and has continued to provide some indication of the annual fluctuations in the birdlife of the county. Attention has been paid to the effect of short term weather variations as well as to more long term influences such as habitat and climate change.

My own experience of birds in the county goes back to the early 1920s, since when I have seen great changes in both the birds and the landscape. I am therefore very glad the opportunity has been taken at the opening of a new century to take stock of the changes which have occurred since the time of Bucknill.

As well as looking at those changes, the present book offers an overview of all time periods for which there is any information, including fossil reports. Additionally, the book includes hitherto unpublished distribution maps of the county's breeding species. These will set a benchmark against which to record whatever changes are to come in the present century.

This book will be a valuable source of reference for all those who are interested in the birdlife of Surrey.

P. A. D. Hollom

Introduction

THIS BOOK IS ABOUT the birds of Surrey in two dimensions, those of geography and time. The structure of the landscape is ancient and for most of its history the birdlife has left little trace, in the soil or on the printed page. Edward Newman's *Letters of Rusticus on the Natural History of Godalming*, published in 1849, was the first substantial regional work. Such written county history as existed by 1900 was well summarised in Bucknill's *The Birds of Surrey*, the first avifauna for the whole of Surrey. The 20th century saw a huge expansion in our knowledge and documentation of Surrey's birds. Donald Parr's *Birds in Surrey 1900-70* was the first modern avifauna for the county and it provides a valuable and well-presented summary of its period.

The inferences that can be drawn from even fragmentary information about the distant past are of value. History illuminates the present and, although the future is always different from what we expect, can suggest directions of future change. The present book therefore starts, where it can, close to the beginning of the story of our birds and goes on to work through the books of Newman, Bucknill and Parr to the present day. The last 30 years or so have seen a general upsurge of interest and a spate of new material which has to be analysed. The book attempts to summarise this in a way that makes it more readily accessible to a wider public and to future researchers.

There is no readily available summary of the occurrences of scarce species in Surrey or (outside the Surrey Bird Report) of the extreme dates of the commoner migrants, and there is no recent account of its commoner birds. The present book has its roots in the stimulus provided by Parr, which prompted further literary and field studies and culminated in work for the new breeding birds atlas started by the British Trust for Ornithology in 1988. A new book, incorporating recent research, and the wealth of new information on the breeding distribution of the birds should be useful and, within the limitations of space and the attention of the reader, an attempt has been made to provide one. The systematic list includes 339 full wild or naturalised species that have been found in the area, 331 of them in the vice-county, together with additional races and several birds whose exact species could not be determined. Escaped and introduced birds are included in an annex. Some of these have interesting histories. Most of the others are of little current biological significance, but a few might in time become naturalised, so it is worth devoting a little space to them.

The Area and Period Covered

The name of the County, Sudergeona or "southern region" in early texts, dates back to the 6th century or earlier. It was part of a wider geographic region, much of it with similar geological and ornithological features. The exact boundary has changed many times and there have been important changes in the 20th century, driven by changing patterns of land use, such as the urbanisation of the countryside, population shifts and changing economic geography. The book takes note of these changes and shows their relationship with its birds. Naturalists have long found it convenient to have a fixed system of boundaries in which to record their observations. This gives continuity and enables a better appreciation of the significance of individual observations to be made. The Watsonian system of vice-counties, fixed in the 19th century, has been useful and the Surrey Bird Club's own recording area has been that of the vice-county of Surrey, which reflects the political boundaries of late 19th century Surrey. It includes Greater London up to the site of the old Surrey Commercial Docks at Bermondsey but has the River Thames as its northern boundary. As the basic biological recording unit, the vice-county retains its interest. We can compare modern knowledge and the present environment with that described by Bucknill in 1900 and more recently by Parr and others in 1970. Some of the best birding in the county is to be had in oases of dereliction and industrial land usage within the heavily built-up areas of the north and east. They make a striking contrast to the heathy commons of the southwest, which have their own ornithological specialities and a rich history of personal observation. The core area which this book covers is therefore the vice-county of Surrey.

The Spelthorne district north of the Thames, which was once in Middlesex, was added to Surrey in 1965 and Spelthorne's own boundaries have been tweaked several times. At the present time, most people would expect a book on the birds of the county to include the Spelthorne district, which has some of the best-known reservoir and wetland sites in the Thames Valley. It has therefore been covered in the text, though in a way that enables the Spelthorne records to be identified and included or excluded by the reader as required. Three main regions are distinguished, to preserve continuity. These and the districts in them are detailed in the table.

	Population (000's) 1999	Hectares	Area Acres	Square Km	People per Square Km
Greater London					
Central London					
Lambeth	272.5	2,724	6,730	27.2	10,004
Southwark	235.9	2,886	7,129	28.9	8,174
Wandsworth	268.3	3,486	8,611	34.9	7,696
Outer London Boroughs					
Croydon	319.2	8,833	21,818	88.3	3,614
Kingston upon Thames	150.1	5,692	14,060	56.9	2,637
Merton	187.0	3,796	9,380	38.0	4,926
Richmond upon Thames	192.2	5,522	13,640	55.2	3,481
Sutton	178.2	4,342	10,729	43.4	4,104
Outer Surrey					
Elmbridge	133.0	9,634	23,796	96.3	1,381
Epsom and Ewell	71.3	3,407	8,415	34.1	2,093
Guildford	129.2	27,094	66,922	270.9	477
Mole Valley	80.2	25,832	63,805	258.3	310
Reigate and Banstead	122.1	12,913	31,895	129.1	946
Runnymede	76.6	7,794	19,251	77.9	983
Surrey Heath	85.9	9,509	23,487	95.1	903
Tandridge	80.7	24,819	61,303	248.2	325
Waverley	116.0	34,514	85,250	345.1	336
Woking	93.5	6,359	15,707	63.6	1,470
Spelthorne	89.6	5,125	12,659	51.3	1,748
Whole area	2,881.5	204,282	504,587	2,042.8	1,411
Vice-county	2,791.9	199,156	491,927	1,991.6	1,402

Using this list, the vice-county consists of Greater London, south of the Thames plus Outer Surrey. The Administrative County consists of Outer Surrey plus Spelthorne. The three regions are shown on the endpapers. The Greater London boundary is taken as at 1988. The Gatwick Airport district of the vice-county, which was transferred to Sussex in 1972, is included. A more detailed note on the boundaries is contained in a note at the back of the book. By convention, birds on or over the Thames and not on one of the banks, have often been counted for Middlesex as well as for Surrey. Thus the same record can be claimed as a first for both counties. For an example, see the Great Skua. Birds on islands in the Thames are assigned to their vice-county, as far as this can be determined. Thus Isleworth Ait, which had a heronry in the 1990s and Jessups Ait, (presumed to be Chiswick Eyot), which was the source of two 19th-century Spotted Crake records for Middlesex (Glegg), are excluded. Places change their names and their nature over the years. The gazetteer has been included to show the location of places under their current names and to indicate some of the alternatives. As far as possible, a single modern name is used for each place in the text. This may mean changing a name used in older references. In some cases, as at Elmers End Sewage Farm, there has been a substantial change in use. In others, there are two names currently used for the same place. A few of the more important changes and alternatives are:

Place	Old or alternative names
Barn Elms London Wetland Centre	Barn Elms Reservoirs, The London Wetland Centre
Chobham Ridges	Frimley Ridges
Earlswood Lakes	Earlswood Pond presumed to be one of these
Ham Gravel Pits	Teddington Gravel Pits
Lonsdale Road Reservoir	Lonsdale Reservoirs (all but one now closed)
South Norwood Country Park	Elmers End Sewage Farm
Tate Modern	Bankside Power Station
Witley Park	Lea Park, Thursley Park
In Spelthorne	
Ashford Common	Littleton Common
Queen Mary Reservoir	Littleton Reservoir
Stanwell Moor	Stanwellmoor

Place names that occur frequently have sometimes been abbreviated in the systematic list where no ambiguity arises, to improve the readability of the text. They are:

Place	Full name(s) and notes
Barn Elms	Barn Elms Reservoirs, The London Wetland Centre
Beddington	Beddington Sewage Farm
Frimley	Frimley Gravel Pits
Holmethorpe	Holmethorpe Sand Pits
Lonsdale Road	Lonsdale Road Reservoir(s)
Papercourt	Papercourt Gravel Pits, Send
Queen Mary Reservoir	May include adjacent gravel pits and feeder streams.
Thorpe	Thorpe Water Park, Thorpe Gravel Pits

Kingston upon Thames and Richmond upon Thames are referred to as Kingston and Richmond. In each case all or virtually all the records refer to the place with the full name. Any which do not are specially indicated.

Several important sites straddle the administrative or vice-county boundary. These are Ash Vale Gravel Pits, South Norwood Country Park, Kempton Park, North Camp Gravel Pits, Perry Oaks Sewage Farm, Virginia Water and Windsor Great Park. Observations from them are included, sometimes with a caveat, unless definitely known or believed to be outside the boundary. A few places given for Surrey in the literature are actually outside the boundary on any definition. These include Bewbush (Crawley), Copthorne Common (Sussex), Lurgashall (Sussex) and Rapley Lake (Berkshire). All records from them have been excluded from the systematic list.

Regions of Surrey

The London area, when referred to in the text, means the recording area of the London Natural History Society, which is a circle of 20 miles in diameter centred on St Paul's Cathedral unless the context indicates otherwise. This includes a good deal of Surrey, inside and outside the present Greater London boundary, which is referred to as northeast Surrey in the text. Inner London was defined by the Society as an oblong 40 square mile area, with boundaries four miles east and west of Charing Cross and 2? miles north and south of Charing Cross. The genesis of this area in 1928-29 is given by Earp (1991). In the context of this book, Inner London refers to the Surrey part of this area

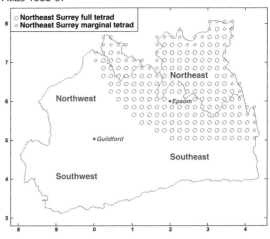

unless otherwise indicated or the context is obviously more general. The *Shepperton Bird Report* covered the Shepperton and Laleham districts, Charlton Gravel Pits south to the Thames, excluding the Queen Mary Gravel Pits and reservoir. Unless otherwise stated, references to Shepperton in the text cover this area. West Surrey lies west of Guildford and is divided into the northwest and southwest regions by the North Downs. It contains most of the heathland. Southeast Surrey is mostly farmland, without hills or heaths.

Sources and Methods

Sources and Citation of Authorities. The text covers all years for which information has been located. Bucknill (1900) has been used extensively for information on 19th century Surrey. References to Graves, Meyer and other 19th century ornithologists are sometimes based on references in Bucknill. Where this is the case, it is normally mentioned in the list of references. The Birds of Surrey (1900) and supplementary papers in the Zoologist of 1901 and 1902 by John A. Bucknill are usually referred in the text as Bucknill. Unsourced 19th century records have come from these publications also. James E. Harting (1866) and William E. Glegg (1935) are important sources for early Spelthorne records but both deal with the whole county of Middlesex and they are often not specific about the Spelthorne District. Two papers by Graham W. Kerr (1906 and 1908) provide summaries of the status of the birds of the Staines district but they include Windsor Great Park in the area covered. The *London Bird Reports* have never treated Spelthorne or Staines as separate districts. For all of these sources therefore, care has had to be exercised in extracting accurate information for Spelthorne alone. Most of Windsor Great Park and Virginia Water belong to Berkshire, but records are often, as in the *South-Eastern Bird Report*, included under Surrey. The earlier *London Bird Reports* listed all records for Dulwich and Elmers End Sewage Farm under Kent.

The recording area of the Haslemere Natural History Society is a six-mile circle based on Haslemere and contains parts of Hampshire, Surrey and Sussex. Three reviews of the birds of the Haslemere district have been published, of which the first was by the Rev. William. A. Shaw, in 1921. Only records which are specifically stated to relate to Surrey have been used for the present work. Shaw himself was Rector of Peper Harow, well inside Surrey. Robert C. Blockey of the Haslemere Museum (see below), con-tributed a considerable number of records in which the location was given as Haslemere to the *South-Eastern Bird Reports*. They were entered into the reports under Surrey, but have only been used without qualification in the present work if it is clear that the county of Surrey and not elsewhere in the HNHS recording area is meant.

The coverage of reservoirs and sewage farms was disrupted by the war of 1939-45, which probably accounts for the absence or scarcity of records of species such as the Slavonian Grebe and Wood Sandpiper during this period. There have been briefer restrictions on access for security reasons and from 28th February to 3rd July 2001 during the foot and mouth disease outbreak of that year. The latest published material which has been used includes the *Surrey Bird Report* for 2001 and London Natural History Society *London Bird Report* for 2003. The virtually complete vice-county records were held by the Surrey Bird Club for 2000 to 2004 and partial records were available for later years. Important records up to mid 2007 have been included, where available. Most Spelthorne records for the years after 2003 have been taken from the London Natural History Society *Ornithological Bulletin* in the absence of a published *London Bird Reports* for these years. Where this has been done, they have been credited to the Bulletin. Such records have not necessarily been cleared by the LNHS Records Committee and publication here should not be taken as implying acceptance. *Bird Watching*, *Birding World* and *British Birds* have also been used as post-2003 sources, mainly for Spelthorne. Where acceptance by national or local records committee is still required at the time of writing, this is indicated. Records known to have been found unacceptable have normally been excluded from the systematic list. If included, this is indicated, with a discussion.

No reference is normally given for records which are in

> *Hants/Surrey Border Bird Reports* for 1971-1997:
> *London Bird Reports* for 1936 to 2003
> *South-Eastern Bird Reports* for 1934 to 1947
> *Surrey Bird Reports* for 1953 to 2001
> *The London Naturalist* for 1917 to 1935

if they can be found in the report for the year of occurrence.

References for other records are given where the record is of particular significance or interest, or where it is needed for clarification, for example where sources conflict. The year of publication given for material from Bird Reports, when cited in the list of references, is the year of publication of the report, if this is available and shown in the report, or otherwise the year to which the report relates. Publication years are not available and shown for the 1952-1956 and 1978-1998 Surrey Bird Reports, the 1936-1943, 1949 and 1952 London Bird Reports and the 1939 South-Eastern Bird Report. Early and late dates are taken from published sources unless otherwise stated. Coverage should be accurate for the vice-county but unpublished Spelthorne records will have been missed. There has been no regular exchange of records for the Gatwick area with the Sussex Ornithological Society after its transfer to Sussex, but national rarities have been picked up and there has been some atlas coverage.

Comments on the recoveries of ringed birds up to 2001 are based on published records only, unless otherwise acknowledged. For 2002-05, draft Surrey ringing reports have been supplied by Richard A. Denyer. Sources searched in full are *British Birds*, *BTO Ringing Reports* for the years from 1970, the Haslemere Natural History Society reviews, *London Bird Reports*, *Surrey Bird Reports* and *The Middle-Thames Naturalist*. Additional recoveries have been supplied by the BTO in a county report. Between them these are thought to cover all foreign records - foreign here meaning involving a country outside the British Isles. They cover all other recoveries for the early years of ringing but later coverage is selective, being determined by what the compilers of ringing reports in these publications thought were noteworthy. This would normally include all movements of more than 50 km and those showing exceptional longevity. Distance travelled and interesting links with other parts of the British Isles are picked out in local publications but less often in national publications, where Surrey is only one part of a larger picture. Richard A. Denyer, Jeremy Gates, David Griffin and Keith Herber have been particularly helpful in providing additional records and helping with the interpretation.

Ringed birds may subsequently be recovered in a variety of ways, for example they may be trapped alive or they may be found dead. Ringers and the BTO distinguish between birds retrapped within 5 km of the ringing site, known as retraps, and those found at more distant places, known as recoveries. Both are generally called recoveries in the text, for simplicity. Details of a few longevity records published in Surrey Bird Reports before 1978 could not be found in the Surrey Bird Club files and they could not be located by a BTO search of its database. Some might be typographical errors and others may have got lost in the post and not reached the BTO. There are also a few technical points to bear in mind.

The national set of recovery records managed by the BTO is compiled from the information sent to it by the people who find the ringed birds, after combining this with the information sent to the BTO by ringers about the birds that they have ringed. All recoveries of dead birds and all recoveries of birds sent in by members of the public are entered into the BTO database. Except in the unlikely event that the ringer retraps his bird away from the ringing site, the longer distance records should therefore be in the BTO database. In earlier times, before the BTO insisted that all local retraps by the ringer should be reported, they may have gone no further than the ringer's log and longevities would only have been reported to the BTO, or even the local organiser, if they were thought to be interesting enough. Even now, retraps are not necessarily entered into the BTO database without a request by the ringer. It is for reasons such as these that some longevity records in the published literature could not be documented.

Recoveries of birds ringed as nestlings differ from those ringed as young fledged birds in that there is certainty about where they were hatched. They provide definite information about movements of the local breeding population, rather than giving information about the movements of young birds that might have moved into the locality from other areas before being ringed. This is of particular importance for migratory races of species wintering in Surrey, such as some gulls, since it may provide stronger evidence of the racial identity of the wintering birds than can be obtained from field observations. Some species, such as Kingfishers, are not ringed as nestlings because there would be excessive risk to the young in extracting them from the nest.

All longevity and distance records claimed in the text refer to their status in Surrey unless they are specifically stated to be national records. Some of the Surrey records may look trivial in a national context. They have been included to mark the boundary of what we know about Surrey birds. If you could tell an old or far-travelled bird by looking at it when it was in its bush, the figures would also provide something to build on.

Treatment of Records. Old bird records tend to lose accuracy and context over time, and modern critical and technical standards are sharper than some of what has gone before. Many of the older records were sifted by Bucknill, who generally included things with his own view on how far they could be trusted. Old or unclear, though, these records give a long perspective on modern observations and have their own intrinsic interest. To take a few examples, one of the earliest written records for the area covered is a 15th century comment on the numerous Red Kites to be seen at London Bridge. Frensham gave Gilbert White sad stories of the birds shot there, including the Osprey and the Black-winged Stilt. The first British record of the Little Gull was of one shot on the Thames near Chelsea. No attempt has been made to reappraise all old records by modern standards, although a few have been re-examined. Decisions made by the British Birds Rarities Committee since its formation in 1958 have been accepted for birds within its period. The Surrey Bird Club Records Committee has reviewed some of its own earlier decisions. Records of birds that have not been specifically identified (mainly divers, geese and gulls) have not been included unless they are of special interest.

Charts and Tables. In the tables of bird months, a bird is counted in each month that it was found, so that one present in January, February and March is counted for all three months. Living birds later found dead are only counted in the months when they were found alive. Birds only found dead are counted in the month when found. The number of birds is used, e.g. two birds in November 1986 will add two to the November total. Records where the month is not known are omitted. In the tables of records by decade, the number of records is used so that an arrival of two birds on the same day and place in 1986 will add one to the 1980s total.

Population Estimates. The Common Birds Census organised by the BTO was the main source of national population trends for breeding birds for the last 30 years of the 20th century. Observers plotted the location of territorial birds on maps in selected areas, making several visits each season. The BTO analysed the information and decided on the number of territories for each species. There was a broad stratification by habitat type - farmland, woodland etc. The mix of habitats changed during the life of the project. County level results are often thin. For the purpose of this book the Surrey results for each species have been aggregated over all habitats to produce an annual figure for the number of territories per ten hectares each year. The trends from 1970 to 2000 for the main breeding species have been esti- mated by linear regression analysis, which gives the best-fitting straight line trend through the annual figures. A five percent level of significance has been used - i.e. the trend is regarded as significant if there is only a five percent chance that any rise or fall that it shows could have arisen by chance. Habitat mix effects have been looked for but not usually found. Although this method of analysis is rather crude, it has surprisingly often produced rising or falling trends that are similar to those observed nationally or by other means.

The number of territories per square kilometre indicated by the trend line for 2000 has been grossed up (without allowance for habitat mix) to county level to produce estimates of the number of territories in Surrey (the vice-county and Spelthorne). The results have to be regarded as very rough, but they often give a feel for at least the order of magnitude of the population size at the end of the 20th century and are a starting point for more thorough work which is beyond the scope of this book.

The Common Birds Census has been replaced by the BTO's Breeding Bird Survey. Observers are allo- cated randomly-chosen 1 km x 1 km national grid squares and asked to walk two transects (normally each 1 km in length) in a single day, twice during the breeding season, counting all the adult birds seen. The number of squares surveyed each year has varied. The BTO has supplied the total of the maximum single day square counts for each species, the number of squares in which the species occurred and the total number of squares covered for each year from 1994-2004. The average number of adult birds of each species counted per square kilometre over the 11 year period can be calculated from this informa- tion. When grossed up to county level the averages become estimates of county adult population sizes. The figures are referred to in some of the species accounts. They have not been adjusted to allow for partial coverage within the square. Large birds like Woodpigeons have a better chance of being counted than small ones like Dunnocks.

There is a developing literature on the relationship between transect counts, 1 km square populations and the number of territories. At least one sophisticated computer model has been developed to esti- mate it for each species. Such work is beyond the scope of this book. Population estimates here have been derived from the transect counts without further adjustment. This is likely to be an underestimate for small birds and does not purport to have the same relationship with total population for each species, or to be directly comparable with the number of territories derived from the Common Birds Census. The crude results have, however, enough interest to warrant inclusion. For some species, the number of territories per square kilometre found nationally in the 1988-91 BTO Atlas has been multi- plied by the size of Surrey in square kilometres to give a comparative figure.

Sequence and Nomenclature. The sequence in the systematic list follows that of the British Ornithologists' Union's The *British List: A Checklist of Birds of Britain (7th Edition)*, published in *Ibis (2006) 148: 526-63*. Species can be thought of as leaves on a tree, each attached by twigs and branches to the trunk. The list is based on current views of the order of avian evolution, with the oldest groups (or lowest branches) at the head of the list. For British birds, this brings the swans to the top, with many changes of sequence within some groups, such as the warblers. Scientific names for species are taken from this list, followed by the older name in brackets if different. English names for species are based on *Birds of the Western Palearctic*, with a few exceptions based on subsequent BOU decisions. Current BOU names, some of which are not in common use, (such as Barn Swallow), are added in brackets where they differ. English names for sub-species were given in *The Handbook* but this work is now well over 60 years old. The BOU published a list which included subspecies in 1971 but did not include English names for them. The current BOU list does not include scientific or English names for sub-species. With the renewed interest in forms, whether or not they are full species, a modern list of English sub-species names is desirable. The list in Gantlett (2000) provides a useful source of English names for all sub-species recorded in the British Isles, and has been followed unless otherwise indicated. The aim is to make it clear, in English and scientific terms, which form the records relate to and not to introduce any innovations.

For most birds, records are not normally reported at the subspecies level by observers and the main text in the systematic list is at the species level. Subspecies are only detailed where they are uncommon and reliably identified.

For birds not known to have been found wild in Britain the sequence has been based on *Birds of the World* (Clements 2000, 5th Edition).

Status Definitions. Notes on the world status of rare Surrey migrants are based on the analysis in Dymond et al. (1989), updated where appropriate. Comments on world distribution are based on the maps in BWP and information in the EBCC atlas. The *Migration Atlas* has been used, with other sources, for background information about bird migration. Harrison (1988) has been used for its long perspectives on the avian history of Britain. The *Historical Atlas* has been used as a source for background information on the period since the 1800s. The 1988-91 Atlas has been used for late 20th century national trends. The main source used for national trends since 1970 is *The State of the UK's Birds (BTO et al. 2003)*. Other works consulted include Mead (2000), joint publications such as *The State of the UK's Birds (BTO et al. 2001-02)* and *Breeding Birds in the Wider Countryside* (BTO, Joint Nature Conservation Committee, 2001 - 2003), *The Population Status of Birds in the UK - Birds of Conservation Concern: 2002-2007* (Gregory et al. 2002) and related publications on the Breeding Birds Survey by M. Raven, D. Noble and S. Baillie in *BTO News 249, 254*. An RSPB press release of 15th May 2000 and RSPB (2002) provided information about House Sparrows. Analyses of national Garden Bird Survey information have been provided by Glue (2000) and others. There are speculations about the future in Mead (1999). In the present text, east coast means the coastal counties from Shetland to Essex, south coast means coastal counties from Kent to the Scillies and British covers England, Scotland and Wales unless otherwise stated. Where Ireland is referred to it includes Northern Ireland and the Republic of Ireland. References to inland counties include those in Ireland.

Wildfowl Counts. Monthly wildfowl counts have been organised by the Wildfowl and Wetland Trust (WWT) and currently they are run as a partnership between the BTO, the WWT and the joint Nature Conservation Committee. They are called Wetland Bird Survey (WeBS) counts and are carried out on nationally-specified dates to reduce duplication. Until recently the WeBS year ran from April to March so that a May count in 1998-99 was carried out in 1998. The WeBS year now ends in June. The maximum WeBS count in each year at the more significant places is published by the WWT in its annual Wetland Bird Survey, together with five-year averages of the maxima and the month of the maximum in the most recent year.

Other wildfowl counts are carried out at most of the Surrey WeBS sites and these often produce higher figures than those in the WeBS counts themselves. Tables of monthly maxima in the *Surrey Bird Report* take the highest available figures.

Weather and climate. Weather changes every day. Climate varies over a long period. For many birds, the severity of the winter is a critical survival factor, so a knowledge of the main years of occurrence helps to interpret bird population information. There is a useful summary of London area weather trends in Brazell (1968). Nationally significant events are summarised in Eden (1995). The main sources of information specifically about Surrey are Davison and Currie (1991) and Currie (1996) unless otherwise stated. References to 1659 use information in Manley's Central England Temperatures series, which starts from that date. It should be a useful indicator of Surrey temperatures, though they would have been somewhat different. The commencement of systematic weather recording at Kew in 1763 enables more precision to be given to the climate's history in Surrey.

Agricultural land use. The long-term perspectives on farmland and its birds that are given by Shrubb (2003) are applicable to much of the farmland development in Surrey. A letter by Bourne (2000b) on open-field systems is also useful.

Geology, Climate, Weather and Land Use

The geological record shows that the land which is now southern England has at various times been a desert (Permian, 220m BC), part of the sea bed (Cretaceous, 140m BC), a tropical rain-forest (Eocene, 50 million BC) and a snowy tundra (400,000 BC). Over such a time scale even the last period of glaciation, which finished some ten thousand years ago, and the separation of the British Isles from continental Europe are rather recent events, though their effect on the bird life of the region has been profound. They also begin to impinge on the events of the present. The unexposed geological strata contain climate and fossil history. Surface features and soils shape land use, vegetation and the potential habitats for birds. The main features of the surface geology are shown in the table.

Main Features of the Surface Geology of Surrey

Formation	Age in millions of years	Typical Localities
Recent and late Pleistocene	0-2	
Alluvium		Battersea, Southwark
Sands and gravels		Wimbledon Common
Lower Eocene	40-70	
Bagshot Sands		Northwest Surrey commons
London Clay		Morden, Oxshott, Burpham
Thanet Sands		Beddington and Waddon
Cretaceous	70-135	
Chalk		North Downs
Lower Greensand		Southwest Surrey commons
Weald Clay		Newdigate, Ockley
Hastings Beds		Horley and Gatwick

Times before history. About 200 million years ago, before there was a bird on earth, the land mass which is now Surrey was part of a group of islands off Africa, drifting slowly north. The sea levels were then much higher and if 'Surrey' was not under water, it was probably a desert. The earliest bird fossils come from the Jurassic limestone, in Germany, and are around 150 million years old. The area forming what is now Surrey was under the sea for much of the succeeding period. Surrey has a number of sites for dinosaurs and other ancient fossils. At one of these, in the Lower Chalk at Betchworth, the remains of a pterodactyl, perhaps 120 million years old, have been found (Wycherley and Anstis, 2001).

The first fossil bird known for the Surrey area is *Gastornis klaasseni*, which dates from early in the Eocene period, some 40 to 70 million years ago. It was in this period that the dome of the Weald and other parts of Britain and Europe rose up from the waters and birds began to arrive. Britain's land mass at this time was still well south of its present position and the eastern coast reached up the Thames Valley, at times as far as Guildford. *Gastornis klaasseni* was a large, flightless bird, perhaps as big as an Ostrich, and probably related to the Geese or the Crakes. It lived about 50 million years ago in the lush forests of the period and was a dominant predator of its time. It had a huge, stout beak, which it used to catch and eat forest mammals, the largest of which was then about the size of a smallish dog. Remains of *Gastornis* were found when the Park Hill railway cutting was dug at Croydon and they were collected by H. M. Klaassen in 1883. There were parts of five tibiotarsi (lower leg bones) and the end of a left femur (thigh) (Newton, 1886). The fragments of three of the tibiotarsi cannot now be traced. Fragments of the other two, together with the femur, are held by the Institute of Geological Sciences, and casts of the tibiotarsi are at the British Museum of Natural History (Harrison and Walker, 1977). Other fossils of the same genus have been found in Belgium and France (Swinnerton, 1958), in Germany (*Gastornis geiselensis*) and in the USA (BBC, 2001).

Left: *Gastornis klaasseni: tibiotarsus*
Right: *Gastornis klaasseni: femur*
© 2001 The Natural History
Museum, London

A beach of flint pebbles was eventually formed along the North Downs, represented today by acidic heaths. The land vegetation at this time was apparently tropical rain-forest (Sherlock, 1960) in Kent and presumably also in what is now Surrey. Fossils in the London Clay of this period include crocodiles, and seeds of a palm tree. The Isle of Sheppey is a famous locality for London Clay fossils. Birds found in it include *Dasornis*, a probably ostrich-like bird (Swinnerton, 1960). Others from the Sheppey clay are *Prophaethon shrubsolei*, a tropicbird, *Odontopteryx toliapica*, a large bird with a 'toothed' beak, *Lithornis vulturinus*, the oldest known vulture, *Halcyornis toliapicus*, a possible kingfisher (Swinnerton, 1958), and three species of *Pediorallus*, a small rail-like genus (Harrison, 1984). *Proherodius* was a heron of the period. It seems reasonable to suppose that some of these might also have reached the modern Surrey land mass. By about 12 million years ago, the British Isles had roughly reached their present position.

The last Ice Age. The European climate remained on the whole warmer than it is today until the beginning of the last Ice Age, some two or three million years ago. Since then there have been around 20 periods of glaciation, the most southerly of which came almost as far south as the Thames, when the climate of southern Britain would have been rather like southern Greenland is today and the North Sea was frozen. Although the whole era is known as the last Ice Age, there were huge climatic variations within it. The glaciations alternated with warmer periods (interglacials) which at times could be very warm indeed, leaving the British Isles clear of ice and the Thames Valley with a climate, flora and fauna rather like the Bay of Bengal. In warmer Ice Age interglacials it would have been mild enough for a species of Jungle Fowl (bones from Kent). Hazel Grouse and Garden Warbler remains have been found in southern England. Early British remains of modern birds including Red Grouse and Ptarmigan have come from the Midlands and the Mendips and date from an interglacial. They are, perhaps, 500,000 to 600,000 years old. The colourful Mandarin ducks, whose current population derives from introductions, may have been Surrey residents about half a million years ago. These may all have bred in our area.

The coldest phase of the Ice Age, the Anglian, came later and drove ice sheets as far south as the Thames perhaps 400,000 years ago. Most temperate species, including any Mandarin, would have been driven out of Britain altogether. Crows may have had a similar history to Mandarins. Western European and eastern Asian populations of Carrion Crows are separated by a central population of Hooded Crows. Surrey at this time would have been tundra, a treeless landscape with ice caps on the tops of the hills. The frozen ground would have been covered in places by gravels, which were moved around by surface water. The River Wey was yet to be formed.

Warmer times returned and flood plain terrace deposits at Swanscombe, in Kent, perhaps from the Hoxnian interglacial some 250,000 years old, have yielded fossils of a number of living and extinct birds that might have been in Surrey, including the Whooper Swan, Greylag Goose, Shoveler, Common Scoter, Red-breasted Merganser, Capercaillie, Cormorant and Eagle Owl (Harrison, 1979). These evidently date from a time when Surrey would again have had a sub-arctic climate or more temperate, and was probably also populated with birds such as the Red Grouse, Ptarmigan, Black Guillemot and Snowy Owl.

Even warmer periods followed. Remains of rhinoceros and a species of elephant have been found in sands at Beddington, possibly from the highest and oldest of the three Thames Valley terraces (the Boyn Hill level), which are perhaps over 200,000 years old. Deposits at Brentford, across the Thames from Kew Gardens and estimated to be about 120,000 years old and from the last of the really warm interglacials, include species of hippopotamus, rhinoceros and elephant.

The warmth gave way to further cold with the Devensian glaciation. This time the ice came no further nearer to Surrey than Norfolk. The tundra returned. During less severe periods of cold the tundra would give way to steppe. Remains of the Woolly Mammoth which were found at Kempton Park and which are estimated to be about 50,000 years old, indicate the kind of wildlife likely to have been about at this time. The last (possibly final) phase of severe cold was from about 11,000 to 10,000 years ago. At some time during the period the Channel was formed, probably as a result of ice sheets melting. This cut Britain off from continental Europe and creating a barrier that some potential European colonists, such as Black Woodpeckers, have been unable to cross.

Overall, Ice Age remains found in caves in Derbyshire, Kent, Somerset and elsewhere relate to at least 155 species of bird which can be found in the British Isles today, of which 146 have been found in Surrey since 1800. The remains of at least 29 extinct species have also been found. Surrey was never glaciated but its current temperate climate might yet prove to be another interglacial.

More modern times. Butler (1970) gives a short, but useful account of the geologically recent climate and landscape development. Burton (1995) provides a link between long term climatic change and bird populations and has been used for inferences about Surrey. Doyle (2000) provides a useful commentary on Surrey climate trends since about 40,000 BC. The beginning of the Mesolithic period, about 10,000 years ago, was marked by a sudden improvement in the climate, which became about 3°C warmer than it was at the end of the 20th century. Afforestation, which had began towards the end of the Mesolithic period on the Weald Clay and the Greensand, moved onto the chalk downland. The transition is marked by pollen grains recovered from the bog at Pudmore, on Thursley Common, which is one of the few sites in Britain to have yielded information about this aspect of the end of the Ice Age in southern Britain. Further evidence comes from Wimbledon Common, where a 6,000 year pollen sequence is laid on sandy grit and begins with bog vegetation. Pine pollen is also found, showing that pines were found on drier parts of the common. At its maximum extent, Surrey would have been almost wholly woodland.

Subsequent temperatures have fluctuated and were highest from about 4000 to 2500 BC, when they were around 2°C above the values of the 1980s (Eden). This period is known as the Climatic Optimum.

The Bronze Age began towards the end of it. There is some evidence for Bronze Age settlement in Surrey, but grassland does not seem to have been important until after Roman times. The climate began to cool from 1000 BC to 400 AD (the Sub-Atlantic phase) but Roman Britain still enjoyed a climate good enough for vineyards. Birds known to have been in Surrey in Roman Times include the Wigeon, Teal, Grey Partridge, Red Kite, Sparrowhawk, Buzzard, Coot, Woodcock, Woodpigeon, Blackbird, Jackdaw and Raven. A cooler period may have followed but the years from 850-1250 AD (the Medieval Warm Period), was on the whole warm and dry. The tree line in Scotland was then about a thousand feet higher than it is today and the climate of southeast England would have permitted a bird life with a noticeably more southern component. Vineyards were cultivated in the Thames Valley at this time, but they gradually declined, for climatic or other reasons, until 1400.

Fisher and Currie identified, mainly from literary evidence, a number of hard winters and famine years when birds probably suffered, some even in the Medieval Warm Period. These were 671 (cold, a year of 'great destruction among the birds' – *Anglo-Saxon Chronicle*), 791-93 (famine years), the 890s, the 930-940s, 976, around 1005 (wet), 1040-44 (wet), 1046 (cold, birds died), 1069-70 (cold), 1086-87 (wet), 1092-93 (cold), 1111, 1114-15 (cold) and 1124, (cold), 1141 (Thames froze) and 1150 (Thames froze). There were some very severe winters and droughts from 1200 to 1400, including 1204-05, (Thames froze), 1210 (bird deaths), the famine years of 1205, 1217, 1224-25, 1233-34, 1256-58, 1269 and 1281-82 (Thames froze), 1294, 1309-10 (Thames froze) and 1315-17, and bird deaths certainly occurred in 1335.

The Little Ice Age. The period from 1400 to about 1850 has been called the Little Ice Age. The number of poor summers increased. Fisher identified bird deaths caused by severe weather conditions in 1407-08 (which wiped out nearly all the thrushes – see *BB*, *11:267*, the Thames froze) and 1462. The Thames froze again in 1506, 1515, 1536/37, 1564 and 1607/08 (many thrushes died). The winter of 1609 was especially severe. The Thames froze again in 1621, 1635 and 1655. John Evelyn described the winter of 1657/58 as the severest winter that any man alive has known and wrote of crows' feet being frozen to their prey. The Thames froze again in 1666/67. Frost fairs were held on the ice in the bitter winters of 1683/84 and 1688/89. January 1684 was the second coldest month on record from 1659 to the present. John Evelyn's diary for 28th January 1684 (Bray, 1966) presents a vivid account:

> *Coaches plied from Westminster to the Temple, and from several other stairs to and fro, as in the streets, sleds, sliding with skates, a bull-baiting, horse and coach-races, puppet-plays and interludes, cooks, tippling and other lewd places, so that it seemed to be a bacchanalian triumph, or carnival on the water, whilst it was a very severe judgement on the land, the trees not only splitting as if lightning-struck, but men and cattle perishing in divers places, and the very seas so locked up with ice, that no vessels could stir out or come in. The fowls, fish and the birds, and all our exotic plants and greens, universally perishing.*

The Thames froze again in 1691 and 1695. At this time the Thames had not been embanked, so that it would have been wider and shallower than it is today. Fisher (1966) noted bird crashes in the cold winters of 1708, 1715/16 (many Goldfinches died, January was the sixth coldest month from 1659 to 1995, vast quantities of snow), 1739/40 (February 1740 was bitterly cold), 1767/68, (thrushes, Redwings) and 1776. January 1776 was the tenth coldest month to be recorded since 1659. Gilbert White (Letter XLIX) writes movingly of the conditions at Selbourne, in Hampshire:

> *January 7th – Snow driving all day, which was followed by frost, sleet and some snow, till the twelfth, when a prodigious mass overwhelmed all the works of men, drifting over the tops of gates and filling the hollow lanes … from the fourteenth the snow continued to increase … on the twentieth the sun shone out for the first time … All this time the cold was not very intense, for the thermometer stood at 29, 28, 25 and thereabout; but on the twentyfirst it descended to 20. At South Lambeth [in Surrey, after more heavy snow in Hampshire,] the temperature fell to 11, 7, 6 and 6 for the four following nights …*

White recounts how the temperature reached a low of zero (Fahrenheit) on 31st January and that the Thames had frozen over so firmly that crowds ran about on the ice. The thaw began next day but 'As to the birds, the thrushes and blackbirds were mostly destroyed; and the partridges, by the weather and poachers, were so thinned that few remained to breed the following year'. It was during this period of severe frost that the first British Red-breasted Goose was shot, near London, possibly in our area. Towards the end of the period the freezing of the Thames became less likely because of the drainage of the marshes at Lambeth and Vauxhall for building, and other construction works which increased the flow of the river. His reference to snow is a reminder of its special significance for heathland birds, where extended snow cover can be a bigger killer than extreme cold. Years of heavy snow are not always among the coldest.

Fisher (1966) notes that the winters of 1781, 1784 (coldest year until 1962/63, Thames froze), 1796 (Thames froze) 1788/89 (Thames froze) and 1794/95 were fatal to many birds. Gilbert White found deep snow on the Hog's Back on 2nd April 1784. January 1795 was the coldest month since 1659. Heavy snow at Falmouth, in Cornwall, in 1796 wiped out the Dartford Warblers there. In the winter of 1798, huge flocks of Fieldfares, Redwings and Starlings moved into Devon after heavy snow in northern and eastern Britain. Many died (Montagu). Many Redwings also died during severe weather in 1799 (Yarrell).

There was an extremely cold spell in 1813/14, the winter of the last great Frost Fair on the Thames and a very bad winter for birds. January 1814 was the third coldest month from 1659 to 1995 and there was a 48-hour snowstorm in Surrey. Yarrell wrote of Redwing deaths in 1814 and again in 1822. The winter of 1829/30 was very cold, with heavy snow. The Thames froze at Richmond and it froze in London for the last time. The next really bad winter was in 1838, a year when the first Red-throated Diver and a Goosander were found in Surrey. Pink-footed Geese were not uncommon in London markets in 1838, though no Surrey birds are on record. A temperature of -10°F (-23°C) was recorded at Cobham on 20th January. This was the day on which the second dated Lesser Black-backed Gull was 'picked up' near Godalming in the great frost that year, which reached a minimum of 46 degrees of frost or -14°F, (-26°C). This was known as Murphy's frost because it had been predicted in an almanac by Patrick Murphy. The winters of 1844/45 and 1853/54 (with heavy snow) were cold. An extremely severe cold spell from January to March 1855 (the 'Crimean Winter') killed some early summer visitors as well as resident birds. Yarrell found Bewick's, Whooper and Polish Swans more abundant than he could ever recall in January and February. The first 19th century Surrey 'Wild Swans' appeared in that year. February 1855 was the ninth coldest month since 1659 and the Thames froze at Richmond. This was the winter in which a Siberian Thrush from near Guildford, a (disputed) first for Britain, was probably found. Strangely, on 25th March 1855, a female Little Bittern was found at Bramley.

In spite of the harsh conditions of the Little Ice Age, species such as the Black Grouse, Red Kite and Raven appear to have prospered and they were eventually lost to persecution rather than the weather.

1850-1895. The Little Ice Age may have ended around the mid-century but there were some fierce winters over the next 50 years. 1860/61 was another bad winter for birds. The winter of 1878/79 was the sixth coldest since 1659. Snow fell on eleven days in December and was especially heavy across Surrey on the 22nd. Further snow fell on fifteen days in January. The winter of 1880/81 was heralded by a six-inch fall of snow in Surrey and Kent on 19th and 20th October. A temperature of 5°F was recorded at Redhill on 16th January (Tyndall, Holmesdale Natural History Club). A snowstorm on 18th-19th January was accompanied by a gale and might have been the worst in the 19th century (Eden). Goosanders appeared at Farncombe and Gatton. A tidal surge driven by the wind flooded riverside areas of Bermondsey and Southwark. Davison and Currie include a photograph of ice flows on the Thames at Putney. It was a winter for which Raynsford (1963) mentions 'memorable falls of snow'. Snow lay for thirteen weeks even in south London. These two winters must have devastated the Dartford Warbler population.

L. J. Raynsford wrote of a single overnight West Surrey snowfall of 'close to two feet' in January 1887.

There were an estimated 20,000 Woodpigeons in Gatton Park during hard weather that year. Further severe weather in the winter of 1887/88 brought large numbers of Black-headed Gulls up the Thames as far as Putney for the first time. There were 127 near Waterloo Bridge on 27th February 1888. F. D. Power saw very big movements of Skylarks over his Brixton garden in the Octobers of 1888, 1891 and 1892. Cold weather in December 1889 brought Power his only Redshank record for Brixton. A frost from 25th November 1890 to January 1891 lasted continuously for 59 days. On 28th November, Power counted roughly a thousand Sklarks moving over his garden in twenty minutes. December was the coldest for 150 years. The woods and wetlands around the Surrey hills were, comparatively speaking, deserted of birds (Jordan, 1892). It was in this winter that a Smew, only the second for Surrey with a known date, was shot near Farnham. A photograph in Murray (1977), taken on 4th January 1891, shows the Thames so deeply frozen from shore to shore at Brentford that the whole surface is cracked and furrowed like a roughly ploughed field. Seven Bitterns were killed at Godalming during the frost. A blizzard in March 1891 was severest in the West Country, but is thought to have covered the whole of the southeast with six inches of snow (Eden) and was very heavy in Surrey. There was an exceptional frost in 1892/93 which brought the Black-headed Gulls up the Thames in even greater numbers. It was in this winter that the police put an end to the shooting of gulls on the river between the bridges, by fining the sportsmen for the offence of discharging firearms to the public danger (Hudson, 1898). It was also the time when Londoners began feeding the gulls.

There were severe frosts in February and March 1895. February 1895 was the eighth coldest month since 1659. F. D. Power saw many Skylarks flying south over his Brixton garden on 18th-21st February. At Beddington the temperature fell to -19°C (-2°F). The Thames froze at Richmond and an ox was roasted at a fair held on the ice. Lapland Buntings were seen on Wimbledon Common. Glegg reported F. O. Forbes as saying there were thousands of Black-headed Gulls, young and old, on the Thames between the London Bridges during the frost. They were fed by the local people. A Little Gull appeared over a river blocked with ice at Charing Cross. The severe winter of 1894/95 marked the start of the first significant Starling movements into London. The further influx of gulls began what has since been a regular winter movement. The winters of the first half of the 1890s would have been very hard on resident heathland birds.

1896 to 1937. The 42 years from 1896 to 1937 were characterised by milder winters, the only really severe winter weather being that of 1916/17. A cold period from November 1916 to April 1917 was marked by abnormal and persistent snowfalls, followed by a drought. Heavy snow fell across Surrey in February 1917. At Walton on the Hill 21 inches fell between the 23rd and 28th. There were very heavy losses among small birds, including a marked diminution of the Dartford Warblers. Graphic notes on this winter were provided at a BOC meeting on 14th February 1917:

> *Mr P. E. Bunyard said he had heard of several Kingfishers being captured by hand in Surrey as a result of balls of ice being formed on their feet.*

> *Mr Carruthers Gould said that during the great frost he walked over the fields between East Molesey and Esher in order to observe the effect of the cold upon bird life. He picked up a dead Heron, which appeared to have been starved and showed no sign of injury. In a ditch overhung by bushes and not quite frozen over he flushed a Greater Spotted Woodpecker and Kingfisher. The Redwings and Fieldfares had come in close to the cottages and fed on scraps thrown out by the cottagers, and picked over the horse-droppings in the road.*

At a later meeting on the 4th November 1917 Bunyard reported the 'apparent extermination of the Dartford Warbler' and also of the Woodlark, both in a group of counties including Surrey. These extracts are from *Birds, Discovery and Conservation*, pp. 68-72. Jourdain and Witherby (1918) gave some specific results for Surrey, including substantial decreases for the Pied Wagtail (50%), Wren (80-90%), Dunnock (at least 50%), Stonechat (wiped out), Song Thrush (50-90%), Mistle Thrush (80%), Dartford Warbler (but at least one pair bred), Treecreeper and Bullfinch. 1919 was mostly a cold year, with a cool spring, arctic winds and snow in September, one of the coldest Octobers on record and an icy November. One of the heaviest snowfalls of the last 100 years began late on Christmas Day 1927, with drifts reaching fifteen feet at Godstone. There was a spell of severe weather in February and March 1929, at its coldest from 11th to 17th February. In Kent, even the sea froze at Whitstable (Currie). Counts of dead birds at the Molesey and Spelthorne reservoirs included over 60 Black-headed Gulls, 12 Coot and four Tufted Duck (*BB, 22:156-57*).

A count of dead gulls around Staines Reservoirs on 26th December 1933, after a long spell of cold weather, found 65 Black-headed, nine Common and four Herring Gulls (Glegg). Great Crested Grebe numbers fell by 12% during droughts in 1933 and 1934.

Colder times 1938 to the 1960s. The cold spell of 17th-26th December 1938 began a run of three severe winters. On the 17th, eight Brent Geese appeared at Island Barn Reservoir, only the second dated vice-county record. Snow fell on the 18th and lay for over a week, killing Dartford Warblers on the heaths. Daytime temperatures at Kew remained below freezing on the 19th, 20th and 21st. Winds were mainly from the north and east and snow fell every day from the 18th to the 26th. The observatory at Kew recorded a total of 64 hours of snowfall. Fitter and Homes (1939) give a full account for the London area. Skylarks were conspicuous immigrants. There were 'many thousands' at Beddington Sewage Farm, of which hundreds starved to death in the cold. Brent Geese (a very unusual species at the time) appeared at Island Barn Reservoir and, equally unusually, at least eleven Pink-footed Geese arrived at Beddington Sewage Farm. Severe weather of 1939-40 had a more serious effect than in 1929 but less than in 1917, when cold was more prolonged. There were three very cold periods, at the end of December 1939 and in mid-January and mid-February 1940. A widespread storm of freezing rain in January 1940 was the most severe of its kind in the 20th century and caused spectacular damage to trees, whose twigs were loaded down with up to fifteen times their weight in ice (Eden). On the South Downs, roosting birds were frozen to their perches. There was heavy snow, after which a huge flock of Skylarks arrived at Beddington. The Thames froze over at Kingston. White-fronted Geese appeared on Staines Moor in the second cold spell. In the third, six Brent Geese were found by Frensham Great Pond and two more on the Thames at Chiswick, the third and fourth dated vice-county records, and a flock of Bean Geese arrived at Staines, the first for the district. Woodlarks, Grey Wagtails and Long-tailed Tits were among the breeding species that suffered badly. Stonechats and Dartford Warblers, already hit by heath fires in 1939, fell further in 1940. No Dartfords bred for more than a decade after that winter. The number of breeding herons fell below the level of the first census in 1928. Water Rail numbers were down.

January 1945 was very cold. One of the most severe winters of the 20th century seems to have been that of 1946/47. February 1947 was the seventh coldest month since 1659. The temperature was -17°C (1°F) at Redhill on the 24th (Davison and Currie) and temperatures at Greenwich did not rise above freezing for fourteen consecutive days. Ashby (1948) describes how the cold spell started with snowfall on 22nd January, followed by more snow which remained on the ground until a partial thaw on 9th February and then further freezing temperatures until 8th March. Snow lay on the ground for 45 days in London and ended with a bad ice-storm a few days before the thaw. A flock of 125 Smew gathered at Walton Reservoirs in February. There was a national invasion of Waxwings. Many other birds died. The mortality list from Oxshott included Green Woodpeckers, Blackbirds, Song Thrushes, Great and Blue Tits and Crows. Heathland species suffered severely. Barn Elms Reservoirs froze over early in February, moving about a thousand Pochard onto the Thames and other unfrozen sites. The Spelthorne reservoirs were partly frozen over in February and almost completely in early March. The relatively deep Walton Reservoir was the only one in the London area to remain unfrozen. Dead Red-throated Divers were found at Island Barn and Walton reservoirs on 1st March. The number of breeding Herons, which had recovered since 1940, fell to a new low. Five Mute Swans were found dead at Hedgecourt on a single day and many Coots were killed by the cold.

Cold spells in the Februarys of 1948 and 1956 brought Curlew and other waders to sewage farms. In the cold winter of 1955/56 there were about 170 shore waders at Beddington Sewage Farm on 2nd February, including 57 Ringed Plovers, 82 Dunlin, 23 Knot, 17 Ruffs and a Purple Sandpiper. Walton and Island Barn reservoirs between them held up to 2,450 Pochard and 4,300 Tufted Duck on 25th-26th February (Homes, 1957). The Grey Heron population fell sharply after the cold winter of 1954/55. A cold winter in 1958/59 seems to have had little effect on the Dartford Warbler population but they did not survive the next cold winter, in 1961/62. A hard frost which began on 14th December 1961 persisted until at least the 28th. On the 31st, five inches of snow fell overnight on the West Surrey heaths and a further three inches the following day. It covered them for three days and wiped out the Dartford Warblers, some of which had survived the frost.

The following winter, of 1962/63, was the severest since 1739/40. Freezing temperatures began just before Christmas and more or less continuous snow from 26th to 28th December left 12-18 inches (30-45 cm) of snow over much of Hampshire, Kent, Surrey and Sussex. The heaviest snowfall began late on the 29th, accompanied by an easterly gale and there were further falls from 3rd to 4th and 19th to 20th January and again from 6th to 7th February. January 1963 was the fifth coldest month since 1659 (Eden, 1995). The Thames froze to a depth of seven inches at Shepperton. Contractors were called in to clear 700 tons of ice, mostly in blocks a foot thick, from Knight Reservoir to keep the works operable. The weather of that winter brought an extraordinary 5,000 Snipe to Beddington Sewage Farm on 26th December 1962. Shore birds driven inland included three Purple Sandpipers at Staines. The newly-opened Queen Elizabeth II Reservoir proved less susceptible to freezing than older reservoirs and attracted 850 Goosander in late January. There were further heavy casualties among resident birds across the county.

Warmer times. None of the Surrey part of the Thames has frozen over since 1963. Cold snaps in the winters of 1965/66 and 1969/70 produced hard weather movements but did not significantly damage breeding populations. There was extensive flooding in the Thames, Wey and Mole valleys after prolonged rain in September 1968. This did little harm to habitats in itself but prompted river bank works which were, in places, more damaging to them. The winter of 1978/79 was cold, with heavy snow in Surrey and the Dartford Warbler population was reduced by at least a third. The December of 1981 was one of the coldest and snowiest in the 20th century and it was followed by severe weather in January 1982. February 1986 was the coldest since 1947, with snow and persistently easterly winds. January 1987 saw another spell of heavy snow and exceptional cold. On the 12th, the temperature did not rise above -9.4°C all day at Warlingham. Dartford Warblers were again reduced.

1987 was the year of the great gale, a violent windstorm or hurricane that swept across southeast England on the night of 15/16th October. Gusts reached 110 mph in the Channel Isles and 99 mph at Gatwick. Fifteen million trees were lost or badly damaged across the country. Heronries were destroyed and unusual birds, including many Sabine's Gulls, were blown into Surrey. Kew Gardens alone lost over 1,000 trees. It was thought to be the strongest wind since the Great Storm of 26th November, 1703, which was documented by Daniel Defoe. A note on the 1987 events is in Wheatley (1989) and there are other details and photographs in Ogley (1988). The long term effect of these events on the birds was small. Neither storm occurred in the breeding season and the woodlands damaged in 1987 are making an excellent recovery. Six inches of snow at Tadworth on 5th April 1989, and no doubt elsewhere in Surrey, does not seem to have stayed long enough to do significant harm. Similarly, heavy snow and a cold spell in February 1991 seem to have done little damage.

The exact path of climate change over the past 2,000 years is a matter of some controversy. The closing decades of the 20th century saw a return to warmer times, but possibly not warmer than they were 1,000 years ago, or in Roman Times.

The Climate and the Breeding Birds. Average world temperatures are thought to have risen by about 0.6°C over the past 150 years and there is a projected further growth of 2°C over the 21st century (Crick, 1999).

For the UK, 0.6°C is similar to a movement of about 150 km (94 miles) south, enough to make a difference to typical bird migration and egg-laying dates. Empirical work by the BTO, summarised by Crick, shows that there is evidence of both effects. In one study, average first arrival dates at Bird Observatories of six common migrants – the Swift, Swallow, Garden Warbler, Blackcap, Chiffchaff and Willow Warbler, were found to have advanced by at least five days for each species since the 1970s.

The use of Bird Observatory information helps to eliminate increased coverage as a source of bias, though it leaves a statistical factor. Samples drawn from a variable population will show an increasing spread as more observations are made, even if the average does not change. The longer you sample, the more chance there is of finding an early date. To be fully convincing, first arrival dates would need to be seen to get later in a period of climatic cooling as well as getting earlier during a period of warming. Another BTO study, based on an analysis of nest record cards since 1940, provides stronger support. For most of the 65 species studied, egg-laying tended to be earlier in the 1940s and 1950s, later in the 1960s and 1970s and then earlier again since 1980 in a way that matches changes in average spring temperatures. Surrey information on first arrival dates is less robust than that used by the BTO but it shows a similar trend, illustrated by charts in some of the species accounts. A study of arrival dates of 23 migrants in Leicestershire in the years 1942-91 (Mason, 1995) showed significantly different trends among species, with the Sand Martin, Sedge Warbler, Blackcap and Chiffchaff arriving earlier and the Cuckoo, Tree Pipit, Whinchat, Whitethroat and Garden Warbler arriving later. Ten species arrived significantly later in the relatively cold late 1950s and 60s. Sussex information for 1966-96 showed a significant negative correlation between February, March, April or March/April temperatures and arrival dates for 16 out of 23 summer migrants (Laxton *et al.*, 1997). Similar features are suggested, though not rigorously proved, for most of these species in the Surrey information in the present work, with the trend to earlier arrivals continuing into the warmer 1990s.

Information of this type is called phenological. Phenology was first investigated seriously in 1917, when it was thought that plant behaviour could help with weather forecasting. This proved unreliable but it was later found that weather affected the future behaviour of plants, insects and birds. Sparks and Carey (1995) examined information covering 1736-1947 from the Marsham estate in Norfolk. Among the birds included in the study, Swallows and Cuckoos were found to arrive earlier in warmer and wetter years. Sparks (1999) shows how the average leafing dates over the past 50 years in Surrey of four common trees have been associated with average January-March temperatures:

Average Leafing Dates and First Migrant Arrivals in Surrey by Decade

	1950-59	1960-69	1970-79	1980-89	1990-99
Tree					
Ash	6th May	7th May	7th May	30th April	24th April
Horse Chestnut	25th March	27th March	31st March	27th March	15th March
Lime	7th April	9th April	12th April	14th April	3rd April
Oak	30th April	26th April	24th April	20th April	10th April
Temperature °C					
January-March average	4.3	4.2	4.5	4.3	5.6

A noticeable feature of the table is that the 1990s were over one degree warmer than the preceding 40 years. Tree leafing has come forward by at least a week, though the results are not uniform among the species. The relationship of temperature with the arrival dates of a number of common migrants is charted in the species accounts.

The Development of the Landscape

Surrey, like most of southern England, has an almost wholly artificial landscape. Very few natural lakes or large ponds exist in Surrey. The damming of streams to form fish ponds and ornamental lakes was, until the late 19th century, the main factor governing the location of sites suitable for significant numbers of waterfowl. In the 20th century it was the creation of reservoirs and the extraction of gravel. Restoration of disused reservoirs and gravel pits for recreational use or as nature reserves, where not used for landfill, is a fairly recent development. The creation of parkland, initially as deer parks, later as country estates, then often converting them to public parks, produced a kind of controlled, ideal landscape.

The wealden woods (Andreaswald) were cleared early. Southwest Surrey may have been fairly widely cultivated by the Bronze Age, some 3,500 years ago. There were evidently cleared areas suitable for substantial settlements. For example on Kings Ridge, which crosses Frensham Common between the Great and Little Ponds, four Bronze Age burial mounds are still clearly visible. These indicate a prosperous local community. It has been suggested that farming methods of the time could have led to the development of heathland. Nutrient minerals were leached out of the exposed sands, leaving a poor, acid soil for which the natural cover was heath. Grazing held back the next stage of development, which would have been pine and birch woodland. It must be obvious to any observer in west Surrey today, that the indigenous birch could take over ungrazed heaths entirely within a few decades. Over a longer period Scots Pine would become the dominant tree, though it may not have been present in the area in the Bronze Age. Elsewhere in Surrey, along the Greensand hills that cross the county to the south or the North Downs, Hill Forts such as Anstiebury Camp at Coldharbour, and Hascombe Camp suggest substantial clearance for agriculture.

Changes to the landscape gathered pace with the growth of a more commercial, but still predominantly agrarian, society from the Middle Ages to the 18th century. Some, such as the enclosure of commonland, made profound changes to bird habitats. Richmond Park was enclosed early.

The effect of changing land use is illustrated by the history of south London. In prehistoric times, the southern margin of the Thames between Battersea and Greenwich merged into the Great South Marsh, an area about eight miles by two and a half with its southern boundary on rising ground at Clapham, Brixton and Camberwell (Besant, 1912). There was a ford at Westminster but those crossing it still had to traverse a mile or so of bog and swamp before they got to higher ground at Clapham Rise. Later a causeway was built and later still the ford became a ferry. At some time, in the Roman period or before, parts of the marsh were embanked and enclosed to permit settlements at Battersea, Bermondsey, Kennington, Rotherhithe and Southwark. Southwark was a Roman town built on sandy ground, with marshes on either side (Brandon, 1998). Battersea Rise was an area of scrub (Old English *hris*, brushwood). Bermondsey had an abbey with substantial grounds. A 14th century visiting bishop left his hawk in a cloister during the service and returned to find it had been stolen. He excommunicated the thieves (Gurney, 1921). The incident shows the popularity of falconry at the time. The south side of the Thames was at this time still mainly rural with a mostly unbanked margin that was probably reedy and marshy in many places. There must have been, in these great stretches of wetland, many herons, ducks, geese and other waterfowl. Spoonbills had once nested across the Thames at Fulham and must have been a moderately common sight in the nearby Surrey wetlands for anyone who went there. There were also woods and some plush country houses on the higher ground and Nightingales could be heard there. Sixteenth century Rotherhithe was the site of Britain's first gunpowder works (Maxwell) and later the docks at Rotherhithe could contain *one hundred sail of square-rigged vessels* (Pigot, 1839) but when Gilbert visited The Borough, now part of Lambeth, in 1791, it was a predominantly rural area. Among the birds he noted were Swifts, which feed on insects and require good air quality. His brother Benjamin had a cow and several acres of hay meadow in South Lambeth. William Wordsworth passed through Surrey on his way to Calais in 1802 and made a well known observation from the top of his coach as it crossed Westminster Bridge:

> Ships, towers, domes, theatres, and temples lie
> Open unto the fields, and to the sky:
> All bright and glittering in the smokeless air.

Later in the century the fields had gone and the air was far from smokeless. It would be far into the 20th century before air pollution had been controlled enough for House Martins to return.

Even so, marshland could be found as far down the river as the Surrey/Kent border at Rotherhithe until at least the middle of the 19th century. In 1811, a Marsh Harrier nested near the Grand Surrey Canal on the Deptford Road; it was placed on a small hillock just above the water's edge ... Graves (1811-21). *The Village London Atlas* (Village Press) includes a map dating from 1822 in which the docks are about half complete. The waterfront had been built on but there was undeveloped land by the Grand Surrey Canal. The canal had two branches by 1839, one running to Croydon via the hamlet of Sydenham and the other to Bermondsey and there were links to the interior of the county. The canal crossed roads, including the Deptford Road, and reached the Thames through the docks. A map published in 1854 (Collins, 1854), a year when 10,000 Londoners died of cholera, shows that a 2 km stretch of undeveloped land ran west from what were then called the Commercial and Grand Surrey Docks, which were still incomplete. The Grand Surrey Canal still passed through a good deal of undeveloped land.

Development of the docks and most of the nearby land continued, leaving Southwark Park (63 acres, 20 hectares) as the last remnant of the open space that had been there, and visited by up to 100,000 people (Hudson, 1898) in a single day. Jefferies (1948) wrote of the masts of ships that were visible from London Bridge Station and of barges loaded with hay and straw to be seen on the river below Waterloo Bridge, towards the end of the 19th century. The docks themselves eventually succumbed to the forces of change as larger and more efficient facilities were set up on the north side of the river and further down, at Tilbury. The Surrey Docks, like others, featured in the labour disputes of the 1960s (Wilson, 1972). They were gradually run down and finally closed to shipping at the end of 1970. During this period they entered a new ornithological phase. Initially the area gradually became overgrown with weeds and scrub and the waters attracted wintering flocks of Pochard, Tufted Duck and other waterfowl. Black Redstarts moved into the abandoned buildings and by 1972 there were five pairs breeding in derelict sheds and offices. Infilling of the docks began before the docks were closed. Lady Dock and most of Lavender Dock had become 60 acres (20 hectares) of flat, overgrown waste ground by 1970. Island, Quebec, Stave and Russia docks had all gone by 1975. Demolition of the dockside buildings provided further habitat changes, as did the start of new construction. Grant (1971), George (1974) and Alderton (1977) give useful accounts of the period. They refer to the whole area as Surrey Commercial Docks, shortened to the Surrey Docks in the rest of this text. Among the other breeding birds listed for this period are the Red-legged Partridge (1973 and 1975), Little Ringed Plover (1973-75), Ringed Plover (1973), Lapwing (1973), Skylark (1973-75) and Yellow Wagtail (15 pairs of which at least nine bred in 1975). This was a remarkable community for an area in central London and doubly so for including two species (Little Ringed Plover and Black Redstart) which were unknown in Britain in George Graves's time.

The most recent phase has been the completion of new construction and the establishment of an 'ecological park' and recreational facilities. Lady Dock is a housing estate. Lavender Dock has been reduced to Lavender Pond and Reed Warblers breed there. Quebec Dock is a site for light industry. Russian Dock has become Russia Dock woodland. Island Dock is parkland. Stave Dock has become Stave Hill. Greenland Dock and South Dock have become marinas. Norway dock is a pool by Norway Gate. The Surrey Basin is all that remains of the Grand Surrey Docks and the adjacent Albion Dock, by Albion Street, has been built over. Canada Dock is now Canada Water, a shopping centre and a car park from which, in January 1997, a Ring-necked Duck could be seen among the Tufted on Canada Water. Later the same year, a pair of Common Terns nested at a dockland site for the first time and raised two young. Graves found nearly two dozen on the Grand Surrey Canal in 1812 but they were not known to breed anywhere in Surrey south of the Thames until over 150 years later.

The Surrey Docks

Cobbett called London 'The Great Wen' in the 1830s, when it did not extend far south of the Thames. Development spread across south London as the 19th century progressed. Waste land that had existed between Brixton and Herne Hill in 1874 was totally covered with houses by 1909 (Power, 1910). The spread of railways facilitated the growth of the London suburbs. The railway came first and housing development followed. Gordon Home, writing in 1901, was able to say that 'Ewell fortunately does not evince any great symptoms of expansion, and both stations are, so far, beyond the reach of houses of any sort' and that from near the platforms 'there are views of the village as typically lovely as may be imagined, for in the meadows down by the stream there grow huge elms …' Although urban development at Worcester Park had begun in the 1890s, it was the electrification of the railway line from Wimbledon to Epsom in 1925 that was the major impetus for growth in this part of Surrey. The fields used by breeding Lapwings were built over in Mitcham by 1926 and New Malden by 1934 (*BLA*). The development of Cheam, Ewell, Stoneleigh, Worcester Park, which took place in the 1930s, is described by Jackson, whose engaging book gives a detailed description of the spread of the London suburbs from 1900 to 1939. The spread was finally controlled by the introduction of the Green Belt in 1938.

Farmland. The open field system of medieval agriculture required very few hedges. These came in with the enclosure movement, which parcelled up the land of the open fields and commons into private farmland surrounded by walls or, in southern England, hedges. The hedges enriched the bird life of the fields. Grassland on the North Downs supported large numbers of sheep from the Middle Ages and for many years after. Flocks grazed on the downs by day and were folded on arable at night. The fold site shifted daily so that the arable land was evenly manured (Shrubb). By the mid 19th century 'high farming' had become the norm. With this method, fodder roots were grown for winter feed, either to be grazed or to be fed to animals in stalls. The manure from the animals was used to fertilise the fields.

Grass was grown in short-term 'leys' on arable land rather than in permanent pasture. There was an extensive reduction of hedge length in the 19th century because farmers wanted more efficient field layouts. By 1860s some said too much downland had been ploughed but sheepwalks persisted into the 20th century. Sheepwalks made up a distinctive type of grassland, favoured by Montagu's Harrier, Grey Partridge, Quail, Great Bustard, Stone Curlew, Lapwing, larks and Wheatear. A thriving rabbit population and intermittent activities such as turf-stripping and temporary cultivation provided extra opportunities for nesting and feeding. Conditions were suitable for species such as the Wheatear to breed. It is clear from a comment by John Aubrey, quoted in the species account, that this was an important habitat for them. Quail and Stone Curlew may also have bred there.

The balance of arable and grassland has not been constant. In the 1860s two out of every three fields in Britain were ploughed but a steady shift towards grass left less than one field in four as arable by 1938. Hop-growing in the Farnham area may go back to 1643 (Howkins, 1987) but the great cultivations have now gone. Heaps of spent hops used by a nursery in west Surrey provided a rich food source for wintering finches into the 1980s. Orchards have now all but gone, as has heathland grazing (except for environmental purposes).

Bucknill gives this summary of rural Surrey (excluding Spelthorne and the County of London) in 1897, drawn from the agricultural returns, which is compared with 2001 figures in the Land Use table.

Farm land use in 1897 and 2001

	Acres 1897	Hectares 1897	Hectares 2001
Corn and cereals	57,681	23,343	
Roots, artificial grasses, brassicas	35,559	14,391	
Clover and grasses	26,471	10,713	
Bare fallow	8,546	3,459	
Crops and fallow	**128,257**	**51,906**	**15,537**
Permanent pasture	152,893	61,875	28,025
Temporary grass			5,090
Rough grazing			3,192
Hops	1,416	573	
Setaside		-	4,994
Orchards	2,460	996	
Other farm land			3,288
Total arable and grass	**285,026**	**115,350**	**60,126**
Woods and plantations	54,437	22,030	5,838
Heathland used for grazing	11,856	4,798	
Total	**351,319**	**142,178**	**65,964**
Reduction in farmland since 1897			76,214

Source: Bucknill, SWT, calculations

In recent years the more intensive use of farmland has resulted in a further widespread loss of hedgerows. Since 1950 alone, over 300,000 miles of hedgerow have been lost in the UK. A 1990 Institute of Terrestrial Ecology report estimated that a quarter of the entire hedgerow stock had been lost in just six years. A measure of legal protection has been introduced but it protects only about twenty per cent of the hedges in England and Wales and none at all in Scotland and Northern Ireland. While Surrey has suffered less than some other parts of the country, hedgerow clearance is one of several factors that have resulted in the loss of what were once typical farmland species.

The three year ley was the dominant farm plan from about 1945 to 1970 (Shrubb). Three years of ley were followed by two of cereals, managed round a dairy herd. The system retained most of the features that enabled birds to adapt to High Farming. Undersown stubbles provided winter food, as did grain-feeding of wintering cattle. Early herbicides were not very efficient. A chemical-based revolution started around 1965-70. The leys were abandoned. Arable fodder crops have now almost gone. Wheat, Barley and Oil-seed rape now account for 75% of arable and 67% of tillage crops now sown in autumn. Animals are no longer needed to provide natural fertiliser. Chemicals are used instead. Specialisation has replaced crop rotations. Field size has increased. Grass herbicides have led to decline of spring tillage. The use of insecticides in standing cereal crops has reduced insect population (Shrubb). These changes have greatly reduced the acreage of winter stubble fields, which in turn has seriously affected finches and buntings which use them as a source of food. RSPB research indicates that the collapse of the Tree Sparrow, Cirl Bunting and Corn Bunting populations can be largely attributed to this. Weed control has reduced another food source.

It is worth remembering that the loss of stubble fields and of farmland weeds are not new factors. Richard Jefferies (1878), writing of Partridge shooting, said that *The old wheat stubbles – which the birds, after all, loved better than anything – have entirely disappeared* and that *The Land is far cleaner than it used to be; and the partridges in dry weather can run between the rows of turnips as easily as on a gravel path.* Nor is the loss of hedges something new. Denham Jordan wrote in 1893 that *Old hedges are rapidly disappearing from the face of the country. … Our present system of farming on a large scale has had much to do with the destruction of fine old hedgerows.*

Unimproved grassland is found on all types of soil. It has been under heavy pressure, with an estimated loss of 97% in the second half of the 20th century. After 1945 the birds of dry grasslands were greatly affected by habitat change. On chalk downland, decline of rabbits on unploughable slopes led to rank grass and loss of Woodlarks and Wheatears (Shrubb). Today the downs are substantially given over to woodland and scrub, with a good deal of arable farming on the north slopes and other areas given over to amenity uses such as municipally managed 'open spaces' and golf courses. The change from chalk grassland to scrub brings gains as well as losses among the birds. Botanists have more substantial concerns about declines among chalk grassland species.

On other grassland the use of seeded grass with fertilisers has reduced plant diversity and caused the loss of insect life. Early grazing prevents seeding, further reducing food supply. There was a switch to silage, replacing haystacks with plastic bailing from the late 1980s. Earlier cutting threatened nests and left fewer ripe seeds to drop.

The loss of rickyards with their associated rats etc has altered the pattern of winter mortality of Barn Owls. There is little 19th century or early 20th century evidence that they were affected by severe winters but severe declines occurred after the winters of 1962/63, 1979/80 and 1981/82, when rickyards had disappeared (Shrubb). Reduced spillage of grain and improved storage to meet European Union regulations has left less for House Sparrows and other birds to eat.

Heathland probably reached its maximum extent in Surrey during the 18th century. According to figures in Webb (1986) there were 136, 838 acres (55,500 ha) of heathland in 1804. At this time the heaths were extensively grazed, which prevented them from being overgrown by grass and scrub. Golden Plovers were once noted as wintering on heathland habitats in Surrey. The habit declined as heathland was enclosed for grazing, and grazing in remaining areas was reduced (Shrubb). The development of towns such as Hindhead and Woking during the 19th century swallowed up areas of heathland and some of the remainder was ploughed. Bucknill recorded nearly 12,000 acres (4,850 ha) of grazed heathland at the end of the century, an area larger than the entire current heathland cover and presumably there were also some ungrazed heaths. During the 20th century the destruction of heathland was accelerated by the cessation of most grazing after the 1930s. Many golf courses have been laid out. Much heathland became overgrown by birch and pine, heading for its natural state, climax woodland, if

Plovers at Milford   *John Davis*

ungrazed. More areas were ploughed during the 1939-45 war, resulting in at least temporary loss. Some 166 acres (60 hectares) of Ashtead Common, 111 acres (40 hectares) of Epsom Common and 114 acres (40 hectares) of Walton Heath were ploughed (*BLA*). Smithwood Common, at Cranleigh, was also ploughed (Watson). The M3 was built across Chobham Common and the M25/A3 Junction straddles heathland at Wisley. The area of heathland had fallen to 14,575 acres (5,901 hectares) by 1983 (figure from Webb). Lindley estimated a sixteen per cent loss from 1975 to 1985. The Surrey Wildlife Trust figures suggest that it is currently only about 7,700 acres (3,100 hectares).

Changes to the heaths are not always well documented and some features are of relatively recent origin. In the 1930s, the Devil's Punch Bowl was devoid of trees. The magnificent beech woods which are such a prominent feature of the western slope, and which have brought in new species such as the Wood Warbler and Firecrest, are the result of later plantings. In bygone years, when the heathland around Hindhead was remote and desolate, Ring Ouzels and Ravens bred there.

Guns, traps and machinery. Greater efficiency of breech-loading guns and improvements in transport to remote areas increased the impact of 19th century persecution, but much trapping was an autumn activity and may not have greatly affected overall mortality (Shrubb). Egging reduced 19th century Lapwing populations, but so did drainage, enclosure and agricultural improvement (see Bucknill). Country landowners were long recognised as being responsible for the decline and often elimination of birds of prey in Surrey, as elsewhere. Great Crested Grebes, like some other birds, would have been killed to provide feathers for hats. The substitution of machines for horses got under way with such devices as the steam plough in the second half of the 19th century. The first real intimation of what was to come, though, was probably the collapse of the Corncrake population. Birds which had previously bred safely in the hayfields harvested with a scythe were cut to pieces by the new harvesting machines.

Pollution Problems. Air quality in the London area deteriorated throughout the 19th century and continued to do so until the 1956 Clean Air Act turned the tide. Legendary London fogs culminated in the smog of December 1952. For 60 hours, visibility was reported at 22 yards or less. This lethal mixture of fog, soot and sulphur dioxide probably killed 4,000 people in London and a further 2,000 in the suburban areas of the surrounding counties. Poor air quality drove out insect and bird populations. The improvements since the 1950s have seen them return.

The switch from coal to smokeless fuels was a major factor in the improvement of air quality. By 1970, the level of atmospheric pollution in Inner London had fallen by approximately 75% against the level of 1956 and had become similar to that in the outskirts of London, where it had fallen by about 50% (Strangeman, 1977).

Water quality in the Thames deteriorated from industrial and sewage pollution to the point where, in places, the water was often black in colour, foul-smelling and producing hydrogen sulphide gas. In the late 1950s, the Port of London Authority and the Greater London Council began an anti-pollution programme. Sewage works were modernised and industrial concerns were required to channel pollutant waste through the new disposal facilities. Oxygen levels slowly improved and by the end of 1972, 66 species of fish had been taken from previously fishless zones (Grant *et al.*, 1974). Improvement was well under way by the 1980s. Fish penetrated further upstream and the Heron population along the Thames Valley increased markedly.

Pollution of the food chain by pesticides based on organochlorine compounds has been detected in Surrey but may have been less severe than in more heavily agricultural counties. The Sparrowhawk was one of the most noticeably affected species, and became a rather scarce bird. A strong recovery began after some of the more dangerous pesticides were withdrawn and the Sparrowhawk is now probably the commonest bird of prey in Surrey.

Conservation Work

Legislation to protect the domestic producers of wool and corn had existed since the Middle Ages, but there was nothing like the elaborate web of agricultural protection and subsidies that has been created in the 20th century, mostly since the 1950s. When rural changes were discussed before the 20th century, it was mainly in forms such as the effect of the Corn Laws on national prosperity or of the enclosure of commons on rural poverty. Bucknill wrote at a time when the shape of the countryside was largely determined by economic and social forces and few people worried about its wildlife, which was on the whole in a healthy state. Huge movements of people from the country to the town had taken place. Urban living conditions, not least in London, were often bad and the subject of widespread concern. The first bird protection legislation was beginning to reduce persecution but habitat management and the creation of nature reserves were ideas for later centuries.

Species and Habitat Management. Modern conservation concerns focus on:

Maintaining biodiversity. Action plans have been worked up for some of the threatened species, with the assistance of government money.

Identification and protection of key habitats. Much of this is done through government-funded initiatives including Habitat Action Plans and some is backed by European legislation for the protection of sensitive habitats, mainly heathland. Planning controls have been tightened up for development within five km of any Nightjar, Woodlark and Dartford Warbler habitat.

Damage to wetlands caused by excessive water abstraction. The RSPB has estimated that more than 50 British rivers suffer from low flows and that 140 key wildlife sites may be threatened by the effects of water abstraction. In Surrey, deliberate land drainage has probably been a bigger problem, at least over the longer term.

At county level, work has concentrated on reserve acquisition and the designation of sites that deserve protection. The creation of the London Wetland Centre by a development of the old Barn Elms Reservoirs has been a huge success for the national bodies concerned. The RSPB is developing a new heathland reserve near Farnham. The Surrey Wildlife Trust has extended and improved its portfolio of nature reserves in the administrative county. The Trust has also drawn up Biodiversity and Habitat Action Plans and it screens planning applications. Information on bird distribution is supplied by the Surrey Bird Club to meet the requirements of the Environmental Impact Assessments that are now required for sensitive new developments and the Club advises on other conservation matters. Similar work is done by other bodies in that part of the vice-county which is in Greater London. Local groups such as those at Beddington and Unstead sewage farms have worked hard to improve the habitat for their local (and sometimes nationally important) birds.

The most conspicuous habitat restoration work in Surrey has been on heathland. Grazing for commercial purposes was a traditional form of heathland management. Nearly 12,000 acres (4,800 hectares) was grazed in 1897. Although this has now ceased commercially, grazing has returned to favour as a form of conservation management. Cattle eat the Purple Moor-grass *Molinia caerulea* and Wavy Hair-grass *Deschampsia flexuosa*, which would otherwise become dominant, in preference to the heather. Grazing can also reduce the extent of scrub and bracken invasion. Provided that there are not too many cows, the heathland bird community benefits, as do insect and other heathland life forms. Grazing may be restricted to the summer, when the grass is growing, the animals being kept elsewhere at other times

Grazing at Chobham Common   *Photo M. B. Lancaster*

of year. Highland cattle have been used for grazing, or sometimes the cattle from a local farm. The British White (a rare and ancient breed) and its hybrids are also used because they have a docile reputation, important in a public place. They have been seen calving on the new grazing marsh at the London Wetland Centre (Barn Elms). New Forest ponies have been used on Prey Heath, near Woking and Highland cattle at Folly Bog, on the northern edge of Pirbright Ranges. There has been grazing on Chobham, Hindhead and Witley Commons and it has been proposed for Bagmoor, Royal and Wisley commons. Grazing requires fencing, gates and cattle grids. This restricts access and reduces the sense of wildness. Tree felling and ground-cover clearance has been carried out on heathland. Total clearance achieves quick results but needs careful planning to avoid the creation of heather deserts and it may reduce biological diversity.

Site designations. A variety of levels of site protection have been introduced:

Sites of Special Scientific Interest (SSSIs). These are created under British legislation Countryside Acts of 1981 and 2001 on the basis of the importance of sites in a biodiversity, geological or other scientific context. There are over 60 SSSIs in Surrey.

Sites of Nature Conservation Interest (SNCIs). SNCI status confers little in the way of legal protection but it carries some weight in planning guidance matters and has been formalised as a way of monitoring numerous Surrey sites that do not qualify as SSSIs.

Special Protection Areas (SPAs). Special Protection Areas are created under EC Directive 79/409 on the Conservation of Wild Birds. They are made up of SSSIs. Four areas in Surrey have achieved this status, three of them for heathland birds.

South West London Water Bodies (Kempton Park, Knight and Bessborough, Staines and Wraysbury Reservoirs, Thorpe No. 1 Gravel Pit and gravel pits at Wraysbury and Hythe End). Between them these sites held 2.4% of the northwest European population of Gadwall and 2.1% of the Shoveler in the five years to 1997/98.

Wealden Heaths I (Thursley, Hankley and Frensham Commons).

Wealden Heaths II (Devil's Punch Bowl SSSI in Surrey and other heathland SSSIs in Hampshire and Sussex).

Thames Basin Heaths (14 SSSIs in Berkshire, Hampshire and Surrey, of which those in Surrey are: Ash to Brookwood Heaths, Bourley and part of Long Valley, Chobham Common, Colony Bog and Bagshot

Heath, part of Bagshot Woods and Heaths, Horsell Common, Ockham and Wisley Commons, Smart's and Prey Heaths, and Whitmoor Common).

Special Areas of Conservation (SACs). These are created under the EC Habitats Directive which specifies habitat types and/or species which are rare or threatened within a European context. None of the species are birds. Four Surrey areas were candidates for SAC status:

Mole Gap to Reigate Escarpment, for Yew and Box woodland

Richmond Park

Thursley, Ash, Pirbright and Chobham, for heathland and exposed peat (approved with effect from 1st April 2005)

Windsor Forest and Great Park

Ramsar Sites. Thursley and Ockley Bogs make up a wetland of international importance as defined by the convention signed at Ramsar, Iran, in 1971. Its status derives from the birds, insects and plants that it supports. The South West London Water Bodies comprise a possible Ramsar site.

National Nature Reserves (NNRs). Ashtead Common, Chobham Common, Richmond Park and Thursley are NNRs

RSPB Reserves. Bourne Woods and Tankersford Common ('The Farnham Heath Project') are RSPB reserves.

Surrey Wildlife Trust and other Reserves. The Surrey Wildlife Trust owns or manages about 70 reserves and open spaces across Surrey. There are others on the Greater London part of the vice-county.

Problems caused by New Colonists and Introduced Species. Some of the birds and animals that have colonised Surrey by natural spread or by introduction do no significant harm to native birds. Others can upset a previous balance. Some, like Pheasants and Rabbits, have been here so long that they have become part of the landscape. Canada Geese are increasing, largely into a vacant ecological niche, but they have had conflicts with other waterfowl. Little Owls also found a niche, but have had rather less breeding success. The current explosion of Ring-necked Parakeets has far from run its natural course but so far, whatever they may do to fruit trees and field crops, the birds do not seem to have had any significant effect on other bird populations. More destructive have been some of the mammals. The native Foxes take eggs and young from ground-nesting birds such as game birds, geese and Nightjars and have moved into urban areas, but in Surrey their overall effect is probably marginal. Cats, on the other hand, destroy large numbers of garden birds in Surrey, as they do elsewhere and they are probably the most significant mammalian predators. Mink predation has been enough to give rise to comment at several Surrey sites. The Mink can climb trees as well as swim. They are an undoubted threat to riverside mammals such as the declining Water Vole and may also be reducing the number of Moorhens and other birds breeding at the waterside.

Habitats and their Birds

Current land use is shown in the table.

Land Use at the end of the 20th century

	Farmland Hectares	Woodland Hectares	Heathland Hectares	Other Hectares	Total Hectares	Sq Km
Greater London	1,275	1,898	51	*34,058*	**37,282**	**373**
Outer Surrey	63,429	37,513	3,060	*57,873*	**161,875**	**1,619**
Spelthorne	471	51	*0*	*4,603*	**5,125**	**51**
Total	**65,175**	**39,462**	**3,111**	*96,534*	204,282	2,043
Vice-county	64,704	39,411	3,111	*91,931*	**199,157**	**1,992**
Administrative county	63,900	37,564	3,060	*62,476*	**167,000**	**1,670**

Farms, Woods and Heaths data for the Administrative County from the Surrey Wildlife Trust

In this table Farmland only includes farms as defined for the Census of Agriculture. Some smaller holdings are omitted from it. Much grassland in the rest of the county is also not included in the farmland total. These figures have been put together from various sources, including the June 1997 Census of Agriculture, The London Biodiversity Audit and Handbooks 9, 12, 21, 22, 26 and 29 of the London Ecology Unit, Drakeford and Sutcliffe (2000), Drewitt (1987), Lindley (undated) and Ordnance Survey Sheet 176 for West London. Italicised figures are estimates based on these.

The changing fortunes of farmland birds are traced in the development of the landscape, above, and in the species accounts. Many of the Common Birds Census areas were on farmland. A pattern of small fields with hedges still persists in many parts of Surrey and is shown in a photograph from Hindhead.

Ridgeway, Highfield and Punch Bowl farms, Hindhead   Photo Flight Images

Woodland. Surrey is one of the most heavily wooded counties in England. Most of the woodland is associated with other habitats and has, where significant, been discussed with them in other parts of this book. A large tract of managed woodland southwest of **Dunsfold**, comprising Botany Bay, Durfold Wood, Fisherlane Wood, Oaken Wood and Tugley Wood is well known for its butterflies and for raptors. Passerines include Nightingale and Hawfinch. **Weatherhill**, near Horley used to be a typical wealden site for Nightingales. The most important of the remaining woodland sites is **Great Ridings Wood,** at East Horsley. The wood, which belongs to the Woodland Trust, has many hornbeams and is currently the most reliable site in Surrey for Hawfinches.

Barfold Copse is an RSPB Reserve but produces very few records. **Staffhurst Wood**, on the eastern boundary of the county, is a non-ornithological SSSI.

Some woodland birds have fallen in numbers over the past 30 years. A national study suggests that changes in the woodland structure arising from deer browsing and reduced management may have resulted in canopy closure and a reduction in the quantity and quality of new tree growth, damaging the habitat for woodland birds (Fuller *et al.* (2005).

Great Ridings Wood   *Photo D. J. Brassington*

Heathland. Surrey heaths account for about thirteen per cent of the UK total and five per cent of all the heathland in Europe. About 60% of the heathland is owned by the Ministry of Defence, which affords a degree of habitat protection and is supported by conservation work made visible in the periodical *Sanctuary* and in local reports such as the one produced annually for the Pirbright Commons. Some of the greensand heaths have held large populations of heathland birds when conditions were right. The early stages of forestry plantations can bring in Nightjars and Woodlarks. Heathland clearance can encourage Stonechats and Dartford Warblers. The pine woods hold Hobbys and Redstarts.

The Greensand Hills. A ridge of sandy hills and commons crosses the county to the south of the North Downs. A few words by A Son of the Marshes (Jordan, 1892), referring to a period about 30 years earlier, gives a feel for what the hills were once like (on a good day, perhaps):

> In the evening, on the top of the Holmbury moor, you could see a flight of Harriers, male and female, – or as the woodlanders term them, blue hawk and ringtail – a most interesting sight. … Bad luck to the blackcock, pheasant or partridge that shows for even one brief moment in any open space …

It is evident from this and other comments by Jordan that the higher ground on these hills was more or less open moor. Today the pine woods are dominant. **Leith Hill** is the highest in Surrey.

Pitch Hill is a good watchpoint for raptors and, if the light is exceptionally clear, offers a view through a gap in the South Downs to the sea. **Hascombe Hill**, which is an old hill fort, and the adjacent **Hurtwood** (Winterfold) are now heavily wooded. The Hurtwood was open heath in the mid-19th century (Yarrell). About 12 square km (3,000 acres) of the Holmbury Hill and the Hurtwood are scheduled for restoration. Work at Winterfold has already brought Dartford Warblers back. Hydon Heath and Hydons Ball are well wooded. There are old records of Goshawk, Nightjar and Firecrest but not much of note in recent years. **Abinger Common** is mainly woodland. **St Martha's Hill** sometimes has Firecrests and Wood Warblers on its slopes, which lead down to Waterloo Pond at Chilworth. A heronry there has been lost.

Limpsfield Common covers about 81 hectares (200 acres) of the greensand hills south of Limpsfield.

Leith Hill and the North Downs   *Photo Flight Images*

The area was surveyed by the Ecology Section of the London Natural History Society from 1936 to 1943, after which the Section switched to surveys of Bookham Common. Oliver (2000) has assessed the changes at Limpsfield Common since that time. Heather and gorse were originally kept open by grazing and burning. Grazing ceased in the mid 1920s but a local committee took on responsibilities for cutting bracken and burning heather from 1935. Ecologically, such open areas of bracken and gorse as still existed in the 1930s have largely been replaced by birch and oak woodland. Ponds which existed in the 1930s have gone and old sand pits have become overgrown. The number of species present in the breeding season has fallen from 53 in 1937 to 29 in 1999. Losses include Turtle Dove, Nightjar, Wryneck, Sand Martin, Nightingale, Wood Warbler, Spotted Flycatcher, Marsh Tit, Willow Tit, Linnet, Redpoll, Hawfinch and Yellowhammer. The only gain (but a good one) was a Redstart. Wintering birds fared little better, with 32 species recorded in 1938 or 1939 compared with 28 in 1999. Losses included Marsh Tit, Willow Tit, House Sparrow and Yellowhammer. Sparrowhawks were gained and Woodpigeons showed a spectacular increase. The changes reflect habitat changes, particularly the loss of open heathland, and wider trends.

Smithwood Common held Whinchats, Stonechats, Wheatears and Red-backed Shrikes before being ploughed. None of these breed there now but recent records include Goshawk, Turtle Dove and Wheatear among the casual visitors and a Lesser Whitethroat was singing in 2000. There is open heathland at **Limpsfield Chart**, **Holmwood** (rather overgrown), **Albury Heath**, **Blackheath** and **Farley Heath**. Overgrown heathland south of Farnham between Bourne Woods and Tankersford Common (169 hectares, 404 acres), is being restored as a heathland reserve by the RSPB under the name of **Farnham Heath**. **Abinger Roughs** and **The Chantries** (Guildford) are good woodland sites. **Reigate Heath**, now mainly a golf course, has a small wet area and is the site of the first Surrey Bar-tailed Godwit, which was in 1816. **Earlswood Common** has man-made lakes, which are its main focus for unusual birds.

Southwest Surrey. The bogs at **Thursley** and **Elstead** were probably formed after clearance of the oak and hazel cover which developed after the end of the last Ice Age. Dormor (1995) provides a useful introduction to their history. Pudmore contains pollen grains about 10,000 years old, dating from the period of woodland cover. Later bog pollens, from about 5,000 years ago, which include cereals and weeds for the first time, suggest temporary land clearance and cultivation in a predominantly forested area, using the slash-and-burn method found in poorer parts of the world to the present day. Further climatic improvement in the Bronze Age, from about 2500 BC, encouraged more widespread clearance of woods on the greensand. A more stable pattern of cultivation, with settlements, appeared on land around Frensham, Elstead, Thursley and Milford. The tree clearances upset the drainage on the poor, iron-rich soil and a water-resistant pan was formed to create bogs. More intensive agriculture seems to have exhausted the poor, sandy soils, which developed into heaths as farmers abandoned their land for more productive areas elsewhere. Most or all of the area may have fallen out of cultivation after a drop in temperatures in the Iron Age which may have led farmers to move to the chalk downland.

The Saxon period presents the first written clues to what the Thursley area might have looked like. A Saxon charter of 909 refers to 'Pudan More' which means the marsh, or moor, of Pudna and might be the bog at Pudmore. Thursley is not mentioned in the Domesday Book and the area was probably regarded as an infertile waste. The commons may not have been much use for growing crops but they were a valuable resource in other ways. They would have had partial tree cover and the 13th century Winchester Pipe Rolls show that wood was being cut. Thick peat deposits had built up by the Middle Ages. These were extracted as fuel for domestic and industrial purposes with increasing intensity until the 17th century, by which time the commons covered some 6,000 acres (24 square km) of which about 50 were bog and quagmire which could not be walked upon without danger of sinking. Iron was produced from furnaces in west Surrey from at least the 16th century. It was worked at forges such as those which were once sited at Hammer Pond. The ore was extracted from local sandstone deposits. Charcoal and peat were used for fuel. A licence of 1634 provided for 10,000 peat turves to be supplied annually to a local ironworks from Witley or Thursley Heath. Up to five feet were removed from Pudmore and some of the present ponds may be old peat diggings. Peat was still being cut for fuel in the 1920s.

Poaching was at one time a problem for land owners. In 1665/66 Charles II commanded a local resident to preserve the hare, pheasant, partridge, heath poult, heron and other wild fowl within an eight-mile radius of his house at Witley (Forster, 1999). The heath poult is today better known as the Black Grouse. It is possible that these birds were present on the Thursley commons at the time, but Hindhead may have been meant. With the decline of the iron industry the area around Witley and Thursley took on a wilder character.

The copse called Will Reeds may have started as a 14th century woodland clearance. There is no evidence of trees at Will Reeds until the publication of an Ordnance Survey map in 1816. Parish Field, a tree-lined field near Will Reeds, has a recorded history which goes back to 1822. It was cultivated during the 1939-45 war. Sewage was being dumped onto it until 1983. The commons at Thursley were grazed from medieval times. Grazing continued on what is now Thursley National Nature Reserve until 1922. It would have been a key factor in keeping the dry and the wet areas open. High ground at the south end was regularly burnt to encourage the growth of grass for extra grazing.

The Scots Pine is now a typical heathland tree. In very distant times, after the ice retreated, the Scots Pine might well have been a dominant tree, as it is in parts of Scotland today. The pines were later replaced by deciduous trees or destroyed by land clearance and the present stock derives from plantings which began in the time of James I (Lousley, 1976). As with the pines, so with the Siskins and the Crossbills. Whenever it was that Crossbills first bred on the commons, it would have been after the Scots Pine arrived. Twelve acres (five hectares) of Scots Pine were planted on Crooksbury Heath in 1776, for use as hop poles. Dormor says that there was a good deal of planting of pine and spruce in Surrey between 1820 and 1850, having been initially recommended by the Board of Agriculture in 1794. In the 1930s, Thursley Common was managed for shooting and forestry and many areas of Scots Pine were planted there.

The writers of the *Letters of Rusticus* refer to a barren, wet, peaty district called the Pudmoors. The present pond at Pudmore, and the nearby Birchy Pond may have taken their present form in Victorian times, for use as duck shoots. In the 1930s, Pudmore Pond was a good deal larger than it is today. Thor's Stone, a rock erected in the bog at Pudmore during some distant age, stands close to the present boardwalk and was probably a village boundary marker. Moat Pond is now surrounded by mature Scots Pines but a photo from the 1930s shows a much more open situation, with deciduous scrub in the background.

Like some other commons, the area has taken a hammering from military activities. Thursley Common was used for training and billeting two cavalry brigades during the Boer War (1899-1902) and more extensively during the war of 1914-18. Tanks were tested there in the 1930s and the troops moved in again for the 1939-45 war. An unsuccessful attempt to drain Moat Pond, which is fed by a spring, was made. Tanks were driven through it. Pudmore was drained. Training was stopped on what is now the Thursley National Nature Reserve in 1965 but has continued in contiguous areas. The Surrey Trust for Nature Conservation (the predecessor of the Surrey Wildlife Trust) made an agreement with the then owner, Colonel Whitbread, in 1965 and Raymond Fry was appointed as the first warden. This and other areas were consolidated into the Thursley National Nature Reserve (3.25 square km, 803 acres), which was created on 4th July 1978.

The general picture of the Thursley area commons that emerges from these brief insights is of an area which, since the Middle Ages at least, has retained most of its physical features - heather, grass, tree and bog, and which for most of the time has been much more heavily used, for forage, fuel, grazing, industry and military purposes, than it has for the past 30 years or so. The heavy usage has been a key factor in keeping the landscape open, sometimes almost treeless, rather than reverting to tree cover and has thereby helped to maintain the uncommon or rare species of wildlife for which it is now best known.

The fairly consistent character of the landscape does not mean that there has been no change in its birds. We know of some, like the Tufted Duck, the Curlew and the Grey Wagtail, that have come and others, like the Wryneck and the Red-backed Shrike, that have gone, for reasons that seem to have little

Thursley, Hankley and Frensham Commons

Photo Flight Images

to do with local habitat changes. Feral species, including Canada Geese and Little Owls, have colonised. Woodlarks and Dartford Warblers were probably more numerous in recent times than at any time before. A 1962 paper by Fry and Welland lists 117 species and with one exception gives a fair impression of what can be seen there now. It does not mention Dartford Warblers, which had been wiped out by heavy snow in the previous year. A few common species are omitted.

Thursley and Ockley Commons form the core of a wider area which has Milford and Witley Commons to the east, Bagmoor, Elstead and Royal Commons to the north and Hankley Common to the west.

Milford and Witley Commons are relatively dry, with extensive stands of pine, birch and hawthorn, the latter hosting a well known colony of Nightingales, now much reduced.

Hawthorns on Milford Common   *Photo D. J. Brassington*

The bird artist David Watson lived in Surrey as a boy and saw 'an immense gathering of crossbills, redpolls, siskins, goldfinches, greenfinches, chaffinches and bramblings' feeding on pine seeds at Witley Common on 9th April 1931. This was a good year for breeding Crossbills, following an invasion in 1929. Bagmoor, a rather wet site, has been acquired by the Surrey Wildlife Trust and is being managed to restore heathland. Elstead and Royal Commons have heather, woodland and *Molinia* grassland. Royal Common was grazed up to 1938. **Hankley Common** is larger, hillier and wilder than any of these, with substantial heather cover and (in good years) a large population of Nightjars, Woodlarks, Dartford Warblers and other heathland birds. Canadian army camps were established on Milford and Witley Commons in both world wars and most of the original vegetation was destroyed (Lawn, undated). It lies to the west of Thursley and Ockley Commons and has a central depression which was used by the army for parachute training (the Dropping Zone). The common is still used for other military exercises. There is normally public access even while these activities are taking place. In the 19th century there were two large ponds at the north end of the common, coming as far south as the west side of Yagden Hill. The south pond was **Abbot's Pond**, referred to by earlier writers and marked on old maps. Today all that remains of the two ponds are **Stockbridge Pond** and a small pond by the golf club buildings (possibly a remnant of Abbot's Pond), together with areas of wet grassland and scrub.

The Dropping Zone at Hankley Common   *Photo D. J. Brassington*

Frensham Ponds and Common. Frensham Ponds were created in 1234 as fish ponds for Waverley Abbey. They were fished on a five-year cycle. The sluice gates were opened to drain the ponds, and the fish were picked up. The ponds are referred to in Manning and Bray (1804-14), where the size of the largest pond is given as 300 acres (1.2 square km, with a circumference of three miles (five kilometres), larger than it was in 1900 or is today. At that time there were 'no woods to adorn its borders'. This remained the case for much of the 19th century. Jordan (1894) described a visit to the ponds. Of the Great Pond he said that it was quite bare at the edges. Heather mixed with a thick grey moss ran down to the edge of the water in many places and there was not enough rush or reed to hide a Teal. Evidently there were no reedbeds and there was no alder carr. The surrounding hills were treeless. The Little Pond was a mere with a rim of white sand in a treeless moor. It had no rushes, reeds or water lilies. Jordan said that many waders could be seen at both ponds. The absence of trees and scrub at Frensham was probably due to grazing.

Hudson (1915) wrote of walking down to Frensham Great Pond on a close, hot morning after a night of rain and watching a huge number of Swifts and hirundines flying to and fro over a green strip, about 130-140 yards in length and 40-50 in width. While doing so, he inadvertently disturbed a hen Pheasant with her chicks on bare ground by a dwarf gorse bush. His description sounds rather like the north side of the pond today, on a May morning, between the old and new car parks. Some 10,000 troops are said to have camped on the Common during the 1914-18 war. The name Kings Ridge derives from a review of the troops there by King George V. The ponds were drained in July 1940. In December 1944, when Frensham Great Pond was overgrown with dense birch and Salix scrub, with water only in the ancient watercourse winding across its bed. L. S. V. Venables found a Spotted Crake there (*BB, 38:259*). Refilling of the Great Pond began in 1945 but the Little Pond was not refilled until 1950 (Parker, 1952). Reed Warblers did not return to the Great Pond until 1954, when the Phragmites had grown back sufficiently for them.

Hindhead Commons. The hills and commons around Hindhead were probably the bleakest part of Surrey in the years before 1800. Signposting in the area was poor and Samuel Pepys, like many others, got lost at Hindhead in the reign of Charles II. The road between Witley and Hindhead was notorious for highwaymen and smugglers, who could hide out on the commons. Early 19th century writers describe Hindhead as a wild place, still inhabited by shy upland species including grouse and the Ring Ouzel. A photograph in the Haslemere Museum shows that there were no trees in or round the Devil's Punch Bowl in 1870. As with Frensham, the bareness was probably due to grazing.

In the latter half of the 19th century the area from Hascombe and Witley out to the hills around Hindhead became popular with writers and artists and with London area residents. The higher parts became known as Little Switzerland, or London's Highlands. The area remained popular until the outbreak of the 1914-18 war, when military activity began to encroach on the commons. Grazing of the heathland by the animals of commoners, often sheep, stopped around 1900, after which birch, pine and bracken began to invade. Current conservation activity is aimed at reducing tree and grass cover in favour of heather. Cattle have been imported to graze the *Molinia* grass, an element of the scene well caught by John Davis in his painting.

One of the finest features of the area is not heathland at all, but the magnificent beech woodland on the west side of the Punch Bowl, of a type known as Wealden Gill to ecologists. In the shelter of the huge trees, on a sunny May morning with the sunlight filtering through the fresh new leaves to an understorey of holly, bilberry, mosses, fallen trees and dead leaves, it is possible to find Redstarts, Wood Warblers and Firecrests as well as commoner woodland birds, like Marsh Tits and Treecreepers.

South London and Thames Basin Heaths. The once extensive commons in the northeast of the county have now become part of south London, partly preserved as open spaces and partly built over. **Wimbledon Common** and **Putney Heath** have a combined area of 1,140 acres (4.2 square km). They lie on London Clay which is capped, in much of the area, by gravels laid down in the last ice age. There is a surprising amount of water on the site, in seven man-made ponds and some boggy patches. Rushmere was known in Tudor times. **King's Mere** is the largest, and the best for waterfowl. **Queen's Mere**, the deepest, was created for Queen Victoria's Diamond Jubilee. **Bluegate Gravel Pit** is one of a number of old gravel pits on the common. The others are dry. The land was occupied in the Bronze Age and later used as manorial wastes for grazing and foraging. Heather grows in places. Drainage in or

Frensham Great Pond, looking east   *Photo J. J. Wheatley*

Frensham Little Pond   Photo D. J. Brassington

around 1874 reduced its attractiveness to Woodcock and Snipe (Hamilton, 1881). The common was extensively used for practice by the National Rifle Association until this was terminated by a fatal accident in 1889. Military activities were substantial in both World Wars. The common was grazed until 1921.

In spite of being such a busy place it attracted the interest of South London birdwatchers from an early date. Bucknill said it was a place to hear the Corncrake. Grey Wagtails bred in 1893, the first in Surrey to do so. Other birds breeding before 1900 include the Nightingale, Whinchat, Mistle Thrush, Blackcap, Dartford Warbler, Chiffchaff, Red-backed Shrike, Jay, Redpoll, Hawfinch, and Cirl Bunting (1890), Vagrants include Stone Curlew (1931), Arctic Skua (1922), Pallas's Sand Grouse (11 in the irruption of 1888), Black Redstart (before 1900), Golden Oriole (1935, 1946, 1954 and 1955), and Lapland Bunting (1895). Woodlarks were well known autumn visitors in the 1920s.

The smaller South London commons at **Clapham** (80 hectares, 220 acres) and **Wandsworth** (70 hectares, 183 acres,) were once in rural settings, with typical heathland and woodland birds, but most were already too heavily used and urbanised to attract these or more than occasional migrants by 1900. In the early 19th century, Clapham was a country village. Donald Maxwell, who was born there, could describe Clapham Common as 'a wild land' as late as the 1890s. Commons at **Barnes** (40 hectares, 100 acres), **Streatham** (20 hectares, 66 acres), **Tooting Bec** (40 hectares, 114 acres) and **Tooting Graveney** (20 hectares, 66 acres) have deteriorated less and were in quite good shape in 1900 (Hudson). Maxwell sketched haymaking in fields adjacent to Tooting Broadway in the 1920s. Like the commons at **East Sheen** (adjacent to Richmond Park) and **Mitcham** though, these commons now have a rather limited range of bird life, albeit the occasional rarity, such as Tooting's Pied-billed Grebe and Wandsworth's Pallas's Warbler, can appear. Mitcham Common (adjacent to Beddington Sewage Farm) had gravel pits and a rubbish tip in the 1950s, attracting shrikes, Short-eared Owls and a variety of gulls. It still produces the occasional scarce bird in its more passive role as a public open space.

In the 18th century, northwest Surrey was a sandy wasteland of heather, bracken and bog. William

Cobbett, whose writings betray little interest in heathland birds, and who did not have the luxury of motor vehicle access on tarmac roads, used Bagshot Heath as a benchmark for barren and unattractive landscapes. As late as 1850, railway travellers on the Southampton Line would find themselves 'whirling through miles of desert' within an hour of London, with only the heathland squatters, or broomsquires in sight (Brandon, 1998).

The heaths in parts of northwest Surrey have been grouped together as the **Thames Basin Heaths** for conservation purposes. They mostly lie on the Bagshot sands. The **Bagshot** and **Chobham** group is the largest, at 5.8 square km (1,444 acres). Together with the contiguous areas of **Westend, Bisley, Ash, Wyke, Cleygate** and **Pirbright Commons**, they contain the largest concentration of heathland birds in the county. Most of the land is used by the army for training purposes. Live munitions, including shells, are used at Westend and Bisley and this area has no public access. Censuses are carried out by special arrangement with the military. There is a somewhat eerie feeling about a Nightjar count here at dusk, along paths edged with '*Keep Out, Live Bombs*' notices and with burnt-out vehicles just visible in the gloom. The Pirbright group of commons has in recent years held over 60 Nightjar and over 250 Dartford Warbler territories. Access to the area is frequently restricted for safety reasons. **Lightwater Country Park** (50 hectares, 146 acres) is one of several contiguous heathland sites which are open to the public.

There is open access to **Chobham Common**, which is a 2 square km (516 acre) National Nature Reserve created in 1994 and makes up the greater part of the Chobham Common SSSI. The nature reserve has around 64 breeding species including Nightjar, Woodlark and Dartford Warbler. Several pairs of Hobbys nest in the surrounding woodland. Harry Witherby lived at Gracious Pond Farm, on the south side, during the 1930s. The common has been used for tank testing in the past. **Olddean Common** is open to the public and is also used by the army, who call it Barossa Training Area. Breeding birds have included Nightjar, Woodlark, Redstart and Dartford Warbler in recent years.

Pirbright Common   *Photo D. J. Brassington*

Whitmoor Common still has enough heathland for a few Stonechats, Dartford Warblers and Nightjars but **Rickford** and **Stringer's** Commons now have too much tree cover. **Pyrford Common** held Woodlarks in 1955. **Wisley and Ockham Commons**, once a relatively undisturbed area, were cut into four pieces by the M25/A3 Junction. Until recently they were too overgrown to be of much value for heathland birds but a collaborative venture between the Surrey Wildlife Trust and the Department for Environment, Food and Rural Affairs has restored some of the heathland and brought back Nightjars, Woodlarks and Dartford Warblers. **Arbrook, Esher, Fairmile and West End Commons** and **Oxshott Heath** (all outside the Thames Basin Heaths area) make up a connected area of 3.6 square km (885 acres) lying on Bagshot Sands and the wetter Claygate Beds. These commons are crossed by roads. They have woods and areas of wet and dry heath. Arbrook Common was a Common Birds Census area for many years. Esher Common, which holds Black Pond, is currently an SSSI, mainly for botanical reasons, and is being improved with heathland management. It was a place fondly remembered by Jefferies: *Who would believe that London could be so near, for in all these three hours stroll only one man and one boy (cutting ferns) did we meet?* He mentioned Woodpigeons, a Jay and an open, treeless, sedgeless rolling hill, literally covered with bright-flowered heath. Woodlarks were present until at least 1961 and there are records of a Honey Buzzard (1959) and an Osprey (1992).

Heath Fires have always been a regulator of the heathland landscape and they have, at different places and times, been a common management method. They keep the woodland and the gorse in check and encourage heather cover. Heath fires may be started by human action or by hot, dry weather. They destroy nest sites and they usually destroy nests, young of birds and the ant colonies and other insects on which the birds feed, yet they also create new habitat, favoured by Woodlarks. The recording of fires has been a bit haphazard but some are known to have been important for heathland birds. After 1869, a large fire destroyed a heath where Dartford Warblers had been common. Bunyard (1924) mentioned a fire in which large tracts of heathland were burnt. Fires in 1938 destroyed several heathland sites in the southwest. Much of the Grasshopper Warbler habitat at Thursley Common was burnt out in 1956 and no birds had returned there by at least 1958.

About 500 acres (two square km) of prime habitat on military land were burnt out on 10th May 1960 (Raynsford 1960). There were huge fires at Elstead and Thursley Commons in the hot summer of 1976. About 1,000 acres (four square km), including two-thirds of Thursley National Nature Reserve, were burnt out. Other fires damaged 700 acres (2.8 square km) of Chobham Common, part of Esher Common, 200 acres (80 hectares) of Hankley Common, 180 acres (70 hectares) of Headley Heath, parts of Horsell and Littleworth commons, 45 acres (10 hectares) of Puttenham Common, 1,200 acres (4.8 square km) of the Pirbright Commons and about 900 acres (3.60 square km) of Westend and Bisley commons (Sage, 1977). A further series of fires on the Pirbright commons in the first few days of August 1990 burnt out most of the Dartford Warblers. On 4th August, the Surrey Fire Brigade tackled 103 grass and heath fires (Davison and Currie, 1991). A fire on the Pirbright Commons in August 1999 destroyed about a quarter of the Dartford Warbler habitat. A fire at the West End and Bisley Ranges began on the unusually early date of 17th April 2003 and was put down to arson. It took 600 firefighters and 34 fire engines to quench the blaze (Surrey Crimestoppers). About 80% of the ground cover was burnt and the Dartford Warbler population there was cut by two-thirds. A fire at Thursley that began on 14th July 2006 burnt out over half of the National Nature Reserve. Birch, Gorse and grasses began to regenerate within weeks but it will be many years before deep heather cover is seen again on Shrike Hill.

The North Downs. A ridge of chalk downland runs across the county from the Hog's Back at Farnham through Guildford and Reigate to Woldingham and the eastern border. The south slopes have a typical chalk flora. White Downs is a site mentioned by John Evelyn. Nore Hill has turned out to be an excellent site for migrant chats and thrushes, including Ring Ouzels. Quarrying for chalk has left cliffs and old buildings, attractive to Kestrels, Jackdaws and, in the case of a large chimney at Betchworth, Barn

Shrike Hill, Thursley Common just before the 2006 fire *Photo D. J. Brassington*

Shrike Hill, Thursley Common just after the 2006 fire *Photo D. J. Brassington*

Owls and Bats. There is a valley between the downs and the greensand hills, called the **Vale of Holmesdale** in the Redhill area and the Tillingbourne Valley at Chilworth.

The downland ridge is in many places capped with plateau gravels which permit the development of heathland, now often overgrown with bracken, birch and conifers. The main sites, west to east, are at the **Hog's back, Newlands Corner, Netley Heath, Hackhurst Downs, Ranmore Common, Headley Heath, Walton Heath, Banstead Heath and Gravelly Hill**. Headley Heath was badly damaged by military vehicles during the 1939-45 war, with its heather and trees largely destroyed (Brandon. 1998) Reclamation work here and elsewhere has restored some of the heather cover and, combined with a run of milder winters, has brought back birds such as the Woodlark, Stonechat and Dartford Warbler on heaths to the east of Box Hill. **Wray Common**, northeast of Reigate, was a site for the Redstart and the Cirl Bunting at the end of the 19th century, but neither breed there now.

Banstead Heath consists of 310 hectares (766 acres) of heather, woods and grassland on the North Downs. Recent birds include Woodcock, Skylark and Yellowhammer and the heathland is of good quality. Banstead Heath is managed as a Site of Nature Conservation Interest, with public access. The adjacent **Banstead Downs** is a Site of Special Scientific Interest, on account of its downland flora rather than the birds. Frederick, son of George II, used to go hawking on Epsom Downs (*Zool. 1880, p.284*).

This was a bleak area in the 18th century. In 1796, William Ravers, a journeyman farrier of Caterham, was lost in the snow near Smitham Bottom, in Woodmansterne and his body was not found for two days (Marshall, 1936), a degree of harshness comparable to that at Hindhead, mentioned earlier. It is hard to imagine the isolation of rural Surrey along the North Downs before 1900. In 1890 the Editor of the *Spectator*, St Loe Strachey, had a house at Newlands Corner, on the North Downs east of Guildford. His daughter wrote that '*No one who knows the two roads over the hill today can have the slightest idea of what a desolate spot Newlands Corner was in the year 1890. There was no post, there was no water; there was no noise*

North Downs: The Tillingbourne Valley

Photo Flight Images

Pewley Down, Guildford

Photo D. J. Brassington

of any sort. Occasionally a cart tumbled past the high hedge which bordered the farmhouse garden, but no one at all seemed to drive up Clandon Hill'. In its day this was a famous place for Nightingales but, for reasons that are none too obvious, they are no longer there. **Hackhurst Downs**, just to the east, were sheep pasture in the late 19th century but are now mainly scrub. **Pewley Down** was the last breeding spot for Surrey Cirl Buntings.

Cheam and Sutton were small villages on the edge of a great stretch of downland. Further east, Frohawk observed that in the 1880s the open country started just north of what is now Purley. The A23 at this point was then a rural roadway with a row of cottages and three Public Houses for travellers. Riddlesdown was a wild and uncultivated place with vegetation typical of the chalk. By 1940 much of Riddlesdown had been built over for residential housing. By 1950 Purley Downs was a Golf Course and much of Sanderstead Downs had been built over. The Shirley (Addington) Hills were very rural and little frequented in the 1880s, in contrast to their busy state today. Only Farthing Down retains some of its old character.

The gentle northern slopes of the North Downs have traditionally been farmland, interspersed with wood and some good chalk downland sites at **Merrow, Fetcham, Mickleham, Epsom, Walton-on-the-Hill, Banstead, Farthing Down and Riddlesdown**. In some places, such as **Coulsdon Common** and **Kenley Common**, the heavier and more acid soils of an overlay of clay-with-flints support woodland. For the most part these sites now hold only the commoner farmland and woodland birds. The chalk eventually dips below the clays of the Thames Valley, giving rise to wetter commonland such as that at Bookham.

Commons on Wetter Soils. Commons of a rather different character are found on the London Clay of the Thames Valley and on the stiff soils of the Weald south of the North Downs. They are often bushy, with deciduous woodland, and some have wet areas.

Blindley Heath (20 hectares, 72 acres and an SSSI) is the most significant site on the Weald and still has the Turtle Dove, Nightingale and Spotted Flycatcher. There are extensive commons in the Thames

Bookham Common   *Photo D. J. Brassington*

Valley. Some of them have patches of acid soil that could hold heather. Commons at Ashtead, Bookham, Effingham and Epsom are still in good condition. **Ashtead Common** was at one time mainly grassland kept open by grazing, but has since become overgrown. It is an SSSI and one of four National Nature Reserves in Surrey. **Bookham** is arguably the best of the four commons for birds and it is certainly the best documented, with the London Natural History Society Survey reaching its 65th year in 2005. The commons at Bookham have a heronry and a strong population of summer visitors including Turtle Doves, up to 12 pairs of Nightingales and various warblers. They are used in winter by Hawfinches, presumed to be from the nearby woods at Horsley.

Effingham Common was ploughed during the 1939-45 war (Douglas) but made a good subsequent recovery and was supporting Nightingales from 1969 or earlier. **Epsom Common** is now best known for the waterbirds on the two Stew Ponds, at one time including nationally significant numbers of Mandarin. Heather is being encouraged to return.

Parks, Ponds and Lakes. Parks in South London hold a surprising variety of breeding birds. There is often enough water to hold Tufted Ducks, Coot and other waterfowl. **Brockwell Park** (30 hectares, 78 acres) has a small lake and it had one of the biggest London rookeries before the park was opened to the public in 1891. **Dulwich Park** (20 hectares, 72 acres) has a larger lake, on which Power saw four Shoveler and five Scaup in 1898. The lake was disturbed when it was opened for rowing boats in 1904. Rowers were on it as early as 6 am. Boats continued to use the lake into the 1990s. A count of 230 Mallard was made there in 1978. **Burgess Park** (54 hectares, 133 acres) was developed after 1945. It has a lake with a small reedbed.

It was at **Battersea Fields**, that Graves recorded a pair of Montagu's Harriers being shot in May 1812. Montagu added the Little Gull to the British List on the basis of a specimen shot on the Thames nearby, prior to 1813. Later a Mr Taylor, of Nine Elms, shot four more at Battersea and presented then to the Charterhouse Museum. There were ponds on open land where Covent Garden Market now stands (*The Village London Atlas*). Riverside meadows were used for fairs (Owen, 2002). By the mid-19th century

Battersea Fields *'were the scene of every description of rough and degraded life. Slums rose in all directions ...'* (Cocksedge (1935).

Battersea Park (80 hectares, 198 acres) fronts the Thames between Battersea Bridge and Chelsea Bridge. It was built on riverside meadows and opened in 1858. During construction, the land level was raised by 24 feet with soil and rubble from the Surrey Docks (Owen). The present lake with its island is shown in *Collins' Illustrated Atlas of London* of 1854, the site being marked as *Intended Battersea Park*. The park, with its lake, is shown on an 1861-71 survey in *The Village London Atlas*. Collins shows a steam boat pier and a shooting ground and the site is adjacent to the now vanished Southwark Water Works. Breeding birds given for Battersea Park 'last season' by Hudson (1898) included Little Grebe, Moorhen, Cuckoo, Pied Wagtail, Reed Warbler and Lesser Whitethroat. With its waterfront and woodland, Battersea Park is still quite a good place to watch birds. Many migrants pass through and there is a heronry. Black Redstarts (unknown in Britain in Graves's time) and Peregrines have bred on the adjacent derelict Battersea Power Station. Traffic noise is substantial.

The Thames at Battersea   *J. P. P. Wilczur*

Kew Gardens (one square km, 251 acres) and the adjacent Old Deer Park (1.4 square km, 350 acres) were well known for their birds a hundred years ago. Hudson (1898) listed 43 breeding species, including the Wryneck, Nightingale, Sedge Warbler, Lesser Whitethroat and Wood Warbler and named six others probably breeding. The long waterfront, ponds and woods have helped to retain most of them, though the Wryneck, Nightingale and Wood Warbler have gone.

Peckham Rye Park (113 acres, 45 hectares) was woodland (*'as perfect a transcript of wild nature as could be found within four miles of Charing Cross'*, according to Hudson) when it was acquired for public use in 1891. It then had an abundance of small birds. Today it is a busy place, with a large number of Carrion Crows among the smaller avian residents. An American Robin caused a stir at Peckham in 2006.

In *South and East Surrey*, Baynards Park, south of Cranleigh, has a history going back to 1066. It is relatively secluded, making it attractive to raptors. Godstone has a small town pond and a larger one, **Bay Pond**, which is run as a reserve by the Surrey Wildlife Trust. Bay Pond was created in 1611 to power a gunpowder Mill. **Vachery Pond** is in a private estate south of Cranleigh. It was originally a hammer pond and later supplied water to the Wey and Arun Canal. It is currently important for Cormorants, Grey Herons and waterfowl and has in the past attracted a Great White Egret and a passing Osprey. **Vann Lake**, at Ockley, once belonged to George B. Blaker, who made plantings to attract Nightingales there. It is currently a Surrey Wildlife Trust reserve.

In the Dorking area, **Dorking Mill Pond**, **Bury Hill Lake** and **Rookery** and **Westcott Ponds** appear on a map dating from 1816 in *The Village London Atlas*. All are man-made. Bury Hill Lake, which is edged with reeds, has produced an exhausted Fulmar and an escaped Purple Gallinule. **Fetcham Mill Pond** is another pond dating back to at least 1816. It is fed by springs welling up from the chalk, which normally used to keep the water from freezing over, attracting wintering flocks of Pochard and other waterfowl. The springs were capped some time between 1955 and 1961 and the associated marsh was drained. Mute Swans and Coots on the pond have both been the subject of special studies. Birds which have been found at the site include Osprey (1999), Spotted Crake (1959) and Grey Phalarope (1960) and there was a Merlin on adjacent land in 2002.

The Tillingbourne rises in sandstone near the summit of Leith Hill and flows west between the chalk downs and the greensand hills to join the Wey, reinforced at Albury by the chalk springs of the Silent Pool and at Chilworth by springs at Waterloo Pond. In the 1600s the valley was an industrial centre, with gunpowder factories, which operated from 1626 to 1920, and mills for processing brass, iron, paper and cloth, all well described by Crocker and Crocker (2000). Chilworth Ponds, one of which is now used for fishing, were built to supply power for local mills in the 17th century. These industries have all gone, but a number of ponds and other structures from the period remain, as do place names such as Abinger Hammer. Postford Pond and the adjacent Waterloo Pond, each served a mill. One of the mills remained in operation until 1990. Cobbett, who was born at The Jolly Farmers in Farnham, had some colourful words about the Chilworth area: *'Here in this tranquil spot, where the nightingales are to be heard earlier and later in the year than in any part of England; … here has the devil fixed on as one of the seats of his grand manufactory; … As to the gunpowder, indeed, we might get over that; … But the Bank-notes!'* (*Rural Rides*). **Albury Park** had a paper mill. Banknotes were made there (Maxwell, 1924). Ponds near **Crossways Farm**, at Abinger, are shown on an 1816 map in *The Village London Atlas*. Birds mentioned in an engaging description of the Tillingbourne valley by Jordan (1894) include Black Grouse, Water Rail and Kingfisher. Trout ponds attracted Herons. Watercress beds in the area appear to be a 20th century development. **Waterloo and Postford Ponds** host Mandarin, Kingfishers, Sedge Warblers and Reed Warblers and, once, a long-staying Osprey. Ponds at **Hedgecourt, Wire Mill and Felbridge**, in the southeast corner of the county, probably originated with the 16th century iron industry. The **Ewood estate**, near Newdigate, was bought by Christopher Durrell, ironmaster, in 1553. A pond of 90 acres was embanked to serve the ironworks. The pond is marked on Bucknill's map but does not now exist. It was given a place in Surrey bird history by hosting the first Collared Pratincole. The pond was drained in the 19th century but traces of the dam remain. Ewood Farm was the property of the Duke of Norfolk in 1921 (Surrey History Service archive).

Gatton Park is a private site, originally landscaped by Capability Brown. The lake is shown on a map dating from 1816 in *The Village London Atlas* and there is a long-established heronry. The park was under military occupation during the 1939-45 war. From a note in the 1969 Surrey Bird Report, anti-aircraft fire drove off the breeding Canada Geese, which were not recorded as breeding there again until 1969. It held nationally significant numbers of Mandarin in the winter of 2000-2001.

Richmond Park was extended to 2,500 acres and enclosed by Charles I in 1637 but had been used as a hunting ground by monarchs at least as early as Henry VIII. Enclosure permitted the introduction of exotic animals and birds, including the deer for which the park is now so well known. Turkeys were introduced in the reign of George I and remained for a number of years. The ground cover at this time was mainly oak woodland and gorse, with thick ivy on the park walls. **Pen Ponds** are the largest waters

Hedgecourt Pond   *Photo D. J. Brassington*

in Richmond Park and have a recorded history which goes back to at least 1650. They were enlarged by gravel excavation in the late 17th century and may have originated in this way. A conservation area was fenced off at the head of the upper pond in 1902, with immediate benefits to the wildlife. The ponds were used for boating and fishing from the early years up to the 1939-45 war. In October 1940 they were drained, like other Surrey waters. The site quickly filled with rushes, which attracted breeding Sedge Warblers and Reed Buntings. In the late 20th century the ponds were a nationally important wintering site for Gadwall.

A dark assessment of the effect of the war on the park was given by Mr Rawlence, in his report of 1942: '*Home Guards practising all day with hand grenades, spigot bombs, trench mortars and other weapons, while during the week there have been occasional enormous explosions from bomb demolition and experimental work. The result has been that bird life has largely left the Park*' (*Birds of the Royal Parks, 1939-46*). Some of the park, though, had been ploughed in the 1940s, bringing back Lapwings, absent as breeding birds since 1835. They stayed until cultivation ceased. The last year of large-scale cultivation was 1950. After the harvest, the stubble field was left to revert to grass (*Birds of the Royal Parks*). Today most of Richmond Park is rough grassland, with scattered oak copses. It is heavily used by pedestrians and motor vehicles, but access away from the roads is restricted and it remains an interesting place for birds, including the waterfowl, breeding Ring-necked Parakeets and visiting rarities such as the Barred Warbler and Ortolan. It is a National Nature Reserve.

Oatlands Park is the site of Oatlands Palace, a large building taken over by Henry VIII in 1538 and pulled down by Oliver Cromwell in 1650. Excavations there have found the remains of edible birds such as the Turkey and a few other birds including a Short-eared Owl. There was a 19th century heronry in the grounds.

Painshill Park was laid out between 1738 and 1773 by Charles Hamilton, over what had been 200 acres of heathland. Elaborate water works raise water from the River Mole and sustain a lake of local interest for breeding waterfowl. The park was acquired by the Elmbridge Borough Council in 1980 and restoration works were begun by the Painshill Park Trust in the 1980s. The nearby **Foxwarren Park** has no lake, but it has secured a niche in the history of Surrey's birds by being the place where Mandarin were introduced in 1928. It is close to **Silvermere**, a lake surrounded by trees, and to **Boldermere**, a lake on Wisley Common, by the A3. Boldermere attracts Goosander in some winters and has held Bewick's Swans.

The landscape garden at **Claremont** is owned by the National Trust and is adjacent to West End Common, Esher. It was begun in 1715 and has a substantial lake. Meyer said he found Red-footed Falcons at Claremont in 1838. Nowadays most bird reports relate to exotic waterfowl, which currently include Black Swans, Greylag and Emperor Geese, Shelduck, Ringed Teal, Wood Duck, Mandarin, Wigeon, Chiloe Wigeon, Pintail, Red-crested Pochard and Sharp-winged (Speckled) Teal. Ring-necked Parakeets are said to breed. Various visiting wildfowl and a long-staying Osprey have been seen there.

In *west Surrey*, **Thursley Lake**, also known as Witley Park Lake, is a small private water in **Witley Park**. It was once a nationally important wintering site for Mandarin but there are no recent counts. The park itself goes back as least as far as 1271, when it was owned by the King. There were 100 or more Fallow Deer in its 900 acres towards the end of the 16th century but, according to Aubrey, they were replaced by iron ore mines and two forges (Maxwell). Most of it was converted to farmland in the 18th century. Lea Park, a property in Witley thought to be Witley Park, apparently had a pond big enough for breeding Pochard in 1906.

Forked Pond, **Hammer Pond** and **Warren Mere** are on the east side of the commons at Thursley. Forked Pond was built as a fishpond in the 16th century. Surrounded by trees, it is not a great pond for birds but it is visited by migrant Ospreys. Hammer Pond held water to generate power for an ironworks. The search for fuel to burn in blast furnaces usually had a devastating effect on the local woodlands, as this one did. Older writers and maps refer to Hammer Ponds, possibly including all the waters in this group. The mill at **Enton**, on the river Ock, probably dates back to the 15th century but the fishing lake is much more recent. The mill was closed in 1899 and later converted to residential accommodation. The present lake was created at about this time by diverting and damming the Ock. Milford House, with a dammed pond of about eight acres on the Ock, featured in 19th century wildfowl records when it was owned by Mr R. W. Webb, who did not allow shooting there. Fish Ponds at Cosford House, a kilometre or so south of Hammer Pond, also featured in 19th century accounts.

Puttenham Common has a group of ponds formed by dams running up its western side. **General's Pond** was created as a fish pond in the mid-18th century, to grow stock for the larger Ponds on the Hampton estate. **Cutt Mill** pond, at the south end, is now a nationally significant site for Mandarin. Puttenham Common is currently owned by Hampton Estate, and is open to the public under an access agreement with the Surrey County Council.

Peper Harow Park, between Godalming and Shackleford, at one time had a herd of deer. Currently it is mixed grazing and arable. It held a heronry at the beginning of the 20th century. Other birds associated with Peper Harow in the past include the Goosander (1838), Buzzard (1898), Waxwing (1849), Golden Oriole (Oxenford Bridge, 1850), Nutcracker (not in the official canon), Raven (19th century) and Hawfinch (1848).

Most of **Windsor Great Park**, including the whole of Great Meadow Pond, is in Berkshire but two important areas, Fort Belvedere and the eastern half of the largest lake, **Virginia Water**, are in Surrey, as are the Savill Garden (created in the 1930s) and Obelisk Pond. A brief history of the park is given by South (1977). The earliest known map of the park is that of John Norden's Survey in 1607, which shows a heronry in the northeast sector, in Berkshire. There were no water bodies in the park when Pepys visited it in 1665. At that time it apparently consisted of woods, heath and swamp (South, 1980). Virginia Water and the two ponds were formed in the 18th century. The original Virginia Water dam burst after torrential rain in 1768. The lake was extended further east into Surrey during rebuilding and currently covers 132 acres. It was drained, wholly or partially, for much of the 1939-47 period (South, 1966). The

The Lower Pond at Cutt Mill   *Photo D. J. Brassington*

heronry moved from Berkshire into Fort Belvedere in 1948 and there is no public access to it. Virginia Water is an important wintering site for Mandarin and has been for many years. Savage (1952) put the population at about 250. There are some fine woodlands. Hawfinches are frequently recorded, usually from the Berkshire side.

The recorded history of **Farnham Park** goes back to at least 1138 and it has, in the past, been a deer park. In 1376, the Bishop of Winchester had a warning to poachers nailed to the door of Witley Church. Deer were kept in the park for over three centuries but were removed in the 1920s because of the cost of maintaining a perimeter fence (*Farnham Herald*, 25th May, 2001). Today the park is mainly open grass-land. Wintering Long-eared Owls have roosted by a small pond, Carron Pond, on the west side. Moor Park, also in Farnham, was established as a garden in about 1690 and is now an SSSI.

There are many other small ponds in west Surrey. **Broadwater,** in the Wey Valley south of Guildford, is mainly used for fishing. It seems to be the 'Old Pond' described by Newman (1849), which lay about a mile north of Godalming, had an island and had been embanked and reduced in size by nearly 100 acres before 1832. Red-crested Pochards have bred on Ponds at **Winkworth Arboretum**. The nearby **Busbridge Lakes** house a wildfowl collection and attract nationally significant numbers of Mandarin.

Reservoirs. Two types of structure are found at water company sites. These are the reservoirs used to store water and the small tanks or filter beds used in water treatment operations. All the reservoirs with open water are of the fully embanked type, with the water level higher than that of the surrounding land. They are fed by pumping. The provision of rafts has attracted breeding terns. From time to time the reservoirs are drained to permit cleaning. This operation creates a beach-like habitat with shallow pools surrounded by mud or sand. Many waders are attracted to them at such times and some, such as Little Ringed and Ringed Plovers, may stay to breed. The water treatment structures generally attract little more than a few gulls and the commoner duck, but they can be locally important. The total area rose from 160 acres in 1900 to 415 in 1914 and 763 in 1973 but has since fallen to about 560 (2.3 square km), after the closure of Barn Elms, Chelsea and Lambeth Reservoirs.

Barnes Group. In the early 19th century, the Barn Elms Farm Estate, which was 'close to a marshy meadow', used its land for arable crops and grazing. Its tenants included William Cobbett (Bullock, 2002). Two groups of reservoirs were constructed at Barnes. The oldest was a string of narrow basins close to the Thames, from Lonsdale Road to Hammersmith Bridge. They are shown on an 1861-71 survey map in *The Village London Atlas*. A Grey Phalarope was shot on the reservoirs during the 1870 influx. Four square basins were added later and the whole group was also known as the West Middlesex Water Works in the 1950s, this being the name of the company that had built the reservoirs. Most of the older ones have now been filled in but **Lonsdale Road Reservoir** still exists as a nature reserve. It is an interesting place, supporting Pochard and Common Terns among its breeding species. The group known as **Barn Elms Reservoirs** included the four square basins, a small pond, filter beds and allotments. It was completed in 1897 and immediately became a winter gull roost. Migrant passerines were attracted to all parts of the site. The Harrods Furniture Repository was at the north end.

The reservoirs feature extensively in the records of scarce birds and waterfowl in the Surrey part of the London area. The Gull-billed Tern, Spotted Sandpiper and Desert Wheatear, all three firsts for Surrey, were recorded there in the 1980s. Late in its life the furniture repository was occasionally used by breeding Black Redstarts and the reservoirs became a nationally important wintering site for Shoveler. Like other reservoirs, the basins were occasionally drained for maintenance and about 150 Linnets were counted on one of the drained basins in 1981. In the late 1990s the site was redeveloped as **The London Wetland Centre**, sometimes known as Barn Elms Wildfowl and Wetland Trust Reserve (BEWWT) in published bird reports. The four basins were completely restructured and landscaped, and most of the land at the north end was built over. The small pond, with its reedy margins, has been retained. The furniture repository was converted to apartments in 1999, retaining its facade along the waterfront.

Interesting birds continued to appear at the site during the reconstruction period and six pairs of Little Ringed Plovers bred there in 1999. The new reserve, opened in the year 2000, has a much greater variety of habitats than the old reservoir basins had, though there is less deep water. Bitterns have been winter-

The London Wetland Centre   *Photo D. J. Brassington*

Island Barn (nearest), Queen Elizabeth II, Walton and Queen Mary reservoirs   *Photo Flight Images*

ing there and a large Reed Warbler colony has been established. An artificial cliff for Sand Martins was finished in 2003. Avocets bred in 2006. Recent rarities include a Cattle Egret.

The reservoirs were nationally important for wintering Shovelers in the 1990s and in 2001/02. Nationally significant numbers of Gadwall were at the reconstructed site in 2000/01 and 2001/02.

Walton-on-Thames. The first reservoirs to be built were the four rectangular basins that made up the **Chelsea** Group. These were opened in 1877. The area was extended with the **Lambeth** basins before 1900 and continued to be used until about 1990. Gravel excavation began in the late 1990s and the area is eventually to be restructured as a nature reserve. **Knight** (Knights on some maps) and **Bessborough** reservoirs, larger and deeper, are shown on a 1903 map revision in *The Village London Atlas* and are still in use. A grassy causeway between the two is used by resting and feeding waterfowl. The reservoirs made up a nationally important wintering site for Shoveler and Ruddy Duck and held notable numbers of wintering Cormorant, Gadwall and Goldeneye in the 1990s but are now less important. Waterbirds such as the Long-tailed Duck, Pied-billed Grebe, Manx Shearwater, Storm Petrel and Leach's Petrel , all rare in Surrey, also use the reservoirs. Drainage for maintenance purposes has brought large numbers of waders, including 25 Ringed Plover in 1971, 13 Golden Plover in November 1990 (Knight), 15 Golden Plover in November 1991 and 150 Dunlin in 1991 and 1992. Chelsea, Lambeth, Knight and Bessborough reservoirs have at one time or another been known as West Molesey Reservoirs, and also as Molesey Reservoirs. They have been grouped as Walton Reservoirs in later Surrey Bird Reports.

Island Barn Reservoir is built on an island encircled by the River Mole and the River Ember at Walton-on-Thames. It was built by the Lambeth Water Company and opened on Saturday 4th November 1911 by the Lord Mayor of London. The reservoir has a circumference of just over 1? miles and a surface area of 121 acres. Until recently it was 27 feet deep, but this is being increased by dredging operations, which are extracting gravel. The original purpose of Island Barn Reservoir was to supply water to Surbiton water treatment works. These works are now redundant and Thames Water is considering whether to treat the water at the company's nearby Advanced Water Treatment Works. Sailing has been permitted on the reservoir since 1972. Access to birdwatchers has generally been rather restricted, apart from the authorisation of the wildfowl counts which have been carried out there since 1952. **Queen Elizabeth II Reservoir** (known as Walton South Reservoir while under construction) covers 317 acres and has an average depth of $57\frac{1}{2}$ feet. Low platform towers well away from the bank are used by roosting Cormorants and breeding Common Terns. There is no public access, apart from that granted for special purposes such as wildfowl counts. The reservoir was a nationally important site for wintering Great Crested Grebes and Cormorants until 2000/01 and remains significant for Cormorants. More intensive watching in recent years has produced rare migrants such as the Purple Sandpiper, Red-necked Phalarope, Roseate Tern and Ortolan Bunting. Exceptional numbers of other migrants, including Arctic Skuas, have also been seen.

Thames Ditton. A group of disused reservoirs by the Thames at Thames Ditton is mainly dry and has been partly redeveloped. This group may be the oldest in Surrey, four small basins being shown there on an 1861-68 map survey in *The Village London Atlas*. Sand Martins have nested in drainage pipes visible from the road. Nearby filter beds, also viewable from outside, were still in use in the 1990s at a site also known as **Seething Wells**.

Spelthorne. The two reservoirs known as Staines North and Staines South (**Staines Reservoirs**) were completed in 1902. They are separated by a causeway over which there is a public footpath, from which both can easily be viewed. Their present configuration is shown on map revisions of 1901-02 in *The Village London Atlas*. The reservoirs make up a nationally important site for Shoveler, Tufted Duck and Cormorants and at times have held very large numbers of Ruddy Ducks. In the 1990s they were nationally significant for Pochard. They are notable for migrant Little Gulls and Black Terns. Common Terns breed on tern rafts during the summer. The reservoirs are drained for maintenance from time to time, for example in 1927, 1975 and 1976 (to September), in late August 1977 to end 1978 (south basin), from late 1982 into 1984 and then intermittently into 1986 (north basin), from December 1984 to March 1986 (south basin, which remained about two-thirds full into 1987), in 1990, 1994 (south), in late 1996 (north basin), in 1997 (north basin) and in late 1998 (south basin). They can attract rare waders at such times as well as large numbers of the commoner species. The potential of the site in this regard first came to light in 1927, when the south basin was drained for five months, from May to October. Three new species for the London area were found, Wood Sandpipers on 17th-18th August, Curlew Sandpipers on 7th and 10th September and two Knots on 10th September. Later rarities during periods of drainage include Dotterel, Baird's Sandpiper, Long-billed Dowitcher, Lesser Yellowlegs and Wilson's Phalarope. Record numbers of Teal were attracted by the drainage of Staines Reservoirs in 1986 (Moon, 1987a). In 1990 Staines North was left unfilled by Thames Water despite a summer drought, permitting fifteen pairs of Little Ringed Plovers to breed. Yellow Wagtails bred at Staines in 1994. The drained north basin attracted many waders in the summer and autumn of 2004.

Queen Mary Reservoir was built in 1925 and used to be known as Littleton. A causeway runs south from the north bank to the middle of the reservoir, which is a nationally important site for wintering Great Crested Grebes and has a large gull roost. The reservoir has attracted many rare birds, including White-winged Black Terns. **King George VI Reservoir** was initially filled in September/November 1947. It was sometimes called Staines New Reservoir. Little Ringed Plovers were found on the site in 1946 and Kentish Plover in 1947. The water level was greatly reduced after the initial filling, leaving islands and pools that attracted many waders. The reservoir was finally filled in the spring of 1950. It was at one time a nationally important site for wintering Great Crested Grebes and until recently was nationally important for Shoveler. There is no public access, apart from that granted for special purposes such as wildfowl counts. Drainage in 1986 attracted record numbers of Canada Geese, Wigeon, Gadwall, Teal, Pochard and Coot (Moon, 1987a). Partial drainage in 1995 attracted an American Golden Plover and a Pectoral

Staines Reservoirs   *J. P. P. Wilczur*

Sandpiper. **Wraysbury Reservoir** is on the border between Spelthorne and Berkshire, indeed until the boundary was realigned it lay in both areas, the boundary followed a winding course under the water on the west side. The reservoir was a nationally important site for wintering Shoveler in the 1990s. There is no public access, apart from that granted for special purposes such as wildfowl counts. Drainage in 1995 brought an unusual number of Ringed Plovers.

Kempton Group. The three reservoirs in the group are **Kempton East**, **Kempton West** and **Red House**. Kempton East and West, just outside the Spelthorne boundary are both disused. Kempton East is being redeveloped as a nature reserve. It was on this reservoir that Avocets bred successfully in 1996. Kempton West is currently empty and scheduled for building development. Red House reservoir, the smallest of the Kempton Group, is the only one which is in Spelthorne and the only one which is part of the South West London Water Bodies SPA and RAMSAR. It is surrounded by private land and a railway, but can just be seen from Hatherop Road Playing Fields, on the other side of the track. The Hersham Ringing Group has operated at Kempton for many years.

Gravel and Sand Pits. The shifts and changes of the gravel pit environment suit many kinds of birds. While they are actively being worked, the pits have cliffs that suit Sand Martins and shingle bars favoured by Little Ringed Plovers. When extraction has ceased the pits fill with water. Marginal vegetation develops and many breeding and migrant birds move in to exploit the new habitat. Old pits may be used as landfill sites, attracting large numbers of gulls and corvids, especially in winter. Pits which are abandoned become less interesting as they get older because the cliffs and banks get covered with vegetation. Mallard and Tufted Ducks, Grebes, Moorhens and Coots become the most obvious species and there are fewer migrants. Old pits can be actively managed to keep the best habitats open to the birds. There are not many examples in Surrey, unfortunately, but a few recent initiatives are promising.

Some of the pits described in *The Birds of the London Area* and *Birds in Surrey, 1900-1970* have been filled in and most have changed their shape. Gravel Pits at Beddington were an early site for colonisation by the Tufted Duck but several of the pits had been filled by the end of 1945, and breeding ceased. In the 1940s and 1950s there were seven pits on land between Walton and Island Barn Reservoirs. Breeding birds of the pits and the surrounding ground included Grey Partridge, Little Ringed Plover, Skylark, Meadow Pipit, Yellow Wagtail, Red-backed Shrike, Tree Sparrow, Yellowhammer, Reed Bunting and Corn Bunting (SBC archive, Keywood and Melluish, 1952). Queen Elizabeth II Reservoir was built over five of them. **Molesey** and **Fieldcommon** gravel pits, on the edge of Molesey Heath, lie approximately on the site of the other two. Both are currently in poor condition. The most prominent feature of Molesey Heath itself is a high spoil heap, over which there are public footpaths affording views of Molesey Gravel Pit and Island Barn Reservoir. Sedge Warblers, a pair of Lesser Whitethroats and numerous Whitethroats breed in the scrub by the path. **Hersham Gravel Pit** lies just to the south, between Molesey Gravel Pit and Hersham Sewage Farm. This area was developed more recently. Mineral extraction has now been completed, leaving a small area of water and a larger area of badly-drained landfill and pasture. The standing water created by the bad drainage has made it attractive to migrants. Lapwing, Little Ringed Plover, Ringed Plover and Redshank have bred there and migrants have included Temminck's Stint and Twite, both rare in Surrey. In recent years there have been wintering flocks of over 20 Dunlin and 1,000 Lapwing. The area can easily be viewed from a public footpath on the south side.

Ham Lands was at one time an area of wet grazing. It featured in an 1819 painting by Turner and was still grazed until the 1970s (*Urbio, Issue 10*). The gravel pits on Ham Lands (Ham Gravel Pits) have mostly been filled in, as have **Hamm Moor Gravel Pits** (Hamm Moor Sand Pits). The Hamm Moor pits were at Hamm, Weybridge, and were active in 1970 and up to at least 1980. **Mitcham Gravel Pit** (TQ297670), which featured in some of the earlier records of the Water Rail, Cuckoo and Reed Warbler, had been built over by 1957 (*BLA*).

A group of pits at **Thorpe**, which were developed in the late 1950s, were later crossed by the M3 motorway. This separated what is now the Twynersh fishing complex from the rest of the site. The layout of the other pits is complex but most of the birds are seen on three parts of it. The first two areas are in **Thorpe Water Park** (also known as Thorpe Park), which lies between the A320 and the M3. They are separated by a footpath running east from Thorpe Church. Three connected areas known as **Manor Lake**, **Fleet Lake** and **Abbey Lake** lie to the north of the footpath. **St Ann's Lake** (also known at Thorpe Park No.1 Gravel Pit) lies to the south of it. The third area lies to the north of the A320, opposite the entrance to Thorpe Water Park, and easily viewed from the road. In recent years this has been the main Surrey station for wintering Smew, for which Thorpe is a nationally important site, and a nationally important site for Gadwall. In 1969 and 1970 Thorpe was the principal breeding station of the Great Crested Grebe in the county and Pochard nested there twice in the mid-1960s. The pits make up a nationally important site for Gadwall and Smew (Wetland Bird Survey 2003-04) and, since the 2000-2001 seasons, nationally significant for Kingfishers. In 1999 St Ann's Lake was nominated as an SSSI for its flock of wintering Gadwall and for significant numbers of other species including Goldeneye and Smew. Longside Lake, a nearby pit on the west side of the M25, was a nationally important site for Gadwall in the 1990s.

Sand and gravel pits have been worked at **Send** since at least 1901, when a Sand Martin egg which is now in the Haslemere Museum was collected from Send Sand Pits. These pits may have fallen into disuse, because eggs collected from the same site in 1907 and 1909 were of Tree Pipits. In 1947, the *South-Eastern Bird Report* recorded two Goldeneyes at 'Send ballast pits'. Two pits in Send village, sometimes called Send Heath ponds, have long since matured and are of more interest to fishermen than birdwatchers. Many fields have been excavated and refilled on the west side of Send at a complex known as **Papercourt Gravel Pits**. Work ceased there in the late 1990s, leaving a large pit which is used for sailing and a small one which become a nature reserve managed by the Surrey Wildlife Trust in 2000. Little Ringed Plovers bred at Papercourt until the pit margins became overgrown. The pit which is used for

Papercourt Gravel Pits   *Photo D. J. Brassington*

sailing has a good record for wintering and migrant duck, including Pochard, Scaup, Eider, Velvet Scoter and Goosander. Other migrants have included Wood Sandpiper and Caspian Tern.

Land east of Redhill, from Merstham to Nutfield, has been extensively worked for sand and fuller's earth (a mineral used for removing natural animal fats from wool). The group is known collectively as **Holmethorpe Sand Pits**. Some of the pits have been used as landfill sites, attracting large flocks of gulls and crows. Others have become overgrown or partly silted up. One, **Mercers Lake**, is used for recreational purposes and as a wildfowl refuge. It is deep, and from time to time has held a wintering diver, various grebes and the occasional sea duck. Another, renamed **Speynes Mere**, is currently being set up as a nature reserve. Adjacent fields to the southeast have large numbers of wintering Lapwings and sometimes a few Golden Plovers. Holmethorpe is one of the more important Surrey sites for Greylag Geese. Fields to the west of Cormongers Lane have become another nature reserve, currently named **The Moors**.

Further east, at **Godstone**, there are other sand pits. Two disused pits were used as reservoirs for a while and held a Surrey Wildlife Trust nature reserve. Infilling has reduced the ornithological interest of the area. There are more old pits further east still, near the county border at **Moorhouse**. These are surrounded by trees and their main interest in recent years has been a Sand Martin colony.

Sands and gravels in the Blackwater valley from Seale, east of Farnham, to Camberley were heavily worked in the second half of the 20th century. **Frimley Gravel Pits** were excavated in the 1960s. A useful account of them is given by Moss. **Hatches Pit**, at Frimley, has a small island and attracts duck, grebes other waterfowl and breeding Common Terns. Some of the Blackwater valley pits, such as **Shawfield**, at Aldershot, have been filled in. Others have now been made over for recreational purposes. **Willow Park,** at Frimley, is used for water sports. The pit beside **Coleford Bridge Road** hosts the occasional rarity. Pits at Seale have been used as landfill sites, attracting many gulls. **Tongham Gravel Pit** can be good for wintering gulls and waterfowl. The nearby **Tice's Meadow** has recently attracted large numbers of waders. Other waters in this area include the gravel pits at **Ash Vale** (a good wildfowl site in the 1970s and 80s but now heavily tree-lined), **Farnborough North Camp**, and a stretch of the Basingstoke Canal with its associated pounding area, **Mytchett Lake**. The canal, which is mentioned by Pigot (1839), originally connected Basingstoke with the Thames but is now largely disused.

Land in Spelthorne, north of the Thames, is on flood plain gravels which were probably laid down in tundra conditions during the last Ice Age. The gravels are over London Clay and, around 500 feet below that, there is the Chalk. The land was farmed in the 19th century but in the 20th a large part of it was given over to gravel extraction and reservoirs. Two groups of gravel pits in the **Ashford** area make up a nationally important site for wintering Smew. Work on the pits to the west of the B3003 (Clockhouse Road) began in 1927 and continued, with infilling and dumping on part of the site, until at least 1951 (Keywood and Melluish, 1952). Much of the area, including all of Bedfont Lakes Country Park, which lies to the east of the B3003, is outside the Spelthorne boundary. The configuration of the pits has changed considerably since the 1950s but the area to the west of the B3003 still supports large numbers of wintering wildfowl and has been made a Site of Nature Conservation Interest with the name Princes Lake.

Charlton Gravel Pit lies to the east of Queen Mary Reservoir. **Queen Mary Gravel Pits** lie to the west of it. They were excavated in 1973. **Laleham** and **Queen Mary** gravel pits held Little Ringed Plovers in 1984. Over 800 Chiffchaffs were ringed there in the period 1970-86. About 86 acres (35 hectares) of worked-out gravel pits either side of the M3 at **Shepperton** have been separately named as Felix Lane, Ferry lane (Ferris Meadow), Halliford Mere, Littleton Lane east, west, north and south and **Sheepwalk** east and west. The **Littleton Lane East** pit south of the M3 was filled in the 1980s but the one north of the M3 is still there. Gravel extraction at Littleton Lane finished in 1967. The Littleton Lane pits are sometimes known as the **Littleton Lakes,** and are currently a Surrey Wildlife Trust reserve. Richard Holleyman described the site in *Surrey Nature No. 128*. Pits at **Laleham Farm**, also to the west of Littleton Lane, have been worked since at least the 1980s. Some have been filled in. The **Ferry Lane West** pit has been filled and replaced by others. Egyptian Geese recently bred at Ferry Lane. The gravel pits on **Staines Moor/Stanwell Moor** made up a nationally important site for wintering Smew in the 1990s. Other old pits form the **Moor Lane Nature Reserve**, to the south of Wraysbury Reservoir.

Holmethorpe Sand Pits   *Photo D. J. Brassington*

Sewage Farms and Refuse Tips. The earliest sewage farms were built in the middle of the 19th century. They reached their fullest development, as bird habitats, in the 1950s and by the end of the 20th century most had been modernised, abandoned or built over. It seems unlikely that sewage farms will be able to make the same contribution to the bird life of the county in the century to come. The Golden Age has gone.

The mile-square wilderness of **Beddington Sewage Farm**, unloved by conservation bodies, is the largest in the county, at about 600 acres. The sewage farm was opened in 1860, part of it on the site of a Roman villa. During the construction of the sewage farm, the skull of a rhinoceros (*Coelodonta antiquitatis*), part of an elephant tusk (probably Mammoth, *Mammuthus primigenius*) and bones from several horses (*Equus caballus*) were found in sands about 17 feet down (*Geological Survey Memoir* in Moorman, 1961), an interesting foretaste of what was to come. Some of the history of the site is contained in Milne *et al.* Until the 1950s it was managed under a regime in which the various fields on the site were first flooded with sewage effluent, forming sludge lagoons, and then dried out to form grassy meadows. Sedimentation tanks and filters for treating the sewage before it went into the lagoons were installed in 1902-12 (Hatton, 1982). The fields were grazed or else ploughed, planted with crops, harvested and left as stubble. By the 1950s there were 37 fields separated by hedges, ditches and dykes, with pump-houses and other buildings scattered across the area. The habitat was a very rich one for birds. Counts in the 1950s showed a daytime total of over 10,000 birds feeding on the farm. There were large numbers of Snipe and other migrants in winter. Shooting rights were let out, with a regular four-gun shoot for Snipe each year (Milne, 1956). Gunners harassed a short-stay flock of eleven Pink-footed Geese in December 1938 and shot one of them. Regular bird surveys were commenced in 1954 and are still being carried out. Of the 500 breeding pairs in 1955, 20 were Yellow Wagtails and 78 were Tree Sparrows.

In the late 1960s, a new method of working was introduced, which used more sludge lagoons and fewer grassy fields. Horses were removed from the site at about this time, allowing bushes and other vegetation to grow. This greatly reduced the number of wintering Snipe and thrushes (Hutson *et al.*, 1971) but benefited Sedge Warblers and Whitethroats. A major new sewage treatment works was opened in 1969 and extended in 1978 (Coleman, 1995). Wet meadows were replaced by gravel-based sludge beds. Sludge lagoons which had previously been left to revert to grassy meadows were now scraped down to the underlying gravel by a bulldozer and the topsoil was transported offsite. New sludge beds were then created. Grazing continued and up to 200 horses used the site in the 1980s. The fields became severely over-grazed, after which the horses were removed. By 1994, all the remaining fields had been converted and there were about 180 sludge beds. A good deal of the site fell into disuse. More recently, a reduction in the number of sludge beds, the commencement of gravel extraction and the provision of a small lake have made further substantial changes to the habitat.

The site has been well worked and has added handsomely to the county list. Red Kite, Short-toed Lark, Richard's Pipit, Aquatic Warbler and Little Bunting have been seen there, as have some barely more common species including Black-winged Stilt, Purple Sandpiper, Alpine Swift, Bluethroat and Lapland Bunting. Gadwall and Water Rail have bred and Spotted Crakes have summered. Lapwing and Snipe have bred and very large numbers are sometimes present in winter. An abundance of mice and voles has from time to time drawn many predators. Over 25 Kestrels and ten or more Short-eared Owls have been present in autumn and winter on occasions. Tree Sparrows remain a Beddington speciality and the breeding population has been boosted by the provision of many nest-boxes. Beddington has by far the largest Tree Sparrow breeding colony in Surrey and, with the national decline in Tree Sparrow numbers, the site is of national significance. The site was nationally important for wintering Shoveler to 2001 at least.

At one time a right of way (Mile End Road) crossed the site but there was no access to the working area, restricting observations. This has been closed. Regular access to the site is now limited to key holders though much of it, including a small lake, can be seen from a newly-constructed footpath along

Beddington Sewage Farm. With more than a square mile of wetland, nettles and sludge lagoons, the sewage farm has attracted a longer list of rare migrants than any other site in Surrey. Its wildness has a strange beauty.

John Davis

its western side. Sand and gravel extraction began in 1998 and there are plans for a complete reconstruction of the site to serve amenity purposes. It seems possible that this will eventually end a remarkable stage in Surrey's ornithological history. However, a Conservation Science Group has been established to oversee the wildlife interest during the development and the mineral workings might be just another chapter. By the end of 2001 at least 243 bird species had been recorded.

Berrylands Sewage Works (Hogsmill Sewage Farm), between Berrylands railway station and the River Hogsmill, has been modernised. A ringing group operates there. They caught a Sardinian Warbler in 1992, the first inland record for Britain. There was a Pectoral Sandpiper in 1984. Ruddy Duck have bred.

Brooklands Sewage Farm used to cover about 35 acres inside the Brooklands motor racing circuit and just east of West Weybridge (now Byfleet) railway station, with the pump building outside the track and close to the station. The site, at TQ0662, was bounded on one side by the track and the other by an airfield. It was probably the first sewage farm in Surrey to be watched regularly (Hollom 1935, 1937). Records from the 1930s include Avocet (1932), Temminck's Stint (1936) and Curlew Sandpiper (1939). Yellow Wagtails bred there. The sewage farm was modernised and reduced in size during the 1939-45 war and the open lagoons were lost. It had no marsh by 1956 and has since been closed and built over. **Weybridge Water Pollution Works** was later built to the north of the circuit. It has open water. An Osprey was seen there in 1993.

When it was constructed, in around 1880, **Elmers End Sewage Farm** straddled the eastern border of the vice-county, part in Surrey and part in Kent. Jones (1961) describes the flora and gives a map. Site history and the birds were described most recently by Birkett (1992). Up to 1930, about 200 acres of fields were flooded as part of the operations. Some of this was turned over to arable in the 1930s. The site was well known to birdwatchers in the mid-20th century but had been modernised by 1960, by which time sports facilities and storage dumps had been laid over fields previously used for sewage disposal. The sewage works was closed in 1966 or 1967. Its name had been changed to **South Norwood Sewage Works** and later, when the mode became popular with local government planning departments, it became **South Norwood Country Park**, the creation of which began in 1988. Sale of land for housing has reduced the area to 125 acres. Boundary changes have now placed the whole area in Surrey. By the 1990s up to 118 species were being recorded each year, with a total site list of 154.

Epsom Sewage Farm, which was about two kilometres south of Ewell West railway station, was a good site for scarce waders and other migrants in the 1950s. There were 73 Jack Snipe on the farm in February 1956 - which would be a remarkable figure for any part of Surrey at the present time. Migrant passerines included Twite and Ortolan. Teal and Yellow Wagtails bred there. Effluent which flowed over the farm was diverted to Berrylands Sewage Works in 1958 and the Epsom Sewage Farm beds gradually dried. A Black Redstart was found on the disused site in 1961. The area has since been built over.

Farnham Sewage Farm held up to 5,000 Snipe before it was modernised in 1971. Other records include Dunlin (1967) and Jack Snipe. Water Pipits were still being recorded there in the 1990s.

Guildford Sewage Farm was built in the 19th century and extended in the early years of the 20th. It did not attract much attention from birdwatchers until the early 1940s, when it had 150 acres of large, shallow lagoons which, as on other sewage farms, were flooded with effluent and then dried out. At this time the farm was owned by the Guildford Council. Modernisation was adversely affecting the habitat by 1960. Shooting rights were let out, and remained in operation until at least the 1970s. A note by Harrison (1947) mentions, among other species, Ruddy Shelduck, Red-necked Grebe and Temminck's Stint, the last being only the second for the vice-county. Teal and Garganey were thought to have attempted nesting in 1945. Hobbys were regularly seen in the summer and Redshank built up to about 60 birds in early April, a few pairs remaining to breed. Waders were a feature in the 1950s, with maximums of 12 Wood Sandpipers in July 1956 and 25 Ringed Plovers in May 1959. Other migrants included Curlew Sandpiper and Black-tailed Godwit (Hollom, pers. comm.). There were up to 600 Snipe in autumn. This period is documented in papers by Adams (1953) and Westwood (1953, 1961 and 1962). Modernisation commenced in 1958 and released much of the land for housing and refuse disposal, but not before the farm became known as a site for Little Ringed Plovers. There was a period in the 1970s when refuse was dumped on open ground and sometimes caught fire, while exotic weeds grew among the rubbish. Today, a few migrants can still be found on the waste ground but open water is virtually absent.

Hersham Sewage Farm (Weylands Sewage Farm) covers 26 acres and was opened in 1900. It was partially modernised in 1962. A pair of Little Ringed Plovers bred there in 1952. In the 1960s over 20 species bred annually, including Yellow and Pied Wagtails, Sedge and Reed Warblers and Tree Sparrows. Larvae of the Hairy Moth Fly (*Psychoda alternata*), a common resident of decaying matter in waste pipes and at sewage farms, provided an abundant food source on the clinker of the new sprinklers and a single Starling might eat thousands of them in a day (Parr, 1963). A rich crop of goosefoots, bur-marigolds, thistles and other weeds on the drying filter beds attracted up to 1500 birds in winter, feeding on the seeds. Most of the area is currently derelict. Yellow Wagtails and Tree Sparrows are no longer breeding but flocks of finches (including a Twite in 1999) still forage there.

Molesey Sewage Farm (Island Barn Sewage Farm, West Molesey Sewage Works), was in the northeast corner of what is now Molesey Heath. It was in operation by 1896. Ringed Plover and Green Sandpiper were among the birds seen there in 1929. The site was still operating in the 1950s but has since been closed and grassed over.

Perry Oaks Sewage Farm was very small in the early 1930s but was extended in 1936 and became known as a major bird site in 1946. Shoveler, Snipe and Black-headed Gulls bred there and it hosted many rare migrants. It had been modernised by 1961 and the site lies within the perimeter of Heathrow Airport. It has now been built over with new airport structures.

Unstead Sewage Farm, also known as Godalming Sewage Treatment Works, is mentioned by Harrison (1947) as being a place where over a hundred Snipe could be seen on one visit. The farm since has been modernised. The administrative buildings and sprinkler beds are on one side of a public footpath and flooded fields with effluent beds on the other. Part of the flooded area was restructured in 1999 with conservation funds provided by Thames Water, who own the site. Access has been greatly improved by the construction, in 1999, of a second footpath which leads round to a hide at the back of the site.

Unstead Sewage Farm   *John Davis*

This gives views over disused flood meadows where water levels are now managed for the benefit of the birds. Breeding and wintering Water Rails are much in evidence. Recent rarities include Little and Great White Egrets. Common Terns recently bred there.

The **Walton-on-Thames** sewage farm was built partly over a disused gravel pit by the Thames at TQ108679 at some time during the period 1935-47. Breeding species included the Mute Swan and Meadow Pipit and other species present in the breeding season included Shoveler, Little Ringed Plover and Redshank. Migrants included Ringed Plover (maximum of seven), Green Sandpiper (maximum of 12) and Wood Sandpiper and there was a Yellow Wagtail roost (Hollom, pers. comm.).

Wandsworth Sewage Works where Yellow Wagtails are thought to have bred in 1950, was probably the sewage farm and works marked on land between the River Wandle and Durnsford Road on maps of the period, but now built over by Weir Road. Durnsford Road Sewage Works (Sedge Warbler 1973, Linnet 1972) was presumably the same site.

Weybridge Sewage Farm had Dunlin, Greenshank, Green Sandpiper, Grasshopper Warbler and two pairs of breeding Redshank in 1929 and breeding Whinchats around this time.

Worcester Park Sewage Farm was a small site in an urban area. Even after modernisation it provided a local haven for about 20 breeding species and for many other birds that came to feed there, or pass through on migration. Up to 200 Carrion Crows could be found, as well as flocks of gulls, Starlings and finches. A few less common birds, including Black-throated Diver and Knot, were seen. The appeal of the site would have been enhanced by adjacent playing fields and allotments and a rubbish tip. The effluent went into the Beverley Brook, where it could provide 90% of the flow. The plant was closed in 1999 but the site has continued, at least temporarily, to attract wetland birds. These included Teal, Jack Snipe, Snipe, Green Sandpiper, Water Pipit and Sedge Warbler in 2001.

Other sewage farms which have provided records from time to time include those at Aldershot Camp (Black-tailed Godwit 1966), Bookham (about 100 Pied Wagtails in a field 1974), Bramley (Water Rail 1971, Jack Snipe, Water Pipit), Brockham (Pied Wagtail Roost 1980), Buckland (Sedge Warbler 1982), Burstow (White Wagtail 2000), Camberley (Jack Snipe and Red-backed Shrike 1954, modernised, part built over), Chertsey Meads, Chobham (thirty-five Snipe 1990), Cranleigh (three Buzzards 2003), Crawley (adjacent to Gatwick Airport, Green Sandpipers etc 2003), Dorking, Earlswood (Jack Snipe, 300 Snipe 1962, White Wagtail 1960), Esher (Wood Sandpiper 1955, Little Stint 1957, 500 Greenfinches 1957), Godstone (Cirl Bunting 1962), Hamm Moor (Sedge Warbler 1975), Haslemere, Holmwood (White Wagtail 1978), Horley (=Meath Green, useful pools, Goldeneye, Smew, Jack Snipe), Leatherhead (probable breeding Redshank 1935), Lyne [Old Lyne, Lyne Old are the same?] (Yellow Wagtails 1962, Water Rail 1971), Malden (Jack Snipe 1960), Merstham, Motspur Park (White Wagtail 1989), Ripley (modernised, still working), Thorpe (Black Redstart 1983), Wandsworth (Yellow Wagtail pair 1950), Wisley (modernised, still working) and Old Woking (modernised, still working, good waders in season, Black Redstart from time to time). The West Middlesex Disposal Works (Black Redstart, 1936) was near Staines Reservoirs. The Wandle Valley Sewage Works, west of Lambeth Cemetery, was converted to the Wandle Meadow Nature Park after closure.

Refuse disposal at landfill and other sites greatly increased in the second half of the 20th century, creating feeding sites for large numbers of gulls and crows. A paper by Gibbs (1963) gives an account of the bird population of tips in the London area, giving Kestrels, gulls, Feral Rock Doves, Pied Wagtails, crows, House Sparrows and Starlings as typical feeding species, mostly attracted by domestic food waste. The area of open sites probably peaked in the 1980s, after which more attention was given to incineration and recycling. Tips which have been important for birds included these:

Camberley Rubbish Tip, to the north of the Frimley gravel pits on what is now an industrial estate, was used by gulls in the 1970s. Possibly the site also known as Aldershot Refuse Tip.

Charlton Rubbish Dump TQ085682. Gravel pits used for landfill, 500 Black-headed Gulls, 250 Carrion Crows, 150 Jackdaws (Gibbs).

Egham Refuse Tip attracted gulls in the 1950s.

Epsom Rubbish Tip, 340 Herring Gulls (Gibbs).

A tip opened on disused parts of **Guildford Sewage Farm** has now been closed.

Ham Rubbish Dump (Gibbs).

At **Holmethorpe**, exhausted gravel pits on either side of Cormongers Lane have been used for landfill over many years and one is still open. Around 2,000 Herring Gulls were feeding there in 1997.

Kingston Rubbish Dump (Gibbs).

Leatherhead Rubbish Dump TQ147578. Water meadows next to a sewage works, 250 Rooks (Gibbs)

Lower Kingswood Rubbish Dump, 200 Herring Gulls (Gibbs).

Mitcham Common Rubbish Dump, 200 Lesser Black-backed Gulls (Gibbs), Glaucous Gull (1955). Several pits at **Papercourt** have been filled and there are currently none open.

Pits at **Runfold** and **Seale** had been used for landfill since at least the 1970s and still attract large numbers of gulls.

Stoke D'Abernon Rubbish Dump (Gibbs).

Thorpe (Laleham) Rubbish Dump (Gibbs).

Walton Rubbish Dump TQ106678. Gravel pits used for landfill, 1,400 Black-headed Gulls, 350 Common Gulls, 300 Lesser Black-backed Gulls, 170 Herring Gulls, 200 Great Black-backed Gulls (Gibbs).

West Molesey Rubbish Dump (Gibbs), (Hooded Crow, 1961).

Worcester Park Rubbish Dump, (200 Lesser-black-backed Gulls and 400 Herring Gulls, 1969).

Wrecclesham sand pits were used for landfill in the 1970s and 80s, when they attracted rare gulls as well as large numbers of the commoner species. Up to 8,000 gulls fed there during cold weather in February 1978.

Spelthorne

Stanwell Moor Rubbish Tip attracted a Hooded Crow in May 1988.

Bankside Power Station (Tate Modern)   *J. P. P. Wilczur*

Rivers, streams and wet meadows. The Thames forms the northern boundary of the vice-county. Two substantial rivers, the Mole and the Wey run south from the Thames and cut through the North Downs, the Mole at Dorking and the Wey at Guildford, to catchment areas on the weald. Wetlands along the valleys provide a remnant habitat for some of Surrey's scarcer breeding birds. Gravel pits along all three rivers have provided rich new sites at all times of the year.

The Thames Valley. Over a long time scale, the water level in the Thames Valley has varied greatly. In prehistoric periods there were large encroachments by the North Sea when the ice melted during interglacial periods. With the end of the last Ice Age, a combination of continued ice melt and the subsidence of southeast England has raised high tide levels by around 12 inches per century, by 15 feet since the Romans left and by 60 feet or more since Neolithic times. The embanking of the London Thames has probably been a piecemeal process, begun by the Romans (Woodley, 1961). The Thames has become deeper, and tidal for more of

Stoke Lake and water meadows with Papercourt in the distance

Photo Flight Images

its length as a result of these changes, though in medieval times it was still relatively shallow, with riverside marshes and meadows that must have supported many birds, not least the celebrated colony of Spoonbills at Fulham. The river is tidal up to Teddington and large stretches of gravel and mud are exposed from the Surrey Docks to Kew at low tide. It is a migration route, especially for sea and water birds, many of which are seen at the reserves and reservoirs along the valley. There are disused power stations at Bankside and Battersea. Mud flats at Wandsworth attract duck, Grey Herons and various scavengers.

The Wey Valley. The River Wey rises just outside the county and drains most of west Surrey. Its valley holds the best of the residual riverside wetlands. They are best developed along the stretch from the Thundry Meadows reserve at Elstead through Eashing (where there was a paper mill from 1658 to 1889), the Lammas Lands at Godalming, the site of the Catteshall paper mill (1661 to 1928) and at Guildford, Send and Pyrford.

Some are still used for grazing. The larger areas, as at Stoke, are used as flood plains to hold water when there is excessive rain. Little Grebes, Kingfishers and Grey Wagtails are fairly frequent. In the 1970s it was moderately easy to find Grey and Red-legged Partridges, Lesser Spotted Woodpeckers, Grasshopper Warblers, Willow Tits and Tree Sparrows in such places, but these are all now much scarcer. **Stoke Lake** was formed from a gravel pit dug for road-making materials when the A3 was rerouted in the 1970s. It quickly became a significant regional site. Meadows at Wrecclesham flood in winter and attract many gulls and other waterbirds. The **Wey Navigation** was built by Act of Parliament in 1651 and allowed barges from the Thames to reach Guildford. In the 19th century it was linked to the Arun Navigation to make an inland connection between the Thames and the Channel. The Wey Navigation is still open, though only used by pleasure craft and the wildlife. For most of its length it provides a quiet habitat for waterbirds. Most of the locks and weirs now attract Grey Wagtails, birds which did not colonise the county until over 200 years after the canal was built. The connection with the Arun did not prosper and most of it has not survived.

The Mole Valley. The River Mole rises in Sussex and drains southeast Surrey. It is mostly too shallow for navigation and its valley does not have marshes and water meadows comparable to those found by the Wey. There are well-wooded sections with plenty of Mandarin. After crossing farmland on the weald and passing parkland at Betchworth it cuts through the North Downs to Leatherhead. The section through the North Downs has gravelly stretches between Dorking and Leatherhead and the bed has occasionally become dry, with the river flowing underground. Migrant Common Sandpipers can sometimes be seen and there is a 19th century record of a nest with four young. Brandon (1998) points out that the charm of this section of the valley, part of which is shown by John Davis in his painting, is mainly due to sensitive landscaping.

In the 19th century this was a bare landscape of rabbit warrens and sheepwalks. The area was made accessible by the completion of the Epsom to Horsham turnpike in 1775. George Lock bought the Norbury estate in 1774, rebuilt Norbury Park and landscaped the Mole Valley at Mickleham as hanging woods, footpaths and ornamental farmland. Bucknill (1900) said of the stretch from Betchworth to Cobham that the reeds were high, the bushes uncut, the stream unnavigable, and the banks mostly inaccessible to the public. There were many Reed Warblers breeding in the reeds from Betchworth to Cobham. The Mole valley changed greatly in the 20th century. The river is still not readily navigable, but the great reedbeds have gone, and so have the Reed Warblers. The river is deeper below Leatherhead. Water meadows at Cobham once had breeding Redshank. The river reaches the Thames at East Molesey after encircling, with the River Ember, the small island that holds Island Barn Reservoir.

Other Watercourses. The River **Wandle** rises at Waddon, in Croydon and passes through Beddington Sewage Farm, Morden Hall Park and King George's Park to reach the Thames at Wandsworth Creek. In Cobbett's day it provided water for one of the most industrialised districts in England, with 39 milling,

The River Mole at Mickleham. This stretch of the Mole is shallow, with swallow holes where the river vanishes into the chalk in very dry weather. Characteristic birds of its bridges and riverside woods include Mandarin and Grey Wagtails.

John Davis

calico printing and other undertakings along a nine mile stretch (Brandon, 1998). As late as the 1880s, when Beddington was still a rural hamlet, the Wandle was famous for its trout. Frohawk was able to show a friend a shoal of 200 in 1883 (Chatfield, 1987). Wandsworth Sewage Farm was on its west bank in the 1950s but has since gone. These days the river is partly piped or enclosed between concrete banks and of no economic importance. **Waddon Ponds** support a large population of Coot and the Wandle, which crosses the south end of Beddington Sewage Farm, is used as a highway by waterbirds. Pilings around **Wandsworth Creek** are used by loafing Cormorants and gulls.

The **Beverley Brook** and the River **Hogsmill** are in the same water catchment area as the Wandle. Until 1999, up to ninety per cent of the water in the Beverley Brook, which rises in Cheam, came in effluent from the Worcester Park Sewage Farm. After the sewage farm was closed, this was replaced by effluent which came from more modern treatment works at Kingston and was pumped back to Worcester Park to maintain the previous volume (Drakeford and Sutcliffe, 2000). After passing through Wimbledon Common and Richmond Park, the Beverley Brook enters the Thames near Putney Bridge. The Hogsmill rises near Epsom and runs past Berrylands Sewage Farm to the Thames at Kingston. Neither watercourse seems to be of major significance for waterbirds, though both maintain riverside vegetation and wetland in the areas through which they pass. The **Redhill Brook** passes Merstham Sewage Farm and the sand pits at Holmethorpe before joining the **Salfords Stream** that reaches the Mole at Sidlow. Earlswood Lakes are connected to the Mole at Sidlow by the **Earlswood Brook**.

The **Falcon** drains ponds on Tooting Bec Common and reaches the Thames at Battersea. The **Efra** runs from Norwood through Brixton to the Thames at Lambeth. The **Peck** runs from Peckham through Dulwich into the piped **Neckinger**, which reaches the Thames at Bermondsey. There are four other rivers. The shortest is the **Ock**, which fills the ponds at Enton and runs into the Wey at Godalming, but not before giving its name to Newman's Ockford Coppice, where he listened to Nightingales before 1850, and to Ockford Pond, which produced 19th century records for the Great Reed Warbler (the third for Britain), Bearded Tit and Golden Oriole. The River **Bourne** rises near Virginia Water and runs east to join the Wey at Weybridge. The River **Eden** drains southeast Surrey and runs into Kent. The **North River** rises south of Leith Hill and runs into Sussex. The main interest of the Tillingbourne lies with its associated ponds, as described earlier.

Spelthorne. The **Colne Brook** forms most of the western boundary of Spelthorne. The River **Ash**, a reedy, rubbish-strewn waterway rising in Shepperton, joins the Colne Brook below King George VI Reservoir. Some of it is good for aquatic plants (Spelthorne Borough Local Plan, April 2001). Mute Swans nest on it (Belsey, 2002).

Birds and Wet Meadows. Riverside meadows can provide a rich habitat for a variety of waders, wagtails, warblers and other birds breeding in marsh and rank grassland. There is little quantitative information about the abundance of these species in Surrey or about historical trends. It is clear, though, that land drainage, assisted by government grants for many years, changes in grassland management and other factors have led to widespread losses in Surrey as they have elsewhere, to the degree that all breeding waders are currently rarer in the county than are birds such as the Nightjar, Woodlark and Dartford Warbler, which are given much higher conservation priorities.

The BTO organised a 1982 survey of the breeding waders of wet meadows. The survey covered England and Wales and aimed to include all significant sites. Thirty-two areas were surveyed in outer Surrey. The percentage of areas in which birds were present was below average for the main species, being 53 for Lapwing, 19 for Snipe and 12 for Redshank against percentages of 66, 31 and 34 respectively in the whole survey (*BTO News 231*). These figures do not include Greater London or Spelthorne. The survey did not cover any heathlands apart from Whitmoor Common (missing the Surrey Curlew, some of the Snipe and a pair of Teal) or gravel pits and sewage farms (missing some Redshank and all the breeding Yellow Wagtails).

Langham Ponds, Runnymede   *Photo D. J. Brassington*

River Wey at Stoke Lock   *Photo D. J. Brassington*

Urban areas. Northeast Surrey is a largely built-up area, with many parks and some larger areas of woods, commons and wetland. The **Norwood** area, which includes Norwood Lake, South Norwood Country Park (once Elmers End Sewage Farm), Beaulieu Heights Wood (Beulah Hill woods), Crystal Palace Park and Penge, takes its name from the Great North Wood, which has a history going back to the Domesday Book. The wood was largely destroyed in the 19th century (Cocksedge, 1933). Birds listed for the Norwood District by Swayne (1934) include the Nightjar (1902), Nightingale (heard 1929) Wood Warbler (Beaulieu Hill Woods 1930, 1932) and Red-backed Shrike (bred 1913). Norwood Lake, also known as South Norwood Lake and apparently the reservoir at South Norwood referred to by Aldridge (1885) held a Pied-billed Grebe in 1998. Beaulieu Heights Wood (Aldridge's Beaulah) has been a good wintering site for Firecrests in recent years and attracted a Red-breasted Flycatcher in 1998. Penge Common was transferred from Surrey to Kent in 1899. **Morden Hall Park**, once a deer park, is a National Trust property with water. Churchyards and cemeteries in towns can be islands of bird life. One such is **Camberley Cemetery** (40 acres). **Nunhead Cemetery** (40 acres), on high ground, is another. Many small birds breed there. Hudson (1898) said it was 'an extremely pretty spot' and a favourite winter resort for Mistle Thrushes, Starlings, Chaffinches and Greenfinches. Magpies and Greenfinches are typical cemetery birds.

Airfields. Airfields and airports have three specialised habitats, large buildings, large areas of tarmac and short grassland and they sometimes have areas of waste ground. Perry Oaks Sewage Farm was finally within the boundary of **Heathrow** Airport. The buildings may attract birds such as Feral Rock Doves and Black Redstarts. The tarmac may be used by roosting gulls (*e.g.* at Heathrow) and the grassland attracts plovers, and other grassland feeders. Little Ringed Plovers have bred or tried to breed on rough ground at two of them. **Brooklands**, **Croydon** and **Kenley**, now closed, had their origins in the 1914-18 war. Black Redstarts bred in ruins at Croydon Airport in 1944. Other birds seen there include Ring Ouzel and a Short-eared Owl. **Gatwick** was set up by the Surrey Aero Club in 1930. **Fairoaks** was built in 1936. **Dunsfold** and **Wisley** date back to the 1939-45 war. Both have now closed. **Redhill** Aerodrome (Black-tailed Godwit in 1991) was built in 1934.

The most frequently watched sites. Some sites are much more heavily watched than others, usually because observers have a better chance of seeing unusual birds. An analysis of over 70,000 records from 1992-97 shows that 40% of them came from eleven places:

Records 1992-97

	Records	**%**		**Records**	**%**
			Stoke, Guildford	1,288	1.8
Walton Reservoirs	5,751	8.2	Island Barn Reservoir	1,241	1.8
Beddington Sewage Farm	5,654	8.0	Frimley	1,080	1.5
Thursley/Ockley Commons	2,515	3.6	Unstead Sewage Farm	1,240	1.8
Frensham Common/Ponds	4,584	6.5	Chobham Common	447	0.6
Queen Elizabeth II Reservoir	2,453	3.5	Other sites	42,269	60.2
Barn Elms Reservoir	1,745	2.5	*Total*	**70,267**	**100.0**

The History of Bird Recording in Surrey

Although this is a book about birds, it is the people that see them who provide all the information. Some, like the shadowy figure of Nicholas of Guildford, are virtually unknown apart from what they wrote, or may have written. Some, like the 'itinerant bird-stuffer named Burls', source of the 1832 Black-winged Stilt claim, live only in the reports of others. Some, like Harry Witherby, lived in Surrey and contributed to the history of its birds but built up their reputations in wider fields. Others, like the observer who found an Eider in the garden pond, were and are people with better than average luck and an interest in what they saw. Today most bird records come from the large and increasing band of amateur birdwatchers, some of them members of bird clubs and many now sharing their observations through the internet, which is itself now proving a valuable communication and research tool. The standard of expertise has increased greatly, assisted by higher quality optical and photographic equipment, better identification guides and a widening and deepening pool of printed and electronic information available.

The earliest written sources are literary and anecdotal rather than systematic. **Nicholas of Guildford** is generally thought to have been the author of the allegorical poem *The Owl and the Nightingale* in which the Nightingale argues for Art and the Owl for philosophy. It is thought to have been written in the late 12th or early 13th century. Nicholas may not have lived at Guildford, or heard a Nightingale there. In the poem, the Nightingale says that he lives at 'Portisham, a seaside town in Dorset'. This could have been an outstation of an ecclesiastical body in Guildford.

The **Evelyn** family developed water power and industries to use it along the Tillingbourne Valley in the 16th and 17th centuries. **John Evelyn** (1620-1706) was a Royalist landowner, garden designer and scholar, best known today for the gardens that he made, and for his diary, which is crammed with details of town and country life of the time and contains some of the early references to Surrey birds. In another work, he warns his grandson not to *'let any of your servants under the pretence of killing crows and kites to have a Gunn without your special leave, for they will shoot Connys, pheasant, partriges, Hares and other game'* suggesting a rather casual attitude to the welfare of the Red Kite. **George Edwards** (1694-1773) published illustrated natural history books in the 18th century. They included the earliest British references to the Mandarin (captive, in Surrey), Little Owl (escaped, in Surrey), Hoopoe and Rose-coloured Starling. The last two might have been in Norwood, Surrey but were only said to have been in Norwood, near London, which leaves another Norwood possibility.

From here on, there are many others and the selection has to be a little arbitrary. The names chosen are mostly of those with a significant relation to the earlier part of the history. **Gilbert White** (1720-1793) was a Hampshire clergyman. He found time to write one of the world's most widely published books – *The Natural History and Antiquities of Selbourne*, with some 200 editions and reprints by 1975, and was the first to separate Willow Warblers, Wood Warblers and Chiffchaffs by their songs. White met and corresponded with the leading ornithologists of his time, including Daines Barrington, George Montagu and Thomas Pennant. He was responsible for adding the Lesser Whitethroat to the British list, along with two mammals – the Harvest Mouse and the Noctule Bat. His book was published by his brother Benjamin, who had a Fleet Street publishing business specialising in natural history and who suggested that Gilbert should get a collected form of the letters into print. White's main Surrey connection is through the many trips he made to London, often to see Benjamin or another brother, Thomas. Both lived in South Lambeth. Thomas had moved there after inheriting an estate and retiring from business. He was interested in natural history and was a Fellow of The Royal Society. Gilbert sometimes attended The Royal Society's meetings as a guest. Thomas and Gilbert shared a common interest in horticulture. Gilbert made some of the earliest records of birds in Surrey in his notes on the birdlife of south London, discussed by Chatfield (1992). Among the birds that he mentioned are the Cuckoo, Tawny Owl, Swift, Green Woodpecker, House Martin, Dunnock, Redstart, Spotted Flycatcher, Red-backed Shrike, House Sparrow and Chaffinch. White's 1754-93 Journals are well presented in an edition by Greenoak and Mabey.

George Montagu (1751-1815) came from a Wiltshire family. He was a professional soldier, retiring with the rank of Lieutenant-colonel in the Wiltshire militia to live in Devon and pursue his interest in natural history. In this capacity he was a painstaking ornithologist who for example, proved that the male and female Hen Harriers were not (as was believed at the time) of different species by taking young Hen Harriers from a nest, keeping them in captivity and observing a male change plumage from brown to grey as it matured. His domestic life and his military career were both rather stormy, the latter ending with a court martial involving personal matters, but as a bird man he ended his life with substantial achievements, culminating in the publication of his *Ornithological Dictionary* in 1802 and a *Supplement* to it in 1813. Of three species added to the British list by his researches, one is the Little Gull, killed on the Thames at Chelsea. The other two are the Cattle Egret and the Gull-billed Tern. There are short biographies of Montagu in Yarrell (2nd Edition, vol. I, pp. 499-501) and Mearns (1988).

George Graves published *British Ornithology*, a multi-volume illustrated work on British birds, which appeared in stages from 1811 to 1821. He included important notes on the birds of Surrey in his time. **Edward Jesse** (1780-1868) was another writer who contributed to the early ornithology of Surrey, particularly from the area around Richmond. His *Gleanings in Natural History* (London, 1835-36) provided a useful source of information about the commoner birds of his time to later researchers. He also located some rarer birds. One of the first Red-breasted Mergansers for Surrey came from him, and his *Gleanings* mentions the first Razorbill, shot in 1831 near Cobham.

Waring Kidd (*c*.1789-?) was an enthusiastic ornithologist and collector who was of independent means and lived at Hatch, in Godalming. He was a mentor of Newman. Stafford wrote of him that for many years he bought every rare bird shot within 20 miles of Godalming (SCCMS). Kidd was an important contributor to the *Letters of Rusticus*. His paper *Some Account of the Birds of Godalming* (Kidd, 1837) appears, with some additions and omissions, in Newman's 1849 work and lists195 species for west Surrey (and in a few cases from beyond its borders). This is the first Surrey bird list of such length. He was an artist, contributing attractive and historically interesting sketches of Godalming sites to Newman's 1849 publication and was working on a list of rarities (not located by Bucknill) in 1868 (Bucknill, 1902). He was still living in Godalming, where he was born, in 1881 at the age of 92.

The family of **Henry Lawes Long** (1795-1868) had a colourful history in Jamaica, where they made money from sugar (Howard, undated). They bought Hampton Lodge, Puttenham in 1801 and Henry lived there from the 1820s or earlier until he moved out in the 1840s. The move was forced by his financial losses in Jamaica after the emancipation of the slaves. Long was well connected. He had, for example, personal recollections of Lord Byron and was Gentleman Usher at the coronation of George IV. Bucknill makes many references to Long, who took a keen interest in birds and owned a copy of Bewick's *British Birds*, in which he made marginal annotations. These and other private notes are the source of the earliest Surrey references to the Goldeneye, Goosander, Great Crested Grebe, Honey Buzzard, Dunlin, Black-tailed Godwit, Redshank, Green Sandpiper, Black Tern and Great Spotted Woodpecker and the first fully dated records of the Cormorant and Ring Ouzel. All but one were from Hampton Lodge and most were of birds shot. Long had a good local collection of stuffed birds, many of which where still on view at the Lodge in Bucknill's time. He assisted in the preparation of Yarrell's *British Birds*. The present locations of his copy of Bewick, his notebooks and the birds he collected, if they still exist, have not yet been traced. Other notes on the family are in Thornton, 2000.

Edward Newman (1801-1876) was born in Hampstead and moved to Godalming in 1817, after leaving school. He began work in the wool trade but moved back to London in 1826 to set up as a printer. He founded *The Zoologist* in 1843 and edited it for the remainder of his life. He is now best known for *The Letters of Rusticus on the Natural History of Godalming* (Newman, 1849), which he edited and printed for John van Voorst, a London publisher associated with many ornithological works and reprints of the period. This book is the earliest avifauna to be devoted to Surrey or any part of it. Other books that Newman published through van Voorst related to Insects and to British Ferns. The letters had originally appeared in the *Magazine of Natural History*, *The Entomological Magazine* and *The Entomologist*. They were written by Newman and others under the pen name of Rusticus and drew heavily on the contributions of local naturalists, including Waring Kidd, James Lewcock, H. L. Long, T. Mansell, J. D. Salmon and William Stafford. He edited the 1866 expanded edition of Montagu's *Ornithological Dictionary*. An appreciation of Newman appeared in *The Zoologist* for 1876.

Edward Blyth (about 1810-1873) contributed to the *Letters of Rusticus* and published a useful, but unfinished, account of the birds of Tooting, where he lived. He later went to India and worked at the Calcutta Museum from about 1842 to 1864, where he obtained considerable experience of oriental birds, enabling him later to play a significant part in the matter of a Siberian Thrush found in Surrey.

Henry Leonard Meyer was the author of a popular, and mid-19th century avifauna (Meyer, 1842), currently somewhat expensive to acquire because of its illustrations. He lived in the Esher area and published a number of personal observations on the birds of the county, often based on observations near his home. Some of these are referred to in the systematic list. His notes on a pair of orange-legged hobbys, now better known as the Red-footed Falcons, at Claremont, near Esher in 1838, established a first for Surrey and were quoted by other writers. Like other men of his time, he sometimes shot birds and the quarry could be of more than passing importance. A Red-breasted Merganser from the Thames near Chertsey was the first that can be dated for the county. He had satisfied himself that the Cirl Bunting bred in Surrey by 1846 and proved his identification of the eggs *'by the only sure test of shooting the bird from the nest'* (Bucknill).

William Stafford (*c*.1810-1890), the son of William Stafford, a Godalming grocer, was a corn merchant and miller by profession, working in Godalming, the town where he was born. He was also a collector and had a museum in the Ockford Road. His collection played an important part in Surrey's ornithological history and is discussed further below. Stafford had more than local interests. The collection included a storm-blown Noddy Tern caught by hand in a fierce gale off Juan Fernandez (SALEC).

Frederick Bond (1811-1889) was a field naturalist, shooter and collector, and lived in Staines. He was the first to describe the nest of the Grasshopper Warbler (from the fens) and he added the Lapland Bunting to the Surrey list. His collection was famous. It included the Siberian Thrush found in Surrey and later bequeathed to the British Museum. There is a memoir of Bond in *The Zoologist* (Harting, 1889).

Denham Jordan (1834(?)-1920), better known under his pen name of A Son of the Marshes, moved from the north Kent marshes to Surrey in the mid-19th century and, after many years observation of the ways of the countryside, produced a series of books on rural themes in the 1890s. He was assisted by J. A. Owen (Mrs Owen Visger), who edited and shaped the works from Jordan's dictated texts. When published, the books achieved great popular success, and they are now a valuable source of information about wildlife and the rural scene in a vanished age. The distance in time between us and that lost landscape is measured, along with its links to the present, by comment that *'The hen-harriers and the sparrowhawks hunt and kill the partridges by the roads after the corn is cut, and the birds are frequently cut down as they clear the hedge to cross over the road'* (Jordan, 1892). Much of the writing was drawn from his experience of the country around Dorking and of the Surrey hills. At times it can be frustrating to read, because Jordan was deliberately vague about locations and gave very few dates. Parr (1972) contains a more extended biographical note. Bucknill referred to him as George Jordan.

Henry Eeles Dresser (1838-1915) had an arduous working life in the City as well as being an acknowledged authority on birds in his day. He wrote an eight volume work on the birds of Europe, published in parts from 1871 to 1881 and, for Surrey, significant in the history of the Siberian Thrush.

James Edmund Harting (1841-1928) published *The Birds of Middlesex* in 1866. It was one of the first county avifaunas, following *Ornithological Rambles in Sussex* by Knox in 1849 and *Birds of Somersetshire* by Crotch in 1851 and he was then 25. Harting had become interested in birds at the age of ten when looking at the collections made by Frederick Bond, who was later to teach him what were then some of the birding essentials - how to shoot and how to make skins. It was an age when well-authenticated records were hard to get. He wrote that:

> In mentioning the only two instances of which I am aware of the appearance of the Great Black Woodpecker in Middlesex, I am, unfortunately, unable to speak from personal observation, and only refer, in the first case, to what I have gleaned from the work of a reliable authority, Colonel Montagu, and in the second case to what has been related to me by an eye-witness.

Any modern records committee member can recognise the dilemma. The Great Black Woodpecker record, which was from Battersea, was first published by George (Colonel) Montagu in 1813 and had appeared in other works. It survived into Harting's *Handbook*, published in 1872 and is discussed later in the text.

There is not a great deal about the Spelthorne (Staines) area which is now part of Surrey, in Harting's book, but there are references to Battersea and other parts of south London. He continued his association with the birdlife of the area in his later years and, for example, gave a lecture on the wildlife of Weybridge over 40 years later, in 1910. He edited *The Zoologist* from Newman's death in 1876 until 1896 and was on the staff of *The Field* for over 50 years until his own death at the age of 87 in 1928. There is an obituary in British Birds (*BB, 21:256*).

William Henry Hudson (1842 1922) was born in Argentina and began to support himself by collecting birds in South America for the Smithsonian Institution in Washington. He emigrated to England in the 1870s and combined a literary life in London with conservation interests and sensitive writings about the countryside, of which *Birds and Man* (1915) is perhaps the best known and *Birds in London* (1898) the most local. He knew parts of Surrey very well and was disgusted by the cruelty of bird and egg collecting as it was practised up to the time of the 1914-18 war:

> *All the localities in which rare resident species may be looked for are known, while the collectors all over the country are in touch with each other, and have a system of exchanges as complete as it is deadly to the birds. And of protests against the bird protection laws The collectors will doubtless cry out that … there is really no more harm in collecting birds and their eggs than in collecting old prints, Guatemalan postage rates, samplers, and first editions of minor poets …'*

There is a short biography in Mearns and Mearns (1998).

Richard Jefferies (1848-1887) was a prolific writer on the countryside and natural history of southern England until his death at the early age of 38. He moved from Wiltshire to Surbiton in 1877 so that he could be nearer to his London publishers and remained there for five years. In 1882 he moved to Brighton, where he hoped that the clean sea air would be better for his health, but not before writing many essays, including those collected in *Nature near London*, a collection which was published posthumously. The essays give an affectionate description of the then rural scene of the district. The book catches the countryside at a time when it still seemed healthy, rich and indestructible. At the same time it was vulnerable in ways that we now recognise. Writing of a December day near Ewell he says:

> *'Small birds swarmed … in every ploughed field. All the birdcatchers in London with traps and nets and limed twigs could never make the slightest appreciable difference to such flocks. I have always expressed my detestation of the birdcatcher; but it is founded on other grounds, and not from any fear of the diminution of numbers only. Where the birdcatcher does irretrievable injury is in this way – a bird, say a nightingale, say a goldfinch, has a nest in the corner of a garden, or an apple-tree in an orchard. The birdcatcher presently decoys one or other of these, and henceforth the spot is deserted.'*

There is good sense in this observation. In the breeding season, disturbance is more damaging than predation, while winter numbers are controlled by food supply. Comparing these Surrey finch flocks with those he had seen elsewhere he said that:

> *'I cannot recall ever seeing such vast numbers of birds … Sparrows crowd every hedge and field, their numbers are incredible; chaffinches are not to be counted; of greenfinches there must be thousands.'*

While much of what he described has long since gone, many who know the Surbiton/Tolworth area will find much of it easily recognisable and the existence of a vigorous local birdwatching society attests to the continued interest of the birdlife to be found there. Like Hudson, Jefferies could be harsh when describing cruelties of the age. An example is his description of the techniques of the professional Nightingale catchers who operated in Surrey woodlands before the bird protection laws that were passed from 1880 onwards began to clamp down on the trade. Even free Nightingales do not sing for more than six weeks or so. The ones that were caught and caged often died within a week.

By the late 19th century writers and artists were becoming interested in the hills and heaths of west Surrey. **William Frederick Foster** (1853-1924) was an artist with an interest in birds and had west Surrey connections. His father moved from London to a substantial property at Wormley Hill in the 1860s. Foster's paintings reflect his birdwatching activities in the neighbourhood and some of them appeared in *British Birds and their Haunts*, by the Rev. C. A. Johns, a popular book of the period, which was published in 1909 (Watts 2004). **George Bernard Shaw** (1856-1950) was invited to visit a west Surrey friend and he left a lively account of the excursion in the *Pall Mall Gazette* for 28th April 1888, quoted in Watts (2004). He travelled by rail from London to Farnham and continued on foot. Shaw was not a countryman and his account of tramping in the rain down muddy lanes from Farnham to well beyond Tilford make entertaining reading. There is only one bird observation in the whole account, of '*Some waterproof variety of bird, screaming with laughter at me from a plantation*' that '*made me understand better than before why birds are habitually shot*'. The following day he got up early to hear the birds but found none, then or in a wet walk to Hindhead by way of Frensham Ponds. He was glad to get back to London. Birding on the commons in wet weather can, even for more dedicated folk, be somewhat disappointing. **Archibald Thorburn** (1860-1935) was born in Edinburgh but moved to London. A short account of his career is given by Watts (2004). By his early twenties, he had established a substantial reputation as a painter of birds and animals. His coloured plates for Lord Lilford's *Coloured Figures of the Birds of the British Isles* have given him a lasting fame. He and his wife moved to a large property at Hascombe in 1902 and he lived there as an artist for the rest of his life. Watts includes a picture of the shed from which he watched wildlife in the garden.

Frederick William Frohawk (1861-1946) was a prominent Victorian naturalist best known as an artist, writer and entomologist. His family moved to Croydon in 1873 and he spent the rest of his life in Surrey, Essex and Kent. He was interested in bird behaviour and made many contributions to *The Field* and other journals on this and other branches of natural history. His place in the history of Surrey birds is secured by records of the first Yellow-browed Warbler in 1930 and what is still the latest Willow Warbler in 1931. Chatfield (1987) provides a well illustrated biography.

The amateur tradition of the time was exemplified by **Arthur Holte MacPherson** (1867-1953), who was a London solicitor by profession. He contributed articles on London birds to *Nature Notes*, *The Selbourne Magazine*, *The London Naturalist* and *British Birds* from 1891 to 1941. His publications included an annual report on the birds of Inner London and an influential paper on the London reservoirs in 1927. In his later years he was on the Councils of the RSPB and the BTO. There is a short memoir in *British Birds* (*BB*, 47:335).

The **Rev. William A. Shaw** (? – 1938), Rector of Peper Harow from 1912 to 1932, was an all round naturalist and was often described in the local press as 'a modern Gilbert White'. Ornithology was undoubtedly his chief interest and he did much to encourage members of the Haslemere Natural History Society to study birds. His work with and for the Society is described further below.

Richard Kearton (1862-1928) and **Cherry Kearton** (1871-1940) were pioneers of nature photography. In the 1890s they produced the first book on nature illustrated entirely by photography. Richard wrote and his brother Cherry took the photographs. The Keartons moved from Yorkshire to Kenley, in Surrey, where they produced work which featured birds of the county, including the Dartford Warbler. A photograph of a Nightingale, taken by Cherry Kearton in 1898 on the Kenley property where he later recorded the song, is in Kearton (1938). The brothers made a feature of their skills and methods, sometimes perhaps with a bit of artifice for emphasis. *Wild Nature's Ways* includes pictures of hides made from mounted sheep and ox carcasses and another in a reed-covered boat and one of a rope descent from a cliff while carrying a camera mounted on a tripod. Richard went on to do some work in Surrey with Howard Bentham. Cherry went abroad in 1908, travelling, writing, taking photographs and making documentary films in distant parts of the world and he did not return until the mid 1930s, living for a while at a house in Kenley called Schunafel. In 1937 or 1938 he bought the old family home. The house itself was in ruins, having been destroyed by an aeroplane which crashed on it and the garden was a wilderness. He had the remains of the aeroplane removed, and a new house built, with The Jungle, Kenley as its address. The Jungle has since gone and the site of this magical episode is now occupied by several houses in Bywood Close.

Sir John A. Bucknill (1873-1926) was a pupil at Charterhouse. His brief, but remarkable Surrey career culminated in the publication of *The Birds of Surrey* in 1900 and some related contributions to the *Victoria County History* and *The Zoologist*. The book was the first avifauna for Surrey and remains a very useful summary of the knowledge available by the end of the 19th century. Legal training made him a tenacious researcher, exemplified by correspondence in the Haslemere Museum that relates to the first Curlew breeding record for Surrey. He evidently had a reference collection which included 20 Curlew eggs. Two years after publication he was posted abroad and did not return to Britain. He initially went to South Africa. A note in Day (1989) mentions him writing about the extinction of the Pink-headed Duck in India, which he blamed on hunting pressure and the drainage of swamps.

Harry Forbes Witherby (1873-1943) was the first editor of *British Birds*, which started in June 1907 and absorbed *The Zoologist* in January 1917. He founded the current British ringing scheme. He was a Hampshire man and moved to Gracious Pond Farm, at Chobham, in 1936 after having retired from full-time participation in the activities of the family printing firm H. F. and G. Witherby. His new home was in an area he already knew, having for example watched Curlew on Chobham Common with P. A. D. Hollom in 1932. He was an enthusiastic gardener as well as an ornithologist and he took much pleasure in developing the garden and he cleared a derelict pond in the grounds as a sanctuary for duck. Many other ornithologists were welcomed as guests, including Ludwig Koch, who made recordings there which were subsequently published by the family printers. Richard Fitter remembers he and E. M. Nicholson being shown the breeding Curlews there (Fitter, 2000). Nicholson himself had strong connections with the Nature Conservancy and was very active in London north of the Thames, though not in Surrey. Notes on Harry Witherby's contributions to bird ringing, ornithological publication and scientific research are given separately below. There is a memoir in British Birds (*BB, 37:162-174*) and an appreciation of his life and work in Tucker (1943). Both amplify these Surrey-based notes.

Charles Howard Bentham (1883-1968) was born in Croydon and started birdwatching in his boyhood. He began keeping a diary in 1906 and made notes on birds in Surrey from then on for more than 60 years. He was an early participant in the Witherby bird ringing scheme and contributed many notes to the early volumes of *British Birds*. After meeting Richard Kearton in the early 1900s, the two worked together in the photography of birds in Surrey, and possibly elsewhere. Bentham began active service in 1916 and subsequently sustained a shoulder injury which prevented his carrying the heavy equipment needed for further photography. He and Kearton co-authored *The Pocket Book of British Birds*, which was published in 1925 and contains 191 photographs, of which several are Bentham's earlier work, including nest studies of the Nightjar, Kingfisher Dartford Warbler (no locations given) and Fieldfare (Norway, *BB, 5:130*) and photographs of a Stonechat and young Little Owls. It is a neat little book, though with very little specific Surrey material in it. The lead author was Kearton. Bentham planned a book on the birds of Surrey and advertised for material in 1927, but the work was sadly not completed. Many Surrey records from his diaries are in the Surrey Bird Club archives. Bentham married Kearton's daughter Grace. He was a member of the advisory committee for the 1953-1956 Surrey Bird Reports and served as vice-president and later President of the Surrey Bird Club.

Clemence Margaret Acland (1889-1973) was an early bird ringer, one of her first recoveries being a Tawny Owl ringed at Banstead in May 1910 and recovered near Coulsdon in January 1912. She became a professional wildlife photographer and took part in the first photographic census of the Gannets on Grassholm in 1922. Her subsequent photographic work took her to many parts of the world. Banstead remained her home base and she was a member of the committee that produced *The Birds of the London Area* (LNHS 1957). Later she was to make useful contributions to *Birds in Surrey, 1900-1970*. An appreciation by David Milne appeared in the *Surrey Bird Report* for 1972.

Phyllis M. Bond had a long and distinguished association with Surrey through her work with the Haslemere Natural History Society, which is described in the review of the Society's activities which appears later in the text. Her book *Watching Wild Life* (Bond, 1937), had no specific Surrey associations but shows her as a fine photographer and a sensitive field worker with a wide range of interests. She was the first editor of the *Surrey Bird Report* and continued sending in records until 1979.

The main contributions to ornithology of **Guy Richard Mountfort** (1905- 2003) were on a much larger scale than the level of the county. They include co-authorship, with Peterson and Hollom, of the pioneering *Field Guide to the Birds of Britain and Europe*. This, with his *Portrait* books did much to stimulate birdwatching travel to the Camargue, Spain and destinations further afield. Mountfort at one time lived in Woldingham and his New Naturalist monograph *The Hawfinch* uses experiences obtained in Surrey. He was appointed as a vice-president when the Surrey Bird Club was established in 1956 and provided valuable help until 1966, when he resigned on moving to Sussex. *Bird Watching* for December 2000 contains a lively interview with him at the age of 94.

George B. Blaker (1912-2001) organised the first survey of Barn Owls in England and Wales, which was carried out in 1932. After a career abroad he moved to Lake House, Ockley in 1964 and developed Vann Lake as a nature reserve. The bird log that he kept for the site from 1965 to 1996 is now in the hands of the BTO.

Richard S. R. Fitter (1913-2005) joined the London Natural History Society in 1934. Two of his books, *London's Natural History* (1945) and *London's Birds* (1949) give a wealth of highly readable information about birdlife of the London area, including a large swathe of Surrey, from the earliest historical times onward and he published research papers in *British Birds*, the *London Bird Report* and *The London Naturalist*. He was one of the team that produced *Birds of the London Area* in 1957. He held other posts with the Society, including a spell as editor of *The London Naturalist* and one as Chairman of the Ornithological Records Committee and he became President in 1999. Martin Woodcock has written more about him in *British Birds* (BB, 99:109-10) and there are other memoirs in *The London Naturalist* for 2006.

Richard Constantine Homes (1913-1978), who lived at Tadworth for many years, made a notable contribution to Surrey ornithology in chairing the committee which produced *The Birds of the London Area* (LNHS 1957), which covers the years since 1900, and an updated edition of the same work in 1964. He co-authored the book with R. S. R. Fitter. It is a fine work which contains much information about northeast Surrey, well written and produced to a high standard. Dick Homes was a banker by profession and well known as a stickler for accuracy in ornithological matters. He had a heavy load of other committee work, initially with the London Natural History Society and then with national bodies including the Wildfowl Trust, the RSPB and the BTO, where he twice served as President. He was a vice-president of the Surrey Bird Club from its foundation in 1956 until his death in 1978. In his later years he trained as a ringer at the Club's ringing station at Kempton, with the Hersham Ringing Group. Short obituaries are given by Parr and Spencer.

Peter Geoffrey Davis (1917-1999) did a huge amount of ringing and nest-recording work in west Surrey and was an expert on the bird life of its commons. He was a mainstay of the Haslemere group and assisted in the production of publications on the birds of the district. The BTO awarded him the Trust's prestigious Bernard Tucker medal in 1982. A note about his career appeared in *BTO News 224* and there are many references to his Surrey work in the text below.

Keith D. G. Mitchell (1924-1993) joined the Surrey Bird Club in 1959, was elected to the Committee in 1979 and from 1981-86 carried out the demanding role of Bulletin Editor. He was a skilful companion in the field, where he could use his excellent knowledge of bird song. In 1984 he was elected

President for a three year term. Later he became a vice-president, holding that post until his death. Keith's interest in field ornithology was a lot older than the Surrey Bird Club. During the war he served in Coastal Command and after it he became a Captain with British Airways. In a 1945 contribution to *British Birds* he described how he had, on a fine day in January, watched a Green Woodpecker following the plough in a field at Cley, feeding in furrows like the gulls. Flying provided him with the spur to write on observations of birds seen from aircraft. His two best known papers were published in 1955 and 1957. In the first of these he mentioned nine Coot seen in flight at 1,500 feet, climbing.

Ronald Keir Merton (1932-1978) started his career as a Scientific Officer at the Ministry of Agriculture, Fisheries and Food and subsequently produced many publications. His work on Woodpigeons, including control studies and a New Naturalist monograph (Merton 1968). He was a founder member of the Surrey Bird Club and edited the *Surrey Bird Report* from 1957 to 1962, after which he continued to chair the Records Committee. A note on his career is given by P. B. Lowe (*Surrey Bird Report* for 1977).

Kenneth C. Osborne (about 1933-2003) lived in Oxted and was best known, as far as Surrey is concerned, for his local records and for the information about Surrey birds in papers that he published in the *London Bird Report*. His first published bird records appeared in the London and Surrey Bird Reports for 1961 and he was a regular contributor from then on. He contributed artwork to LNHS publications and edited the *London Bird Report* and he was part of the team that produced the 1977 *Atlas of the Breeding Birds of the London Area*.

Rupert Benedict Hastings (1955-1993) was a highly skilled observer who made many rare bird finds at Barn Elms Reservoirs and others at Staines Reservoirs and at Kew Gardens, where he worked as a scientist. A full appreciation of his career is given by Andrew Moon and others in the *London Bird Report* for 1993.

The current scene is busier and more complex than it has ever been before. National organisations have moved into online record collection. The BTO's Birdtrack system has greatly increased the volume of records available to bird clubs and its other Atlas and survey schemes are mobilising amateur efforts on a large scale. A perusal of the systematic list will reveal a number of observers whose names recur over the past twenty years or so because of their birdfinding and identification skills. There are many others whose skills or interests attract less attention because they are in other fields. The dedication of some patch workers is formidable. One put in at least 1,400 hours at a Surrey sewage farm in a single year.

Museums and Collections

Museums can be a valuable source of information about the bird life of earlier ages. The museum of curiosities established by a Dutchman, John Tradescant, at South Lambeth in the 17th century was the first to be created anywhere in Britain. Its catalogue, published in 1656, mentions no Surrey material but the collection did include the skin of a Dodo, which may have been the bird seen caged in London in 1638 (*BB, 4:267-73*).

Local archaeological collections make up a largely unexploited source of information about birds in Surrey and what is presented here is a sample rather than a summary. Alan Pipe, Jane Liddle and Kevin Reilly of the Museum of London provided very helpful information about bird remains at archaeological sites going back, in some cases, to Roman times and coming from Beddington Sewage Farm, Merton Priory and 21 sites in Southwark. The information is drawn from these papers:

Site	Site code	Citation
Beddington Sewage Farm	BSewage Farm86	*Howell
Merton Priory	MPY86	*Sankey
4 St Thomas Street, Southwark	4STS82	*Cowan, Westman and Wheeler
10-18 Union Street, Southwark	USB88	*Cowan, Westman and Wheeler

Site (cont)	Site code	Citation
15-23 Southwark Street, Southwark	CB81	Cowan (1992)
18 Park Street, Southwark	PRK90	*Cowan
104 Borough High Street, Southwark	BGH95	*Drummond-Murray and Thompson
179 Borough High Street, Southwark	179BHS89	*Cowan, Westman and Wheeler
Arcadia Buildings, Sylvester Street, Southwark	AB78	*Cowan, Westman and Wheeler
Bermondsey Abbey, Abbey Street, Southwark	BA84	
Chaucer House, Southwark	CH75	*Cowan, Westman and Wheeler
Courage's Brewery, Park Street, Southwark	CO84-7	*Cowan
Escalator shaft, London Bridge, Southwark	LB195	*Drummond-Murray and Thompson
Fastolf's Palace and Rosary, Southwark	BFS/SYM88	*Blatherwick and Bluer
Fennings Wharf, Tooley Street, Southwark	FW84	Watson, Brigham and Dyson (2001)
Globe Theatre, Southwark	GLB96	*Barber
Redcross Way, Southwark	RWG94	*Drummond-Murray and Thompson
Union Passage, Tooley Street, Southwark	UPP88	*Blatherwick and Bluer
Winchester Palace, Clink Street, Southwark	WP83	*Yule, Seeley et al.

*forthcoming at the time of writing

Michael Rowe has provided information about bird remains found at Oatlands Palace. The Surrey County Archaeological Unit has provided excellent information about finds at Guildford Castle (Poulton, forthcoming) and Little Pickle, Bletchingley (Poulton et al.). Special thanks for these are due to Rob Poulton and, for Guildford Castle, Naomi Sykes. The Museums of Farnham (Anne Jones) Guildford (Mary Alexander) and others were kind enough to respond to provide information about their holdings which, although including little of value for the current work, were worth checking.

Many private egg and skin collections were built up in the 19th century. Some of the collectors, like Yarrell, were distinguished writers of the period. Others were pursuing sporting or hobby interests. This was a time when optical instruments, field guides, cameras and ornithological knowledge were much less developed than they are today. Sight records were generally distrusted. Contemporary misgivings about single-observer sightings of rare birds, unsupported by photographs, are not a new phenomenon. The collections themselves were of more than ornamental value. They contained specimens of regional and national interest and might change hands for considerable sums on the death of the owner.

The best known of these collections, as far as Surrey is concerned, is that of William Stafford. He built up a large collection of British birds, many from Surrey and all personally mounted by him. Local people contributed to the collection, as did contacts from a wider area. A farmer from Elstead provided a pair of Golden Orioles that were shot near Peper Harow. One Lillywhite, the landlord of the Half Moon Inn, which was until recently on the A3 at Thursley, sold him a Turnstone that had been killed at the nearby Hammer Pond (still the only Turnstone known for the site). A packman named Megenis gave him an Avocet that had been shot at Frensham in the winter of 1839. Sometimes he would shoot a specimen himself, a Blue-headed Wagtail obtained near Godalming and a Rock Pipit from Eashing Bridge being examples. The latter would be a rather unusual find today - no other Rock Pipit has been recorded at Eashing since the shooting. Stafford's collection included some rare or historic birds, including the first Ferruginous Duck and Dotterel for Surrey and the first Pacific Golden Plover for Britain (the last given to him by a Mr Aubrey, then a clerk at Nine Elms Station). The same Mr Aubrey gave Stafford a Little Stint killed at Battersea in 1869, another first for Surrey. Stafford exhibited his birds at the Surrey Art Loan Exhibition, which was held at Guildford in 1884. There is a copy of the exhibition catalogue in the Surrey History Centre at Woking. This has been fully consulted for the present work. After Stafford's death in 1889, the collection was divided up and sold. The Charterhouse School bought 332 cases for

£400. This purchase, together with Stafford's private notebook, the exhibition catalogue (*SALEC*) and the Stafford Collection catalogue were used as sources by Bucknill. Bucknill adds a few details to the notes in SALEC, presumably from his perusal of Stafford's notes. It has not been possible to trace the Stafford Collection catalogue with certainty, but the Charterhouse Library holds a small manuscript notebook (SCCMS) which may be part of the original or a copy of it. Many of the entries in the notebook are identical to Bucknill's text in wording. The manuscript only covers non-passerines. The Charterhouse Collection was overhauled and enlarged in the 1930s by the curator, P. J. Mountney (*The Carthusian, March 1954*) and was cleaned and debugged in about 1992 (Ian Merling-Blake, pers. comm.). The links between the specimens now held and the originals in the Stafford Collection are not always clear. Also, as Merling-Blake has indicated, Stafford was a collector and may have been too ready to accept the provenances given to him by the people from whom he bought birds.

Mr Plasted, a Chelsea resident, had a collection which included the first British Little Gull and an early Little Crake. It was later bought by a Mr Leadbeater, whose name appears several times in Yarrell (1845). Yarrell mentions seeing one of the specimens and probably saw all of them. Some collectors would only keep birds that they shot themselves. Others were supported by professional birdcatchers, who also provided live birds to the many people who wanted to keep them in captivity, usually as songbirds, for millinery purposes or for shooting – see Starling and House Sparrow in the systematic list. Yarrell (1845) has an engraving showing a clap net in use, and another showing a bat-fowling net with a lantern held up behind it, being used to catch birds at night. Kearton (1911) has a photograph of men poking sparrows out of a haystack with a stick and holding up an identical net. Bat-fowling nets were used to catch 307 Swifts that were ringed at Ewell Court in July 1954 (*SBR*).

Bat-fowling net   *Alexander Fussell in Yarrell*

There were also the taxidermists, or 'bird-stuffers' as they were known at the time. The names of Smither, a retired gamekeeper living in Farnham, a 'bird-stuffer of Churt' and Mr Smither of Churt are cited several times by 19th century authors as the source of Surrey specimens, including a Great Northern Diver, Black Grouse eggs, a Siberian Thrush and numerous Dartford Warblers. H. Smither of Churt shot a Little Gull at Frensham in February 1875. These notes might relate to two individuals, possibly the 56-year old Henry John Smither, resident at the Devil's Jumps in the 1871 census, and the Alfred Smither of Churt who was a well-known west Surrey supplier of birds, nests and eggs to the London market and to local collectors such as Phillip Crowley, mentioned in Bucknill (1901).

There were substantial markets for birds, eggs and skins. Nineteenth century writers often referred to London markets as a source of living and dead birds. According to Kearton, the live birds caught on the South Downs were sold in Great Andrew Street, Seven Dials and the dead ones at Leadenhall. It is not always clear whether sales were at ordinary game and poultry markets or markets for collectors. Some were certainly the latter. Saunders, for example, wrote of the Little Owl that *Cages-full, brought from Holland, may often be seen in the Leadenhall Market.* Many specimens and collections changed hands at J. C. Stevens' Auction Rooms in Covent Garden, famous for natural history offerings. Sales of Great Auk remains provided its telegraphic address, Auks, London (Fuller, 1987).

Phillip Crowley built up a 'magnificent' collection of eggs which was very rich in rare Surrey birds, mostly taken in the 1860s near Farnham (Bucknill, 1901). Among the treasures were many clutches from Teal, three from Black Grouse, 60 or 70 Dartford Warbler clutches, and a Raven's egg from Churt. Crowley was one of the subscribers to Bucknill's *Birds of Surrey*. Egg collection continued well into the 20th century, when it made less contribution to history while retaining some of its ornithological interest. An account of it, with brief biographies of a number of Surrey collectors, is given in Cole and Trobe. Some of the collectors contributed valuable observations and insights as field ornithologists. Percy Frederick Bunyard, who died in 1937, lived at Croydon and was an important contributor to Surrey field studies as well as a collector – see references. Edgar Percival Chance (1881-1955), whose book and film *The Cuckoo's Secret* (1922) broke new ground with great skill, was one of the people behind the reintroduction of Buzzards to west Surrey. His egg collection contained over 24,000 specimens (Letter at Haslemere Museum, reference LD 129). C. W. Colthrup lived in East Dulwich and is known to have been active from 1915 to 1927. Surrey interests included Woodlarks. Kenneth L. Skinner (1876-1956), who bought much of his worldwide collection, lived at Weybridge where he studied the local Yellowhammers. He founded the *Oologists' Record* and tried to improve standards of documentation and preparation in collections (Cole and Trobe). Lack of documentation has greatly reduced the value of some of the material researched for the present book. Skinner's bookplate was a coat of arms with finches, eggs and feathers. Gordon Douglas (1913-1988) found unusual Curlew eggs and a clutch of six Lapwing eggs, both in Surrey and had two clutches of Surrey Hobby eggs (Cole and Trobe). He was an expert on Bookham Common (see Parr, 1972) and egg collections from the area are also recorded in Maitland and Turnbull. Major Harry Theodore Gosnell (1897-1954), who was educated at Charterhouse and fought in both World Wars, is best known for collections outside Surrey but his collection, which was left to Charterhouse, included heathland species from the Frensham and Thursley areas. These are recorded in a card index at Charterhouse, which has been examined. Alfred Pearman (1880-1957), who was an expert on the Hobby, appears to have operated in Surrey (Cole and Trobe, 2000). Harry Kirke Swann (1871-1926) was the author of books and papers which included *Bird Life on Epsom Common* in *The Naturalists Journal* that he founded in 1892 and *Birds of London* (Swann, 1893). Anthony G. Wootton seems mainly to have worked in Sussex but *'was successful with Dartford Warbler on Thursley Common'* in 1960 (Cole and Trobe). Douglas Hadley Meares (1881-1949), who collected Hobby eggs in northwest Surrey in the 1930s and 40s, worked there with Percy M. Meason in 1937 and published field note papers in *British Birds*, not always under his own name. He last climbed to a nest in 1948. Cole and Trobe quote the final entry from his diary: *'This season about ends my Hobby nesting; the work is now too strenuous at 67!'*, a human touch.

Some of the museums built up collections, now rather out of fashion but useful where they still exist. The Haslemere Educational Museum was established by Sir Jonathan Hutchinson in 1888. It was initially at his home in Inval but is currently in Haslemere High Street. Education has always played a prominent part in its work. The Museum collection includes early 20th century nests and eggs of species such as the Wryneck, now lost to Surrey as a breeding bird. It has a collection from Samuel Staines Boorman (1865-1952), a farmer with land at Molesey and Send, which includes the eggs of many local farmland birds, most of which were then common species. Scarcer Surrey eggs included those of Dartford Warbler and Red-backed Shrike. Swanton (1947) mentioned a Red-footed Falcon bought from a gamekeeper in Selby, purchases from Stevens' Auction Rooms, 183 cases given by Col. Herbert French and other specimens of local origin. This and the Museum's extensive library have proved very useful in researching material for the present book. The role of the Museum in Surrey natural history is discussed more fully below, in the Haslemere Natural History Society section.

The Booth Museum in Brighton, which started from the private collection of Edward T. Booth, still has Surrey specimens of the Avocet, Alpine Swift and Two-barred Crossbill. Booth wanted to display every British Bird in every plumage in his collection (Mearns and Mearns). At some time in the period

1885-1900, international collectors Osbert Salvin and Frederich DuCane Godman gave birds and eggs that they had collected in Surrey in their youth to the British Museum of Natural History (Mearns and Mearns, 1998). Harry Witherby built up a collection of over nine thousand skins of around thirteen hundred species for scientific purposes over a period of more than 40 years. He later sold these to the British Museum (*BB, 27:174-175*). Some museum collections proved little more durable than those privately held. Montagu (*Supplement*) lamented that the Leverian Museum collection, to which the first Surrey specimens of the Dartford Warbler were sent, was dispersed because the British Museum could not find the £20,000-£30,000 required to save it for the nation. Most of Lord Rothschild's collection of birds at Tring were offered for sale in New York in 1931 (*BB, 26:17-21*).

Bird Ringing and Nest Recording

The month of August 2006 marked the 107th anniversary of the first scientific bird ringing scheme, which started in Denmark when Hans Christian Mortenson put individually numbered rings on 164 Starlings. Ringing in Britain began in the British Isles ten years later, with schemes organised by Harry Witherby in London and Arthur Lansborough Thompson in Edinburgh. Among early workers in the Witherby scheme Mrs Patteson (Limpsfield), Clemence Acland (Banstead) and Howard Bentham had each ringed over 60 birds by 1912. The Witherby scheme was taken over by the then recently founded BTO in June 1937. Further notes on the national scheme are in Clark (2000).

Ringers and Ringing Groups often work at sites outside the recording areas of their local bird clubs. The London Natural History Society's 1938 Bird Ringing Report (*LBR* for 1938) explains that the Society's return to the Bird Ringing Committee of the BTO only totals 673 birds, compared with 1,976 in the previous year, because of a reduction of about 800 in the number of Manx Shearwaters ringed and 240 in the number of Sandwich Terns. The Hersham and Runnymede Ringing Groups have operated across both administrative and vice-county borders. The London Natural History Society and Surrey Bird Club have both included information from outside their recording areas in their annual Bird Reports.

Ringing began at Beddington Sewage Farm in 1938 when Stuart Baker, then a London Natural History Society Member and Mayor of Croydon, cooperated with the London Natural History Society to obtain permission for the erection of a suitable trap on the site. The trap was completed in September and, by the end of the year, 63 birds of eight species had been ringed, predominantly Starlings (*LBR* for 1938). At that time, rings could be obtained through the Society at a cost of a shilling (5p) for a packet of 20. Notable captures in its history include a Bluethroat trapped in 1997 and retrapped in 1999.

The Hersham Ringing Group was established with Donald Parr as its Secretary in 1960, when it began ringing at the now disused Weylands Sewage Farm, also known as Hersham Sewage Farm, which is adjacent to the railway at Hersham. The Surrey Bird Club supported the ringing activities from 1962 under the name of the Hersham Ringing Station. Changes in effluent management reduced the attractiveness of the site to birds and ringing activities were extended to a Metropolitan Water Board site in woodland and adjacent filter beds by the Thames, opposite Rivermead Island. This site was called the Walton Ringing Station. Ringing at the Hersham Ringing Station had ceased by 1971. In 1967 permission was obtained to ring in Kempton Park, on the Middlesex side of the Thames. Kempton Park is a large site which includes Kempton East, Kempton West and Red House Reservoirs, together with about 20 acres of woodland, stream and marsh. It lies wholly in the vice-county of Middlesex and is crossed by the Spelthorne boundary. Ringing began there in 1967, on 11th March. Ringing began at Queen Mary Reservoir in 1969.

From its earliest years the Group made contributions of a more general kind to ornithology. Donald Parr published a paper on the ecology and feeding preferences of its birds in the 1962 *London Bird Report* (Parr, 1963). In 1969 the Kempton site was used for part of the BTO film *Rings for Research*. In the same year the Metropolitan Water Board gave permission for the rescue of birds trapped at the outlet towers of Knight and Bessborough Reservoirs. Two rescues in the winter of 1969/70 were of Red-necked Grebes, which became only the third and fourth Red-necked Grebes ever to be ringed in the UK. Other notable captures in its history include a Common Rosefinch in 1971. In 1971 the Group began supplying ticks to Cambridge University for research purposes. Work was carried out on Barn Owl pellets. Papers on these and other aspects of the Group's work appeared in the Hersham Ringing Group Reports, the first two of which covered 1967-68 and 1969-71. Monthly Bulletins initiated by Charles Ogston were issued from January 1971. Donald Parr was Secretary until he resigned in 1982.

The Runnymede Ringing Group was registered with the BTO in March 1978 after having worked informally at Wraysbury (Yeoveney) Gravel Pit from 1977 and from earlier at Englefield Green and Kingswood. Founder members were Keith Herber and Mike and Linda Lewis. Its area straddles the borders of Surrey, Berkshire, Greater London and Hertfordshire. In association with the Maple Cross Ringing Groups it is also active in Oxfordshire. Among the projects in Surrey that the Group has been associated with are habitat preservation at Wraysbury during the construction of the M25 and survey work at Runnymede and Coopers Hill on behalf of the National Trust. The Group has co-operated with ringers in Israel and Portugal and assisted with the designation of Bedfont Lakes as a National nature Reserve, a Mandarin Duck ringing project and various projects with Royal Holloway College. Current Surrey ringing sites include Chobham Common, East Molesey, Kingswood (Englefield Green) and Tythebarns (Ripley). By August 2000, Group members had ringed nearly 100,000 birds of 110 species and trained many ringers to work elsewhere. The Group produces a monthly Newsletter, editions of which had reached 300 by December 2003. Many other groups and individuals have worked in Surrey.

The Surrey Bird Club

The Surrey Bird Club was founded in 1957 as the first ornithological society or club to cover the whole of Surrey. It took its recording area as the Watsonian vice-county of Surrey. As amplified below, it grew out of the Haslemere Natural History Society to take on the increasing load of the Surrey Bird Report, which was initially produced by the Society. One of the Society members, Harold F. Dickinson, was given the job of advertising for and collecting the names of possible members. He and K. E. W. Doughty announced the formation of the Surrey Bird Club in British Birds for December 1956. As mentioned below, there were some initial misunderstandings between the two organisations but the Club quickly established itself as the as the county-wide body for collecting and publishing bird records. The first President was Sir Norman Boyd Kinnear. C. Howard Bentham was the second, after service as vice-president. Other early vice-presidents included Phyllis Bond, Richard Homes and Guy R. Mountfort. P. Bruce Lowe, another of the founder members, succeeded Bentham as President until 1978 and then served as a vice-president until his death in 1982. His special interest was in wildfowl. There is a brief obituary in the *Surrey Bird Report* for 1982.

The Club had, from the outset, a strong interest in bird ringing, an interest shared by many of its Presidents and Chairmen. Donald Parr (1921-88) was a founder member of the Club, serving in turn as Ringing Secretary, Auditor, Secretary, Chairman and President, finally becoming a vice-president and he founded the Hersham Ringing Group. Another interest was survey work, which he organised during his time as BTO Representative for Surrey. He personally operated the Common Birds Census at Ashtead and Chessington and carried out Wildfowl counts at Island Barn Reservoir for many years. His work on the Records Committee and the *Surrey Bird Report* led eventually to his finest achievement, the production of *Birds in Surrey, 1900-1970*, a work whose clear, concise and exact style has served birdwatchers well for more than 30 years. Donald Parr was a Yorkshireman and those who knew him will remember his dry, understated humour and his smile. His wife Joyce edited the *Surrey Bird Report* from 1968 to 1973 and provided support to Donald and the Surrey Bird Club support in many other ways. She and Donald retired to Malvern.

Phillip A. D. Hollom (Phil) joined the Surrey Bird Club Records Committee in 1957. He already had a distinguished career in the wider birdwatching world, beginning long before and it continued long after. His work in wider fields is summarised in Pemberton (1997). His early notes on birds in Surrey appeared in *British Birds* in the 1920s. He made many observations on the Curlews that bred on Chobham Common up to the 1940s and kept Harry Witherby informed about them, indirectly assisting Ludwig Koch to find a suitable site for recording Curlews in the early days of sound recording. Interest in the Surrey sewage farms was greatly stimulated by his work at Brooklands Sewage Farm in the 1930s, when he showed that many wader species previously considered rare in Surrey occurred more commonly on passage. As a member of the Surrey Records Committee he would base his judgment on the practicalities of fieldwork as much as on written notes and sketches, for example in expressing surprise at the ability of an observer to identify an uncommon bird at a range of two miles, even with field glasses. On another occasion he said of the description of a large bird of prey that it was 'too perfect'. How could the observer really have seen all that? Later, after other records from the same source had come under something of a cloud, this judgment was reinforced. He finally left the Records Committee in 2003 and still serves as a vice-president. His dry wit can raise a smile.

The work of the Records Committee continues. It must be said that the foregoing records were put up in good faith by observers who were convinced of what they saw, and who may well have been right in their identifications. With an eye to the accuracy of a note laid down for posterity though, the Committee has to go on the evidence presented and in the foregoing cases it was not enough, or was flawed. For example, do observers always get distances right?

Field meetings have been an important aspect of the Club's activities, particularly in its earlier years. Victor (Vic) Edwards led field meetings from at least 1962 until his death in 1978. He was a real countryman an excellent field ornithologist and many will have sharpened their skills under his tutelage. Lowe gives an appreciation of his work (*SBR* for 1977). Others, including David Hollow, have continued the work.

The Club has built up a computerised database of over 600,000 records and a paper archive of similar size. These are used for research and conservation purposes.

Other Clubs and Societies Operating in Surrey

The **Haslemere Natural History Society** has an important place in the ornithological history of Surrey. For over a century it has been a focus for naturalists in the southwest of the county and has played a significant part in gathering bird records from its base at Haslemere Museum. It initiated the *Surrey Bird Report* in 1953, supporting its publication each year up to and including 1956.

The Society was founded as the Haslemere Microscope and Natural History Society on Christmas Eve 1888 by a small band of enthusiastic naturalists whose chief interest was microscopy. For the first 18 years its main purpose was to hold regular discussion meetings for its own members and to provide learned lectures to educate the general public. The membership included Sir Arthur Conan Doyle and eminent scientists such as the physicist Professor John Tyndall and geologist Sir Archibald Geikie. 'Natural History' apparently encompassed anything of a scientific, archaeological or literary nature and the only fieldwork was the collection of specimens, such as pressed flowers. Birds hardly featured at all, except as zoological specimens for demonstration. Even when local author Grant Allen lectured on Swallows and Martins in December 1894, he included Swifts and Nightjars under this heading and concentrated on various myths and fashionable theories of migration rather than scientific fact. The same lecture series included *Goats, Our Free Press, The Antiquity of Man* and *Modern Astronomy*.

In 1906 the Society was relaunched with a single new objective, 'the study of local natural history and archaeology'. Observation, 'with use of the Camera and notebook' was to be encouraged and wanton destruction strongly discouraged. A recording area with a radius of six miles from the Haslemere Post Office was set up – this was chosen as it was considered 'a reasonable cycling distance for ladies'!

In 1907, for the first time, local records were mentioned when Mr Roger Hutchinson, a doctor of the district, lectured on *Birds* from his own notebook, which covered 1879 to 1907. He remarked that

Nightjars were common on Lythe Hill (now completely covered in woodland) and that the Hawfinch, which could crack plum stones, frequently visited his garden. The then rare Dartford Warbler had been seen in the Devil's Punch Bowl, where Ring Ouzels could be seen when the whortleberries were ripe. The Goldfinch, rare 20 years previously, had become common, but House Martins had declined.

Later in the year, Roger Hutchinson was appointed branch leader for ornithology, to 'co-ordinate the compilation of local records, to be embodied in the annual report'. However, it appears that he did not manage to persuade the members to produce any records, as nothing ever appeared in the report. It was not until the Rev. W. A. Shaw joined the Society in 1914 that the study of birds began to be taken seriously. Surprisingly, most seemed to think that bird study was extremely difficult - one local reporter who joined him for a walk on Thursley Common in May 1914 was effusive about his abilities, remarking that it was almost uncanny that he could identify birds *by detecting minute differences in the notes*. He continued *Perhaps of all the branches of natural history ornithology is the most difficult … anyone who hopes to attain such eminence … must be peculiarly gifted with unbounded perseverance and unusual keenness of observation.* On that occasion they found breeding Curlew, Wheatear and Dartford Warbler and saw Teal and Wryneck. Within a year, the Rev. William. A. Shaw was working on a list of local birds, to be published by the Society as one of their occasional series of Science Papers. Its publication was delayed until 1921, first by wartime printing restrictions and then by his other commitments (these included examining schools throughout the country for the RSPB). Meanwhile, he gave annual lectures, which he continued until shortly before his death in 1938, on his natural history observations for the preceding year. For 1917 he reported Redshank breeding at Frensham, which he thought to be a first for the county (in fact it had bred at Beddington in 1910 and Howard Bentham found a nest in outer Surrey in 1915). He also led regular rambles, to Thursley and the Devil's Punch Bowl, where he insisted that members should learn songs and calls and observe and make notes on behaviour. His enthusiasm was infectious and he must have inspired the young Phyllis Bond, who joined the Society when her family moved to Haslemere in 1921 and who became one of a new generation of very able Surrey birdwatchers.

Phyllis Bond soon met Margaret Hutchinson (niece of Roger and granddaughter of Sir Jonathan Hutchinson, founder of the Haslemere Museum) and the two became lifelong friends. Both were passionately interested in birds but while Margaret was a loner, undertaking meticulous studies on her own, including one on the territorial behaviour of Woodlarks, Phyllis was a natural team organiser. Together they influenced the activities of the Society for the next 60 years and built up its reputation in the field of ornithology. They were joined in 1930 by Robert Blockey, newly appointed assistant curator at the Museum, who was very keen on scientific fieldwork. In 1933 he was involved in a survey of Dartford Warblers on local commons, when 90 pairs were estimated. Unfortunately, his own notes have not been found so it is not known exactly which commons were covered. He contributed local records to the *South-Eastern Bird Report* and joined its committee in 1938.

In 1935 Haslemere Museum was awarded a £250 grant from the Carnegie UK Trust to set up a Regional and Ecological Survey covering 100 square miles around Haslemere. Robert Blockey led the team of HNHS members who undertook the bird recording and the work was carried on with enthusiasm up to and including 1938. The 1939-45 war curtailed most activities (although Phyllis Bond continued to collect local records for the card index which she had begun in the 1930s) and the loss of Blockey, Assistant Curator from 1933 to 1939, who died in action as a Flight Lieutenant while in Egypt in 1944, was a serious blow to the Society.

In 1947 Phyllis Bond and Margaret Hutchinson decided to monitor the birds of Frensham Great Pond when it was refilled after wartime drainage. They recruited a small team of helpers from the Society who became known as the 'Frensham Watchers' and who visited the Pond every week. In 1948 and subsequently they contributed to the International Wildfowl Enquiry (later the Wildfowl Counts and now Wetland Bird Survey), the Grebe Census and the Investigation of Swifts. The Little Pond was included as it also was refilled and the weekly visits continued (except when prevented by heavy snowfall) for 52 years, until December 1998 and less regular counts were made until at least December 2000.

The enthusiasm for fieldwork continued and in April 1950 the Society monitored 200 nest boxes in Alice Holt Forest for the British Trust for Ornithology, which was carrying out research into the Breeding Habits of Tits for the Forestry Commission. However, in 1952 they regretted that they were unable to repeat the work *owing to the distance and the arduous nature of the investigation*. The uphill cycle ride from Haslemere each week (rather more than the recommended six miles!) and scrambling up and down stepladders must have proved a strain. By then most of the active members were involved also in the joint Ecological Survey of the Devil's Punch Bowl, which was co-ordinated by Col. Bensley and continued until 1955. The ornithological contribution was a study of bird territories, mostly in the woodland areas.

Conservation matters had concerned the Society from its early days. In 1908 the committee discussed *the wanton destruction of Kingfishers and Moorhens in the neighbourhood* and the Secretary was instructed to see the local police sergeant on the subject. In the 1920s egg collecting and malicious heath fires (the two were thought to be linked) were a considerable worry. In 1933 the Hindhead Commons Management Committee requested a note, not later than New Years Day each year, of the whereabouts of any rare birds on Trust property in order that the limits of proposed burning for the year could be decided. In 1952 the Society was protesting about the Boxing Day Coot Shoot, held at the Frensham Pond Hotel, and the following year they wrote to object to the destruction of a colony of Buzzards at Witley Park.

In 1953 Phyllis Bond was asked to prepare a revised bird list to update Shaw's 1921 publication. This must have been a busy time for her as, in the same year, she was approached by Bruce Campbell (then Secretary of the BTO) who was concerned about the lack of coverage of bird records in Surrey, following the demise of the *South-Eastern Bird Report*. He suggested that she might do something to remedy this and that the Museum would be an appropriate collecting centre for information. John Clegg, then Museum Curator, was keen on this idea and together they wrote to all the serious birdwatchers they knew in the county, asking them to support an annual Surrey Bird Report. She also reported the proposal to the HNHS Committee and asked if the Society would fund the publication of the first Report. This was agreed and a budget of £25 was provided. Report No. 1 was issued in the autumn of 1954 and went on sale for two shillings. Phyllis continued to compile the Surrey Bird Report for the next three years, even financing the printing herself, but was still able to work on *A Revised List of the Birds of the Haslemere District* which appeared in 1955.

It was soon apparent that the Bird Report needed its own supporting organisation, as the Society could not continue to fund it. A small advisory committee had been set up, including representatives of other natural history societies in the county, and one of its members, H. Dickinson, was given the job of advertising for and collecting the names of possible recruits to a Surrey Ornithological Society. Unfortunately he left the district suddenly and the ensuing reshuffle of responsibilities led to a number of misunderstandings and some serious rows, which overshadowed the launch of the new organisation.

The newly formed Surrey Bird Club took over the Bird Report from the 1957 issue (No. 5) and since then the Society has contributed all its relevant records each year. Unfortunately, the ill feeling continued, with serious antagonism between some members of the Bird Club and Phyllis Bond, which meant that the Society was virtually ignored in *Birds in Surrey 1900 – 1970* (Parr 1972).

In 1959 Peter Davis joined the Frensham Watchers and within a year had qualified as a BTO Registered Ringer. By 1961 he was ringing regularly at Frensham and contributing his records to the Society. This added a new dimension to the Society's activities and became especially significant after the severe 1963 winter, when he reported that Grey Wagtails and Wrens had suffered the most severely, in addition to Dartford Warblers which had disappeared from Surrey. He was also deeply involved a few years later, with the full support of the committee, in efforts to prevent Frensham from losing its SSSI status and being developed for leisure pursuits, such as gun dog trials.

The birdwatching activities of the Society continued to be popular, with no shortage of keen observers. In 1965 they assisted with the collection and identification of ants at Frensham for the BTO, which was investigating the status of the Wryneck in England. In 1968 a new *Review of the Birds of the Haslemere District* was published, with Peter Davis, Helen Barlow and Margaret Hutchinson joining Phyllis Bond as compilers. However, despite all this enthusiasm, the Society did not become involved with the BTO's landmark project, the fieldwork for the Atlas of Breeding Birds. Apparently it was never discussed or even mentioned at any meeting, so it can only be surmised that Phyllis Bond was finally running out of energy and that no one else was prepared to take on the paperwork.

In 1969 Penny Kirkpatrick (later Hollow) joined the Museum staff and was soon recruited to the Society, becoming the latest of many young birdwatchers to be trained up by Phyllis Bond. Phyllis's standards were exacting (standards now maintained by the Surrey Records Committee) and she insisted that all records should be properly submitted, with supporting evidence if required. The value of this was obvious when John Clark used the Society archives to prepare *Birds of the Hants/Surrey Border*. Ten years later Penny became Secretary of the Society and both Phyllis and Margaret Hutchinson handed over their tasks of maintaining bird records and organising participation in current surveys.

The most urgent task was to replace the 1968 Review, which was long out of date. The increased interest in birdwatching meant that far more records were available from sources other than Society members, and *The Birds of the Haslemere District* (1980), written by Penny Kirkpatrick with contributions from Peter Davis, was more comprehensive than its predecessors.

The BTO Atlas of Wintering Birds (Winter Atlas) was the next major project, with fieldwork running over three consecutive winters and being much enjoyed by members taking part. The summer of 1980 was occupied by the BTO Nightingale survey, for which Peter Davis was national co-ordinator. In the following years Cormorants, Nightjars, Woodlarks, Dartford Warblers, Wood Warblers and Rooks were targeted, with varying degrees of success. Fieldwork for the new Breeding Atlas began in 1988 and the Surrey Tetrad Atlas project ran alongside it from 1989 and continued thereafter, the Society managing comprehensive cover of the extreme southwest corner of the county. However, in the 1990s, the ever-increasing quantity and complexity of paperwork required by the BTO made it virtually impossible to recruit volunteers for surveys and reluctantly the Society had to withdraw.

Throughout its existence the Society has attracted members with a wide range of interests and specialised abilities and thus has benefited from access to more varied skills than may be available in a purely ornithological group. This shows particularly in the results of the 1950s Devil's Punch Bowl survey, where the bird records are far more interesting when considered alongside the vegetation plan. Similarly, in 1983 when Penny Kirkpatrick was studying Firecrests around Haslemere, local experts were on hand to survey the flora of the breeding sites and to identify insects being carried to feed the young.

The links with Haslemere Museum have also been extremely valuable, not only for the provision of a base and a home for records and reference library, but also for much practical support. Until 1988, when Arthur Jewell retired, each Museum Curator was a naturalist and although they had their own specialities, all regarded bird study as an important discipline. Indeed, John Clegg, who preceded Arthur Jewell and was a freshwater life expert, left the Museum in 1962 to work as Education Officer for the RSPB.

There is no doubt that ornithology in Surrey owes a great deal to this and other local natural history societies, which formed the basis of bird recording long before birdwatching became the popular activity that it is today.

The **Holmesdale Natural History Club** was founded in 1857 and is the oldest natural history organisation operating in Surrey. Its recording area is based on the Vale of Holmesdale, which runs across

Surrey and into Kent between the North Downs and the greensand hills. From its earliest days the Club was recording birds, including some Ring-necked Parakeets shot by the stationmaster of Dorking in 1857 and the first dated Black-headed Gull in 1877. The Club has a museum and a collection of birds and eggs. Most of these do not, unfortunately, have obvious Surrey provenances though there will undoubtably be some local specimens. Its archive is easier to use. Among the papers held is one giving the average number of pairs of breeding birds in a 14 acre (5.7 hectare) estate at Wray Park in around 1881. This is the earliest breeding bird survey that has been located for Surrey. With 114 pairs and 32 species, its 20 pairs per hectare compares with the average of 20-40 pairs found in Common Birds Census studies in Surrey 80-100 years later.

The **London Natural History Society** (LNHS) was formed by an amalgamation in 1914 of the City of London Entomological and Natural History Society, which was founded in 1858 as the Haggerston Entomological Society, and the North London Natural History Society, which was founded in 1892 (Fitter, 1956). Aris (1925) says that the Haggerston Entomological Society took its name from the Haggerston Arms, where it met. The LNHS recording area, a circle 20 miles in diameter centred on St Paul's, dates from the amalgamation, so it has included part of Surrey since 1914. The circle is well known and useful among London naturalists but not immediately suitable for more general purposes.

The Society has two major annual publications, *The London Naturalist* and the *London Bird Report*. *The London Naturalist* has been published in much the same format since 1921, with research papers, sectional reports and matters relating to the society as a whole. Earlier publications go back to at least the year 1917, the year for which the Ornithological Section was able to report first records of the Eider Duck (Essex), Buzzard (Essex) and Goldeneye (on the Thames at Kew), bringing the species total for the LNHS area to 147. Further short reports by the Section were made for the years to 1923 (in *The London Naturalist* from 1921) and the edition for 1924 carried the forerunner of the *London Bird Report*, a paper entitled *London Birds*, by A. Holte Macpherson. This appeared annually until 1928, when it was replaced by Ornithological Records of the London Area and then Birds in the London Area from 1932 until it was finally split off as a separate publication, the *London Bird Report* for the year 1936 at the instigation of R. C. Homes. Further articles on London birds appeared in *British Birds until* 1950.

The Slough Natural History Society, later renamed the **Middle-Thames Natural History Society**, was founded in about 1947 and closed in 1983. It originally covered the area within five miles of Slough but from 1953, coverage was extended to the whole of Buckinghamshire, and to eastern Berkshire including Virginia Water. *The Middle-Thames Naturalist*, which was annually published by the Society, generally covered the Surrey part of the Virginia Water area as well as the part in Berkshire and is a useful source of information about the Lake and the adjacent heronry at Fort Belvedere.

The **Surbiton and District Bird Watching Society** was founded in 1954 by Hockley Clarke and records in a 12 km square around Surbiton. The area includes parts of Greater London (Richmond and Bushy parks), Spelthorne (Sunbury) and outer Surrey (Cobham, Walton-on-Thames). The Society has a very active membership and publishes an annual bird report. Records are shared with the London Natural History Society and the Surrey Bird Club.

The **Croydon Natural History and Scientific Society** was founded in 1870 as the Croydon Microscopical Club. It has a museum, whose ornithological specimens include material from Major F. W. Proctor (1862-1916) a noted egg-collector for whom no other Surrey connection has been located. Current ornithological work is co-ordinated through the Croydon RSPB Group. The **Guildford Natural History Society** was founded in 1893. Other organisations with an interest in birds at some time in the past include the **Camberley Natural History Society** (1946), the **Charterhouse Natural History Society**, the **Elmbridge Natural History Society** (1951), the **Spelthorne Natural History Society** (1976) and the **West Surrey Natural History Society** (1979). The **Eton College Natural History Society** published records for what is now Spelthorne, including one relating to the first Snow Buntings.

The extensive heathlands on either side of the Hampshire/Surrey border have been well worked by **John M. Clark,** who published his *Hants/Surrey Border Bird Report* from 1971 to 1997 and whose 1984 book on the area remains a useful guide to its birds. He was joint editor of the last Hampshire avifauna, published in 1996 and is currently the Recorder for Hampshire.

The Royal Society for the Protection of Birds has a large membership in Surrey, with a network of local Groups. Recording work carried out includes local surveys, as at Croydon, and Wetlands Birds Survey counts by the Northwest Surrey Group at Thorpe. The Surrey Wildlife Trust manages a large portfolio of reserves, which has recently been expanded to include some important bird sites such as Holmethorpe Gravel Pits. Bird information is published mainly on its website. The Wildfowl and Wetlands Trust manages the most important wetland site in Surrey, the London Wetland Centre at Barn Elms. A bird report has been published from time to time.

County Recorders

The North London Natural History Society commenced bird recording north of the Thames in 1908. In 1914, after its amalgamation with the City of London Entomological and Natural History Society, it began recording south of the Thames. The first two recorders, C. L. Collenette (1908-13) and W. E. Glegg (1913-17) were later to make distinctive contributions to the ornithology of our area, Collenette by his book on Richmond Park and later as a member of the committee that produced *The Birds of the London Area* and Glegg by an avifauna for Middlesex. The society set up a separate Ornithological Section in 1917 and began producing annual reports, the first of which covered the same year.

When **Ralph Whitlock** started the *South-Eastern Bird Report* in 1934, various local societies covered parts of Surrey and other parts were not covered at all. Whitlock was the first person to collect records across the outer Surrey area for annual publication. The report was published for the years 1934-47 and covered the counties of Hampshire, Kent, Surrey and Sussex. It was published from his home in Wiltshire. Whitlock also edited it, later assisted by E. M. Cawkell (Kent), G. Des Forges (Sussex) and Dr J. G. Harrison (Surrey). Coverage was rather thin but it was, at the time, the only publication which nominally covered the whole of the county outside the London area. The *South-Eastern Bird Report* was established as an organisation at a General Meeting held at Horsham on 26th November 1938 and attended by about 30 people, with Dr J. M. Harrison of Sevenoaks presiding. The area within 20 miles of St Paul's Cathedral, covered by the London Natural History Society in the *London Bird Report*, was formally excluded from 1937 onwards. R. S. R. Fitter edited the Surrey section of the Report for 1939-41 and Dr J. G. Harrison edited the 1947 section, which was the last to be published.

There was no further formal coverage until 1953, when the first *Surrey Bird Report* was published. Unlike the *South-Eastern Bird Report*, the new publication attempted full coverage of the whole vice-county including the Surrey part of the London area. After an uncertain start while relationships were being established with the London Natural History Society over the coverage of Surrey within 20 miles of St Paul's Cathedral, the *Surrey Bird Report* has covered the whole of the vice-county. There was, at this time, no formal post of recorder for Surrey. The job was often discharged by the Editor of the Bird Report, which was how the current recorder, J. J. Wheatley, took over in 1982. The Surrey Bird Club did not formally appoint a County Recorder until 1994, when the tasks of the County Recorder and the Report Editor were separated.

The present arrangement, whereby the Surrey Recorder covers the recording area of the Surrey Bird Club, which is the vice-county, may seem administratively untidy since Greater London also has a recorder, while the Spelthorne district is left to the Middlesex recorder of the London Natural History Society, but it works well enough.

Sound Recording

Surrey has a place in the history of sound recording. Vocalisations in imitation of the songs of common birds have long been an important way of learning the songs and identifying the singers. Even the best of these, though, lacks the immediacy and accuracy of a recording of the song. The earliest surviving sound recording is of an Indian (White-rumped) Shama *Copyschus malabaricus*. It was made by Ludwig Koch (1881-1974) in 1889 but was not published until after his death, when the BBC included it on a gramophone record commemorating his work. The first commercial recording of a singing bird was made in 1910 by Karl Reich. This was of a Nightingale singing in Germany. Both of these involve captive birds. The first recording of a wild bird may be one mentioned by Joyce Parr (Parr 1972). It was of a Nightingale and made in the Limpsfield area of Surrey. The recordist is not known, but a George Wickham is said to have been mainly instrumental in having it broadcast in Canada. The original source of this reference has been sought but not been located. Neither the recording nor the broadcast are mentioned by Boswall (1964), who says that Cherry Kearton probably made the first recording. Kearton caught a few notes of a Song Thrush and later the song of a Nightingale on a wax cylinder in 1900. These recordings were made at Kenley in Surrey (Kearton, 1938). The horn used to catch the song had to be within two feet of the song post. Kearton describes how he bought about £50 worth of Edison equipment for the job, and had trouble with a faint hissing sound made by the stylus on the cylinders, which was amplified by the horn and disturbed the birds.

Surrey was also the site of a better known 'first'. Wilfred Whitten, then editor of John O'London's Weekly, visited the Savoy Hill studios in March 1924 and subsequently wrote an article in which he said he wouldn't become a radio listener until there was 'an exchange of experiences between the silences of Nature and the hum of the city'. This caught the attention of John Reith (later Lord Reith), Managing Director of the BBC, who commented favourably on it. Another visitor to the studios that year was Beatrice Harrison, a leading British cellist of the day. In 1922, at the age of 30, she had moved with her family to Foyle Riding, which was in woodland south of Oxted. In the spring of the following year, while playing Rimsky-Korsakov's *Chant Hindou* in her garden, she noticed a bird, which was identified as a Nightingale by the gardener, responding to the sound of her cello. After her broadcasting debut, which was in 1924, she thought of introducing her Nightingales to a wider public over the air. The main account of the unique episode that followed is in Copeland *et al.* (1988) and its associated references. Other material appears in Mabey (1993 and 1997) and BTO (1998). Reith met Beatrice Harrison at the Savoy Hill studios and she told Reith of her discovery and her idea. Reith, after some initial doubts (he thought people might come to prefer the recording to the song of a live bird), was finally persuaded to try it out. The first broadcast was made on Monday 19th May 1924, at intervals from 10.30 to 11.10 pm. Miss Harrison sat down with her cello, wearing a concert frock and close to a bush where there was a Nightingale song post, then began to play. The bird failed to respond to *Danny Boy*, the Elgar Cello Concerto or bits of Dvorak but it finally responded to an improvisation. The song was sent out over all BBC stations and generated huge public interest. The broadcast reached audiences as far afield as Hungary and in parts of the world, such as Scandinavia, outside the Nightingale's breeding range. Mabey (1993) says that a million people listened in. Beatrice Harrison received 50,000 letters of appreciation. This was the BBC's first live outside broadcast of any kind. There was a second broadcast in June and further broadcasts of the duets continued for twelve years, until Beatrice Harrison moved house. There were occasional broadcasts of the Nightingales on their own up to 1942.

At Miss Harrison's request, the HMV record company had made recordings in her garden on 3rd May 1927. These recordings were published on two 78 rpm double-sided disks, numbered B2469, B2470. The disks bore HMV's plum label (price three shillings and threepence (17p) in 1950) rather than the more expensive black label on which Beatrice Harrison usually recorded. B2469 and B2470 appeared in June 1927, and are considered to be the first commercial recordings of any wild creature. A third record, D2853, which contained 1927 recordings together with additional Nightingale material recorded at Oxted on 19th May 1928, was published in November 1928 (Copeland *et al.*).

The music used to encourage the Nightingales on B2470 was the *Londonderry Air* and Rimsky-

Korsakov's *Chant Hindou*, with Beatrice Harrison credited as cellist and recorded on 3rd May. B2853 used Dvorak's *Songs my Mother Taught Me* with Beatrice Harrison as cellist, and on the other side two Nightingales in her garden on 19th May 1928 with church bells dubbed in. B2469 had Nightingales and Beatrice Harrison, on one side, with *Dawn in an Old-World Garden*, which included a Nightingale and two Song Thrushes. A keen-eared contemporary reviewer also claimed to hear the Wren, Robin, Blackbird, Blue Tit, House Sparrow and Chaffinch. This disk remained in the catalogue until 1958. The *Londonderry Air* and *Songs my Mother Taught Me* were reissued by the BTO on the CD *Nightingales: A Celebration* as recently as 1998. The latter was also on the CD *An English Musical Heritage*, produced by Claremont in 1992. The episode also lingers on in fiction. The 1943 war film *The Demi-Paradise* has Beatrice Harrison playing to Nightingales in the garden during an air-raid.

Before finally leaving her work, one other recording in the series should be mentioned. A further live radio broadcast was planned from the same Oxted garden for the night of 19th May 1942, the 18th anniversary of the first broadcast. While the recording was being made it was realised that bombers could be heard flying over, on their way to Germany. They were taking part in a massive raid on Mannheim. The plugs were pulled on the broadcast to prevent a security leak but the recording survives, and was issued by the BBC as HMV BD.1016 in September 1942, to raise money for the RAF Benevolent Fund. The BTO reissued it on their 1998 Nightingale CD, with the additional information that 197 bombers (from various parts of Britain) were involved in the raid. However many bombers were involved, the throbbing song of a single bird, unaccompanied by any music, against the rising engine noise of the aircraft as they get nearer, and then the fading sound as they move further on, is a powerful and disturbing image of the war.

Copeland mentions another early record, HMV B3345, which was published in April 1930 and has a side entitled *Daybreak at a Surrey Farm*. It was created by dubbing in bits of other records, including one of a Nightingale and another of dawn chorus which included a Blackbird. The source of this material and its connection, if any, with Surrey do not seem to be known.

Ludwig Koch took a job with EMI and conceived the idea of a sound-book, a text illustrated with pictures and accompanied by gramophone records. He produced a number of these in Germany, one of which had the song of 25 species of wild birds. He had worked with a world famous bird-recordist, Dr Oscar Heinroth, and through him obtained an introduction to Harry and George Witherby. This meeting led him to E. M. Nicholson. Koch worked with Nicholson to produce two books on bird song accompanied by gramophone records, *Songs of Wild Birds* and *More Songs of Wild Birds* (Nicholson and Koch, 1936 and 1937), each published by H. F. & G. Witherby. Many of the recordings were made in Surrey, including the Robin at Leatherhead in 1936, the Cuckoo and Nightingale at Oxted in 1936, the Grey Heron, Stock Dove, Tree Pipit, Redstart, Mistle Thrush, Wood Warbler (see Collenette for this species) and Chiffchaff in or near Richmond Park in 1937 and the Curlew, Little Owl, Woodlark, Skylark, Blue Tit, Willow Tit, Blackcap, Garden Warbler, Jackdaw, Rook and Carrion Crow at Chobham in 1937. Harry Witherby provided facilities on his estate at Chobham. Practical problems were considerable. The recordings were made on wax and the equipment had to be on stable and absolutely level mountings if it was to work successfully. The birds had to be found and microphones had to be close to them to obtain good quality. Cable runs were sometimes as long as 400 yards. Koch (1955) gives his own account of the story behind the Surrey recordings as part of a more general memoir of his recording career. One of the Curlew recordings in *More Songs of Wild Birds* was used for introducing *The Naturalist*, a programme broadcast weekly on BBC radio for many years from 1964. In the book, E. M. Nicholson describes in considerable detail the trials and tribulations endured in making the recording on Chobham Common. It entailed rising in the small hours and setting up equipment at 2 am in bad weather on 3rd May and waiting for hours for the first sounds to be captured.

Koch's British recordings became widely known through broadcasting. He was later to work with Witherby and other sound-recordists in the production of Witherby's *Sound-Guide to British Birds*, a set of 13 disks with two accompanying books which covered 195 species, published in 1958. This collection includes some of Koch's earlier recordings, such as the Skylark recorded in Surrey in June 1937 and published in the 1937 bird song book, as well as subsequent material such as a Blackbird recorded in Surrey in May 1939.

Another well-known recordist was Victor C. Lewis, who published a number of albums of bird song, mostly recorded in Surrey. He moved to Herefordshire (where he was born) in 1970. The recordings in track order, many made in Surrey, were:

1964 *A Tapestry of British Bird Song* HMV CLP 1723: Skylark, Pheasant, Tawny Owl, Canada Goose, Robin, Song Thrush, Blackbird, Blackcap, Greenfinch, Willow Warbler, Woodlark, Dartford Warbler, Mandarin and Sedge Warbler.

1965 *Bird Song Recognition – An Aural Index* HMV 7EG 8923-25: recordings of 47 species.

1969 *Bird Sounds in Close-up* Marble Arch MAL 1102: Robin, Song Thrush, Blackbird, House Sparrow, Mistle Thrush, Blue Tit, Skylark, Woodlark, Dartford Warbler, Garden Warbler, Willow Tit, Green Woodpecker, Sparrowhawk, Great Spotted Woodpecker, Long-tailed Tit, Hobby, Willow Warbler, Chaffinch, Kingfisher, Sand Martin and Little Grebe.

1970 *Bird Sounds in Close-up, Volume Two* Marble Arch MAL 1316: Surrey recordings – Greenfinch, Goldfinch, Chaffinch, Dunnock, Stonechat, Nightjar, Whitethroat, Grasshopper Warbler, Wood Warbler, Willow Warbler, Jay, Turtle Dove, Chiffchaff, Blackbird, Song Thrush, Willow Warbler (again), Coal Tit, Siskin, Chaffinch, Robin and Coot.

These were followed in 1979 by *British Bird Vocabulary*, an even more comprehensive set of recordings on six two-cassette volumes published privately, and in 1984 six single cassette sound guides comprising shorter selections from the earlier publication.

This short survey is meant to highlight the significance of Surrey in the history of published sound recording. There have, of course, been many other sound recordists working in Surrey since the 1950s. In a more general way, and sometimes not specifically linked to Surrey, other county ornithologists have made substantial contributions. Some, such as P. J. Sellar, have become well known through talks and public demonstrations of their work and contributed to many published collections. An expert bird sound recordist and winner of the 'Golden Nightingale' award in a European Broadcasting Union competition, he was a co-founder of the British Library of Wildlife Sounds in 1969 and, as an Assistant Editor of BWP, selected the recordings used for the preparation of sonagrams. P. A. D. Hollom has made some remarkable sequences of recordings, including those of nesting Nightjars on Pirbright Common and Tawny Owls in a box in his garden at Worplesdon in the 1970s. At least 380 of the sonagrams in Birds of the Western Palearctic are credited to him. R. H. Kettle was Curator of the British Library of Wildlife Sounds (BLOWS, later the Wildlife Section of the National Sound Archive in the British Library) in 1972-88. He was the compiler/editor of two tape cassettes, *British Bird Songs and Calls* (1987) and *More British Bird Sounds* (1989) and joint compiler/editor of *British Bird Sounds on CD* (1992). Others, like R. H. B. Forster, once the Surrey Bird Club Conservation Officer, have published tape recordings made by themselves for helping the local groups with which they worked to develop their field skills. K. F. Betton has made many recordings in Britain and has written and spoken about them.

Bird Photographers

The birds of Surrey have attracted the attention of many fine photographers. Reference has already been made to the pioneering work of the Keartons, who were the first well-known known workers to have published photographs taken of birds in Surrey, and to Howard Bentham who later worked with them. In more recent years Frank V. Blackburn produced many outstanding studies of Surrey birds. His picture of a Hobby at its nest appeared on the dust jacket of Parr (1972). Other photographs appeared in Surrey Bird Reports of the period. Photographers whose work has featured in Surrey Bird Reports include Robert J. Arnfield, Stephen Dalton, Richard Denyer, Davis S. Dicker, F. Sanderson Dolley, Peter

Gasson, Alan Greensmith, David M. Harris, Eric Hosking, Mike McDonnell, Garry D. J. Messenbird, John Uhlig, Derek Washington and Ron Wells among others. Derek M. Turner-Ettlinger took the habitat photographs for Parr as well as birds for Surrey Bird Reports, the latter including a breeding Whinchat. The Little Ringed Plover has been a popular subject. Ian Beames produced the text and photographs for an attractive review of major British wildlife areas with Thursley Common as its lead site (Beames 1988). Four recent books by Derek Belsey (1997, undated, 2002 and 2006) include local bird pictures and follow the Kearton tradition of providing narratives about the birds, the sites and the photography. David J. Brassington has taken most of the habitat photographs used in this book.

Bird Atlases

BTO initiatives have led to winter distribution atlas and two atlases of breeding birds.

1981-84 Winter Atlas. The British Trust for Ornithology and the Irish Wildbird Conservancy organised surveys of birds wintering in the winters of 1981/82, 1982/83 and 1983/84. The recording unit was the 10 km national grid square. The results were published in Lack (1986). The Surrey survey was mainly organised by Keith J. Herber. Five squares in the Surrey part of the London area were covered by the London Natural History Society. The distribution maps in Lack are scaled by comparative abundance, in three size ranges that vary between species. For most species, the counts obtained by field workers were adjusted from numbers of birds actually seen to a notional number that they would have seen if they had observed for six hours, using factors contained in Lack. In all cases, the base number is the largest number found in any of the winters in a single visit, regardless of how many visits were actually made. Neither the base nor the adjusted numbers can be regarded as a census.

Apart from the maps in Lack, none of the Surrey information has been published. The Surrey Bird Club archive holds many of the unadjusted figures and these contain useful information additional to that in Lack. In view of the striking differences between the totals (92,000 in the figures held compared with 174,000 in the adjusted totals) and features of the adjusted information which would not have been important in the size range presentation of the Winter Atlas maps, it has been felt prudent to use the unadjusted figures, where held, in the main body of this book. These are uneven in coverage basis but are consistent with other information used, in being what was actually seen. The Winter Atlas information has particular value for species such as the Feral Rock Dove, for which it is the earliest quantitative Surrey study of such breadth. The comparative numbers of Marsh and Willow Tits and of House and Tree Sparrows are other examples of its usefulness.

1968-72 BTO and LNHS Atlases. There are four sources of information about the Surrey breeding season results obtained from fieldwork in 1968-72. Parr (1971) contains a set of 10 km square maps. These derive from information collected for the BTO Atlas. They cover the 22 main Surrey squares, but overlap into neighbouring counties and the marginal squares may include non-Surrey information. Some marginal 10 km squares, such as TQ44 and TQ45 are omitted. All the 10 km squares can, with some effort, be extracted from the 1968-72 BTO Atlas (Sharrock, 1976). Forster (1973) includes tetrad maps for the LNHS area of Surrey, together with an account of a parish survey attempted from 1964 to 1968. Tetrads in the LNHS area can be extracted from the 1968-72 LNHS Atlas prepared by Montier (1977).

1988-91 BTO Atlas, 1988-94 London Atlas and 1988-97 SBC Atlas. The framework used for the fieldwork was the tetrad (two km square) grid. Each 10 km national grid square is divided into twenty-five 2 km squares. Fieldwork for the breeding distribution maps was carried out for all tetrads by the Surrey Bird Club from 1988 to 1997 with no limit on the time spent in each tetrad. This was an extension of the New Atlas survey of 1989-91 organised by the BTO (the 1988-91 BTO New Atlas), which used only a sample of tetrads with limited time in each. Dr Ernest Garcia organised most of the initial work, which was carried out through the BTO Square Stewards. The actual surveying was carried out by a team of well over 400 people, to whom many thanks are given and without whom there would have been no Atlas.

Final polishing was put in hand by Jeffery Wheatley and Hugh Evans. Tetrad data for the LNHS area was exchanged with the LNHS, which also carried out a full tetrad survey for its area.

The general coverage achieved for the county was good, though not completely uniform. All marginal squares were looked at, even though the Surrey element for some was very small. Records for marginal squares which are known to relate to Surrey are shown by solid symbols. Others, which may not relate to Surrey, have not been used. Even small fractions of a tetrad could produce a wide variety of species if the habitat was favourable. The location of ponds and other specialised features could be critical for the Surrey element. One small segment consisted of half of the car park and other public areas of Heathrow Airport's Terminal 4, an almost totally concrete habitat which nevertheless produced half a dozen breeding birds. The work is called the 1988-97 SBC Atlas in text that follows. The London Natural History Society also extended the survey period and has published an Atlas for 1988-94, the 1988-94 London Atlas in what follows.

Records for marginal tetrads are only included if they are known to be within the county boundary. Maps for the 1988-97 SBC Atlas are included in the species accounts and titled Atlas 1988-97. Large dots indicate breeding, probable breeding or the holding of territory (by mated or unmated birds). Evidence for this includes song on two dates in the same place, song flight and aerial displays, roding and signs of agitation near a possible nest site. For common birds, the presence of many birds in the same area during the breeding season is taken as breeding evidence. Small dots indicate presence at least once in a suitable habitat during the breeding season, without any other indications. The definitions follow those used by the BTO for the 1988-91 Atlas.

Population Changes and Bird Movements

There have been great changes in the number of breeding pairs of many species in the county. While those in decline have been given a good deal of publicity in recent years, others have prospered and there have been more gains than losses. The breeding populations of most farmland birds are smaller than they were, but the Collared Dove has invaded and other breeding birds which have established themselves since 1900 include Little Ringed Plovers, Redshanks, Common Terns, Black Redstarts and, since 2000, Peregrines. Human factors have sometimes helped. Collared Doves, having arrived under their own steam in the 1950s, found the empty television aerials and Lawson's Cypresses waiting for them. Little Ringed Plovers flourish in actively worked gravel pits. Common Terns are one of the great conservation successes, now widely breeding on artificial rafts. Redshanks found a new wetland habitat on sewage farms in the early 20th century as part of a wider national expansion. Black Redstarts first colonised bombed sites and even now they prefer old or derelict buildings. Dartford Warblers have been at a record high since the year 2000. These gains and the growth of heathland populations have largely happened through the efforts of the birds themselves and the milder climate of recent years, though there has been some assistance from sensitive habitat management. The most broadly based success has been at the London Wetland Centre, where new reedbeds planted on the site of the old Barn Elms reservoirs have been colonised by a large population of Reed Warblers and other wetland birds.

Some birds, such as Dartford Warblers, have been protected by living on rare habitats which have themselves been protected and improved for the wildlife that they support. Others, such as Woodcock, Lesser Spotted Woodpeckers and Nightingales which use widely distributed, unprotected types of habitat, have been affected by land use changes. This is particularly true of farmland birds, where substantial declines among the characteristic species have taken place. The changes are described in the systematic list. The table below analyses some of the more notable of these.

Rising numbers of breeding pairs since 1900

Greylag Goose	New colonist	Vacant niche, introductions in Kent.
Mandarin	Introduction	Vacant niche.
Tufted Duck	Increase	National range expansion.
Ruddy Duck	Introduction	Vacant niche.
Great Crested Grebe	Increase	More gravel pits, legal protection.
Grey Heron	More than doubled since 1928	Milder winters, less pollution.
Buzzard	Recolonisation	National range expansion, less persecution.
Hobby	Increase	Egg collection stopped.
Peregrine	New colonist	National range expansion, less persecution.
Avocet	New colonist	Habitat change, national increase led by habitat management.
Little Ringed Plover	New colonist	More gravel pits.
Redshank	New colonist, now declining	National range expansion, habitat loss.
Common Tern	New colonist	More gravel pits, tern rafts.
Collared Dove	New colonist	Genetic change, vacant niche.
Ring-necked Parakeet	Introduction	Vacant niche.
Little Owl	Introduction	Vacant niche.

Grey Wagtail	Increase	National range expansion.
Black Redstart	New colonist, now declining	National range expansion, habitat loss.
Dartford Warbler	Record high	Milder winters, habitat management.
Magpie	Large increase	Fewer gamekeepers, less persecution, more carrion on roads.

Falling numbers of breeding pairs

Wryneck	Lost breeding species	National range contraction.
Grey Partridge	Severe decline, perhaps lost	Intensification of agriculture
Skylark	Severe decline	Intensification of agriculture
Turtle Dove	Severe decline, perhaps lost	Intensification of agriculture
Red-backed Shrike	Lost breeding species	National range contraction.
House Sparrow	Heavy decline	House design, refuse clean-up in farms and gardens, loss of winter stubbles.
Tree Sparrow	Heavy decline at natural sites	Intensification of agriculture.
Cirl Bunting	Lost breeding species	Intensification of agriculture.
Corn Bunting	Lost breeding species	Intensification of agriculture.

Rising numbers of non-breeding migrants

| Little Egret | Potential new colonist | European range change. |
| Cormorant | Potential new colonist | National range expansion. |

Falling number of non-breeding migrants

| Smew | Well down since mid-20th century | Milder winters. |
| Hooded Crow | Well down since the 1930s | Climate and range change. |

Bird Movements

One of the many things that make watching birds so enjoyable is their mobility. A bird may travel thousands of miles and finish up in a suburban garden. That same garden may be flown over morning and evening by roosting gulls or Rooks. The right supply of bird food can attract winter wanderers such as Bramblings or, less easily these days, Yellowhammers from surrounding woods and fields. An Eider has been found on a small garden pond and a Little Auk on a doorstep with the morning milk.

The daily tides of roosting movements and the great seasonal migratory movements have a basic regularity but they are never quite the same. Population levels vary. Weather patterns modify the migratory pattern and what is seen of it from the ground depends a good deal on such factors as cloud cover, and sudden storms which may ground migrants in unexpected places.

Black Terns may suddenly appear after heavy rain at Frensham. Huge numbers of migrating House Martins may be brought down by heavy showers. Then there are the storm-driven birds, often seabirds blown scores of miles off their migratory course by high winds. Occasionally gales, such as the great gale of 1987, will bring in sea birds normally found far out at sea, driven inland by the wind.

From April onwards the resident birds are joined by a huge influx of summer visitors and passage migrants. Many of these have wintered in North, West or Sub-Saharan Africa. Others will have travelled much further. Swallows reach Southern Africa. Common and Arctic Terns make extraordinary journeys which may take them to the Antarctic. These long distance travellers have the double benefit of long northern summer days while they are feeding young and long southern winter days when they are feeding themselves and preparing for their return journey.

Most winter visitors come from Scandinavia and northern Europe east to Novaya Zemlya and the other bird regions of the Russian Arctic. Some of them are moving west to the milder climate of the British Isles. Others, such as the Black-headed Gull, may have come from the Russian north. Some come from high northwest regions. Most Brent and White-fronted Geese from these areas finish up on the coast but a few get as far as Surrey and other parts of southeast England. Many passage migrants from the far north pass through Surrey to regions further south, as do many summer visitors to northern Europe. There is at least circumstantial evidence to suggest that even though a species such as the Firecrest may be found at any time of the year, two populations of birds may be involved. The breeding locations, which are mostly in the southern half of the county, are deserted outside the breeding season and the birds that breed there may be summer migrants. Wintering Firecrests are mostly found in woods in the northern half of the county, often in the Surrey part of the London area where the weather is milder. These might well be migrants from northeast Europe.

The movements so far mentioned are regular and they mostly involve large numbers of birds. A much smaller number of migrants are birds which are many miles away from their normal migration routes. Birds from Africa may overshoot their normal breeding areas in southern Europe. Rollers, Hoopoes and other breeding birds of southern Europe have overshot their routes, or they may be young or inexperienced birds flying in a wrong direction. Most, presumably, never make it back to their proper destinations. North American species occasionally appear. The American Robins found in Surrey, for example, must have come down the wrong side of the Atlantic, or got carried across it, on their autumn migration. Some North American waterbirds, such as the Ring-necked Duck and Pied-billed Grebe, have wintered in Surrey in successive years but have been missing in the summer, presumably summering elsewhere. Drift migrants of eastern origin are well-known as stragglers which may reach the British Isles in the autumn on easterly winds if the right weather patterns occur at migration time. An anticyclone, which is an area of high pressure round which the winds move in a clockwise direction and the weather is good, can create such conditions. Other weather patterns can influence spring migration. Waves of Black Tern arrivals from the south in Surrey and elsewhere have been correlated with periods of warm weather in the Bay of Biscay and north-easterly winds in the Channel (Hinde, 1951).

Another type of bird movement is the irruptive behaviour of some species that follows an unusually good breeding season, or a winter food shortage. Waxwings and Crossbills are the best known examples. Other species, such as the Ruddy Shelduck have irrupted into Europe in the second half of the 20th century and may have reached Surrey. In earlier years, Pallas's Sandgrouse made spectacular invasions from the Middle East, though sadly none has reached Surrey since the early years of the 20th century. The arrival of the Collared Dove in the 1950s represents movement of a different and more encouraging kind – the sustained success of a breeding species which has colonised Europe without any help to become one of its most familiar birds within a space of 40 years.

Most migrants pass through at night, or are too high to see. Visible migration can be conspicuous though, in spring and autumn. The first person to study it systematically in Surrey was F. D. Power. Among other work, he recorded and published daily movements, wind direction and strength in Brixton for each October from 1885 to 1909 (Power, 1910). Power's experience has been that of many subsequent observers: *Given a fair morning, between the second week and end of October, following one or two days of WNW wind – still holding from the same quarter – the passage of birds from about 7.30 to 10.30 am is remarkable. Flock after flock crosses my garden in steady flight, and apparently the fixed purpose is to get as far West as they can while the wind continues favourable. Chaffinches were the commonest, followed by Larks and then Starlings.* It was Power who noticed that there was a partial migration of locally-bred birds in July and August. He also described how visible migration was much less obvious in spring and how, in autumn, Blackbirds and Song Thrushes were not seen on the move, but suddenly became common in parks and gardens at times when the migration of other species was observed.

Migration may be on a broad front. The arrivals of winter thrushes seem to sweep across broad swathes of Surrey. Sometimes the movement is funnelled along particular routes or flylines that follow natural features. The valley of the Thames is one such feature, first recognised by Clarke (1912). In one of his comments Clarke described a huge northwesterly movement of Skylarks, Fieldfares, Rooks and

Starlings over Bermondsey on 22nd October 1896. Glegg (1928) distinguished between the valley's use as an east-west route in autumn and as a route for storm-driven birds at any time of the year. Throughout the 20th century, bird ringing threw a great deal of light on the pattern of these movements and the detailed findings are to be found in the species accounts of the systematic list.

There was renewed interest in visible migration in the 1960s. Following a discussion at the Bird Observatories Conference in 1962, inland observation points were set up in several counties, including Surrey. The Surrey sites were at Brooklands, Chessington, Dorking, East Molesey, Ewhurst, Godalming, Haslemere, Tilford and Woking and all nine were operating by February 1963. Parr (1965) and Ogston (1966) provided details of the first two years of operation. It has to be said that the results were not spectacular, at least by coastal standards, but they did show that local inland observations could be correlated with national movements.

Many species which are resident in Surrey, or in the British Isles, make seasonal movements during the year. Most Woodlarks, for example, leave the heathlands in the late autumn to winter on local farm fields. Curlews and most Stonechats also leave the heaths in winter. Some move to marshes and sewage farms but most probably leave the county altogether, and are thought to winter in coastal areas. Dartford Warblers, alone among the characteristic heathland species, remain in their breeding areas all the year round, taking their chance with the rigours of the winter. This is one factor which leads to their periodic extinction in the county. The survival value of this behaviour is presumably positive in the very long term but does not seem to have been much studied.

The bio-mechanics of migration have prompted a number of homing and displacement experiments, some involving Surrey. A Rook that was caught near Chipping Norton and released at Addlestone, 65 miles southeast in January 1931 was recaptured where it was originally caught in June 1933 (*BB, 27:238*). In 1935, Dr Werner Rüppell arranged for seven Swallows to be caught at their nests in Scheessel, near Bremen at 10 pm on May 20th and released at Croydon Airport, 428 miles away, on the following morning. Five of them were seen back at Scheessel on dates from 25th May. (*BB, 30:31*). Later in the year fourteen House Martins from the same region of Germany were released at Croydon and two or three of them got back after delays of two or more days. R. M. Lockley carried out some similar experiments with Manx Shearwaters. Two adults were taken from their eggs on Skokholm and released at Frensham on 8th June 1937. They got back within 24 hours (Lack and Lockley, 1938). There have been at least two homing experiments with House Sparrows (Summers-Smith, 1956). In 1936, Mr C. I. Blackburne, Secretary of the Haslemere Educational Museum organised part of a study in which five-week old White Storks from nests in East Prussia were reared on cartwheel nests in the Museum grounds and in North Kent. All were marked and released in Kent in August. Their progress was tracked along the south coast and in France, where two were shot. Nothing more was heard of the birds, which may have migrated further south to Africa. There is a photograph of the Museum Storks being fed on their cartwheel nest by Robert Blockey in Swanton (1947). An egg from East Prussia was hatched under a Heron, but died in inclement weather before fledging (Blockey, 1936). In June 1939, six breeding adult White Storks were brought by air from their nests in Pinsk, Poland and released, after marking, at the Haslemere Museum. They were seen in Norfolk and in various other counties down to the south coast and contact was then lost. None returned to Pinsk (Swanton, HNHS, 1955).

Early and Late Dates of Summer Migrants

The first few migrants of a common species are an advance guard, with the main arrival perhaps weeks later. These early migrants are not of great statistical significance but they are one of the pleasures of bird-watching. They may also be useful markers of an underlying trend. Of course allowance has to be made for the great increase in the number of birdwatchers since the 1950s, so that there is a greater chance of early migrants being found. It is difficult to do this at all rigorously but it may have offset the declining numbers of some species, such as the Grasshopper Warbler.

Robert Blockey feeding the Storks   *from Swanton (1947)*

Some information about main arrival dates before 1900 is given in Bucknill. Annual first arrival dates for the London area (but not specifically for Surrey) were published more regularly from the early 20th century onwards by the London Natural History Society and there is a useful summary for London south of the Thames from 1929 to 1939 in Parrinder and Parrinder (1940). The *South-East Bird Report* contained a certain amount of annual information from 1934-46, but again not specifically for Surrey. Early and late dates from the 1950s onwards have usually (but not always) appeared in the *Surrey Bird Report*. Information about departure dates can be found in these sources but it is a good deal sparser. No arrival or departure date information specific to Spelthorne has been located.

Early and late dates may be difficult to interpret but many species do show a pattern of earlier arrivals. Two examples, concerning species with Surrey populations that are stable or declining, are the Sand Martin and the Tree Pipit. Climatic factors are presumably responsible. This may not be a major long-term trend in global warming, but it has been a feature of recent years.

Movement to and from roosts

Gulls. The earliest known gull roost was on the Thames at Chiswick Eyot, some time before 1895. By about 1895, gulls were roosting on the small reservoirs at Lonsdale Road and in 1896 they were on the newly created Barn Elms reservoirs, where large numbers came each evening, as they do to this day (Rowberry, 1934). Rowberry adds that at the present time our gull population is so immense that practically all the Thames valley reservoirs are utilised as roosting grounds. Gulls were roosting on Staines Reservoirs by 1906.

There is little quantitative information about gull roosts before the 1950s. Glegg counted 600 gulls, along the Thames between Richmond and Hammersmith Bridges on 16th March 1930 and estimated that there were at least 2,000 Black-headed Gulls along the Middlesex section of the Thames in the winter. They began to arrive in July and started to leave at the beginning of March. A note in *The Handbook* (Hollom, 1941) shows that the roost at Queen Mary Reservoir was very large in 1936 and 1940. National surveys of wintering gulls were carried out in the winters 1953/54, 1963/64 and 1973 (Hickling, 1954, 1967, 1977, Homes, 1955). There was a Thames Valley survey in 1970 (Parr, 1972) and further surveys were carried out by the BTO in 1983 and 1993 (Burton *et al.*, 2003). Up to 1973 the only known Surrey roosts were in the London area but in that year an outer Surrey roost was discovered at Frensham Great Pond. A summary of the number of roosting gulls is in the table. Species information, where available, is given in the systematic list.

Gull Roosts in winter

	1936 Jan	1953 Jan	1963 Dec	1968 Dec	1969 Jan	1973 Jan	1983 Jan	1993 Jan	2004 Jan
Barn Elms Reservoir	n/a	10,200	20,400	24,100	25,000		6,546		
Frensham Great Pond	0	0	0	0	0	1,400	110	900	813
Holmethorpe Sand Pits									335
Island Barn Reservoir		11,200	100	20,000	50,000				1,503
Lonsdale Road Reservoir									
Walton/Molesey Reservoirs:									
Knight and Bessborough			1,850	4,950	1,840			890	1,314
Chelsea and Lambeth			300	1,650	2,100				
All four		5,000				5,325			
Queen Elizabeth II Reservoir	Not built	Not built	100,000	53,000	107,500	91,000	84,278	45,340	23,700
Spelthorne									
Queen Mary Reservoir	42,000	17,500	24,000	30,000	75,000	18,113	42,931	28,000	43,716
King George VI Reservoir	Not built	3,000	4,010	26,000	30,000				
Staines Reservoirs		4,000	7,750	9,220	12,600				1,000
Staines and King George VI					11,173	3,191			
Wraysbury Reservoir	Not built	Not built	Not built	Not built	Not built	30,570	712	618	3,304
Total	42,000	50,900	158,410	168,920	304,040	157,581	137,768	75,748	75685

Sources: London and Surrey Bird Reports, Hickling, Burton et al. Wraysbury 1993 includes Lesser Black-backed Gulls only. No information available for blank cells.

An accurate count of gulls coming in to roost is difficult to make. Gulls move between reservoirs on the same day, as well as varying in number from day to day, adding to the counting difficulties. The highest recorded total for a single reservoir was of 250,000 at Queen Elizabeth II Reservoir in December 1963. This was made the day after a count of 50,000 by a different observer on the previous day (Hickling, 1967). Hickling used a compromise figure of 100,000 in the table above for 1963. Day to day variation accounts for an unknown amount of the difference between December 1968 and January 1969 at the same reservoir.

It is evident from the table that the total number of roosting gulls rose to a peak in 1960s, followed by a decline. From the earliest days of the winter gull invasions, gulls have been quick to make use of reservoir sites and some of the increase can be attributed to the construction of new reservoirs, particularly Queen Elizabeth II Reservoir. The extension of feeding areas that came with the rolling out of huge rubbish dumps and landfill sites in the post-war years must also have played a part. Reasons for the decline are less obvious, not least because a further reservoir, Wraysbury, has been constructed. Many, perhaps most, of the wintering gulls breed in Scandinavia and other parts of continental Europe. On the whole, the number of gulls breeding in these areas has been stable or increasing, so adverse population factors cannot explain the decline. It is tempting to look to climatic factors for an explanation. Elsewhere in the text, use will be made of a chart of average temperatures by decade. The 1960s were the coldest decade in the second half of the 20th century and the 1990s were the warmest. We know that gulls moved into Surrey in a big way during the cold winters of the 1890s, so it may be that gull numbers have fallen because of the milder winters of recent years.

The feeding areas of these gulls does not seem to have changed much since Rowberry (1934) mentioned the importance of the new sports grounds that were created in Middlesex from derelict pasture and rough meadowland. He described how the first birds straggled in from the western reservoirs at dawn and fed on the short, rich grass until 8 or 9 am, after which they spent several hours resting and preening. One Lesser Black-backed Gull ate 45 worms in five and a half minutes, so that a flock of gulls would create a formidable rate of depletion for the worms. Although he was writing about an area just outside the county, this kind of behaviour can be seen across Surrey on any winter day. Rubbish tips and ploughland are important feeding sites now, as they might have been earlier.

In southwest Surrey, the development of landfill sites at Runfold, Seale and Wrecclesham in the 1970s attracted large numbers of gulls, some of which, mainly Black-headed, were probably the origin of a new roost at Frensham Great Pond. At least 6,000 gulls were counted at Wrecclesham in February 1977, most of which flew southwest to roost, presumably in Langstone Harbour, Hampshire. Feeding numbers reached 8,000, mostly Black-headed, in February 1978. Frensham Great Pond was frozen at this time in both years. The larger gulls mostly flew northwest to roost, presumably at Thames Valley reservoirs (*HSBBR*).

The roosts and flylines of the Thames Valley gulls have been described in the complementary papers of Parr (1970), Sage (1970) and Bourne (1971). Parr described the gull movements to and from reservoirs in Surrey and Spelthorne during the winter of 1968/69. Dispersal from the reservoirs began before dawn and the first birds were seen arriving on feeding grounds up to ten miles away at first light. The movement was protracted, with gulls stopping off at playing fields, parks and other sites before reaching the feeding destination up to two hours after setting off. Before starting the return flight, gulls would often spiral upwards in a milling flock to a height of 1,000 feet or more. They would then drift off in the direction of the return flyline. Once the return flight was under way, it was generally faster than the flight out and stops were uncommon.

Most of the gulls roosting at King George VI and Staines Reservoirs came down the Thames Valley from the west (Bourne). Some were seen to come in from the Uxbridge and Denham Vale areas to the north, beyond Spelthorne. 10,000 of them were found at a single tip (Sage). Some of the Staines birds moved on to Queen Mary Reservoir later in the evening. Other birds arriving at Queen Mary Reservoir came from the northeast and may have followed the River Crane at Twickenham. The largest flow to Queen Mary came from the south and south southwest, many following the River Wey from Godalming about 17 miles to the south. Others came from the direction of Camberley, over Chobham Common, and from the northwest, along the Thames.

The biggest roost in the Walton group of reservoirs was at Queen Elizabeth II Reservoir. Most of the birds came from the east (*e.g.* over Worcester Park, - see Smith) with a smaller flow from the southeast. Many followed two flyways, along the river valleys of the Thames and the Mole. Most of the gulls roosting at Barn Elms came from the southeast, from unidentified sites in east Surrey. There was also a flow from the northwest. The morning and evening flights had a similar pattern. In the morning the Mole valley birds moved through the Mole gap in the North Downs and fanned out across the country south of Dorking in the same way that those in the Wey valley fanned out south of Guildford.

Fieldfares and Redwings. Winter thrushes roost in many rural areas. Fieldfares and Redwings can be seen flying in to the bushes on Pudmore at dusk on winter afternoons.

Starlings. Records of Starling roosts in central London go back at least as far as 1894, when Sir T. D. Piggott drew attention to the fact that Starlings were flying to a roost on Duck Island, in St James's Park. Contemporary literature suggests that this was then a recently-formed habit and that numbers remained fairly low until the severe winter of 1894/95, during which gulls also began to come into the City in large numbers (Fitter, 1942). Of 59 roosts identified by Fitter, Battersea Park (on an island), Southwark Cathedral and Southwark Park (both in trees) and the Albert Bridge (on girders) were the only ones in Surrey. Fairly large numbers came into London from the Barnes, New Malden, Richmond/Kew and Wimbledon areas. A 1932/33 survey (Nicholson, unpublished) was the first to show that the roosting birds were suburban residents choosing to roost communally after the breeding season, and not immigrants that roved the countryside in large flocks by day, and flew into London to roost. Starling roosts are discussed in more detail in the species account.

The 21st Century and Beyond

Change, with birds more than most parts of the natural world, is a fundamental feature of the daily scene. Birds have a much greater mobility than plants or mammals. The bird life of a particular site changes from day to day. Birds can respond to environmental changes very quickly. So in looking ahead, will Surrey be a friendlier or a more hostile place for this shifting avian population to inhabit?

Although some worrying trends emerged in the latter part of the 20th century, the birdlife of the county has entered the 21st century in good shape. The varied nature of the Surrey landscape, which provides habitats for many different species within a small space, gives it plenty of scope to adapt. Warmer winters have pushed some heathland species to levels they have not seen for many years. Late 19th and early 20th century colonists such as the Tufted Duck, Curlew, Redshank and Grey Wagtail are still with us. Willow Warblers have crashed, perhaps due to problems in their African wintering areas, a reminder that Surrey birds have a global context. Some range extensions, such as those of the Buzzard and Peregrine, owe nothing obvious to climate change and more of these can be expected. Ravens are set to move in very soon. Habitat creation at the Barn Elms London Wetland Centre has brought back breeding Avocets. Warmer times will no doubt bring in other birds to breed, while making it less likely that others breeding further north will need to winter with us. .

But such perspectives are geologically short. A hundred years may be a long time for Surrey in terms of a human life but even a thousand is not very much in the history of the birds. Beyond global warming lies the next Ice Age.

Systematic List of the Birds of Surrey

Mute Swan
Cygnus olor

Moderately common breeding resident

The native range extends across northern and central Europe and there are naturalised populations in many other parts of the world. British birds are of mixed origin, a wild population augmented by domesticated stock and kept for profit, food and ornament from medieval times or earlier. National breeding numbers are thought to have increased substantially since 1970. The *Migration Atlas* shows only 45 foreign recoveries of British-ringed birds, mostly from southeast England.

Early Surrey history. The edibility of Mute Swans helped to make them an early addition to the county list. The Sergeant of Kennington seized cygnets on behalf of the King in 1246 and, in 1249, the Sheriff of Surrey was commanded to deliver swans to Westminster for the Feast of St Edward, held on 18th March (Ticehurst, 1924). In 1377, John Drayton was appointed Master of Swans for a territory that specifically included Surrey (Ticehurst, 1928). Surrey later had its own deputy. Young swans were caught to have their bills carved with distinctive marks that indicated ownership, a procedure known as upping. Some marks are known to go back to the time of Henry IV (1399-1413) and might be older, since a means of proving ownership would have been needed in earlier times (Ticehurst, 1934). Yarrell (1845) contains correspondence about the date for the 1593 swan-upping. Yarrell and Bucknill reproduce swan-marks. There are others, including the mark of the Abbot of Chertsey, in Ticehurst (1926). Bill marking was replaced by ringing in the 1990s. 'Upping' is said to be derived from the call of "All up" when eligible cygnets are spotted (*The Times*, 18th July 2002).

Swan remains found at Fastolf's Palace and Rosary, Southwark, were dated at 1480-1520, a period when the swans of the Thames were an internationally famous sight. In 1496 or 1497 someone, probably the secretary to Capello, the Venetian Ambassador, wrote on Capello's behalf that it was *Truly a beautiful thing to behold one or two thousand tame Swans upon the River Thames*. And so it would be regarded today. This was part of *A Relation of the Island of England*, written about 1500 and reprinted by the Camden Society in its *Transactions* for 1847 (Gurney, 1921; Glegg, 1929). William of Dunbar is credited with writing a 'ballade' recited at a dinner party held during Christmas week, 1501 in honour of the visiting Scottish Ambassador and which described the Thames at the City of London as a place

> *Where many a swan doth swim with wingés fair,*
> *Where many a barge doth sail and row with oar.*

Numbers remained high in the 16th century. A visitor, the Duke of Najera, said of the Thames that *Never did I see a river so thickly covered with swans as this* (Gurney, 1921). Numbers were large because the swans were eaten like ducks and geese, and they were not only found on the Thames. The Carew family had them on their property at Beddington where, on 6th March 1608, one Blake received 4d for a half day's work *to fence in the Swanes* (Carew Household Book). Gilbert White saw cygnets on the Mole at Cobham on 10th June 1789.

19th century. Swans continued to be eaten in the 19th century. Samuel Gurney, writing to report a brood of twelve in Beddington Park in 1850, said he had a brood of eight *which I shall soon shut up, and fatten for the autumn* (*Zool.*, 1851:3234). Bucknill gave little hard information apart from saying that Mute Swans were frequent on the larger ponds around Godalming, that they were sometimes shot in mistake for Bewick's and Whoopers at Frensham and elsewhere and that eleven flew over a wood on Epsom Common in the winter of 1895/96. During the Swan-upping between Staines and London, 114 juveniles were marked in 1893, 167 in 1894 and 146 in 1895 (Glegg). Mute Swans were evidently fairly common in the years up to 1900 at Staines. Staines Reservoirs were used as a feeding area by birds on the Thames (Kerr, 1906).

After 1900. Glegg walked the banks of the Thames between Hammersmith and Staines in January and February 1930 and counted 117 Mute Swans, not a high figure by comparison with later counts. There were 418, including 60 cygnets, between Battersea and Staines in 1938 (*BLA*). Numbers fell substantially during and after the 1939-45 war but picked up again and 479 were counted between Putney and Staines in 1954. Numbers in the London area as a whole crashed thereafter, and were at a very low level in the 1970s (Oliver, 1982). The exact Surrey position is not known, but a slight recovery followed in the London area. There were 166 between Hampton Court Bridge and Hurst Park on 16th February 1993. The Winter Atlas found partial survey counts and estimates totalling 217 birds in 1981-84, with birds present in all 21 of the 10 km squares surveyed, suggesting a minimum size for winter population.

Breeding. Older records of breeding are rather sketchy. Mute Swans attempted at Send in 1903 (Boorman egg collection) and they bred at Beddington Gravel Pits, Fetcham Mill Pond, Godstone and Weybridge fairly often in the 1920s. They later bred at Barnes and they resumed breeding, after a 20 year lapse, in Richmond Park in the 1930s. Censuses for the Surrey part of the London area found 31 birds in 1955, 34 in 1956 and 38 in 1961. A pair bred at Clapham Common in 1962. Twelve pairs bred at Barn Elms in 2002 compared with one in 1996, before the construction of the London Wetland Centre on the site. Large broods include nine at Esher in 1987 and Woking in 1991. Mute Swans were breeding at Queen Mary Reservoir (Geen) and Shepperton (*Shepp. BR*) in the 1980s.

Trend since 1970. The table shows the number of breeding pairs and sites reported from 1970 to 2001. Breeding numbers since 1970 seem to have been increasing:

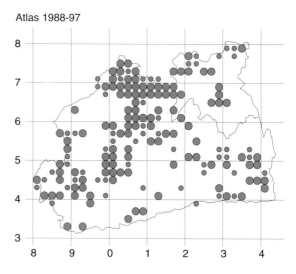

Atlas 1988-97

Breeding pairs and breeding sites in the vice-county

Year	1970	71	75	76	77	78	79	80	81	82	83	84	85	86
Pairs LNHS area						33	24	17	20	15	31	14	6	15
Pairs vice-county			16	18	15	16		11	13					
Sites	23	17	15	18	10	14	18	16	9	12		19	17	25

Year	87	88	89	90	91	92	93	94	95	96	97	98	99	2000	2001
Pairs LNHS area	9	6	12	4	3	8	12	12	14	19	19	20	29	26	17
Pairs vice-county						17		24	23	41	23	30	50	44	41
Sites	17	17	18	18	20	15	22		20	37	18	25	39	39	32

Of the 231 tetrads in northeast Surrey (the LNHS area in the table), 33% were found to hold territories in the 1968-72 Atlas survey and 34% in the 1988-97 Atlas, indicating a slight increase. In the county as a whole, territorial Mute Swans were found in 170 areas in the 1988-97 Atlas.

Population size. A BTO census in 1978 found 33 territories in eleven of the 10 km squares outside Greater London and at least 16 pairs bred raising a minimum of 61 young. The 1994-2004 Breeding

Birds Survey found an average of 0.36 adults per square km, which would gross up to 726 adults for the county as a whole. This seems a high figure, but it may have included many non-breeding adults as well as sampling variance. Female Mute Swans do not usually breed before they are three years old (*BWP*). If Surrey held a proportionate share of the British breeding population as given by the *New Atlas*, the population would be nearer to 195 territories, or 0.1 per square km. This is similar to the 170 tetrads in which territorial birds were found in the 1988/97 Atlas but may be on the low side. In 1999, which was not a census year, at least 50 breeding pairs were reported.

Large counts

Ash Vale Gravel Pits: 22, February 1978 (*HSBBR*)

Badshot Lea: 32, 17th July 1977

Barn Elms: 56, 9th April 2002

Beddington Sewage Farm: 20, August 1997

Burgess Park Lake: *c*.20, October 1997

Earlswood: 26, March 1994

Earlswood Lakes: 30, 21st January 2003

Enton: 45, 1990

Frensham: 60, 1977 and 1st December 1973

Frimley Gravel Pits: 75, October 1996

Hedgecourt: Up to 60, 1910

Holmethorpe: 26, January 2000

Hurst Park: 149, May 1997

Island Barn Reservoir: 36, May 1995

Longside Lake: 44, October 1998

Papercourt Gravel Pits: 40, 26th March 2002

Pen Ponds: 48, November 1996

Queen Elizabeth II Reservoir: 71, 25th August 2001

Ripley Sewage Farm: 23, 9th January 1984

Send Water Meadows: 42, 9th March 1984

Shalford: 20, January 1969

Stoke Lake, Guildford: 30, 11th February 1985

Surrey Docks: 21, 28th February 1976

Thames Barnes/Putney: 230, 1963

Thames Putney/Staines: 479, 1954

Thorpe Water Park: 80, September 1991

Tongham Gravel Pits: 34, March 1997 (*HSBBR*) and November 1998

Unstead Sewage Farm: 16, October 1999

Walton Reservoirs: 84, July 1999

Spelthorne

King George VI Reservoir: 70, November 1997.

Queen Mary Reservoir: 62, 18th July 1984

Shepperton Gravel Pits: 45, 15th November 1989.

Staines Reservoirs: 68, 24th December 1986.

Movements. Most Mute Swans are rather sedentary but a few long distance movements have been recorded. A bird ringed at Wonersh in April 1996 was recovered at South Moulton, Devon in October 2000, a movement of 237 km. The longest domestic movement located is of a bird ringed at Beddington Park in September 1995 and recovered 504 km north at Berwick-on-Tweed in April 1999. There are two overseas recoveries, from Germany and Denmark, the latter being only the fourth British-ringed Mute Swan to be recovered in that country. The swan was a second-summer bird ringed at Staines on 5th May 1963 and controlled at Nykøbing, Denmark, about 800 km northeast, on 5th January and 2nd February 1970 (*Bird Study* 19 Supplement). The Thames at Laleham Park was a release point for Mute Swans treated at the nearby swan sanctuary. They were given white plastic Darvic rings as part of an Edward Grey Institute research project (*Shepp. BR*).

Longevity. A Mute Swan colour-ringed at Rack End, Oxfordshire on 30th August 1978 was seen over 15 years later at Wonersh Park, on 15th June 1994. An even older bird, which had been ringed in County Cork on 27th February 1985, was found freshly dead at Outwood on 8th November 2004. Mute Swans are sometimes killed or injured in collisions with overhead wires. Many have lead-poisoning, presumably from fishing weights. Swan Lifeline knew of 39 poisoned birds on a 500 yard stretch of the Thames at Hampton in 1987.

Bewick's/Whooper Swans

Cygnus columbianus/cygnus

It is not always possible to obtain specific identification of wild swans but, since these two species are both uncommon, generic records are sometimes published, such as one at Richmond Park in 1950. Others include four going east over Hinchley Wood on 1st January 1970, those seen over Kingston Vale and North Sheen in 1971 and over Ashtead (1980), Beddington (1994, 1997), Dulwich (1979), Egham (1978), Enton (1988), Epsom (1981), Frensham (1972, 2001), Ham (1986), Purley (1990), Staines Reservoirs (23 in 1959), Surbiton (1978), Thursley (1996) and Worplesdon (1972).

Bewick's Swan (Tundra Swan)

Cygnus columbianus (Cygnus columbianus bewickii)

Scarce winter visitor

Breeds on the Russian tundra, further north than the Whooper. A winter visitor to the British Isles and south to the Mediterranean and Caspian Seas.

Early Surrey history. Newman (1849) included Bewick's Swan as a winter visitor to the Godalming area without further comment. Jordan (1894) noted a herd of six near Dorking. There are no dated records in Newman, Bucknill or the writings of Denham Jordan.

Since 1900. The first dated occurrence is of a pair on Frensham Little Pond on 13th-27th January 1929 in very hard weather. An immature bird on a frozen lake at Felbridge (presumably Hedgecourt) on 17th December 1933 was captured the following day and sent to the London Zoo. An immature at Staines Reservoirs on 27th October 1935 (*BB, 29:216*), was apparently the first recorded for the Spelthorne district. In 1939 there were five at Frensham on March 18th and there was one at Hedgecourt on April 3rd. Sixteen at Barn Elms Reservoirs on 3rd-7th March 1946, after a national influx in the previous month, were the first for the Surrey part of the London area.

Overall there were 89 records for the vice-county and Spelthorne in the 20th century, 57 of them after 1970 and there were at least five more for the vice-county from 2001 to 2004. The total of 774 vice-county bird months was distributed as shown in the table. Of these, 608 were after 1969. A third of all the bird days were in March. There was a continuous increase in bird month numbers during the 20th century, though they fell back after 1999:

Bird months by decade 1900 to 2004 (to 2001 for Spelthorne)

	1900s	1910s	1920s	1930s	1940s	1950s	1960s	1970s	1980s	1990s	2000s	Total
Vice-county	0	0	2	7	24	31	102	105	187	302	14	**774**
Spelthorne	0	0	0	1	1	17	23	23	85	18	0	**168**

Over half of the vice-county records have been from Frensham (fifteen), Barn Elms (thirteen), Beddington (thirteen) and Queen Elizabeth II Reservoir (seven). Others have come from Boldermere (1968), Bricksbury Hill (1982), Burpham (1980), Camberley (1996), Chertsey Lock (2001), Cobham (1992), Cutt Mill (1979), East Molesey (1989), Elstead (1980), Enton (1958, 1962, 1965), Epsom (1979, 1993), Ewell (1989), Farnham Park (1999), Felbridge (1933), Frimley (1985), Guildford (1956, 1965,

1980), Hedgecourt (1939, 1949, 1972), Holmethorpe (1979, 1989, 1993), Island Barn Reservoir (1989, 2001), Limpsfield Chart (1993), Manor Brook (1979), Merrist Wood (1993), North Camp Gravel Pits (1991), Papercourt/Send (1970, 1981, 1991), Richmond Park (1948, 1963, 1980, 1991), Shalford (1956, 1963, 1966), Thursley Common (1994, 1996), Tooting (1985) and Walton Reservoirs (1966, 1980).

In Spelthorne, Bewick's Swans were seen at King George VI Reservoir (1949, 1954, 1955, 1971, 1979, 1981, 1985, 1991), Queen Mary Reservoir (1954, 1956, 1973, 1985, 1987, 1989, 1990), Staines Reservoirs (1935, 1954, 1957, 1967, 1969, 1970, 1971, 1978, 1980, 1981, 1982, 1983, 1985 (two records), 1987, 1993, 1997 (two records)) and Wraysbury Reservoir (1997).

Calendar. Bewick's Swans begin to arrive in October. They are passage migrants, rarely staying more than a day or two. Peak numbers pass through in March:

Bird months 1929-2004

	Jan	Feb	Mar	Apr	May	Jun	Jul	Aug	Sep	Oct	Nov	Dec	Total
Vice-county	174	191	269	3	0	0	0	0	0	31	45	61	**774**
Spelthorne	51	65	3	0	0	0	0	0	0	17	22	10	**168**

The earliest known arrival in autumn was one that came down at Beddington Sewage Farm on 4th October 1992. The latest known spring bird was one at Beddington Sewage Farm which lingered from 25th March to 15th April 1996.

Large counts

Cobham: 34 over, 16th March 1992

Cutt Mill: 34, 1st March 1979

East Molesey: 29 over, 11th March 1989

Farnham Park: 108 northeast, 20th February 1999

Frensham Little Pond: 35, 2nd March 1984 and on the Great Pond next day.

Frensham Little Pond: 32, 24th February 1988

Merrist Wood College: c.30 ENE, 9th March 1993, also seen at Epsom Common on the same day

Queen Elizabeth II Reservoir: 40 northwest, 1st January 1997

Spelthorne

Staines Reservoir: 38, 10th February 1980

Whooper Swan

Cygnus cygnus

Scarce winter visitor, 45 vice-county records 1900-2005 and a few earlier

Present in Britain in prehistoric times (Harrison and Hollom, 1932). Breeds in Iceland and in northern Europe, south of the tundra. In the British Isles, mainly found wintering in Scotland and Ireland, where it has occasionally bred, and in northern England.

Early Surrey history. Some of the earlier notes are a little vague, but the Whooper Swan seems to have been commoner than Bewick's in the 19th century. Jesse (in Bucknill) mentioned that 'wild swans' were shot on the Thames near Richmond in the severe winter of 1837/38. This was a notable winter for swans (Yarrell) and the birds might presumably have been of either species. Newman (1849) more persuasively wrote that the Whooper, *whose grand trumpeting note I have heard while skaiting here by moonlight*, had been killed on Old Pond, Godalming. Meyer (1842) saw six or seven at Chertsey Meads in the winter of 1847, two flew over the Wandle in the winter of 1861 and there are several undated records prior to 1900 (Bucknill). Jordan (1894) wrote of one that had been shot at Frensham Great Pond.

1900 to 1970. Two at Frensham on 27th February 1922 and four there on 8th March 1953 were the only ones from 1900 to 1955. There was an influx in February 1956, with birds at Barn Elms (three), Island Barn Reservoir (two) and Old Coulsdon (five) on the 5th, and eight at Gatton on the 26th. One was reported in March. Two adults and one juvenile were at Enton on 6th October 1956. After single records in 1960 (Island Barn Reservoir) and 1962 (East Molesey) there was a further influx in the cold weather of early 1963. They came from Hersham (three on 6th January), Queen Elizabeth II Reservoir (six on 20th January), Tilford/Elstead (four on 4th and 23rd February), Sutton Place (up to nine from 4th February to 12th March), Unstead Sewage Farm (five on 8th-10th March), Walton Common (two on 8th March), Shalford (nine to twelve on 17th-18th March), Broadford (twelve on 23rd March), Cutt Mill (one on 28th-29th March), Chessington (fifty over on 22nd March) and Bletchingley (two on 1st-8th April).

The cold winters of the 1960s proved to be the high water mark for Whooper Swans in Surrey:

Bird months by decade 1900-2003

	1900s	1910s	1920s	1930s	1940s	1950s	1960s	1970s	1980s	1990s	2000s	Total
Vice-county	0	0	2	0	0	26	113	18	5	17	5	**186**
Spelthorne	0	0	0	0	0	4	22	14	0	2	0	**42**

Where Found. Of the 44 vice-county and five Spelthorne records, ten have been at Frensham and five at Island Barn Reservoir. No other place has seen more than three, the other places being Ash Vale Gravel Pit (1972), Badshot Lea (1967), Barn Elms (1956, 1967), Beddington Sewage Farm (1981, 1996), Bletchingley (1963), Chessington (1963), Cutt Mill (1963), East Molesey (1962), Enton (1956), Epsom Sewage Farm (1956), Frimley Gravel Pits (1992), Gatton (1956), Godalming (1974), Hersham (1963), Holmethorpe (1995, 1997), Kew Gardens (1981), Ockley Common (1965), Old Coulsdon (1956), Queen Elizabeth II Reservoir (1963), Shalford/Broadford (1963), Sutton Place, Guildford (1963), Thursley Common (1986), Tilford/Elstead (1963), Unstead Sewage Farm (1963), Walton Common (1963) and in Spelthorne King George VI Reservoir (1956, 1961, 1998), Staines Moor (1956) and Staines Reservoirs (1979). The most recent was a family party of five at Island Barn Reservoir on 18th October 2002.

Calendar. Whooper Swans are rarely seen before November and numbers peak in March. Almost all are seen flying over, though they occasionally linger.

Bird months since 1900

	Jan	Feb	Mar	Apr	May	Jun	Jul	Aug	Sep	Oct	Nov	Dec	Total
Vice-county	36	35	90	4	0	0	0	0	1	8	8	4	**186**
Spelthorne	15	4	0	0	0	0	0	0	0	0	0	23	**42**

Early and late dates are:

Arrivals

7th September 1973　over Wrecclesham (*HSBBR*)
6th October 1956　Enton

Departures

1st-8th April 1963　Bletchingley

Two at Frensham in April 1967, on 23rd-24th April (Parr)/23rd-30th (Clark 1984) might not have been wild in view of the dates.

Large counts

Chessington: *c*.50 ENE, 22nd March 1963
King George VI Reservoir: 22 flew in, 28th December 1961 during a very cold spell.

Movements and longevity. One ringed at Martin Mere, Lancashire in 1984 was found exhausted in a field at Godstone in the spring of 1987, where it recovered and flew off next day (*Natureline*, Winter 1995/6).

Bean Goose

Anser fabalis

Twelve records, including three A. f. rossicus

Breeds on the tundra from Scandinavia east to Siberia, moving south in winter. Numbers are falling. A few hundred winter in Britain. These are mainly of the race *A. f. fabalis*, which is the most westerly population, but birds of the race *A. f. rossicus*, which breeds further east, on the Siberian tundra, are occasionally found and may be the commonest race in the southeast.

Early Surrey history. Jordan saw Bean Geese flying *over the lowlands at the base of the Surrey hills* at migration times but gave no dates (Jordan, 1892). Dated occurrences are:

1841:   below Godalming Wharf, one shot by a bargeman (*SALEC*) was still in the Charterhouse Collection in 2001.

1892:   Cannon Farm, Fetcham, one shot in the winter (*Bucknill, 1902*).

1940:* Staines Reservoirs, eight on 10th-11th February increasing to eleven on 15th-16th (*BB, 33:315*) and last seen on the 22nd, were apparently the first recorded for the district. They had arrived during a period of intense cold during the winter of 1939/40.

1945:   Frensham Great Pond, one on 8th December (Eric Parker, *Surrey Naturalist*).

1958:   Beddington Sewage Farm, two on 4th-6th January.

1963:   Queen Elizabeth II Reservoir, seven for a few days from 21st January.
        Walton Reservoirs, one on 2nd March.

1981:   Smallfield, two on 26th-28th December.

1984:* Staines Moor, 11 on 16th January, during a cold spell on the Continent.

Spelthorne

Tundra Bean Goose   *Anser fabalis rossicus*
Three records:

1993:   Holmethorpe Sand Pits, five on 28th November (G. W. J. Hay and P. Kerry).

1997:   Beddington Sewage Farm, one on 1st February (R. D. Weller).

2003:   Island Barn Reservoir, one on 1st, 2nd and 20th March (D. M. Harris *et al.*).
        Several other recent reports, including Barn Elms (11th December 2004) and Staines (8th-9th December 2004), fit the pattern but have not yet been confirmed.

Pink-footed Goose   *Anser brachyrhynchus*
About 14 records of apparently wild birds since 1900, latest 2003
Breeds in Greenland, Iceland and Spitzbergen (Svalbard) and winters in Europe, mainly in coastal areas.

Surrey. This has always been a rare goose:

1929:* Staines Reservoir North, T. H. Harrison and P. A. D. Hollom saw four on 18th January (*BB, 22:374, BB, 23:22*). The geese flew off but were present again on the following day.
        Between Runnymede and Stanwell, J. R. Crawford saw six flying low and calling loudly, on 3rd December.

1938:   Beddington Sewage Farm, ten on 23rd and 24th December (on the ground). One was apparently shot on the previous day.
        Barn Elms Reservoirs, three on 27th and 30th December. Severe weather at the time but very tame. They might have been escapes, or the Beddington birds.

1950:* Staines Moor, one on 24th-27th December.

1956:   Old Coulsdon, 75-80 north on 26th February.

1963:   Beddington, one on 6th January.

1968:   Brockwell Park, four over on 28th March.

1970:* Staines Reservoirs, two east on 28th February.

1971:* Queen Mary Reservoir, two west on 9th December.

1995:   Holmethorpe Sand Pits, an adult and a juvenile, probably wild, flushed by a dog on 2nd November.

1996:   Chertsey Meads, a first-winter bird on the bank of the Thames on 19th January.

2001*:   Staines Moor, three on 16th February (*LNHSB, Bird Watching*) were thought to be part of a small influx to southeast England.

2003:   Wimbledon Common, two on 26th February.

*Spelthorne

White-fronted Goose (Greater White-fronted Goose)   *Anser albifrons*
Scarce winter visitor

Breeds on coasts and islands inside the Arctic Circle and winters in Europe, Asia and North America. Numbers are declining. Members of the Greenland race, *A. a. flavirostris* winter in northern and western Britain but have not been found in Surrey.

Early Surrey history. Most occurrences relate to skeins of migrants presumed mainly to be of the Eurasian race *A. a. albifrons*. Bucknill gave four dated occurrences. A White-fronted Goose was shot at Frensham Pond in 1820 and others are said to have been shot there by 1837. One was shot at Unstead Old Water [Broadwater?] in 1841 (*SALEC*). Meyer and others shot one of a flock that stayed for several days on gravelly ground by the Thames during snowy weather in February 1847. One was killed near Godalming in 1851.

1900 to 1969. A flock of twelve over Caterham on 25th February 1927 (Bentham in *BLA*), would appear to have been the first birds in Surrey for 76 years. Two were at Beddington Sewage Farm on 16th January 1943 and two on 20th April 1955 and there were several at Barn Elms and Walton on 3rd March 1963. The first 20th century record from Frensham was in 1964, when two flew over on 3rd February. In Spelthorne, there were ten on Staines Moor on 24th January 1940 during a spell of intense cold. About 60 flew over the same site on 20th December 1950 and twelve were seen there a week later.

Other vice-county places and counts up to 1969 include Cheam (March 1953), East Surrey (seventeen, January 1947), Epsom (sixty-seven, 5th February 1961), Ewell (nineteen, 1955; 180, 1968), Farnham (six, 22nd December 1962), Frensham (a hundred and thirty, 18th February 1968), Hersham (twenty-seven, 7th January 1967), Ockley Common (fifty, 1969), South Norwood Lake (three, 1953), Sutton (sixty-four, February 1954), Walton Reservoirs (seven, 1st March 1952) and Weybridge (eleven, 25th December 1961). White-fronted Geese were seen in Spelthorne in 1953, 1960, 1962-64, 1967-69.

Where found from 1970. There were 604 vice-county bird months, excluding two uncounted flocks, in the vice-county and 177 birds in Spelthorne from 1970 to 2003. The largest vice-county flocks for the period were 70 over Kew Gardens on 9th January 1984 and 54 over Capel on 15th January 1994. Other records and major flocks were at Alderstead Heath (1997), Ash Vale Gravel Pits (1973), Badshot Lea (1979), Barnes (1983, 1986), Barn Elms (22 in 1992, 1999), Beddington Sewage Farm (1984, two records 1985, 21 in 1991, 1993, 1998, 2002), Cranleigh (2002), Croydon (25 in 1999), Frensham (1972), Frimley Gravel Pits (twenty in 1979, 1986, 1991 (possible escapes), 1992), Ham (thirty in 1987), Holmethorpe (1990, three records 1993, 1996, 1997), Island Barn Reservoir (1985, 2003), Molesey Heath (eighteen in 1993), Old Woking (1996), Olddean Common (1994), Papercourt Lock (1994), Queen Elizabeth II Reservoir (1998), Redhill Aerodrome (1995), Sanderstead (1994), South Norwood (1997 Country Park and Lake), Thursley Common (1981, 1983, 1996, 1997, 30 in 2001), Walton Reservoirs (1993) and Witley (1996).

Twenty five of the bird months were of single birds. There is always a suspicion that such birds are escapes, especially when with Canada Geese. Two with Canada Geese at Halliford Mere on 9th February 1986, at a time of severe weather, just might have been feral (*Shepp. BR*). There were three at King George VI Reservoir from January to March 2001(*LBR*) and three at Staines Moor in February and March 2003. Very few White-fronted Geese have been found in the period April to September, so it seems reasonable to include these winter records with the wild flocks.

Calendar. The majority of the vice-county birds, 350 bird months, occurred in January.

Bird months 1972 to 2003

	Jan	Feb	Mar	Apr	May	Jun	Jul	Aug	Sep	Oct	Nov	Dec	Total
Vice-county	350	108	6	2	0	0	0	0	0	5	74	59	**604**
Spelthorne	85	14	11	0	0	0	0	0	0	2	22	43	**177**

The earliest of autumn were two adults and two immature birds at Frimley Gravel Pits on 10th October 1991, thought at the time to be possible escapes in view of the date.

Arrivals		Departures	
10th October 1991	Frimley Gravel Pits	30th March 1983	Thursley Common
17th October 1999	Staines Moor	3rd April 1995	Beddington Sewage Farm
6th November 1994	Sanderstead (heard)		(two, escapes?)
13th November 1983	near Barn Elms (single bird)		
25th November 1990	Holmethorpe Sand Pits (nine)		

Large counts. The largest vice-county parties go back to the 1960s:

Ewell: *c.*180 flew northeast at *c.*500 ft on 4th March 1968, calling loudly

Frensham Great Pond: 130 flew northeast on 18th February 1968 (Clark, 1984).

Spelthorne

Queen Mary Reservoir: *c.*200 northwest on 12th January 1985

Greylag Goose   *Anser anser*

Locally common feral breeding resident

Greylag Geese were present in Britain over half a million years ago. They have the most southerly range among the grey geese, breeding from Iceland (the source of most British winter visitors) through Britain and Europe east to China. Northern birds move south in winter but are almost unknown in Surrey. Greylag Geese have been domesticated from ancient times and more recently have been widely introduced by wildfowlers. There is now a large and increasing British population of feral birds. They nest in trees more commonly than *BWP* suggests. Hewlett mentions a London area nest that was found 20 feet up a plane tree. A pair brought off young from a pine tree in Kent in 2005 (*BB, 99:365*).

Early Surrey history. Newman (1849) included them without comment as winter visitors. The only dated 19th century record is of one on the river at East Molesey in the winter of January 1880.

1900 to 1963. One at Hedgecourt Pond on 9th April 1947 was extremely wary. The severe winter of 1963 brought three exhausted birds to Barn Elms Reservoirs from 5th January to 9th February.

1964 to 1979. Most or all of the later records up to the 1980s are likely to relate to vagrants from stock introduced in southern Britain. Wild birds and many of the introduced birds are likely to be of the western race *A. a. anser,* though racial identifications are rarely given by observers. Birds had been introduced as close as Sevenoaks by 1965 (*London Bird Report*), possibly the origin of birds found in 1967 at the Barrow Green and Holmethorpe sand pits, both in east Surrey, and at Lyne Sewage Farm. They reached Unstead Sewage Farm in 1969, Barn Elms in 1970, Weybridge (a very tame bird) in 1971, the Surrey Docks in 1974 and Beddington Sewage Farm in 1976. They were picked up by the Common Birds Census from 1996.

Breeding. The first breeding colony was also in the eastern part of Surrey, at Hedgecourt, where probably two pairs had 11 young in May 1980 and a count of 25 adults and young was made in the following month. A pair with nine young was seen at Gatton in June 1983. By 1984, breeding flocks had become established at Battersea Park, Gatton and Hedgecourt and in 2000, 12 or 13 pairs bred at seven sites. These figures probably understate the true size of the breeding population because, at one time or another, Greylag Geese are known to have nested at over 20 places, including Barn Elms (35 pairs in 2005), Battersea Park (20 pairs, 17 goslings in 1985), Baynards, Britten's Pond (2001), Buckland (1985), Claremont, Elstead, Enton, Ewell Court, Gatton, Hedgecourt (from 1985), Holmethorpe (from 1991, *BHSP*), Hurst Green, Kew Gardens, Lambeth Bridge (2001), Painshill Park (2001), Richmond Park,

Trevereux/Swaynesland (2000), Vachery Pond, Wimbledon Common, Winkworth Arboretum and Witley Park. A pair bred at Shepperton Gravel Pits in 1985 and 1986. Greylag Geese are now spread widely across the county. There were records from 49 sites in 1999 and a similar number in 2001. It is perhaps surprising that a colony breeding at Stratfield Saye, in northeast Hampshire, since 1964 has not had more impact on northwest Surrey.

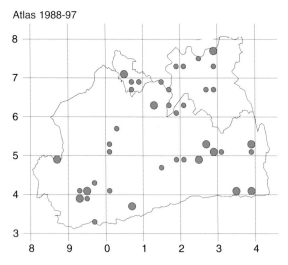

Atlas 1988-97

Nest sites. One apparently tried to nest in a hole 30 feet up in a large, dead oak tree at Oxenford Farm, Peper Harow, in 1999. The bird was seen peering out of the hole on a number of occasions and was not disturbed by the presence of point-to-point racing with bookies, a public address system and the last jump near the tree. A second bird, presumed the male, was seen by the nearby river, with Canada Geese. No young were seen. (Redfern (2002), pers. comm.). No other records of hole-nesting in Surrey have been located, although *BWP* mentions that tree nesting occurs exceptionally in or near low trees on flooded areas, especially in what was then the USSR and that they have been found nesting in pollarded willows in Czechoslovakia (*BWP*, vol. 1 pp.414, 420). Greylag Geese have nested in pollards elsewhere in the UK (Editorial note to Redfern, 2002).

Large counts. Numbers have been rising, with no sign of levelling out:
Barn Elms: 26, 3rd November 2002
Claremont: 51, 6th December 2001
Enton: 232, roosting, 30th September 2003 (also feeding on Tuesley Farm, 30th September 2003)
Holmethorpe: 172, 22nd September 2002
Trevereux, Limpsfield: 115, 22nd October 2000 (probably Holmethorpe birds)
Vachery: 165 in fields, 12th January 2002
Witley Park: 43, June 1998

Movements and longevity. Although the Surrey birds are largely resident there is some evidence of regular movements. Frensham records for 1945-94, for example, showed an April peak (S. P. Peters). A Greylag Goose ringed at Sevenoaks, on 1st July 1985, was found at Hedgecourt over two years and eleven months later, on 20th June 1988. Two different Greylag Geese that had been ringed at Sevenoaks were found dead or dying at Nutfield Marsh, 28 km west, in 1988.

Western Greylag Goose
Anser anser anser

This is the orange-billed form common in Surrey but rarely indicated as such by observers. Birds with characteristics of *A. a. anser* were reported in 1978 from Effingham and Papercourt Gravel Pits.

Canada Goose (Greater Canada Goose) — *Branta canadensis*
Common breeding resident

Canada Geese had already been introduced as a parkland species before 1672. Francis Willughby (1635-72) wrote of them as being in King Charles II's collection in St James's Park. In the 18th and 19th centuries it was frequently to be found on country estates. The first reference to an escape appears to be of one recorded as shot on the Thames at Brentford, on the edge of our area in or before 1731 (Albin, 1731). Feral breeding was not recorded until 1885, when a pair bred in Birmingham. Numbers increased, but in the 1930s most records of free-flying Canada Geese still came from southern England and the Midlands. Numbers have increased hugely and they are currently the commonest breeding geese, still increasing after a pause in the 1990s. Canada Geese are mainly resident, but there is a significant moult migration to the Beauly Firth, mostly from the Midlands and the North but including a few from Surrey (*MA*).

Early Surrey history. Bucknill knew of a few that had been shot in the years up to 1900, but thought they were all escapes and made no reference to feral breeding.

Since 1900. A pair bred in Richmond Park in a semi-wild state in 1904 (Mouritz). A pair bred at Godstone in 1905 (Bentham in *BLA*). Power saw five flying low near Dulwich on 25th May 1907 and assumed they were from Brockwell Park. Four were seen in Gatton Park in 1909, a pair bred there 'in the early years' of the 20th century (Bentham, 1970) and there was one at Godstone in 1926 (*BLA*). A pair bred on private land at Oxted, unknown to the owner, in 1931 and a pair bred on Elstead Common in 1932, possibly the birds seen in wildfowl counts at Frensham in that year. By about this time, Canada Geese had become established at Painshill Park, Cobham. They were lost during the 1939-45 war but bred again in 1949 and were doing so regularly from 1956 (Baker, 1985). A pair bred at Godstone in 1940.

Canada Geese took up residence in Gatton Park in 1929 or 1930. They increased quickly and there were at least 130 there by 1936 and 200 by 1938, in spite of the destruction of eggs. Most left during the wartime military occupation of the park, driven off by anti-aircraft fire (*SBR* for 1969). Up to 70 had returned by 1952 but they were not reported as breeding again there until a pair with young were seen in 1968.

A substantial flock built up in the Englefield Green area in the 1940s and early 1950s. Eggs were destroyed at Englefield Green from 1952 (Baker, 1985). Birds were often seen flying to Windsor Great Park but they were slow to colonise it. South (1980) put this down to the absence of small islands, where the geese would be safe from foxes and other predators. Canada Geese were still not common in most of Surrey in the 1950s. The 1953 Surrey Bird Report mentions only two birds, one at Frensham and the other at Send, though there were 60 at Virginia Water in September 1954. Two Canada Geese were killed by Mute Swans in Battersea Park in 1965. The swans were then removed. Three pairs bred there in 1966.

Others bred at Ash Vale Gravel Pits (1958-59), Broome Hall (1968), Bury Hill Lake (1962), Camberley (1957), Chertsey (Botley's Park, 1967), Cobham (Painshill, 1956-58, 1959, 1962 etc), Enton (1959), Godstone (1940), Holmethorpe (1965), Kew Gardens (1964), Reigate Priory (by 1957, *BLA*), Send Gravel Pits (1962), Vann Lake (by 1967, Blaker Log), Winkworth Arboretum (1962) and Wisley RHS gardens (1958). Five pairs bred in Battersea Park in 1967. In 1971, eggs from an abandoned nest at Thorpe were rescued and three young were later released on Botley's Lake, Chertsey. The largest flock mentioned by Parr was of 200 over Ewhurst in September 1970. Numbers have increased substantially since that date. Of the 231 tetrads in northeast Surrey, 18% were found to hold territories in the 1968-72 Atlas survey and 49% in the 1988-97 Atlas, a very big advance.

The colonisation in Spelthorne extended up the Colne Valley in spite of control measures in the 1950s (Baker, 1985). One flew over King George VI Reservoir with two Mute Swans on 11th February 1954. Two were seen at Queen Mary Reservoir in July/August 1959 and two flew over on 27th March 1960. Sightings became fairly regular from 1962. Canada Geese first bred at Shepperton in 1973 and by

1985 there were 14 breeding pairs, when 76+ young were raised. They have bred at other sites, such as Halliford Mere (2000-02) and Queen Mary (annual in the 1980s).

Population size. It was estimated that in 1975 there were at least 250 adults in the county, of which about 20% fledged young, bringing the population up to about 450 by August, and that numbers were increasing by between 6 and 10% per annum (*SBR*). Canada Geese were found in Common Birds Censuses from 1972, territories rising to 2.1 per ten hectares by 2002, which probably over-represents them in Surrey as a whole. They were found in 272 tetrads during the 1988-97 SBC Atlas survey and breeding was proved in more than half of them. The 1991 Feral Goose survey found 3,350 adult and young Canada Geese at 54 sites in July. The Breeding Bird Survey which is supposed to exclude juveniles, found an average of 1.76 Canada Geese per square km in 1994-2001, which grosses up to about 3,400 for the vice-county plus Spelthorne.

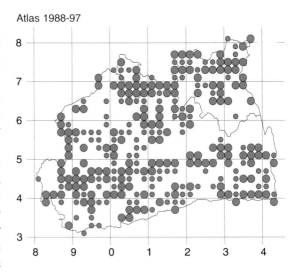

Atlas 1988-97

Breeding behaviour. Many pairs may breed at a single site. There were 49 young at Effingham Fish Ponds on 31st May 1978 and 110 goslings in Battersea Park on 30th May 1985. A pair with 22 goslings at Thorpe Water Park on 20th May 1992 were evidently in charge of a crèche. There were 13 territories at Beddington Sewage Farm in 2004.

Canada Geese have expanded mainly because they have few natural rivals. Mute Swans, to which they might be thought of as a threat, have also been increasing and where the two do compete, they can get the better of the Canadas. Aggressive Mute Swans prevented breeding at Barn Elms and Lonsdale Road Reservoirs in 1995, recalling the events at Battersea Park in 1965 except for the removal of the swans. At Shepperton in 1985, Canada Geese greatly outnumbered Mute Swans and there were conflicts involving three pairs of Mute Swans. Two of these raised young and the third was driven off. On the River Ash, goslings were also lost and one pair of Canada Geese was driven off (*Shepp. BR* for 1985).

'Excited' birds were observed diving at Holmethorpe on 5th August 1970 and at the Royal Military Academy, Camberley on 18th October 1970. One seen perched in a dead oak tree at Oxenford Farm, Peper Harow by Robin Redfern in 1999 (the tree used as a nest site by a Greylag Goose and mentioned above), was rather unusual for the species, though tree nesting has been reported from Middlesex (*LBR* for 1995).

Large counts. In the maximum counts shown below, those for Papercourt, Send and Stoke Lake all refer to the same group. The largest published count of all, over 700 at Papercourt in September 1986, may have marked a peak, or at least a levelling off in the numbers in the vice-county. The stability was at least partly because of control measures. Much larger numbers remained in Spelthorne until at least 1996. More recently there has been a record count in the Milford area and the growth in numbers may have been resumed, following a national trend.

Ash Vale Gravel Pits: 103 adults and 12 juveniles in 1991 (Feral Goose Survey)
Badshot Lea: 351, September 1987
Barn Elms: 250, August 2001; 376, 5th September 1996 (*Barn Elms Bird Report* 2001-02)
Barnes Pond: 120, 13th September 1989
Battersea Park: 260 adult + 80 juveniles in 1991 (Feral Goose Survey)

Bay Pond, Godstone: 225, October 1985
Beddington Sewage Farm: 200, September 1991
Buckland Sand Pits: 300, 16th February 1986
Capel landfill: 253+, 20th September 2003
Chertsey: 220, December 1983
Chertsey Meads: 144, 3rd July 1998
Chilworth: 136, October 1978
Clandon Park: 380, November 1984
Cutt Mill: 122, October 1972
Effingham Fish Ponds: 330, September 1985
Enton: 158, 25th August 1999
Epsom Common/Stew Ponds: 250 August and
    September 1998
Frensham: 217, 10th September 1992 (SBC
    archive)
Frimley Gravel Pits: 305, February 1991 (*HSBBR*);
    375, 16th September 2001
Gatton Lake: 310, September 1985
Godstone – Bay Pond: 225, October 1985
Godstone: 123, September 1981
Hamm Moor, Weybridge: 200+, 21st January
    1984
Hedgecourt: 201, December 1990
Hersham Gravel Pit: 332, September 1999
Holmethorpe Sand Pits: 434, 13th January 1985
Hurst Park: 238, June 1997
Island Barn Reservoir: 232, October 1997
Kew Gardens: 210, 27th August 1980
Lammas Lands: 215, 12th December 1994
Lonsdale Road Reservoir: 145, 3rd November
    1996
Milford (Tuesley Farm): 900, 26th September
    2003
Molesey Gravel Pit: 125, 17th October 1982
North Camp Gravel Pits: 65, 18th January 1970
Outwood Swan Sanctuary: 158, October 1998;
    302, 12th October 2003
Papercourt Gravel Pits: 700+, September 1986
Pen Ponds: 116, October 1990
Queen Elizabeth II Reservoir: 128, 28th
    November 1999
Reigate Priory: 167, September 1994
Seale Sand Pits: 179, 22nd October 1978
Send Water Meadows: 350, 11th October 1987

Shalford Meadows: 170, 25th January 1976
Shalford Park: 132, December 1975
South Norwood Country Park: 250, September
    1991
South Norwood Lake: 135, 16th September 2000
Stoke Lake, Guildford: 472, February 1992
Sutton Green: 270, January 1986
Sutton Place: 211, 10th January 2003
Tangley Mere: 136, October 1998
Thames Hampton Court – Walton-on-Thames:
    358 including young, June and/or July 2000
    (Naturalised Goose Survey, *LBR*)
Thames Putney Bridge – Hampton Court: 943
    including young, June and/or July 2000
    (Naturalised Goose Survey, *LBR*)
Thorpe Water Park: 158, 1999; 411, September
    2000
Thursley Common: 98, September 1995
Tongham Gravel Pit: 390, August 1995
Unstead Sewage Farm: 421, November 1999;
    462, November 2000
Vachery: 44, 31st January 1970; 70+, 20th August
    1978; 161, 1st January 2001; 190, 26th
    September 1998; 218, 1st January 2001; 256
    on nearby field, 12th January 2002
Walton Reservoirs: 305, 2nd December 1989
Wanborough: 665 on stubble, 21st September
    2001
Wandsworth Common: 62, 8th September 1978;
    92, (not aged) on Central Pond in 1991 (Feral
    Goose Survey)
Waverley: 53, 30th July 1977; 98, January 1997
Wimbledon Park Lake: 168, November 1989
Wrecclesham: 260, 21st October 1987, 260 on
    Floods, 8th January 1998
Spelthorne
King George VI Reservoir: 1,139 on 6th
    September 1986
Queen Mary Reservoir: 55 on 26th October 1975
Queen Mary Gravel Pits: 750 on 23rd August
    1986
Shepperton Gravel Pits: 650 in August 1986.
Staines Moor: 450 on 17th October 1993
Staines Reservoirs: 1,400 on 27th August 1996

Movements. For most of the year, large flocks of Canada Geese roam locally, over a radius of several miles. They flock up to moult from about July and are flightless for a period. The Thames is an important moult site (Baker and Coleman) but some birds move considerably further. One that was shot at Guildford in January 1979 had been ringed as an adult 737 km north at Beauly Firth, Highlands, in the previous July, presumably part of the nationally important moulting flock there. This is the longest known Surrey movement. Other Canada Geese came from Kings Bromley, in Staffordshire to Cobham in 1980 and to Dorking in 1981. Not all moulting birds move so far. One colour-ringed on the Thames at Isleworth in July 2004 was seen at Hedgecourt in December 2005.

Longevity. One ringed at Sevenoaks on 24th June 1990 and recovered at Buckland 26th December 1998 established a Surrey longevity record of over 8 years 6 months (national oldest over 24 years).

Barnacle Goose   *Branta leucopsis*

Five vice-county records of apparently wild birds since 1900, latest 1984. Many records of feral birds, usually with Canada Geese.

Barnacle Geese breed in the Arctic from Greenland east to the Baltic and Novaya Zemlya, moving south in winter. Those coming to Britain are mostly found on the north and west coasts. The geese are commonly kept in wildfowl collections. There were occasional breeding records of feral birds in Britain up to the 1970s and by the end of the 20th century feral breeding was reported from many localities.

Early Surrey history. A Barnacle Goose that had been shot near Elstead in 1849 (*SALEC*) was in the Charterhouse Collection in Bucknill's time and is presumably the specimen which was still held there in 2001, with Surrey as its provenance. Another was shot on the Thames at Thames Ditton in the winter of 1875 (Bucknill, 1902).

Wild birds since 1900. There are five other records that appear to relate to migrant wild birds. A gaggle of eight frequented a flooded meadow near Dorking for a few days from 2nd October 1909 after rough weather. Two were in Witley Park in February 1919. Four flew over Beddington Sewage Farm on 5th April 1959. One at Walton Reservoirs on 29th January 1967 was grazing with Wigeon. One at Frensham Little Pond on 2nd March 1984 was with a flock of Bewick's Swans.

Feral birds. The existence of large feral flocks at Eversley Gravel Pits and Stratfield Saye in north Hampshire have made it difficult to isolate any long distance migrants from the increasing numbers of Barnacle Goose reports in recent years. Apparently feral birds have been seen annually since at least 1974, usually one at a time and with Canada Geese. A Barnacle Goose with an aluminium ring on its left leg was seen throughout 1979 at various west Surrey sites, usually with Canada Geese. It was probably an escape. There were six at Staines Moor in August 1977, five there in 1994, up to six at Gatton and Holmethorpe in 1982, eight there throughout 1983 and seven in 1984. Records came from 14 sites in 1998 and subsequent sightings included a party of six at Copthorne on 27th March 2000. One at Barn Elms Reservoirs on 31st December 2000 was said to have appeared wild, but four seen there in June 2001 would certainly not have been. One was seen at Halliford Mere lakes on 6th April 2001. A number of *leucopsis* hybrids have been reported.

Breeding. A pinioned pair bred at Effingham Fish Ponds in 1979 and breeding took place again in 1980 and in 1981, when Barnacle Geese were present in some numbers. A pair with two goslings was seen at Holmethorpe Sand Pits on 4th June 2002 (G. W. J. Hay). No other records involve breeding in Surrey.

Brent Goose

Branta bernicla

Scarce winter visitor, increasing

Breeds on coasts and islands all round the Arctic Circle and moves south in winter. There are three races. The Dark-bellied *B. b. bernicla*, breeds on the Siberian tundra, where numbers are said to be at a 20-year low. These birds winter in northwest Europe, including southeast England and Surrey. Numbers in Britain declined during much of the 20th century but have since more than recovered in spite of the fall in breeding numbers. The Pale-bellied *B. b. hrota* is from around Arctic waters of the North Atlantic. The Black Brant, *B. b. nigricans* comes from western North America and was treated as a separate species by some 19th century writers, *e.g.* Saunders.

Early Surrey history. Brent Goose occasionally visited the Godalming district up to 1849 (Newman).

Since 1900. The earliest dated record is of two at Frensham Great Pond on 23rd April 1923 (HNHS 1954). Eight were preening in severe weather at Island Barn Reservoir on 17th December 1938. Another six were found at Frensham in the very severe weather of February 1940. Two others were on the Thames at Chiswick from the 14th to the 18th of the same month. Brent Geese were not seen again until 1964, when five appeared briefly at Walton Reservoirs on 11th January (not Bean Geese as in the *SBR*).

There was a striking increase in the number of records in the 1980s and 90s consisting, it is thought, mainly of birds flying between the Thames estuary and the south coast:

Records by decade

	1900s	1910s	1920s	1930s	1940s	1950s	1960s	1970s	1980s	1990s	2000-01	Total
Vice-county	0	0	1	1	2	0	2	4	38	85	23	**156**
Spelthorne	0	0	0	0	0	0	4	2	11	22	4	**43**

Of 199 records up to 2001, 126 came from six sites: Beddington Sewage Farm (42), Frensham (19), Queen Elizabeth II Reservoir (16), Barn Elms (12), Holmethorpe Sand Pits (11) and, in Spelthorne, Staines Reservoirs (26). The rest came from Addlestone, Artington, Ashtead, Bookham, Camberley, Cobham, Crooksbury Hill, Elstead, Fieldcommon Gravel Pit, Frimley Gravel Pits, Hersham, Island Barn Reservoir, Limpsfield Chart, the M25, Newdigate, Pen Ponds, Reigate Priory, South Croydon, South Norwood Country Park, Stoke Water Meadows, Sutton, the Thames, Thursley, Tooting, Walton Heath, Walton Reservoirs, West Ewell, Witley, Wrecclesham Floods and, in Spelthorne, King George VI Reservoir, Perry Oaks Sewage Farm, Queen Mary Reservoir, Staines Moor and Stanwell Moor.

After 2001 there were others at Barn Elms, Beddington Sewage Farm, Queen Elizabeth II Reservoir (including 16 on 11th December 2002), Queen Mary Reservoir (Spelthorne), South Norwood Country Park, Staines Reservoirs (Spelthorne) and West Ewell.

Calendar. October is the peak month for migrants, which are then generally moving south or southwest. December and January movements tend to be related to hard weather and there is a less obvious return passage from February to April. The 199 records generated 1,841 bird months. Most records were of flocks flying over, so that the average record was of about nine birds.

Bird months 1900-2001

	Jan	Feb	Mar	Apr	May	Jun	Jul	Aug	Sep	Oct	Nov	Dec	Total
Vice-county	158	140	19	96	1	1	0	0	26	861	452	87	**1,841**
Spelthorne	84	10	10	38	0	0	0	0	0	0	145	25	**312**

Early arrival and late departure dates are:

Arrival

23rd September 1998	Thames at Sunbury (three)
23rd September 2000	Beddington Sewage Farm (23)
25th September 1976	Frensham Great Pond (one)

Departure

20th April 1995	Beddington Sewage Farm (22)
23rd April 1923	Frensham Great Pond (two)
26th April 1981	Staines Reservoirs (one)
28th April 1983	Staines Reservoirs (seven)

Single birds were seen at Frensham Little Pond on 15th May 2001 and over Queen Elizabeth II Reservoir on 5th June 1998.

Large counts

Beddington Sewage Farm: 267 in two flocks, 20th October 1997
Beddington Sewage Farm: 240+ in two flocks, 10th October 1991
Beddington Sewage Farm: 97 in two flocks, 8th November 1992
South Norwood Country Park: 80-90, 28th January 1991

Pale-bellied Brent Goose · *Branta bernicla hrota*

Two definite, four others

One was shot at Bramley (undated in Bucknill). There are two well authenticated occurrences:

1998: Beddington Sewage Farm, one on 7th February (R. D. Weller *et al.*, *LBR*, *SBR*).

2003:* Staines Reservoirs, one on 29th December.

Two other reports are:

1852: Eashing, a bird shot in this year (*SALEC*) was seen in the Charterhouse Collection by Bucknill, who made no reference to its race. One was still held in the Charterhouse Museum in 2001, with Surrey as its provenance. Rather surprisingly, this bird is Pale-bellied and if it really is the Eashing bird it raises a question about the relative frequency of the two races in southern England at the time. The Pale-bellied race is not mentioned by Yarrell (1845) or Saunders (1899).

1995:* Queen Mary Reservoir, two were claimed in the November wildfowl count (BTO, not in the *LBR*).

* Spelthorne

Black Brant · *Branta bernicla nigricans*

One, Spelthorne

There was one at Staines Reservoirs from 27th October to 23rd November 1984 (D. Coker, R. B. Hastings and A. V. Moon, *BB, 78: 536*; P Naylor, *BB, 79:534*).

Egyptian Goose · *Alopochen aegyptiaca*

Uncommon feral breeding species.

Egyptian Geese are native to Africa, where they are found in wetland habitats across the region, breeding in riverside vegetation and holes in trees. They were included in the King's collection at St James's Park in the 17th century and were common in wildfowl collections by 1785. By the 19th century there were unpinioned breeding groups in Bedfordshire, East Lothian and Norfolk and winter reports of flocks (presumably from these collections) were being made, apparently because of seasonal movements. Currently increasing in Britain. There are feral populations in Belgium and the Netherlands.

Early Surrey history. Bucknill referred to 'many occurrences' of escaped birds in Surrey, including specimens killed at Frensham and other ponds at dates up to 1862 but did not mention breeding. Three were killed 'at one shot' on Frensham Pond in or around the end of February 1862 (*Zool., 1862:8005*).

1900 to 1970. The 20th century Surrey history up to the 1960s is poorly documented, but Egyptian Geese were not very common. Some were probably ignored as scarce escapes and there are again no breeding records. There are no references in Parr (1972) or in *BLA*. Glegg (1935) and Clark (1984) give a few records but none in Surrey.

Vice-county since 1970. There was a full-winged bird at Silvermere on 2nd November 1973. Towards the end of the 20th century, reports became more frequent and the first breeding record was in central Surrey at Effingham Fish Ponds in 1974. East Surrey breeding records seem to have been generated by an introduction on private land near Oxted. Research by N. J. Donnithorne (pers. comm.) suggests that pinioned birds were brought into a local estate in 1991 and that they bred in most years up to 1998, when up to 15 adults were present. This colony was probably the source of full-winged birds that colonised four other local places, where they later bred, and used a variety of nest sites. One pair nested on a flat roof and another on an island. K. E. Noble found a pair nesting in tree holes by Townland Pond in 1996, where there was an attempt in 1997. By 1998, about 20 chicks a year were being produced at one of these sites.

There were breeding and non-breeding records from 19 sites in 1999: Apps Court Green, Barn Elms, Bay Pond (Godstone), Burgess Park, Burpham, Esher, Guildford, Hersham Gravel Pit, Hurst Green, Kew Gardens, Lammas Lands (Godalming), Oxted, Queen Elizabeth II Reservoir, Reigate Priory, Richmond Park, Stoke Lake, Thorpe Water Park, Unstead Sewage Farm and Walton Reservoirs.

A female with five tiny young was seen in the Berkshire part of the lakes at the Royal Military Academy, Camberley in 2000. It is not known if the nest was on the Berkshire side or in Surrey. There were three definite breeding records elsewhere in the same year. A pair with three juveniles was seen on the Thames at Shepperton (the Spelthorne family, below?), two adults and five goslings were seen at Sutton Place, Guildford and a pair raised two young at Thorpe Water Park.

Family parties were seen at Kew Gardens in 2001, 2002 and 2003. Breeding was recorded at Sutton Place in 2001, Burhill Golf Club in 2001-03 and Kew Gardens in 2001. Young were raised in an owl nesting box on a farm at Thorpe in 2001, 2002 and 2003. Family parties were seen in Richmond Park in 2002 and 2003 and at Sutton Place in 2002 and 2003. A pair fledged six young at Secretts Garden Centre, Milford in 2005 as did another pair at Eagle Pond, Clapham in 2007.

Other places where Egyptian Geese have been seen since 1970 include Beddington Sewage Farm, Chertsey, Claremont, Dorking, Earlswood Lakes, Egham Swan Sanctuary, Frensham, Frimley Gravel Pits, Gatton, Godstone, Holmethorpe, Island Barn Reservoir, Leigh Place, Lightwater Country Park, Old Woking, Papercourt Gravel Pits, Reigate Priory, South Norwood and Tongham Gravel Pit.

Spelthorne. Egyptian Geese were occasional at Shepperton in the 1980s (*Shepp. BR*) but have increased considerably. A pair with six juveniles was seen at Ferris Meadow Gravel Pit on 24th March 2000 and adults with young were seen there again in 2001 and 2002. They nested on the ground on a small wooded island (H. W. Evans). Ten were seen on Shepperton Golf Course on 3rd February 2003. A flock of 45 at the same place in January 2004 appears to be the largest flock so far for Surrey.

Movements and longevity. One ringed as a bird of the year in Bushy Park, Hampton on 7th

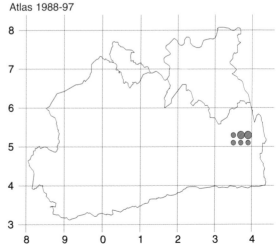

Atlas 1988-97

July 2000 was found at Stoke, 22 km south one year and ten months later, on 15th May 2002. Another Bushy Park bird, ringed on 26th June 2001, was found at Sunbury, 7 km away and over three years later, on 13th July 2004.

Ruddy Shelduck   *Tadorna ferruginea*

Rare, feral birds have bred

Breeds from the Balkans east to Manchuria and with a mainly resident population in northwest Africa. More northern birds winter mainly in the Middle East. There are infrequent irruptions into Europe. Introduced to Britain in the 19th century. Escaped or feral birds have confused the records of birds from abroad. Most of the Ruddy Shelducks found in Britain are thought to be escaped or feral. The occurrence of genuinely wild birds in the past 50 years has yet to be proved to the satisfaction of the BOU Records Committee, though there are a few older records. There have, however, been significant European influxes, including the appearance of some 262 individuals in Finland and Scandinavia in 1994 (Vinicombe and Harrop, 1999), a year that also saw flocks of up to 12 in northern Britain and smaller numbers elsewhere.

Early Surrey history. There is a pre-1885 record of a possibly wild bird found dead at Farnham (*SALEC*). Bucknill mentions two shot at Ripley on the 22nd October 1892. This was a year of very severe drought in southeast and southern Europe and when at least 118 others were recorded in the British Isles (Vinicombe and Harrop, 1999), a fact which Bucknill does not mention and may not have known, when he wrote that they were 'perhaps not really wild specimens'. In Bucknill's time the Charterhouse Collection held two, one of the Ripley birds and a male found dead in a ditch at Farnham, but they are not now there.

Breeding. There are two breeding records for 1991, presumably of feral birds. The first is of a pair seen with four large juveniles on June 29th at Chertsey Weir, after earlier sightings in the area. The nest site is not known. The second is of a pair at Queen Mary Reservoir, Spelthorne, which is less than three km to the northeast. Present 'for much of the year', they nested in July, raising three young (Evans, 1992). Given the reported date of nesting, this must be a second pair. The London Bird Report for 1991, incidentally, gives the Queen Mary details as two on February 16th and three from 10th August to 6th September and does not mention nesting. Vinicombe and Harrop give the year for the Chertsey record as 1992 but this is an error (Vinicombe, 2000). The 1994 national influx, of whatever origin, included six individuals in Surrey, at Beddington, Holmethorpe and Staines.

Since 1995 and up to at least 2003 there was a mixed flock of Ruddy, Cape and Paradise Shelducks in the Walton-on-Thames area. These have apparently hybridised, producing offspring of somewhat puzzling appearance - mainly resembling the Paradise species and discussed further in the annexes. Birds presumably from this group have been seen as far away as Stoke Lake, at Guildford.

Where found from 1975 to 2001. There were 145 vice-county Ruddy Shelduck bird months from 1975 to 2001. The birds were seen at Barn Elms (1981, 1984, 1986-89, 1991), Beddington Sewage Farm (1982, 1987, 1989-90, 1992, 1994), Brockwell Park (1983),

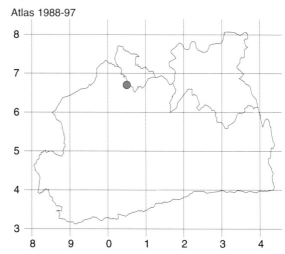

Atlas 1988-97

Carshalton (1983), Chertsey (1991, 1996), Claremont (1996), Dulwich (1992), Frensham (1977, 1992-93), Frimley Gravel Pits (1989), Hedgecourt (1984), Hersham (1997, 1999), Holmethorpe (1994), Island Barn Reservoir (26th April 2001), Kew (1979, 1984, 1984-86, 1989, 2000), Papercourt (1977, 1991), Queen Elizabeth II Reservoir (1995-98, 2000), Richmond Park (1981), Stoke Lake (1997, 2000), Thames at Westminster (1988), Thorpe (2000), Unstead Sewage Farm (1995), Walton-on-Thames/Reservoirs (1995-98), Wandsworth (1982-83, 1986) and Windsor Great Park (1999) and in Spelthorne at Laleham (1990), Perry Oaks Sewage Farm (3rd July 1994), Queen Mary Gravel Pits (1990), Queen Mary Reservoir (1991-92, three from 20th July 1994 into August), Shepperton (1997), Staines Reservoirs (1990, 29th May to 16th July 1994, 1997) and Wraysbury Reservoir (2000).

Calendar. The 145 vice-county Ruddy Shelduck bird months from 1975 to 2001 were distributed as in the table. This shows noticeable spring and autumn peaks, which would be more prominent if several long-staying birds were excluded. The peaks would be consistent with some movement through the county at these seasons.

Bird months 1975-2001

	Jan	Feb	Mar	Apr	May	Jun	Jul	Aug	Sep	Oct	Nov	Dec	Total
Vice-county	7	10	14	20	19	8	7	13	11	13	13	10	**145**

Shelduck (Common Shelduck) *Tadorna tadorna*
Scarce migrant and rare breeding resident

Breeds from the British Isles east to Siberia. In the mid-19th century the British breeding population was limited to Scotland after a contraction of range that may have been due to persecution, but an extension of range was under way by 1900. Sussex was colonised in 1904 (*Historical Atlas*). National breeding numbers are thought to have doubled since 1970 but wintering numbers have been falling. There is a major moult migration from the British Isles and elsewhere to the German Waddenzee area of the Heligoland Bight in June and July, after which many return to their breeding areas. Winter ringing recoveries in Hampshire and Sussex have included several birds which were ringed in nearby continental countries during the breeding season.

Early Surrey history. Remains found at Chaucer House, Southwark, during an excavation were judged to be Post-Roman, but were not aged more precisely. Newman (1849) listed Shelducks as winter visitors to the Godalming district without further comment. One killed at Frensham Pond (*SALEC*) was in the Charterhouse Collection in Shaw's time and might be the bird held there in 2001, of unknown provenance. Others in Bucknill are one shot at Ashtead (*c*.1894), several on the Mole near Fetcham (undated) and a possibly escaped bird on the Thames (summer of 1898).

1900 to 1970. There were six at Staines Reservoirs in severe weather on 31st December 1906, the first record for Spelthorne. Lesser numbers were recorded there in the autumn of 1928 (two), in 1929-33 and 18th October 1934 (one all year) and 1936 (one all year). Shelduck were recorded from Queen Mary Reservoir in 1929-30 and 1934-35 and eight were there on 6th May 1936. They became fairly regular in Spelthorne after this date.

Bentham heard of five at Hedgecourt on 6th March 1914 and saw two at Godstone on 19th December 1920, where one had been found dead in December 1914. There were eight at Barn Elms Reservoirs on 18th September 1926 and twelve there in August 1929, with smaller numbers in other years. Shelduck were recorded at Brooklands Sewage Farm on 22nd March 1931 (one), 23rd April 1933 (a pair), 31st May and 14th June 1934 (a pair) and May 1936 (three pairs and an odd bird). There are further records from Barn Elms, Battersea (1968), Beddington Sewage Farm (from 1933), Chertsey (1967), Cutt Mill (1966), Dulwich (1961), Enton (1957, 1964), Earlswood Sewage Farm (1970), Frensham (1935, 1947-50, 1953, most years 1956-70), Gatton (1958), Guildford Sewage Farm (from 1942), over the Hog's

Back (1960), Island Barn Reservoir (many records, a party of 16 in 1957), Kew Gardens (1966), Merstham (from 1945), Mitcham Common (1958), Molesey Sewage Farm (1960), Papercourt (1968, 1969), Queen Elizabeth II Reservoir (from 1963), Richmond Park (from 1954), Send Gravel Pits (1964), Sutton Place (1946), Thorpe (1969), Walton Reservoirs, Wandsworth and Wimbledon Common (1967). Possible escapes were seen in other areas.

Where seen since 1970. There have been many records since 1970, from sites including Battersea Park, the Blackwater Industrial Estate, Broadwater, Burgess Park, Busbridge, Chertsey, Effingham Fish Ponds, Enton, Frensham, Frimley Gravel Pits, Kew Gardens, Kingston, Moat Pond, Papercourt Gravel Pits, Richmond Park, the River Thames, Snowdenham, South Norwood Country Park, Surbiton, the Surrey Docks, Tilhill, Vachery, Wimbledon Common, Wimbledon Park Lake and Wrecclesham Floods. Shelduck are currently most often seen around and near the reservoirs at Barnes and Walton, at suitable gravel and sand pits such as Hersham, Holmethorpe and Papercourt and at sewage farms, especially Beddington. Shelduck are sometimes seen on lakes and pits such as Gatton, Frensham, Stoke and Thorpe. They are casual visitors elsewhere,

Breeding. Breeding was not established in Surrey until 1984, when a pair was seen with recently fledged young at Walton Reservoirs, which was the site of several later breeding records. Sites since 1984 were these: *Beddington Sewage Farm*: a pair raised two young in 1989, one brood seen in 2004; *River Wandle near Beddington Sewage Farm*: a pair bred in 1993, no young survived; *Holmethorpe Sand Pits*: a pair with nine juveniles on 13th June 1987, bred in 1988 (*BHSP*), a pair with nine juveniles on 13th June 1993 (breeding site not known) and in 1994 a pair hatched nine young of which three fledged; *Island Barn Reservoir*: two pairs in 1992 (probably from Walton Reservoirs); *Molesey Gravel Pit*: A pair with a juvenile on 6th

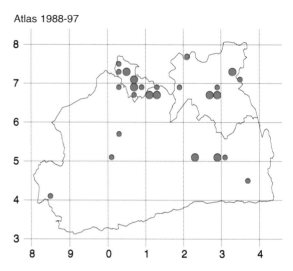

Atlas 1988-97

July 1986 possibly bred in the area; *Queen Elizabeth II Reservoir*: a pair with nine small young on 15th June 1990 'had probably bred there', a pair with two young on 4th August 1994, three pairs bred in 1997; a pair with eight juveniles on 13th June 2002; ten, including eight juveniles, on 20th July 2003; *Walton Reservoirs*: bred 1991, 1992 (young seen), 1993 (a pair with six young on 1st July); *Watermeads, Mitcham*: a pair with seven juveniles on 19th May 1993.

In Spelthorne, Shelducks bred at *Perry Oaks Sewage Farm* in 1983, 1989, 1991-93 and 1998; *Queen Mary Reservoir* in 1974-77, 1979, 1983-84, 1987, 1989, 1991-93, 1996 and 2001; *Stanwell Moor* by the late 1980s (Hewlett); at *Staines Reservoirs* in 1994-95 and at *Wraysbury Reservoir* in 1987-89, 1994-95 and 1998. Juveniles of unknown origin were seen at King George VI Reservoir in 1980-81, Perry Oaks Sewage Farm in 1981-82, at Staines Reservoirs in 1985, at Stanwell Moor Gravel Pits in 1988 and at Wraysbury Reservoir in 1982.

Full-winged feral birds have been in Surrey for many years (see *e.g. LBR* for 1970), and may account for some of the birds seen in the breeding season. Feral birds bred at Dulwich in 1994 and 1995.

Large counts. Shelduck numbers have been increasing and the biggest counts have been made since 1990:

Barn Elms Reservoirs: 12 + 22 (two flocks), 24th February 1965

Beddington Sewage Farm: 34 over, 25th September 1987

Beddington Sewage Farm: 21, 14th May 1989
Frensham Great Pond: 16, 4th January 1996
Hersham Gravel Pit: 11, 22nd May 1988
Island Barn Reservoir: 16, 13th April 1957
Holmethorpe Sand Pits: 10, 3rd June 1988
Queen Elizabeth II Reservoir: 14 plus nine
    young, May 1997
Richmond Park: 10, 30th January 1994
Rodborough Common: 20+ over, 23rd January
    1966 (Clark, 1984)

Walton Reservoirs: 51, 13th May 1992
Spelthorne
King George VI Reservoir: 60, 15th February 2002
Perry Oaks Sewage Farm: 48, May 1998
Queen Mary Gravel Pits: 16, 10th January 1988
Queen Mary Reservoir: 33, 11th March 1993
Shepperton Gravel Pits: ten, 20th March 1991
Staines Reservoirs: 68, May and June 1994
Stanwell Moor Gravel Pits: ten, 22nd April 1996
Wraysbury Reservoir: 52, 14th September 1987

Calendar and movements. Occurrences during the year are irregular but there is some evidence, for example in the large counts, of a spring passage from February to May. Shelducks are scarcest in June and July, when British adult birds elsewhere begin their moult migration. An autumn passage peaking in September may be connected with the return of British birds from their moulting grounds. Wintering parties on Surrey reservoirs and gravel pits probably include migrants from more northern and eastern populations as well as British birds. Bird-ringing has not yielded any specific information about the movements of Shelducks seen in Surrey.

Mandarin (Mandarin Duck)   *Aix galericulata*

Moderately common breeding resident.
Probably increasing in Britain. The current home of native Mandarin Ducks is in the Far East, China, Japan and Korea, where they inhabit mature deciduous forests in which there are streams, rivers and lakes. They nest in holes in trees. Mandarins are migratory and dispersive in their native range (*MA*). The Far East population has been declining because of deforestation and until recently it was thought that the feral colony in Britain was now of sufficient size to be of world significance, almost certainly exceeding the number in China according to the *New Atlas*. Davies (1985) speculated that the British population might be the biggest in the world. Marchant *et al.* (1990) quote Lever, *in litt.*, for the view that the Japanese population still exceeded that of Britain though. More recent estimates, cited in Brown and Green (Birds in England, 2005), also put the numbers in China, Japan and Korea higher, at about 70,000 birds. The first record of an escaped bird came from Berkshire in May 1866 (Lever, 1977).

Mandarins have been kept in captivity in Britain since shortly before 1745, in which year George Edwards made a drawing of one in the gardens of Sir Matthew Decker, on Richmond Green in Surrey (Edwards, 1743-51). Decker, a director of the East India Company and High Sheriff for Surrey from 1729, had been importing exotic birds, animals and plants to his Surrey home for some years (Lever, 1977). The *Historical Atlas* gives the date as 1747, a small inconsistency with the Lever account which may have had something to do with publication delays. None were successfully bred in captivity until 1834, when two pairs that the London Zoo had bought for £70 four years earlier produced young. The Duke of Bedford established a free-flying colony at Woburn from around 1900 and this was followed by attempts by others in the London parks and elsewhere.

Early Surrey history. The most important British release was by Alfred Ezra in Surrey at Foxwarren Park, Cobham. Six pairs were introduced there in 1928. They had been given by M. Jean and were left full-winged and they are believed to be the origin of the present wild population. An unstated number seen by D. Goodwin on the River Bourne, near Virginia Water in 1929 is the first record of free-flying birds and there was a colony at Virginia Water itself by 1932 (South, 1980). There was one at Staines Reservoirs on 18th November 1938.

Since 1940. Mandarins bred at Thorpe in 1946, the first for the London area (Hewlett) and a family party was seen on the Surrey side of the Thames at Runnymede in 1953. The Surrey and East Berkshire population was estimated at 400 in 1951 (Savage, 1952). An empty nest was found at Wisley Common in 1958. Mandarins bred at Addlestone in 1959 and in Claremont and Painshill Parks in 1967, when an old-established colony was found on the Mole at Leigh. A family party was seen at Fetcham in 1968. I. R. Beames found 55-60 pairs on or near the Mole from Esher to Mickleham in 1969. A nest with eggs was found at Gatton in 1970 and a pair bred at Holmethorpe in 1976. In central Surrey, Mandarins were breeding in the Clandon area by 1973. Mandarins were not proved to breed in Richmond Park until 1987. In the south, Mandarin bred at Vann lake in 1968 (Blaker log). In the southwest, Mandarin were first recorded at Cutt Mill in 1965 and then at Warren Mere in 1968. Breeding was proved at Forked Pond in 1974, Tilford in 1976, Peper Harow in 1977 and Frensham in 1979 (Clark, 1984). Colonisation in west Surrey may have been accelerated by the release of birds at Busbridge Lakes in 1972. The site has been of national significance, with an average peak count of 40 birds in the five years to April 2003 (*Wetland Bird Survey* 2001-03). Of the 231 tetrads in northeast Surrey, 12% were found to hold territories in the 1968-72 Atlas survey and 16% in the 1988-97 Atlas, showing further colonisation in that area.

In Spelthorne, there was one at King George VI Reservoir on 16th October 1962. Two drakes were seen at Shepperton in 1968. Other sightings followed and pairs bred at Staines Moor in 1977 and at Shepperton Gravel Pits in 1992.

Population size. The Winter Atlas found partial survey counts and estimates totalling 356 birds in 1981-84, similar to the number of Gadwall and mostly in the 10 km squares SU93, SU96 and TQ15. Mandarin were found in Common Birds Censuses from 1970, territories rising to 0.04 per ten hectares by 2000, grossing up to a Surrey total of around 900 pairs by the end of the period. A thorough analysis of the Mandarin distribution in Surrey, based on historical records for 302 sites at which Mandarins had sometime or other been found, was made by A. K. Davies (Davies, 1986). The majority of breeding season birds were in the 10 km squares SU96, SU97, TQ05 and TQ15. This is similar to the distribution found in the 1988-97 SBC Atlas survey, where Mandarin were found in 131 tetrads, although by the Atlas date they had achieved a greater penetration in the south and southwest. Davies estimated the population size at 1,400-2,000 in the breeding season and 1,400-2,300 in the winter. His estimates look high compared with most other figures, but broadly consistent with the Common Birds Census estimate. Mandarins are difficult to survey and likely to be underestimated in casual observations.

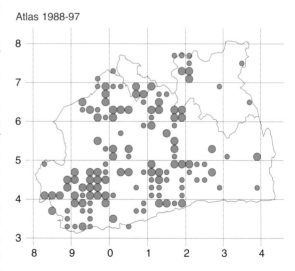

Atlas 1988-97

The BTO's Breeding Bird Survey picked up a total of only 106 adults in the whole of 1994-2004, grossing up to an average breeding season population size of around 160. This must be too low, since the winter maximum counts for the ten main sites alone totalled over 900 birds. The Davies estimate may, after all, prove to be a good guide. Surrey has had three nationally significant sites for Mandarins. Average annual wildfowl count maxima from 1994/95 to 1998/99 at these were 74 at Virginia Water, 55 at Cutt Mill Ponds and 14 at Thursley Lake. More recently Busbridge Lakes and Gatton Park have come into prominence.

Breeding behaviour. Some of the Asian sites in which Mandarins are found, such as parkland around Tokyo, are uncannily like Surrey strongholds such as Virginia Water and the ponds at Cutt Mill, with the low branches of deciduous trees and rhododendrons sweeping down to the waterside to provide cover for resting birds. Oak and Ash trees provide typical Surrey nest sites. Mandarins will also use suitably-placed nestboxes. The Surrey Bird Report for 1986 contains a photograph of an occupied box. Their success may be due to a diet preference as well as a similar habitat. Marchant *et al.* give the favoured foods as aquatic insects in summer and acorns, chestnuts and beechmast in winter, enabling Mandarins to exploit a vacant ecological niche. The food preference and success in nestboxes may bring Mandarins into competition with the hole-nesting and insectivorous Goldeneyes in Scotland (P. Cosgrove as quoted in *Bird Watching*, October 2003).

Nest holes are sometimes a mile or more from water (Davies, 1985). The normal clutch size is 9-12, rarely 14 (*BWP*). P. A. D. Hollom watched 14 ducklings emerge in seven minutes from a nestbox in his Hydestile garden on 21st May 2003 (pers. comm.). A female with 18 ducklings, thought to be one day old, was seen on the Tillingbourne at Chilworth on 7th April 2004 by Dr E. F. J. Garcia, who considered that the female may have been a victim of egg-dumping or had perhaps accidentally acquired members of another brood.

A lost native? The discovery of a possible fossil Mandarin bone in Norfolk (Langley, 1998), has put the known Surrey history of the species in a completely new light. It would appear that before the last Ice Age, Mandarins may have bred across Europe and Asia from Britain to China. Extending glaciation could have first divided the population into two and then wiped out the western birds. The Mandarin may not, therefore, have been introduced to Surrey in the 1930s as an alien, but reintroduced as a lost native.

Large counts. The largest counts come from west Surrey but others are well distributed along the Mole and Wey valleys:

Betchworth Park: 60, 3rd-20th October 1986
Bookham Common: 20-30, 3rd January 1970
Buckland, Rectory Lane: 120, 1st May 1994
Buckland Sand Pits: 105, 27th August 1983
Burwood Park: 48, 2nd December 2001
Busbridge Lakes: 72, 25th January 2004
Claremont Park, Esher: 92, 15th and 27th November 1997
Cutt Mill: 225, 22nd December 2001
Enton: 50, 22nd October 2002
Epsom Common Stew Ponds: 133, 10th October 1995
Esher Common: 38, 27th January 1980
Frensham: 28, 21st November 1998
Gatton Lake: 25, December 1995
Hurst Gate Lake, Milford: 120, 15th December 1981

Hurst Green: 30, January 1983 (*LBR*)
Kew Gardens: 33, 6th November 1998
Ottershaw: 26, 8th October 1984
Painshill Park: *c*.40, 27th October 1979
Pickhurst: 21, 18th September 1976
Pudmore Pond: 91 over, 11th October 1987
River Mole at Cobham: 40, 27th October 1979 (*LBR*)
Send Grove: 23, 15th January 1978
Vachery Pond: 64, 31st January 1996
Virginia Water: 180, 2nd November 1993;
Waterloo Pond: 30, maximum in 2000
Witley Park: 180, 17th November 1986, 15th February 1987
Woodlands Park (Leatherhead): 35, 7th January 1979 (*LBR*)

Movements and longevity. Three ringing recoveries show only local movements but lives of up to 5 years eleven months:

Ringed		Recovered		Distance/age
Ottershaw	16th May 1981	Ottershaw	10th May 1987	5 years 11 months
Ottershaw	16th May 1981	Ottershaw	12th May 1986	
Berkshire	13th Feb 1994	Egham	18th Mar 1996	16 km

There are several other recoveries. Mandarins at Virginia Water were severely affected by the frost of early 1963 (S. R. South, *Middle-Thames Naturalist 23:4*).

Wigeon (Eurasian Wigeon)   *Anas penelope*

Moderately common winter visitor

The breeding range extends from Iceland east through northern Europe to Siberia. In Britain, since the late 19th century, the range has extended south from Scotland with sporadic breeding (possibly of escapes) through eastern England to Kent. Winter numbers in northwest Europe were increasing from 1975 to at least 1994 (*MA*).

Early Surrey history. Roman remains from the Winchester Palace site at Southwark, dated to 70-120 AD, and four other remains from dates between 1440 and 1650 from the same place suggest early acceptability as a food item. Wigeon seem to have been fairly common as winter visitors at the beginning of the 19th century, appearing on small ponds such as those at Cutt Mill and near Godalming. Meyer (1842) mentioned flocks on flooded meadows near Chertsey. They became scarcer as the century progressed. At Pen Ponds, they were uncommon winter visitors from 1883. Bucknill gave no dated records but mentioned occurrences at Epsom, Forked Pond ('recent seasons'), Frensham (frequent), Milford House Pond, Painshill Park and Poynter's (both Cobham), Reigate (winter of 1899-1900), near Sutton and Witley (one male). Larger numbers appeared in cold winters. One of Bucknill's correspondents had seen a flock of 250 at Frensham Little Pond in February. Scarcity is a relative term. A bird of unknown provenance in the Charterhouse Museum in 2001 might have been one of the two specimens, from the Wey and the Thames, that were there in Bucknill's time. Wigeon were at Staines Reservoirs early in the 20th century (Kerr, 1906).

Since 1900. Wigeon were uncommon winter visitors to Pen Ponds until at least 1936. By 1970, up to 30 were being recorded from Frensham, Godstone and Hedgecourt, 50-80 at Walton Reservoirs, where they could graze on the grass between reservoirs (Parr) and 200 were being found at Queen Elizabeth II Reservoir.

Wintering numbers continued to increase in the last decades of the 20th century and the largest count of all, 720, was made at Walton Reservoirs on 10th February 1996. Maxima at the other main sites are detailed below. Site maxima (not all on the same day) peaked at 1,048 at 20 sites in January 1996.

Breeding. Stafford said that Wigeon had been *known, but rarely, to breed in west Surrey* but no documented instances have been traced.

Calendar. In a typical season, small numbers arrive in September, gather at up to 30 sites by the end of the year with the main winter arrivals in November and December. Numbers remain high in January and February but the birds have mostly gone by the end of March. Autumn arrivals may come as early as August (2nd August 1970 at Barn Elms, 15th August 1964 at Hersham) and a few may linger into June, as for example at Barn Elms on 13th June 1925 and the Thursley area ponds in 1994. There have been July records from Barn Elms (1956), Stockbridge Pond (30th July 1974, possibly an escape), Frensham (1990) and Walton Reservoirs (1999). There was one at Staines on 3rd May 1925. Up to three pairs were at King George VI Reservoir on 20th and 27th May, 24th June and 1st July 1951 (*BB, 45:419*). A pair summered at Barn Elms in 1976 and a female with a damaged wing summered at Holmethorpe in 1997.

Large counts. The severe winters of the 1960s affected Wigeon less than some other ducks and the largest counts date from the 1980s or later:

Badshot Lea: 34, 12th December 2004
Barn Elms: 200+, 28th October 2003
Beddington Sewage Farm: 101 in three flocks, 5th November 1984
Coleford Farm Gravel Pit: 58, 11th and 18th January 1997
Frensham: 53, 31st January 1985
Frimley Gravel Pits: 155, 22nd January 2005 (K. B. Wills)
Hersham Gravel Pit: 76, 9th February 2001
Holmethorpe Sand Pits: 67, January 1997
Island Barn Reservoir: 50, 10th January 1985
Longside Lake: 209, 16th October 1998
Stoke Lake: 128, 6th March 2003
Papercourt Gravel Pits: 54, 4th January 1986
Pen Ponds: 192, November 1990

Queen Elizabeth II Reservoir: *c.*200, 18th February 1962
Sutton Place: 282, 21st January 2005
Thorpe Water Park: 323, 21st February 1999
Tongham Gravel Pit: 102, 15th January 2006
Unstead Sewage Farm: 42, 20th January 1985
Walton Reservoirs: 720, 10th February 1996
Spelthorne
King George VI Reservoir: 823, 8th February 1986 (a London area record at the time)
Perry Oaks Sewage Farm: 120, March 1999
Queen Mary Reservoir: 280, 20th January 1987
Staines Moor: *c.*530, 18th January 1985
Staines Reservoirs: 759, 18th January 1987
Stanwell Moor: 420 over, 8th October 2002
Wraysbury Reservoir: 180, 19th January 1985

Movements and longevity. A Wigeon ringed at Vlijmen, in the Netherlands, on 12th January 1993 was recovered at Thorpe Green, 402 km west, on 18th October 1995.

American Wigeon   *Anas americana*

One

Breeds in North America, wintering south to Panama. British records have been scattered across the British Isles, most often in Cornwall and County Kerry. They have occurred throughout the year, with a well-marked peak in October and November. Full-winged birds are not uncommon in wildfowl collections.

Surrey. An adult male was seen at the Surrey Docks on 29th August 1973 (R. E. Alderton, *BB*, *67:316*).

Gadwall   *Anas strepera*

Moderately common winter visitor. Has bred. Most immigrant wintering birds are from eastern Europe (MA).

The breeding range extends through the temperate regions of North America, Europe and Asia and may have increased during the 20th century. Gadwall were regarded as rare in the 19th century (*Historical Atlas*). The British breeding population seems to have been started by introductions in Norfolk from 1849 onwards and is increasing.

Early Surrey history. Newman (1849) listed Gadwall as winter visitors to the Godalming district without further comment. In 2001 the Charterhouse Collection still held a Surrey specimen, possibly the male shot at Elstead in the spring of 1850 or the female, once in the same collection, that was killed at the Hammer Pond around the same date (*SALEC*). One was shot in early spring (year not given) on the Mole (Jordan, 1895).

Since 1900. Bentham saw four near Lingfield in August 1910, there was an adult at Frensham on 12th November 1920 (Shaw) and there were single birds at Godstone on 27th November 1932, in March and December 1933, January 1934, April 1935, March/April 1937 and in April 1938. Gadwall were first recorded at Staines Reservoirs on 22nd April 1928 (Glegg, not in *BLA*) and then on 29th October 1931.

Fifteen locally-raised full-winged birds left St James's Park after the lake was drained in 1932 and early London area records, such as that of one at Staines Reservoirs on 22nd October and 24th December 1932 and one at Richmond Park from 14th November to 27th December 1935, tended to be regarded as likely to be from this source.

Gadwall were seen at Guildford Sewage Farm, Send and Frensham in 1945 and, whatever their origin, by then they were becoming more common. Even so, the next at Frensham were not until 1954, 1958, 1963 and 1971, after which they were seen in most years. A count of 49 at Barn Elms on 11th February 1968 was the largest for the London area as a whole up to that time. The main wintering sites during the 1970s were Barn Elms, Lonsdale Road Reservoir and Richmond Park but more recently significant winter flocks have built up at the Walton group of reservoirs and sometimes at Frimley and Thorpe. Smaller numbers had been seen at Ash Vale Gravel Pits, Badshot Lea, Beddington Sewage Farm, Busbridge, Coleford Farm Gravel Pit, Cutt Mill, Effingham Fish Ponds, Enton, Epsom Common, Forked Pond, Gatton, Godstone, Hammer Pond (Thursley, first 1987), Hedgecourt, Holmethorpe, Kew Gardens, Long Ditton, Moat Pond, Mytchett Gravel Pit, Papercourt, Royal Common Pond (1992), Stoke Water Meadows (from 1975), Sutton Green (1974), Tongham Gravel Pit, Virginia Water, Warren Mere (Thursley), Wimbledon Common, Winkworth Arboretum, Witley Park Lake, Wrecclesham Floods and other sites by 1997. The range is still increasing and there were records from over 30 sites in 2000. Gadwall are present in the county throughout the year but the largest numbers are in winter, when there may be a total of up to 500 at the main sites.

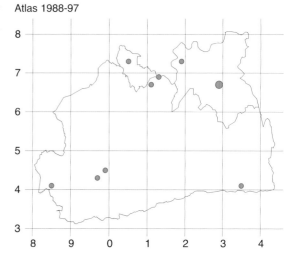

Atlas 1988-97

Breeding. Gadwall first bred in Surrey at Barn Elms Reservoirs in 1936 and they may have originated from the St James's Park stock. A pair nested at Beddington in 1938 (*LBR*) and 1939 and possibly in other years (*BLA*). Broods were seen at Lonsdale Road Reservoir in 1942 and 1945. Breeding continued at least intermittently at Barn Elms until the 1960s. After an absence, a pair bred in 1969, when ten ducklings were seen. Juveniles were seen in 1996 and there was an attempt in 2000. A pair bred there in 2001. Pairs bred at Godstone in 1967 (Leigh Place) and 1969 (Bay Pond), at Chertsey Reservoir

(1996) and at Walton Reservoirs (2000). Half-grown young were seen at Molesey Gravel Pit in 2003. A brood was seen at Beddington Sewage Farm in 2004. In Spelthorne, a pair bred at Perry Oaks Sewage Farm in 1997 and a brood was seen there in 1998, followed by two in 1999 and three in 2000. A pair bred on Stanwell Moor in 2003.

Large counts

Barn Elms: 240, 22nd December 2001
Beddington Sewage Farm: 92, 12th January 1999
Epsom Common: 20, 11th February 1989
Frimley Gravel Pits: 112, 15th February 2004
  (S. P. Peters)
Holmethorpe: 35, 22nd December 2002
Island Barn Reservoir: 129, 7th December 1998
Longside Lake: 178, 16th October 1998
Lonsdale Road Reservoir: 208, 5th January 2003
Papercourt Gravel Pits: 123, January 2003
Pen Ponds, Richmond Park: 230, 8th January
  2000

Queen Elizabeth II Reservoir: 160, 3rd January
  2002 (S. J. Spooner)
Thorpe Water Park: 285, December 1991
Walton Reservoirs: 298, 27th December 1996
Spelthorne
Large counts since 1970 have been:
King George VI Reservoir: 379, 16th November
  1986
Perry Oaks Sewage Farm: 80, September 1999
Queen Mary Gravel Pits: 81, February 1991
Queen Mary Reservoir: 164 in February 1986
Shepperton Gravel Pits: 167, November 1989
Staines Reservoir: 200, September 1997
Wraysbury Reservoir: 99, 12th February 1984

Gadwall are among the waterfowl that have a degree of protection under environmental legislation. Thorpe Water Park has been a nationally important site for them, with an average peak count of 249 in the five years to April 2004 (*Wetland Bird Survey* 2003-04). There were nationally significant numbers at Lonsdale Road Reservoir in 2001/02 and 2002/03 (*Wetland Bird Survey 2001-03*). Much higher numbers have been recorded at Thorpe, including 252 there in January 1993 and 285 in December 1991. Numbers are lower at Longside Lake, which was also a nationally important site for Gadwall in the 1990s.

Movements and longevity. There is one foreign ringing recovery, of a bird ringed at Dobersdorfer See, Plon, Germany on 13th September 1992 (*LBR*) and seen at Thorpe, 727 km away, on 21st October 1992. On November 26th, this bird was seen in Kent, at Sevenoaks.

Teal (Eurasian Teal) *Anas crecca*

Common winter visitor. Irregular breeder

Breeds in the more northerly parts of Europe and Asia and is replaced in North America by the Green-winged Teal *A. carolinensis*, until recently treated as a race of *A. crecca*. Teal bred in most parts of Britain in the 19th century and may have increased their range in spite of loss of habitat. More recently, further loss of habitat has led to a decline in southeast England. Most autumn immigrants are from northern Europe (*MA*).

Early Surrey history. Excavations in the Surrey part of the London area have located 20 dated sets of remains, ten of them dating back to Roman Britain. Four were at 104 Borough High Street, Southwark, with dates of 50-70 AD (two), 70-100 and 350-400. Three were in a London Bridge escalator shaft, with dates of 50-160, 70-100 and 120-140. One in a well at Fennings Wharf, Southwark was dated at 200-400 and another at Hibernia Wharf was put at 250-275. The tenth was at Beddington Sewage Farm. Bermondsey Abbey produced remains dated at 1140-1200, 1350-1500, 1480-1600 and 1630-1680. Remains from Chaucer House, Southwark, were dated at 1500-1700. Five from Winchester Palace fell within the period 1440 to 1600. Teal would have been hunted for food and the exact provenance of all of these birds is uncertain, but they could have been procured locally if not wild.

Newman (1849) described Teal as winter visitors to the Godalming district, occasionally staying to breed. Phillip Crowley had many clutches from the Churt district. Like Newman, Bucknill offered no dated records but said they had often been seen around Bagshot, Farnham and Godalming and at least once at Weybridge in the breeding season and that they had bred near Epsom in about 1880 and in Surrey in 1900. He said they were fairly plentiful as winter visitors on the upper Wey and in West Surrey and that up to 30 might be seen at Frensham in hard weather. Power mentioned eight over Clapham Common on 12th July 1897, three on Dulwich Park Lake on 6th October 1898 and a flock of 20 or more over Peckham on 8th October 1907. A few were wintering on Staines Reservoirs by 1906 (Kerr). A count of 200 at Staines Reservoirs on 16th January 1927 (London Naturalist) was unusual for the period. There was a pair at Brooklands Sewage Farm in May 1936 (Hollom, 1937).

Breeding up to 1950. Hudson (1898) wrote that Teal had reared young in Richmond Park but Collenette thought this was an exceptional case and that the birds might even have been pinioned. They were no longer nesting in Richmond Park in 1906 (Mouritz). Bunyard found a nest with ten eggs, most of which fledged, in heather 150 yards from water and presumably in west Surrey, in 1912. Baynes knew of a marshy moor where, he said, five or more pairs bred annually (*BB, 6:190*). Bunyard (1924) said they were still breeding in fair numbers. A pair bred near Cobham in 1930 (*BLA, London Naturalist*). Two pairs probably tried to nest near Guildford Sewage Farm in 1944. There was a strong possibility of a nesting attempt at Guildford Sewage Farm in 1945 (Harrison, 1947) and a female with ten young was seen there in 1957. Teal nested at Pudmore in 1939 and 1946 (CNHS, 1959) and bred at Hedgecourt (an unusual site) in 1947. E. C. Rowberry found a female with three small young in the Colne valley on 28th May 1931(*BB, 25:134*). This was the first breeding record for Middlesex but might have been north of Spelthorne.

Breeding after 1950. A nest with 18 eggs, of which 15 hatched, was found on Epsom Sewage Farm in 1951. Teal bred at Frensham Little Pond in 1953 (brood) and 1954 (eggs) and probably in 1956 (HNHS). A pair nested at Barn Elms Reservoirs in 1956, fledging nine young. Young were seen at Wisley Common in 1959 and 1960. A west Surrey nest with ten eggs in 1963 was predated. Unpublished reports suggest intermittent breeding at Frensham from 1953 to 1975. Teal bred at Frensham Great Pond in 1976 (HNHS).

Teal were present in the breeding season at Ockley Common and Stoke Water Meadows in 1969 and at least one pair bred at Ockley Common in 1970. In 1971, nests with eggs were found in TQ06 and at Ockley Common and a third pair was thought to have bred in SU95. Subsequent breeding records were from Ash Vale Gravel Pits (probable in 1974), Epsom Common Stew Ponds (1989, 1993), Esher Common (1972 two nests, one predated; 1973-75), Ockley Common (1973 three pairs, 1974, 1981, 1988), a site in SU95 (1974) and Walton Reservoirs (1999). Birds have summered at several of these and other sites since 1970 without firm breeding evidence being obtained.

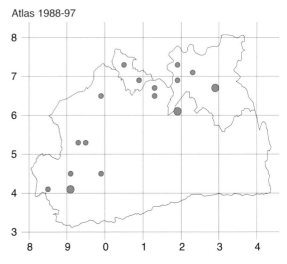

Atlas 1988-97

The 1982 BTO Breeding Waders of Wet Meadows survey included the Teal as an additional species. Only one bird was found, a drake at Whitmoor Common on 20th April. The survey did not cover other heathlands, missing a pair possibly breeding at Ockley Common. There were no other actual or possible breeding records from anywhere in the area. Although breeding has become less frequent, the number of Teal wintering in the vice-county was probably at its highest recorded level at the end of the period. Wintering numbers build up to a peak which in recent years has been well over 1,500, as shown by the table below for the main sites in 1999.

At Staines Moor a female with one young was found at the end of June 1977 and a female with four flying young was seen there on 8th August 1978. A 'hybrid Teal x Wigeon' pair bred at Shepperton Gravel Pits in 1984 but the eggs were lost. One or both of the birds were probably feral (*Shepp BR* 1985).

Calendar. Wintering numbers now build up to a peak which in some years has been well over 1,500, as shown by the table for the main vice-county sites in 1999. The largest numbers have usually been found where there are large areas of flooded fields or reedy lagoons, as at Beddington Sewage Farm, Guildford Sewage Farm before modernisation and Walton Reservoirs during reconstruction.

Teal in the vice-county in 1999

	Jan	Feb	Mar	Apr	May	Jun	Jul	Aug	Sep	Oct	Nov	Dec
Barn Elms Reservoirs	212	250	218	20		1	4	29	102	182	369	220
Beddington Sewage Farm	300	350	120	45	3	9	6	65	560	600	700	1,100
Berrylands Sewage Works	60	70							7	50	50	80
Frimley Gravel Pits	16	30	10					1	7	9	16	15
Hersham Gravel Pit	75	40	46	10		2		7	61	74	80	120
Papercourt Gravel Pits	90	90	16	13					40	20	23	54
Unstead Sewage Farm	50	14	9	1	1	1		4	17	35	30	51
Walton Reservoirs	60	142	27	39	2	13	52	57	73	36	20	34
Vice-county total	863	986	446	128	6	26	62	163	867	1,006	1,288	1,674

Large counts. The biggest counts came from the Spelthorne reservoirs in the 1980s:

Ash Vale Gravel Pits: 75, February 1981

Barn Elms: 617, January 2003

Beddington Sewage Farm: 1,250, 14th December 1996

Berrylands Sewage Works: c.300, February 1986 and January 1987

Broadford Marsh: 120+, 2nd March 1996

Buckland Sand Pits: 31, February 1986

Buckland – Dungates Farm: 150, September 1978 in barley stubble

Clandon Park: 100, 8th December 1973

Enton: 200, December 1956

Frensham: 33, 23rd February 1969 (Clark, 1984)

Frimley Gravel Pits: 70, December 1985

Gatton Lake: 25th January 2004

Gatwick Airport: c.80, 15th December 1985

Guildford Sewage Farm: 600, 13th February 1954

Hersham Gravel Pit: 290, 30th October 2000

Hersham Sewage Farm: 200+, 18th December 1981

Holmethorpe Sand Pits: 156, December 1981

Island Barn Reservoir: c.550, 14th January 1968

Molesey Gravel Pit: 80, 15th November 1986

Old Woking Sewage Farm: 350+, 10th February 1996

Ockley Common: c.50, 17th January 1970

Papercourt Gravel Pits: 200+, 25th January 1998

Queen Elizabeth II Reservoir: 458, January 1977

Reigate Priory: 100, November 1993

Ripley Sewage Farm: 55, March 1975

Send Water Meadows: 65+, 8th December 1972

Sutton Place, Guildford: 152, 30th December 2002

Unstead Sewage Farm: 250+, 31st December 2001

Vann Lake: 35, 12th November 1978

Walton Reservoirs: 940, January 1991

Wisley Common: 60, 16th-26th February 1974

Spelthorne

King George VI Reservoir: 1,568, February 1986

Perry Oaks Sewage Farm: 400, November 1998

Queen Mary Gravel Pits: 40, January 1990

Queen Mary Reservoir: 400, 31st December 1929 (Glegg)

Staines Reservoirs: 2,000, January to February 1986

Wraysbury Reservoir: 150, 13th December 1975

Movements and longevity. A young female was colour-ringed at S. Jacinto Dunes Nature Reserve, Portugal, on 15th January 2005 and seen at Frensham Little Pond, 1,332 km northeast, on 11th September in the same year (S. P. Peters). A bird ringed in the Netherlands on 6th October 1980 was found dead at Frensham Little Pond on 23rd November 1981. Three foreign ringing recoveries involve exchanges between Surrey and Denmark. One ringed at Buckland on 26th October 1985 was recovered in Denmark, 776 km northeast, on 1st September 1988 and another ringed at Buckland on 20th September 1986 was recovered there, 960 km northeast, on 1st September 1988. The longest-lived was a Teal ringed in Denmark on 30th July 1964 and recovered over five years and five months later at Ewhurst on 4th January 1970.

Green-winged Teal *Anas carolinensis* (*Anas crecca carolinensis*)

Seven birds, of which three were in Spelthorne

The North American equivalent of the Teal found in Europe.

Surrey:

1971:   Barn Elms Reservoirs, a male on 11th April (J. E. Harvey, *BB*, *65:328*).

1971:* King George VI Reservoir, a male on 13th April (A. R. J. Paine, *BB*, *65:328*).

1997:   Beddington Sewage Farm, one on 14th December and from 17th January to 8th February 1998.

2002:* Staines Reservoirs, a male on 9th March (*LBR*).

2004:   Barn Elms, one on 5th December (SBC archive).

2005:   Beddington Sewage Farm, a male on 1st-2nd May (P. R. Alfrey).

2005:* Staines Reservoirs, one on 23rd-27th April (*LNHSB*).

*Spelthorne

Mallard *Anas platyrhynchos*

Abundant breeding resident

Present in Britain in prehistoric times (Harrison and Hollom, 1932). A cosmopolitan species, breeding around the northern hemisphere. Habitat loss had reduced breeding numbers in Britain even before 1800 and breeding was considered comparatively infrequent in southern England in the early 19th century. There has since been a recovery, still continuing. Breeding numbers are thought to have more than doubled since 1970. Many northern birds winter in the British Isles and wintering numbers are said to be in long-term decline (BTO *et al.*). Mallard have been extensively hunted for food and sport and many have been introduced for these purposes. Most autumn immigrants are from northern Europe (*MA*).

Early Surrey history. Mallard or domesticated duck remains from the 16th century were found at Little Pickle, Bletchingley (Poulton *et al.*). Remains dated not later than 1650 were found at Oatlands Palace (Cohen). Bucknill mentions three duck decoys in Surrey, at Ottershaw Park, Pyrford and Virginia Water. John Evelyn saw the Pyrford decoy in use on 23rd August 1681 (Evelyn) and Daniel Defoe saw it in 1724 (Parker, 1954). Many Mallard were and still are put down for sporting interests.

Numbers seem to have been lower in the late 19th century than in earlier years, at least in the London area and no doubt due to heavy shooting pressure. They were apparently seen but not breeding in the Norwood area Aldridge (1885). Power only had about a dozen records for the Dulwich area from 1874 to 1909, mainly in spring and late summer. None involved breeding. Bucknill noted that the duck-gun was a common weapon at Battersea but knew of nesting on the Mole, on the Wey at Unstead water meadows and elsewhere, at Cutt Mill, Milford, Pudmore, Pen Ponds and 'very many other localities'. In the spring of 1905 several pairs stayed to breed on small ponds in the Staines area (Kerr, 1906). Things may have improved in the early 20th century. There were four nests at the Surrey Docks in 1922, where Mallard bred nearly every year, and broods were seen in Chelsea Reach (Macpherson, 1929).

Breeding since 1960. Mallard were found in Common Birds Censuses from 1964, rising to 1.1 territories per ten hectares until 2002. This probably over-represents Mallard in Surrey but the increase is statistically significant and implies that the population has more than doubled since 1970, following the national trend. The 1982 BTO Breeding Waders of Wet Meadows survey included the Mallard as an additional species. Birds were found at all but nine of the 32 outer Surrey sites that were visited, a total of 199 representing a hundred or more pairs. The Mallard was the commonest of the species surveyed.

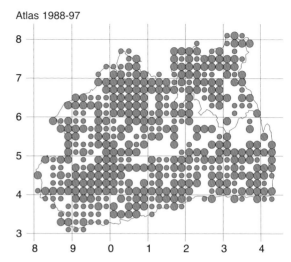

Atlas 1988-97

Population size. The Breeding Bird Survey figures for 1994-2004 gross up to an average breeding season population of about 5,300 adults. Of the 231 tetrads in northeast Surrey, 68% were found to hold territories in the 1968-72 Atlas survey and 71% in the 1988-97 Atlas, a small extension of range. Across the whole county, Mallard were located in 430 tetrads in the 1988-97 SBC Atlas survey, 75% of the total and a slightly higher density than in the London area. If Surrey held a proportionate share of the British breeding population as given by the *New Atlas*, the population would be nearer to 720 territories, or 0.35 per square km, which looks on the low side given the Atlas distribution and the number found in wildfowl counts.

Territory counts. Significant numbers bred at Barn Elms Reservoirs even before the site was converted to a wetland centre. There were 25 broods in 1966 and over 30 in 1969. There were twelve broods at Thorpe in the latter year. Mallard commonly bred at Shepperton in the 1980s and no doubt have done so since. Beddington Sewage Farm has had around 30 pairs in the years since 2000 and Barn Elms WWT has had around 20.

Breeding behaviour. Mallard may breed very late in the year. A brood was seen at Tooting Bec Common on 14th November 1983 and another at Send Heath Ponds on 14th December 1995. Recently hatched young were seen in Dulwich Park on 19th November 1997.

Calendar. Winter numbers are swelled by successful breeding and by immigration but the summer population of resident birds remains high, as the table for 1998 shows:

Totals of monthly maxima at the main vice-county sites in 1998

	Jan	Feb	Mar	Apr	May	Jun	Jul	Aug	Sep	Oct	Nov	Dec
Birds	1,828	1,506	1,150	545	626	727	1,026	1,535	1,768	1,564	1,887	1,871
Waters	27	26	25	19	19	20	18	22	23	26	26	26

Large counts. In Spelthorne, Mallard at one time only appeared in hard weather, on the Thames. By 1904, several hundred were wintering on Staines Reservoirs. In Richmond Park, wintering numbers increased in the 40 years to 1936. Parr estimated that in a normal winter there would be about 5,000 in the vice-county, of which 1,000 were on the Thames. In September 1975 the wildfowl counts at 27 waters totalled 3,100 birds. In the following year they totalled 3,660 on 29 waters. Even in good years, these counts only cover 30 or so of the numerous places where this common duck can be found.

As the table shows, the wildfowl counts for 1998 were considerably lower than in 1975 and 1976.

The counts at 27 waters (not all formal wildfowl counts and not all counted every month) peaked at 1,887 in November. This may reflect a lower level of immigration due to milder weather and possibly to fewer Mallard being put down for sporting purposes. The high counts for Clandon Park (1975), Effingham Ponds (1974), Gatton (1977) and Vachery (1965) which are shown in the list below all reflect such introductions.

Ash Vale Gravel Pits: 160, 8th January 1978
Badshot Lea: 131, January 1979
Barn Elms: 600, 16th January 1966
Bourne Hall: 88, October 1998
Broadwater: 172, August 1996
Buckland Sand Pits: 232, 16th November 1993
Busbridge: 207, 17th September 2000
Cannon Hill Common: 58, January 1998
Clandon Park: 320, September 1975
Clapham Common: 99, November 1964
Cutt Mill: 360, August 1978 (*HSBBR*)
Dorking Mill Pond: 89, November 1984
Dulwich: 230, 12th February 1978
Earlswood: 137, 25th December 1996
East Clandon Common: *c.*200, 11th September 1992
Effingham Fish Ponds: 712, 29th November 1994
Enton: 64, 26th November 1970
Epsom Common Stew Ponds: 101, September 1998
Ewell Court: 20th December 2003
Fetcham Mill Pond: 250, 18th January 1970
Frensham: 171, August 1993 (*HSBBR*)
Frimley Gravel Pits: 159, January 1982 (*HSBBR*)
Gatton Lake: 1,200, September 1977 (*LBR*)
Hammer Pond: 54, 9th December 1972
Holmethorpe Sand Pits: 178, December 1981
Island Barn Reservoir: 250, January 1977
King George's Park, Wandsworth: 86, 16th September 1972
Lammas Lands: 106, January 1999
Lonsdale Road Reservoir: 759, 12th January 1964
Moat Pond: 150, August 1998
Outwood Swan Sanctuary: 139, October 1998
Papercourt Gravel Pits: 600, September 1986
Pen Ponds, Richmond Park: 305, October 1989
Queen Elizabeth II Reservoir: *c.*500, 14th

November 1971 (*LBR*), 506, autumn 1971 (*SBR*)
Reigate Priory: 30, 13th January 1974 (*LBR*)
Shottermill Ponds: 54, December 1988
Snowdenham: 210, 23rd September 1979
South Norwood Country Park: 123, September 1992
Stoke Water Meadows, Guildford: 102, 6th October 1997
Surrey Docks: 207, September 2000
Tangley Mere: 84, December 1984
Thames Barnes/Kew: 656, 1964
Thames Barnes/Putney: 1,790, 13th January 1963
Thames Putney/Teddington: 3,552, 13th January 1963
Thames Richmond/Kew: 1,323, 1963
Thorpe Water Park: 228, January 1979
Tongham Gravel Pit: 150, 7th January 1997
Unstead Sewage Farm: 280, October 1999
Vachery Pond: 3,000+, 26th September 1965
Vann Lake: *c.*100, 3rd December 1995
Virginia Water: 582, January 1977
Waddon Ponds: 180, October 1996
Walton Reservoirs: 162, February 1992
Waterloo Pond: 59, 17th January 1971
Wimbledon Common – Queen's Mere: 120, 3rd November 1971
Wimbledon Park Lake: 180, January 1968
Winkworth Arboretum: 92, November 1978
Wrecclesham Floods: 132, 23rd November 1996
Spelthorne
King George VI Reservoir: 1,255, 24th December 1964
Perry Oaks Sewage Farm: 350, 24th December 1978
Queen Mary Reservoirs: *c.*1,500 January 1930 (*BLA*)
Staines Reservoirs: *c.*1,100 November 1950 (*BLA*)

Movements and longevity. One of the five foreign recoveries relates to a Mallard ringed as an adult in Denmark in July 1970 and recovered at Ewhurst in December 1972 and another was ringed as an adult in Poland in June 1981 and recovered 1,063 km west at Godalming in November 1992. These indicate winter immigration from the continent. A third bird was ringed at Frensham in August 1980 and recovered in northern France in October 1981. Two others show a similar pattern. The longest life established by ringing, apart from the Polish bird, was of a bird ringed at Hersham on 22nd July 1978 and recovered at Dorking on 8th November 1986, over eight years and three months later. At least 60 young found dead at Kew Gardens in 1970 were thought to have been infected by snails.

Pintail (Northern Pintail) *Anas acuta*
Uncommon winter visitor and feral resident

Breeds around the northern and temperate regions of the northern hemisphere. Has bred in parts of the British Isles, including Kent, since 1898. Winter visitors to Britain come from Iceland and northern Europe east to Siberia. The most significant wintering site near Surrey used to be on the Thames estuary at Rainham, where counts of 100 or more were made in the 1980s, before drainage of the main habitat there.

Early Surrey history. Newman (1849) included Pintails as winter visitors without further comment. Bucknill gave seven dated records and an undated reference to Frensham Little Pond. Two birds were shot on Old Pond near Godalming in January 1836. Others were shot near Eashing Mills in 1838 (*SALEC*) and at Compton and Elstead in 1839. One was shot on the Thames near Walton in February 1875. Pinioned birds at Witley attracted five wild ones, of which a male was shot on 11th March and a female on 18th March in 1890. The Eashing birds, a pair, eventually went to Charterhouse and are presumably the pair still there in 2001, with Surrey as their provenance.

1900 to 1945. There was one was at Frensham on 8th February 1908 and the next were two at Frensham Little Pond on 1st November 1932. Collenette (1937) knew of eight records for Richmond Park, in the months from December to April. The first was on 23rd March 1907. In 1937 a party of six were seen on 5th November. There were four at Barnes on 22nd February 1924 (*BLA*). A pair stayed on a pond near Godalming for three weeks until 21st May 1934. A pair was seen near Godalming on 22nd-30th March 1935 and at Brooklands Sewage Farm on 7th May 1936. Two in eclipse at Brooklands Sewage Farm on 13th August 1936 appeared tired and hungry. Others appeared there and at Island Barn Reservoir and Richmond Park in 1938 and 1939. Elsewhere, Pintails were most often seen on the Thames and at adjacent sites. There was one at Chiswick on 26th December 1938 and in the Barnes area until March 1939 (probably the bird in Richmond Park in January), one on Chelsea Reach on 16th March 1942 and others were opposite Sion House later in 1942 and at Isleworth on 24th January. One or two were at Lonsdale Road Reservoir (one in 1941 and 1944, two single birds in 1943). Others were seen in the Thames area in 1943 and 1945.

Pintails were seen at Staines Reservoirs on 7th March 1926 (*London Naturalist*, first record located for Spelthorne), then three times in 1927, and annually to 1933 (maximum of four birds on 24th November 1932). There was one at Staines Moor on 12th March 1932 and one at Staines Reservoirs in May 1938. At Queen Mary Reservoir, there were up to three from March to 28th May 1936 and a pair was seen in April 1937.

1945 to 1970. Pintails were seen at Beddington Sewage Farm (1954-55), Churt (1954), Earlswood Lake (1967) and Sewage Farm (1962), Enton (eight on 13th February 1954), Frensham (1947, 1952, 1954-56, 1960, 1961), Godstone (1958), Guildford Sewage Farm (1954, 1968), Hedgecourt (1946), Hersham (1967), Holmethorpe Sand Pits (1960, 1961, 1965), Island Barn Reservoir (1949, 1954, 1958, 1960, 1961, 1965), Kew Gardens (1958, 1966), Milford (January 1943), Queen Elizabeth II Reservoir (1966), Reigate Priory (1967), Send (1945), Shalford (1963), the Thames area (1946-60 and into the 1970s), Vachery Pond (1954, 1965) and Walton Reservoirs. Twenty-six at Walton Reservoirs on 8th and 9th March, 1947 were the largest party in the London area and Surrey up to that date. In January 1949 there were ten at Staines Reservoirs, where they became fairly regular in small numbers from about this time.

Since 1970. Pintails were somewhat more frequent in the 1970s and numbers increased hugely in the 1990s. The average annual number of vice-county records rose from four in the 1970s and five in the 1980s to at least 25 by the 1990s. Bird months show an even sharper rise:

Bird months by decade

	1970s	1980s	1990s	2000	Total
Vice-county	82	197	904	161	**1,344**

Nearly all of them are from the London area. Wild Pintails are still uncommon in the south and west. Vice-county sites and years at which Pintails have been recorded from 1970 to 2000 include: Ash Vale (1979), Barn Elms (18 years), Battersea Park (1996-98), Beddington Sewage Farm (20 years), Bell Creek (from 1995), Berrylands (eight in 1981), Bourne Hall (1997-98), Broadford Marsh (1996), Broadwater (1976, 1996), Broome Hall (1975), Buckland (1990s), Burgess Park (1997), Burpham (1992), Busbridge Lakes (1990s), Capel (1991), Carshalton (1991), Cutt Mill (1985, 1991), Enton (1993), Esher (1986), Fetcham (1995), Frensham (13 years), Frimley Gravel Pits (seven years), Godstone (1979), Ham Moor Sand Pits (1970), Hammer Pond (1986, 1991-92), Hersham (1985, 1999), Hurst Green (1996), Holmethorpe (13 years), Island Barn Reservoir (seven years), Lonsdale Road Reservoir (1995), Lowick's Pond (Churt, 1984), Moat Pond (1981, 1994), Old Woking Sewage Farm (1990s), Papercourt (six years), Peasmarsh (1991), Queen Elizabeth II Reservoir (from 1996), Ravensbury Park (1991), Reigate (1987), Richmond Park (four years), River Ember (1990-91), River Wandle (1997), River Thames Southbank to Teddington (six years), Send Water Meadows (1971), South Norwood Country Park (six years from 1987), South Norwood Lake (1987), Stoke Water Meadows (three years), Surrey Docks (1971, 1975-76), Tangley Mere (1982), Teddington Lock (1987), Thursley/Ockley Commons (1971 and 1985), Tongham (1975), Tooting Bec (1981), Unstead Sewage Farm (four years), Vachery Pond (1971, 1988, 1989), Virginia Water (1981), Waddon Ponds (1991), Walton Reservoirs (from 1991), Watermeads (1991), Wimbledon Common (1997, 1999), Winkworth Arboretum (1992), Wisley (1991), Woking (1990) and Wrecclesham (1997). One at Shepperton Gravel Pits on 23rd February 1985 was said to be the first recorded for the site. No new sites have been reported since 2000. Small numbers have been seen at the Spelthorne reservoirs throughout the period.

Feral breeding. In the late 1990s a regular and apparently feral flock built up at Bell Creek, Wandsworth. The focus has since shifted to the new London Wetland Centre at Barn Elms, where up to 30 have been wintering. The habitat changes at Barn Elms will certainly have attracted wild immigrants but the summer location of most of the Barn Elms birds and the increasing number of others seen outside the breeding season at Battersea Park (nine on 21st October 1998) and Wandsworth (twenty on 30th November 1999) is unknown. It has been conjectured that many are of feral origin, perhaps from St James's Park, north of the Thames. A female with two downy young was seen at Barn Elms on 25th May 2001, the first known breeding in Surrey. A pair hatched nine young there in 2002 but none fledged.

Calendar. The main autumn arrivals are in October, with numbers remaining at a high level until March. Occurrences from May to September were rare until the 1990s. A drake of unknown origin was at Broome Park, Betchworth on 18th June 1975. There was a female at Barn Elms Reservoirs on 14th August 1976. One at Barn Elms and on the Thames on 11th and 25th September 1948 was the first for September. Two at Walton Reservoirs on 18th September 1966 were unusually early for the period.

Bird months 1970-2000

	Jan	Feb	Mar	Apr	May	Jun	Jul	Aug	Sep	Oct	Nov	Dec	Total
Vice-county	180	193	99	42	28	26	5	93	157	235	122	164	**1,344**

Large counts at selected sites. Despite the rising frequency, the largest go back to the 1980s or earlier. They will have been wild, not feral birds:

Barn Elms: 30 feral, 5th October 1998

Beddington Sewage Farm: 35, 14th September 2002; 60+ circled over, 17th October 1988

Cutt Mill: 25, January 1939

Richmond Park: 12 over, 7th November 1964

Thursley Common: 36 southwest, 3rd February 1985

Walton Reservoir: 26, 8th-9th March 1947

Spelthorne from 1970

King George VI Reservoir: 13, 16th February 1986; 28, February 2002 (BTO)

Queen Mary Reservoir: 15, 14th January 1994

Staines Reservoirs: 65, 3rd February 1985

Garganey

Anas querquedula

Scarce passage migrant, has bred

Present in Britain in prehistoric times (Harrison and Hollom, 1932). Breeds across Europe and Asia, except in the far north and wintering in West Africa and just south of the Sahara. Bred in some east coast counties and Hampshire in the late 19th century and extended its range more widely until the 1950s as part of a more general expansion which some have attributed to climatic factors.

Early Surrey history. Newman (1849) listed Garganey for the Godalming district but neither he nor Bucknill gave any dated records. A pair in the Charterhouse Museum with Surrey as their provenance might be the birds given to Stafford by John Hawkins of Cosford House, Bowlhead Green who said that they had sometimes been known to breed at the site (Stafford Collection Catalogue). Bucknill thought that, since Garganey were often kept in collections and since he knew of no breeding records from neighbouring counties, these might not be wild birds.

1900 to 1955. There was a drake on Pen Ponds, Richmond Park on 17th March 1927 and there was a pair at Barn Elms on 31st March 1928. There are later records from Barn Elms (6th May 1930, 1937, 1947), Brooklands Sewage Farm (two, August 1937 *LBR*), Earlswood Common (15th April 1938), Frensham (four, April 1947), Guildford Sewage Farm (1945), Hedgecourt (1946-47), Island Barn Reservoir (three, 9th April 1938), Richmond Park (25th March 1940), Send (1943, 1945) and Walton Gravel Pits (two, 2nd June 1951).

The first Spelthorne record is of a male at Staines Reservoirs for a few days from 21st May 1933 (A. Holte Macpherson). In 1948 there were many reports from 20th March to 9th October, with a maximum of seven at King George VI Reservoir on 22nd August and 4th September and none in July. Later records were of up to five at Staines Reservoirs in 1949 and one at Queen Mary Reservoir on 19th March 1955 (Geen).

Since 1955. Records became much more frequent from the 1950s, averaging over three per year for the rest of the period. Migrant Garganey have been seen most often at Barn Elms, Beddington Sewage Farm, Frensham, Send and the Island Barn, Queen Elizabeth II and the Walton-on-Thames gravel pits and reservoirs. There have also been reports from Addlestone, Badshot Lea, Berrylands, Bookham Common, Britten's Pond, Broadford, Brooklands Sewage Farm, Buckland, Cobham (Slyfields), Earlswood, Effingham, Enton, Epsom, Esher, Frimley Gravel Pits, Gatton, Godstone, Guildford Sewage Farm, Hamm Moor, Hammer Pond, Hersham, Holmethorpe, Kew Gardens, Lonsdale Road Reservoirs, Moat Pond, Molesey, Morden Hall Park, Old Woking Sewage Farm, Papercourt Gravel Pits, Richmond Park, Shalford, Silvermere, South Norwood Lake, Stoke Water Meadows, Thorpe, Tongham Gravel Pit, Vachery Pond, Virginia Water, Warren Mere and Wisley and at various spots on the Mole, the Thames and the Wey. There were over 30 vice-county bird months from 2001 to 2004. Garganey have been seen regularly in Spelthorne over the whole period.

Breeding. Garganey bred in the Leatherhead area at some time between 1945 and 1951 (Douglas). There was a strong possibility of a nesting attempt at Guildford Sewage Farm in 1945 (Harrison, 1947). Two pairs at Walton Gravel Pits in 1951 may have bred. Garganey definitely bred in 1952, when a duck with two young too small to fly were seen on the Wey at Weybridge. At Effingham Fish Ponds a pair first seen on 9th April 1972 had four fully fledged young on 4th August (DP). Breeding was attempted in Surrey in 1993 but not next proved until 2000, when a female was seen with up to five juveniles at Beddington Sewage Farm from 7th July to 22nd August and a female was seen with four downy young at Stanwell Moor on 20th August.

Calendar. Garganey begin to arrive in March with spring passage peaking in April. There are many summer records. Autumn passage peaks in August but a few birds linger into December:

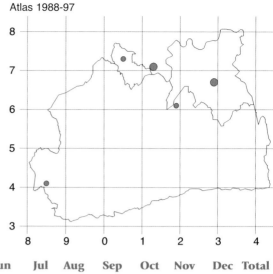

Atlas 1988-97

Bird months 1900-2004

	Jan	Feb	Mar	Apr	May	Jun	Jul	Aug	Sep	Oct	Nov	Dec	Total
Vice-county	2	1	66	91	56	32	56	108	54	8	3	2	**479**

Numerous records from Spelthorne show a similar pattern. Early and late dates include:

Early

3rd March 1970	River Mole near Royal Mills, Esher, adult male before snow storms
4th March 1961	Island Barn Reservoir, a pair
6th March 1960	Britten's Pond, Guildford, five drakes and a duck
12th March 1945	Send, a pair
14th March 1954	South Norwood, a drake
19th March 1976	Staines Reservoirs, a pair
3rd April 1961	Island Barn Reservoir, a pair

Late

11th November 1977	Staines Moor, two
13th November 1960	Frensham, one
19th November 1983	Staines Reservoirs, one
22nd December 1994	Barn Elms Reservoirs, an immature male

A female at Perry Oaks Sewage Farm on 30th January 1988 was unusual. A female on and near Island Barn Reservoir from 12th October 2001 to 23rd April 2002 was the first Garganey known to overwinter.

Large counts. Ten at Barn Elms Reservoirs on 18th March 1947 (*LBR*) are thought to be the largest group up to 1970. There were 12 at Staines Moor/Reservoirs on 31st August 1976 and ten at Staines Reservoirs on 13th August 2004 (*LNHSB*).

Blue-winged Teal   *Anas discors*

Two birds

Breeds in North America and winters south to Brazil. British records have occurred most often in Cornwall and the Scottish islands but many have been inland. Arrivals are most frequent in September and October, and are presumably displaced migrants. Quite common in collections.

Surrey. There was a male at Barn Elms Reservoirs on 16th-19th February 1981 (R. B. Hastings, Mrs W. Roberts and P. J. Strangeman, *BB, 75:491*). A rather tame female on Frensham Great Pond from 29th October to 26th November 1989 was seen in flight and on the water by many observers (*HSBBR, SBR*) and was accepted by the BBRC as a possible escape, at least partly on a disputed claim that one wing was clipped (J. M. Clark, pers. comm., nothing in *BB*). It arrived on a typical date for a wild bird and was not seen again after the pond froze in late November.

Shoveler (Northern Shoveler) *Anas clypeata*
Locally common winter visitor. Has bred

Breeds around the northern hemisphere, mainly in the northern and temperate regions, wintering south to Africa, India and Central America. In Britain, a rare breeding bird in the early 19th century but has since increased. Autumn immigrants to Britain are mostly from northern Europe (*MA*).

Early Surrey history. On 5th March 1793, Gilbert White received a Shoveler that had been shot on 'Frinsham pond' (*sic*, Journals). Newman (1849) listed Shovelers as winter visitors to the Godalming district without further comment. In 2001, the Charterhouse Collection still held a pair shot at Cosford Pond in the 19th century and handled by Stafford. A male was shot at Horsley in the autumn of 1887 (Fitzgerald, 1888). Bucknill included a couple of undated records, from Milford House Pond and near Poynter's, at Cobham. There were four on Dulwich Park Lake on 8th October 1898 (Power, 1910).

1900 to 1940. Collenette knew of seven reports of wild birds for Richmond Park up to 1936, the earliest being of one in the autumn of 1902 and all in the months from autumn to April. A pair of pinioned birds from St James's Park was also present in 1906. Bentham (*BB, 14:139-40*) listed a pair at Hedgecourt on 19th April 1905, six at Godstone on 10th April 1910, one at Hedgecourt on 30th November 1913 and others there in October and November 1914, one on Frensham Little Pond on 6th March 1915 and a pair there on 13th March 1920. Several on the lakes at Puttenham on 25th July 1920 (*BB, 14:118*) were on an unusual date for the time. There were up to four at Barn Elms Reservoirs from October 1926 to early January 1927. Two were at Molesey in January 1929 and one was there in September. This became a regular site for Shovelers. A female at Frensham on 28th January 1933 was an unusual winter occurrence there but there were others in December 1936.

Shovelers were present at Staines Reservoirs from 16th December 1923, with one as late as 3rd May in 1925 and 8th June in 1927, up to ten in October 1931 and January 1932. At Queen Mary Reservoir there were single birds in January and April 1929 and up to seven in December. They were regular in increasing numbers from about this time and 30-40 were at Queen Mary Reservoir in September 1937.

Since 1940. From the 1940s and 50s, Shovelers were recorded fairly regularly at wetland sites, including Barn Elms, Battersea Park (1965), Brooklands, Enton (1961), Earlswood Lakes (1970), Frensham (every month except July, by 1967), Guildford Sewage Farm, Hedgecourt (1945-47), Island Barn Reservoir, Mitcham Common/Gravel Pits (1938, 1943), Painshill Park (1956), Queen Elizabeth II Reservoir, Richmond Park, Send/Papercourt Gravel Pits, South Norwood Lake (1943), Stoke Water Meadows (1947), Sutton Place (1946), Thorpe, Vachery (1937) and they have been seen at Broadford, Broadwater, Clapham Common, Godstone and Moat Pond. Flocks of 20-30 were being recorded at Walton Reservoirs by the mid-1940s (Parr). Wintering numbers increased in the second half of the 20th century and at most of the main sites the largest numbers were found in the 1990s, as may be seen from the list of large counts. Shovelers are currently found at 35-40 sites in a typical year.

Breeding. A young bird was shot at Beddington in 1932 where adults had been present in the breeding season (Parr, 1972). A pair were at Beddington on 4th and 5th June 1931 (*BB, 26:232*), apparently the first for June. Shovelers were seen in May and June at Brooklands Sewage Farm each year from 1931 to 1934 and in 1936 but no nest or young was found. Breeding was thought possible at Queen Mary Reservoir in 1936. Ten adult males were seen there on June 10th. Females were seen with broods at Queen Mary and Staines Reservoirs in 1939 (*BLA*). A pair with twelve ducklings was seen at Send on 3rd April 1943. Shovelers occasionally bred at Guildford Sewage Farm (Harrison, 1947). Three or fours pairs tried to breed in the Wey Valley between Guildford and Send in 1944 but no young were found. A pair nested near the Moat in 1950 and a brood of six was found at Sweetwater, Witley in 1954.

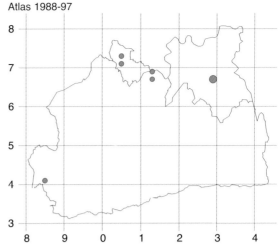

Breeding was proved at Perry Oaks Sewage Farm in 1948, a first for Middlesex. Shovelers bred there again in 1949 and in 1950 a pair bred about a mile to the southwest (*BB, 44:28*) and there was further breeding in the area in most years up to 1959. Shovelers bred at King George VI Reservoir twice in the period 1955-61 (*BLA, LBR* for 1959). They bred at Stanwell Moor Gravel Pits in 1971, Staines Reservoirs in 1978 and Staines Moor in 1979. Staines Reservoirs were drained in 1985 and four pairs raised 20 young. A brood of ten was seen in late July 1994 at Beddington Sewage Farm. Shovelers bred at Perry Oaks Sewage Farm in 1996 and 1997.

Calendar. Wintering birds begin to arrive in August. An annual peak up to October probably includes passage migrants. Numbers begin to fall in February or March, with a noticeable return passage, and most birds have gone by the end of April. A few remain in the summer months.

Large counts. The largest counts date from the 1980s and 90s:

Barn Elms: 259, December 1994
Battersea Park: *c.*130, 15th February 1990
Beddington Sewage Farm: 198, October 1996
Frensham: 20, July 1992 (*HSBBR*)
Gatton Lake: 16, 7th October 1979, 10th March 1996 and 29th February 2004
Holmethorpe: 18, October and December 1980
Island Barn Reservoir: 313, 22nd December 1985
Kew Gardens: 33, January 1982
Lonsdale Road Reservoir: 180, 3rd January 1995
Papercourt Gravel Pits: 78, 14th January 1995
Pen Ponds: 50, February 1997
Queen Elizabeth II Reservoir: 570, November and December 1975
South Norwood Country Park: 40, 22nd February 2002

Thorpe Water Park: 30, November 1980
Unstead Sewage Farm: 38, 7th November 2000
Walton Reservoirs: 588, 10th November 1994
Wimbledon Park Lake: 80, November 1993
Spelthorne since 1970
King George VI Reservoir: 660, 28th October 1978; 1,134, November 1995 (BTO)
Perry Oaks Sewage Farm: *c.*200, 2nd December 1984
Queen Mary Reservoir: 621, 22nd January 1984
Shepperton Gravel Pits: 160, 17th September 1991
Staines Reservoirs: 638, November 1982
Wraysbury Reservoir: 290, 7th January 1985; 325, September 1996

From 1994-95 to 1996-97, King George VI Reservoir was internationally important with an average winter maximum of 409. In this period there were nationally important averages at Knight and Bessborough Reservoirs (223), Wraysbury Reservoir (186) and Barn Elms Reservoirs (113). Staines Reservoirs were internationally important in the 1990s. The ratings have since slipped but Surrey still had one nationally important site for Shovelers, Staines Reservoirs (327), in the five years to 2003/04. Numbers are lower at Barn Elms, Beddington Sewage Farm, Knight and Bessborough Reservoirs and Wraysbury Reservoir all of which were of national importance in the 1990s. The average was 118 at Beddington Sewage Farm from 1996-97 to 2000-01.

Movements and longevity. In 1961, an adult ringed in the Netherlands on 30th September was recovered at Stanwell, 395 km away, on 2nd December.

Red-crested Pochard   *Netta rufina*

Scarce passage migrant and feral resident, has bred

The heartland of these handsome ducks lies east of the Caspian Sea, with scattered colonies west to the Netherlands and Spain. Western birds mainly disperse rather than migrate. In the 19th century, Red-crested Pochards were only rare winter vagrants to Britain. The first attempts at breeding them in captivity were made at Woburn in the 1930s. Eggs were hatched in incubators and free-flying young were released. Other releases were made in London (St James's Park) in 1933 and 1936, one pair raising young on each occasion, and in 1950 (Regent's Park and St James's Park). Meanwhile, they were extending their breeding range northwest into Denmark, Germany and the Netherlands. A pair which bred on the Lincolnshire coast in 1937 may have been genuinely wild birds. The first (or next) feral breeding was in Essex in 1958. Feral breeding is now quite common.

Early Surrey history. The first for Surrey was at Frensham Great Pond on several dates from 19th November 1931 to 29th January 1932. Since this is before the London introductions and some distance away from Woburn the bird could well have been wild. The next records, of single birds at Staines on 26th April and 10th May 1934 and in Richmond Park in April and May 1935, may be connected with the London introduction. There were only two others before 1950, at Beddington on 23rd November 1940 and at Barn Elms Reservoir on 2nd May 1946.

Since 1950. Because of the London introductions, all records since the 1950s, especially those from the London area, have been under suspicion of being of feral or escaped origin, though there is some evidence of migrant wild birds, particularly in the autumn. There were single birds at Barn Elms in December 1950 and from 27th November to 1st December 1955 and at Enton on 5th August 1959. (For the latter, with a caveat, see *BB, 53:485*). Sightings became more frequent from about this date. Red-crested Pochards have been seen annually since the mid 1970s, initially concentrated on Barn Elms and other sites in the London area, but more recently from many west Surrey sites, with scattered records from elsewhere. A few birds are now reported from the reservoirs and gravel pits each year and most are probably of feral origin. A female at Shepperton Gravel Pits on 15th October 1983 stayed for two weeks and might have been an escape. From 2001 to 2005 there were records from Badshot Lea, Barn Elms London Wetland Centre, Battersea Park, Beddington Sewage Farm, Claremont, Enton, Fieldcommon Gravel Pit, Hersham Gravel Pit, Island Barn Reservoir, Outwood Swan Sanctuary, Queen Elizabeth II Reservoir, Thorpe Water Park, Waddon Ponds and Walton Reservoirs.

Breeding. A female with four small young was seen at Winkworth Arboretum on 19th June 1994. Two adults and two young were seen there in 1995 and a female with six young was seen there on 21st May 1997. A female with

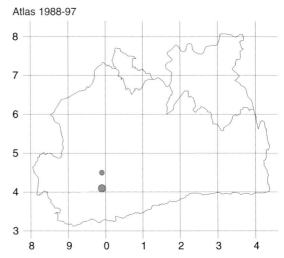

Atlas 1988-97

three juveniles was seen at Kew Gardens in 2000. At Claremont, a female with clipped wings was seen with a juvenile on 6th June 2001.

Calendar. The bird month distribution for the years 1950-73 suggests that a resident population was being more than doubled by wintering immigrants:

	Jan	Feb	Mar	Apr	May	Jun	Jul	Aug	Sep	Oct	Nov	Dec	Total
Vice-county	10	8	3	2	1	2	4	3	1	3	9	8	**54**

The most likely source of any immigrants is a feral population in the London area. There are no foreign ringing recoveries to provide definite evidence but a few of the wintering birds might come from Europe and possibly further east. A duck at Queen Mary Reservoir in October 1960 and a drake there in November 1975 might have been such birds. The monthly pattern of the records has since changed and the peak is now in August and September:

Bird months 1994-2001

	Jan	Feb	Mar	Apr	May	Jun	Jul	Aug	Sep	Oct	Nov	Dec	Total
Vice-county	10	5	7	8	7	3	13	15	22	10	5	10	**115**

This probably reflects a larger feral breeding population, in Surrey as well as elsewhere. It remains possible that the smaller peak from December to January includes one or two foreign birds. The pinioned birds at Thorpe Water Park are not included in these figures. Nor are birds that bred at Winkworth.

Plumage variations. A buff-coloured pair at Frensham in 1995 were especially likely to have been escapes.

Pochard (Common Pochard)   *Aythya ferina*

Moderately common winter visitor, rare but increasing breeder

Breeds mainly in temperate parts of Europe and Asia east to Lake Baikal, moving south or west in winter. Many Pochards migrate from other parts of Europe to wintering grounds in Britain and the breeding range has extended northwards in continental Europe. In Britain, the breeding range extended from a base in Norfolk to a number of other counties in the 19th century and has since spread further.

Early Surrey history. There were about 50 on Old Pond, Godalming not later than 1837 (Newman in Yarrell). Meyer (1842) found them as regular winter visitors to muddy creeks and alder carr by the Thames. Bucknill gave a few dated records: Witley (one, December 1846), West Molesey (8th January 1869), Gatton Lake (25 in March 1875 and two drakes on 5th January 1881), Thames at East Molesey (one, 25th December 1878), Earlswood Pond (a pair in March 1889), Wey near Godalming (one, January 1893) and Witley (five for six weeks in 1893). He mentioned Pochards as winter visitors to some of the larger lakes of west Surrey, including a male on Forked Pond on 8th January 1902, and wrote that Pochard had been seen at Milford House pond and shot on the Mole near Cobham.

There were up to sixteen in Richmond Park during March 1905 (Mouritz) and 121 there the following February (*BLA*). Power had records of only three in the Dulwich area from 1874 to 1909. Two of them, an immature from 21st February to 13th March and a male on 10th December, were on Dulwich Park Lake in 1899. The third was a male on Tooting Common Lake on 4th December 1905. Pochards were using Staines Reservoirs at least as early as 16th December 1923. There were 300 present on 17th November 1932 and 450 on 30th August 1936.

Breeding. Dalgliesh saw a Pochard that was sitting in Lea Park, Witley on 1st May 1906. Eggs were laid but did not hatch. The pair remained there until late summer (Mouritz, 1907). This is the first record of attempted (and unsuccessful) breeding in Surrey, though it does not seem to have been mentioned in *British Birds* or elsewhere. Six nests were found in the reeds round 'the pond in Windsor Park' in May and June, 1907 and a brood of six was seen on 20th June (Kerr). It is not known how many, if any, of the nests were in Surrey. Six newly hatched ducklings were seen at Barn Elms Reservoirs on 2nd June 1927 and a pair nested there in 1929, 1930 (possibly) and 1931. R. S. R. Fitter saw a female with one newly hatched duckling on a gravel pit at Beddington on 22nd July 1931 and seven fair-sized ducklings there from the 25th (*BB, 26:230 and 27:171*). Collenette wrote that Pochards bred in Richmond Park in 1930 (two young seen), 1931 (four young) and 1932 (one young). Breeding at Richmond Park did not resume until 1969 (*LBR*).

A pair bred at Beddington from 1931 to 1933. Pochards attempted to breed in Battersea Park in 1954 and were successful in 1955. They bred at Kew Gardens in 1950 and from 1967 to 1977. There was successful breeding at Thorpe Gravel Pits in the years 1966-68. Subsequent proven breeding records were more frequent. Places (single pairs/broods except where indicated), were at *Barn Elms*: 1989, 1992, 1994, 1995 (two), 1998 (two), 1999 (two), 2000, 2001, 2002 (two), 2004 and 2005 (two); *Battersea Park*: 1987; *Chertsey Works Reservoir*: 1997, 1999; *Dulwich Mill Pond*: 1994; *Effingham Fish Ponds*: 1986, 1992, 1994, 1997-2000 (two each year), 2001 (two), 2002 (three) and 2003 (three); *Kew Gardens*: 1972 (two), 1973, 1981, 1997, 2000; *Lonsdale Road Reservoir*: 1986, 1988 (two), 1989, 1990, 1993, 1998; *Papercourt Gravel Pits*: 1974 (two), 1975 (two), 1976 (three), 1978 (two), 1979, 1981; *Pen Ponds and Richmond Park*: 1971-72, 1973 (two), 1974-75, 1976 (three), 1990, 1994-97 and *Walton Reservoirs*: 2000, 2001(two). Pairs were present in the breeding season at several other sites. The two pairs that bred at Papercourt Gravel Pits in 1974 were suspected of being the product of one drake Pochard mating with two Tufted Duck x Pochard hybrids (J. J. Bowley) though no such suggestions were published about breeding there in subsequent years. Five broods were seen in 1997, the largest number on record with the possible exception of 1907. In Spelthorne, pairs bred at Queen Mary Reservoir in 1988, Shepperton Gravel Pits in 1993 and Stanwell Moor in 2002.

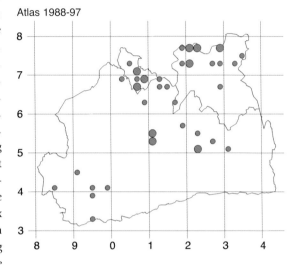

Atlas 1988-97

Other places where found. By 1970, Pochard had been seen at many other places including Badshot Lea (1958), Broadwater, Enton (1958, 1960), Fetcham Mill Pond, Frensham, Gatton, Guildford Sewage Farm (1958), and Winkworth Arboretum. Pochards can now be found even on the smaller waters such as Moat Pond, in some winters, often in association with Tufted Ducks.

Calendar. Wintering birds begin to arrive in July and in a typical year build up rather slowly to a peak in December and January, with most wintering birds away by the end of March. Peak Pochard numbers depend, more than for most other waterfowl, on the severity of the winter.

Large counts. Numbers at Barn Elms in November and December 1925 peaked at 500 or more. Fetcham Mill Pond could hold 30 or more in winter because the springs usually kept it from being frozen over (Bucknill, 1902). The number of wintering birds on the 30 or so larger waters was usually in the region of 1,000 in the 1990s. This is probably more than in the early years of the 20th century and is likely to be a consequence of the creation of many new reservoirs and gravel pits over the period. The really large counts date back to the 1970s or earlier and were associated with hard weather:

Ash Vale Gravel Pits: 94, January 1979
Badshot Lea: 270, January 1973 (*HSBBR*)
Barn Elms: 500, December 1925; 3,000, 17th January 1971
Battersea Park: 20, 10th January 1990
Beddington Sewage Farm: 84, December 1992

Broadwater, Farncombe: 75, February 1967
Burgess Park: 50, 8th February 1997
Clandon Park: 32, 15th January 1978
Claremont Park, Esher: 22, 1st March 1979
Earlswood: 25, 1969 and 8th February 1970
Effingham Fish Ponds: 118, 11th January 1997

Enton: 84, 12th November 1961
Fetcham Mill Pond: 35, December 1988
Frensham: 370, February 1973 (*HSBBR*)
Frimley Gravel Pits: 283, 26th December 1996 (*HSBBR*)
Gatton Lake: 77, 17th December 1961
Godstone: 53 (Pounds, undated)
Hammer Pond: 46, 6th January 1996
Hedgecourt: 40, 17th December 1988
Hersham Gravel Pit: 63, November 1988
Holmethorpe Sand Pits: 100, December 1981
Island Barn Reservoir: 237, 20th January 2001
Lonsdale Road Reservoir: 144, January 1998
Papercourt Gravel Pits: 250, 12th January 1997
Pen Ponds: 435, 13th February 1952
Queen Elizabeth II Reservoir: 3,000, 9th February 1963
Stoke Lake, Guildford: 91, 18th January 1999

Surrey Docks: 1,700, 17th January 1971
Thorpe Water Park: 246, October 1981
Tongham Gravel Pit: 38, December 1999
Virginia Water: 80, 19th February 1970
Walton Reservoirs: 1,500-2,000, March 1947; 2,000, 2nd March 1963
Wimbledon Park Lake: 30+, February 1980
Spelthorne
King George VI Reservoir: 1,584, December 1986
Queen Mary Reservoir: 2,000 on 2nd March 1963
Queen Mary Gravel Pits: 550 on 11th August 1976
Staines Reservoirs: 5,000, 23rd November 1979 to February 1980
Wraysbury Reservoir: 400 in January 1978 and January 1979

Staines Reservoir (Spelthorne) was a nationally important site for Pochard in the 1990s. The average annual wildfowl count maxima from 1994/95 to 1998/99 was 494.

Movements and longevity. A Pochard ringed in Latvia on 23rd June 1992 was recovered 1,660 km WSW near Great Bookham on 5th October 1996. One ringed near Peterborough on 5th February 1996 was recorded over eight years and two months later at Laleham on 12th April 2004.

Ring-necked Duck   *Aythya collaris*
About ten birds to 2003

Breeds in North America, wintering south to Costa Rica. British records are spread throughout the year, with fewest from June to August. Once in Britain, birds not infrequently remain for long periods and may return to the same wintering site for several years running.

Surrey. Records date back to 1985:

1985:   Frimley Gravel Pits, a first-winter male found by K. B. Wills on 17th November moved to Fleet Pond (Hampshire) and was later seen at Frimley on 23rd November to 13th December. It then moved between Ash Vale, Badshot Lea and Frimley gravel pits until its final day at Badshot Lea on 16th April 1986 (*BB*, 79:537, *BB*, 80:528, *HSBBR* 1996). A male at Frimley Gravel Pits on 9th September 1986 was seen there and at Ash Vale Gravel Pits until at least 6th April 1987 (P. M. Troake *et al.*, *BB*, 81:548) and was presumably the same bird.

1992:   Lonsdale Road Reservoirs, a male on 20th April (B. P. Aris, M. J. and Mrs A. P. Earp *et al.*, *BB*, 86:462).

1996:   Vachery Pond, a male from 20th January to 9th March.

1997:   Surrey Docks, a first-winter male from 11th January to 3rd February (*LBR*).
        Gatton Park Lake, a male on 23rd March.

2000:   Bessborough Reservoir, Walton-on-Thames, a male on 7th April.
        Frensham Little Pond, a male that was first seen on 29th-31st October was later at Frensham Great Pond on 5th and 12th-22nd November, Tongham Gravel Pits (many dates 12th December to 8th January 2001), Moat Pond (19th December), and Cutt Mill (3rd January 2001).

2001:   Virginia Water, one on 17th January has been accepted as being in Surrey.

Walton and Island Barn reservoirs, a first-winter female from 25th November to 4th May 2002, also seen on the adjacent rivers Ember and Mole and at Fieldcommon Gravel Pit.

Bourne Hall, Ewell, a different first-winter female from 22nd December to at least 16th February 2002.

2002:   Barn Elms London Wetland Centre, one or other of the 2001 birds on 3rd February.

Beddington Sewage Farm, one or other of the 2002 birds on 24th February.

2002:* Shepperton Gravel Pits, a female on April 6th (*LNHSB*) was probably the Island Barn Reservoir bird of 2001.

2002:   Bourne Hall, Ewell, a female from 5th December to 26th February 2003 (*LBR*).

2003:   Island Barn Reservoir, one on 1st March.

Spelthorne

Ferruginous Duck   *Aythya nyroca*

At least forty-four records, including eleven from Spelthorne

Breeds from southern Europe across the steppes to Asia, wintering south to Africa and India. It is currently declining in the west of its range.

Early Surrey history. Bucknill (1900) mentions only one 19th century occurrence, undated. A specimen which was then in the Charterhouse Collection was said to have been killed at Bramley (*SALEC*) and sent to Stafford, the collector, by a Guildford poulterer. This bird is no longer held in the collection. The early 20th century records for Surrey and the London area were not free of suspicions about the origin of the birds. A pinioned pair was introduced into St James's Park, Westminster, in 1912. The pair did not breed but others were seen at the same site and a brood of seven was produced in 1938. A pair seen at Barn Elms Reservoir on July 17th of that year probably came from the park (*LBR*). An adult drake seen at Barn Elms on 12th and 29th January 1947 was considered a possible escape. A note in the *London Bird Report* for 1947 quotes a letter written by the Duke of Bedford to the *Manchester Guardian* on 3rd May 1947 warning that "The war has had a devastating effect on collections of waterfowl …" and warning that, for the next few years, any full-winged duck, rare or common, might be an escape. While the *LBR*'s caution is understandable, the date is quite consistent with this having been a wild bird and it has been counted as such in what follows.

There were identification problems while reliable information about the characteristics of *Aythya* hybrids was being collected, see the section on escapes for an example. The records which are considered reliable are below. All are single birds unless otherwise stated. Numbers peaked in the 1960s:

Bird months by decade 1900-2003

	1900s	1910s	1920s	1930s	1940s	1950s	1960s	1970s	1980s	1990s	2000s	Total
Vice-county	0	0	2	4	4	11	26	9	12	8	10	**86**
Spelthorne	0	0	0	58	2	9	31	13	23	10	0	**146**

Staines Reservoirs, with 106 bird months, has been by far the most heavily used site, followed by King George VI Reservoir with 28. The busiest vice-county site has been Walton Reservoirs, with 25. Detailed records are these:

Vice-county: *Barn Elms Reservoir*: 12th and 29th January 1947; 19th-20th February 1956; 10th-27th January 1960 (*BB, 54:182*), arrived with influx of other ducks; 9th-14th February 1969; 24th and 27th January 1971; 9th-24th December 1973; *Beddington Sewage Farm*: 11th December 1990; *Bramley*: before 1900; *Domewood Lake*: 8th December 1946; *Enton Ponds*: 5th August 1959 (*BB, 53:415*); 17th December 1978; *Frensham*: 8th October 1920 (Shaw); 29th December 1960 to 12th January 1961 (17th January

1961 in HNHS, 1968); *Frimley Gravel Pits*: single females (same?), 18th September 1986 (*HSBBR*) and 10th January to 5th February 1987; *Gatton*: 30th December 1951 and 10th March 1952; *Godstone*: 3rd, 16th and 26th January 1952, 13th March 1952 (the Gatton bird?), 11th and 13th January 1969; *Hedgecourt*: 15th-23rd January 2000 (K. E. Noble *et al.*, *BB, 95:488*); *Papercourt Gravel Pits*: a female on 2nd January 2002 (J. Gates, *BB, 96:558*); *Queen Elizabeth II and Walton Reservoirs*: 15th October 1972; *Surrey Docks*: 7th January 1971 a pair, one staying to 10th January 1971; 7th-13th December 1971; 31st October 1972 to the end of the year (six dates); 13th-14th December 1973; 2nd-24th January 1974 and 11th February 1974; 14th-28th November 1974; a male from 2nd-16th January 1975, 18th-22nd February 1975 and 11th March 1975; a female on 3rd and 6th February 1975; *Tooting Bec Common*: 5th-6th January 1981; *Virginia Water*: 22nd December 1932 (*BB, 26:279*); 29th December 1949 to 5th March 1950 mainly at the Berkshire end (*BB, 43:340*); 7th October 1956, a pair, county not known (*Middle-Thames Naturalist 23:5*); *Walton Reservoirs*: 23rd, 25th-26th and 28th February 1956 (Barn Elms bird?)' *Wandsworth Common*: 15th-19th January 1980.

Spelthorne: *King George VI Reservoir*: an adult male on 19th December 1964 (J. B. Cox, S. Greenwood and D. M. Putman on 19th, *BB, 58:358*), still there on the 31st (*LBR*); *Queen Mary Reservoir*: a male on 8th December 1958 (D. W. Taylor, *BB, 53:411*); *Staines Reservoirs*: 24th September 1928, a pair (Glegg, who was not fully satisfied); 2nd to 3rd January 1965 (the King George VI Reservoir bird, *LBR*); 28th September 1966 (A. D. Prowse, G. Walker, *BB, 60:314*); 26th October to 26th November 1986, a female which arrived with Pochards and Tufted Ducks; a drake on 29th October 1971; two females 2nd and 15th November 1986; a juvenile on 1st October 2002 (also Berkshire and Harmondsworth, *BB, 96:558*); *Wraysbury Reservoir*: 17th January 1982; 20th September 1986.

Calendar. Peak months are December and January. There have been none from April to July:

Bird months since 1900

	Jan	Feb	Mar	Apr	May	Jun	Jul	Aug	Sep	Oct	Nov	Dec	Total
Vice-county	16	9	3	0	0	0	0	1	0	3	2	11	**45**
Spelthorne	2	0	0	0	0	0	0	0	2	2	2	2	**10**

Tufted Duck

Aythya fuligula

Common breeding resident and winter visitor

Breeds from northern Europe east to Siberia, wintering south to Africa and points east. Tufted Ducks were regular but uncommon visitors to Britain in the first half of the 19th century, with very sketchy evidence of breeding. Since then, they have become much more common and were still increasing from

1970 to 2005. Autumn migrants to Britain are mostly from northern Europe (*MA*). Tufted Ducks were introduced to the London Zoo in 1831 and bred regularly in Regent's Park up to 1848. They bred in St James's Park in 1838 and later colonised other London parks (*LBR* for 1938).

Early Surrey history. Tufted Ducks were seen at least occasionally in west Surrey in the first half of the 19th century, though the only dated record available is one in Newman of a flock of five at Milford in January 1841. Spicer (1854) knew of an occurrence in the Farnham district. Bucknill gave a few later occurrences, as near Witley (three, spring of 1870), Gatton Lake (three, 25th March 1876) on the Thames at East Molesey (one, 5th December 1879), Poynter's near Cobham (undated) and as regular visitors to Milford House Pond and the larger western lakes. He said they bred freely in captivity.

Since 1900. Tufted Ducks were on Fetcham Mill Pond in December 1901 and on other dates. There were 50 at Barn Elms in 1902 and 90 in Battersea Park in 1905 (*BLA*). Mouritz saw three in Richmond Park on 26th February 1905, five in the following month and eleven on 5th November. Dalgliesh counted fifteen on the Hammer Ponds, Thursley on 17th February 1906 and they were first seen at Gatton in 1908. Tufted Ducks were using Staines Reservoirs by 1906 (Glegg). Wintering flocks were seen at Staines Reservoirs in the 1930s, arriving as early as July, reaching 600-700 by the end of September and leaving during April (Glegg, based on 1930-31).

Breeding. The first breeding record for wild birds appears to be of a pair that bred annually from 1901 to 1904 at Dulwich Park Lake, raising four young in 1901 and then two in 1902, three in 1903 and two in 1904 (Power). Disturbance by the boats permitted on the lake from 1904 prevented successful breeding in subsequent years. The date is earlier than that of P. E. Bunyard's breeding pair on 'a large Surrey pond' in 1912 (*BB, 6:158*). Tufted Ducks first bred at Richmond Park in the 1920s and at Godstone in 1922. They bred at Barn Elms in 1925 and 1928-30. A pair bred on Wandsworth Common in 1927, Beddington Gravel Pits were colonised in 1929 and Gatton Park in 1930. In Spelthorne, a brood of eight was seen at Staines Reservoirs on 22nd July 1934, the first breeding record for Spelthorne. A nest with eggs was found at Queen Mary Reservoir in 1936 and another in 1937. By 1938, Tufted Ducks were breeding at many sites in the London area and winter counts of 700 or more (Barnes, 1935) were being made. G. Douglas found a nest with nine eggs on Thursley Common in 1952. Tufted Ducks first bred at Battersea Park in 1955. Since then, they have colonised large and small waters across the county. They were nesting at Vann Lake by 1964 (Blaker Log). Breeding at Holmethorpe was first proved in 1975 (*BHSP*). Oliver (1985) estimated the May/June population of the Surrey part of the London area in 1984 at 64-99 pairs (24-39 of them at Barn Elms), with 36-91 extra males and 2-7 extra females. The map shows that Tufted Ducks are strongly represented on the small ponds of parks and commons in this area. Tufted Ducks bred at Shepperton in the 1980s.

Of the 231 tetrads in northeast Surrey, 24% were found to hold territories in the 1968-72 Atlas survey and 34% in the 1988-97 Atlas, showing a significant extension of range. The 1988-97 SBC Atlas survey found birds in 134 tetrads across the county. This is only 23% of the total, showing a lower density in rural areas than the more heavily built-up region of northeast Surrey. The conversion of Barn Elms Reservoirs to a wetland reserve has increased the number of northeast Surrey breeding pairs further and 33 broods were raised there in 2002

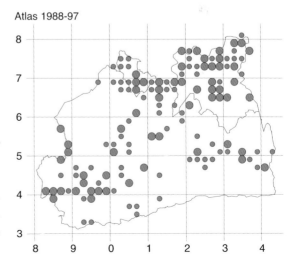

Atlas 1988-97

(*Londen Wetland Centre Bird and Natural History Report 2001 and 2002*). Beddington Sewage Farm has held between seven and 15 pairs from 2000 and 2004. Breeding reports for the vice-county as a whole currently come from around 20 sites annually, a small fraction of the true total.

Population size. Tufted Ducks were occasionally found in Common Birds Censuses from 1964. The number of territories depended mainly on the amount of wetland covered, the underlying trend being inconclusive. The Breeding Birds Survey of 1994-2004 suggested a breeding season population of around 1,400 adults, which looks a little high. The Common Birds Census, on a much smaller sample, suggested more but probably over-represented them. If Surrey held a proportionate share of the British breeding population as given by the *New Atlas*, the population would be fewer than 60 territories, showing how well Tufted Ducks fare, in relative terms, in Surrey.

Calendar. Moulting flocks build up at Barn Elms, Island Barn, Queen Elizabeth II and Walton reservoirs from late July, *e.g.* 1,407 at King George VI Reservoir in 1973, 1,200 at Queen Mary Reservoir in 1976 and 1,400 at Wraysbury Reservoir in 1975, a feature often commented on in the 1970s and still apparent from recent counts. Many disperse in September, numbers remaining lower until the arrival of later winter immigrants, which in recent years have been few in number, in December. This is illustrated in the table, which has been compiled for sites where a full set of monthly counts is available.

Vice-county monthly maxima in 1999

	Jan	Feb	Mar	Apr	May	Jun	Jul	Aug	Sep	Oct	Nov	Dec
Barn Elms	91	150	110	128	87	102	66	61	83	98	116	169
Beddington Sewage Farm	70	65	64	36	35	60	30	25	100	90	45	18
Frensham Ponds	37	50	20	64	26	11	7	8	16	26	45	43
Island Barn Reservoir	95	71	97	19	6	9	18	240	260	113	78	31
Papercourt Gravel Pits	92	50	39	28	22	12	24	22	60	98	140	150
Queen Elizabeth II Reservoir	4	7	18	10	14	69	398	327	434	119	65	47
Stoke Lake	48	22	17	18	2	3	0	1	5	10	15	31
Waddon Ponds	52	46	59	22	9	3	17	14	21	12	29	45
Walton Reservoirs	85	60	62	82	28	21	433	565	111	108	136	235
Total	**574**	**521**	**486**	**407**	**229**	**290**	**993**	**1,263**	**1,090**	**674**	**669**	**769**

Large counts. Bentham found 200 drakes at Hedgecourt on 30th May 1935, still a record for the site and, although not stated, presumably a bachelor party. Flocks often contain a preponderance of males, as analysed for Walton Reservoirs by Homes (1942). The biggest counts date back to the 1970s and earlier:

Ash Vale Gravel Pits: 125, January 1979
Badshot Lea: 280, January 1973 (*HSBBR*)
Barn Elms: 2,700, January 1964; 2,400-2,800, January 1966
Battersea Park: 280, January 1990
Beddington Sewage Farm: 125, October 1993 and 24th January 2004
Effingham Fish Ponds: 40, March and December 1985
Enton: 102, 1969
Epsom Common Stew Ponds: 80, 5th March 1989
Frensham: 466, 23rd November 1958
Frimley Gravel Pits: 171, February 1991 (*HSBBR*)
Gatton Lake: 114, 4th February 1960
Hammer Pond: 51, March 1987 (*HSBBR*)

Hedgecourt: 200 drakes, May 1935
Holmethorpe Sand Pits: 170, 25th November 2004
Island Barn Reservoir: 868, November 2003 (*LBR*)
Long Ditton: 91, 29th October 1989
Lonsdale Road Reservoir: 300, February 1987
Mytchett Gravel Pit: 48, February 1989 (*HSBBR*)
North Camp Gravel Pits: 62, 28th February 1970
Papercourt Gravel Pits: 200, 1974
Pen Ponds: 154, 1965
Queen Elizabeth II Reservoir: 3,130, 13th January 1963
Stoke Lake: 48, January 1999
Surrey Docks: 800, 7th January 1971

Thorpe Water Park: 893, October 1982
Tongham Gravel Pit: 87, 2nd December 2000
Virginia Water: 86, November 1976
Waddon Ponds: 98, 18th March 1996
Walton Reservoirs: 3,000, 3rd March 1963
Wimbledon Park Lake: 120, 1962
Spelthorne
King George VI Reservoir: 7,230, 3rd January 1971

Queen Mary Reservoir: up to 2,000, 2nd March 1963,
Shepperton Gravel Pits: 574, December 1986
Staines Reservoirs: 1,118, October 1958; 3,332, September 1995; up to 4,500, January and February 1980
Wraysbury Reservoir: 1,500 in January 1979

Staines Reservoirs, with an average peak count of 1,325 from 1999/2000 to 2003/04, is a nationally important site for wintering Tufted Ducks.

Movements and longevity. A Tufted Duck that was ringed at Walton Reservoirs in January 1934 and retrapped there by P. A. D. Hollom in December 1934 before being recovered in Finland in 1935 was the first British proof by ringing of a migrant bird of any species wintering in the same place in different winters (*BB, 29:138*). Eight Tufted Ducks ringed in winter at Walton Reservoirs and two ringed in winter at Queen Mary Reservoir have been recovered abroad. Three of them were in Finland in April (1935, two in 1959), two were in France in July (1935 and 1972), one was in the Netherlands (August 1982) and one in the old USSR (May 1958). The two from Queen Mary Reservoir were recovered in the old USSR in May and August 1981. Four foreign-ringed birds have been recovered in Surrey, one from Estonia, two from Finland and one from Latvia. Notable distances travelled and longevity are:

Ringed		Recovered		Distance/age
Pembrokeshire	1st February 1938	Barnes	January 1952	13 years 11 months
Walton Reservoirs	3rd December 1956	Old USSR, Komi	3rd May 1958	3,306 km
Queen Mary Reservoir	23rd January 1991	Old USSR, Katravozsh	18th May 1991	4,098 km

Severe winter weather can cause extra Tufted Duck deaths at the reservoirs. Examples given in the weather section above included four at Staines in 1929.

Scaup (Greater Scaup)   *Aythya marila*
Scarce winter visitor

A circumpolar arctic and sub-arctic breeding species wintering south to the Mediterranean. Has occasionally bred in England and Scotland, possibly associated with periods of climatic cooling. Most winter immigrants ringed abroad and recovered in Britain are from Iceland, with a few from the Russian Arctic (*MA*).

Early Surrey history. A pair said to have been shot near Hampton Lodge (*SALEC*) were in the Charterhouse Collection in Bucknill's time but are no longer held there. One was shot on a pond near Milford House, Milford on 8th December 1846 (*Zool.,1847:1641-42*). Bucknill gave four other records, of six or seven over Gatton on 8th January 1871, one on the Thames at Molesey in February 1874 and another there on 10th January 1877 and one shot at Poynter's, Cobham. There were five on Dulwich Park Lake on 8th October 1898 (Power).

Since 1900. Shaw saw one that had been shot at Witley (undated). There were two at Frensham on 28th November 1908 (Bentham) and two on 30th December 1920 (Shaw). One at Staines Reservoirs on 15th December 1923 and two on the 29th (*London Naturalist* for 1924) appear to be the first for the Spelthorne district. There were seven at the Molesey reservoirs on 21st and 25th February 1926 (*LN*). Others were at Barn Elms (1928-30) and at Frensham Great Pond in the winter of 1931/32 and on 23rd December 1932. One or two were seen at Frensham in most winters up to the 1950s. There was a female on a large pond at Godalming on 11th January 1936 and one on the Thames at Waterloo in early 1941.

One on a gravel pit near Molesey on 5th May 1946 was apparently the first Surrey record for the month of May. Other places where Scaup were seen up to 1970 include Barn Elms Reservoirs, Carshalton (1963), Enton (1957), Frensham, Lonsdale Road Reservoir, Richmond Park (1958, 1959, 1961, 1965) South Norwood Lake (1956), Wimbledon Park Lake (1961). The intense cold of the 1947 winter brought unusual numbers to Surrey as did, to a lesser extent, severe weather in early 1963 and early 1997.

Vice-county numbers peaked in the cold decades of the 1940s and 1960s:

Bird months by decade 1900-2003

	1900s	1910s	1920s	1930s	1940s	1950s	1960s	1970s	1980s	1990s	2000s	Total
Vice-county	2	0	30	57	119	73	96	77	72	73	37	**636**

Since 1970, Scaup have been seen most frequently at the adjacent Walton area reservoirs, rivers and gravel pits, with Barn Elms/Lonsdale Road and Frensham the next most frequent sites. Birds have also been seen at Ash Vale, Beddington, Chertsey, Chobham, Crystal Palace, Earlswood, Frimley, Godstone, Hammer Pond, Henley Park, Holmethorpe, Mitcham, Moat Pond, Papercourt, the Surrey Docks, Teddington and Thorpe. There were at least 25 vice-county bird months from 2001-03, records coming from Barn Elms London Wetland Centre, Beddington Sewage Farm, Island Barn Reservoir (five on 9th November 2003), Queen Elizabeth II Reservoir, Tongham Gravel Pit and Walton Reservoirs. Others were at the Spelthorne reservoirs, which have continued to attract similar numbers to the rest of Surrey, with 15 bird months from 1998 to 2001, all of them from King George VI Reservoir or Wraysbury Reservoir and with a maximum of five at Wraysbury on 17th January 2000.

Calendar. Single birds at Queen Mary Reservoir on 2nd June 1958 and at Staines Reservoirs on 17th August 1947 appear to be the first for these months in any part of Surrey. Other summer records include a female at Wraysbury Reservoir on 19th July 1999 and one at Staines Reservoirs on 2nd August 1949. None have been recorded in the vice-county in June or July.

Bird months 1900 to 2003

	Jan	Feb	Mar	Apr	May	Jun	Jul	Aug	Sep	Oct	Nov	Dec	Total
Vice-county	139	177	110	34	7	0	0	2	3	26	63	75	**636**
Spelthorne*	28	19	81	9	1	2	0	5	2	15	16	21	**199**

* to 1963 only

Large counts. The largest counts are before 1960:

Barn Elms Reservoirs: up to seven, January to March 1951; seven, 4th February 1956; seven, 3rd and 16th February 1962
Frensham: six, 14th October 1931
Surrey Docks: eight, 2nd and 4th April 1974
Thames at Chiswick: 17, 9th March 1947
Thames at Wandsworth: 18, 1st March 1947

Walton Reservoirs: eight, 16th March 1947
Spelthorne
Queen Mary Reservoir: 20, 6th March 1954 (Geen).
Staines Reservoirs: five, 17th-18th March 1979; five, 23rd March 1985; five, 12th February 1991

Movements and longevity. One ringed in Iceland on 6th August 1947 was recovered at Lonsdale Road Reservoir on 5th March 1950, a day short of two years and seven months later. Hudson (1898) mentioned one that was killed and partly eaten on an island in Battersea Park by a large cat. The cat, which could swim, was hunted by 18 men and a dog but escaped.

Eider (Common Eider) *Somateria mollissima*

An irregular winter visitor, sometimes making prolonged stays

Breeds on northern coasts of Europe and North America, moving further south in winter. Ringing recoveries in the *Migration Atlas* show an exchange between Britain, Denmark and the Baltic.

Surrey. Jordan (1895) mentioned a storm-driven female that was shot on a Surrey moor '39 years ago' (*i.e.* in about 1856). Dated records, which include some long-stayers, are:

1957:* King George VI Reservoir, six from 12th November to 1st December (S. Greenwood *et al.*), the first for Middlesex.

1965: Frensham Great Pond, a drake on 10th July,

1968: Virginia Water, one on 15th September (*Middle-Thames Naturalist* 23:5) may not have been in Surrey.

1973: Island Barn Reservoir, one from 16th December to 19th June 1976 was also seen at Walton Reservoirs.

1976:* Queen Mary Reservoir, one in March and two there on 4th November.
Staines Reservoirs, one on 28th April.
Wraysbury Reservoir, one on 10th August.

1978: Island Barn Reservoir, a drake on 17th December and on 7th January 1979.

1982: Streatham, a female in worsening condition on a garden pond for three days from 1st November.

1988:* Staines Reservoirs, a female on 31st March.

1988: Barn Elms Reservoirs, a female on 16th November.

1993: Papercourt Gravel Pits, a female from 31st October to 1st November, when it moved to Stoke Lake, where it stayed until the next day.
Holmethorpe Sand Pit, a female on 31st October, not the Papercourt bird.
Two briefly at Beddington Sewage Farm on 2nd November.
One on the Thames at Isleworth Eyot on 10th November.

1998: Queen Elizabeth II Reservoir, eight on 21st November, five staying on into 1999 and one until 13th March 2000.

1999:* Queen Mary Reservoir, four on 29th October and 8th November.

Spelthorne

Food. Recent Surrey birds are thought to have been feeding on the introduced Zebra Mussel *Dreissena polymorpha*, now common in northwest Surrey reservoirs (*LBR* for 1999).

Long-tailed Duck *Clangula hyemalis*

Scarce winter visitor

A circumpolar arctic breeding species which has occasionally bred in northern Scotland, and winters in southern Britain in small numbers. Most Long-tailed Ducks wintering in Britain are probably from northern regions of Finland and Scandinavia and northwest Russia (*MA*).

Surrey. Appearances have been irregular, with peaks in the 1930s and the colder 1960s:

Bird months by decade

	1900s	1910s	1920s	1930s	1940s	1950s	1960s	1970s	1980s	1990s	2000-03	Total
Vice-county	0	0	2	4	4	11	26	9	12	8	10	**86**
Spelthorne	0	0	0	58	2	9	31	13	23	10	0	**146**

Vice-county records are these:

1928: Barn Elms Reservoirs, a female or immature bird was found on 13th November by Donald Gunn. It remained until 17th December (to 17th in Parr, to 15th in the *LN*).

1938: Walton Reservoirs and Island Barn Reservoir, one on dates from 27th January to 19th April (*LBR*).

1947: Walton Reservoirs, one on 25th February, 9th March and 16th March (*LBR*).
Thames, one at Kew/Hammersmith on 1st-9th March and at Southwark on 14th-18th March, not the Walton Reservoirs bird.
Barn Elms Reservoirs, one on 16th, 21st-22nd and 29th June (*LBR*), appears to be the only Surrey record for June.

1951: Barn Elms Reservoirs, one on 22nd-31st December, also at Barn Elms and Lonsdale Road reservoirs until 20th January 1952, two on 8th January.

1952: Pen Ponds, one on 12th-15th January.
Thames near Hungerford Bridge, one on 7th February.
Barn Elms Reservoirs, one on 30th November and 7th December.

1957: Island Barn Reservoir, one from 6th January to 4th February.
Enton, one on 15th December.

1961: Frensham, an immature bird on 9th-10th November.

1965: Queen Elizabeth II and other reservoirs, one from 12th December to 20th March 1966, at Island Barn and Walton reservoirs on some of the dates.

1966: Island Barn Reservoir, one on 23rd January and 13th February. The Queen Elizabeth II bird.
Walton Reservoirs, one on dates from 19th February to 20th March. The Queen Elizabeth II bird.

1967: Frensham, two on dates from 28th October to 26th November, three on 5th November (*SBR*, HNHS 1968).
Barn Elms Reservoirs, one from 6th November to 18th February 1968, second bird present in November.
Island Barn Reservoir, one on 12th November, also one at Walton Reservoirs on the 24th, presumed the same.

1968: Barn Elms Reservoir, one from 17th March to 10th May (not the 1967 bird).

1969: Walton Reservoirs, one from 23rd November to 11th May 1970.

1972: Barn Elms Reservoirs, one on 18th November.

1975: Beddington Sewage Farm, one on 22nd September.

1978: Walton Reservoirs, one from 26th December to 1st May 1979.

1979: Walton Reservoirs, one on 10th November.

1980: Island Barn Reservoir, one on 21st December.

1981: Walton Reservoirs, one from 18th January to 19th March (not 29th, as in the *SBR*).

1983: Island Barn Reservoir, one from 20th November to 22nd February 1984, presumably the one seen at Walton Reservoirs on 12th February.

1984: Holmethorpe Sand Pits, one from 21st October to 9th December.

1991: Island Barn Reservoir, one from 22nd December to 15th February 1992, then at Walton Reservoirs from 20th February to 31st March 1992.

1992: Walton Reservoirs, one on 21st April, a different bird.
Walton Reservoirs, one from 15th November to at least the 20th.

1993: Barn Elms Reservoirs, one from 7th November (6th in the *LBR*) to 23rd December.

2001: Papercourt Gravel Pits, on 19th November.
Longside Lake, one on 21st November.

Walton Reservoirs, one on 9th December.

2003:   Walton Reservoirs, one on 27th September.

Island Barn Reservoir, a female or immature bird on 4th November and dates to 17th March 2004, also seen at Walton and Queen Elizabeth II reservoirs.

Spelthorne. There are numerous records, the earliest being:

1932:   Staines Reservoirs, one was found by F. R. Finch on 6th November (Glegg), apparently the first for Middlesex. One or two were then seen on dates to 25th April 1933, with four on 18th November.

1933:   Staines Reservoirs, one for a day or two from 5th November 1933 and probably the same bird on 19th January and dates to 7th April 1934 (Glegg).

1934:   Staines Reservoirs, four on 18th October and one on dates from 23rd October to 24th March 1935 (*LN*).

1935:   Staines Reservoirs, one from 29th September to 21st March 1936.

1936:   Staines Reservoirs, one from 11th October to 6th April 1937 (Glegg).

There were others at Staines Reservoirs up to 1940 but the next was not until 22nd January 1949. Another long gap followed, with the next not until 1954. Long-tailed Ducks were almost annual from 1957 to 1971 but have since been irregular, most often seen at Staines Reservoirs and often staying for long periods. Single birds at Wraysbury Reservoir in 1998 and Staines Reservoirs in 1999 were the first since 1992. There were none in 2000 or 2001.

Calendar. Arrivals are usually from October onwards with many birds lingering until April:

Bird months 1900 to 2001

	Jan	Feb	Mar	Apr	May	Jun	Jul	Aug	Sep	Oct	Nov	Dec	Total
Vice-county	14	14	11	5	3	1	0	0	2	2	19	15	**86**
Spelthorne	22	19	26	23	3	0	0	0	3	10	20	20	**146**

Common Scoter   *Melanitta nigra*

Uncommon mainly winter visitor

Breeds in the northern and Arctic regions from Europe east to Siberia and North America, wintering south to northern Africa. Also breeds in Scotland and Ireland and has bred in northern England. Little change in status up to 1900 or since has been traced. Has bred in Ireland since 1905, peaking in the 1960s. Recently separated from the North American and east Siberian Black Scoter *M. americana* (previously *M. n. americana*).

Early Surrey history. This bird was rarely seen in the 19th century, with only three dated records. A Common Scoter was shot on a pond near the [Basingstoke?] canal at Farnham on 2nd November 1843, another was killed at Hampton Lodge on 31st October 1855 and one was shot at East Molesey on 17th April 1878 (Bucknill). One shot on the Wey near Godalming on an unknown date was in the Charterhouse Collection in Bucknill's time and was still there in 2001. Two were shot on the Thames at Bell Weir Lock, Runnymede some years before 1906 (Kerr).

1910 to 1969. A female on the Thames at Lambeth on 2nd March 1912 was the first for Inner London (Macpherson). There was one on The Flashes at Churt on 16th April 1924. In Spelthorne, there was one at Staines Reservoirs on 13th April 1922 (*BB*, 16:25) and another there on 21st November 1926 (*London Naturalist*). From April 1929, when there were two present, Common Scoters became fairly regular visitors to the Spelthorne reservoirs.

Vice-county sites to the 1960s include Badshot Lea (1962 and 1969 in Clark 1984), Barn Elms,

(March 1929, April 1930, April and October 1935, September 1936, 1937-39 and later dates), Beddington Sewage Farm (1937, 1951), Carshalton (1953), Dulwich Mill Pond (1958), Enton (1958, 1966), The Flashes (Churt), Frensham (1931, 1933, 1952, 1955, 1957-58, 1961, 1963), Godstone Bay Pond (1958), Island Barn Reservoir (1932, 1953, 1956 etc), Kew Gardens (1952), Lonsdale Road Reservoir (1930, 1944), Moat Pond (1966), Queen Elizabeth II Reservoir (from 1963), Richmond Park (1948), South Norwood Lake (1957), the Thames (Kew 1949, Chiswick 1963), Virginia Water (1967, county uncertain) and Walton Gravel Pits and Reservoirs (1955, 1957-58, 1960 and later). There is an undated record for Wimbledon Common in *BLA* and for the Beverley Brook in Parr.

Where seen since 1970. There were 85 records from 1970-2000, of which 63 were at Barn Elms, Frensham and Walton Reservoirs. Sites and records were: Barn Elms 19; Frensham 22 (of which at least 17 were at the Great Pond); Frimley Gravel Pits three; Holmethorpe five; Papercourt Gravel Pits five; Thames three; Walton area reservoirs 22 (of which Island Barn eight, Queen Elizabeth II six and Walton Reservoirs eight); one each at Beddington Sewage Farm, Clapham Common, Moat Pond, Mole at East Molesey, Seale Sand Pits, Stoke Water Meadows and Warren Mere. Common Scoters rarely linger for more than a day. After 2000 there have been further reports from Barn Elms, Frensham, Holmethorpe Sand Pits, Island Barn Reservoir, Queen Elizabeth II Reservoir and Walton Reservoirs. The largest party was three at Queen Elizabeth II Reservoir on 6th April 2003.

In Spelthorne, sightings include three immature birds at King George VI Reservoir in November 2001, four at King George VI Reservoir in June 1998 and eight at Staines Reservoirs in May 2002 (BTO, *LBR*).

Calendar. Although Common Scoters are mainly spring migrants, they have been seen in every month of the year, as the table shows:

Bird months 1970-2000

	Jan	Feb	Mar	Apr	May	Jun	Jul	Aug	Sep	Oct	Nov	Dec	Total
Vice-county	1	5	16	103	25	12	19	14	12	9	7	1	**224**
Spelthorne	5	4	19	55	21	26	15	5	14	58	39	6	**267**

Large counts. Common Scoters are sometimes seen in parties of 20 or more. The largest party dates from 1996:

Barn Elms: 50, 7th April 1996; 22, 30th May 1992

Frensham Little Pond: eight, 18th November 1959

Holmethorpe Sand Pits: ten, 25th April 1993

Papercourt Gravel Pits: four, 4th April 1987

Queen Elizabeth II Reservoir: seven, 13th July 2000

Spelthorne

Queen Mary Reservoir: 22, 10th April 1958

Staines Reservoirs: 16, 3rd April 1932; 27, 27th July 1964 and 30th October 1993

King George VI Reservoir: 18-20, 7th June 1953

Velvet Scoter *Melanitta fusca*

24 records in the vice-county, others from Spelthorne

Breeds around fresh and salt water in northern parts of Europe and Asia, wintering south to the Mediterranean. Those found in Britain probably come from Scandinavia, Finland or northern Russia. The scarcest of the scoters and apparently decreasing. North American birds have recently been split off as a separate species.

Surrey. Velvet Scoters have appeared most frequently in the colder decades of the 1940s and 1960s. Recent numbers have been boosted by a long-staying party in the winter of 2001/02:

Bird months by decade

	1900s	1910s	1920s	1930s	1940s	1950s	1960s	1970s	1980s	1990s	2000-02	Total
Vice-county	0	0	1	1	1	15	7	1	5	8	26	**65**
Spelthorne	0	0	2	1	22	9	31	20	11	5	0	**101**

There was a young bird at Barn Elms Reservoirs on 3rd December 1927 (*BB, 23:223*). Single birds at Staines Reservoir on 13th December 1927 (possibly the Barn Elms bird) and 23rd November 1929 were the first records for Middlesex. Subsequent occurrences, of single birds unless otherwise indicated, were these:

Barn Elms: 18th April 1937

Walton Reservoirs: 30th October 1948

Barn Elms Reservoirs: 14th November 1948

Barn Elms Reservoirs: 10th February 1952

Pen Ponds: 30th January 1956

Walton Reservoirs: up to 6, 23rd February to 31st March 1956, with a maximum of six (Parr) on 25th February.

Island Barn Reservoir: 26th February 1956 (*LBR, SBR*, 25th in Parr)

Frensham Great Pond: 4th-24th November 1956

Barn Elms Reservoirs: 29th November 1958

Frensham Great Pond: 26th March 1961

Teddington Weir: 26th-27th January 1963

Walton Reservoirs: 9th-10th February 1963

Barn Elms: A duck and drake, 24th October 1969, the duck stayed until the 28th

Barn Elms Reservoirs: 27th January 1979

Island Barn Reservoir: two drakes, 19th January 1985

Frensham Great Pond: a male, 8th March 1989

Barn Elms Reservoirs: a pair, 16th November 1989

Papercourt Gravel Pits: two, 26th-27th October 1991

Papercourt Gravel Pits: 1st November to 10th December 1991

Beddington Sewage Farm: 11th-16th October 1993

Holmethorpe Sand Pits: 2nd November 1993

Island Barn Reservoir: two, 5th December 1998

Walton Reservoirs: one first seen on 7th December 2001, increasing to five and later seen at Island Barn, Queen Elizabeth II and Walton Reservoirs up to 14th April 2002.

Spelthorne

Staines Reservoirs: 18th April 1937

Staines Reservoirs: 20, 30th October 1948

Staines Reservoirs: two, 7th July 1949

Staines Reservoirs: dates from 25th October 1951 to 6th January 1952

Staines Reservoirs: two, 27th December 1953

King George VI Reservoir: 27th-28th January 1954.

Queen Mary Reservoir: 28th November 1954.

Staines Reservoirs: 31st January 1959

Queen Mary Reservoir: six, 29th October to 4th November 1964, then up to three to the year end and one on 2nd January 1965.

King George VI Reservoir: 13th and 15th December 1968

Queen Mary Reservoir: two from 22nd December 1968 to 26th January 1969

Queen Mary Reservoir: nine, 12th and 18th October 1970, up to six in November

Queen Mary Reservoir: one, 9th February to 7th March 1971,

Queen Mary Reservoir: three on 7th December and one on 22nd December 1971.

Staines Reservoirs: 22nd February 1979,

King George VI Reservoir: 16th November to 6th December 1981

Staines Reservoirs: 27th December 1981

Wraysbury Reservoir: four, 19th January 1985

King George VI Reservoir: 26th January to 23rd February 1985

Staines Reservoirs: a female, 1st November to 20th December 1991, an immature male 21st November 1991

Wraysbury Reservoir: two, 30th November 1981,

Staines Reservoirs: an immature female, 5th December 1995

King George VI Reservoir: 7th-22nd December 1996

Calendar. Arrivals begin in October, which is also the peak month. Most have gone by the end of March:

Bird months 1900-2002

	Jan	Feb	Mar	Apr	May	Jun	Jul	Aug	Sep	Oct	Nov	Dec	Total
Vice-county	11	15	14	6	0	1	0	0	0	6	6	6	**65**
Spelthorne	12	3	1	1	0	0	2	0	0	45	19	18	**101**

Goldeneye (Common Goldeneye) — *Bucephala clangula*

Locally common winter visitor. Most British immigrants are from Finland and Scandinavia (MA).
Goldeneyes have a circumpolar breeding distribution in the northern forests and have bred in Cheshire and Scotland. They nest in tree holes. Breeding numbers in the UK have increased since 1970. Large numbers now winter round the British coasts. Uncommon in inland counties until the 20th century.

Early Surrey history. A young male and female were killed at Hampton Lodge, Puttenham on 31st December 1836 (Long in Bucknill). A pair in the Charterhouse Collection in 2001 (*SALEC*, at least one) were from Godalming and are presumably the undated pair mentioned by Bucknill. Other records in Bucknill are from Witley (one, 22nd February 1885 and another on 20th January 1893), Frensham Great Pond (one, spring of 1894), and near Kew (spring of 1898), Fetcham Mill Pond, Milford House Pond and Poynter's, near Cobham. The creation of the Thames valley reservoirs from the 1890s onwards has provided a large extension of inland winter habitat and Goldeneyes have become more regular at other inland waters such as Frensham Great Pond.

1900 to 1969. There was one at Shamley Green on 17th November 1901 (Dalgliesh, 1902). G. W. Kerr saw Goldeneyes at Staines Reservoir on 29th December, 1906. About 25 wintered there in 1921/22 and there were 35 in April 1938. Collenette knew of six records for Richmond Park by 1936, the earliest being of a female in early February 1904. One of these, in August 1925, seems unlikely to be a wild Goldeneye in view of the date. There are later records from Badshot Lea (1958, 1962), Barn Elms Reservoirs, Barnes (1933), Beddington Sewage Farm (1930, 1934), Enton, Fetcham (1917 *BLA*), Frensham, including two on 13th May 1906 (Mouritz, 1907) and six on 28th November 1937, Gatton (1962), Hamm Moor Gravel Pits (1962), Hammer Pond (1938, 1955), Hedgecourt (1909-10 SBC archive, 1937, 1943, 1946-47), Island Barn (1937 onwards), Kew Gardens (1954-56), Lonsdale Road Reservoir (1938), Mitcham Gravel Pits (1937), Moat Pond (1962), Putney (1920 *BLA*, 1933), Queen Elizabeth II Reservoir (1962 onwards), Richmond Park (1938), Send Gravel Pits (1947), the Thames at Kew (1917 *BLA*), Walton Reservoirs and Winkworth (1957). They were occasional at Enton to 1967 at least. Numbers increased in the 1960s and 70s (Oliver, 1978).

Where found since 1970. Places where Goldeneyes were found from 1970-2000 (with maxima if more than three) include Abbey Farm, Ash Vale Gravel Pit (four, 18th February 1979), Badshot Lea, Battersea Park, Barn Elms (27, January 1985), Beddington Sewage Farm (four, 13th March 1994), Bookham Common, Black Pond (Esher), Broadwater, Buckland, Burgess Park, Chertsey Reservoir (five, 22nd February 1999), Chilworth, Cutt Mill, Effingham Fish Ponds, Enton, Epsom Common, Fieldcommon (28, January 1997), Frensham (11, 20th March 2000), Frimley Gravel Pits, Gatton, Godstone, Ham Lands, Hamm Moor, Hedgecourt, Holmethorpe, Horley Sewage Farm, Island Barn (26, December 1985), Longside Lake, Lonsdale Road Reservoir, Moat Pond, Molesey Gravel Pit (five, 9th February 1997), Morden Hall Park, Oxenford Pond (Peper Harow), Papercourt Gravel Pits, Queen Elizabeth II Reservoir (27, January 1982), Richmond Park (five, 14th April 1977), Send, South Norwood Country Park, Stoke Lake, the Surrey Docks, the Thames (34, 1st February 1987), Thorpe (43, February 1995), Unstead Sewage Farm, Vachery Pond, Walton Reservoirs (109, 17th March 1986), the River Wandle and Windsor Great Park.

Lambeth Reservoir, one of the Walton reservoirs, consistently attracted the largest number of birds, which fed on freshwater mussels on a submerged wall that ran across the reservoir. With the redevelopment of the site in the late 1990s, the Goldeneyes have dispersed to other reservoirs in the area or left it altogether and Thorpe Water Park has become increasingly important. Barn Elms, Beddington, Cutt Mill, Fieldcommon Gravel Pits, Frensham, Frimley Gravel Pits, Hedgecourt, Holmethorpe, Island Barn Reservoir, Longside Lake, Papercourt, Queen Elizabeth II Reservoir, Shepperton Gravel Pits (Spelthorne), Staines Reservoirs (Spelthorne), Stoke Lake, Tongham Gravel Pit, Walton Reservoirs and Wrecclesham are among the sites where Goldeneyes were found after 2000.

Breeding behaviour. Courtship display is not uncommon in winter quarters, for example at Frensham on 31st March 1979.

Calendar. One at Staines Reservoir on 4th October 1936 was an early arrival. The average arrival date in the London area south of the Thames from 1929 to 1939 was 17th October. In the vice-county from 1970-2001, the average departure date was 17th April and the average arrival date was 19th October. The latest spring bird was at Wrecclesham on 17th June 2001 and the earliest of autumn was at Barn Elms on 4th September 1976. There are occasional summer records. Two summered at Staines Reservoir in 1929 (*LN*) and one summered at Queen Mary Reservoir in 1978. In 1963 an immature bird stayed at Barn Elms from 23rd April to 15th July (Parr). A bird stayed at Frensham from 21st July to 15th December 1963, when the pond was frozen. In 2000 and 2002, a male lingered at Walton Reservoirs through the summer. One at King George VI Reservoir on 25th June 2005 was 'unseasonable' (*Bird Watching*). The summering birds are sometimes suspected of having stayed to moult, being injured or being oiled. The largest numbers are usually seen in March, a few weeks before the last departure.

Large counts. The largest numbers were found in the 1980s and early 1990s:

Ash Vale Gravel Pits: four, 18th February 1979
Barn Elms Reservoirs: 27, January 1985
Fieldcommon Gravel Pit: 27, March 1996
Frensham: 16, 14th November 1952
Island Barn Reservoir: 26, December 1985
Queen Elizabeth II Reservoir: 27, January 1982
Thorpe Water Park: 43, February 1995
Walton Reservoirs: 109, 17th March 1986
Spelthorne
King George VI Reservoir: 147, March 1987
Queen Mary Reservoir: 95, 1981
Shepperton Gravel Pits: 32 in February 1990
Staines Reservoirs: 164, February 1991
Wraysbury Reservoir: 73, April 1986

Smew   *Mergellus albellus*

Scarce winter visitor

Nests in tree-holes in the forests of northern Europe and Asia east to Siberia, wintering south to the Mediterranean. Most breed in European Russia and winter in the Baltic or the Netherlands.

Early Surrey history. Remains found in at ditch at the Chaucer House archaeological site in Southwark were dated at 1500-1700 AD, perhaps a lucky find since Smew, like other sawbills, were rare in Surrey until the 1920s. Perhaps it was a relic from the 'Little Ice Age'. Bucknill cites several references, including a female at Hampton Lodge, but could find only three dated records, of a female shot at Wallington Bridge on 2nd January 1871, one near Thursley in 1874 and of a bird shot near Farnham in the severe winter of 1890/91. A pair killed at mills near Albury (*SALEC*) was in the Charterhouse Collection in Bucknill's time and was still held there in 2001. Glegg mentions a female which was shot on the Thames at Kingston on 31st January 1869 and which was brought to Harting.

1900 to 1970. Smew tend to favour the shallower waters. There was one at Frensham on 30th April 1907 and a male there on 10th January 1915. An increase was noticed in the 1920s. Eight or nine at Barn Elms on 25th February 1922 are the earliest records located for the site and numbers there peaked at 48 in November and December 1925. One at Pen Ponds on 11th, 12th and 24th January and 21st February 1926 was the first for Richmond Park. Others were seen there in 1927, on 9th March 1934 (Collenette) and in later years. Twenty or more were seen at Walton Reservoirs in the 1920s and 1930s. Severe weather in 1938 brought 117 to them on 28th December.

Glegg saw a Smew at Staines Reservoirs on 16th December 1923, the first record which has been located for Spelthorne. Ten were there on 10th March 1929, at a time when the smaller reservoirs were frozen. There were 26 on 9th January 1949. Other places where Smew were seen up to 1970 include Barn Elms, Beddington Farm Pond, Carshalton, Elstead, Enton, Frensham, Gatton, Hedgecourt, Holmethorpe, Island Barn Reservoir, Kew Gardens, Lonsdale Road Reservoirs, Ockham, Richmond Park, West Molesey Gravel Pits (21 in 1946), Wire Mill and the Mole, the Wey and the Thames.

Since 1970. During the 1970s and 80s, Smew appearances were irregular. In some years there were none, in others there were none in the second half of the year. Vice-county numbers picked up in the 1990s. There were arrivals before Christmas in every year from 1989 and, as shown in the table, a maximum of about 65 birds were present in the winter of 1995/96:

Number of birds in the vice-county

1989/90	1990/91	1991/92	1992/93	1993/94	1994/95	1995/96	1996/97	1997/98	1998/99	1999/2000	2000/01
1	30	10	2	4	10	65	60	35	25	11	16

Thorpe, where Smew were first recorded in 1979, became a nationally important site, with an average annual wildfowl count maximum from 1994/95 to 1998/99 of 15 (down to ten in the five years to 2003/04) and the only site where Smew were seen regularly. These birds were usually on the pit outside the gates of the Water Park.

Vice-county sites at which Smew have occurred since 1970 are: Abbey Farm Gravel Pit, Ash Vale Gravel Pits, Badshot Lea, Barn Elms, Battersea Park, Beddington Sewage Farm, Buckland, Carshalton Ponds, Clandon Park Lakes, Earlswood Lakes, East Molesey, Effingham Fish Ponds, the River Ember, Enton, Fieldcommon, Frensham, Frimley Gravel Pits, Hedgecourt, Hersham, Holmethorpe, Horley Sewage Farm, Island Barn Reservoir, Long Ditton, Longside Lake, Molesey Gravel Pit, Morden Hall Park, Mytchett Lake, Newdigate, Oxted, Papercourt Gravel Pits, Queen Elizabeth II Reservoir, Queen's Mere, Ravensbury Park, Richmond Park, Send, South Norwood Country Park, Stoke Water Meadows, the Surrey Docks, the Thames, Thorpe, Unstead Sewage Farm, Walton Reservoirs and Wimbledon Park Lake. All the Spelthorne reservoirs have been visited and Staines Moor Gravel Pits was a nationally important site when counted in 1993. There were 18 at Thorpe on 18th January 2004 and 6th January 2006 and three at Staines Reservoirs on 26th November 2005.

Breeding behaviour. Display and mating is not uncommon in winter quarters. Early references came from Barn Elms, Lonsdale Road and Walton Reservoirs (Hollom, 1937, *LBR* for 1946, Parmenter 1937).

Calendar. The average arrival date in the London area south of the Thames from 1929 to 1939 was

27th November. The average arrival date in the vice-county from 1989 to 2000 was 3rd December. There was one at Barn Elms Reservoirs on 5th November 1960. The earliest, from 1970-2000, was at Thorpe on 12th November 1995. One at Thorpe Park in September-October 2003 had a badly injured wing and may have stayed from the previous winter. There are occasional April records, including one from Newdigate in 1985, but the last Smew usually leaves by about 20th March and sometimes in February. The latest spring bird remains one at Frensham on 30th April 1907.

Large counts. The largest counts date back to the 1940s, an indication of the decline in wintering numbers which took place in the second half of the 20th century. A national influx in the winter of 1996/97 was picked up at Thorpe Water Park:

Barn Elms: peak of 48, 28th November to 27th December 1925; up to 78 in January 1947.

Island Barn Reservoir: 24, 17th February 1963

Lonsdale Reservoirs: 13, 31st December 1931; 24, 24th February 1957

Queen Elizabeth II Reservoir: 25, 3rd February 1963

Queen Elizabeth II/Walton reservoirs: 12, 28th December 1995

Thorpe Water Park: 30, 2nd January 1997

Walton Reservoirs: 125, 1946/47 (*BLA*, citing Keith Shackleton in *Country Life* 103:539, the figure is not in the *LBR*)

Spelthorne

King George VI Reservoir: 18, 17th February 1991

Queen Mary Reservoir: 53, 1st February 1987

Shepperton Gravel Pits: 31, 27th January 1985

Staines Reservoirs: 62, 1st February 1964 (*LBR* for 1987)

Wraysbury Reservoir: 31, February 1987

Red-breasted Merganser   *Mergus serrator*

Scarce winter visitor

Breeds in northern parts of Europe, Asia and North America, wintering south to the Mediterranean. The range increased in Scotland during the 19th century. A southward spread into England, Wales and Ireland continued until at least the 1980s. Breeding numbers have increased since 1970.

Early Surrey history. A male was shot on Frensham Pond on 7th February 1829 (Long in Bucknill). The Thames in London was evidently a favoured 19th century area. The first edition of Yarrell (1837-43) mentioned one that was killed in severe weather above Putney Bridge, from Jesse. Meyer recorded 34 on the Thames near Chertsey in November 1842, the first dated record for Middlesex. James Dutton told Harting that two were shot on the Thames at Hammersmith in January 1854 and that another, in his (Dutton's) brother's collection was killed on the Thames near Chiswick in the winter of 1855. There was a female at Merstham early in April 1883 (Bucknill).

1900 to the 1960s. There were two at Frensham Little Pond on 28th December 1913. Four on Upper Pen Pond on 20th February 1916 were the first for Richmond Park and the only ones there to at least 1936. Another was at Frensham on 11th May 1921. Four brown-headed birds at Staines Reservoirs on 18th February 1922 seem to comprise the first dated record for Spelthorne. Another brown-headed bird was found there on 19th February 1931 (Glegg).

Other vice-county records up to 1970 came from Barn Elms (winter 1928/9, 1938, 1947, 1954, 1956), Battersea Park (March 1950), Beddington Sewage Farm (1958, 1963), Dorking (1937), Enton (1964), Frensham (1949, 1954, 1960, 1968, 1969, all December to April), Hedgecourt (1947), Island Barn Reservoir (1947, 1956, 1958), Richmond Park (1966), the Thames (1940, 1942, 1946-47, 1963, 1966) and Walton Reservoirs (winter of 1928/9, 1938, 1944, 1947, 1954-59, 1968 etc). In Spelthorne, there was an adult male at Staines Reservoirs from 16th December 1934 to 13th January 1935 and brown-headed birds were seen on 20th January, 24th February and 2nd to 3rd March. Two were at Staines in January 1936 and there were others up to 5th April. One was found there in late January 1937, after an easterly gale. They were by then fairly regular visitors to the district.

Since 1970. Vice-county records became more frequent from 1970 to the 1990s but seem to have fallen back since:

Bird months by decade

	1970s	1980s	1990s	2000-01	Total
Vice-county	42	72	152	9	**275**

Vice-county sites in this period, with their number of records if more than two, were: Barn Elms (thirteen), Badshot Lea, Beddington Sewage Farm (five), Boldermere, Cutt Mill, Enton, Epsom Common Stew Ponds, Fieldcommon, Frensham (thirteen), Frimley Gravel Pits, Ham Lands, Hersham, Holmethorpe (six), Island Barn Reservoir (eight), Kew, Lonsdale Road Reservoir, Molesey Gravel Pits, Newdigate Brickworks, Papercourt Gravel Pits (thirteen), Queen Elizabeth II Reservoir (eight), South Norwood Lake, Stoke Lake, the Surrey Docks (five), the Thames (four), Thorpe (six in January 1997), Witley Park and Walton Reservoirs (seventeen). Later records came from Beddington (2002), Frensham (2003, 2004), Island Barn Reservoir (2004), Queen Elizabeth II Reservoir (2003-04) and Walton (2002-04). Red-breasted Mergansers have been almost annual visitors to Spelthorne for many years, most often at Staines Reservoirs. There were none in 1976, 1978, 1986, 1990 or 1999. Later vice-county records include five at Beddington Sewage Farm on 1st November 2002 and one at Frensham on 9th December 2004.

Calendar. Three females were briefly at Queen Elizabeth II Reservoir on 24th June 1995. An eclipse drake at Walton Reservoirs on the morning of 20th July 2000 is the only vice-county bird for July. The 275 vice-county bird months from 1970 to 2001 show a clear peak in January. Spelthorne records since 1998 have shown a peak in March and April:

Bird Months 1970-2001

	Jan	Feb	Mar	Apr	May	Jun	Jul	Aug	Sep	Oct	Nov	Dec	Total
Vice-county	82	68	24	13	2	3	1	0	3	10	42	27	**275**
Spelthorne*	2	4	5	5	0	0	0	0	0	1	3	3	**23**

*1998-2001

Large counts. The largest counts go back to the 1980s or earlier:

Barn Elms Reservoirs: up to nine, 25th February to 4th March 1956

Papercourt Gravel Pits: fourteen, 15th February 1987

Queen Elizabeth II Reservoir: up to 11, 20th-24th June 1985

Thames at Chiswick: fourteen, 30th December 1939

Walton Reservoirs: thirteen, early 1956

Spelthorne

Queen Mary Reservoir: nine, 5th November 1994

Staines Reservoirs: ten, 24th-25th February 1979

Wraysbury Reservoir: nine, 22nd November 1972

Goosander

Mergus merganser

Locally common winter visitor

Breeds beside lakes and rivers in northern parts of Europe, Asia and North America, wintering south to the Mediterranean. Colonised Scotland in the second half of the 19th century. Goosanders reached northern England in the 1940s and have since spread into Wales. British breeding numbers are still increasing. Winter immigrants to Britain are mainly from around the Baltic. No birds ringed in northern or western Britain have been recovered in the southeast (*MA*).

Early Surrey history. Goosanders were rarely seen in Surrey or Middlesex until the 1920s. Bucknill could only find eight records, the earliest of which was a female killed at Hampton Lodge on 16th November 1825. Other Goosanders were found at Frensham Pond on 9th January 1827, Ockford Pond

(*SALEC*, undated, in the Charterhouse Collection), Eashing (two killed, undated), Peper Harow Park in the winter of 1838 and West Molesey on 10th January 1877. One was shot at Frensham before 1881. Severe weather brought one to Farncombe, where it was shot on 28th January 1881. A female at Gatton Lake on 26th February of the same year stayed on for nearly two months. One was killed at Frensham in or about 1885. Harting (1866) described Goosanders as rare in Middlesex, without more detail.

1900 to 1969. There was an adult male at Vauxhall Bridge in 1908 (*BLA*). Bentham saw one at Frensham on 14th February 1909, a pair there on 2nd December 1911 and thirteen on 13th March 1920. Another was there on 20th March 1921. Goosanders first appeared in Richmond Park on 15th November 1925 and wintered regularly in the 1930s. Three immature Goosanders were seen on Mount Pond, Clapham Common on 16th January 1936. They remained until mid-September, the last two being seen on the 24th, and were probably the three found on Pen Ponds, Richmond Park during late September. All three were gone by 2nd October (*BB, 30:192-194*). At both sites the birds were very tame, but they were included as wild birds in *BLA* and there seems no reason to take a different view.

A count of at least 60 at Staines Reservoirs on 19th February 1922 was the first dated record for Spelthorne. Staines Reservoirs were initially not much watched by birdwatchers and the birds might have been present earlier. Later and larger counts at the same site were 86 on 12th February 1933 and 174 during a cold spell in December 1933, the last staying until 18th May in 1934. There were 14 at Queen Mary Reservoir on 12th January 1935. One at Staines Reservoir on 30th May and 1st June 1937 might have been the one seen a few days later at Barn Elms. There was one at Staines Moor on 1st June 1948.

Others in the years 1930-1969 were seen at Barn Elms Reservoirs, Boldermere (1961), Carshalton (1963), Cobham (1963), Cutt Mill (1954), Earlswood Lakes (1965), Enton (1961), Farnham (8th April 1936), Fetcham Mill Pond (1962, 1965-66), Frensham (1932-37, 1951, 1953-54 etc), Gatton (1961), Hedgecourt (1947, 1963), Island Barn Reservoir (1937, 1949 etc), Kew Gardens (1961), Ockham (1963, 1969), Papercourt (1969 etc), Queen Elizabeth II Reservoir (from 1962), Richmond Park, Send (1946), Silvermere (1962), the Thames, Virginia Water (1968), Walton Reservoirs (62 in March 1931, 101 in December 1937, 550 in 1947 etc) and Weybridge.

Since 1970. In the years from 1970, reports came from over 50 other sites, including most of the main waters in the southwest. Some of the others, from rivers and other waters near Queen Elizabeth II Reservoir, were probably local dispersal. Parties of up to 85 were seen at Boldermere, Wisley in the mid 1990s. These probably came from Papercourt or the Walton area. London sites included Battersea Park and the Surrey Docks. There were seven at the Docks on 13th December 1973. In the south and southeast, Goosanders were seen at Broome Hall, Earlswood, Godstone, Leigh Place, Oxted and Smallfield. None of the later reservoir counts reached the maxima of the 1946-47 and 1962-63 winters. Numbers generally have been low since 2000.

Calendar. The average arrival date in the London area south of the Thames from 1929 to 1939 was 30th October. In the vice-county from 1970-2000, the average arrival date was 9th November and the average departure date was 9th April. The earliest of autumn was at Holmethorpe on 29th September 1989 and the latest spring bird was at Barn Elms Reservoirs on 1st May 1984. Three at Barn Elms Reservoirs on 9th September 1962 were early arrivals. In Spelthorne, one at Queen Mary Reservoir on 5th May 1984 was late in leaving. Three stayed at Clapham Common through the summer of 1936 (see above). In 1939, an adult male was seen at Staines in June and July (*BLA*). In 1962 there was a drake at King George VI Reservoir until 7th July. One was at Barn Elms Reservoir on 5th June 1937. Single males summered on the Thames in 1996-1998 and one was seen there on 23rd May 1999 (possibly all the same bird, variously speculated to be feral, injured or non-migratory). A full-winged female that was present on the Thames between Teddington and Kingston throughout 1988 was treated as an escape in the *SBR*.

Large counts from 1970, with some earlier if larger and some smaller where of local interest. The largest counts go back to the cold years of the 1940s and 1960s:

Barn Elms: 80, January 1947
Beddington Sewage Farm: 38 over, April 1954
Boldermere: 85, 8th January 1996
Cutt Mill: 15, 27th January 1996
Frensham Great Pond: 32, 13th February 1997
Frimley Gravel Pits: 30, 10th March 1996
Holmethorpe: 16, 19th January 1997
Island Barn Reservoir: 370+, March 1963; 65, January 1985
Papercourt Gravel Pits: 112, 11th January 1997
Queen Elizabeth II Reservoir· 850+, 27th January 1963; 218, January 1997
Richmond Park: 61, 11th February 1936; 31, 1st January 1970
Thorpe Water Park: 125, 29th January 1985
Walton Reservoirs: 550, 28th February 1947; 79, February 1996

Wimbledon Common: 13, January 1976
Wimbledon Park Lake: 16, 16th February 1975
Spelthorne
King George VI Reservoir: 96, 16th December 1973,
Laleham: 100 flew over, 23rd January 1985
Queen Mary Gravel Pits: 27, 31st December 1983
Queen Mary Reservoir: 14, 12th January 1935; 600, February 1947 (*BLA, LBR*); 440, 16th January 1985
Staines Reservoirs: 125, 24th February 1935; 128, 5th December 1964; 130 in February 1979
Stanwell Moor Gravel Pits: 17, 18th December 1971; 19 on 13th January 1985
Wraysbury Reservoir: 140, January 1987.

Movements and longevity. Information about foreign links comes mainly from birds ringed at Walton Reservoirs in the 1930s, when recoveries were obtained from Finland, the Netherlands, Russia and Sweden. Notable recoveries, including one showing site fidelity and another showing the longest life, are:

Ringed		Recovered		Distance/age
Molesey	24th December 1934	Surbiton	Winter 1936/7?	
Walton Reservoirs	28th January 1935	Walton Reservoirs	18th April 1938	3 years 2 months
Molesey	28th November 1936	Sweden	15th April 1937	
Walton Reservoirs	11th January 1937	Russia, Arkhangel	25th April 1939	2,789 km
Walton Reservoirs	9th February 1937	Sweden	April 1938	
Molesey	8th December 1937	West Finland	26th September 1938	
Walton Reservoirs	19th December 1937	Sweden	3rd April 1938	
Walton Reservoirs	2nd March 1962	Netherlands	29th December 1966	4 years 9 months
Walton Reservoirs	26th February 1963	Finland	14th September 1963	2,280 km
Walton Reservoirs	10th December 1971	Sweden	November 1973	

Ruddy Duck
Oxyura jamaicensis

Scarce but increasing breeding resident of feral origin, now being culled.

The Wildfowl Trust imported three pairs of this North American duck in 1948 but found the young difficult to rear by artificial methods. Better results were obtained when the birds were allowed to rear their own young and some of the ducklings used this freedom to escape unpinioned. The first feral breeding attempts were made in Somerset in 1960 and by 1997-98 there was a well established and widely distributed British population of about 3,600 individuals.

The appearance of Ruddy Ducks in 15 European countries by 1992 has been attributed (by the RSPB and others) at least in part to the increasing British population, though this does not seem to have been supported by direct evidence such as the recovery of ringed birds, at least up to the year 2000 and Britain may not be the only European country into which the species has been introduced. Ruddy Ducks are not a significant threat to any native birds in Britain, where they seem to have found an unexploited ecological niche, but those in Spain are said to prejudice the survival of the closely-related White-headed Duck, with which they may compete and hybridise.

Early Surrey history. Up to 1970, Ruddy Ducks had only been seen at Island Barn Reservoir (from February 1958) and Walton Reservoirs (from 1964). There were two at the Surrey Docks on 29th November 1971. There were single birds at Staines Reservoirs in 1974 and up to six at Shepperton Gravel Pits in 1985. The first at Papercourt Gravel Pits was on 7th January 1977 and at Thorpe on 18th February 1979. Ruddy Ducks were recorded at Frensham from October to December 1980. There was one at Barn Elms in December 1981 and, in 1985, the first was at Richmond Park.

Since 1986. By 1986/87, over a hundred were wintering at Walton Reservoirs. This remained the main vice-county wintering site for many years, though smaller numbers later wintered at Lonsdale Road Reservoirs. Sites and large counts from this date are: Barn Elms (18, December 1998, 21 in 2000); Battersea Park; Beddington Sewage Farm (ten, August 1997); Buckland; Chertsey Reservoir; Cutt Mill; Effingham Fish Ponds; Enton; Epsom Common Stew Ponds; Fieldcommon; Frensham Ponds (six, 1988); Frimley Gravel Pits; Gatton; Hersham; Holmethorpe; Hurst Park; Island Barn Reservoir (114, January 1997, Walton birds); Longside Lake; Lonsdale Road Reservoirs (28, October 1996); Molesey Gravel Pit (five, May 1995); Papercourt Gravel Pits; Queen Elizabeth II Reservoir (103, February 1987, Walton Birds); Richmond Park (17, 17th September 1996); South Norwood Country Park; South Norwood Lake; Stoke Lake; the Surrey Docks, the Thames; Thorpe (eight, January 1997); Walton Reservoirs (239, 14th January 1997), Wimbledon Common and Wimbledon Park Lake.

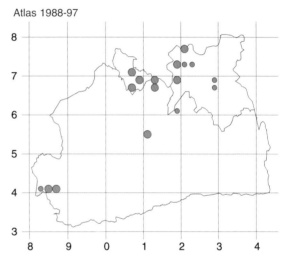

Atlas 1988-97

Breeding. A female at Frensham Great Pond on 22nd October 1980 (*HSBBR*) was the first Ruddy Duck for the site. A few were seen there in most subsequent years and Ruddy Ducks were proved to breed there in 1987. The young were thought not to have survived. Despite further territorial behaviour, definite breeding was not recorded there again until 1992. The breeding population has since increased in size and range. A pair with five juveniles was seen at Shepperton Gravel Pits on 8th July 1992. Single pairs bred at Queen Mary Gravel Pits in 1994 and 1997.

Vice-county Ruddy Duck broods 1987-1999

	1987	1988	1989	1990	1991	1992	1993	1994	1995	1996	1997	1998	1999
Barn Elms												1	1
Beddington												1	
Berrylands				1									
Central Surrey						1						1	1
Frensham Ponds	1					1	1	1					
Lonsdale Road								4	1	2		1	
Molesey Gravel Pit									1				
Ottershaw													
Papercourt													1
Richmond Park											1		
Walton Reservoirs							1	2	2	2		2	5
Total broods	**1**	**0**	**0**	**1**	**0**	**2**	**2**	**7**	**4**	**4**	**1**	**6**	**8**

Information is incomplete or has to be confidential for the later years but nine broods were raised in 2000 and five in 2001. Ruddy Ducks are known to have bred at Barn Elms London Wetland Centre (two broods in 2001, seven broods in 2002, nine in 2003, ten in 2004, two in 2005), and at several other places. Surrey had four nationally significant sites for Ruddy Duck in 2004. Average annual wildfowl count maxima from 1999/2000 to 2003/04 at these were: 43 at Knight and Bessborough Reservoirs, 31 at the Barn Elms London Wetland Centre, 531 at Staines Reservoirs (Spelthorne) and 57 at King George VI Reservoir (Spelthorne).

Many Surrey birdwatchers are pleased to see these perky and sometimes elusive birds. Culling (=killing) them to protect the White-headed Duck has become a controversial issue. Four speedboats were said to have been used in a cull at Staines Reservoirs on 8th February 2006 (*Bird Watching*). The effect of attempting to kill Ruddy Ducks is not quite clear. Certainly large numbers have been driven from some of the main wintering sites. On the other hand, Ruddy Ducks were still breeding in 2005. There is a reluctance to report Ruddy Ducks or have records published among some observers because of the killing.

Large counts and some smaller ones of local interest are shown below. Numbers at the main wintering sites were increasing until 2003:

Barn Elms London Wetland Centre: 86, 1st December 2004

Frensham: ten, 3rd October 2005

Island Barn Reservoir: 114, 11th January 1997

Lonsdale Road Reservoir: 28, October 1996

Queen Elizabeth II Reservoir: 103, February 1987

Walton Reservoirs: 239, 14th January 1997

Spelthorne

Charlton Gravel Pits: 12, January 1989

King George VI Reservoir: 195, February 1996

Queen Mary Reservoir: 284, 10th December 2001

Staines Moor: 200, 1st March 2003

Staines Reservoir: 30, March 1987; 103, February 1991; 141, January 1993; 150, February 1996; 209, January 1997; 547, 29th November 2002; 670, 16th February 2003; 696, February 2003 (BTO); 697, March 2003; 879, 22nd December 2003

Wraysbury Reservoir: 17, 17th January 1982

Movements and longevity. A first-year Ruddy Duck ringed in Sussex on 25th August 1997 was recovered at Barnes, 90 km away, on 2nd February 1998.

Red Grouse/Black Grouse   *Lagopus lagopus/Tetrao tetrix*
(Willow Ptarmigan/Black Grouse)

Surrey. Nathaniel Salmon's *Antiquities of Surrey* (1736) notes that '*Here is the Chert, next to Hind Head, a wild and desolate hill, whose heath, like those of Wales, afford sometimes the red game upon it*'. Bucknill, who gave this quote, thought that Salmon was mistaken and that the birds were Black Grouse.

Black Grouse   *Tetrao tetrix*
Lost breeding species

A resident in northern and upland forests from Wales, northern England and Scotland east through Europe to Siberia, declining over most of its range. The British range extended south to Berkshire (where it was introduced, not indigenous), Surrey and the southwest in the late 19th century but had withdrawn from virtually all these areas by the 1930s and was absent by the time of the *New Atlas* (1988-91). The Berkshire birds originated from releases 'in the royal preserves at Windsor' in the mid-1860s, which persisted only until 1884 (Swash 1996). The decline elsewhere has been ascribed mainly to a failure to adapt to habitat changes.

Surrey. The history of the Surrey birds goes back to at least 1665 or 1666, when Charles II ordered Anthony Smith, a local landowner and ironmaster, to protect those that were within an eight-mile radius of his house at Witley. Two brace were killed at Hindhead not later than 1752 (Hill). Gilbert White mentioned that 'A *grey hen* was lately killed' in the Devil's Punch Bowl (*Journals*). Yarrell (1845) gave the Surrey distribution *as from Pudmores along the brows of the heath-hills towards Tilford and again from Tilford up to the Devil's Punch-bowl on Hindhead,* quoting from the *Letters of Rusticus* (1832). Newman (1849) makes much the same comment. At this time, and until at least the closing years of the 19th century, Hindhead was a much wilder place than it is today. It was remote, with few inhabitants and poor access. Phillip Crowley had clutches of six taken at Churt in May 1862 and May 1863 and a clutch of nine taken from Hindhead in May 1866. Bucknill refers to undated introductions just over the Sussex border, at Blackdown, including one in 1840 but thought that the native population in Surrey was in a healthy state up to the beginning of the 1880s. The Haslemere Museum has a mounted specimen which was shot at Blackdown, in November 1890. A cock was seen near Hindhead in 1899.

Black Grouse were present in the Leith Hill area before 1760. It does not seem to be known what happened there from that date until 1815, when birds were turned out on the Hurtwood (Yarrell), though some writers thought they were extinct. They bred there in 1816 and descendants were subsequently found on heaths between Farnham and Bagshot. At least one bird strayed as far as Finchampstead, in Berkshire. Stafford had a specimen from Cranleigh (*SALEC*, undated). Black Grouse were abundant on Leith Hill in the 1830s, when Borrer saw 20 males together (*Birds of Sussex*, in Bucknill) and in 1866 and they were still there around 1876 (Thomas, 2001). Jordan (1892) has an undated reference to Holmbury. They nested in a copse just north of High Ashes Farm and were seen in the area until at least 1888. Young birds released in the Hurtwood during the 1890s were killed in a heath fire.

A statement that there were *a good many black game in a wild tract of country not far from Frimley Ridges* (J. W. G. Spicer, writing in 1854, in Bucknill) suggests that the Pirbright commons were another stronghold for the species and they were said to be nesting near Bagshot in 1863. There were also birds on lower ground. Two frequented an estate near Farnham for some years prior to 1888. Others were at Peper Harow around 1890 and there were at least five at Frensham in 1891 and other sightings there in 1894 (one dead) and 1896. A pair were shot on Chobham Ridges some time before 1900.

Ten were released on Witley Common around 1875 but Black Grouse were practically extinct there by 1900. There was a pair at Pudmore, Thursley in 1891 and 1892 and there were two pairs near Thursley in 1898 and 1899. These may be connected with the Witley Common releases. A pair shot on Hankley Common went to the Haslemere Museum.

Black Grouse last bred 'in a certain wild tract of country' in 1905, when two pairs were present (G. W. Swanton in Mouritz (1907). The last birds were said to have been shot in 1905 (*Bird Study 226:4*), but Mouritz saw a greyhen in the spring of 1906. The decline of the West Surrey Black Grouse population was probably due to road improvements and the increased house-building as much as it was to shooting pressure.

Red-legged Partridge   *Alectoris rufa*
Uncommon breeding resident

Native to Spain, Portugal, France, and Italy, including Corsica and a few other islands. After some failed introductions, a successful attempt was achieved in Suffolk in 1770 (Lever). By the late 19th century, escapes and releases had established a viable breeding population in southern and eastern Britain north to the Humber. Little seems to be known about historical population trends, which have been complicated at both home and abroad by introductions of this species and the related Chukar *A. chukar*. The *New Atlas* and more recent studies show mixed pictures of gains and losses between 1970 and 1990, but overall numbers seem to be down.

Early Surrey history. The first attempted Surrey introduction was in or soon after 1673, when a Mr de Mouchant went to France to get the stock for release in the parks at Richmond and Windsor. An intro-duction was made at Wimbledon at some time between 1712 and 1729 by the Duke of Leeds. He raised young from eggs and released them. The colony grew for a while, but was wiped out by a neighbour (Lever, 1977). Reports from the Farleigh district go back to at least 1858 (Sanderstead). Red-legged Partridges had become common breeders in rural Surrey by 1900 (Bucknill). Glegg gave no 19th century records for Spelthorne.

1900 to 1953. A pair bred at Woodmansterne in 1901 (SBC archive). The Boorman egg collection in the Haslemere Museum includes a Red-legged Partridge egg taken at Send in 1902. There was a Red-legged Partridge at Frensham Little Pond on 2nd June 1906 (*Zool.*, 1906). A London area survey for the period 1900-33 found records of breeding in Surrey only from Addington, Caterham, Limpsfield and Wallington, with birds being seen in another fourteen localities and no breeding anywhere in 1933 (*London Naturalist* for 1933). They were less common than Grey Partridges in the Warlingham area (Beadell, 1932) and in Richmond Park (Collenette in *BRP*). They bred at Limpsfield in 1935 and in the Leatherhead area before 1939. In Spelthorne, a nest was found on Staines Moor in 1928, where they then bred regularly. Up to 50% of the partridges shot at Stanwell were at one time Red-legged, 20 or 30 of them on one occasion, but there were no records from 1930 to 1933. Glegg cited the area north of Staines as the Middlesex stronghold of the species by 1935.

1954 to 1969. In the succeeding years, up to 1969, Red-legged Partridges nested or bred at Beddington Sewage Farm (1956-59), Chessington (1955), Chobham Common (1964, 1968), Cobham (1968), Compton (1968), Cutt Mill (1957), Esher Sewage Farm (1955), in the Haslemere area (1934), Hersham (1963), Holmethorpe (1961), Island Barn Reservoir (1958-59), at Kew Gardens (1953), in the Leatherhead area (1955), Richmond Park (1958), Sandown Race Course (1963), Thursley Common (1963), Wanborough (1964) and Wey Manor Farm (1959, 1965).

Since 1970. Breeding reports have come from Buckland (1970, 1976), Elstead/Tilford (1972), Epsom (1989), Fieldcommon (1977), Frensham in 1972 and 1976, Godstone (1980, 1984), Hersham (1989), the Hog's Back (1983), Hookwood (1984), Milford (1975), Ockham (1976), Ripley/West Horsley (20 territories and definite breeding in 1973, 40 territories in 1974 and 1975), Stoke Water Meadows (1971), the Surrey Docks (1971 - first breeding record for any part of Inner London, 1974-77).

Currently the Surrey population is in decline. The Winter Atlas found partial survey counts and esti-mates totalling only 33 birds in 1981-84. The last Common Birds Census territory was found in 1971. Of the 231 tetrads in northeast Surrey, 13% were found to hold territories in the 1968-72 Atlas survey but only 6 % in the 1988-97 Atlas, perhaps a fair measure of the decline. Across the county as a whole, Red-legged Partridges were found in 77 of the 575 tetrads, or 13%, indicating that 19% of the tetrads outside the northeast were occupied. No breeding was reported anywhere from 1992 to 2000 even though there have been further releases. A pair bred at Shalford in 2001.

In Spelthorne, breeding continued into the 1970s, for example at Shepperton in 1970. Staines was the main area in Middlesex for the species at the time of the 1968-1972 LNHS Atlas. At least five of about seven Middlesex tetrads where Red-legged Partridges were recorded were in Spelthorne and the other four

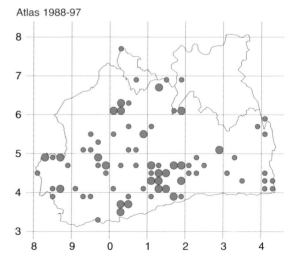

Atlas 1988-97

were on or close to its border. Much the same was true in the 1988-94 London Atlas, where two of about five occupied Middlesex tetrads were in Spelthorne, although Red-legged Partridges were rare, at least in Shepperton (*Shepp. BR*). No breeding records have been published for subsequent years up to 2001.

Population size. In spite of the infrequency of breeding reports, Red-legged Partridges continue to be fairly widely reported as being present, as shown in the table. This is probably because they are still being released for sporting purposes. Up to 1,000 were put down on an estate at Ewhurst in 1972 and some escaped to surrounding areas. About 200 were released near Dorking in 1991. A release resulted in 42 being seen in the Beddlestead Valley in 1999. About 5,000 birds are released each year on a farm in northeast Surrey (*RSPB East Surrey Local Group Newsletter April 2007*). In these circumstances, casual reports of breeding and even the Breeding Bird Surveys, which suggest an adult breeding season population of under 150 adults, may not mean very much.

Vice-county breeding and non-breeding places reported 1960-2001

Year	1960	61	62	63	64	65	66	67	68	69	70	71	72	73
Places	20	9	10	15	13	9	9	11	6	6+	6	13	12	4
Year	74	75	76	77	78	79	80	81	82	83	84	85	86	87
Places	2	3	5	5+	7	3+	5	12	9	7	10	8	9	2
Year	88	89	90	91	92	93	94	95	96	97	98	99	2000	2001
Places	4	3	11	9	15	7	11	9	15	11	13	11	8	14

Movements and longevity. The only ringing recovery located is of a bird ringed at Byfleet on 2nd May 1982 and found locally, freshly dead (hit glass), later that day.

Behaviour. A Red-legged Partridge flushed at Staines Reservoirs in 1980 landed on the water a good way out and then swam to the bank.

Grey Partridge *Perdix perdix*

Uncommon breeding resident

Breeds from the British Isles east through central and southern Europe to central Asia and has been introduced in North America. The British breeding population increased substantially during the 19th century, perhaps as much as fourfold and probably due to changes in farming practice as well as protection from poaching and predation. In the 20th century, the British population may have fallen by 95% (*MA*) and there was a 40% fall from 1994 to 2005 (*BTO News 266*).

Early Surrey history. Desirability as a food item ensured the Grey Partridge an early place on the Surrey list, well illustrated by archaeological evidence from Southwark. An excavation at Winchester Palace produced remains from the Roman period, 70-120 AD and another at 104 Borough High Street produced remains dated at 120-200. Three sets of remains from Bermondsey Abbey were dated at 1140-1350, 1480-1600 and 1730-1770, a wide range of history. Remains dated to the Tudor period were found at Royal George Wharf. There is also evidence from Merton. Of nineteen sets of remains found at Merton Priory, one was dated at 1150-1200, one at 1200-1300, five at 1230-1300, two at 1230-1350, two at 1230-1400, one at 1350-1400, two at 1350-1450, one at 1400-1500, one at 1500-1550, one at 1580-1650 and two at 1580-1910. On 1st December 1247 the Sheriff of Surrey was ordered to deliver a hundred partridges to Henry III's castle at Windsor. Partridge remains dated from about 1170-1230 and later were found at Guildford Castle (Poulton) and others not later than 1650 were found at Oatlands Palace (Cohen). There were 16th century remains at Little Pickle, Bletchingley (Poulton *et al.*).

Grey Partridges were protected within a radius of eight miles around Witley in 1665-66 by order of Charles II - see Black Grouse. John Evelyn noted that there were partridges on Denzil Onslow's estate at Pyrford when he visited it on 23rd August, 1681. He apparently regarded the poaching of partridges to be more serious than shooting Red Kites.

Yarrell (1845) mentioned a view that in some heathy districts, such as the Hurtwood and Bagshot Heath, the partridges lived on *heath and hurtle berries* and not corn, and that they were not so white in the flesh and tasted more of grouse. Much the same was said by Jordan (1893). The *Historical Atlas* describes the Partridge as an abundant breeder in the last quarter of the 19th century. Bucknill's comment that the species was *'a very common resident in Surrey, and, being well looked after, is perhaps rather on the increase in the rural districts'* is consistent with this. It suggests that the national increase in the 19th century was experienced, in general terms, in Surrey as well, although as Bucknill himself pointed out, the county was not of the best and shooting bags (of over 50 brace on occasions!) were relatively modest. A few could be still found in Richmond Park (where they had long been preserved, with as many as 165 killed in 1839) and Wimbledon Common (Hamilton). Jefferies (1878) was more cautious about numbers, suggesting that the loss of wheat stubbles, the clearing of weeds from farm fields (also a more modern concern) and excessive hunting were making the species scarcer than it was before 1850. Power knew of only three or four records in the Dulwich area from 1874 to 1909.

1900 to 1960. A nest was found at Sandcross Lane, Redhill in 1905 (G. T. Winter). There were several Grey Partridges at Oxted on 30th September 1906 (*Zool.*) and they were not uncommon in the lower parts of the North Downs (Mouritz), around Warlingham (Beadell, 1932) and in the Farleigh district (Pounds, 1952). Five or six pairs bred in Richmond Park in the 1930s (Collenette). Numbers there rose sharply with the extension of cultivation during the war and a partial count yielded 113 birds in 1950. Grey Partridges nested at Elmers End Sewage Farm in 1936. Pairs bred at Dulwich in 1947, Kew Gardens in the 1950s and Old Deer Park in 1957. There were two pairs at Beddington Sewage Farm in 1954 and 1955 (Milne, 1956).

At the beginning of the 20th century, Grey Partridges were well distributed throughout the Staines district (Kerr, 1906). The biggest partridge bag at Stanwell Place was 140 of which, as above, 20 to 30 were Red-legged.

Since 1960. The breeding population has since been in decline. Subsequent breeding reports have come from Addlestone (1984-85), Beddington (1976), Bookham (1969), Bricksbury Hill (1982), Brook (1971), Buckland (1970), Chertsey (1970), Chessington (1969, 1976), Chobham Common (1966, 1979, 1981, 1987, 1991), Compton (1970), Downside (1975), East Wyke Farm (1973), Godstone (1979), Guildford (1976), Hersham (1989), the Hog's Back (1968), Holmethorpe (1971, 1989-90, last pair seen in 1992), Newlands Corner (1971), Old Woking (1972), Ottershaw (1969, 1986), Papercourt Gravel Pits (1971, 1974-75), Richmond Park (1973), Ripley/Ockham/Clandon (1973-74), Stoke Water Meadows (1971-72), Thorpe/Chertsey (1970), Walton Reservoirs (1970), Wonersh (1986), and Woodlands Park (1970, 1979).

Spelthorne

By 1960 Grey Partridges had become much scarcer in Spelthorne, although Geen mentioned 25 at Queen Mary Reservoir on 6th November 1971. Two pairs bred at Staines Moor in 1976 and pairs bred at Perry Oaks Sewage Farm in 1979, Charlton Gravel Pits in 1982 and Shepperton Gravel Pits in 1986. The *LBR* gives occasional records into the late 1990s.

In Surrey as a whole, Grey Partridges were found in Common Birds Censuses at densities of up to 0.3 territories per ten hectares from 1963 to 1981 but only one territory was found in later years. The Winter Atlas found partial survey counts and estimates totalling only 68 birds in 1981-84, a small number, but twice as many as for Red-legged Partridges. There have been no reports of confirmed breeding anywhere since 1991 and Grey Partridges are now being seen at fewer than ten sites annually.

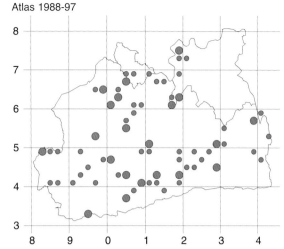

Atlas 1988-97

Releases in Bushy Park (Middlesex) and Richmond Park during the 1980s and 1990s have probably boosted nearby populations. The 1994-2004 Breeding Bird Survey grosses up to an average of 36 adults across the county in the breeding season, but its interpretation is complicated by releases.

Behaviour. Young birds that are too large to be incubated will roost together (jug), usually together and typically in a circle. A covey of 26 roosting together in a cornfield at Eashing Farm on 23rd September 1991 formed a circular jug at about mid-day.

Plumage variations. Bucknill mentioned white specimens, from Box Hill in 1811 (one, in Graves) and Shirley in the autumn of 1881 (eleven from one estate) and also a buff bird and one with a white horseshoe on its breast.

Quail (Common Quail) *Coturnix coturnix*
Scarce summer visitor, has bred

The British Isles are on the northwest edge of a breeding range that extends through central and southern Europe to Central Asia, European birds wintering from southern Europe south to sub-Saharan Africa. Quail are grassland birds which, in Britain, did better in the medieval open fields than in enclosures. The range covered most parts of the British Isles in the late 19th century, though Quail were by then lost to much of Ireland. The Irish extinctions were probably due to changing agricultural patterns and human predation for food as a result of the famine years of the 1840s, after which much tilled land reverted to pasture and moor (*HA*). There is evidence of an increase in the rest of Britain up to about 1865, followed by a crash from which numbers did not recover, and which is ascribed to changed farming techniques (*HA*). The 20th century saw a further national decline, though even during the *New Atlas* period (1988-91) Quail were breeding, or attempting to breed, throughout England. There have been occasional 'Quail years' when large numbers of migrants have reached the British Isles.

Early Surrey history. Quail were among the game that John Evelyn noted when he visited Denzil Onslow's estate at Pyrford on 23rd August, 1681. One obtained at Halliford on 18th September 1841 (Meyer in Glegg) is the first recorded for the district. J. E. Harting said they were heard frequently at Laleham in 1890 (Glegg).

Quail were occasionally found in the Godalming district (*Letters of Rusticus*, 1837), at Tooting (Blyth, probably 1830s) near Shackleford in 1842 (Bucknill) and in the Dorking district (Jordan, 1893). There were occasional 'Quail years', of which 1870 and 1893 are the best documented. Bucknill, who knew of the 1870 and 1893 national influxes, cited a nest with sixteen eggs at Epsom in 1870. He gave records for Churt (nested, undated), Horsell (nest and nine eggs, May 1874), near Guildford (September 1880), Epsom Downs (1884, a covey in 1886, five in 1893), a chalkpit near Guildford (1893), Little Bookham (eggs taken June 1893), Morden (November 1893), near Milford (clutch 1893), Puttenham (1893), Ashtead (1895), Wanborough (autumn 1895), Headley (8th October 1895) and Ashtead/Epsom (1897). Several introductions did not stem or reverse the decline. Bucknill mentions the release of twelve at Epsom in 1882 and of about seventy which 'quickly vanished', near Lingfield in 1890. Most of Bucknill's records related to autumn migrants and his own assessment was that breeding Quail were rare.

1900 to 1945. Power heard one calling from a turnip field near Banstead on 8th June 1907. One was calling at Old Oxted in 1909 (*BLA*), one was found at Haling Down, near South Croydon on 17th April (*BLA*) and/or 7th May 1912 (Pounds) and there was one calling in Richmond Park from 20th June to 11th July 1913. Beadell heard one calling at Warlingham in June 1917. One was calling at Belmont in 1938.

1945 to 1964. In this period, 1947, 1952-53 and 1964 were national Quail years. Calling was heard at Perry Oaks Sewage Farm and Staines Moor in 1952 and Quail were found at Addington (June) and Sanderstead (June and July) 1953. There was one at Tilford in May 1954 and another at Oxenford (Peper Harow) in September 1956 (CNHS). One was found at Perry Oaks Sewage Farm on 13th September of that year and another in May and August 1964.

Breeding. This period accounts for the only attempted or proven breeding records for Surrey since the 1893 influx. A nest was reported from Purley in 1958. There were up to seven calling from a site at Chertsey in 'Quail year' of 1964 and at least two pairs bred.

Where found from 1965. The Quail years of 1970, 1983 and 1989 did not find much reflection in Surrey. There were up to four Quail at Chertsey and several at Compton in 1970. The 1989 Quail year will have boosted the *New Atlas* results, though it was not a particularly good year for Surrey, where there were only two records, one at Walton Heath and the other at West Clandon. There were no Surrey records at all in 1983. From 1965 to 2000,

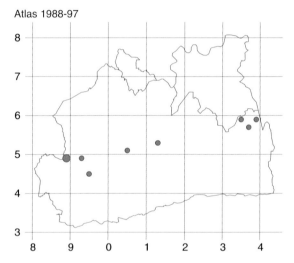

Atlas 1988-97

Quail were recorded outside the Quail years at Ashtead Common (1978), Beddington Sewage Farm (1987, 1997), Bookham (1972, 1979), Chelsham (1965, 1972), Chertsey (1968, 1974), Chiddingfold (1994), Cranleigh (1998), Elstead, (Red House Farm 1991), Epsom Common (tame, near a Quail farm in 1988), Ewhurst (1965), Frimley Gravel Pits (1972), Gomshall (1990), Guildford (1981), Horsell (1998), Polesden Lacey (1976), Purley (1960), Send (1996), Shackleford (1995), South Norwood Country Park (1989, 1991, 1992), Thorpe (1974), Tongham (1990), Walton Heath (1989), Wanborough (1995), Wonersh (1973) and Worplesdon (1974). The majority of the records were for June, with a few in May and July. Three at Beddington on 28th August 1987 were the only ones outside this period since the 1960s. Most recent records have been from fields on the back slopes of the North Downs, potentially suitable for breeding if other conditions were right. Single birds were heard at Hydestile in 2001 and Riddlesdown in 2002. There was at least one in 2005, near Conduit Farm, Guildford on 4th June and there are several as yet unconfirmed reports for 2004 and 2005.

Calendar. Quail are typically found when they are heard calling in June. They are less often seen. Extreme arrival and departure dates are:

Early		Late	
3 April 1991	Elstead	1st September 1964	Chertsey
17th April 1912	South Croydon	September 1956	Oxenford, Peper Harow
30th April 1992	South Norwood Country	8th October 1895	Headley
	Park (possible escape)	27th October 1968	Old Lyne Sewage Farm
3 May 1965	Ewhurst	November 1893	Morden
		11th November 1918	Haslemere area (Shaw – may not have been in Surrey)

		Spelthorne	
		13th September 1956	Perry Oaks Sewage Farm
		18th September 1841	Halliford

Movements and longevity. An adult Quail was ringed at Cranleigh on 3rd May 1995 and recovered at Zarazoga, Spain on 15th September of the same year.

Pheasant (Common Pheasant)   *Phasianus colchicus*
Moderately common breeding resident

The indigenous range runs from the Black Sea to Japan but, as introduced birds, Pheasants are well established in Europe, North America and elsewhere. The European introductions are of ancient origin, possibly going back to Roman times, and of several different races. British birds are thought to have been introduced by the Normans and may have been of a dark-necked race. Ring-necked birds, probably of far-eastern origin, were present in Britain by 1768 (*BB, 18:84*). In the late 19th century, Pheasants were breeding throughout the British Isles, apart from in the Isle of Man.

Early Surrey history. Pheasants breeding in rank wetland vegetation, such as that found at Beddington Sewage Farm and Stoke Water Meadows today, are using a habitat very similar to that of native birds in Asia. There was much more of this type of ground in earlier years. Pheasants were protected within a radius of eight miles around Witley in 1665-66 by order of Charles II - see Black Grouse and Grey Partridge. They were among the game that John Evelyn saw, or heard of, on 23rd August 1681 when he visited Denzil Onslow's estate at Pyrford and they were protected as gamebirds around Wotton. Pheasants were present in the Godalming district before 1849 (Newman). In Richmond Park, 267 were shot in 1839 when the park was keepered (Collenette). Pheasants were occasional on Wimbledon Common (Hamilton, 1881). A pair at Norwood might have been escapes (Aldridge, 1885). They were common in most of Surrey at the end of the 19th century. There are no Spelthorne records in Kerr or Glegg.

1900 to 1960. In Richmond Park, where numbers had been reduced by 1905, about 190 were counted in 1952 following wartime cultivation (*BLA*). Pheasants bred in Dulwich Wood in 1901 (Power). There were *c.*100 in Kew Gardens in 1936, and they were still common there in 1950 (*BLA*). They bred at Beddington Sewage Farm in 1948 (*LBR*).

Since 1960. Pheasants were found at territorial densities of up to 0.5 per ten hectares in Common Birds Censuses from 1962 to 2002, peaking in 1996, when there were also four territories on Pirbright Common and Ash Ranges (*HSBBR*). The Winter Atlas found partial survey counts and estimates totalling 456 in 1981-84, fourteen times the number of Red-legged Partridges and mostly in TQ03 and TQ14. Of the 231 tetrads in northeast Surrey, including Spelthorne, 54% were found to hold territories in the 1968-72 Atlas survey but only 40% in the 1988-97 Atlas, a notable decline. Pheasants were found in 81% of the 344 tetrads in the rest of Surrey, which were on average more rural. In Spelthorne, Pheasants have

This secluded pool, part of Papercourt Gravel Pits, is a favourite with dabbling duck. It was host to a flock of Goosanders in the winter of 1997/98 and held a Scaup in the following spring.

John Davis

most consistently been reported from Staines Moor. They were present in seven Spelthorne tetrads in the 1968-72 LNHS Atlas and in at least five in the 1988-97 SBC Atlas. A few residents were picked up by the 2003 BTO Migration Watch.

Breeding behaviour. Gardens in rural areas provide good opportunities for observing Pheasant behaviour. Territorial disputes, crowing and the elegant lateral display of courting males, who may be accompanied by up to a dozen females, have been seen in my Elstead garden. In this display, the cock circles a hen, leaning towards her with his inner wing drooped, his outer wing raised and his tail twisted and fanned, all to enhance his size. And he may be ignored. A less subtle male may seize a female by the wing tip with his beak to bring her down.

Population size. A Breeding Birds Census estimate grosses up to around 4,900 adult birds for a 1994 to 2004 average and is of a similar

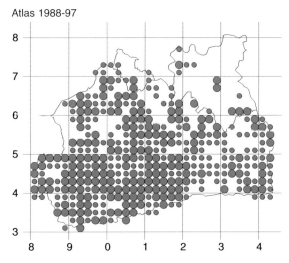

Atlas 1988-97

order to the 6,000 territories implied by the Common Birds Census. If Surrey held a proportionate share of the British breeding population as given by the *New Atlas*, the population would be nearer to 6,100 territories, a surprisingly close figure. These estimates should relate only to feral or wild birds but frequent releases for sporting purposes make any assessment of numbers difficult. Most large aggregations, such as some of those above and 120 at West Horsley in 1972, 100-200 at Chipstead in 1979 and 200 at Capel in 1994 are presumably from this source. At least 2,500 birds were reared on a keepered estate in central Surrey in 1987. The *Surrey Advertiser* for 22nd July 2005 mentioned an estate near West Horsley where 9,000 Pheasants, imported from France, were being reared.

Plumage variations. Variants such as the melanistic birds reported from Clandon in 1972 and 1977 and Lonsdale Road in 1975, the albinos reported from Ranmore Common (Mouritz in 1906), Kingswood in 1982 and Clandon in 1992 and dark green or barred birds of the *tenebrosus* type seen in an Elstead garden in 2002 reflect the mixed nature of the introduced stock. Individual males are often so distinctively marked that they can easily be recognised. They may visit the same site, for example a garden, for up to a year before being replaced by a different male.

Golden Pheasant   *Chrysolophus pictus*
Escapes, possibly feral

As native birds, Golden Pheasants are confined to a mountainous part of China. Attempts at introduction to the British Isles date back to the late 19th century. These have not been very successful, though they have been enough to get the bird onto the British List as a feral species. Numbers are currently falling.

Surrey. Although birds of unknown origin are seen in Surrey from time to time, no evidence of feral breeding is available. There was an apparently feral bird near Cranleigh in 1983 and 1984. All records are listed in the Annex concerned with escapes.

Divers of unidentified species   *Gavia species*

A diver at Virginia Water from 6th December 1936 to 17th January 1937 was 'almost certainly' Black-throated. It no doubt visited the Surrey part of the lake but has been excluded from the records below. A Great Northern Diver reported at Frensham from 20th-21st December 1959 (HNHS1980) has been placed in the broader category of Diver *species*. Other unidentified divers were at Frensham Great Pond in mid January 1970, at Frensham Great Pond and Enton on 11th January 1974, at Staines in early 1977, at Walton Reservoirs in January 1980, at Queen Mary Reservoir on 15th November 1985, at Wraysbury Reservoir on 15th January 1987 and over Thursley Common on 19th December 1993 (possibly the Black-throated Diver found at Frensham on that date).

Red-throated Diver   *Gavia stellata*

Winter visitor with at least 103 records and 107 bird months up to 2005, including 36 records from Spelthorne

Red-throated Divers breed in northern America, Russia and Europe, including Scotland and Ireland. They have been increasing in Britain since 1950. The *Migration Atlas* shows that Red-throated Divers wintering in southern Britain have come from Greenland, Scandinavia and Scotland.

Early Surrey history. The earliest report is of a 'young specimen' at Chertsey Weir in 1838, the first for Middlesex and the London area as well as for Surrey. A winter-plumaged bird was killed on the Thames between Richmond and Twickenham, nearly opposite Eel Pie Island. It was seen by Harting (Harting, 1866). Among the five other 19th century records, the most noteworthy is of eight seen on the ground at Clandon on 18th October 1848. This is one of the very few multiple occurrences and the only one involving more than two birds. One at Guildford on 18th October 1848 was thought to be one of the eight at Clandon. One from Surrey in the Charterhouse Collection in 2001 could be the female shot on Abbot's Pond (Hankley Common) in 1843 (*SALEC*), the male from Hammer Pond in 1846 (Bucknill) or the male shot at Guildford in 1865 (*SALEC*), all of which were handled by Stafford. There was one at Cobham in February 1892.

Since 1900. The table shows that occurrences peaked in the 1950s. There seems be some correlation with climate information, the lows coming in the cold decades of the 1940s and 1960s and the highs in warmer periods.

Bird months by decade 1900 to 2005

	1900s	1910s	1920s	1930s	1940s	1950s	1960s	1970s	1980s	1990s	2000-05	Total
Vice-county	1	4	5	3	16	3	7	10	11		4	**64**
Spelthorne		2	3	2	12	5	2	8	4		5	**43**

One at Richmond Park on 13th February 1921 was found by Col. R. Meinertzhagen. It was seen by other observers on 13th and 20th March (*BB, 14:261*). Five places, three of them in Spelthorne, account for about half of the occurrences after 1921: *Frensham*: 12th February 1931, 15th October 1931, 3rd-12th February 1933, 12th December 1948, 24th October 1952, 24th January 1954, 12th February 1956 (dead), 17th February 1957, 28th February to 27th March 1960, 25th February to 3rd March 1978, 12th March 1978 (probably the same), 8th February 1993, 16th December 1997; *Island Barn Reservoir*: 1st March 1947 (dead), 5th February 1955, 25th February 1956, 4th February 1985, 13th February 1994, 16th March 1998, 3rd November 2003; *King George VI Reservoir*: 6th March 1955, 4th February 1956, 15th March 1958, 17th February 1985, 15th November 1987, 8th April 1989, 19th November 1989; *Queen Mary Reservoir* 1st February 1937 (dead), 6th March 1948, 17th January 1960 (dead), 17th January to 21st February 1960, 16th February to 12th March 1985, 17th February 1986, 23rd January 1987, 23rd January 1993, 19th December 1993, 2nd February 1996, 20th December 1997, 14th January 2001 (*LNHSB*); *Staines Reservoirs*: 2nd-5th May 1929 (identified on 4th May) and 9th June 1929, 20th-

Stoke Water Meadows. In the 1970s it was proposed that this marsh should be excavated for gravel and surrounded by a high embankment. Riverside willows would have been felled. The proposal was resisted and a new water, Stoke Lake, created. In 1993 a Red-throated Diver was found on the channel in the foreground.

John Davis

21st November 1932 (two), dates from 16th December 1934 to 20th January 1935, 20th December 1938, 11th February 1940, 26th March 1951, 12th September 1953, 8th January 1955, 17th December 1955 to 29th March 1956 (second bird present on 25th-26th February, 17th March), 9th-10th February 1957, 18th-20th February 1961 (also 4th and 19th March), February/March 2003 (also King George VI Reservoir).

The others were: *Badshot Lea*: 6th-14th February 1960, 28th-29th December 1995; *Barn Elms Reservoirs*: 20th December 1938, 21st January 1950, 1st January 1955, 21st February 1978, 19th February 1985, 11th March 1986; *Beddington Sewage Farm*: 2nd-4th December 1991, 7th June 1996; near *Chiddingfold*: 20th February 1950; *Cutt Mill*: 6th-20th January 1957; *Enton*: 31st December 1952, January 1957; *Hamsey Green Pond*: February 1956; *Hedgecourt*: 23rd January 2003; *Hersham Gravel Pits*: 20th-21st February 1996; *Lonsdale Road Reservoir*: 3rd January 1984; *New Lines [Lyne?] Pond*: 16th-17th February 1979; *Pen Ponds, Richmond Park*: 12th and 19th March 1922, 7th-14th March 1982 (placed there by the RSPCA, provenance unknown); *Queen Elizabeth II Reservoir*: 15th February 1982 (dead), 22nd-24th January 1985, 22nd-23rd February 1986, 15th February 1991; *Royal Military Academy, Camberley*: 29th March 1977; *Stoke Water Meadows, Guildford*: 14th February 1993; *Surrey Docks*: 17th March to 23rd April 1977; the *Thames* between Kew and Richmond: 2nd, 9th, and 16th-17th March 1956; Twickenham 1st-15th November 1939; *Walton Reservoirs*: 1st March 1947 (dead), 25th February to 5th March 1956, another 5th March 1956, 17th-18th January 1987 (also Island Barn Reservoir on the 18th), 29th January 1997 and one on 28th October 1998; *Wraysbury Reservoir, Spelthorne*: 20 January 1979, 24th February 1979. One found oiled on 7th May 1938 'near Haslemere' (*SEBR*) and 'near Linchmere' (Clark, 1984) was probably not in Surrey.

Calendar. The table shows that for records since 1900 the peak month was February, that none have been found in July or August and that only one (in Spelthorne) has been found in May and September:

Bird months 1900-2005

	Jan	Feb	Mar	Apr	May	Jun	Jul	Aug	Sep	Oct	Nov	Dec	Total
Vice-county	12	23	13	3	0	1	0	0	0	3	2	7	**64**
Spelthorne	9	14	9	1	1	1	0	0	1	1	3	3	**43**

The earliest arrival was at Staines on 12th September 1953 and in the vice-county at Frensham on 15th October 1931. The latest of the early year was at Staines on 9th June 1929 and in the vice-county at Beddington on 7th June 1996.

Ringing and longevity. Red-throated Divers ringed in Greenland, Scotland and Scandinavia have all been recovered in southern Britain, the majority being from Scandinavia. Presumably Scandinavia is the main source of those seen in Surrey. No ringing recoveries involving Surrey have been located. At least 12 of the birds found since 1950 were reported as oiled and seven were found dead or died after arrival. The cold spell of early 1947 killed two. They were at Island Barn and Walton reservoirs.

Black-throated Diver   *Gavia arctica*
Winter visitor with at least 82 records, including 40 from Spelthorne
Black-throated Divers breed in northern North America, Russia and Europe, including Scotland. They have increased in Europe in recent years but are only winter visitors to Surrey.

Early Surrey history. There are no dated records before 1881 and, although occasionally shot on Frensham Pond (Kidd, 1837), it was evidently a rare bird in the county. A Black-throated Diver was shot at West Molesey on 26th March 1881. This is four years after the opening of the first reservoir in the area which has since been one of the most regular localities for these birds.

Since 1900. One was seen at Richmond Park in late December 1907 by Col. R. Meinertzhagen and

Claude Borrer and was found dead there on 1st January 1908 (B. A. Marsh pers. comm., listed in *BLA* for Richmond Park in 1908 without details). A young male was found exhausted by the roadside near Caterham Valley on 6th November 1909. It died shortly after capture and was reported by Bentham (*BB*, 5:28). The table shows that bird months peaked in the 1980s, with a smaller Spelthorne peak in the 1960s:

Bird months by decade

	1900s	1910s	1920s	1930s	1940s	1950s	1960s	1970s	1980s	1990s	2000-06	Total
Vice-county	2	0	2	8	3	12	3	2	7	7	9	**55**
Spelthorne	0	0	1	4	2	11	18	6	20	7	4	**73**

Three places, two of them in Spelthorne, account for over half of the occurrences after 1909: *Walton Reservoirs*: 1st March 1929, 24th December 1929 to 18th January 1930, 2nd-21st February 1937 (two), 25th February to 18th March 1956 (Walton Gravel Pits 7th-8th March 1956 presumably the same), 21st-28th December 1957, 20th January 1985 to 3rd February 1985, 21st December 2002, 6th February 2005 (in the area from 29th January to 28th March); *Queen Mary Reservoir (Spelthorne)*: 21st December 1957 (Staines Reservoirs bird?), 8th January to 16th March 1958 (one or two), 30th November 1958, 15th November 1959 to 27th December 1959, 17th January to 17th February 1960, 24th February 1962, 14th November 1962, 30th December 1977, 29th December 1995 to 7th January 1996, 31st December 1996; *Staines Reservoirs (Spelthorne)*: December 1927, 13th December 1930 to 18th January 1931, 31st January and 14th February 1937 (one of the Walton Birds?), 11th January to 8th February 1948, 29th September to 8th October 1957, 27th December 1959, 28th January 1962, 2nd February to 5th May 1962 (up to three), 16th January 1966 to 1st March 1966, 19th November 1972, 17th-26th November 1974, 9th-29th December 1977, 2nd March 1979 to 14th May 1979, 9th January 1981, 21st March 1982 and 3rd April 1982, 15th March 1986, 1st January 1996 and 6th January 1996, 20th November 1996 and dates to 30th December 1996; up to three from December 2000 to February 2001, one until May; one from 14th January to 12th February 2002 (also at King George VI Reservoir in January), 20th December 2003 (*LNHSB*); *Staines and King George VI Reservoirs*: 20th April 1951.

The others were: *Alfold*: 3rd February 1957; *Barn Elms Reservoirs*: 15th February 1953, 10th-12th March 1955, 2nd to 4th February 1956; *Barn Elms and Lonsdale Road Reservoirs/adjacent Thames*: 31st January to 5th June 1937 (at least two, one staying to June), 9th March to 12th April 1948, 1st-9th January 1955; *Camberley*: 3rd February 2006; *Cranleigh (Baynards)*: 28th October 1998; *Earlswood Lake*: 13th-24th April 1956; *Frensham*: 3rd and 6th-12th February 1933 (Great Pond), 6th January 1957 (Little Pond) and 26th-27th January 1957 (Great Pond) - the Thursley bird; 26th January 1957, 18th February 1965 (found dead on 22nd January 1965), 18th-27th January 1970, 19th-27th December 1993, (Great Pond); *Goldsworth Park, Woking*: 25th-27th November 1996; *Holmethorpe*: 9th January 1983 to 3rd February 1983; *Island Barn Reservoir*: 16th and 29th January 1988, 29th December 1993; *Lightwater*: 3rd February 2006; *Moat Pond*: 26th December 1956; *Papercourt Gravel Pits*: 16th-23rd November 1991, 16th December 2005 into January 2006; *Queen Elizabeth II Reservoir*: 25th November 1997; *Richmond Park*: 16th October to 3rd November 1965; *Surrey Docks*: 8th-12th December 1977, 31st December 1981; *Thames opposite Isleworth Eyot*: 30th November 1941; and *Worcester Park*: 26th February 1986. In Spelthorne: *King George VI Reservoir*: 27th February 1982 (the Wraysbury Reservoir bird), 26th-27th January 1985 (two, Wraysbury Reservoir birds), 1st March 1986 (two), 7th January 1994 to 6th February 1994, 6th-23rd December 2000; *Shepperton Gravel Pits*: 27th December 1984 to 7th January 1985; *Wraysbury Reservoir*: 16th-17th January 1982 (two) also three on 31st January 1982, one on 28th February 1982 and 27th March 1982; 19th January 1985 (two) also one on 20 January 1985 and 22nd January 1985, two on 3rd February 1985; 25th February to 9th March 1986, 7th February 1987, dates to 22nd March 1987 and 2nd May 1987 (Berkshire bird).

Calendar. The table shows that the peak period is in January and February, with none found in July or August:

Bird months 1900-2006

	Jan	Feb	Mar	Apr	May	Jun	Jul	Aug	Sep	Oct	Nov	Dec	Total
Vice-county	13	13	5	3	1	1	0	0	0	2	6	11	**55**
Spelthorne	18	16	13	3	4	0	0	0	1	1	5	12	**73**

The earliest arrival was at Staines on 29th September 1957 and in the vice-county at Cranleigh on 28th October 1998. The latest departure was at Staines on 14th May 1979 and in the vice-county in the Barn Elms area on 5th June 1937.

Great Northern Diver   *Gavia immer*
Winter visitor with at least 143 bird months, including 84 from Spelthorne

Great Northern Divers breed from North America across to Iceland and many winter on British coastal and inland waters. They would probably have been common in Britain after the end of the last Ice Age, some 8,000 years ago (Thomas, 1999). Summer records are not uncommon in northern Britain, where they have bred.

Early Surrey history. One was killed on Frensham Pond in 1824 and there were two others, at Frensham and Old Pond (Broadwater), not later than 1837 (Kidd, 1837 in Newman, 1849). Long shot another on Puttenham Common on 26th February 1838 (Bucknill). The Stafford collection contained a female shot at Broadwater (*SALEC*, possibly the Old Pond bird and at Charterhouse in 2001). Stafford noted that a male was found dying between Godalming and Guildford (*SCCMS*). Bucknill mentioned two others, one on Frensham Pond at the end of 1869 (recorded in *The Field*, 8th January 1870 by Mr Smither, of Churt) and an immature bird shot there in 1885. There was one at Kew Gardens in 1876 (*BRP* 1949). One took bait meant for a Pike and was caught with a rod and line at Virginia Water in December 1881. One was shot on a flooded field at Egham in 1889 (Kerr, 1906).

1900 to 2005. Great Northern Divers have been seen more frequently in recent decades, peaking after the 1980s. Some of the birds make long stays, during which they visit more than one of the Spelthorne and Walton-on-Thames reservoirs and they may visit others outside the county. As a consequence, those of the 79 birds that were seen from 1900 onward gave rise to 143 Surrey bird months:

Bird months by decade

	1900s	1910s	1920s	1930s	1940s	1950s	1960s	1970s	1980s	1990s	2000-05	Total
Vice-county	0	0	0	7	0	5	6	7	12	19	3	**59**
Spelthorne	2	0	3	7	0	6	4	3	12	16	31	**84**

Where found. Barn Elms Reservoirs hosted a few Great Northern Divers up to 1984 but the restructuring of the site in the 1990s seems not to have left water deep enough to attract them. Three reservoirs, two of them in Spelthorne, account for over half of the birds since 1900. In the following account of the records since 1900, the reservoir of arrival is generally used: *Island Barn Reservoir*: 19th November to 10th December 1938, 6th-27th December 1953, 29th November 1986 to 15th February 1987 and a second bird from 12th to 26th January 1987, 24th December 1989 to 31st March 1990, 26th January 1991, 2nd November 1995 and dates to 24th January 1996 (also seen on Queen Elizabeth II Reservoir), up to two from 20th November 1999 to 16th January 2000, 4th December 2005; *King George VI Reservoir* (*Spelthorne*): 7th-30th November 1967, winter 1982/83, 14th April 1985, 12th December 1987 to 24th January 1988, 13th-20th March 1988, 17th December 1989, 8th January 1999, up to two from 9th January to 9th May 2000, a juvenile from 26th November to 2nd December 2000, an adult on 14th-21st

December 2000, 16th October 2002, two in November 2002, one from 14th November 2002 to 3rd January 2003, 15th January 2005 (*Bird Watching*); *Staines Reservoirs* (*Spelthorne*): 25th December 1905 to 28th January 1906, 6th November 1927, 30th November to 6th December 1929, up to three from 23rd November 1930 to 1st February 1931, 5th-6th December 1931, 1st November 1932, 23rd October 1934, 11th December 1938 to 5th January 1939, 15th December 1951 to 18th May 1952, 4th November 1968 (dead), 22nd October 1974, 2nd-4th December 1974, 20th February to 17th March 1983, 3rd-6th November 1996, 5th-26th January 1999, 20th February 2000 and up to three from 31st October 2000 to 28th May 2001. There was one on 7th November 2005 (*LNHSB*).

The others were at *Barn Elms*: 15th December 1936 to 28th February 1937 (*BB, 30:294*), 17th November into December 1951, 5th-23rd December 1954, 3rd December 1960 to 7th January 1961 (two on 4th-5th December), 18th-28th January 1961 (possibly the second bird of December 1960), 21st December 1983 to 19th January 1984; *Earlswood Common*: 27th November to 4th December 1977; *Frensham Great Pond*: 5th January to 21st February 1964; *Hedgecourt*: 15th February 1953; *Holmethorpe Sand Pits* (*Mercers Lake*): 19th February to 9th March 1995; *Queen Elizabeth II Reservoir*: 27th-28th December 1985, 11th April and 5th May 1990, 14th February and 17th-28th May 1996; *Stoke Water Meadows*: 24th February 1990; *Walton Reservoirs*: 22nd November to 28th December 1935, 11th December 1977 to 9th April 1978 (also at Island Barn Reservoir), 8th November 1996, 28th October 1998; *Walton-on-Thames area*: 19th January 2005, 12th November 2005.

Calendar. Arrivals are from October. Numbers peak in December and most are gone by the end of March.

Bird months since 1900

	Jan	Feb	Mar	Apr	May	Jun	Jul	Aug	Sep	Oct	Nov	Dec	Total
Vice-county	14	10	3	2	2	0	0	0	0	1	9	18	**59**
Spelthorne	15	16	8	6	6	0	1	0	0	4	11	17	**84**

The earliest arrivals have been at Richmond Park on 13th October 1965 (*LBR*, *SBR* says 16th) and in Spelthorne at King George VI Reservoir on 16th October 2002. The latest to leave the vice-county was at Queen Elizabeth II Reservoir on 28th May 1996. The same bird was in Spelthorne, at Queen Mary Reservoir on 25th May 1996. There was a summer bird at Queen Mary Reservoir on 18th July 1993.

Pied-billed Grebe   *Podilymbus podiceps*

Three in the vice-county

Pied-billed Grebes breed in the Americas and Canadian birds migrate south to the USA. Nearly all British records have been in coastal counties, though there has been one in Oxfordshire. Some of them have stayed for several months.

Surrey. There have been three occurrences, perhaps only involving one bird. They are presumably from the Canadian population. The first was an adult found by J. G. Flynn on South Norwood Lake, where it remained from 26th January to 30th March 1997 (*BB, 91:459, LBR* for 1997). Photographs appeared in the *SBR* for 1997 and in other journals. An adult at Tooting Bec Common, only a mile to the west, from 5th December of the same year to 12th February 1998 (*BB, 92:557*) was presumably the same bird. There was one at Knight and Bessborough Reservoirs, Walton-on-Thames on 16th March 1999 (D. M. Harris, *BB, 93:516*).

Little Grebe

Moderately common breeding resident

Tachybaptus ruficollis

Breeds from Europe east to Japan and in Africa south of the Sahara. The recent breeding population trend in Britain is uncertain, but numbers appear to have increased since 1994 (*BTO News 266*). Most British Little Grebes winter away from their breeding areas, often on the coast, with maximum WeBS counts in September and October (*MA*). Little Grebe movements tend to be on an east-west axis extending to continental Europe (*MA*). The Wetland Bird Survey shows a national increase in winter numbers.

Early Surrey history. Newman (1849) saw one on the river bank at Eashing on St Valentine's Day, 1835. They were common in Surrey in the 1880s, with specimens from Cranleigh and Shalford (*SALEC*) and flocked up in winter and dispersed to breeding sites in spring (Bucknill). At the end of the 19th century Fetcham (=Leatherhead) Mill Pond held good numbers. Others were to be found breeding on the reedier upper parts of the Mole and the Wey, on many large and small lakes and, occasionally, at Battersea Park and Kew.

1900 to 1960. A nest was found at Horley in 1905 (G. T. Winter). Dalgliesh saw a pair at the Hammer Ponds, Thursley, a site with a long history of observations, on 17th February 1906. Three young just hatched, were seen at nearby Lea Park [=Witley Park] on 8th September 1906. Hascombe was a regular nesting site (Mouritz, 1907). Power (1910) knew of no breeding records for the Dulwich area but saw and heard Little Grebes on Dulwich Park Lake from time to time. Little Grebes were breeding in the Staines district at the beginning of the 20th century (Kerr, 1906). They bred at Stanwell Moor Park in the 1930s (*London Naturalist* for 1934). Glegg said that only occasional birds were seen at Staines Reservoirs.

Little Grebes were irregular winter visitors to Richmond Park up to 1936. One at Clapham Common in November 1964 was the first there for about 30 years. They bred at Addlestone (1929), Beddington (1908, 1929-34), Bookham Common (1933-34), Chertsey (1934), Fetcham Mill Pond (1906, six broods; 1928-33), Godstone (1915-34), Ham Gravel Pits (1929), Kew Gardens (1934, most/all years 1949-60), Kingston (1933-34), Leatherhead (1934), near Mitcham (1907), Molesey Gravel Pit (1931-32), Oxted (1907-11), Richmond Park (most/all years 1948-60, 1973), South Norwood (1933-34), Waddon (1933), Walton-on-the-Hill (1930-31), Weybridge (1930) and Wimbledon Common (1929) and continued to breed at most of these sites.

As originally noted by Bucknill, Fetcham Mill Pond remained a good place to see Little Grebes as they dived into the clear water of springs bubbling up from the chalk. Twelve pairs bred there in 1931 and 1932 (Parr). Hartley (1933) describes their breeding behaviour, noting that they were '*more than a match for both Coot and Moorhen, which seem to have no means of defending themselves against the smaller birds' submarine attacks*'. Large numbers wintered at Fetcham Mill Ponds in the 1930s. In 1934 the site was partially drained for the construction of (Leatherhead) watercress beds. This reduced the size of the wintering flock. The capping of the springs in the 1960s put a stop to underwater observations.

Further sites were colonised or discovered as the century progressed, including Windsor Great Park (Obelisk Pond) in 1946. Large numbers were seen at Frensham Ponds in the 1940s, with a peak of 165 at Frensham in October 1949. Flock numbers then fell and have never recovered. Reported breeding places have increased a little in number since 1960, possibly through better coverage.

Vice-county breeding places reported to the Surrey Bird Club from 1960 to 2001

Year	60	61	62	63	64	65	66	67	68	69	70	71	72	73
Northeast Surrey	8				7	9	10	2	6	8	6	8	5	7
Remainder	8				2	11		8	6	6	2	7	8	9
Total	**16**	**8**	**7**	**7**	**9**	**20**	**n/a**	**10**	**12**	**14**	**8**	**15**	**13**	**16**

Year	74	75	76	77	78	79	80	81	82	83	84	85	86	87
Northeast Surrey	6	6	6	5	4	5	7	6	4	5	7	3	6	6
Remainder	5	4	4	5	14	16	16	11	7	1	4	3	7	4
Total	**11**	**10**	**10**	**10**	**18**	**21**	**23**	**17**	**11**	**6**	**11**	**6**	**13**	**10**

Year	88	89	90	91	92	93	94	95	96	97	98	99	2000	2001
Northeast Surrey	1	4	4	5	9	4	7	8	11	6	14	9	14	7
Remainder	8	2	6	6	7			11	13	12	11	8	7	12
Total	**9**	**6**	**10**	**11**	**16**	**n/a**	**n/a**	**19**	**24**	**18**	**25**	**17**	**21**	**19**

Of the 231 tetrads in northeast Surrey, 19% were found to hold territories in the 1968-72 Atlas survey and 18% in the 1988-97 Atlas. This, like the table of breeding sites, suggests some stability in breeding numbers after the colonisation of earlier years. Little Grebes were found in 15% of the tetrads elsewhere in Surrey in 1988-97. The Winter Atlas found partial survey counts and estimates totalling 102 birds in 1981-84, suggesting a minimum size for winter population.

Population size. Little Grebes were rarely found by the Common Birds Census but a grossed-up estimate from the 1994-2004 average comes to about 50 adults in the breeding season. This looks on the low side unless the casual reporting of sites in the table has been unusually comprehensive. If Surrey held a proportionate share of the British breeding population as given by the *New Atlas*, the population would be about 0.27 per square km, or 50 territories, which again looks low. Little Grebes were found in 92 tetrads during the 1988-97 Atlas but since a territory only had to be established once in the ten year period, it might be that the annual total fluctuates in a range of 25 to 100 territories.

Territory counts. Six pairs were present at Ash Vale Gravel Pits in 1967 and at least 15 young were raised, the largest county site for the 1960s (Parr). Little Grebes bred at the Surrey Docks in 1977. There were four territories at Beddington Sewage Farm in 2003. Little Grebes bred on Bookham Common in 2004 (A. D. Prowse). A pair or two have bred on Spelthorne gravel pits in most, if not all, years since 1970 with up to three at Queen Mary from 1975-88 (Geen, 1990). Little Grebes bred at Perry Oaks Sewage Farm and Stanwell Moor in 2000 and 2001.

Large counts. Most flocks since 1950, apart from 52 at Perry Oaks Sewage Farm in 1999, have not exceeded 32:

Ash Vale Gravel Pits: 10, September 1976
Badshot Lea: 18, 1973 (*HSBBR*, 14 in *SBR*)

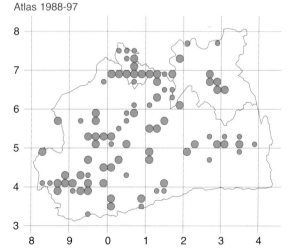

Atlas 1988-97

Barn Elms: 32, including six juveniles, 5th August 2001

Barrow Green: c.12, 16th September 1906

Beddington Sewage Farm: 32, September 1999

Buckland Sand Pits: 11, 12th October 1993

Effingham Fish Ponds: 10, July 1997

Enton: 18, 26th November 1970

Fetcham Mill Pond: 60, December 1930; 60, January 1934

Fieldcommon: 19, 23rd February 1992

Frensham: 165, October 1949 (HNHS)

Frimley Gravel Pits: 22 on 21st August 1971 and 11th September 1971

Gatton Lake: 17, November 1971

Hammer Pond: 8, 28th January 1996

Hedgecourt: 25, 1947

Hersham Gravel Pit: 16, 16th September 1990

Holmethorpe Sand Pits: 28, 12th January 2003 (S. Gale)

Island Barn Reservoir: 8, 10th October 1971

Lonsdale Road Reservoir: 17, 8th September 2002

Purley: 9, 11th January 1978

Richmond Park: 8, December 1928

Snowdenham: 6, 14th October 1973

Stoke Lake, Guildford: 19, 12th October 1985

Surrey Docks: 8, 11th February 1971 and 1st December 1973

Thames Richmond/Kew: 39, 13th January 1989

Thorpe Water Park: 16, 1969

Tongham Gravel Pit: 11, November 1998

Unstead Sewage Farm: 18, September 1999

Walton Gravel Pits: up to 23, August/September 1950

Walton Reservoirs: 18, April 1996

Watermeads, Mitcham: 16, 25th October 2001

Wrecclesham Sand Pits: 31, 23rd August 2003

Spelthorne

Perry Oaks Sewage Farm: 52, 4th September 1999

Queen Mary Reservoir: 20+, 21st October 1978

Shepperton Gravel Pits: 33, 16th March 1980

Movements and longevity. Like other Little Grebes, those in Surrey often move to other areas after breeding. Surrey Bird Club ringing reports since 1977 have included a longevity record of two months. The bird travelled from Queen Mary Reservoir to Carshalton (per Richard A. Denyer) but no further information about this or any other Little Grebe recovery has been located.

Great Crested Grebe   *Podiceps cristatus*

Moderately common breeding resident

Breeds from Europe east to China and in Africa, Australia and New Zealand. Present in Britain in pre-historic times (Harrison and Hollom, 1932). In the 19th century, persecution reduced the breeding population to under 50 pairs by 1860 but there has been a substantial increase since 1900, which is still continuing. Most Great Crested Grebes winter away from their breeding areas. Movements tend to be on an east-west axis extending into Europe. Moult takes place between August and October in areas safe from predators (*MA*).

Early Surrey history. Bucknill thought that Great Crested Grebes probably bred on all the large waters in the rural area at the beginning of the 19th century but he gave no evidence to support this. The earliest available record is of a young bird shot at Hampton Lodge, Puttenham on 11th February 1835. The Charterhouse Collection included one shot at Frensham in 1837 and another from Forked Pond. One of these may be the one currently held there with Godalming as its provenance. Great Crested Grebes were breeding at least occasionally at Forked and Hammer Ponds in the 1840s and 1850s. Yarrell mentioned a first-winter bird that was shot on the Thames at Penton Hook in February 1844. Breeding numbers are thought to have fallen sharply after 1850, under pressures from shooting for the millinery trade (*BB, 26:108*), building development and improved travel facilities which made remote areas more accessible. For the later 19th century, the birds were best known as uncommon winter visitors. There was one, season unknown, at Wimbledon Park Lake in the 1860s. Harting (1866) did not know of any summer records for Middlesex. One was shot at Forked Pond on a date before 1885 (*SALEC*). Bucknill (1900) knew of only five places, Frensham, Gatton Park, Richmond Park and two others, where the species had recently bred. One of the unnamed sites, 'one of the western lakes' might have been Obelisk Pond in Windsor Great Park, which was colonised in 1898 or Virginia Water, colonised by 1899 and the other, 'a southern sheet of water', was probably Vachery Pond, colonised in 1899.

Since 1900. The colonisation of Pen Ponds preceded the fencing off of a reserve area in 1902, the birds breeding on an island. From then onward there are records of between one and three pairs breeding in almost every year up to 1940. The birds were lost when the ponds were drained in 1940 and did not return until 1949, when there were two pairs. Gosnell collected a clutch of five eggs at Frensham Great Pond in 1912. On the Surrey side of the Thames, the reservoirs at Barn Elms, completed in 1897, attracted Great Crested Grebes from an early date and a pair bred there in 1929. Gravel pits have provided a major new, if often transitory, habitat since the 1930s. Many gravel pits in Spelthorne, which were opened up during the 1939-45 war, attracted Great Crested Grebes, some lost again when pits were filled in to create housing land in the late 1940s.

The 1931 Great Crested Grebe Inquiry, organised by *British Birds*, showed much improved breeding numbers, with many new sites colonised after 1900. A national sample census, carried out in 1935 to test the effect of droughts in 1933 and 1934, showed a small reduction, from 26 to 23, in the number of adults on the thirteen Surrey waters re-sampled from 1931 (Hollom, 1936). The Surrey reduction of 12% compared with 6% in the national sample. Later sample surveys produced vice-county estimates of 130 adults for the years 1946-50 and 168 for 1951-55 (Hollom, 1959). The 1965 estimates are from Prestt and Mills (1966). The BTO 1975 census produced a figure of 187 breeding and non-breeding adults for the vice-county (Parr, 1976) with a further 221 in Spelthorne (Oliver, 1977). These figures relate to adults in the breeding season, generally May/June. Wildfowl counts for 1995 came out at 261 for May, of which 114 were in Spelthorne, suggesting a decline but the vice-county total for selected wildfowl counts alone in May 2000 came out at 178, plus 33 breeding pairs at other sites. The total population was then at a historically high level.

The date of colonisation, where known, and counts numbers are shown in the table:

Colonisation dates and censuses (number of adults)

Place	Colonised	Census			Wildfowl Counts
		1931	1965	1975	1995
Vice-county					
Ash Vale	1916	2		9	
Badshot Lea	1916 or earlier		8	4	
Barn Elms	1929		7		
Boldermere		6	2	2	
Broadwater, Farncombe	1921	2	9	4	
Broome Hall			2	2	
Bury Hill, Dorking		2	2	2	
Cox's Lock Mill				1	
Cutt Mill Ponds				4	
Enton	*c.*1910	2	2	2	
Fetcham Mill Pond				2	
Forked Pond				2	
Frensham Great Pond	1899	12	4	4	
Frensham Little Pond	1907	4	2	2	
Frimley Green	1921 or earlier	2			
Frimley Gravel Pits				4	
Gatton	1897	18	2	6	
Godstone, Ivy Mill	1931	2			
Godstone Reserve			2	2	

| Place | Colonised | Census | | | Wildfowl Counts |
		1931	1965	1975	1995
Hamm Moor Gravel Pits			2		
Hammer Pond	1858 or earlier				
Hampton Park		2	6		
Hedgecourt	1904	6	10	2	
Hersham Gravel Pit				6	
Holmethorpe Sand Pits				2	
Island Barn Reservoir			9		
Lonsdale Road			2	2	
Mytchett	1913	2	3	2	
New Lines Pond			2	2	
Nutfield Reserve				2	
Obelisk, Windsor Great Park	1898	2	2	2	
Oxshott Brickworks				2	
Papercourt Gravel Pits			6	8	
Penton Hook Gravel Pit			2		
Richmond, Pen Ponds	1899	6		4	
River Thames				2	
River Thames, Staines-Chertsey			1		
Royal Military Academy, Sandhurst	1922 or earlier	2			
Send Heath Gravel Pits				3	
Silvermere	1916	2	2	2	
Snowdenham				2	
South Norwood Lake			2	2	
Stockbridge Pond				1	
Surrey Docks				2	
Tangley Mere	1928 or earlier	2		2	
Thorpe Gravel Pits			6	10	
Thorpe Water Park				12	
Vachery	c.1899	6	4	8	
Walton Gravel Pits				2	
Warren Mere		0	2		
Weybridge Mill Pond	c.1910	2			
Weybridge, Seven Arches	c.1922	2			
Wimbledon Park Lake	1906 or earlier	4	8	5	
Wire Mill Lake	1904	2	2		
Witley Park	1931	2	4		
Others, not breeding		25		48	
Subtotal vice-county		119	117	187	147
Spelthorne					
Staines Group	One pair. 1930, none 1931				
Subtotal Spelthorne		0	58	221	114
Grand Total		**119**	**175**	**408**	**261**

Virginia Water, not included in this table, was colonised in 1899 or earlier. There were three pairs in 1906. Numbers there varied up to 19 (1946) between 1930 and 1965 (South, 1966). Great Crested Grebes were nesting in Kew Gardens by 1934 and Richmond Park by 1938. They bred at Battersea Park in 980 and later at the Surrey Docks (1984-85). In Spelthorne, up to five pairs bred at Queen Mary

Reservoir from at least 1976-88 (Geen). There were 17 pairs with young and three pairs on eggs at Shepperton Gravel Pits in 1985. One pair bred there in 2000.

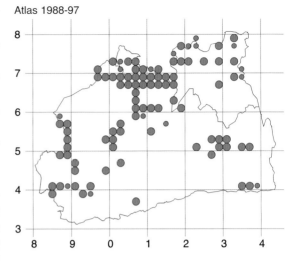

Breeding behaviour. A juvenile at Chertsey Meads was 10-14 days old on 15th March 1993. Belsey (undated, 2002) mentions photographing a chick at Chertsey on 15th February 1988, said to have been hatched on 12th February and the first for Britain in that year.

Calendar and movements. In some areas, the local population has been heavily augmented by autumn immigrants since 1919 or earlier. Large numbers were wintering on the reservoirs in the 1930s. Combined counts for the reservoirs at Barn Elms, Molesey and Spelthorne in 1930 showed the number of birds rising from 40 in June to a peak of 360 on 15th October (*BB, 26, p.130*). There were 330 on 29th September 1934. A count on 18th December 1937, found 141 at Molesey, 35 at Barn Elms, nine at Lonsdale Road and 123 at Staines. The completion of the Queen Elizabeth II reservoir at Molesey in 1962 created a nationally important wintering site. There were 250 in the vice-county wildfowl counts on 18th October 1981.

In Spelthorne, the creation of Staines Reservoirs in 1902, the Queen Mary Reservoir in 1925 and King George VI Reservoir in 1947 transformed the status of the bird. The only records mentioned by Glegg (1935) for Spelthorne are at Staines Reservoirs, where over 200 had been counted in August and September though none were known to have bred. Queen Mary Reservoir later became a nationally important site for wintering birds and held 330 as early as 19th September 1934. The number of Great Crested Grebes present in the London area in late 1958 and 1959 was abnormally high, with 670 at Queen Mary Reservoir alone on 15th November in the latter year. Average annual wildfowl count maxima from 1994/95 to 1998/99 at the four nationally important reservoir sites in the area were 331 at Queen Mary Reservoir (Spelthorne), 147 at Queen Elizabeth II Reservoir, 128 at Wraysbury Reservoir (Spelthorne) and 124 at King George VI Reservoir (Spelthorne). By 2003/04 the only one of these to qualify was Queen Mary with a five year average of 495, though significant numbers sometimes appeared at Queen Elizabeth II.

At other sites, especially the smaller waters, Great Crested Grebes may be absent in winter, as noted by Venables (1934a) for Frensham, where there was a spring passage peaking at 40 birds in mid-March. A spring passage of about this volume still occurs at Frensham but the ponds are no longer deserted in winter. Overall, there has been a decline in recorded numbers since the 1980s.

In spite of the substantial movements implied by the seasonal counts, Great Crested Grebes are not often seen flying more than a short distance. Ten flew south over Frimley Gravel Pits on 3rd January 1979, when the waters were frozen. A Great Crested Grebe ringed at Morden on 2nd February 1965 was recovered 68 miles (109 km) away at Stanton Fitzwarren, Wiltshire, on 25th February 1966.

Large counts. The large autumn counts at reservoirs are consistent with national experience:

Ash Vale Gravel Pits: 20, April 1971 (*HSBBR*)
Badshot Lea: 37, April 1984 (*HSBBR*)
Barn Elms: 113, 1962
Enton: 23, 31st October 2003
Frensham: 60, including 40 young on 2nd

August 1970
Frimley Gravel Pits: 53, January 1996
Gatton Lake: 25, February 1977
Holmethorpe Sand Pits: 40, February 1996
Island Barn Reservoir: 141, 1966

Lonsdale Road Reservoir: 13, April 1931
Papercourt Gravel Pits: 18, March 2001
Queen Elizabeth II Reservoir: 375, 13th January 1963
Thorpe Water Park: 106, January 1996
Virginia Water: 44, 26th March 1959 (South, 1980)
Walton Reservoirs: 305, March 1963

Wimbledon Park Lake: 22, 19th November 2000
Spelthorne
King George VI Reservoir: 401, July 1995
Queen Mary Reservoir: 679. January 1997
Shepperton Gravel Pits: 59 in September 1995
Staines: 600, 4th January 1962 (*LBR*, Staines Reservoirs presumed)
Wraysbury Reservoir: 515, 16th January 1979

Longevity. One ringed at Frensham on 29th October 1978 and recovered (shot) there on 3rd June 1981 is the greatest known longevity.

Red-necked Grebe   *Podiceps grisegena*

Scarce winter visitor

Breeds in North America, Europe and Asia. Birds occasionally summer in the British Isles. Breeding attempts were first proved, in England and Scotland, in 1988. Little is known about the origin of those wintering in Britain.

Early Surrey history. The Red-necked Grebe is included in Newman's 1849 list for the Godalming area. As with other birds in this list, it should be remembered that his area ran well beyond the Surrey border, reaching at least as far as Winchester. In Bucknill's time the Charterhouse Collection held a female in winter plumage which had been found by John Jones, a farmer of Tuesley, in a small stream (*SALEC*, *SCCMS*), but the specimen was not in the collection in 2001. A shot-damaged adult was picked up dead at Farthing Down in April 1890 and one was killed at Poynter's, near Cobham (Bucknill).

Since 1900. After a slow start, the 1950s saw a surge in reports which continued and peaked in the 1980s. Numbers have fallen back a little:

Bird months by decade

	1900s	1910s	1920s	1930s	1940s	1950s	1960s	1970s	1980s	1990s	2000-06	Total
Vice-county	0	0	3	6	9	8	25	24	51	44	24	**194**
Spelthorne*	0	0	2	5	3	25	42	27	69	60	6	**239**

*to 2003

There was one at Barn Elms Reservoirs in 1922 (*BLA*) and another on 10th September 1929. Two at Frensham on 9th July 1925 were the first there for the 20th century and possibly the first ever. One that appeared at Barn Elms Reservoirs after an easterly gale in January 1937 was part of a national influx of divers and grebes (*BB, 30:370-74*). It stayed from 30th January to 10th February. The next was in shallow water at Guildford Sewage Farm on 19th September 1944.

The first for Spelthorne was one at Staines Reservoirs on 24th January 1926. There were others there on 1st December 1928, 13th and 15th July 1930, and from the end of November to 7th December 1930 (Glegg), then in November 1936.

Where found. Over half of the bird months have come from the Spelthorne reservoirs. All have featured but Staines Reservoirs dominates. There have been a few at Shepperton Gravel Pits. Over 70% of the 194 vice-county bird months have come from Barn Elms Reservoirs (56), Walton Reservoirs (33), Queen Elizabeth II Reservoir (19), Island Barn Reservoir (17) and Frensham (14). The remainder have been at Badshot Lea, Bay Pond (Godstone), Beddington Sewage Farm, Brittens Pond, Buckland Sand Pits, Chobham, Fieldcommon Gravel Pit, Frimley Gravel Pits, Goldsworth Park Lake, Guildford Sewage Farm, Holmethorpe Sand Pits, Leatherhead, Mitcham Common, Molesey Gravel Pit, New Lines Pond, Papercourt Gravel Pits, Richmond Park, the Surrey Docks, the Thames, Thorpe Water Park, Virginia Water and Wimbledon Park Lake.

Most recently, Red-necked Grebes have been seen at Fieldcommon Gravel Pit (2001), Island Barn Reservoir (2001), Queen Elizabeth II Reservoir (2001, 2003, 2004), Thorpe Water Park (2003, 2006) and Walton Reservoirs (2001, 2002, 2003). No Spelthorne records have been located for 1998-2000. There were single birds at King George VI Reservoir on 9th December 2002 and in February, August and September 2004, at Queen Mary Reservoir on 14th February 2004, at Staines Reservoirs in September 2001, October 2002, November-December 2003 and August 2004 (*LNHSB*) and at King George VI Reservoir in November and December 2003 (*Bird Watching*).

Calendar. Red-necked Grebes have appeared in every month of the year. The monthly table shows a clear spring passage, peaking in February, with a return passage peaking in November.

Bird months 1900-2006

	Jan	Feb	Mar	Apr	May	Jun	Jul	Aug	Sep	Oct	Nov	Dec	Total
Vice-county	35	40	24	10	4	4	5	8	14	9	22	19	**194**
Spelthorne*	38	34	34	20	6	2	4	8	12	22	34	25	**239**

*to 2003

The first August record for the vice-county was of one at Walton Reservoirs from 31st August to 2nd September 1975. The first June record for the vice-county was of one at Island Barn and Queen Elizabeth II reservoirs in 1996.

Large counts. Most are seen as single birds. There were seven at Queen Mary Reservoir on 19th January 1985.

Slavonian Grebe   *Podiceps auritus*

Scarce winter visitor

Breeds in North America, Europe and Asia. Mainly winter visitors and passage migrants in the British Isles. There has been a small Scottish breeding population since the early years of the 20th century.

Early Surrey history. The earliest reliable record is of one shot at Cosford Pond and given to Stafford by John Hawkins in 1839 (*SALEC*). This bird was seen in the Charterhouse Collection by Bucknill, though it is no longer held there. Others were shot at Carshalton on 15th February 1870 and at East Molesey on 23rd December 1876 (Bucknill).

1900 to 1969. There was one on the Thames at Richmond on 16th February 1917 (*The Field, 139:385* in *BLA*) and another at Barn Elms Reservoirs from 5th-12th October 1924, after which Slavonian Grebes became irregular winter visitors there. One at Staines Reservoir on 9th March 1924 (*BLA*) was the first for Spelthorne. There were others at the same place on dates from 12th October to 26th December 1925, on 27th December 1926, November to December 1928 and January and December 1929 (*LN*). In 1930, there were three at Queen Mary Reservoir on 14th December (Glegg) and four at Staines Reservoirs on 30th November (*London Naturalist*). By this date Slavonian Grebes were established as regular winter visitors to the district, though none were recorded from 1940-45.

Slavonian Grebes were at Walton Reservoirs in 1929 and 1931, establishing another fairly regular site for the species. One at Richmond Park on 16th December 1939 was a first for the park. There was one at Walton Reservoirs on 7th March 1939. Others were at Island Barn Reservoir in March 1956 and in 1958 (September). Slavonian Grebes were first recorded at Frensham on 16th December 1923. There were others in 1937 (February/March), 1948 (November/December), 1951 (April), 1952 (November), 1953 (October/November), 1954 (October and November, CNHS and Haslemere Museum archive), 1955 (January), 1958 (November), 1962 (November), 1965 (1st August) and 1967 (November). One was on the Wandle at Carshalton on 28th January to 6th February 1963.

Where found since 1970. In the years from 1970 to 2000, about 70 Slavonian Grebes were found, appearing in every year except 1982, 1993 and 2000, most often at Barn Elms (nine years), Island Barn Reservoir (nine years),Walton Reservoirs (eight years) and Frensham (seven years). Some stayed for a day and others longer, a few wintering. The sites at which they have appeared are: *Barn Elms* (1978-79, 1983-85, 1988-89, 1992, 1994); *Cutt Mill* (1973); *Fieldcommon* (1997); *Frensham* (1973-76, 1978, 1981, 1984, 1986, 1988, 1996); *Frimley Gravel Pits* (1986-87); *Hersham Gravel Pit* (1979, 1985, 1991); *Holmethorpe* (1987-88, 1996); *Island Barn Reservoir* (1970-71, 1976, 1985, 1987, 1989, 1996-99, 2003); *Moat Pond,* (1971); *Queen Elizabeth II Reservoir* (1985, 1987); *the Thames* near Barn Elms (1985-86), at Ham Lands (1986), at Mortlake (1986) and at Teddington (1986); *Thorpe* (1972, 1977, 1979-81, 1996-97); *Walton Reservoirs* (1975, 1978-79, 1985-86, 1988, 1990, 1992); and *Wimbledon Park Lake* (1996). At least eleven more birds were recorded from 2001 to 2004.

Slavonian Grebes were found in Spelthorne in all years except 1974 and 1976. Most were single birds but there were up to four at Queen Mary Reservoir in March/April 1973. Single birds were recorded at Shepperton Gravel Pits on 6th March 1979, 26th October 1985 and 8th January 2000. Others in 2000 were at King George VI Reservoir (December) and Staines Reservoirs (January, April, November). Spelthorne records after 2000 include *King George VI Reservoir*: January-February 2001, up to three in September-November 2001, 9th December 2002, February-April 2003, November-December 2003; *Queen Mary Reservoir*: two in January 2001, 13th January 2002; *Shepperton Gravel Pits*: February 2001; *Staines Reservoirs*: January, September-October and December 2001, January-April and August-October 2002; up to four in February-March 2003 (LNHSB), one in December 2003 (LNHSB); *Wraysbury Reservoir*: 3rd March 2002, two on 4th March 2002 and two on 14th December 2002.

Calendar. One at Frensham on 1st August 1965 was very early. The earliest vice-county autumn arrivals since 1970 were on 12th August 2001 at Island Barn Reservoir and on 16th September 1975 at Walton Reservoirs. The main arrivals were in January and February. Most birds had left at the end of March, the latest being on 1st May 1992, at Walton Reservoirs. There was one at Island Barn Reservoir on 16th July 2002. Spelthorne dates have ranged from 9th September (Staines Reservoirs, 2001) to 5th May (Staines Reservoirs, 1970).

There are no vice-county records for June. A bird that made a nesting attempt just outside the Spelthorne boundary in 1948 was seen at Staines on dates from 6th June to 26th September and there was one at Staines Reservoirs in late July 1975.

Large counts. There were four at Staines Reservoirs on 30th November 1930 and three at Queen Mary Reservoir on 6th December of the same year. Slavonian Grebes at Mitcham from 31st January to 26th March 1937 were part of a national diver and grebe influx, peaking at four on 6th and 20th February. In the vice-county since 1970, the biggest numbers in any one year were eight in 1985 and seven in 1986, all single birds in each case. No more than two were seen at any one time during the period. There were seven at Queen Mary Reservoir on 4th April 1996.

Black-necked Grebe   *Podiceps nigricollis*

Regular winter visitor and passage migrant, recorded in all months.

Black-necked Grebes breed in parts of North America, Europe, Asia and Africa. The *Migration Atlas* suggests that those wintering in the southeast are of European origin. Although mainly winter visitors and passage migrants to the British Isles, Black-necked Grebes have bred in Britain in small numbers since 1904, as part of an extension of range north and west across Europe.

Early Surrey history. A male obtained from the Hammer Pond, Thursley in the summer of 1840 and a female of the same year from Forked Pond (*SALEC*) were in the Charterhouse Collection during Bucknill's time but are no longer held there. One was shot at Frensham not later than 1854 (Spicer, 1854).

1900 to 1969. The next dated record came in 1920, when Bentham saw one at Frensham on 14th March. Another was there in November/December 1922. At Barn Elms Reservoirs, an early record was of one from 14th-27th September 1926. One was there in December 1934 and others in July 1935, December 1937 and September 1938. Black-necked Grebes became fairly regular at the site, as they did at Island Barn Reservoir (1958) and Walton Reservoirs and later at the Queen Elizabeth II Reservoir. There was one at Walton Reservoirs on 21st December 1930 and October 1931 and two there on 19th and 20th December 1931. A pair were seen on an unidentified Surrey pond on 7th April 1935 (*BB*, *29:117-18*) and there was one near Godstone on 28th December 1938. There were two at Hedgecourt in August 1947. At Frensham, Venables saw one on the Little Pond on 21st and 30th July 1932 and in 1934 three were there on 12th February and one from 16th-18th May. Three on 9th September 1956 and some others made a total of twelve records from 1920 to 1970 (HNHS, 1980). Other places where they have been seen include Badshot Lea (1960), Boldermere (1960), Enton (1954), Fetcham Mill Pond (1940), Gatton Park (1959), Godstone (Ivy Mill Pond 1943), Guildford Sewage Farm (1955), Kew Gardens (1948), Mitcham Junction Gravel Pit (1936) and Papercourt (1969). Black-necked Grebes were recorded at Island Barn Reservoir in 1954, 1956 and from the mid-1960s, with a maximum to 1970 of ten on 19th October 1969.

The first for Spelthorne was of one at Staines Reservoirs from 13th-26th October 1907 (Kerr). Black-necked Grebes were often seen there in subsequent years (Glegg). There was one at Queen Mary Reservoir on 28th August 1931 and another there in January 1937. Staines Reservoirs remains the most important Surrey site for them, with up to eight in 1939 and 21 (the maximum to 1950) on 21st September 1945. By 1950 some were staying as late as December.

Since 1970. In the years from 1970, Black-necked Grebes have appeared annually in small numbers, nearly half of them at Island Barn Reservoir. The vice-county sites at which they have appeared, together with the totals of the annual maxima for 1970-2000 at each are: Badshot Lea: one; Barn Elms Reservoirs: seventeen; Beddington Sewage Farm: six; Chertsey Reservoir: one; Frensham: 17; Frimley Gravel Pits: four; Hammer Pond: one; Holmethorpe Sand Pits: six; Island Barn Reservoir: 79; Moat Pond: one; Papercourt Gravel Pits: four; Queen Elizabeth II Reservoir: sixteen; Richmond Park: three; Send Heath: one; Surbiton: one; Thames: eight; Thorpe Water Park: five; Tongham Gravel Pit: one; Unstead Sewage Farm: one and Walton Reservoirs: 27. The peak years were 1972 and 1976 (fourteen), 1971 and 1998 (twelve) and 1970 and 1984 (ten).

In Spelthorne, annual maxima at Staines Reservoirs began to fall in the later 1980s and have fallen further to around five through the 1990s. Black-necked Grebes were recorded every year from 1970-99, the annual maxima for these years totalling 412 birds. The totals of the annual maxima at other Spelthorne sites were: King George VI Reservoir: 77; Perry Oaks Sewage Farm: nine; Queen Mary Reservoir: 34; Queen Mary Gravel Pits: one; Shepperton Gravel Pits: four; Stanwell Moor Gravel Pits: two and Wraysbury Reservoir: eighteen. There were records for all months in the period.

Places visited from 2001 to 2005 include Barn Elms London Wetland Centre, Frensham, Island Barn Reservoir, Queen Elizabeth II Reservoir, Thorpe Water Park, Tongham Gravel Pit and Walton Reservoirs. Numbers in Spelthorne remained generally low after 1999,

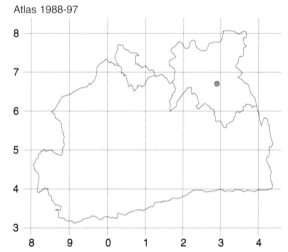

Atlas 1988-97

but there were fourteen at Staines Reservoirs on 4th January 2006 (*LNHSB*) and five at King George VI Reservoir from 26th September to 2nd October 2000 (*LBR*).

Breeding behaviour. A pair were seen displaying at Beddington Sewage Farm on 24th-25th May 1993 and a juvenile was seen there on 13th September. Breeding was not established.

Calendar. There were records for all months of the year, with passage peaks in February/March and August/ September, for example in 1970 a spring peak of eight at Island Barn Reservoir in March/April and an autumn peak of eight there on 26th October (Parr and *SBR*).

Large counts. The maximum single day counts for individual sites from 1970 to 2005 were:

Frensham Great Pond: six, 24th March 1984

Island Barn Reservoir: 11, 25th March 1972 (all-time vice-county high)

Queen Elizabeth II Reservoir: eight, 1998

Thorpe Water Park: three, 1995

Walton Reservoirs: four, 1976

Spelthorne

King George VI Reservoir: ten, 5th October 1985

Queen Mary Reservoir: seven, 5th August 1981

Staines Reservoirs: 39, 13th September 1981

Wraysbury Reservoir: seven, 3rd February 1974

None of the other vice-county waters ever held more than two.

Fulmar (Northern Fulmar)   *Fulmarus glacialis*

Twenty-four records, including six from Spelthorne

The Fulmar breeding population spread south from Iceland and the Faeroes to reach Scotland in the 19th century and had reached Norway, northwest France and most of the British coast by the end of the 20th.

Surrey. The few which have been found in Surrey have mainly been storm-driven, and about half of them were exhausted or dead:

1941:   Whitmoor Common, one dead on 20th April, in a wood.

1962:*   King George VI and Staines reservoirs, an apparently uninjured bird on 4th-5th March.

1977:   Farthing Down, one freshly dead on 25th September (R. Price).

1981:*   Queen Mary Reservoir, one on 27th April.

1981:   Barn Elms Reservoirs, one in a weak condition for several hours until evening on 27th April.
Coopers Hill, Runnymede, one over on 27th April.

1981:*   King George VI Reservoir, one on 2nd May.

1983:   Woodmansterne, one WSW on 14th November.

1985:   Moat Pond, one southwest on 29th June.

1986:*   Staines Reservoir, one on 12th June.

1986:   Beare Green, a ringed bird found dead on 11th April.

1987:   Thames at County Hall, one on the foreshore on 3rd February was probably injured, as it trailed its right leg.
Thames at Battersea, one found dead on the river bank on 10th March.

1987:*   Ashford Cemetery, one west on 16th December.
Queen Mary Reservoir, one on 17th December.

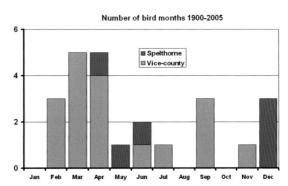

Number of bird months 1900-2005

1994: Tower Bridge, one flew east on 14th February.

Stoke Lake, one flew up the Wey valley on 20th February.

1996: Epsom, one found in September was taken into care and released later at Beachy Head.

1997: Bury Lake, Dorking, one found on 26th September died two weeks later while in care.

2000: Queen Elizabeth II Reservoir, one on 1st July, also seen at Walton Reservoirs.

2001: Single Fulmars on 1st March at Barn Elms WWT, Beddington Sewage Farm (taken into care on 2nd March), Stoke Lake (1st-2nd, found dead on 3rd), and one found dead at Effingham on 2nd March were related to an east coast wreck which brought Fulmars to at least seven other inland sites (*Rare Birds* 7:2, p.140).

Spelthorne

Calendar. March is the most frequent month of occurrence

Movements and longevity. The 1986 ringing recovery is remarkable, and gives an indication of where other Surrey birds may have come from. The bird had been ringed as an adult at Eynhallow, Orkney on 13th July 1964 and was found dead 21 years eight months later and 870 km (540 miles) south at Beare Green on 11th April 1986.

Manx Shearwater   *Puffinus puffinus*

At least 23 vice-county birds and nine from Spelthorne

Manx Shearwaters breed around the coasts of the British Isles, where they are thought to be increasing, and on a few Atlantic island groups. There are closely related forms, treated by some authors as races, in the Mediterranean. Outside the breeding season the birds disperse widely over the North and South Atlantic. All foreign-ringed birds recovered in Britain have involved exchanges with colonies in France (*MA*).

Early Surrey history. The first four are due to Stafford. A Manx Shearwater was killed at Normandy Farm, near Seale in 1838 or 1839. Two others occurred in March 1872, one at Farnham and the other between Aldershot and Godalming. A starving bird killed at Aldershot and given to Stafford on 11th September 1873 may not have been in Surrey. Two of the 1872-73 birds were at one time in the Stafford collection (*SALEC*) but the specimens currently held at Charterhouse are of unknown origin, except for one from the Scilly Isles. An injured bird was picked up at Haling Park, Croydon, on 6th September 1888 (Bucknill). One found at Staines on 30th August 1882 was the first for Middlesex (Glegg).

Later records, all single birds:

1930: Honor Oak, one was picked up alive in Netherby Road on 23rd September (*LN*).

1946: Clapham, one alive in Kings Avenue in September, taken to the Zoo.

1953: Barn Elms Reservoirs, one on the water on 8th September.

1953: Mitcham Common, one on 12th September was found on a pond, badly oiled.

1963:* Staines Reservoirs, one on 12th September, (notes in the *LBR*).

1968: South Norwood, one picked up in a garden, exhausted, on 9th September and released at Brighton.

1969: South Norwood, an exhausted bird on 6th October.

1974:* Wraysbury Reservoir, one on 3rd September.

1977:* Queen Mary Reservoir, one on12th-14th September.

1980:* Staines Reservoirs, one on 6th September.

1980: New Malden, an exhausted bird on 11th September, released at Selsey Bill.

1983:* Staines Reservoirs, one on 5th-6th September.

1984: Ottershaw, one under a wood pile on 1st September after gales.

1984:* Wraysbury Reservoir, one on 1st September.

1985:* Wraysbury Reservoir, one on 1st-2nd September.

1985:   Hersham, one flew over rough ground on 5th September.

1988:* Queen Mary Reservoir, one on 14th September.

1990:   Woking, one found on 8th September.

1991:   Barn Elms Reservoirs, one on 21st- 23rd July.

1992:   Camberwell, London SE5, one found exhausted on 3rd September.

        Putney, London SW15, one found exhausted on 4th September.

        Croydon, one found exhausted on 7th September.

1997:   Guildford Railway Station, one found exhausted in August and released at Selsey in September.

1998:   Walton Reservoirs, one from 30th July to 2nd August.

        Beddington, one taken into care in September.

2003:* Staines Reservoirs, one on 18th September.

2004:* King George VI Reservoir, one on 12th September (*LNHSB*).

Spelthorne

There was an exhausted bird probably of this species at Guildford on 14th September 1973.

Calendar. Most of the birds found in Surrey are storm-driven, usually found in September, at the end of the breeding season.

Balearic Shearwater   *Puffinus mauretanicus*

One bird

Surrey. One was found by M. Lawford and finally identified by R. B. Hastings at Island Barn Reservoir on 17th August 1984 (Hastings, 1985).

Petrel species   *Hydrobates or Oceanodroma*

Surrey. A white-rumped petrel was on the Thames at Waterloo on 15th January 1947 and one was picked up in Battersea Park on 24th November 1949 (*BLA*).

Storm Petrel (European Storm-petrel)   *Hydrobates pelagicus*

At least fifteen birds, three of them in Spelthorne

Breeds around the northern and western coasts of the British Isles and around other island groups in the eastern Atlantic and the western Mediterranean, dispersing to the oceans in winter, when some reach Southern Africa.

Surrey. Records are mainly of storm-driven birds, often dead or dying.

1825:   Thames, a bird which was flying along the river between Blackfriars and Westminster Bridges was shot from a coal barge in 1824 or 1825. The record is due to Yarrell, who, as Harting pointed out, gives two dates - November 1824 in Yarrell (1825) and March 1825 in Yarrell (1845). The latter date appears to be correct. Possibly there was another in November 1824, when *between two and three hundred were shot after severe gales* [!] (C. and J. Paget, *Sketch of the Natural History of Yarmouth and its neighbourhood* in Yarrell, 1845).

1835:   Richmond, an exhausted bird on the Thames in March was shot *by a man named Arris* (Bucknill). This might be the bird mentioned by Glegg as being *taken on the Thames near Richmond about the end of January 1835*, but the date is different, so it might have been another bird.

1837:   Wormley Hill, one picked up dead (*SALEC*).

1840:   Milford, one found (*SALEC*). This and the previous specimen were in the Charterhouse Collection in Bucknill's time, but they are no longer held there.

1852:   West End, Esher, one shot in October (*Zool.*, 1902).

1865:   near Haslemere, one picked up dead on a road (*Zool., 1902*), not definitely in Surrey.

1896:   Nork Park, Banstead, one killed by flying into glass in or around 1896.

1901:   St Catherine's, Guildford, a male was caught alive at a street lamp on 28th December (Dalgliesh, 1902).

1932:   Frensham Great Pond, one swimming and flying on 5th October, when there had been no recent gales (*BB, 27.27*).

1950:*   Staines Reservoirs, one on 11th November was the first LNHS area record for the 20th century.

1951:   Hambledon, one found on 26th August. It did not survive. (Parker, 1954 contains a full account).

1959:*   King George VI Reservoir, one on 27th October.

1961:*   Staines Reservoirs, one on 18th November.

1986:   Cranleigh, one found dead on 10th September.

1999:   Queen Elizabeth II Reservoir, a healthy bird on 10th October.

* Spelthorne

There is an undated reference to one shot on the Thames near Brentford a few years before 1888 in Glegg

Calendar. As the table shows, most occurrences are in the autumn, most often in October:

Bird months 1835 to 2000

	Jan	Feb	Mar	Apr	May	Jun	Jul	Aug	Sep	Oct	Nov	Dec	No month	Total
Vice-county	1	0	1	0	0	0	0	1	1	3	0	1	4	**12**
Spelthorne	0	0	0	0	0	0	0	0	0	1	2	0	0	**3**

Leach's Petrel (Leach's Storm-petrel)   *Oceanodroma leucorhoa*

At least 26 vice-county records and 24 from Spelthorne to 2004

Breeds in the North Atlantic, including Scotland, and in the North Pacific, moving south in winter. Also breeds off South Africa (*MA*). Storms during the southward autumn migration drive some of the birds inland.

Early Surrey history. Those found in Surrey have typically arrived in the period September to December, often associated with storms and always single birds. Many of them have been found dead. One was shot on the Thames near Chelsea in October 1827. Several had occurred in the Godalming district by 1837 (Newman, 1849). Dead birds were found near Haslemere on 21st November 1840 (Bucknill, presumably the 1840 bird in *SALEC*), Dunsfold/Haslemere on 2nd February 1841 and Cranleigh on 29th November 1881. The Charterhouse Collection at one time included a specimen from Rodborough Hill (*SALEC*). One found alive on Busses Common, Hambledon on 12th November 1899 went into a private collection (Bucknill).

Since 1900. These are the subsequent records, all of them from September to January:

1911:   Frensham Great Pond one on 30th December.

1927:   Dorking, one on 27th December, captured in a snow drift.

1949:*   Staines Reservoirs, one on 7th January.
        Staines Reservoirs, one on 13th November.

1952:   A nationwide wreck of Leach's Petrels in late October and early November 1952 involved at least 6,700 birds and was brought about by severe westerly gales from the Atlantic (*BB*, *47:137-63*). Most of the casualties were in western Britain but there were a few in Surrey.

Cranleigh, one found alive on 31st October.

Haslemere, one found dead on 1st November.

Petersham, one found dead on the towpath on 2nd November, 'between Ham and Richmond' in *British Birds*.

Kingston Hill, one on 14th November, *British Birds* says it was found dead.

Unstead Sewage Farm, one reported on 28th September was not well seen but could have been part of the wreck. Notes are in Parker (1954).

1952:* Two were found as a result of the wreck.

Queen Mary Reservoir, one found dead on 2nd November.

Staines Reservoirs, one found alive on 3rd November.

1957:* Queen Mary Reservoir, one on 18th September.

Staines Reservoirs, one found dead on 27th September.

1958:* Queen Mary Reservoir, one on 19th October.

1959:* Queen Mary Reservoir, one on 1st November.

1962:* Queen Mary Reservoir, one on 28th October.

1964:* Staines Reservoirs, one on 29th November.

1966:* Staines Reservoirs, one on 30th November.

1969:* Staines Reservoirs, one on 1st November.

1972:* Wraysbury Reservoir, one on 9th November.

1977:* Staines Reservoirs, one found dead on 11th September.

1978:* Queen Mary Reservoir, one on 4th November.

1979:* Staines Reservoirs, one on 23rd September.

1981:* Staines Reservoirs, one on 12th September.

1982:* Queen Mary Reservoir, one on 24th October.

1983:* Queen Mary Reservoir, one on 3rd September.

1983: Thursley Common, one flew east, low, on 3rd September. A northwest gale on the previous night brought twelve to the London area.

1985:* Wraysbury Reservoir, one on 27th December.

1986:* Staines Reservoirs, one on 6th September.

Queen Mary Reservoir, one on 17th October.

1986: Walton Reservoirs, one on 25th October.

1987: Lambeth Reservoir, one on 11th October.

New Haw, one on 16th October, brought in by the Great Storm of that month.

1987:* Staines Reservoirs, one on 17th October.

1988: Barn Elms Reservoirs, one on 30th September.

1989: Barn Elms Reservoirs, one on 17th December.

Walton Reservoirs, one on 17th December was watched for over two hours.

Ashtead, one picked up in late December and released at Berry Head, Devon.

Frensham Little Pond, one found dead on 26th December.

1989:* Queen Mary Reservoir, one on 17th December.

Staines Reservoirs, one on 17th December.

1991: Walton Reservoirs, one on 1st November.

1995: Frensham Great Pond, one in calm weather on 22nd October.

1997: Walton Reservoirs, one on 11th September.

1999: Queen Elizabeth II Reservoir, one on 12th October.

2000:   Queen Elizabeth II Reservoir, one on 30th October.
2003:   Walton Reservoirs, one on 24th September, after strong winds.
          Queen Elizabeth II Reservoir, one on 2nd October.
          Barn Elms London Wetland Centre, one on 17th October.
          Frensham Great Pond, one on 31st October in calm weather.
2004:*   King George VI Reservoir, one on 24th September (*LNHSB*).
2004:   Queen Elizabeth II Reservoir, one on 6th December.

* Spelthorne

Gannet (Northern Gannet)   *Morus bassanus (Sula bassana)*

Twenty-nine records to 2004, including four from Spelthorne

Breeds in colonies around North Atlantic coasts and mostly winters on the continental shelf off West Africa. The British population was held back by persecution in the 19th century but has been increasing since.

Early Surrey history. An exhausted bird was found near Frensham Pond in 1840 (*SALEC*). Spicer (1854) mentioned one from Frensham in his collection (the 1840 bird?). Another was killed by a boy with a stick in a field near Haslemere in 1844. Both finished up in the Charterhouse Collection (Bucknill) and one might be the bird still held there, said to be of unknown provenance. Charterhouse records show that one killed at Guildford was bought for six shillings in November 1892.

Later records are:

1906:   River Wey near Godalming, one on 17th February (Dalgliesh, 1906).
1927:   Kenley, one in a cottage garden on 8th November (Pounds).
1930:   Wandsworth Common, one at a pond in May, sent to the Zoo on the 29th.
1941:   Waterloo Bridge, one in flight on 28th January.
1950:*   Staines Reservoirs, one on 18th June.
          Staines Reservoirs, one on 13th September.
1956:   Barnes Railway Bridge, one picked up exhausted on 31st January.
1957:   Bermondsey, an adult found in a garden on 18th January.
1958:   Tolworth, one on 25th November, flying east.
1963:   Frensham Little Pond, a sick bird first seen on 27th August was sent to London Zoo on 1st September and died there of haemorrhagic enteritis on the 4th. It was thought to be a three year old female.
1979:   Beddington Sewage Farm, one on 15th September, flying over.
          Epsom Common, one on 31st December.
1981:   Pen Ponds, Richmond Park, one flying east on 14th February.
1981:*   Staines Reservoirs, one on 27th April.
1985:*   Stanwell, one on 6th September.
1985:   Dorking, one found in a field, underweight, on 29th October. It was taken into care and released in Cornwall.
1989:   Beddington Sewage Farm, an immature bird flew over on 16th September.
1996:   Beddington Sewage Farm, an adult and a juvenile flew west on 2nd May.
1997:   Knaphill, one flew over on 9th October.
1998:   Beddington Sewage Farm, one flew over on 5th October.
1999:   Wrecclesham Floods, one flew over on 15th October.
2000:   Epsom, one found injured on 30th September and taken into care. It died on 4th October.
          Queen Elizabeth II Reservoir, a juvenile flew south on 26th October.

2001: Beddington Sewage Farm, a juvenile flew over on 19th September.

2003: Beddington Sewage Farm, one on 31st December.

2004: Stoke Water Meadows, one flew over on 8th May.

Calendar. Gannets have appeared in all months except July, with a small autumn peak:

Bird Months 1900-2004

	Jan	Feb	Mar	Apr	May	Jun	Jul	Aug	Sep	Oct	Nov	Dec	Total
Vice-county	3	2	0	0	4	0	0	1	4	5	2	2	**23**
Spelthorne	0	0	0	1	0	1	0	0	2	0	0	0	**4**

Cormorant (Great Cormorant)   *Phalacrocorax carbo*
Locally common, with large roosts and has attempted to breed

Races of the Cormorant breed across Europe, Africa, Asia, Australia, New Zealand and parts of North America. Some are very distinctive and have been split off as species. *P. c. carbo* breeds in Norway, Britain and eastern Canada. The British population was held back by persecution in the 19th century but has increased since. The increase has continued into the 21st century. Immigration by birds of the southern race *P. c. sinensis* is thought to account for part of the increase. An increase in tree-nesting, which used to be rare in the British Isles but is common among continental birds, lends support for this view. Successful inland breeding began in Essex and Staffordshire in 1981 and in the London area in 1987. Cormorants from British coastal colonies, where most ringing takes place, move south or east after the breeding season (*MA*).

Early Surrey history. King James I (reigned 1603-25) kept Cormorants, Ospreys and tame Otters on the Thames at Westminster (Gurney, 1921). His successor, Charles I, had a Master of the Cormorants whose job apparently included training Cormorants to catch fish, in a manner still used by the Chinese (Yarrell). There was a Cormorant on top of the steeple at Kingston on 11th July 1629 (Parker, 1952).

An adult was shot in high alders at Hampton Lodge, Puttenham on 8th October 1822 and there were single birds at Hampton Lodge on 6th March 1827, in September 1845, in August 1847 (*SALEC*) and in 1848. The next record was not until 12th September 1884 at Witley. These records are from Bucknill, whose further notes include one near Lambeth Bridge in 1889, one near Hampton Court on 11th August 1891 and one on the Putney reservoir [= Barn Elms?], all of which he thought might have been escapes from a collection in Richmond Park. He mentioned others, one (undated) at Poynter's, Cobham and one on Frensham Great Pond in the autumn of 1899. There was one in Surrey in August 1894 (Jordan, 1896). Several local birds that were in the Charterhouse Museum in Bucknill's day are no longer there.

1900 to 1959. Cormorants were not common in the first half of the 20th century. At Frensham there was an immature on 28th August 1906 and one on the Great Pond from 31st October to 7th November 1932. The next there was one in September 1948. Others were seen in 1953-55. Cormorants were found at Barn Elms Reservoirs in August 1926 and on the Thames, with up to three in January and February 1940, in 1941 and in 1942. Others were seen at Island Barn Reservoir on 25th October 1930 (one), Walton Reservoirs on 24th December 1930 (one), in the Farleigh district on 2nd January 1940 (one), at Hedgecourt (1946-47), and at Enton (1953). The first substantial gathering in the vice-county was 30 at Walton Reservoirs in March 1954 (Parr). In Spelthorne, Cormorants were reported from Staines Reservoirs on 9th-10th August 1924 (*London Naturalist*), the earliest record that has been located for the district. In the 1930s, numbers at the reservoirs were low. A count of 27 at Queen Mary Reservoir on 18th September 1931, apparently migrants, was regarded as unusual at the time as was a group of up to eight roosting on a buoy at King George VI Reservoir in 1950. There was a further increase in the 1950s, with 43 on Staines Moor on 15th February 1953 and 86 at King George VI Reservoir in January 1959. The roost at this site was later abandoned.

Where found since 1960. From the 1960s, Cormorants were often found at outer Surrey ponds and pits, including Enton, Frensham (almost annually by 1980), Hamm Moor (1971), Hedgecourt, Holmethorpe, Papercourt (1970), Thorpe (1970), Vachery (22nd November 1970) and Vann Lake. They were seen flying over other localities including Caterham (July 1966), Ewell (November 1969) and Thursley Common (November 1967). Small numbers were seen at the Surrey Docks.

Roosts. Cormorants began roosting on the towers in Queen Elizabeth II Reservoir as soon as it was opened in 1962 (Parr). Roosting numbers were initially low but they were increasing erratically, to peak at 130 in 1969, 216 in 1979, 350 in 1986 and over 500 in 1994 at which level, apart from a peak of 1,149 in January 1997 (D. M. Harris), they have broadly stabilised.

Wraysbury Reservoir was opened in 1971 and was immediately occupied by Cormorants. They roosted on three towers in the reservoir. It had a nocturnal roost with winter peaks of 85 birds in January 1980, 118 in November 1984 and 101 in March 1986 (Strangeman, 1988). A nocturnal roost on an island at Shepperton Gravel Pits was unoccupied in the winter of 1979/80 but held 63 in January 1985 and 128 in March 1986 (Strangeman, 1988).

With the increase in the Cormorant population, larger numbers are being seen in outer Surrey. Most of the Queen Elizabeth II Reservoir. Cormorants disperse to other wetland sites during the day, returning to the roost at dusk. An indication of where they go can be obtained from the maxima at other sites which are tabulated below. Non-breeding birds are present throughout the year but are scarce away from the Barn Elms, Beddington and Walton-on-Thames areas in the summer. Strangeman (1988) drew attention to roost flights along the Thames.

A roost in trees at Vachery Pond held 60 birds on 17th January 1998. A few Cormorants have recently roosted overnight in a dead tree at Hedgecourt. It is possible that some roost at Virginia Water, where Cormorants have perched during the day.

Breeding. An immature bird was seen carrying twigs into a tree at Shepperton Gravel Pits in May 1985 (*LBR, Shepp. BR*). A nest was built on one of the structures in Queen Elizabeth II Reservoir in 2002, when a pair laid eggs and sat for a month but the nest was deserted on 13th June. In 2004 a nesting pair was first noted on May 2nd. They were incubated until May 12th, when the nest was deserted (D. M. Harris).

Population size and calendar. The size of the Surrey population as a whole throughout the year is probably best judged from the Queen Elizabeth II Reservoir roost counts. Monthly averages for 1996-2005, together with each month's maximum and its year are in the table:

Monthly Cormorants counts at Queen Elizabeth II Reservoir 1996-2005

	Jan	Feb	Mar	Apr	May	Jun	Jul	Aug	Sep	Oct	Nov	Dec
Month average	606	526	359	199	101	89	192	345	482	575	539	489
Month maximum	1,149	830	450	326	168	153	325	456	670	740	710	866
Year of maximum	1997	1997	1996	1996	1996	1996	1999	1999	1997	2005	1996	1996

The Wildfowl and Wetlands Trust measures the national importance of a site by taking the average of the maximum counts in each of five consecutive winters. Average annual Cormorant count maxima at three sites in the area qualified as nationally important for the five winters to 1998/99. There were 345 at Queen Mary Reservoir (Spelthorne), 259 at Queen Elizabeth II Reservoir and 226 at Wraysbury Reservoir (Spelthorne). In the five years to 2003/04, Queen Mary Reservoir had dropped out but Queen Elizabeth II Reservoir (average 205), Staines Reservoirs (average 286) and Wraysbury Reservoir (average 244) reached levels qualifying as nationally important.

Large counts. Large numbers have roosted at Queen Elizabeth II Reservoir and at the Spelthorne reservoirs:

Badshot Lea: 21, November 1996 (*HSBBR*)

Barn Elms: 286, March 1993

Battersea Park: 24, 18th January 1987

Beddington Sewage Farm: 34, October 1992

Cutt Mill: 18, December 1997 (*HSBBR*)

Effingham Fish Ponds: 30, 1965

Enton: 14, 5th February 1988

Frensham: 16, November 1997 (*HSBBR*)

Frimley Gravel Pits: 52, December 1996

Gatton: 45, 14th December 2003

Hedgecourt: 27, 27th January 1986

Holmethorpe: 42, 16th January 1999 (R. D. Weller)

Island Barn Reservoir: 525, 30th November 2003

Lonsdale Road Reservoir: 78, March 1995

Papercourt Gravel Pits: 100+, 24th January 1991

Queen Elizabeth II Reservoir: 1,149, January 1997

Surrey Docks: 11, 23rd October 1972

Thames Richmond/Kew: 55, March 1993

Thorpe Water Park: 88, 21st December 2003

Vachery Pond: 60, January 1998 and December 1997

Walton Reservoirs: 735, January 1997

Spelthorne

King George VI Reservoir: 376, 17th October 1993

Queen Mary Reservoir: 678, January 2000; 1,050 in January 1997 (BTO) were in the peak month for the Queen Elizabeth II Reservoir roost.

Shepperton Gravel Pits: 128, 8th March 1986

Staines Reservoir: 560, 17th September 1998; 950, 6th September 2003 (*Bird Watching*)

Wraysbury Reservoir: 520, October 1999; 899, September 2003 (BTO)

Movements and longevity. Notable Surrey ringing recoveries include:

Ringed	Age	Date	Recovered	Date(s)	Distance/age
Glamorgan	?	14th June 1930	Staines Reservoirs	23 August 1930	
Walton Reservoirs	Adult	30th October 1964	Denbigh	c.26th June 1976	
Farne Islands	Pullus	15th July 1971	Walton Reservoirs	18th December 1983	475 km
Anglesey	Pullus	1st July 1984	Thorpe	26th October 1998	318 km, 14 years 3 months
Tenby	Pullus	18th June 1992	Island Barn Reservoir	3 May 1997	
	Pullus	16th June 1995	Guildford	28th December 1995	
	Pullus	18th June 1995	Guildford	25th November 1995	

Apart from those taken to be *sinensis*, there is no ringing evidence to show that any of the Cormorants wintering in Surrey come from abroad, or move abroad, though some of them may do so. The relatively large summer numbers are likely to be mostly non-breeding birds of British stock.

Behaviour. Cormorants are sometimes seen to soar and may reach great heights. Donald Gunn saw one rise an estimated 2,300 feet at Staines on 7th July 1925 (*BB, 21:82-85*).

Southern Cormorant

Phalacrocorax carbo sinensis

Uncommon winter visitor

Individuals of the race *sinensis* have been proved by DNA evidence to breed at English sites including Walthamstow (Hughes *et al.*). Gular pouch angle is the preferred external race identifier and the races may hybridise (Hughes *et al.*). Colour-ringed birds of apparently undetermined race from St Margaret's, Tenby that have wintered in the London area have sometimes attained full white heads before they leave for their breeding grounds (*LBR* for 1988). It seems likely that the increase in wintering Cormorant numbers may be partly due to greater numbers of *sinensis* now reaching Britain.

Surrey. At least two birds resembling this race were found by P. A. D. Hollom at Queen Mary Reservoir on 19th March 1950 and others were at King George VI Reservoir on 4th April 1952, Walton Reservoirs on 29th April 1962, Barn Elms Reservoirs on 12th February 1978, Queen Elizabeth II Reservoir on 2nd and 12th March 1978 (at least ten), Virginia Water (one) and Walton Reservoirs on 12th March 1978, Holmethorpe in April 1992, Thorpe Park in January 1993 and the Surrey Docks on 15th January 2001 (two).

Movements and longevity. While most Surrey birds are believed to be of the Atlantic race *P. c. carbo*, it has been proved by ringing that birds of the Baltic and southern race *P. c. sinensis* are now sometimes present, especially in winter. Definite evidence of continental origin has been provided by at least four Cormorants ringed as nestlings at Vorso, Denmark. The first, and longest lived, was ringed there on 1st July 1980 and was found dead on the Thames at Kingston over 14 years later, on 22nd January 1995 (BTO). Another of them was colour-ringed in June 1982 and seen at Queen Elizabeth II Reservoir on 11th December 1988. It had wintered on Lake Geneva, 712 km southeast of the reservoir, in most years and was back in Denmark by March 1989 (*LBR*). A third, colour-ringed on 16th May 1988, was seen at Fleet Pond (Hants) late in 1989, Farnborough (Hants) early in 1990 and at Frimley Gravel Pits in December 1991, February and March 1992, January 1993 and January and February 1994. The fourth was ringed on 27th May 1990 and found dead at Baynards Park, 869 km southwest, on about 12th January 1991. A Cormorant colour-ringed as a chick in Denmark on 8th June 2001, was seen outside the breeding season at Island Barn Reservoir in 2002 and 2004.

Shag (European Shag)

Phalacrocorax aristotelis

Far less common than Cormorants, though a few are seen in most years.

Shags breed on rocky coasts around Europe and the Mediterranean and are mainly resident, though some northern birds move south and others disperse. In 19th century Britain they were shot and sometimes eaten. Reduced persecution may account for a subsequent increase in breeding numbers. British Shags are mainly resident but some move south and others, particularly young birds, move to inland localities after the breeding season. Most of those recovered in the southeast are from northeast Britain (*MA*).

Early Surrey history. The first known for Surrey was killed at Cutt Mill in 1820. Many Shags have since been seen along the Thames. One killed at Vauxhall in 1865 (*SALEC*) and obtained from Mr Aubrey, a railway clerk at Nine Elms, was presumably the bird seen by Bucknill in the Charterhouse Collection.

1900 to 1955. A young bird was found in a garden near Woking in calm, but misty weather on 29th August 1927 (*BB, 21:158*). An immature bird on the Thames between the Waterloo and Charing Cross Bridges on 5th January 1928 was only the second for Middlesex (Glegg). The first for Spelthorne was at Staines Reservoirs on 18th February 1931 (Glegg).

One was found in a garden at Childown, near Chertsey on 9th February 1935 and there were two at Barn Elms on 20th January 1936, with one on the following day. In 1937 there was one at Frensham on 27th February, three were on the Thames at Mortlake on 24th March and one at Barnes in April and May. There were over 20 bird months along and close to the Thames from Barnes to Kew from 1938 to 1947, all but one of them in the first five months of the year. There were no more records until 1953 (Morden) and 1954 (Lambeth).

Since 1955. The nine reported in February/March 1958 (*BB, 51:131*) cannot all be located but there were up to three on the Thames until May and two at Island Barn Reservoir. From this year, with the exception of 1964, 1967, 1970, 1972-73, 1978 and 1981, Shags were seen annually until 2000. A national wreck in mid-March 1962 brought at least ten immature birds to Surrey.

In 1979, two or three Shags were in the Thames in the Waterloo Bridge area from January to the end of May. Two roosted on Hungerford Bridge in 1985 (*LBR*). In 1988 there was a huge London area influx of about 67 birds (*LBR*) and a roost of up to a dozen developed near Waterloo Bridge, persisting until early July. A bird or two is now seen along the river in most years.

Records from other places in the vice-county since 1959 have come from: *Badshot Lea* (1962); *Barn Elms* (1960, 1965, 1968, 1976, 1985, 1990); *Battersea Park* (1986); *Beddington* (1962, 1991-94, 1997); *Burgess Park Lake* (1992); *Camberley* (1986); *Croydon* (1974, 1986); *Frensham* (1961-62, 1980, 1990, 1993); *Frimley Gravel Pits* (1990, 1994); *Godalming* (1963); *Ham Lands* (1988); *Haslemere* (1963); *Hersham* (1993); *Holmethorpe* (1989, 1992-93); *Island Barn Reservoir* (1966, 1988, 1996, 2001); *Kingston Vale/Richmond Park* (1971, 1990); *Ockley* (1977); *Oxshott* (1975); *Queen Elizabeth II Reservoir* (1985, 1999); *Reigate* (1962); *Shottermill* (1974); *South Norwood* (1969); *Stoke Water Meadows* (1991-92, 1994); *the Surrey Docks* (1997) and *Walton Reservoirs* (1962-63, 1965-66, 1988, 1993, 1995). From 2000 to 2005 there were at least eight more reports, from Barn Elms London Wetland Centre (one or two in February 2002), Fieldcommon (January 2003), Island Barn Reservoir (November 2001 to January 2002, December 2002 to January 2003, November 2005), Queen Elizabeth II Reservoir (December 2002) and the Thames at Barnes (August 2001) and Wandsworth (two in February 2002, others to June).

One at Ferry Lane East on 15th December 1985 was the first for Shepperton Gravel Pits. Shags remain scarce in Spelthorne, one at Wraysbury Reservoir in August 2000, one at Staines Reservoirs in November 2000 and another at Staines Reservoirs in November 2005 (*LNHSB*) being the most recent records to hand.

Calendar. There were almost 300 vice-county bird months from 1900 to 2001, peaking in March:

Bird months 1900 to 2001

	Jan	Feb	Mar	Apr	May	Jun	Jul	Aug	Sep	Oct	Nov	Dec	Total
Vice-county	28	53	69	37	33	9	3	2	6	14	15	30	**299**

Movements and longevity. There are five recoveries of birds ringed as young from the Farne Islands and two from the Isle of May. The furthest-travelled was a Shag ringed at the Bass Rock on 10th July 1965 and found dead at Frensham, 566 km south, on or about 20th December in the same year. This reflects the national pattern. A ring found at Hove in May 1971 had been put on a Shag released at Frensham 11 years previously (A. Davis pers. comm.).

Bittern (Great Bittern)   *Botaurus stellaris*
Scarce winter visitor
Breeds from Britain east to Japan. Present in Britain in prehistoric times (Harrison and Hollom, 1932). British birds are mainly resident. The British breeding range has contracted substantially, mainly because

of habitat destruction, which goes back to at least the 17th century. The *Historical Atlas* shows it as an extinct breeding species in Hampshire and Sussex but the current avifaunas for these counties (Clark, 1993 and James, 1996) say that there is no firm evidence that it ever bred in them. There are breeding records from Kent. The *Migration Atlas* says that no British-ringed Bitterns have been recovered abroad but that a few foreign-ringed birds have been recovered.

Early Surrey history. Bitterns presumably bred in Surrey in the distant past, in swampy areas along the Thames and perhaps elsewhere, but historical evidence is lacking. In the 1830s they were scarce winter visitors, though perhaps not as scarce as today. One was shot at Gatwick (near Puttenham, undated) and later one was killed just below the Hog's Back in the winter of 1831/32. Two or three were shot each winter near Eashing Bridge, there was one in Richmond Park (in or around 1836) (Bucknill) and one at Burwood Common (*c*.1840). Another shot by the Wey at Gatwick (near Puttenham) in January 1848, was dressed and eaten for dinner. H. L. Long said that it 'proved excellent'. Later birds were at the Thames near Chiswick (7th January 1854), Kew Bridge (*c*.1854), Esher and Molesey (both October 1855), Chobham Common (1869), near Godstone (winter of 1879/80), Lingfield (1884), near Malden (before 1888), Godalming (seven in the frost of 1890/91), Beddington Corner (17th January 1891), Epsom Common (*c*.1891), Hurtmore (3rd January 1893), near Apps Court (1894), Weybridge (9th January 1895), Duxhurst (1895), Cobham (*c*.1896) and Fetcham (1898-99) with undated occurrences at Churt, Egham, Ewell and Gatton (Bucknill) and Eashing and Elstead (*SALEC*). One at Grayshott in January 1895 might not have been in Surrey.

1900 to the 1960s. Bitterns were extremely scarce in the first half of the 20th century, with records of one at Tangley Mere in January 1900, one at Forked Pond on 12th January 1907 (Shaw), one shot near Cranleigh on 13th February 1919 (*BB, 14:139*), one tangled in a bush at Kew Gardens in December 1921 (*BLA*), one at Beddington Sewage Farm on 28th March 1928 and one near Mitcham on 28th February 1934. The terrible winter of 1947 brought one to Beddington Sewage Farm on 1st February, one to a garden at Carshalton on 18th March and one to Peper Harow Park in January. There were others at Oxted in the winter of 1948 (*BLA*) and at Walton-on-Thames in January 1949. Bitterns were more frequent from 1956, when there were records from Frensham and South Munstead, followed by others at Frensham (1959, 1962), Abinger, Shere and Peper Harow in 1963, and Brook in 1965.

Since 1970. The next was not until 1970. There were at least 132 bird months from 1970 to 2006. About half of them have come from Frensham Ponds. Barn Elms London Wetland Centre and Frensham are currently the most regularly reported sites. Others were: Badshot Lea (1970-71); Enton (1979, 1997); Epsom Common (1998); Esher Common (one found dead in 2005); Farnham (1991); Frimley Gravel Pits (1996); Gatton (1970, 2002); Hedgecourt (1984, 1986-87, 2000-01, 2004, 2006); Henley Park Lake (1980); Holmethorpe Sand Pits (2002); Milford (1992); River Mole (1989); Newdigate (1979); Old Oxted (1985); Raven's Ait, Kingston (1981); near Reigate (1970); Richmond Park (1976, 2002-03); Ripley Sewage Farm (1985); Shalford/Tangley Mere/Waterloo Pond (1979); South Norwood Country Park (1998); Stoke Water Meadows (1985, 1993); Thorpe (1993); Thursley Common (1994, 1997); Unstead (1982, 1985); Vann Lake (1988); Virginia Water (1979, 1994); Walton Reservoirs (1996) and Witley (1979).

One at Queen Mary Gravel Pits on 20th January 1979 is the earliest Spelthorne record that has been located. There have been a few more since then, including others there on 31st December 1981 and 30th January 1982 and one at Ferris Meadow on 20th January 1986.

Calendar. Wintering birds begin to arrive in September and normally leave by the end of April. The earliest arrival since 1970 was at Frensham on 24th September 1989 and the latest spring bird was at Hedgecourt on 16th April 1984. There was an exceptional occurrence of one at Barn Elms London Wetland Centre on 22nd August 2003.

Vice-county bird months 1970-2006

	Jan	Feb	Mar	Apr	May	Jun	Jul	Aug	Sep	Oct	Nov	Dec	Total
Frensham	20	12	11	1	0	0	0	0	0	0	3	11	**58**
Elsewhere	17	20	18	0	0	0	0	1	1	1	3	13	**74**
Total	**37**	**32**	**29**	**1**	**0**	**0**	**0**	**1**	**1**	**1**	**6**	**24**	132

One at Frensham on 26th July 1959 is the only bird for the period May to July. The first September and November records came in 1989 and the first October record was not until 1997.

Large counts. Until recently, the largest number found was three circling over Frensham Little Pond at dusk on 14th March 1974. The appearance of three Bitterns at the Barn Elms London Wetland Centre in January 2002 was a hopeful indication for the future of the species in the reedbeds newly created by the Wildfowl and Wetlands Trust.

Movements. Bitterns visiting Surrey may have come from continental Europe.

Little Bittern

Ixobrychus minutus

Nine records in the vice-county. Breeding has been suspected but not proved.

Breeds from southern Europe to western China, to Australia, and south into Africa. Most British migrants arrive from April to June and less frequently into August. They have been found mainly in southern coastal counties. Breeding in Britain has frequently been suspected from the 19th century onwards. No nests have been found, but a young bird in down was found in Norfolk in 1885 and a pair raised four young in Yorkshire in 1984. May is the peak month for British migrants.

Surrey. All but one of the dated records fall in the June-August period:

1854: near Guildford, a female with eggs inside her body was shot not later than June (Spicer, 1854).

1855: Wintershall, one shot on 25th March (*the Thanksgiving-day after the Crimea*, Bucknill) by a Mr Barrett.

1855: Bramley, one shot a few years after 1855 was eventually held in the Charterhouse Collection (Bucknill) and might be the bird still there in 2001 with Godalming as its provenance.

1954: Pen Ponds, an immature bird on 20th-24th August then one in similar plumage at Beddington Sewage Farm on 27th and 29th.

1956: Beddington Sewage Farm, a pair from 18th June to 14th July, one on 6th and 14th August (*LBR* for 1958, *SBR* for 1958).

1961: Weybridge, one found dead on 22nd August (*BB, 55:568*).

1984: Send Heath Ponds, one on 15th September (L. Norton, *BB 88:498*).

1989: Milton Court, Dorking, a male at a small lake at the entrance on 28th May, fishing from 0845 to 1130 (G. C. Maples, *BB, 83:44; BB, 62:463*). .

1996: Epsom Common Stew Ponds, a male from 30th May to 1st June (A. Greensmith *et al.*, *BB, 90:468*, photograph in the *SBR* for 1996).

No definite Spelthorne records have been located. Birds shot in Middlesex in 1782 and at Uxbridge Moor in 1831 were probably outside the border.

Night Heron (Black-crowned Night Heron)

Nycticorax nycticorax

Seven vice-county birds

Night Herons of various races breed from France and the Netherlands across to Japan and in Africa and the Americas. Most British records are in coastal counties from April to June. The records have been confused by the existence of an Edinburgh Zoo colony in an aviary which was unroofed from 1951 until at least 1968. (*BB, 54:179*). In August 1997 there were 35 full-winged birds, including five juveniles. In the same year unfledged young were dispersed to other collections. A pair which had escaped from a collection bred in 1997 (*BB, 93:429*). Ringed birds have been reported from counties as close as Cambridgeshire and Oxfordshire in 2002 and there is a free-flying colony in Norfolk (*Newsacre* 23).

Surrey. It is worth noting, in a Surrey context, that Edinburgh is further away than the Netherlands and hence a less likely origin of birds found in the county. Others in British wildfowl collections are nearer. The earliest record is from 1855:

1855: Ditton Marsh, an adult male was shot on 12th June (*Zool, 1902:305*).

1884: Bramley, a female killed there in 1884 or earlier and acquired for the Charterhouse Collection might be the one still held in 2001, with Surrey as its provenance.

1884: near Molesey, an immature was captured alive on a Thames eyot by one Hawkes in the autumn (Bucknill).

1968: Farnham, an immature on the River Wey on 1st-2nd December (R. W. Byrne, T. A. Guyatt, J. E. Hunt *et al.*, a possible escape in *British Birds* (*BB, 60:463*). Given as 15th November to 31st December 1968, Gostrey Meadow, Farnham in Clark (1984),

1990: Bookham Common ponds, an immature bird on 7th and 16th April (D. Connell and D. Element, *BB, 85:511*)

2001: Barn Elms London Wetland Centre, one on 18th August.

2004: Barn Elms London Wetland Centre, one on 5th-8th May.

One was shot in Middlesex 'near London' in May 1782 (Pennant in Glegg). It was probably not within the modern Spelthorne boundary.

Squacco Heron   *Ardeola ralloides*

Two birds

The breeding range extends from southern Europe across to southwest Asia and south into Africa. Birds winter south of the Sahara. In Europe, they decreased in the 19th century but have since been extending their range northwards. Most British records are in the coastal counties of the southwest, during the period April to October with May and June as the peak months.

Surrey. There is an undated reference to one killed at Vachery Pond (*SALEC*). The date was probably before 1884. The bird is mentioned in Bucknill and in *British Birds* (*BB 1:348*). It was in the Charterhouse Collection in Bucknill's time but is not there now. A Squacco Heron at Lambeth Reservoir, Walton-on-Thames in 1997 from 0645 to 1343 hrs on the very typical date of 17th June was found by D. M. Harris and seen by many observers (D. M. Harris, *BB, 91:462*).

Cattle Egret   *Bubulcus ibis*

One bird

Cattle Egrets greatly extended their range during the 20th century and are now found around the world in the warmer climates. Some European birds winter in Africa but on the whole the species is dispersive rather than migratory. British records have been most frequent in coastal counties from Cornwall to Kent and in Norfolk and in April and May.

Surrey. There was one at the Barn Elms London Wetland Centre on 18th August 2001 (H. Bradshaw, S. Elliott *et al.*, *BB, 95:481*).

Little Egret
Egretta garzetta
Thirteen dated vice-county records and others from Spelthorne up to 1998, then many.

Little Egrets lost ground in the 19th century but have extended their range since 1900. They are now found in Europe and in temperate and tropical parts of Asia, Africa and Australia. While most European birds migrate south to Africa in winter, many individuals do not. During the period 1958-85, records were mostly of birds seen in the spring in southern coastal counties, with a scatter of others throughout the year. Since 1996 they have been breeding in southern Britain and, by 2001, Little Egrets were breeding at 16 sites, with autumn numbers estimated at over 2,500 (Musgrove, 2004).

Early Surrey history. Little Egret remains dated to 1500-1700 AD were reported from an archaeological excavation on the Chaucer House, Southwark site (Cowan, Westman and Wheeler). They were in a pit. How they got there is impossible to say. The find supports the speculations of Stubbs (1910) and Bourne (2003a), based on culinary evidence rather than field observations, that Little Egrets bred in Britain in medieval times and perhaps up to 1600. The species was not recorded alive and wild in Britain before the early 19th century.

Since 1990. The invasion of Surrey in the 1990s is a local reflection of a national trend. Spelthorne records include three at Staines Reservoirs on 27th May 1985 (F. J. Chandler, C. Watson. R. Wells, *BB, 79:531*) and one at Queen Mary Gravel Pits on 3rd-6th July 1985 (D. C. Bailey, A. J. Beasley, G. R. Geen *et al., LBR, BB, 79:531*). The first vice-county bird was found at Beddington Sewage Farm on 1st June 1990 (P. R. Alfrey).

Others to 2000, single birds except where stated, were:

1991:   Beddington Sewage Farm, 3rd June.

1993:   Frensham Common, one west on 3rd May.

1995:   Beddington Sewage Farm, 15th August.

1996:   Unstead Sewage Farm, 10th February.
        Papercourt Gravel Pits and Stoke Lake, 14th May (two).
        Island Barn Reservoir, 13th June.
        Axe Pond, Churt 10th-12th July.

1997:   Beddington Sewage Farm, 2nd-16th January.
        Badshot Lea, 12th-27th January then Tongham Gravel Pit, 28th January.
        Barn Elms Reservoirs, 11th June (two), 20th July.

1998:   Barn Elms Reservoirs, 4th June (two), 4th August, 10th-11th August.
        Stoke Lake, 14th June.

1999:   Stoke lake, 11th February (two).
        Stoke Lake and Unstead Sewage Farm, 30th May.
        Thames at Wandsworth, 18th July.

Barn Elms Reservoirs, 25th July, 10th August;

Unstead Sewage Farm, 21st August.

Beddington Sewage Farm, 21st December.

2000:   Cranleigh, 31st January.

Beddington Sewage Farm, 23 April, 27th May.

Thursley Common and Frensham, 27th July.

Frensham Great Pond, 28th July.

Queen Elizabeth II Reservoir, 17th August (two), 21st August (two).

In total there were 38 bird months from 1991 to 2000. Numbers have since risen sharply and the larger groups seen include four at Barn Elms WWT on 25th May 2002, six at Beddington Sewage Farm on 4th January 2002 and four at Waterloo Pond, Chilworth on 6th February 2004 and six there on 11th March 2005. There has also been a large roost at Watchmoor Park (Camberley). Other places where they were reported from include Badshot Lea, Barn Elms London Wetland Centre (eleven on 24th March 2005), Bay Pond (Godstone), Blackheath, Cranleigh, Enton, Ewell Court, Fetcham Mill Pond, Frensham, Frimley Gravel Pits, Haslemere, Island Barn Reservoir, Lingfield, Molesey Gravel Pit, Moorhouse, Papercourt, Queen Elizabeth II Reservoir, Send, South Norwood Country Park, Stoke Water Meadows, Sutton Place (Guildford), Thursley Common, Unstead Sewage Farm, Vachery Pond and Wrecclesham.

In 2000 there were single birds, possibly one wandering individual, at King George VI Reservoir (July, August, September), Queen Mary Reservoir (August), Staines Moor (July-September), Stanwell Moor (July-September) and Wraysbury Reservoir (July-September) and there were two at Wraysbury Reservoir from 27th August to 4th September. Little Egrets have been reported annually since then, with records of up to two from various sites, including Laleham, Staines Moor, Staines Reservoirs and Stanwell Moor (*LNHSB*).

Calendar. As the table shows, August is the commonest month of occurrence and Little Egrets are scarcest from September to December:

Bird Months 1991 to 2006 (incomplete after 2001)

	Jan	Feb	Mar	Apr	May	Jun	Jul	Aug	Sep	Oct	Nov	Dec	Total
Vice-county	24	22	24	7	23	13	16	18	4	7	4	7	**169**
Spelthorne	3	5	3	4	6	4	8	13	8	0	3	2	**59**

A likely colonist. With the increasing number of records, it will probably not be long before Little Egrets breed in Surrey as they did, for the first time, in Buckinghamshire in 2003 (*BTO News 2004*).

Great White Egret (Great Egret)   *Ardea alba* (*Egretta alba*)

Four or five birds, including two in Spelthorne

Great White Egrets have a world range which includes Europe, Asia, Africa and the Americas. They have bred as close as the Netherlands since the 1970s and it is perhaps surprising that so few have been found in Britain. The 33 British records up to 1985 were mainly on the east coast and all (except for one which was undated) from April to November. Since then there have been December and January records. May is the peak month. The change of genus from *Egretta* to *Ardea* might, one could suppose, justify the return of the fine old vernacular name of Great White Heron.

Surrey. The first bird broke with this pattern:

1997:   near Cranleigh, one found by Robin Stride on 22nd-23rd December (*BB, 91:463*).

1999:   Unstead Sewage Farm, one seen flying over on 30th August by B. Milton and J. S. Winder and subsequently seen at Frensham Little Pond by Shaun Peters and D. Gibbs (*BB, 93:519*).

2000:* Kempton Park nature reserve, Middlesex, one on 7th October (*BB, 95:483*) was seen to fly off and cross the border into Spelthorne (K. Purdey, pers. com.).

2002:* Staines Moor, one on 6th September (F. J. Maroevic. P. J. Naylor, K. I. Purdey *et al.*, *BB, 96:552*) may have been the one seen at Pudmore Pond on the following day.

2002: Pudmore Pond, one on 7th September (A. J. Fisher, *BB, 96:552*).

*Spelthorne

Grey Heron   *Ardea cinerea*
Moderately common breeding resident

Breeds in Europe, Asia and Africa. British colonies can be reduced by severe winters (*e.g.* by two or three days of freezing temperatures icing over waters), but recover in milder years. Persecution and habitat destruction reduced numbers in the 19th century but until recently there had been little overall change since 1928, when the national heronry census was started. There has since been an increase and a BTO survey in 2003 showed that numbers were still rising.

Early Surrey history. Remains of Grey Herons have been found at three Southwark sites: Bermondsey Abbey (dated to 1350-1500), 15-23 Southwark Street (medieval) and Union Passage (1500-1550). Remains found at Merton were dated at 1350-1450. Presumably Grey Herons from the colony north of the Thames at Fulham in 1523 occasionally crossed into Surrey (see Spoonbill below). Sixteenth century remains were found at Little Pickle, Bletchingley (Poulton *et al.*). John Williams was paid eightpence (worth rather more today) *for takinge the herrons* at Beddington on 12th April 1607 (Carew Household Book). In the same year there was a census naming the heronry in Windsor Great Park. John Evelyn had '*Never seen so many*' as he did at Denzil Onslow's duck decoy at Pyrford on 24th August 1681. Herons were protected within a radius of eight miles around Witley by order of Charles II – see Black Grouse.

Persecution and habitat destruction reduced Grey Heron numbers in the 19th century. Writers of the period, such as Yarrell, knew of a few heronries but gave little indication of their size and evidently regarded Grey Herons as regular, but very local, breeding birds, a judgement later reflected in Bucknill and the *Historical Atlas*.

Since 1900. Power (1910) knew of no heronries in the Dulwich area and had only three records from 1874 to 1909. Grey Herons from Virginia Water were feeding at Staines Reservoirs at the beginning of the 20th century (Kerr, 1906). They are still commonly seen around the reservoirs and on Staines and Stanwell moors and will mostly have come from nearby heronries including the one at Kempton Park.

Breeding. National Heron Censuses were started in 1928 and since that date there have been fairly complete annual nest counts at most Surrey heronries. The harsh winter of 1939/40 brought the Surrey nest count down to the lowest level since 1928. The severe 1946/7 winter was followed by the lowest national nest count since 1928 (Fisher, 1966 p.153), as it was in the vice-county. The addition of the Kempton figures brings the total up, but there is still a marked dip. Numbers recovered to rise to new heights in later years but the severe winters of 1961/2 and 1962/3 again brought a substantial reduction. Nationally the numbers did not get back to the previous level until 1970 (Reynolds, 1979). In Surrey the process took even longer and it was not until 1977 that a full recovery was made. In more recent years they have increased steadily.

Figures for some heronries have been published in more than one place. For example, the London and Surrey Bird Reports both cover Gatton Park. The Middle-Thames Naturalist and the Surrey Bird Report have both covered Windsor Great Park. Review papers by Chappell and Chappell (1989) and Suckling (1997, 1999) have extended and taken forward the earlier material. The available information has been pulled together and updated for each heronry in the accounts that follow.

The difficulty of counting breeding pairs should not be underestimated, even at heronries where local conditions permit all the nests to be seen well from the ground. The old BTO census categories of *certain*, *probable* and *possible* nest occupation and the more recent *definite* and *best estimate* seem not to have been followed consistently in publications, though it is hard to be sure since counters typically send in figures for two or three different dates, each date producing a different result. Two observers may produce a different result on the same day. For example, a ringer who climbed the trees at Kempton saw eggs in many nests which, for their flimsy nature or other reasons, a terrestrial counter thought were unoccupied. On the other hand, Suckling thought that some of the past Battersea Park counts had been too high and his lower estimates have replaced them in what follows. The figures below follow the most common practice in attempting to present the highest figure for the number of certain or probably occupied nests (old definition) or the highest best estimate (current definition), omitting possibly occupied and empty nests, where the information permits. The Chappell figures have normally been used for years up to 1988, those of Suckling for later years up to 1999 and BTO Census information from 2000 onward. Over 40 heronries have been found in Surrey, of which at least 20 are still active. These are the heronries:

Heronries in use after 2000

Ash SU9051. There were 21 nests in 2001, 21 in 2003 and 17 in 2004.

Barn Elms Playing Fields/London Wetland Centre TQ2276. Single nests in 2000, 2001 and 2003, two in 2005.

Battersea Park TQ2877. On an island with no public access in a public park by the Thames.

			Number of nests						
1990	2	1993	11	1996	15	1999	25	2002	27
1991	9	1994	15	1997	18	2000	27	2003	21
1992	8	1995	23	1998	22	2001	30		

Bookham Common TQ1256. SSSI on National Trust land which is open to the public, allowing actual or potential disturbance from under the trees. The nests are in Pedunculate Oaks, situated close to the River Mole. Suckling records that nests in the more disturbed parts of the site have been less successful.

			Number of nests						
1988	1	1992	4	1996	18	2000	25	2004	14
1989	4	1993	7	1997	20	2001	23	2005	15
1990	1	1994	6	1998	22	2002	23	2006	14
1991	8	1995	10	1999	16	2003	26		

Brentford Ait TQ1877. Another newly-established heronry, on two uninhabited islands in the Thames, in poplars and willows.

			Number of nests						
1990	2	1993	8	1996	15	1999	21	2002	24
1991	3	1994	12	1997	23	2000	23	2003	26
1992	7	1995	17	1998	23	2001	19		

Bury Hill Lake, Dorking TQ1548. One nest in 1927, none in 1929 but four in 2003 (reported as Dorking, probably this site) and five in 2004 and 2005 after re-occupation.

Churt (Lowicks) SU8640. No public access. The surrounding area is an SSSI with SPA status.

			Number of nests						
1969	3	1973	18	1977	10	1981	14	1985	13
1970	0	1974	15	1978	13	1982	13	1986	16
1971	5	1975	12	1979	12	1983	15	1987	27
1972	14	1976	14	1980	17	1984	14	1988	29

1989	20	1993	24	1997	40	2001	n/c	2003	34
1990	23	1994	24	1998	43	2002	34	2004	25
1991	21	1995	30	1999	59				
1992	20	1996	33	2000	43				

Corporation Island (Richmond Ait) TQ1774. Limited public access from moorings. No nests in 1997, six in 1998, 11 in 1999, 2000, 2001 and 2002.

Dorking TQ1548. Four occupied nests in 2003. Had been nesting for three or four years.

Gatton Park TQ2752.

Number of nests

1930	1	1945	8	1960	17	1975	8	1990	16
1931		1946	c.8	1961	18	1976	7	1991	17
1932	1	1947	2	1962	18	1977	7	1992	18
1933		1948	11	1963	12	1978	7	1993	21
1934		1949	7	1964	8	1979	5	1994	18
1935	1	1950	8	1965	6	1980	9	1995	15
1936	1	1951	10	1966	8	1981	5	1996	14
1937		1952	12	1967	4	1982	7	1997	19
1938	2	1953	10	1968	4	1983	8	1998	24
1939	3	1954	10	1969	5	1984	8	1999	21
1940	3	1955	9	1970	4	1985	13	2000	22
1941	2	1956	10	1971	5	1986	7	2001	22
1942	4	1957	12	1972	7	1987	12	2002	n/c
1943	7	1958	14	1973	8	1988	14	2003	29
1944	5	1959	17	1974	8	1989	16		

Horton Country Park TQ1962. No nests in 1998, two in 1999, three in 2000, six in 2001 and 2002, 11 in 2003, three in 2004, six in 2005.

Isleworth Ait TQ1775. Seven nests in 1999, eleven in 2000, seventeen in 2001, seven in 2002, six in 2003.

Lonsdale Road Reservoir TQ2177. No nests in 1997, one in 1998, two in 1999, four in 2000, 2001, 2002, 2003.

Moor Park, Farnham SU8645. SWT Reserve, four nests in 2002, three in 2004.

Morden Hall Park TQ2669. two nests in 1999, three in 2000, eight in 2001, six in 2002. seven in 2003.

Munstead Park SU9943. Known to have been active from before 1963 to 1974, no nest counts.

Number of nests

1975	6	1986	12	1991	22	1996	12	2001	n/c
1976-81	n/c	1987	13	1992	12	1997	22	2002	14
1982	10	1988	12	1993	12	1998	19	2003	17
1983	21	1989	21	1994	15	1999	17	2004	18
1984	11	1990	15	1995	18	2000	17	2005	22
1985	15								

Richmond Park TQ1973. A long-established heronry that may have originated from birds at Hampton Court, Middlesex (*BB, 23:328*). There was a single nest in about 1880, 13-14 in 1890, 16 in 1893 and 20-30 in 1906, when it was in Sidmouth Wood. There were 30-40 nests from 1909 to 1928, after which regular counts began. The heronry was abandoned from 1961 to 1992.

Year	Nests	Year	Nests	Year	Nests	Year	Nests	Year	Nests
1929	25	1938	53	1947	10	1956	6	1997	13-14
1930	30	1939	61	1948	11	1957	8	1998	25
1931	30	1940	55	1949	12	1958	7	1999	7
1932	33	1941	56	1950	12	1959	7	2000	13
1933	43	1942	40	1951	18	1960	7	2001	15
1934	48	1943	38	1952	20	1993	1	2002	13
1935	48	1944	36	1953	23	1994	7	2003	11
1936	44	1945	39	1954	13	1995	5		
1937	49	1946	11	1955	6	1996	6-8		

Sutton Place, Guildford TQ0153. Three to five nests in 2000, 11 nests in 2001, 13 in 2002, 16 in 2003, 11 in 2004, eight or more in 2005.

Vachery Pond TQ0737. On private land, with about 20 nests from 1986 to 1988, counts of 20 to 25 in most years from 1989 to 2000, 27 in 2002, 25 in 2003 and 22 in 2004.

Watermeads TQ2767. A single nest in 1984, three in 2002, five in 2003.

Windsor Great Park (Berkshire and Surrey) Present location Fort Belvedere SU9768. On land with no public access. The history of this ancient heronry goes back to at least 1607, when John Norden prepared a survey and plan of the park for King James I. At that time the nests seem to have been in the Berkshire sector. It was recorded again by W. J. Smith at a date some time between 1823 and 1856 and again by Menzies in 1904. The move from Berkshire to Surrey is not well documented. There was a period in the first half of the 20th century when the heronry straddled the county border. The desertion of Berkshire for Fort Belvedere, in Surrey, was not complete until 1948. The early history of the park is described by South *et al.* (1979). Nest counts and further details are in Chappell and Chappell (1988).

Year	Nests	Year	Nests	Year	Nests	Year	Nests	Year	Nests
1607	Active	1939	42	1956	54	1972	24	1988	25
1853	Active	1940	40	1957	44	1973	32	1989	24
1868	Active	1941	28	1958	34	1974	33	1990	23
*c.*1900	Active	1942	18	1959	43	1975	28	1991	*c.*20
1900	*c.*10	1943	24	1960	36	1976	34	1992	18
1910	*c.*10	1944	?	1961	32	1977	45	1993	16
1928	32	1945	49	1962	18	1978	50	1994	22
1929	23	1946	47	1963	20	1979	43	1995	17
1930	31	1947	25	1964	17	1980	53	1996	19
1931	30	1948	?	1965	16	1981	41	1997	19
1932	32	1949	48	1966	23	1982	35	1998	22
1933	29	1950	55	1967	30	1983	27	1999	18
1934	32	1951	69	1968	27	1984	26	2000	n/c
1935	36	1952	62	1969	23	1985	24	2001	n/c
1936	42	1953	57	1970	37	1986	28	2002	10
1937	50	1954	70	1971	22	1987	24	2003	7
1938	45	1955	53						

Kempton Park/Hydes Field (Partly in Spelthorne) TQ1269. No public access. On the Spelthorne/Greater London border. The failure of numbers to recover after the severe winter of 1962/63 followed the commencement of gravel excavation nearby and may have been caused by resultant disturbance (Oliver, 1975).

				Number of nests					
1942	1-2	1955	88	1968	24	1980	c.50	1992	38
1943	c.20	1956	83	1969	18	1981	40	1993	35
1944	c.30	1957	88	1970	7	1982	?	1994	35
1945	39	1958	86	1971	34	1983	?	1995	50
1946	52	1959	91	1972	8	1984	?	1996	35
1947	52	1960	91	1973	6	1985	24	1997	60
1948	57	1961	95	1974	c.20	1986	39	1998	72
1949	71	1962	83	1975	20	1987	44	1999	65
1950	81	1963	49	1976	55	1988	46	2000	60
1951	93	1964	47	1977	65	1989	55	2001	62
1952	88	1965	12	1978	48	1990	48	2002	47
1953	87	1966	44	1979	34	1991	42	2003	44
1954	85	1967	?						

Disused heronries. Grid references are not available for many of these.

Albury Park. A nest recorded before 1907 might have been a precursor of the Chilworth heronry.

Ash Vale. A heronry first noticed with one nest in 1995 had three in 1996 and four in 1997. The following year the site was destroyed by building work.

Ashley Park. Active before 1836 and around 1855. Deserted by 1872.

Betchworth. One nest in 1928.

Broadwater, Godalming. Single nests 1928, 1948-50.

Burwood Park, Hersham.

				Number of nests					
1925	c.30	1929	31	1933	16	1937	8	1940	7
1926	c.30	1930	28	1934	17	1938	7	1941	8
1927	15-20	1931	20	1935	16	1939	16	1942	1
1928	20+	1932	15	1936	14				

Chilworth. Founded in 1962, no counts until 1964.

				Number of nests					
1962	?	1966	10	1969	4	1972	3	1975	5
1963	?	1967	8	1970	5	1973	6	1976	4
1964	4	1968	4	1971	4	1974	3	1977	2
1965	2								

Cobham Park. Active from before 1846 (Yarrell) until about 1875.

Godstone Village Pond. Single nests in 1946, 1947 and 1948, none 1949-52.

Kew Gardens. Single nests in 1907 and 1981.

Mickleham. TQ1652. Two nests in 1999.

Oatlands Park. A heronry at Oatlands Park was abandoned by 1866 (Harting) and perhaps as early as 1855.

Ockley Court. On private land. Single nests from 1970 to 1973.

Old Norwood Woods (Dulwich Wood). A small colony around 1850 until about 1855.

Peper Harow Park. Active from before 1900 until at least 1908, when there were one or two nests.

Pirbright – Furze Hill. Active from 1960 to 1973. One to six nests in 1966, none in 1971, one in 1973.

Sendholme. Up to six nests from about 1928 to 1937. Deserted in 1938.

Unstead. A single nest in 1885.

Waverley. Initially at Black Lake. The Black Lake heronry was destroyed when the trees were felled during the 1939-45 war, so later records must refer to a different site.

Number of nests

1892	18	1920	?	1929	0	1934	Active	1946	9-10
1899	Active	1928	1	1930	1	1941	4	1947	4-7
1913	15								

Wrecclesham. Two to three nests from 1969 to 1984 (three in 1981).

The chart shows how the Grey Heron population has grown:

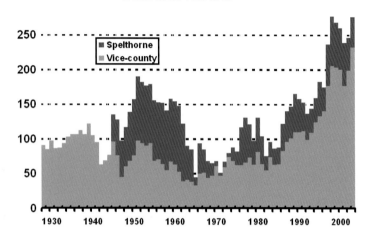

Heron Nests 1928-2003

Environmental factors. Reynolds was not able to make a direct link between temperature variables and number of Grey Herons' nests. Even so, the freezing over of feeding areas, even for a few days as may happen in otherwise mild winters, is likely to be detrimental to adults, and the recent rise in nest numbers has at least coincided with recent warmer temperatures even if not directly caused by them. Suckling (1997) suggested that the increased numbers since 1987 may be partly due to a reduction of river pollution. He pointed, for example, to the increase in Thames Valley heronries such as the one at Kempton, and others on islands and parks in Middlesex further downstream.

Despite the upward trend in breeding pairs, Suckling (1999) found strong circumstantial evidence that disturbance was having a significant adverse effect on breeding success. As he illustrated, most heronries are at locations to which the general public do not have access or which they are discouraged from visiting (see table). These are factors which usually (but unfortunately not always) prevent significant disturbance.

Nest sites. Suckling highlighted the fact that, in 1999, half of the heronries were on islands in lakes or the River Thames. Virtually all nests were in trees at heights in excess of ten metres and frequently considerably higher. Heronries tended to be in commanding positions. Wherever circumstances permit in Surrey, Grey Herons nest high in the crowns of mature trees. Typically, they do so at heights ranging from 12 m to 20 m, but sometimes as high as 30 m (as at Fort Belvedere and Churt Common). However, where shorter trees are available at chosen locations (as on the islands in Battersea and Gatton Parks), Grey Herons are prepared to nest lower down. (Suckling 1997 and 1999). Suckling studied the trees favoured by Grey Herons as nest sites. In both 1997 and 1999, 121 trees in Surrey carried occupied nests of Grey Herons. The favourite species was Scots Pine *Pinus sylvestris*. Pedunculate Oaks *Quercus robur* and Common Alders *Alnus glutinosa* were also popular.

Heronries in the Vice-County of Surrey, 1997 and 1999
Use of trees as nest sites.

Tree	1997		1999	
	Number of trees used	Number of pairs using tree species	Number of trees used	Number of pairs using tree species
Scots Pine	52	81	57	94
Pedunculate Oak	30	40	16	23
Alder	16	20	27	47
Poplar species	7	15	6	8
Willow species	6	12	11	23
Ash	2	8	1	10
London Plane	1	4	1	3
Silver Birch	2	2	0	0
Other	5	17	2	10
Totals	121	199	121	218

This table includes the occupied nests in Morden Hall Park in 1999 (Suckling 1997 and 1999).

Multiple nesting in some trees probably reflects a shortage of suitable trees at some heronries (*e.g.* Battersea Park and Gatton). It is less explainable at other locations (*e.g.* Richmond Park and Fort Belvedere), (Suckling 1999). Only one heronry in Surrey (Fort Belvedere – previously located elsewhere in Windsor Great Park) has remained active each breeding season since the end of the 19th century. Only two were lost during the period 1986 to date (Ash Vale due to housing development, and Mickleham).

Feeding and foraging. In 1999, Suckling also studied the foraging and feeding patterns of breeding birds. He found that the distance between heronries varied between 3.5 km in the Thames valley (and even less to heronries immediately outside the vice-county) and 19 km in the southwest. Observations of Grey Herons in Surrey indicate that they like to forage at sites with clear views in most, if not all, directions. Favoured locations are often in flood-plains. When foraging in groups, Grey Herons are normally well spaced out. Still, clear waters free of vegetation and with gently sloping banks free of shrubs and trees seem to be preferred for fishing (Suckling 1999). Single Grey Herons may be found fishing at small, tree-lined waters such as Moat Pond. Prey items are not often reported but include Frog, Mole (Staines Moor), Roach and Water Vole. Freshwater mussel shells were found under a nest on Bookham Common in 2001 (*LN*).

Limited studies in Surrey have found Grey Herons to be most active foraging and feeding early in the morning, shortly after sunrise, and late in the day, just before sunset. They also feed their young during the night. Studies of departure patterns of adult birds from heronries revealed marked concentrations in certain directions. These in many cases matched known or likely foraging sites (Suckling 1999).

Large counts away from heronries

Barn Elms: 39, June 1999

Beddington Sewage Farm: 45, February 2002

Bell Lane Creek (River Wandle)/Thames at Wandsworth: 32, 21st September 2000

Lavender Dock: 18, 24th August 1970.

Surrey Docks: 38, 26th July 1972

Walton Reservoirs: 38, 8th July 1962

Wrecclesham Floods: ten, 23rd February 1981 (*HSBBR*)

Spelthorne

Queen Mary Reservoir: 75, mostly juveniles, 10th July 1987.

Movements and longevity. The few ringing recoveries of birds ringed as pulli indicate post-fledging dispersal rather than migration, supporting Suckling (1999). The furthest known Surrey movements within the UK, Suffolk to South Godstone in 1957/58 (132 km) and Faversham to Staines Moor in 2001 (102 km) are of this type. There is, however, some evidence of immigration from abroad. Herons ringed as pulli in Denmark (three), France, the Netherlands (two) and Norway have been recovered in Surrey. The Norwegian bird was ringed in Rogaland on 14th June 1969 and found dead at Staines, 883 km SSW, on 3rd January 1970. Ringing has found one Surrey Grey Heron with a life length of over eight years (national maximum 23 years). The Surrey bird was ringed in the nest at Hersham on 12th April 1930 and recovered at Walton-on-Thames on 2nd October 1938.

Behaviour. Grey Herons are occasionally seen floating or swimming on water, *e.g.* at Queen Mary Reservoir in 1947 (*LBR*).

Plumage variations. A bird with bluish-grey tinged white plumage was seen and heard at Beddington Sewage Farm on 23rd July 2003.

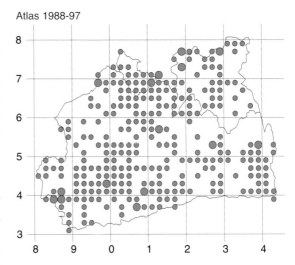

Atlas 1988-97

Purple Heron   *Ardea purpurea*

Eight birds, of which one was in Spelthorne.

The breeding range extends from Europe and North Africa east to Asia. European birds winter in Africa. The majority of British sightings are in the spring, from April to June. While most are seen in coastal counties, Purple Herons have appeared in nearly all the counties of southern England.

Surrey. Three of the seven dated records are later than June:

1884:   Frensham, one was killed at Frensham before 1884 (*SALEC*). No details and no skin are available.

1955:   Frensham Little Pond, one on 18th-25th September (*BB, 49:148*).

1970:*   Shepperton Gravel Pits, one flew east on 2nd June 1970 (F. R. Cannings, *BB, 64:342*).

1992:   Beddington Sewage Farm, one flew over on 11th April (*BB, 78:535*).

1993:   Stoke Lake, Guildford, one flew over and then northeast up the River Wey on 10th May.

1999:   Beddington Sewage Farm, one on 22nd September.

2001:   Unstead Sewage Farm, one flew over on 13th June.

2005:   Beddington Sewage Farm, one on 18th August.

*Spelthorne

Black Stork   *Ciconia nigra*

Two birds

Black Storks breed in Iberia and France east to Manchuria and in South Africa. Most European birds winter in tropical Africa. The European population has been increasing and this may account for the more frequent British records in recent years. Nearly all the reports are from coastal counties, from April to September.

Surrey. The two records, one in each migration period, fit the seasonal pattern. One flew over Pirbright Common at 7.30 pm on 2nd May 1990 (P. M. Troake, *BB, 84: 548*). Another flew over Kennington Oval at 2 pm on 25th August 1990 (G. C. Davey, H. S. and Mrs B. J. Joliffe), also seen in Essex and Suffolk (*BB, 84:458*).

White Stork
Ciconia ciconia

Up to eleven vice-county records, including three possible escapes, one from Spelthorne

Ice Age remains have been found in southern Britain. The current breeding and wintering ranges of White Storks are similar to those of Black Storks but the population size is larger and British records are far more numerous. Birds have been seen in all months of the year, with a marked peak in April and May. Escapes are a persistent problem and the reintroduction of breeding birds into the Netherlands has made it difficult to separate wild birds from those which are feral, escapes or introduced. The British Birds Rarities Committee stopped considering records in 1982.

Surrey. The records have mainly been from April to June:

1890: Frensham, one killed at some time before 1890 (Stafford in Bucknill). No details, no date, no skin. This might be the basis for it being described as an occasional visitor in the *Letters of Rusticus*.

1930: Richmond Park, one on the ground on 11th May. Collenette thought it might be an escape but the date is good for a wild bird.

1967: Holmbury St Mary, near Abinger, one soaring on 3rd June (W. Ruttledge, *BB, 61:335*), at the time of a national influx.

1978: Croydon and Beddington Sewage Farm, one on 6th August (Croydon area, D. A. Hougham and J. McEachen, *BB, 73:496*).

1979: Povey Bridge, Gatwick, one from 9th July to at least the 26th (Mrs P. Copper *et al.*, *BB, 73:496*).

1993:* Staines Reservoirs, one circled on 24th April.

1993: between Horley and Salfords, one flew northwest on 13th June.

1994: Bramley, one flew over on 1st May.

2000: Sutton Place, Guildford, two adults on 30th-31st March.

East Sheen, one flew over on 17th June (*LBR*).

2002: Merrow, one north on 11th May.

2004: Leatherhead, one on 1st April.

Fetcham, one on 2nd April, presumably the Leatherhead bird.

* Spelthorne

Glossy Ibis
Plegadis falcinellus

Two shot, none Spelthorne

Breeds from southern Europe to Asia, Australasia, Africa, the eastern USA and the Caribbean. European birds winter in Africa. British records have almost all been from coastal counties and from March to December, peaking in September and October.

Surrey. One was shot at Whitmore Pond in March (Yarrell) or May (*Letters of Rusticus*) 1833. One said to have been killed at Woking in 1867 (*SALEC*) was in the Charterhouse Collection in Bucknill's time but is no longer held there.

Spoonbill (Eurasian Spoonbill)
Platalea leucorodia

About 22 records

Breeds in the Netherlands and in Southern Europe east to India and China and in Africa. Most of those seen in Britain are probably from the Netherlands (*MA*). Land drainage is reducing the range. They bred in Britain until the 17th century and may have done so in Surrey, though firm evidence is lacking. Harting showed that they were breeding on the other side of the Thames at Fulham in the 16th century.

The Year Book of 14 Hen. VIII., fol.1 contains a report of an action for trespass brought by the Bishop of London in 1523 against a defendant to whom the Bishop's park at Fulham was leased for grazing, accusing him of taking Herons and Shovelers (the name then used for Spoonbills) from the colony in the park (Glegg). Spoonbills began breeding in Britain again in 1998.

Surrey. Presumably the Fulham birds occasionally crossed the river and entered Surrey even if they did not nest there. Dated records go back to 1839:

1839: Vachery Pond, one shot in the summer (*SALEC*) was in the Charterhouse Collection in 2001.

1844: Frensham, a bird of the year was shot on 24th October (*Zool., 1845:878*). This may be the Frensham bird mentioned by Spicer (*Zool., 1854:4367*).

1862. Frensham, one was killed 'a short while ago' (Bridger, 30th October 1862 in *Zool., 1862:8283*).

1889: Camberwell, Power (1910) wrote that C. P. Johnston had seen one fly north over his garden in August 1889.

1901 Clandon Park, a female was shot on 26th November (Dalgliesh, 1902).

1972 Unstead Sewage Farm, one was flushed on 30th August.

1973:* Staines Moor, one on 27th-28th September.

1976: Richmond Park, one flew on 30th June.

1980: Holmethorpe Sand Pits, one on 12th-13th August.

Papercourt Gravel Pits, two stayed for two and a half hours on 20th September.

1982: Beddington Sewage Farm, two for an hour on 1st June.

1986:* Queen Mary Gravel Pits, one on 4th July.

King George VI Reservoir and Queen Mary Gravel Pits, single birds on 23rd August.

1989:* Staines Reservoirs, one on the north basin on 7th October, when it was partly drained.

1989: Beddington Sewage Farm, two on 25th May (*LBR*).

1995: Queen Elizabeth II Reservoir, one flew over on 2nd December.

1999: Barn Elms, one on 13th May.

2001:* Stanwell Moor, four juveniles on 11th September.

2005:* Staines Reservoirs, two on 6th September (*LNHSB*).

2006: Crooksbury Common, one flew over on 26th April.

Beddington Sewage Farm, one on 6th May.

Spelthorne

Movements and longevity. One of the four juveniles at Stanwell Moor in 2001 had been ringed in the Netherlands, 424 km northeast, on 7th June 2001. One of the two Spoonbills at Staines Reservoirs in 2005 was a male that had been colour-ringed on the nest at Schiermonnikoog, in the Netherlands on 18th May 2003. It had earlier been seen in Yorkshire in July and Kent in September (L. G. R. Evans, e-mail 8th September 2005).

Honey Buzzard (European Honey Buzzard)   *Pernis apivorus*

Scarce passage migrant and rare breeding species

Breeds in the temperate parts of Europe and western Asia, wintering in Africa. The Honey Buzzard was a rare British breeding species in the 19th century, with a distribution much as it is now.

Early Surrey history. One was caught at a wasp nest at Hampton Lodge, Puttenham on 1st September 1824, a great year for wasp nests according to H. L. Long (Bucknill). Two others were caught at Lea Park, Witley, (undated, *SALEC*). One of them had been trapped while attacking a wasp nest and another was caught there in the following year. These two, and another shot at Peper Harow, were in the Charterhouse Collection during Bucknill's time but the one held there in 2001 was said to have come from Scotland. Others were found near Bagshot (1871 or earlier) and at Chobham (November 1890 or earlier). There is a vague reference to a heathland site in Jordan (1892).

1900 to 1986. There were in all only sixteen records from 1900 to 1986, the first of which was not until 1954.

Early records: single birds except where indicated, likely breeding localities excluded.

1954:   Juniper Top, Box Hill, one flying west on 27th July.

1959:   Esher Common, one flew over on 22nd August, notes in the *LBR*.

1965:   Tilford, one on 7th June.

1976:   Barn Elms Reservoirs, one on 16th-21st November. Taken to London Zoo. Died on the 23rd.

1979:   Ewell, one flew over on 27th May.
        Bricksbury Hill, one on 11th August.

1980:   Pirbright Common, one flying north on 20th July.

1981:   Normandy, one flew over on 27th June.
        Ockley and Elstead, one flew over on 19th July.
        Beddington Sewage Farm, one flew southeast on 11th October.

1983:   Boundstone, one flew east on 11th July.

1984:   near Oxshott, one mobbed by Carrion Crows in a wood on 18th June.

1985:   Thursley Common, one flew over at 0930 hrs on 26th May.
        One adult at another vice-county locality on 11th July.

1986:   South Croydon, one feeding on lawns at Maywater Close on 23rd May.
        Godstone, one, possibly two, soaring on 7th September.

After 1986. After 1986 there were more sightings, and occasional suspicions of breeding, not established until 1990. The first four records in 2000 were typical for a good year, with one at Thursley on 1st May, one at Limpsfield on 13th August, one at Milford on 28th August and another at Thursley on 31st August. An extraordinary autumn irruption of Honey Buzzards into Britain then brought up to 75 birds into Surrey between 17th September and 6th October. The number of records peaked at 12 on 28th September and 15 on 1st October. There were 54 birds in September and 21 in October. They appeared in most parts of the county but were most reported in the London area and at well-watched sites such as the Thursley/Ockley Commons. The daily autumn count for 2000 is shown in the chart:

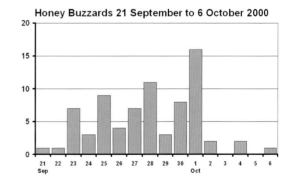

Honey Buzzards 21 September to 6 October 2000

Later records have come from Beddington (2001), Limpsfield Chart (2001), Moorhouse (2001), Pewley Down (2001), Thursley Common (2001), Lightwater (2002), Stoke Lake (2002), Walton Heath (2003) and Horton Country Park (2004).

Spelthorne

There was one over Queen Mary Reservoir on 4th October 1981 and one over Staines Moor on 10th October 1993. In the exceptional national influx of 2000 there was one over Staines Reservoirs on 24th September and two over Shepperton on the 28th.

Breeding. There were no breeding records before 1900. The first known successful breeding since then took place in 1990, when a nest with two well-developed young was found in south Surrey on 9th August by D. C. Bailey and J. R. Mullins. The young flew from the nest site on about 20th August and flying young were seen up to 10th September. Birds were seen in the area again in 1991 but there was no suggestion of breeding. The 1990 nest was re-occupied in 1992 and an egg was found under the nest, broken. Disturbance was suspected. In 1993, breeding was suspected about two miles away but no evidence of success was obtained. Two chicks were ringed at a vice-county locality in 2004 and two more in 2005.

Calendar. September, with 25 bird months up to 1999, has been by far the most frequent month for migrants, followed (before 2000) by August with ten. In the years from 1954, the earliest were on 12th April 2001 (Beddington) and 1st May 2000 and the latest was the sick bird at Barn Elms on 16th-21st November 1976.

Black Kite *Milvus migrans*

Four birds, one of them in Spelthorne

With a breeding range covering most of Europe, Asia, Africa and Australia, the Black Kite is still an elusive bird in the British Isles, though becoming less so. Most records are from April to June, peaking in May, and many of them come from the five coastal counties from Sussex to Norfolk. Very few have been from inland locations.

Surrey. The four birds were:

1986: Haslemere, one SSW over Inval on 18th May (P. A. Kirkpatrick, *BB, 80:531*).

1994: Capel, one flew over Old Stores Meadows Reserve on the afternoon of 15th May (W. Attridge, *BB, 88:504*).

2003: Barn Elms London Wetland Centre, one flew over on 30th August (N. P. Senior, *BB, 98:645*).

2003:* Staines Moor, one flew over on 29th September (R. E. Innes *et al.*, *BB, 100:30*).

Spelthorne

Red Kite *Milvus milvus*

Lost resident, now a scarce but increasing passage migrant

Ice Age remains from one of the warmer interglacial periods, and at least 120,000 years old, have been found in Wales (Harrison, 1988). Red Kites now breed from Britain across to central and southern Europe. Some, including the Welsh population, are resident, others move south towards the Mediterranean. In medieval times, Red Kites appear to have been common in England, including London. Numbers declined in the 17th and 18th centuries but they could still be found in Scotland, Wales and most of England outside the southeast, until the beginning of the 19th century. Since 1989, the English population has been boosted by introductions, to reach an estimated 146 pairs by 2000 (Ogilvie *et al.*, 2002). Flocks of up to 200 birds are sometimes seen in the Chilterns (Carter and Grice, 2000; *Bird Watching*, July 2002). A pair, (possibly of continental origin), bred in Suffolk in 1996 and 1997 and a territorial pair was present at a Sussex site within 20 miles of the Surrey border in 2000, a year during which, according to the RSPB, three pairs bred in southern England, with another five pairs holding territories. The Welsh Kite Trust website has reported that by 2005 there may have been as many as 300 pairs breeding in southern England. The southern introductions are from non-migratory Spanish stock and, while some of the younger English birds are dispersive, most of the older ones remain in the same area all year. All five of the Red Kites that were shown as ringed abroad and recovered in Britain in the *Migration Atlas* came from Denmark or Germany.

Early Surrey history. The history of Red Kites in Surrey goes back at least as far as Roman Britain. While there is no definite evidence that they have ever bred in the county, circumstantial evidence suggests that they must have done so, up to at least the 16th century. Lovegrove (1990) says that bones found in the midden (waste tip) of a settlement at Putney come from this period, making the Red Kite one of the earliest birds to have been listed for Surrey. Red Kites were common in medieval times. Further information on their Surrey status comes from continental observers visiting London.

An early written account is given by Gurney (1921), who quotes from a 1465 diary entry of Baron Leo von Rozmital, brother-in-law of the King of Bohemia. The diary was written in Latin by Schaschek, the Bohemian who was his guide and Latin Secretary. The Baron said he had never seen as many Kites as were present in the vicinity of London Bridge, that it was a capital offence to kill them and that there was probably not a large town in England without them. Charles Lécluse (Clusius), the Flemish naturalist, visited London in 1571 and thought that Red Kites were as numerous in London as Black Kites were in Cairo (Nisbet, 1959). Lécluse described them feeding on garbage thrown into the Thames (Harting, 1866).

Since Red Kites scavenged in the filth around the towns and, as Lécluse and others testified, they were sometimes present in considerable numbers, reminiscent of Black Kites in parts of Africa and Asia, there has been some doubt about whether the London birds were Red or Black Kites. However, Red Kites can be found flocking to offal at tips and feeding stations in mid-Wales and French birds flock similarly in winter. In the Midlands, Red Kites will take carrion put out for them in village gardens (Carter and Grice, 2000), so this behaviour is not unusual. Other evidence that the London birds were Red rather than Black Kites includes bone measurements (*e.g.* those in Bramwell, 1976) and a statement by the 16th century ornithologist William Turner (1544) that he had only ever seen a Red Kite in Britain.

Persecution over the next three hundred years probably wiped out Red Kites as breeding birds in London and Surrey by 1800 at the latest. John Evelyn, writing soon after 1700, refers to servants shooting kites, as if they were still fairly common at the time. Red Kites last bred in London in 1777 (W. H. Hudson, *Rare, Vanishing and Lost British Birds* in Shrubb (2003)). Recorded 19th century occurrences are few. There are early and undated references to a pair at Hindhead and Farnham. Jordan (1893) saw one that had been killed about 40 years previously (*i.e.* around 1850). One was said to have been killed near Godalming in March 1870. One was caught at Box Hill in about 1878. The Haslemere Museum has a note by J. C. M. Nichols of one shot near Holmwood around 1884. One was seen flying near Lingfield in September 1892 (*Naturalists Journal*, 1892 in Bucknill). Jefferies (1893) said he once saw one over Surbiton.

20th century. The first record in the 20th century was of an immature bird at Beddington Sewage Farm on 15th August 1966. There were six more from various sites in the 1970s and thirteen in the 1980s. The increase continued through the 1990s, when 35 birds were seen, including two together at Compton on 26th April 1994 and there were eight birds in 2000. All records were single day sightings, and all but the two at Compton and two at Barn Elms on 7th May 2000 were of single birds. Sightings of Red Kites became more common in the 1990s. It is tempting to ascribe this to the establishment of introduced breeding populations in southern England, though dispersal from the release sites has been slow (Carter and Grice, 2000).

Where found. Up to 2000, most records were from rural areas in central and west Surrey, but

Beddington Sewage Farm in the northeast, with seven, was the busiest single site. Others were at Banstead Downs, Barn Elms, Baynards (Cranleigh), Buckland, Capel (three), Caterham, Cheam, Chelsham, Chiddingfold, Clandon, Eashing, Egham, Frensham, Godstone, Guildford (three), Hankley, Haslemere (two), Heath End (Horsell), Kew (two), Lightwater, Merrow, Milford (two), Oxted, Papercourt/Send (two), Peaslake, Pirbright, Pyrford, Redhill, Richmond Park, Ripley, Stoke Lake, Tadworth, Thursley/Ockley/Elstead (five), Unstead Sewage Farm (two), Wanborough, Windsor Great Park, Witley, Woodmansterne, Worplesdon and Wrecclesham. In Spelthorne, there was one at King George VI Reservoir on 1st April 1958 (R. Adams, *BB*, *53:163*). One flew southwest over Perry Oaks Sewage Farm on 10th January 1982 (*LBR* for 1984) and one south on 3rd May 1997.

After 2000. The pattern has continued since 2000, with a rising number of reports, most of them from March to June. New sites up to 2005 included Addington, Ash Vale, Berrylands, Bookham, Broadstreet Common, Chessington, Chilworth, Dorking, Ellens Green, Elstead, Epsom Common, Ewell, Farncombe, Frimley Green, Holmbury St Mary, Holmethorpe, Little Woodcote, Island Barn Reservoir, New Haw, Newdigate, Purley, Putney, Queen Elizabeth II Reservoir, Reigate, South Norwood, Titsey, Walton Reservoirs, West Byfleet, West Horsley, Wimbledon Common and Wrecclesham. There were at least 12 vice-county reports in 2005, all from March to June and most from outer Surrey. In Spelthorne, single birds flew over Staines Reservoirs on 17th October 2004 (*Bird Watching*) and 2nd May 2005 (*LNHSB*) and at Staines Moor one was seen in September 2005 and there were two on 18th October 2005 (*LNHSB*). Given the rising volume of reports, it may not be too long before a breeding pair is found in the vice-county.

Calendar. The monthly pattern of occurrences since 1900 given on the table shows that 2005 was not untypical. Most of the reports are from the period March to June and Red Kites are scarce from July to February.

Bird months 1900-2005

	Jan	Feb	Mar	Apr	May	Jun	Jul	Aug	Sep	Oct	Nov	Dec	Total
Vice-county	3	5	18	22	21	12	2	4	3	0	4	6	**100**

Movements. The monthly pattern remains consistent with passage migration of some European birds, albeit with a spring dispersal from British sites, and few if any resident birds. Definite evidence of dispersal was provided by wing-tagged birds seen in 2006. One of these was sitting in the middle of the road near Ockley, eating a dead rabbit. The tags indicated a bird raised in the Chilterns in 2005 (W. Attridge).

White-tailed Eagle   *Haliaeetus albicilla*

Eight records, latest 1906

White-tailed Eagles have a northern breeding range which extends from Greenland, Scandinavia and Scotland to eastern Asia. They bred in England up to the 18th century and may have been widespread in Bronze Age Britain. Inland records are now very uncommon in the south.

Surrey. The records are all over 100 years old and all but possibly the earliest are likely to have been wandering birds from northern Europe:

300 AD: London. Remains of a White-tailed Eagle were found during an excavation at 18 Park Street, Southwark, in a group of Roman and medieval deposits dated 300 AD or later.

1847:   Weybridge. The first White-tailed Eagle recorded alive was one that landed in a tree in Lord Portman's park in 1847 or earlier. It perched so close to the house that it could be shot from a window (Meyer, 1847).

1850:   Wimbledon. Yarrell (1845) mentioned one that was shot in Coombe Wood and stuffed for the Duke of Cambridge. Bucknill gave the date as about 1850 but it must have been between 1838 and 1845 because the record was in Yarrell's 2nd Edition of 1845.

1858:   Godalming. One was shot near Godalming on 27th February, during rough and windy weather (Bucknill).

1876:   Windsor Great Park. There is a remarkable account of three appearing at about the end of October. One was trapped and presented to H. R. H. Prince Christian. The other two were seen again in November, wheeling round and over the surface of Virginia Water, by Mr H. S. Styhan while he was fishing there. Attempts to capture them were unsuccessful and they remained in the district for some time (Bucknill, 1902). It seems highly likely that these birds visited the Surrey part of the park, at least occasionally. The record is not mentioned in The Birds of Berkshire (Swash *et al.*, 1996), though two other records for Windsor Great Park are given.

1893:   South Surrey. A female shot in Wadhurst Park, Sussex on 26th December had frequently been seen in Surrey (Bucknill).

1900:   Wintershall, one was killed before 1900 (*SALEC*).

1906:   Titsey, a male was shot in Pitchers Wood, just north of Titsey Plantation, on 12th November (Pycraft, 1907).

Bucknill also gave an undated record in which the location might not have been in Surrey, so it must be discarded.

Harriers   *Circus spp.*

Unidentified harriers, usually thought to be Hen or Montagu's, have been published for Ashtead (a pair, 1922), Barn Elms (1954), Bourne Woods (1955), Frensham (28th June 1953, (*SBR*), Hen Harrier in HNHS 1955), Grayswood (1955), Headley Heath (1968), Oxshott (1948), West Molesey (1948) and Winterfold (1957). Later published records include: Ash Ranges (2000), Banstead Heath (1970), Churt (1986), Farthing Down (1966, SBC archive), Felbridge (1973, 1977, 1991), Haslemere (1970), Moorhouse (1986), Netley Heath (1973), Old Woking Sewage Farm (1994), Pirbright Commons (1976, 1977), Richmond Park (1973), Thursley/Ockley Commons (1968, 1977, 1995, 1996), Tongham (1980), Vann Lake (1973), Westhumble (1972) and Wimbledon Common (1978).

In Spelthorne there have been single harriers at Queen Mary Reservoir (1982), Staines Moor (1949) and Staines Reservoirs (1975).

Marsh Harrier (Eurasian Marsh Harrier)   *Circus aeruginosus*
Scarce passage migrant

Races of the Marsh Harrier breed from Europe east to Australasia and the Pacific. It is likely to have bred widely in Britain many years ago but had already become very local by the late 19th century as a result of habitat loss and persecution. British breeding numbers have increased since the 1970s. Some European birds winter in the region but others move further south, in Spain or northwest Africa.

Early Surrey history. Graves (1811-21) described a nest in osiers (willows used in basket-work) near the Grand Surrey Canal on the Deptford Road in 1811. Five eggs were laid and the female was shot from the nest. This remains the only breeding record for Surrey.

Birds shot at Elstead and Frensham, both in 1847 (*SALEC*), were in the Charterhouse Collection when Bucknill knew it. Currently the Collection holds one (the Elstead bird?) which is said to come from Godalming. There were two near Guildford on 15th November 1880. One was seen at Headley in January 1896 and one was killed at Cheam on 5th September of the same year (Bucknill). The November and January dates are unusual by more recent experience. There are a few undated 19th century records. Waring Kidd said that he had stuffed three that had been shot near Godalming (Newman).

1900-1970. There were very few Marsh Harriers in the first 70 years of the 20th century. A pair near Haslemere on 16th May 1914 was 'on the commons', and perhaps not in Surrey. A female was seen at the Lammas Lands, Godalming on 3rd May 1933 and may have been associated with a male that was seen at Ockley Common on the 4th and in Godalming on the 7th of the same month. There were single birds at Pudmore on 16th August 1951 and at Beddington Sewage Farm on 5th September 1954, two were at Thursley on 10th May 1959 and single birds were at Frensham in October 1960, Elstead in July 1961 and on 2nd November 1963 and at Ockley Common on 25th May 1966. One hunting along the banks of King George VI Reservoir on 28th April 1957 was only the second for Middlesex.

Where found, 1900-2005. There were 121 vice-county bird months from 1900 to 2005, increasing sharply towards the end of the period:

Bird months by decade 1900-2005

	1900s	1910s	1920s	1930s	1940s	1950s	1960s	1970s	1980s	1990s	2000-05	**Total**
Vice-county	0	1	0	3	0	4	4	6	7	59	37	**121**

They were nearly all single birds up to 2000. Beddington Sewage Farm, with 38 records and 42 bird months, was by far the most frequent site. The Thursley/Ockley/ Elstead area provided another 20 records and 21 bird months. The remainder came from Albury (2000), Barn Elms (2000), Beddlestead Valley (1993), Buckland Sand Pits (1988), Chertsey Meads (1995), Chiddingfold (1994), Dulwich (1991), Enton (1999), Frensham (1960 (HNHS), 1996, 1999, 2000), Godalming (1933), Hambledon (early summer 1986), Hankley Common (1979), Haslemere area (1914), Holmethorpe (1994), Milford (2000), Nore Hill (1999), Pewley Downs (1980), Papercourt Gravel Pits (1993), Richmond Park (1998), Runnymede (1980), Stoke Lake (1996, 1998), Unstead Sewage Farm (1999 (two), 2000), Walton Reservoirs area (1988, 1993, 1995, 1996), Warlingham (1997), West End (1995), Winkworth (1989), Woking (1998) and Woodmansterne (1982). There was one in the King George VI Reservoir area on 14th September 1985.

Since 2000. There have been records from Barn Elms, Beddington, Putney, Stoke Lake and Thursley in 2001, from Beddington, Papercourt and Worplesdon in 2002, from Beddington in 2004 and from Barn Elms, Frensham and Worplesdon in 2005 (*Bird watching*, London Wetland Centre and SBC archive). Later Spelthorne records have come from Staines Moor on 11th May 2001, from King George VI Reservoir on 6th September 2001 and September 2004 (*Bird Watching, LNHSB*), from Staines Reservoirs on 16th May 1984, 14th June 1985, 21st September 1994, 25th May 1997, 12th September 1999, 11th May 2001, 8th August 2004 (*LNHSB*) and 9th September 2004 (*LNHSB*) and from Stanwell Moor on 13th May 2004 (*LNHSB*).

Calendar. The table shows clear spring and autumn peaks, with two winter records, 14th January 1994 and 2nd January 1997, both from the Thursley/Ockley Commons:

Bird months 1900 to 2005

	Jan	Feb	Mar	Apr	May	Jun	Jul	Aug	Sep	Oct	Nov	Dec	**Total**
Vice-county	2	0	4	26	33	2	1	24	20	7	2	0	**121**

Apart from the winter birds, the earliest was at Dulwich on 25th March 1991 and the latest were at Elstead Common on 2nd November 1963 and the Thursley/Ockley Commons on 12th November 1993. The only July bird was at Elstead in 1961.

Hen Harrier
Scarce winter visitor, has bred

Circus cyaneus

Breeds in Europe, northern Asia and North America. Most Hen Harriers leave the breeding area for more southern parts of Europe, Asia and the Americas in winter. The British breeding range has been contracting as a result of habitat loss and persecution during the past two centuries. Hen Harriers are mainly winter visitors to southern England. They feed on small mammals, particularly voles, and birds.

Early Surrey history. Graves (1811-21) wrote that he often saw a Hen Harrier skimming over Rolls Meadows, beside the Kent Road. This would be in about 1820 (Bucknill). Rolls Road, in Bermondsey, is just to the north of the Old Kent Road and might be the site. Blyth (1836) said that they were, rarely, seen on heaths some distance from Tooting. References in Bucknill mention fields on the Hog's Back and around Loseley as sites up to 1837. Newman (1849) has them as occasional visitors to the Godalming district and records that Waring Kidd had stuffed several. Stafford wrote that they were sometimes seen near Hammer Pond (Bucknill). A male and female were shot near Farnham not later than 1854 (Spicer).

Jordan (1892) mentions a pair of harriers ('Blue hawk and ringtail') hunting Black Grouse, pheasants and partridges on Holmbury Hill in the 1860s. No season is mentioned and they might, on the brief note given, have been Montagu's Harriers. The prey species mentioned are unusually large for either harrier, so this part of the observation looks a little problematic. In *Within an Hour of London Town* he gives an undated reference to the Hen Harrier as *a large grey bird… He looks like a gull* on high moorland at Leith Hill. Later records in Bucknill come from Wisley (December 1869), near Tadworth (1875), near Banstead (20th January 1880), Chelsham (winter of 1880/81, *Zool*.1881, p.211), Olddean Common (22nd January 1892), Clandon Park (about January 1894), Milford (December 1895) and, in the 1890s, Betchworth, Headley and Walton Heath. There are undated references to Frensham Common, Poynter's, (near Cobham) and near Thursley.

1900-1950. During the first 50 years of the 20th century, records were scattered and infrequent. A pair was seen near Godalming in February, 1906 (Dalgliesh, 1906). Others were found at the Devil's Jumps (March 1907), southwest Surrey (April 1919) and a Surrey common (March 1922), but no definite pattern of wintering was established. Records became more frequent in the 1930s, including one on the North Downs at Beddlestead and Mickleham in 1935 and Banstead in 1947. There were others at Tilford and Worms Heath in 1958. A female on Staines Moor on 17th November 1940 was the first for the Spelthorne district and only the fourth for Middlesex, the previous being in 1880. There was one at Kempton Park race course on 3rd November 1946.

Since 1950. By 1960 one or two Hen Harriers were often found to spend part of the winter in southwest Surrey, possibly because of colder winters. Frequent absences suggested that the birds had larger territories and had connections with those seen at Woolmer, in Hampshire. Others were seen at Queen Elizabeth II Reservoir in 1961, Epsom Common in 1965, Cobham in 1969 and, in Spelthorne, Staines Reservoirs on 28th September 1966.

Where found. Over half (172) of the 336 bird months have come from the Thursley/Ockley Commons, 42 are from the Pirbright Commons, which are less heavily watched and 40 from Frensham, Tilhill and Churt. Military land on West End and Bisley Commons (six bird months) is suitable but very little watched in winter. There are nine records from Beddington Sewage Farm. Other sites where the Hen Harrier has been recorded since 1970, include: Badshot Lea, Baynards Park, Betchworth, Capel, Chobham (nine bird months), Enton (two bird months), Frimley Gravel Pits, Hedgecourt, Hersham Gravel Pits, Hindhead, the Hog's Back, Holmethorpe Sand Pits, Island Barn Reservoir, Molesey Heath, Netley Heath, Olddean Common, Papercourt Gravel Pits/Old Woking Sewage Farm/Send (eight bird months), Puttenham Common, Pyrford, Redhill, Tilford, Unstead Sewage Farm, Walton Heath, Warlingham, West Horsley, Wimbledon Common and Winterfold.

Sites where Hen Harriers have been seen since 2000 include Ash Ranges (2006), Barn Elms (9th

November 2003), Beddington Sewage Farm (2005), Bisley Ranges (2003), Headley Heath (2001), Cleygate Common (2002), Thursley (several years),West End Common/Ash Ranges (2003) and White Downs (2002).

Most Surrey sightings are on the western heaths. If there were fewer trees on the chalk downland, Hen Harriers would probably take to hunting there in the winter, as they do in Sussex. Hen Harriers are still uncommon in the Spelthorne district, but there was one on 29th December 2001 and another at Staines Moor on 11th September 2005 (both *LNHSB*).

There are two breeding records. Meyer (1842) wrote that he had seen a nest of young birds on a boggy heath in Surrey. A pair bred at West End Common in 1932 (site from Clark, 1984 which is based on original Nethersole-Thompson correspondence). Five eggs were laid and four young were hatched.

Calendar. The monthly distribution of 368 bird months from 1900 to 2001 shows a January peak and spring birds continuing to June, with one later summer record, from Chipstead on 21st August 1973 (*LBR*, *SBR* for 1973). Apart from this one, the earliest autumn arrival was from Thursley/Ockley Commons on 1st September 1991. The latest seen alive in spring was one at the same site on 2nd June 1990. One was found dead, full of shot, at Haslemere on 14th June 1963.

Bird months 1900-2001

	Jan	Feb	Mar	Apr	May	Jun	Jul	Aug	Sep	Oct	Nov	Dec	Total
Vice-county	64	56	51	36	5	2	0	1	6	37	54	56	**368**

Bird month figures are indicative rather than exact. Hen Harriers rove widely and are rarely seen at the same site on two days running. A significant number of Thursley birds are almost certainly included in the totals for Frensham, Hankley and other places in west Surrey.

Large counts. Up to three Hen Harriers have been seen together but most reports are of single birds.

Montagu's Harrier $\qquad$ *Circus pygargus*
Rare summer visitor and passage migrant

A summer visitor to Europe and Asia as far east as Siberia, wintering in Africa and India. Montagu's Harrier was not distinguished from the Hen Harrier until 1802, so its early British history cannot be traced, but it has bred in small numbers in southern Britain since that date. Shrubb said that it failed to adapt to the enclosure of land and changed cultivation methods.

Early Surrey history. Graves knew of a pair shot in Battersea Fields in mid-May, 1812 and based his illustration on them. Montagu's Harriers were occasional visitors to the Godalming district, where Waring Kidd had stuffed several (Newman (1849). Other references in Bucknill come from a farm near Guildford (shot in the spring of 1872, present in several previous springs), Combe Wood (Coombe Wood, Wimbledon, mid-1880s), Farnham (winter 1882/3), Royal Common (a pair killed 1890, one seen spring 1891) and Frensham Ponds.

One that was found dead in 1840, on Royal Common (*SALEC*), was seen in the Charterhouse Collection by Bucknill, who added in *The Zoologist* for 1902 that Stafford informed Mr F. Styan that the bird had been found by its nest, which had contained four eggs. *SALEC* gives the season of finding as winter, which, if it is the same bird, is something of a puzzle. This is not too convincing as proof of breeding. Other problems beset the story of a pair that were thought initially to be Hen Harriers. They were watched at Ockley Common on dates from 28th May to 6th August 1906 but no nest was found (Mouritz (1907), Bentham and Mouritz (1908)). A nest was found at the same place in 1907, again thought initially to have been of a Hen Harrier. Four eggs were laid, of which two were taken by a collector. Two young birds fledged and proved to be Montagu's when examined in the nest. One of these was shot in August by a local gamekeeper and again identified as a Montagu's. Both the adults were also shot (*BB, 1:237-42 and 351-54*). In the following year a pair nested a mile or so away on Hankley Common, between Lions Mouth and Hospital Pond. The eggs failed to hatch in spite of RSPB surveillance, possibly because of disturbance by observers (*BB, 2:140*). Not surprisingly, after all this harassment, there were no further attempts.

Later birds. There are fifteen later records.

1917:   Thursley area, an immature bird was nearly run over by a cyclist.

1935:   Frensham, a female or immature bird on 15th March.

1935:*   Staines Moor, a juvenile on 5th August is the earliest record that has been located for the Spelthorne district.

1946:   Devil's Punchbowl, one reported from the Punch Bowl on 11th November (rather a late date).

1954:   Frensham, two from 8th May to early June.

1967:   Thursley/Hankley area, an immature bird on 14th-28th May.

1968:   Chobham Common, a sooty grey melanisitic male at Longcross on 24th August.

1969:   Richmond Park, an immature bird on 11th October.

1979:*   Staines Reservoirs, one on 7th May.

1986:   Hambledon, an adult male was watched for over five minutes near Burgate House on 18th May. Ockley Common, a juvenile on 20th August.

1994:   between Capel and Vann Lake, a female on 26th April.

2000:   Unstead Sewage Farm, a female flew over on 29th May. Nore Hill, a dark morph bird on 12th August.

2002:*   Staines Reservoirs, a juvenile on 5th August.

2004:   Barn Elms London Wetland Centre, one on 17th May.

* Spelthorne

Goshawk (Northern Goshawk)   *Accipiter gentilis*

Scarce. Has bred.

Breeds in Europe and the more northern parts of Asia and North America, mainly wintering within its breeding range. The *MA* shows few movements over 20 km. Deforestation and persecution led to its extinction in Britain by the mid-19th century but Goshawks have now become re-established.

Early Surrey history. The earliest record is of one caught near Egham at the beginning of 1846. The circumstances were rather strange. It was *perched on a gate-post, so intently watching a flock of Starlings, that he did not perceive the approach of a man, who captured him by seizing the legs* (Horn, 1846). A female was caught at Beddington (undated, in Bucknill). Birds shot near Godalming in 1856 or caught there (undated) were in the Charterhouse Collection in Bucknill's time but are not there now.

Where found since 1900. There were at least 80 records and 87 bird months from 1900-2005, none earlier than 1959. Most of the reports came from south and west Surrey but Goshawks have also been seen at Barn Elms/Putney (2001, 2005), Beddington Sewage Farm (1960), Bookham Common (1984), Epsom (1980), Hersham Gravel Pit (2001), Nutfield Ridge (1993) and Woldingham (1959). There were two adults with two juveniles in East Surrey in 2002. In Spelthorne, one at Staines Reservoirs on 16th June 1957 is described in the *LBR*. Belsey (2002) mentions a pair seen occasionally in the Shepperton and Laleham area 'last year'.

Breeding. There are no 19th century records of breeding and none for the 20th century until 1990, when a pair laid five eggs at a site to the west of central Surrey. Three males and two females fledged. In the following year, five eggs were laid at the same site and three males and two females again fledged. Five eggs were laid at the site in 1993 but the nest was later deserted. In the same year a pair bred within 20 km of the site. Five eggs were laid. The male was found shot and died in care, leaving the female to fledge two males and three females. A pair nested in south Surrey in 1994. Three young were fledged and an empty nest was found after fledging. A pair built a nest in central Surrey in 1997 but were unsuccessful. Although Goshawks are still seen from time to time, particularly in west Surrey, confirmation of breeding anywhere since 1994 is not available.

Calendar. The bird months show a noticeable peak in April and a smaller one in August, suggesting passage.

Bird months

	Jan	Feb	Mar	Apr	May	Jun	Jul	Aug	Sep	Oct	Nov	Dec	**Total**
Vice-county	8	5	7	16	9	3	1	12	8	8	8	2	**87**

Sparrowhawk (Eurasian Sparrowhawk) — *Accipiter nisus*
Moderately common breeding resident

Common breeding birds in Europe and the northern parts of Asia. The British population is partly resident but most of the more northern birds winter further south. Some presumably pass through Surrey as passage migrants, though evidence on this is lacking. Numbers were much reduced in the 19th century. Persecution by gamekeepers does not seem to have had much effect on its numbers since the 1930s but Sparrowhawks were badly affected by pesticides in the mid-20th century. They have since made a full recovery. Numbers have doubled since 1970.

Early Surrey history. Remains found at 104 Borough High Street, Southwark dated back to Roman Britain, 270-350 AD. Sparrowhawks (if this is what they were) had a use in falconry at Beddington according to an entry in the Carew Household Book for 13th November 1608. This details a payment for earthen pots 'for the sparowhawkes to bowse' *i.e.* drink (*Surrey Archaeological Collections* 31:8).

19th century. Sparrowhawks were uncommon at Tooting even in the 1830s (Blyth). Meyer (1842) knew of Sparrowhawks that were nesting at Weybridge. Newman (1849) listed them as resident in the Godalming district, without further comment. Bucknill said they were still common, though declining, in rural districts and had records of recent nesting in most parts of the county, 'and even in this, the Epsom neighbourhood (1895)', suggesting that 'rural' meant the south and southwest. They were occasional in Richmond Park (Bucknill) and on Wimbledon Common (Hamilton). Power (1910) had only three records for the Dulwich area from 1874 to 1909, none of which involved breeding. Sparrowhawks were sparsely distributed in the Staines District (Kerr, 1906).

1900 to 1970. A recovery may have begun in the early years of the 20th century, as instanced by breeding at Newdigate (1905), Chart (1906) and by a nest, eggs and young birds at Warlingham from 6th June to 20th July 1918 (LNHS 1918). Eggs collected by Boorman at Clandon Common (1901, 1906), Ockham Common (1906, 1908) and Ripley (1908, 1909) are in the Haslemere Museum. Up to two pairs were breeding in Richmond Park after the cessation of gamekeeping (Collenette). Sparrowhawks bred at Bookham (eggs collected by Douglas, 1936), Farleigh (1938-39), Headley (1937), Limpsfield (1935-36), Oxshott (1935) and Pirbright (eggs collected by Douglas, 1939). A further increase came

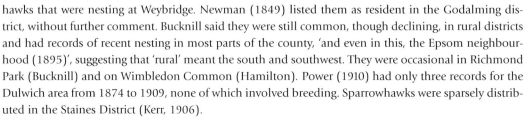

with the relaxation of gamekeeping in the 1940s. Eggs were collected at Effingham (1946) and eighteen pairs nested around Oxted and Limpsfield in 1948 (*BLA*). Sparrowhawks bred at Bookham (eggs collected 1951), Dulwich (1957), Oxshott (1957) and Wimbledon Common (regular by 1956). A population crash associated with toxic chemicals followed and only a pair or two were found breeding in the mid-1960s. There were eleven known vice-county breeding localities in 1970. There were three Spelthorne records in 1970 and in 1971, but none anywhere in Middlesex in 1972.

The recovery since 1975. There has since been a strong recovery. By 1978 there were 16 pairs in west Surrey alone, of which eight were proved to breed (*HSBBR*). Sparrowhawks were seen at 60 Surrey localities in the London area in 1984 and by the end of the 20th century they were being commonly seen across the county, soaring over parks, commons and farmland and sweeping through gardens with well attended bird tables, right up to the Surrey Docks. Sparrowhawks colonised Wimbledon Common/Putney Heath in 1984 and eight nests produced 26 young in 1996 (Wills and Kettle, 1997). The 1988-97 SBC Atlas survey found Sparrowhawks present in 310 tetrads, 300 of them in the vice-county, suggesting a breeding population of at least 300 pairs. This is broadly consistent with the 1994-2001 Breeding Bird Survey which grossed up to an average of 393 birds. There have been some substantial local studies. In 1974, P. A. D. Hollom and F. V. Blackburn found 16 occupied nests in 60 square km of northwest Surrey (an average of one per tetrad). In 1978, M. J. Cowlard and J. R. Mullins found 53 nests in central and west Surrey, of which 25 failed. In 1990, M. J. Carter found 26 nests in the London area and 69 nests in the rest of Surrey. A pair bred in Battersea Park (Inner London) in 1997. There were ten pairs (seven nests) on the 346 hectares of Wimbledon Common in 1997 (about eight nests per two km square, a very high figure). By the late 1990s, without special surveys, observers were reporting around 80 breeding season sites annually. Spelthorne numbers remained low but by 1983, the year of the first Middlesex record of successful breeding for 20 years, Sparrowhawks were being seen frequently at Shepperton and Staines Reservoirs outside the breeding season.

Population size. Sparrowhawks were not found in Common Birds Censuses until 1989 but were then reported annually at around 0.05 - 0.1 territories per ten hectares . The more recent Breeding Birds Census suggests about 350 adults (0.02 adults per ten hectares) might be on the low side. If Surrey held a proportionate share of the British breeding population as given by the *New Atlas*, the population would be about 230 territories (0.1 per square km). These three estimates seem broadly consistent. Whatever the number, the increase since the 1970s is significant and probably at least as great as that experienced nationally. Six pairs bred on Wimbledon Common in 2001 and Sparrowhawks are now frequent visitors to gardens. The Croydon RSPB Garden Bird Survey found that each month up to 20% of the surveyed gardens were visited by Sparrowhawks in 2003.

Food. Prey items and species attacked include Teal, Red-legged Partridge, Grey Partridge, juvenile Kestrel, Snipe, Woodcock, Feral and domestic Rock Doves, Stock Dove, Woodpigeon, Collared Dove, Budgerigar, Cuckoo, Green Woodpecker, Great Spotted Woodpecker, Skylark, Swallow, House Martin, Tree Pipit, Pied Wagtail, Dunnock, Robin, Stonechat, Blackbird, Fieldfare, Song Thrush, Redwing, Mistle Thrush, Blue Tit, Great Tit, Jay, Starling, House Sparrow, Chaffinch, Brambling, Greenfinch, Goldfinch, Siskin, Bullfinch,

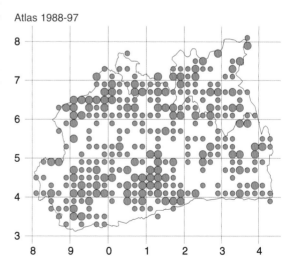

Atlas 1988-97

Hawfinch, Reed Bunting, a Pipistrelle Bat (caught), a gerbil (safe behind glass) and a half-grown rat. Even the largest of the birds listed has been taken. The increase in Collared Doves has provided a new food source, sometimes distressing since the victims may be caught and eaten alive in gardens. A strange incident occurred at Guildford in 1993, when a male Sparrowhawk chased a Collared Dove into the United Reformed Church sanctuary. The dove was rescued but the hawk remained perched on light fittings until the following day, when it found its own way out.

Movements. A raptor movement on 23rd September 2000 saw 13 over Beddington Sewage Farm. Young ringed in Surrey have been recovered in Dorset, Essex, Kent, Northamptonshire (Oxendon) and Sussex. The only foreign ringing recovery is of a male ringed in Belgium on 11th January 2001 and controlled at Gomshall on 8th December, 227 km away, in the same year. The greatest established longevity is of a bird ringed at Blackheath on 4th July 1982 and recovered at Peaslake on 15th December 1990.

Plumage variations. There was an albino at Hambledon in 1933 (Parker, 1947). Melanistic birds were seen at Bookham Common on 20th November 1997 and South Norwood Lake on 7th January 2000.

Buzzard (Common Buzzard) — *Buteo buteo*

Scarce but increasing passage migrant and breeding species.

Breeds from Europe east to Siberia and Japan. Mostly resident in Europe but some move south to winter elsewhere. Buzzards bred in almost every British county at the beginning of the 19th century but were extinct in much of the south and east, including Surrey, by 1875. A gradual recolonisation began from about 1950, accelerating in recent years. Buzzards are now making a spectacular eastward push across England, facilitated by reduced persecution and an increase in the rabbit population (Clements, 2002). By 1999 there were 38-50+ pairs in West Sussex alone (Kalahar, 1999). The total Sussex breeding population was estimated at 130 pairs in 2002 (*Sussex Bird Report*). Ringing evidence shows that Buzzards breeding in Britain rarely move to other countries but contains little information about possible migrants from elsewhere.

Early Surrey history. The recorded history of Buzzards in the Surrey part of the London area goes back to Roman times. Two sets of remains found at excavations in the Borough High Street, Southwark, were dated at 101-120 and 120-140 AD. Others at Winchester Palace, Southwark were dated at 250-400 AD. Remains dated to 1230-1300 AD were found at Merton Priory.

19th century. Bucknill gave fourteen dated records, from Mitcham Common (winter of 1834/35), Dorking (1858), Woodmansterne (October 1875), Walton Heath (October 1880), Sanderstead (8th July 1881), Cobham (November 1881), Bramley (15th November 1890), Pudmore (1st January 1891), Royal Common (pair, 31st March and the following week, 1891), Wonersh (December 1895), Peper Harow (two, 1898), Frensham (spring of 1899) and Kingswood Warren (November 1901). There were undated occurrences at Cheam, Egham, Headley Heath, Mickleham and Thursley. Shrubb put the last Surrey nesting at 1820-29 but Bucknill mentioned two successful breeding records, including a pair thought by Meyer to have nested near Claremont around 1840. A pair 'killed while nesting at Witley' (Stafford) were presented to Stafford by a Mr Richardson, master of the Witley workhouse (*SALEC*), in 1851. They had bred there for three successive years (years not located) but were shot because they were thought to be a danger to chickens (Bucknill, 1902). No later 19th century breeding records have been located.

1900 to the 1950s. There were two at Banstead in the autumn of 1909 (*LN* for 1933) and others were in the Haslemere area in 1913 and a year or two earlier (Shaw). In 1922, Buzzards were seen at Epsom Downs (4th June), Dulwich (27th August) and Tadworth (1st October). There was a pair at Warlingham in July 1923. In 1925, single birds were seen at Farleigh on 26th June, Epsom Downs on 3rd October and Godstone on 26th October. Two at Chelsham in the first quarter of 1927 stayed for over six weeks. There was one at Titsey around 1928 and one at Frensham on dates from 8th February to 7th April 1933. One was seen at Farleigh on dates from 3rd December 1932 to 4th March 1933 and one from October to December 1935, when it was shot. A Buzzard wintered there again in early 1934 and 1934-35. Buzzards were seen at Selsdon (1935), Fairchildes (1937), Oxted (pair shot 1937), near Godalming (1937), Kew Bridge (1938), Nore Hill (1940), Putney and the Thames near Richmond (1942), Guildford (1943), Croham Hurst (1943 and 1945), Seale (1944), Baynards (1947), Clandon and Witley (1947), Hindhead and Tooting (1946), near Godalming in 1946-47, Richmond Park (1948, 1951, 1953-54), and Holmbury Hill, Newlands Corner and Virginia Water in 1954.

The Witley reintroduction. An experimental reintroduction of Buzzards was made by Sir John Leigh, together with his younger son David and his estate agent, on his 5,000 acre estate at Witley Park in 1939. The experiment was at the suggestion of Edgar Chance. Seven six to nine week old young were obtained from central Wales in July and put into a large aviary with two adults and fed on newly-shot rabbits. They were released at intervals through August and September. Five of them were still present on 22nd November and there was evidence that they had been feeding on the abundant local rabbit population. Two were seen in January 1940. Territory was held in 1940 and three pairs nested on the estate in 1941 (E. P. Chance, letter of 2nd December 1953 in the Haslemere Museum). From then until 1954 at least one pair nested every year (Chance, 1939 and *Surrey Bird Report* for 1954). In 1953, following a change of ownership, the Haslemere Natural History Society sent a letter to the new owner of Witley Park to object to the destruction of the colony of Buzzards. Nothing more was published about the colony after the 1954 breeding season, when at least one pair nested, until the 1960 *Surrey Bird Report* mentioned its continued existence. Parr (1972) says that, though documentation was lacking, Buzzards probably continued to breed in the Witley Park area until 1970. Pairs bred not far away at Chiddingfold in 1966 and 1968 (HNHS1980).

1955 to 2006.There was a noticeable increase in the number of records, particularly in west Surrey, from the mid-1950s. 1955 saw birds at Barn Elms, the Blackwater Valley, Chipstead, Farncombe, Hindhead, Kingswood, Puttenham, Sanderstead, Unstead, Walton Bridge, Wimbledon Common and Winterfold. There was one over Lambeth in 1957, one over Tulse Hill in 1965 and one at Vann Lake in 1969. One at Perry Oaks Sewage Farm on 24th January 1965 may have been in Spelthorne. Buzzards bred in 1969 and very occasionally in the years up to 1990. At least two young fledged at a locality south of Wotton in 1987.

By this time, four or five sightings a year were being reported to the Surrey Bird Club. There was a surge in the 1990s and the Club received about 70 records in 1998, 135 in 2000 and 130 in 2001. Territorial birds were initially seen mostly on private land but, if the rabbits can stand it, there seems to be plenty of suitable habitat for Buzzards elsewhere. Buzzards were recorded at King George VI Reservoir in 2000 and 2001 at Staines reservoirs in 2000 (*LBR*), at Staines Moor in 2003 and at Shepperton in 2004 (*LNHSB*) and 2005 (H. W. Evans). There were probably others.

Breeding was proved again in 1999 and the Buzzard is now a regular breeding species. By 2005, Buzzards were breeding on common

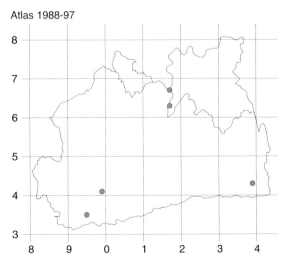

Atlas 1988-97

land in west Surrey and along the Surrey Hills. The average of 16 breeding season adults suggested by the 1994-2004 Breeding Bird Survey may not be too far from the mark as an average but now looks very much on the low side. Ten nests were found within ten miles of Guildford town centre in 2006 and the county population is probably fifty to a hundred pairs.

Jeremy Gates has made notes on recent breeding behaviour at seven sites. At one of them, a private estate with coniferous and deciduous woods and open grassland, birds were displaying in 1998 and they nested in 1999-2006, failing only in 2000. Nearly all the prey remains found were rabbit. At a second, in deciduous woods with scattered Scots Pine and Douglas Fir, territorial birds were seen in 2001 and there was successful breeding in 2002 and 2003 but the site was abandoned in 2004. At a third, heavily-keepered, mixed woodland, birds were present from 2000 to 2006 and bred in at least four of the years. The 2001 nest contained Crow, Magpie and Jay remains (probably shot by the gamekeeper) as well as the usual rabbit. Nest trees at the other four sites were Scots Pine, Norway Spruce, Oak and Turkey Oak. Nine more sites were established from 2003 onward and, in 2006, nests were found in eight of them. By the end of 2006 a total of 43 birds had been ringed.

In the main, the recolonisation of Surrey is a reflection of the national trend. There is no established link between the Surrey rabbit population and the number of Buzzards, though recovery may have been helped by the reduction in pesticides. Introductions may have played a part. N. J. Donnithorne saw both ringed and unringed birds in the Felcourt area from 1997 to 2000 and suspected nesting.

Calendar. The monthly distribution of records up to 2001 was consistent with a significant spring and autumn passage and a resident population of several pairs:

Bird months 1996-2001

	Jan	Feb	Mar	Apr	May	Jun	Jul	Aug	Sep	Oct	Nov	Dec	Total
Vice-county	21	22	58	81	59	26	28	40	58	38	18	23	**472**

Buzzards were ringed in the 1940s. Ringing was resumed in 1999 and, by the end of the 2005 breeding season, 28 young had been ringed in Surrey. There have been three recoveries of Surrey-ringed birds up to 2005:

Ringed	Age		Recovered		Distance
Thursley	Young	June 1942	Hampshire	14 November 1942	
Surrey	Young	18 June 2001	Hampshire	16 March 2003	53 km
Surrey	Young	8 June 2004	Cobham	15 November 2004	

A nestling ringed in Dorset on 7th June 1996 was found dead at Waterloo Station in the same year. One of the 1999 adults at Jeremy Gates's first site had been taken from a nest in Dorset, hand reared and then released at Nuthurst, West Sussex, in the autumn of 1996. Four other birds were released in the Thursley area. Radio tracking showed that one of them settled in central Surrey, where it was still present in 2003.

Rough-legged Buzzard   *Buteo lagopus*

About 14 records, including two from Spelthorne.

Circumpolar breeding distribution in the arctic and sub-arctic zones, including Norway, moving south in winter. In Britain, mainly found in eastern coastal counties and probably of Scandinavian origin.

Early Surrey History. Birds killed near Busbridge and Munstead (*SALEC*) were in the Charterhouse Collection in Bucknill's time. In 2001 there was one in the collection, with Surrey given as its provenance. There is a vague reference to a heathland site in Jordan (1892).

Dated records are

1876:   Walton Heath, one shot in 1876 by a gamekeeper named Shuttle was presumably part of a national influx during the winter of 1875/76, though the exact date is not available.

1879:   Croydon, one (Bucknill).

1880:   Guildford, one in October (Bucknill).

1881:   Chelsham, a female on 7th February (Bucknill).

1887:   Horsley, autumn (Fitzgerald, 1888).

1891:   Baynards Park (Bucknill).

1891:   Wonersh, January (Bucknill).

1909:   Wonersh Park, one shot on 24th November (*Zool.,1909:468*) was later housed in the Charterhouse Museum (Charterhouse records).

1912:   Croydon, one on 21st April (*Bull. BOC* 32:179).

1953:   Guildford Sewage Farm, one on 9th May.

1968:* Perry Oaks Sewage Farm, one on 15th September appears to be the first possibility for Spelthorne.

1973:* Wraysbury Reservoir, one flew NNE over the reservoir on 17th October.

1975:   near Unstead Sewage Farm, one on 28th March, circling.

1994:   Papercourt Lock, one drifted over on 21st October, at the time of a national influx.

*Spelthorne

Golden Eagle   *Aquila chrysaetos*
One bird

Breeds in upland areas throughout the northern hemisphere south to Mexico, North Africa and Japan. Mainly resident. Currently breeds in Scotland and, very locally, in northern England. The British population is increasing slowly, after a decline in the 19th century which bottomed in the 1870s in Scotland but continued in Ireland until the last bird was killed in 1926.

Surrey. Graves mentioned a male shot near Godalming in June 1810. The record was not listed by *Newman* and is not in Yarrell (1845). Montagu, Saunders and Bucknill all drew attention to possibly misidentified White-tailed Eagles. Saunders (1899) does not list the Godalming bird and the date seems unusual. The record satisfied Graves though and, as Bucknill wrote, *must stand for what it is worth*.

Osprey   *Pandion haliaetus*
Scarce but increasing passage migrant

Breeds throughout the northern hemisphere in coastal regions of Southeast Asia and Australia and in parts of Africa. Northwest European birds winter in West Africa. Some Scandinavian birds reach Britain though none have been found in southeast England (*MA*). Widespread in Britain after the last glaciation (Harrison, 1988). Ospreys bred in Scotland up to 1916 and recolonised in 1954. There are late 18th century records of apparent breeding from Westmoreland. Attempts are currently being made to establish breeding birds in England and have been successful at Rutland Water. Pairs have reached Cumbria and north Wales without assistance.

Early Surrey history. As mentioned above in the Cormorant account, James I kept Ospreys on the Thames at Westminster. Gilbert White mentioned one that was shot at Frensham Pond in 1772 while sitting on the handle of a plough and eating a fish that it had caught.

19th century. Ospreys were well known to the Godalming group. Kidd said that birds shot at Pudmore, Frensham Pond and elsewhere had often been brought to him. The Charterhouse Collection

Frensham Little Pond. A favourite spot for the passing Osprey, especially in autumn, and for the occasional Bearded Tit in winter. Breeding birds include Water Rails and numerous Reed Warblers.

John Davis

at one time included a bird shot at Abbot's Pond in 1840 (Bucknill). One in the area in September 1843 (Newman, 1849) is presumably the bird shot at Hammer Pond in 1843 by a man called Keen (*SALEC*). Bucknill gave records for Milford House (18th October 1852 and another about the same time), Weybridge (11th September 1853), Gatton (August 1868), River Mole at East Molesey (October 1881), Puttenham (30th November 1881), Frensham Pond (about 1884) and Frensham Little Pond (winter of 1885). One in Alton Museum was shot at Frensham in 1876 (HNHS 1955). In 1889 there were single birds at Richmond Park (22nd September, *Zool.,1889:435*) and Barnes (November 1889, *Zool.,1889:18-19*). There were records from Frensham and other ponds (summer of 1897), Kew and Richmond Park (December 1898) and Painshill Park (about 16th October 1899). Another was at Kew in 1899 (*BRP*).For Spelthorne, Glegg added one on the Thames at Laleham in 1855 and gave an extra date of 21st October for the 1889 bird. There was another at Laleham in 1863.

1900 to 1970. Cecil Harmsworth saw a pair at Vachery in September 1904. They stayed for many days, until one was shot on a nearby estate (Harmsworth, 1930 in Parker, 1952). The next record was not until 1930, when one was seen at an undisclosed locality on two dates in September. One at Cutt Mill from 19th October to 19th November 1940 was the latest from 1900 up to that date.

There were single birds at Hedgecourt on 15th May 1944, Enton in 1949 and Frensham Little Pond on 27th April 1953. The next Spelthorne birds appear to have been at Staines Moor and Reservoirs in August 1951. In the spring of 1952, birds were seen there on 14th April and from 29th April to 1st June and there was one in the autumn on dates from 20th August to 19th September. Another was at King George VI Reservoir on 23rd May 1953. In the 1960s there were Ospreys at Thursley/Ockley Commons on 10th June 1967, 10th September 1968 and 21st September 1968, at Frensham/Churt on dates from August to October 1967 and at Wonersh in September and October 1968. There was one at Queen Mary Reservoir, Spelthorne, on dates from 17th September to 3rd October 1965.

After 1970. There were about 20 records in the 1970s and 25 in the 1980s. The number more than quadrupled to 113 in the 1990s and there were 20 in 2000 alone, presumably reflecting greater breeding success in Britain and elsewhere.

Where found. Of 182 records (197 bird months) from 1970-2000, some 39 came from the Frensham area and 34 from the Thursley/Ockley Commons. Beddington Sewage Farm provided twelve and the others were from sites mentioned above and from Ash (three), Barn Elms (four), Bletchingley/Redhill, Brooklands, Buckland, Burpham, Capel (five), Caterham, Chessington, Chiddingfold, Chobham, Churt, Claremont, Cranleigh, the Devil's Punch Bowl, Dockenfield, Dorking, Eashing, Egham, Elstead, Enton (four), Epsom Common (two), Esher Common, Ewhurst Green, Fairoaks, Felbridge, Fetcham, Frimley (two), Gatton (six), Godstone (two), Guildford (Stoke, nine), Hammer Pond, Hankley Common, Haslemere, Hersham, Hindhead, the Hog's Back/Bricksbury Hill, Holmethorpe (three), Island Barn Reservoir (two), Lambeth, the M25, Merrow, Morden Park, Newdigate, Nore Hill (two), Pirbright, Pyrford, Queen Elizabeth II Reservoir, Reigate, Riddlesdown, Send, Tilhill Nurseries, Unstead Sewage Farm (four), Virginia Water, Wallington (two), Walton Reservoirs, Warlingham, Witley Park, Woking and Wonersh. For Spelthorne, there are published records for June 1973 (Geen), May 1984 (Geen) and May 1988.

Subsequent records have come from sites which include Barn Elms, Chilworth, Crooksbury Common, Enton, Farnham, Frensham, Frimley, Guildford (Stoke), Ham Common, Holmethorpe, Hurst Green, Milford, Morden, Papercourt (one on 8th December 2004, W. McCubbin), Queen Elizabeth II Reservoir, Richmond Park, Thursley, Unstead, Walton Reservoirs, Wisley, Witley Park, and Worplesdon (*Bird Watching*, London Wetland Centre, SBC archive) and, in Spelthorne, Staines Moor (2002) and (2004, *LNHSB*) and Staines Reservoirs (2004, *LNHSB*), probably a somewhat incomplete account.

Breeding? A remarkable report in Baker and Minchin (1938) states that *a pair of Ospreys nested in a fir tree near the [Devil's] Jumps* around 1890 and that *the keepers had them*. Baker saw one catch a fish at

Frensham and carry it off to its nest. No other details or references to this record have been located and it must be rated as tantalising rather than definite. One displayed over Witley Park on 15th June 2005 (J. Gates).

Calendar and movements. The bird month distribution to 2005 shows a broad April/May spring passage and a sharper return passage peak in September. The relatively few available Spelthorne records show a different pattern to that of the vice-county, with a summer peak.

Bird months 1970-2005 \

	Jan	Feb	Mar	Apr	May	Jun	Jul	Aug	Sep	Oct	Nov	Dec	Total
Vice-county	0	0	12	47	39	9	4	21	68	21	1	2	**224**
Spelthorne	0	0	0	2	4	2	12	11	5	0	0	2	**38**

There has been a shift to earlier spring arrivals. There have now been twelve in March, all from 1989 onwards, at Dockenfield (28th March 1998), Frensham (28th March 1989), Island Barn Reservoir (24th March 2000), Queen Elizabeth II Reservoir (28th March 2000, 29th March 2005), Stoke (31st March 1995), Thursley/Ockley Commons (24th March 1996, 27th March 1997 and 17th March 2000 seen by M. R. Pankhurst, the earliest for Surrey), Unstead Sewage Farm (31st March 1999), Walton Reservoirs (26th March 2000) and Witley Park (31st March 2001). The last birds usually leave in October but one lingered at Gatton from 17th November to 13th December 1979, the latest for Surrey. There have been other lengthy autumn stays. An Osprey spent about three weeks at Waterloo Pond, Chilworth in October 1956, an example of what became a not uncommon pattern of autumn migrants lingering and sometimes moving from pond to pond. Another visited Frensham and other local ponds from 27th August to 6th October 1967 and in the following year an Osprey visited a private pond at Wonersh for seven weeks up to 21st October. There was one at Claremont for two weeks in the autumn of 1980 and another at Witley Park for about three weeks in 1989 and there have been other long stays in the southwest. One at Frensham from 25th May to 1st June 1977 was unusual for its length of stay in spring. No more than two have been seen together.

Kestrel   *Falco tinnunculus*

Moderately common breeding resident

Breeds in most parts of Europe, and in Asia, Australasia and Africa. Some northern birds move south in winter. Those from Scandinavia winter in Britain (*MA*). Some British Kestrels move to the nearer parts of continental Europe south to Spain. Kestrels bred throughout the British Isles in the 19th century, though they were declining, probably because of persecution and the removal of dead and dying trees, which provided nest sites, for lumber. Numbers in Britain recovered in the 20th century, with a move into towns widely noted in the 1930s. There was a population crash from 1959, caused by toxic farm chemicals, but a good recovery was made until the 1970s. Numbers have since fallen by at least a third, possibly related to the intensification of agriculture.

Early Surrey history. One was killed at Deanery Farm, Godalming, by W. Smeed in 1838 (*SALEC*). Kestrels were then resident in the Godalming district (Newman, 1849). They became much scarcer during the 19th century but still bred throughout rural Surrey and in some areas close to London at the century's end (Bucknill). Localities mentioned by him were Wimbledon Park (1830s), Reigate (nesting in 1881) and Dulwich. Kestrels seem to have become uncommon in Surrey by the 1870s. Hamilton (1881) mentioned one or two on Wimbledon Common. Aldridge (1885) listed it for the Norwood district. Power (1910) had one over his Brixton garden on 10th October 1875 and only four subsequent records for the Dulwich area. In the Staines area, Kestrels had decreased and were not known to have bred for many years (Kerr, 1906).

1900 to 1950. Boorman collected eggs at Hatchlands (1909), Newark Priory (1901) and Ockham Park (1908). A pair nested at Newdigate in 1905 (G. T. Winter). There were three in Richmond Park on 26th February 1905 (Mouritz, 1905) and at least one pair seems to have nested in most of the 1920s and 30s. Kestrels bred in a chalk quarry at Warlingham in 1915. There were a few pairs around Epsom, Haslemere and Limpsfield in 1934. A pair bred at Guildford in 1944 and one was seen over County Hall, Lambeth, in November of the same year. Numbers increased during or after the 1939-45 war. In 1948, a nest was found in Lambeth and six pairs nested in Richmond Park. A nest in Battersea Park at around this time was robbed (*BLA*).

Trends since 1950. A decline associated with toxic chemicals began in about 1953. It bottomed out in about 1964 and was followed by a recovery. A survey of the Surrey part of the London area in 1967 found 52 breeding pairs (Montier, 1968). The first quantitative survey for Surrey as a whole was carried out in the same year by Donald Parr. It showed proven breeding for 58 pairs, with breeding suspected for 32 others. Allowing for coverage, the total Surrey population was estimated at 130-160 pairs, with a remarkable 20 pairs in Richmond Park (Parr, 1969a), where Kestrels bred annually from 1951 to 1976 (and still do), but in smaller numbers. The atlas survey carried out from 1988 to 1997 found Kestrels in about 400 tetrads (414 including Spelthorne). The use of a ten year survey period and the inclusion of birds seen in the breeding season without other breeding evidence make the Atlas more generous than Parr, but suggest a further increase. Breeding Bird Survey information for 1996-2004 grossed up to an average of about 500 birds and also suggests a higher figure. Annual reports of breeding have fluctuated in the range 10 to 30 since 1970. The Common Birds Census shows a decline from 1970 to 2000, probably due to the changing mix of Common Birds Census habitats rather than any trend in the county as a whole.

Where found. There were Kestrels at Vann Lake, in south Surrey, in almost every month from 1964 to 1996 (Blaker Log). Kestrels have often been seen in the most built-up parts of the London area throughout the past 30 years and have bred at sites such as St Thomas's Hospital and the Surrey Docks. A family party including six juveniles was seen at Runfold Sand Pits on 22nd July 1976 (*HSBBR*). Kestrels were reported in the breeding season from 54 sites in 1998 and 51 in 2001. The Croydon RSPB Garden Survey for 2003 showed that, in gardens, Kestrels were less commonly recorded than Sparrowhawks were. In Spelthorne, Kestrels bred at Perry Oaks Sewage Farm and Staines Moor in 1963, at the reservoirs in 1965 and at Shepperton in the 1980s. The BTO Migration Watch for the spring of 2003 produced 16 records for the Spelthorne area.

Nest sites. Kestrels use holes in trees where these are available. In built-up areas, the nest sites include cavities in buildings and other structures such as the sawn-off wing of an aircraft used as a cabin-trainer.

Large counts. Beddington Sewage Farm: held 25+ in October 1970 and 30 in March 1971, attracted by voles and mice. There were 36 on 8th August 1993. Recent counts from Beddington have been lower, probably reflecting habitat changes. There were eight at Queen Mary Reservoir on 10th October 1965.

Food. A Kestrel caught a bat on 15th November 1889 (*Zool.*, *1890:107* in *British Birds* (*BB, 14:136*)). H. F. Witherby saw one carrying a Turtle Dove as prey at Chobham on 9th

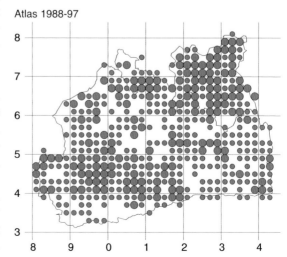

Atlas 1988-97

August 1938 (*BB, 32:125*). In London, Kestrels take feral Rock Doves, mainly young ones (Hewlett). Smaller prey species include Mallard ducklings, Stonechats, House Sparrows, Starlings, Greenfinches, rats (Milford 1975), flying ants and Elephant Hawk Moth caterpillars (Surrey Docks 1971). They have also been known to take Tree Pipits – see Tree Pipit.

Movements and longevity. Nestlings ringed in Surrey have been recovered in Berkshire, Buckinghamshire, Cambridgeshire, Dorset, Essex, Gloucestershire, Hertfordshire (per J. Gates), Humberside, Kent, Lincolnshire and Nottinghamshire. There is one overseas recovery of a young Surrey bird, ringed at Thursley on 15th June 1940 and recovered in Spain (Cortes), some 940 km south, on 14th December of the same year. A nestling ringed in the Netherlands in June 1976 was seen at Dunsfold in the following October. A young bird ringed at Thorpe on 25th June 1975 was recovered over eight years and five months later, at Little Marlow, Berkshire on 5th December 1983.

Red-footed Falcon   *Falco vespertinus*

At least eight birds

Red-footed Falcons breed from Poland east to Siberia and winter in Southern Africa. Most British records are from April to June, most commonly in Shetland and the southeastern coastal counties but with many inland sightings.

Early Surrey history. The earliest Surrey records are not without some ambiguities. Two birds, of the same size but different colours and believed to be a pair, were found by Meyer at Claremont, Esher on a summer evening in 1838 and seen on several subsequent evenings. Their behaviour suggested to Meyer that they might be nesting. He was unable to prove this but, in a further note, adds that a female (which he did not himself see) was caught in a hole in a tree 11 or 12 feet up in the summer of 1840. This bird too, he thought might be nesting (Bucknill). Birds said to have been shot at Compton (dated 7th February in *SALEC*, and the spring of 1871 in Bucknill) and Binscombe (undated) were in the Charterhouse Collection in Bucknill's time but are no longer held there. The February date suggests an error with the Compton bird or its documentation.

Later records:

1890:   Normandy, one was shot around 1890 (Bucknill).

1892:   Nunhead, a female was shot in the summer by a man who, while testing rifles, noticed an unfamiliar bird land on a nearby fence and *happening to have a shot-gun with him, killed it as it rose from its perch* (Bucknill). It has been suggested that this might have been an escaped bird, perhaps from the cages of the collector A. G. Butler, who lived nearby at Penge.

1915:   Witley Park, one shot some years before 1915 (Shaw). No supporting details have been located.

1915:   Haslemere area, a male on 11th July (Shaw) may not have been in Surrey.

1961:   Ockley Common, one on 13th May, watched for 1½ hrs (R. M. Fry, *BB, 55:571*).

1971:   Godstone, a female on 8th and 9th May (M. Pellett, *BB, 65:330*).

1994:   Winterfold, an adult male on 30th May (N. Broomer, *BB, 93:527*).

1997:   Shamley Green, an exhausted first-summer male was found beside the B2128 just south of Shamley Green on 3rd July. It was taken into care at the Hydestile Wildlife Hospital and released at Thursley Common on 30th May 1998. An account is given by Harris (1997a). Possibly the same bird was seen by B. Milton at Unstead Sewage Farm on 12th and 27th June 1998 (*BB, 91:471, 92:569, 93:527*).

Merlin   *Falco columbarius*
Scarce winter visitor

Merlins breed in northern moorland and tundra regions of Europe, Asia and North America, moving south to the Mediterranean, Southeast Asia and Central America in winter. The *Migration Atlas* suggests that those in Surrey are likely to be from northern Britain or Iceland. The 19th century breeding range included most parts of the British Isles away from southern England but was in decline because of persecution. Since then the range seems to have stabilised.

Early Surrey history. Blyth (1836) said that Merlins were common winter visitors to Tooting, with a few shot every season. They were regular in winter in the Godalming district at this time. One in the Charterhouse Museum with Surrey given as its provenance may be the bird shot by Mr Dykes, a gamekeeper, at Compton on 10th May 1870 (*SALEC*), and seen by Bucknill in the collection. Others mentioned by Bucknill were at Weybridge (autumn of 1872), Ashtead Woods (undated), near Guildford (winter of 1880/81), Richmond Park (late autumn of 1892) and Normandy (about 1893). The Normandy bird was also in the Charterhouse Collection and so might be the bird currently held at Charterhouse. Power mentioned one flying west over his Brixton garden on 4th January 1899, 'sufficiently near to be plainly identified'. This is a confident statement and the date is good, but, in more recent years, garden sightings have been difficult to prove.

1900 to 1970. Merlins were seen from time to time in the early 20th century, for example at Caterham in September 1912 and March 1913, Frensham in November 1910 and 1911 and Titsey Park in November 1910. Merlins were recorded in 15 of the years 1910-1956 in the Walton-on-the-Hill/Tadworth/Banstead/Caterham area (*BLA*).

Nearly all Merlins up to 1969 were in the October to March period. Sites included Banstead Downs (1948), Beddington Sewage Farm (1956, 1962), Charterhouse (1947, SEBR), Churt (1936), Coulsdon Common (1956), East Molesey (1968), Epsom Sewage Farm (1950-51), Frensham (1934, 1936-37, 1954), Godalming (Charterhouse 1944 and 1947), Hankley (1967), Herne Hill (1956), Lonsdale Road Reservoir (1952), Marden Park (about 1937), Milford (1957), Oxshott (1954), Peckham (1966), Richmond Old Deer Park (1942), Tadworth (1930, over a garden in 1947), Thursley/Ockley Commons (1936, 1951, 1957, 1961, 1964, 1968), Walton Heath (1945), Walton Reservoirs (1936) and Wandsworth (1967), but Merlins remained very infrequent visitors until about 1967. There were Merlins in Spelthorne on 23rd March 1946, in November and December 1953 and in March 1958, 1959 and 1969.

Merlin sightings from April to September included Addington (September 1967), Beddington Sewage Farm (April 1954), Epsom Sewage Farm (September 1952), Guildford Sewage Farm (August 1954), Ockley Common on 15th September 1957 (Clark, 1984), Oxshott (1955), Richmond Park (1950), Streatham Common (1956) and Tadworth (27th August 1930, 6th May 1954). One at Staines Reservoirs on 15th April 1938 is the first that has been located for Spelthorne. There were others from King George VI Reservoir (21st August 1949), Perry Oaks Sewage Farm (8th April 1954, 25th August 1956), Staines Moor (30th August 1954) and Staines Reservoirs (22nd April 1956, August 1959).

Where found, 1970 onward. There are no breeding records from Surrey but Merlins now come as winter visitors in most years. They are mainly found on the western heaths and they also hunt over farmland and other areas where they can find the small birds, such as Meadow Pipits, that they prey on. Over half of the bird months from 1970 to 2000 were at Thursley/Ockley Commons (107) and the larger but less accessible Pirbright group of commons (52). The only other sites with more than four bird months were Frensham/Tilhill (twelve), Milford/Tuesley (ten), Beddington Sewage Farm (nine), South Norwood Country Park (seven), Unstead Sewage Farm (five) and West End/Bisley (five).

The remaining records came from Badshot Lea, Baynards, Box Hill, Bricksbury Hill, Buckland, Busbridge, Capel, Chelsham, Chiddingfold, Chobham (two), Clandon Downs, Crooksbury, Dunsfold,

East Clandon, East Horsley, Effingham, Elstead (four), Enton, Epsom Common, Farnham Park, Frimley Gravel Pits, Hankley, Highcombe Bottom, the Hog's back, Hurtmore, Island Barn Reservoir, Kew, Olddean Common, Papercourt, Queen Elizabeth II Reservoir, Ripley Sewage Farm, Shackleford, Stoke Water Meadows, Tadworth, Thursley, Tongham, Vann Lake, Walton Heath, Walton Reservoirs (two), Wimbledon Common, Witley Park, Worplesdon (two) and Wrecclesham. Spelthorne records came from Queen Mary Reservoir in 1976, 1979 and 1985 and (per H. W. Evans) Staines Reservoirs on 9th November 1988. There were no doubt others. Like other raptors, Merlins are sometimes mobbed by crows. Merlins have rarely, if ever, been seen in or over gardens, even rural ones.

The most recent records have come from Barn Elms (2004, 2005), Beddington (2001, 2002, 2006), Chelsham (2003), Elstead (2001), Fetcham (2002), Island Barn Reservoir (2002), Milford (2001, 2002), Nore Hill (2003), Pirbright Common (2001, 2002), Queen Elizabeth II Reservoir (2001), Royal Common (2002), Stoke Lake (2001), Thursley (2001, 2002, 2003), Walton Reservoirs, (2001), Wanborough (2003) and Worplesdon (2001, 2002). Merlins remain uncommon migrants in Spelthorne, but there was one at Staines Reservoirs on 10th October 2003.

Calendar. The 290 vice-county bird months recorded from 1970 to 2004 show an almost level peak from October to December, with a fall in the colder months of January and February and none in June or July. The latest spring bird was on 22nd May 1996 at Thursley/Ockley Commons and the earliest of autumn was on 15th August 1996 at Thursley Common.

Bird months 1970-2004

	Jan	Feb	Mar	Apr	May	Jun	Jul	Aug	Sep	Oct	Nov	Dec	Total
Vice-county	44	32	31	7	4	0	0	3	11	58	52	48	**290**

Food. Prey items are rarely noticed by observers. Meadow Pipits certainly feature. Dartford Warblers are often numerous on their sites but they rarely break cover and may be less at risk.

Hobby (Eurasian Hobby) *Falco subbuteo*
Uncommon summer visitor, breeding annually

Breeds in most parts of Europe and Asia and in North Africa. European birds winter in southern Africa. Others winter in northern India. In the late 19th century Hobbys bred in many counties of southern Britain and occasionally in Scotland. Since then the British range has extended. Breeding numbers are thought to have at least doubled on farmland since the 1970s (Shrubb) but may currently be falling (*BTO News 266*). Very few British-ringed Hobbys have been recovered abroad and recoveries of foreign-ringed birds are rare (*MA*).

Early Surrey history. Hobbys probably bred in the early 19th century but became scarcer as the century progressed. At Tooting there were usually two or three in late summer but they did not nest (Blyth, 1836). They were said to be breeding in the Godalming district by 1849 (Newman), though without further details. Bucknill knew of specimens from Godalming (*SALEC*, 1842), Binscombe and Compton (two, spring of 1874) in the Charterhouse Collection but none are now held there. Other Bucknill records are of birds at Clapham (July 1851), East Molesey (16th July 1873), near Wimbledon (late August, about 1874), Weybridge (17th June 1878), Thursley (not later than 1880 in Bucknill, 1902), on the Thames at Kew (25th May 1890), Epsom (12th August 1891), Cheam (autumn of 1892), near Epsom (5th August 1892), Betchworth (about 1894), Caterham (about 1897), Ashtead (August 1898) and Epsom (12th August 1901 in Bucknill, 1902).

Breeding. The first documented breeding records, (apparently overlooked in the *Historical Atlas*), were at Normandy Farm, near Wanborough in 1879, when the nest and young were taken, and in 1880, when young were safely reared (Bucknill, 1902). A family party was seen at Ockley Common in 1907 and at least four pairs bred on nearby commons in 1914. Hobbys were well established by 1920, though Bunyard thought that numbers had been cut back by a shortage of crows' nests when the shooting of Carrion Crows resumed after the war.

In 1935, Hobbys were said to be *much harried by gamekeepers, except on commons and Government areas*, breeding most successfully on the heaths (*SEBR*). Further information for this period is rather sparse but the birds seem to have been scarce. Egg collection, for which the Hobby was a target species, may have held back numbers, at least until more recent years. Gosnell, for example, took a clutch of three from Ockley Common in June 1936, Douglas had two Surrey clutches (Cole and Trobe), taken some time before his companion Alfred Pearman's death in 1957. Meares collected from pairs at Ash Ranges (with Meeson in 1937 and on the final occasion in June 1948), Bisley, Pirbright and Wentworth. A pair nested in the Wisley/Esher area in 1937 and 1938. Hobbys bred in the HNHS area (not necessarily in Surrey) up to 1939 (HNHS, 1955). The *SEBR* for 1941 reported two nesting pairs on a west Surrey heath in 1940 and one in 1941, at a time when access to other commons was probably restricted. In 1946, pairs nested at one site in the Surrey part of the London Natural History Society area and probably at another 17 miles away (*LBR*). Two pairs nested there in 1948 (*BLA*). The next breeding record in the Surrey part of the London area was not until 1959. None bred again in the HNHS area until 1951, when a single pair bred, possibly not in Surrey. Two pairs bred in Surrey in 1956 and several in 1957, including one in the Thursley area. Two pairs were known to have bred in 1963. Numbers increased in the 1960s. There were twelve pairs in 1962-64 (*BB, 60:43* Parslow, 1967), and nine or ten in 1969 (*SBR*). Persecution and egg collecting continued. Of three nests on Ash Ranges in 1970, the eggs disappeared from one, and the young from a second. At the third, one of the parents was shot. There was a further increase to an estimated 27 territories in the hot summer of 1976 but numbers then fell back. As late as 1978 Hobbys did not breed in east Surrey (*SBR*) and they were infrequent visitors to Richmond Park (*BRP*). At this time also, Hobbys did not breed every year in the Haslemere district where they had declined since the first decades of the century (HNHS, 1980). The number of territories was almost

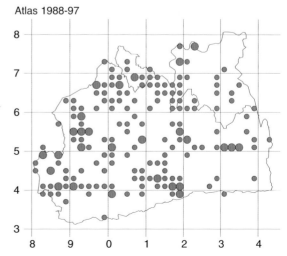

Atlas 1988-97

back to its 1976 level by 1988 and there was a surge in the 1990s, peaking at 47 in 1998 but with only 32 in 2001. By the end of the period, breeding Hobbys were thinly spread over most of the rural areas of the county and in the larger parks and open spaces in the suburbs. It is possible that a full census would show a considerably larger population than this account suggests, but no territories were found in Common Birds Censuses and the Breeding Birds Survey for 1994 to 2004 grosses up to a total of only 64 adults.

Nest sites. The typical nest site, in west Surrey at least, is a disused crow's nest in a Scots Pine. Trees in which nests have been found include the Ash *Fraxinus excelsior*, Corsican Pine *Pinus nigra laricio* Oak *Quercus sp.* and *Wellingtonia*.

Calendar. The chart suggests a connection between Hobby arrival dates and average temperatures, getting earlier in the recent warmer decades. Extreme arrival and departure dates are:

Arrival

21st March 2000	Barn Elms (J. P. P. Wilczur)
1st April 1990	Lightwater
1st April 2001	Beddington Sewage Farm
3rd November 1982	Northwest Surrey

Departure

11th November 1996	Chertsey Meads
12th November 1911	North Downs near Oxted (*BTO Guide 15*)

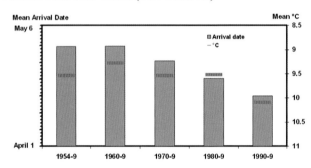

Feeding. Hobbys often hunt at wetland sites such as Beddington Sewage Farm and the Spelthorne and Walton-on-Thames reservoirs even if they do not breed there. In 2001, four were reported from Beddington Sewage Farm and Barn Elms WWT. Six were seen feeding on large flying beetles (Summer Chafers?) near Reigate in July. On the western heaths, Hobbys catch dragonflies, sometimes a hundred feet or more in the air but more often when skimming low over boggy ground. They are fast enough to catch Swifts (Beddington 1968, Guildford 1973, Queen Elizabeth II Reservoir 2004, Shepperton 1999). Other prey caught includes Sand Martins, Swallows, and House Martins. Hobbys have been reported with Black-headed Gulls catching flying ants and they follow migrating parties of hirundines across the county in autumn. Spelthorne had become a regular feeding area for Hobbys breeding at nearby sites by the 1980s.

Movements and longevity. Recoveries of ringed birds show only one foreign recovery, from Belgium, and none from winter quarters. Two birds have a proven age of over ten years.

Ringed	Age		Recovered		Distance
Northwest Surrey	Young	27th July 1978	Kent	11th July 1982	
Frimley*	Young	22nd August 1983	Merrist Wood	6th August 1995	8 km
Woking	Young	7th July 1987	Belgium	2nd August 1988	357 km

*11 years, 11 months and 15 days – the national longevity record.

Gyrfalcon (Gyr Falcon)   *Falco rusticolus*

Two birds, one in Outer Surrey and the other in Spelthorne

Breeds in arctic and sub-arctic zones of northern Europe and Canada, moving south in winter. British records are spread fairly evenly throughout the year outside the breeding season, peaking in March. Gyrfalcons have mostly been in the north but a few have been in southeast England. They are generally of the white *candicans* phase which predominates in Greenland and the Canadian Arctic and is found less frequently in other populations.

Surrey. One of unpublished phase was seen by T. A. Guyatt, J. E. Hunt, J. A. Lucas and others at Queen Mary Reservoir on 6th March 1971 (*BB, 65:330*). A light phase bird was found by S. Greenwood on Rushett Farm, at Chessington on 14th March 1972. It stayed until the 19th (*BB, 66:339*).

Peregrine (Peregrine Falcon)   *Falco peregrinus*

Scarce breeding resident and migrant.

Breeds on every continent except the Antarctic. Northern birds move south in winter. Those breeding in the British Isles are mainly resident. In the last quarter of the 19th century, Peregrines bred throughout Wales, northern England and Scotland and in coastal counties of southern Britain, and had not been reduced by persecution to the same degree as other raptors. They were hit badly by pesticides in the 1960s but since then have made a remarkable recovery, extending their range to areas where they had not bred for many years, if ever. They have moved into inland and urban areas and used pylons, viaducts and other man-made structures in a number of countries across the world, including Britain.

Early Surrey history. Peregrine remains found at Bermondsey Abbey, Southwark, were dated at 1480-1600. The bird seems more likely to have been a falconer's bird than a wild one. There is no evidence that, up to 1999, Peregrines had ever bred in Surrey, even in the distant past.

19th century. Newman (1849) mentioned one shot at Hindhead on an unstated date and taken to Waring Kidd, a record first published in 1837 (Bucknill). One that had been caught in a rabbit trap at Puttenham in 1835 (*SALEC*) used to be in the Charterhouse Collection (Bucknill). Other records in Bucknill come from Munstead Heath (*SALEC*, spring of 1849), near Munstead Heath (about the same time), near East Molesey (26th April 1876), near Leigh (October 1876), Thursley (before 1880), Merrow Downs (spring of 1880), near Wimbledon (about 1890) and near Mickleham (one caught in Starling nets, September 1898).

20th century. The first 20th century records were of single birds at Marden Park (Pounds) in 1917, Richmond Park (Collenette) in 1917 and 1919 and Peper Harow in the spring of 1920 (Shaw). Peregrines remained less than annual visitors to Surrey until the early 1990s and there were no records at all during the periods 1968-72 and 1977-87. There were over 60 bird months from 1917 to 1992. They were spread over all months of the year but were least frequent from May to September. They came from across the county. The sites were: Addlestone, Barn Elms (two), Battersea Park, Beddington, Betchworth, Bisley, Chiddingfold, Chipstead, Earlswood, Epsom (three), Fairchildes Park, Farnham, Freelands Wood, Frensham, Guildford (three), Hankley, the Hog's Back (two), Hydon Heath, Island Barn Reservoir, Kew, Lambeth, Limpsfield, Lonsdale Road Reservoir, Mickleham, Newark Priory, Ockley, Oxted (two), Papercourt/Send (four), Peper Harow, Ranmore, Richmond Park (five), Salfords, Southbank (two), Tandridge, Thorpe, Thursley (three), west Surrey (four), West Horsley, Weybridge and Woldingham.

Where recently found. The last decade of the 20th century saw a rapid increase, with 129 bird months from 1993-2000. There were 42 from sites along the Thames between Bankside Power Station and Barn Elms and there were 28 from Beddington Sewage Farm. The remainder were from Capel, Chertsey Meads, Chiddingfold, Croydon, the Devil's Punch Bowl, Dulwich, Elstead (four), Enton, Farnham, Frensham, Guildford (five), Haslemere, Hersham (two), Holmethorpe (four), Island Barn

Reservoir, Limpsfield Chart, Littleworth Cross, Morden Hall Park, Queen Elizabeth II Reservoir (two), South Norwood, Sutton, Thursley/Ockley Commons (eleven), Tuesley, Unstead (two), Walton Reservoirs, West Horsley and Worplesdon. In Spelthorne, there was one at Staines Reservoirs on 16th April 1936. Later in the year, Glegg saw a Peregrine at Queen Mary Reservoir on 6th and 18th May. He found a family party of four perched on posts at the same site on 8th July 1937. Further records were infrequent for many years, but in the 1980s Peregrines became more frequent as autumn migrants. In Spelthorne, there were also a fair number of records outside the breeding season from the 1990s and later. New sites since 2000 include Artington, Broadstreet Common, Chelsham, Chessington, Enton, Farnham, Limpsfield Chart, Holmethorpe, Nonsuch Park, Normandy, and Tice's Meadow.

Breeding. In Spelthorne, display was seen in February and August 2000. The presence of apparently territorial birds on old buildings by the Thames, including Bankside and Battersea Power Stations, suggested coming colonisation. Available food along the river and in London streets includes Gulls, Terns and feral Rock Doves. Expectations were rewarded when, after a report of breeding in 2000 about which no primary information is held, a pair raised two or three young at Battersea Power Station in 2001. The event was reported, with a photograph, in London's *Evening Standard* on 1st June, an indication of its wider interest. They bred there again in 2002, raising three young but not in 2004, when contractors blocked off their usual nest site and a more exposed nest failed (*LNHSB*). They bred there again in 2006 (*The Times*, 26th August 2006). The adoption by wintering Peregrines of a nest box installed on the tower of Guildford Cathedral in 2001 suggested further scope for colonisation but it happened elsewhere.

Peregrines fledged young at a North Downs chalk quarry in 2004 and 2005, the first records for the Administrative County. Photographs have appeared on a Surrey Wildlife Trust website. Territorial birds had been seen in Croydon by 2005 and, per Richard A. Denyer, eggs were laid in a tower block nest at Woking in May 2006.

Food. Prey remains found at Guildford Cathedral have included Teal, Golden Plover, Lapwing, Woodcock and Black-headed Gull. Richard A. Denyer checked a tower block roost site in Woking in the spring of 2006 and found the remains of Teal, Little Grebe, Jack Snipe, Snipe, Fieldfare, five Lapwings, seven Woodcock, and about 30 feral Rock Doves. The way in which these rather choice birds were caught is a matter for speculation. Some, like the Lapwings, Black-headed Gulls and doves would have been caught in the air, but who has seen a Little Grebe or Jack Snipe flying at any great altitude for any distance? The thought remains, though, that the sharp-eyed Peregrines may have seen and caught both of them, along with the Woodcock and the others, while they were flying across in local movements or migration. More likely for the Woodcock, perhaps, is that the Peregrine hunted down roding birds at dawn or dusk.

Calendar. While most Peregrines have been seen in autumn and winter, spring and summer have also been well represented.

Birds months 1900-2000

	Jan	Feb	Mar	Apr	May	Jun	Jul	Aug	Sep	Oct	Nov	Dec	Total
Vice-county	28	19	22	17	10	6	14	17	28	23	23	31	**238**
Spelthorne	7	7	7	2	2	0	4	10	10	8	7	8	**72**

Movements. The *Migration Atlas* says that Peregrines wintering in southern England, including Surrey, may be mostly of continental, rather than British origin. For Surrey, there is no ringing evidence to illustrate this. More recently, some of the wintering birds have probably bred locally, along with others breeding elsewhere in southeast England.

Water Rail
Scarce winter visitor and breeding resident

Rallus aquaticus

Breeds from the British Isles east to China and Japan and south to Morocco, with some birds moving as far south as Morocco in winter. Water Rails breeding in Britain are largely resident but some continental birds winter in Britain (*MA*). They are absent from much of Scotland. Land drainage during the 19th century would have caused local declines but Water Rails were, even so, widely distributed and common in some counties. Pressure on the habitat continued through the 20th century and the *New Atlas* showed a population reduction from 1970 to 1990.

Early Surrey history. Kidd (1843) wrote that Water Rails had nested at Ockford Pond, Godalming on one occasion. Newman (1849) said they had been seen locally on the Wey near Catteshall and elsewhere. Smither took clutches from Frensham in 1866 and 1867 (Bucknill, 1901). A young bird was seen on the Wey near Stoke in the summer of 1881 (Bucknill, 1902). Other writers of the period mentioned Water Rails at Abinger, Bletchingley, Esher, Gatton, Hampton Lodge/Cutt Mill, Pudmore, near Sutton, Virginia Water and Wimbledon and along the Mole and the Thames (Bucknill).

20th century. After 1900 they were recorded occasionally in the Haslemere district at Cutt Mill, the Devil's Punch Bowl and Pudmore. Other regular sites in the first half of the 20th century were Barn Elms, Beddington Sewage Farm, Elmers End Sewage Farm, Fetcham Mill Pond, Godstone, Mitcham Gravel Pit (*BLA*) and Richmond Park and they were also seen at Lingfield (1939) and the Rookery (Dorking, 1939).

Kerr (1906) said that Water Rails were rarely seen in the Staines area but that men cleaning out osier (willow) beds along the river banks often brought him eggs. Later published records for the district have been infrequent. One or two were reported at Shepperton and elsewhere in Spelthorne in most years from 1970 but no information about breeding has been located.

Breeding since 1939. A nest with nine eggs was found at Frensham Little Pond in 1939, before the pond was drained. Water Rails were present at Frensham again from 1952. This is the most consistent site for Water Rails, where

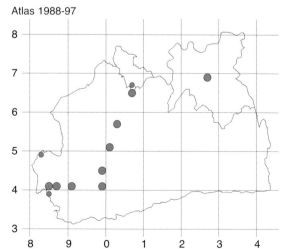

Atlas 1988-97

they are now present all year, with several breeding pairs and winter numbers of up to 8 (1977). Water Rails bred at Beddington in 1955. Two pairs at Unstead in 1955 probably bred and juveniles were seen there in 1956. Juveniles were seen at Guildford Sewage Farm in 1957 and Ockham Common in 1959 (Parr). Later breeding records came from Barn Elms (2001-2005), Chiddingfold (1976), Forked Pond (1993, *HSBBR*), Frensham Little Pond (1980 (*HSBBR*), 1982, 1985-87, 1989-98), Hedgecourt (2000), Morden Hall Park (nest abandoned 2000), Papercourt Gravel Pits (1994, 2002), Richmond Park (1975, 1989), Stoke Water Meadows (1986, 1994, 1996-2000, 2002), Thursley (1974), Unstead Sewage Farm (1996-2000). A territory found in 1972 at Frimley Gravel Pits is the only Common Birds Census record.

Where else found. Water Rails have been found at many other sites and have probably bred at some of them. Sites since 1970 include Addlestone, Apps Court Gravel Pit, Ash Vale, Badshot Lea, Battersea Park, Beddington Sewage Farm, Berrylands, Black Pond (Esher), the Blackwater Valley, Bletchingley, Blindley Heath, Bramley Sewage Farm, Broadstreet Common (1971), Broadwater Lake, Brooklands, Buckland, Capel, Charlwood, Chertsey Meads, Deepcut, Earlswood Sewage Farm, Effingham, Enton, Epsom Common, Esher, Ewell Court, Farnham Park, Fetcham Mill Pond and River Mole, Frimley Gravel Pits, Gatton Park, Godstone (Bay Pond), Hackbridge, Hamm Moor, Hammer Pond, Hersham, Holmethorpe/Merstham, Horley Sewage Farm, Horton Country Park, Hurst Green, Island Barn Reservoir, Kew Gardens, Kingston, Leatherhead, Lingfield, Lonsdale Road Reservoir, Lyne Sewage Farm, Mitcham, Moat Pond, Molesey Gravel Pit and Heath, Moorhouse, New Lines Pond [Lyne?], Old Woking Sewage Farm, Pitch Place (Thursley, *HSBBR*), Putney, Pyrford, Reigate Priory, Ripley Sewage Farm, the River Ember, the River Mole at Island Barn Reservoir, Send, Shalford, South Holmwood, South Norwood Country Park, Stoke D'Abernon, the Surrey Docks, Thorpe, Thursley/Ockley Commons,Tolworth, Tongham Gravel Pit, Vann Lake, Waddon Ponds, Walton Reservoirs, Waterloo Pond (Chilworth), Weybridge, Winkworth, Wire Mill and Worplesdon.

Large counts. An exceptional number of Water Rails were at Fetcham Mill Pond and cress beds in 1959, when up to eight were easily seen at close range The restructuring of Barn Elms has created large reedbeds. Water Rails have bred in them and 52 were counted there, using a tape lure, on 15th December 2001. Only 12 were found by normal counting methods in the previous month, showing how elusive these birds can be.

Movements and longevity. There is one foreign ringing recovery, of a Water Rail ringed at Leatherhead in February 1959 and found dead at the Lower Rhine, France, 629 km away, in March 1960. One ringed at Stoke, Guildford, on 16th January 2002 was recovered at the same site over three years and one month later, on 10th March 2005.

Behaviour. One at Frensham Little Pond on 21st October 1979 was flushed from reeds and flew to a willow bush, where it fed on insects and caught a fly in mid-air (*HSBBR*).

Spotted Crake   *Porzana porzana*
At least 23 vice-county records 1900-2006 and a few earlier

The core breeding range lies in central Europe east to central Siberia, with a more scattered range west to Spain, France and the British Isles, wintering in Africa, India and parts of Europe. Land drainage would have reduced Spotted Crake numbers in Britain from at least 1700 but they seem to have been fairly common up to the mid 19th century. They were thought to have bred, at least occasionally, in most English counties up to about 1860 but evidence has always been hard to collect. Numbers continued to fall during the 20th century, with a small rally in the 1990s. No British ringing recoveries involve other countries.

Early Surrey history. Spotted Crakes were said to be occasional visitors to the Chertsey district (Meyer, 1842) and Godalming district (Newman, 1849, *SALEC*). Two that were said to have been shot at Laleham by W. K. Heseltine in 1857 passed into the collection of a Mr Minasi (Harting, 1866). Glegg said that these were taken on the south side of the Thames and not in Spelthorne, as implied by Harting. One was killed by a telegraph wire at Thames Ditton in the spring of 1871, one was shot at East Molesey on 10th May of the same year, one was shot on Reigate Heath in about 1887 and there is an undated reference to one on the Mole (Bucknill).

Subsequent records, providing some 45 bird months, are:

1906:   Brook, one on 1st May, also seen subsequently (G. Dalgliesh in Mouritz, 1907). Witley Park, one on 1st May (Shaw) may have been the same.

1930:   near Witley Farm, a pair from April to July, on a marsh.

1944:   Frensham Great Pond, one on 31st December (L. S. V. Venables),

1955:   Epsom Sewage Farm, one on 11th December, described in the *LBR*. The *SBR* includes December 5th.

1959:   Guildford Sewage Farm, one on 5th August and dates to 11th September. Fetcham Mill Pond, one on 3rd October, remains found there on 7th November.

1963:   Beddington Sewage Farm, one calling in July.

1964:   Beddington Sewage Farm, at least four from June to 1st August. May have bred.

1965:   Beddington Sewage Farm, may have bred.

1971:   Frensham Great Pond, one on both sides of the county boundary through the swamp near the sailing Club from 18th September to 7th October was seen almost daily.

1974:   Stoke Water Meadows, Guildford, one on 20th April.

1975:   Papercourt Gravel Pits, one from 18th August to 16th September.

1978:   Frensham Great Pond, one from 27th November to 5th December.

1980:   Beddington Sewage Farm, one from 12th November to 9th December.

1981:   Beddington Sewage Farm, one on dates from 15th August to 3rd October.

1982:   Waterloo Bridge, one found in a car park on 29th September had an injured claw.

1985:   Buckland Sand Pits, one on 2nd-5th September.

1990:   near Dorking Sewage Farm, a dead one was brought into a house by a cat on 15th September.

1996:   Beddington Sewage Farm, a juvenile on 21th-27th September.

1999:   Barn Elms, an adult on 10th-17th October.

1999:   Unstead Sewage Farm, an adult from 31st October to 1st November.

2004:   Beddington Sewage Farm, one on 22nd-30th October.

2006:   Beddington Sewage Farm, one on 12th August (photographed).

Breeding. The only nest known to Bucknill dated back to about 1810, at Rolls Meadows, near what is now the Old Kent Road. They might have bred occasionally since, but evidence is lacking. The *Historical Atlas* shows them as probable breeders, unconfirmed, for the last quarter of the 19th century.

Spotted Crakes occur in Surrey on migration from time to time and, in 1964 and 1965, they may have attempted to breed at Beddington Sewage Farm, where several calling birds were present. Published references to this as a breeding colony go somewhat beyond the information available to the Surrey Bird Club, though it seems likely (Gooders, *Birds that came back*, Simms, *Birds of Town and Suburb*, SBR for 1985 p.48). None were found in the 1999 Spotted Crake National Survey (Gilbert, 2000).

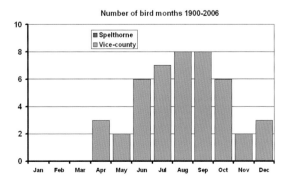

Number of bird months 1900-2006

Little Crake
Porzana parva

Up to three birds

Little Crakes breed from the Netherlands and Germany through southern Europe to Kazakhstan and Iran and winter south to Kenya. British records are mostly outside the breeding season, with a peak in March. Nearly all are in southern England.

Surrey. The birds are:

1812: On the bank of the Thames near Chelsea, one shot in May, in or around 1812 (Yarrell, 1845) may not have been in Surrey.

1860: Bramley, one shot at a farm in 1860 by Jeffrey, the Guildford gunmaker (*SALEC*). It was in the Charterhouse Museum in 2001.

1910: Haslemere, one on a pond on 17th September (Shaw). The date is consistent with autumn migration but the bird was not definitely in Surrey and is not listed by Evans or Naylor. Best ignored in the absence of further detail.

Little/Baillon's Crake
Porzana parva/pusilla

Two vice-county birds, not specifically identified

Surrey. One seen at Beddington Sewage Farm on 13th November 1955 is described in the *LBR* for 1955. The bird was flushed from an overgrown dyke. The other was seen at Frensham Great Pond on 17th February 1973 and at least four dates up to 11th March.

Baillon's Crake
Porzana pusilla

Two vice-county birds

A more southern breeding range than Little Crakes, with a breeding distribution running from the Iberian Peninsula east to Japan and south to Africa and Australasia. Possibly common in the boggier parts of Britain 4,500 years ago (Thomas, 1999). They are now scarcer than the Little Crakes but used to be much commoner and they occasionally bred in the 19th century, at least three nests having been found. Breeding has not been proved since 1889. Northern birds move south to Africa, India and points east in winter.

Surrey. One that was 'taken' at a spring off Church Street, Godalming in 1837 by a leather dresser named Rainbow (*SALEC*) is in the Charterhouse Collection. An adult female was caught in a meadow between Mitcham and Carshalton at about the end of May 1874 (*The Field* 30th May 1874:515, *BB*, 2:146). Naylor has this record in twice, as 1847 and 1874, *British Birds*, apparently wrongly, gives the year as 1847. Neither record is in Saunders.

Corncrake
Crex crex

Once a common summer visitor, now rare, no longer breeds

The breeding range runs from the British Isles east to Siberia. Birds winter in eastern countries of Africa. A Scottish-ringed bird was recovered in the Congo Basin. Corncrake bred throughout most of the British Isles until about 1880 but since then the population has crashed. They adapted to commonland enclosures and cultivation but could not cope with mechanical haymaking. By 1970 Corncrakes had disappeared from most of lowland Britain and the *New Atlas* showed a further substantial decline to 1990.

Early Surrey history. Corncrakes appear to have been common in rural Surrey up to the latter part of the 19th century, being for example often heard in fields around Norwood (Aldridge, 1886) and heard regularly at Tooting in 1880. They were in a wheatfield at Haslemere in 1887 (HNHS 1980) and a summer resident on Streatham Common in 1890. A nest with eight eggs was found in a hay meadow at Bugg Hill Farm, Woldingham in 1894. Young were seen later. Some were shot at Warren Barn Farm, Warlingham in 1895. Bucknill said they were very plentiful in the summer of 1896, five brace being shot in several places early in September. Corncrakes were well established around Staines in 1906, though numbers varied considerably from year to year (Kerr).

The finish of breeding. A decrease had begun in the 1890s, largely accounted for by the introduction of mechanical harvesting. Corncrakes had been at risk even before its introduction - Jordan (1895) described how a hen would sit tight, and young ones might get cut in two by the scythe - but whole nests of youngsters were destroyed at Chelsham from 1892 to 1895, after the introduction of mowing machines. Beadell wrote of young ones cut to pieces in a field at Woldingham in 1895. Two nests were mown out on Tillingdown, Caterham in 1913 or 1914. A national inquiry showed that over the previous ten years there had been occasional breeding pairs in Surrey but none at the same place in successive years (Alexander, 1914).

Corncrakes held on for a while. Nests had been found at Hambledon in 1901 and Dorking in 1907. Corncrakes bred at Caterham in 1911 and 1912 and at Beddington Sewage Farm in 1918. They did best on parts of the North Downs, breeding for example at Limpsfield up to at least 1928 and on Epsom Downs up to 1934. A new problem was now emerging. The tendency to mow hay earlier in 1938 than 50 years previously was thought to be a factor in the decline (Norris, 1947). Corncrakes had disappeared from the Leatherhead district by around 1939. A nest with two eggs in the Wey Valley below Farncombe on 14th June 1946 (SEBR) was robbed, but the adults were seen again. There was no further breeding in Surrey.

Where else found. Other sites and dates where Corncrakes have been found include Addington (1905, 1945), Banstead (1938), Beddington Sewage Farm (1952, 1964), Carshalton (1949, dead in a garden), near Caterham (1905, 1913), Chelsham (1948), Chessington (1958, 1980), The Devil's Jumps (1951), Ditton Hill (1954, in a garden), Dulwich (1901 and 1905), Elmers End (1935), near Felbridge (1910), near Gatton Park (1901-03), near Godstone (1913), Guildford (1902, three injured by telephone wires), Headley (1948), Hersham Sewage Farm (1958), Lambeth (1967), Leigh Mill (1918), Ockley (1966), Ockley Common (1954), Outwood (1913), Oxshott (1947), Oxted (1906, 1914), Prince's Coverts (1958), Redhill (1901-03), Richmond Park (1912), near Sanderstead (1945, 1946), Tandridge (1909), Thursley Common (1955, 1990), Upper Caterham (1910), Waddon (1907, 1912), Warlingham (1926), Witley Park (1946), and Woldingham (1913). In Spelthorne, one was flushed from long grass three times near Staines Reservoirs on 29th January 1950. There were single birds at Perry Oaks Sewage Farm on 3rd August and 3rd October 1953.

One with an injured wing was found in Shamley Green on 4th September 2004. It was taken into care but died after about three hours. A photograph was taken by D. M. Harris.

Calendar. There are no dated records for February, March or November. Extreme dates and three old winter records are:

Early

15th April 1954	Ditton Hill

Late

early October 1980	Chessington Farm

Winter

mid December 1834	near Tooting, one shot, (*Loudons Magazine of Natural History* vol.viii p.512 in Bucknill)
27th January 1914	Oxted, one shot
29th January 1950	Staines

Moorhen (Common Moorhen)

Common breeding resident

Gallinula chloropus

The breeding range extends to most parts of the world away from the Arctic, Antarctic and Australian continents. Northern birds disperse or migrate in winter, though little information seems to be available about their movements. Apart from a contraction of range in Scotland, and set-backs following severe winters, the British population was more or less stable throughout the 19th century and up to the 1960s but has since declined in farmland. Most British Moorhens are resident but there is ringing evidence for winter immigration, mainly from Denmark and the Netherlands (*MA*).

Early Surrey history. Newman (1849) included Moorhens as breeding residents in the Godalming district without further comment and they were common throughout the vice-county until the end of the 19th century and beyond. Aldridge (1885) noted them breeding at Crystal Palace. They were breeding in Battersea Park prior to 1898 (Hudson) and in Dulwich Park, Kew Gardens and Tooting Bec Common by 1900 (*BLA*).

Since 1900. Boorman collected eggs at Send in 1902 and at East Clandon in 1907. Moorhens were very common along the river banks in the Staines area (Kerr, 1906). They were breeding on Wimbledon Common in 1925 although not again there until at least the 1950s. There were three or four pairs in Richmond Park in the 1930s. Kew Gardens held 16 breeding pairs in 1952. Eight pairs bred at Hersham Sewage Farm in 1963. In Inner London, up to three pairs have bred at the Surrey Docks in most years since the 1970s. Seven pairs bred there in 1999. Moorhens remain common birds in the Spelthorne district. The 2002 and 2003 BTO Migration Watch information show counts of up to 20.

Other selected territory counts since 1965

Ash Vale Gravel Pits: 10+ pairs, 1965

Barn Elms: 50 broods in 2002, 24 broods in 2005

Battersea Park: six pairs bred, 1989

Beddington Sewage Farm: 38 pairs, 1994, 48 territories in 2000 and 42 in 2003

Buckland Sand Pits: 16 pairs, 1988

Capel: 18 pairs, 1993

Cobham: 19 pairs on 2.6 km of the River Mole, 1979

Frensham Little Pond: eight broods totalling 19 young in 1993, 13 pairs bred in 1997

Hersham Sewage Farm: eight or nine pairs bred, 1964

Holmethorpe: eight pairs, 1995-96

Lonsdale Road Reservoir: five pairs and seven broods, 1987

Painshill Park: five pairs, 1965

River Wandle between Morden Hall Park and Butterhill: 56 territories, 1997

Southwark Park: three broods, 1976

Unstead Sewage Farm: 20 pairs bred, 2000

Watermeads, Mitcham: eight pairs, 1990

Wimbledon Common: 12 pairs, 1999

Spelthorne

Perry Oaks Sewage Farm: five pairs bred, 1996

Shepperton: around four pairs in the 1980s (*Shepperton Bird Reports* 1983-85)

Nest sites. Newman wrote of Moorhens nesting some 20 feet up a Spruce tree on an island in Old Pond, about a mile from Godalming (*Magazine of Natural History* Volume 5 in Yarrell, *Zool.*, *1845:879*). Gurney (1854) reported a nest in a fir tree, a few feet above the water, at Carshalton. Two of the young were carried down from the nest in the feet of an adult on 8th June. Kerr (1906) described nests placed 15 to 20 feet up in the crowns of willows near Staines. A nest built against wire netting in Battersea Park in 1896 was nearly three feet high and shaded with four Peacock feathers (Hudson, 1898). One pair nested eight feet up a pine tree at Wisley RHS Gardens in 1985. A nest found at Felix Lane Gravel Pit in May 1986 was 16 feet above the ground (*Shepperton Bird Report*).

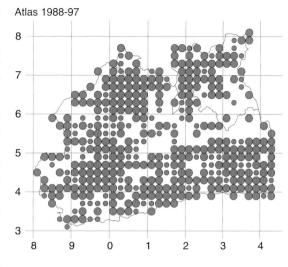
Atlas 1988-97

Population size. The 1982 BTO Breeding Waders of Wet Meadows survey included the Moorhen as an additional species. Birds were found at fifteen of the 32 outer Surrey sites that were visited, rather fewer than might have been expected. Moorhens were recorded at Vann Lake monthly from 1964 to 1996 (Blaker Log). They were found in 385 tetrads, 72% of the total, in the 1988-97 SBC Atlas survey. The Breeding Birds Survey for 1994-2004 suggests a minimum current population of about 1,100 pairs, possibly a considerable underestimate. Recent figures suggest that the size of the breeding population may have been increasing. In 1999 a total of 198 breeding pairs at 33 sites was reported in local counts. Common Birds Censuses suggest that the county breeding population might have doubled since 1970, after allowing for changes in the Common Birds Census habitat mix, though the margin of error in this estimate is wide. Better river bank management has helped the Moorhen along the Wandle, where the number of territories rose from 15 in 1983 to 47 in 1994 (Coleman, 1995).

The longer term position does not look so good. Certainly the days of really large non-breeding counts, of which the biggest was 500 at Guildford Sewage Farm in 1959, have passed with the modernisation of the sewage farms where these gatherings took place.

Large counts

Barn Elms: 208, 2nd December 2001
Beddington Sewage Farm: 138, September 2000
Bramley Sewage Farm: 50, 31st January 1971
Busbridge: 36, 16th December 1996
near Cranleigh: *c*.100, 1963
Cutt Mill: 84, 10th December 1972
Earlswood Sewage Farm: *c*.80, early 1966
Effingham Fish Ponds: 40, 1974
Farnham Sewage Farm: 50+, 22nd December 1968
Frensham: 60, 12th November 1961
Godstone area: *c*.100, 28th December 1967
Guildford Sewage Farm: *c*.500, 1959
Hedgecourt: *c*.50, December 1990
Hersham Sewage Farm: 120, 11th February 1979

Holmethorpe Sand Pits: 70, December 1970
Horley Sewage Works: 32, 5th October 1996
Kew Gardens: 75, December 1983
Morden Hall Park: 55, 14th December 2001
Papercourt: 90, 24th February 1974
Pennymead Lake East Horsley: 40, 16th December 1974
Reigate Priory: 30, December 1993
Richmond Park: 49, November 1990
Ripley Sewage Farm: 60, 16th January 1976
River Wandle, Carshalton to Morden Hall Park: 138, 13th November 1999
Shalford Meadows: *c*.70, 1st February 1969
Stoke Lake: 42, 23rd August 1998
Surrey Docks: 65, 30th November 1972

Thorpe: 40, 9th January 1971
Unstead Sewage Farm: 118, August 2001
Waddon Ponds: 36, 15th November 1997

Spelthorne
Queen Mary Gravel Pits: 60, December 1990
Queen Mary Reservoir: 65, January 1991
Staines Moor: 60, 14th February 1996

Food reported as taken includes a Mallard egg and fallen apples.

Movement and longevity. The two Surrey foreign ringing recoveries are consistent with the national picture. A Moorhen ringed in Denmark in August 1962 was recovered at Godalming, 1,002 km west, in November of the same year. Another ringed at Stoke, Guildford in January 2002 was recovered in Germany, 799 km east, on 11th April 2003. A Moorhen ringed at Hersham Sewage Farm on 16th December 1978 was recovered 10 km away and over four years four months later at Albury on 2nd May 1983.

Moorhens suffered badly in the severe winter of 1962/63 but recovered quickly (Marchant *et al.*, 1990; specific Surrey information not available). Young were killed by a Mute Swan on the Basingstoke Canal in 1975. Mink predation has been reported from Vann Lake in 1972 and Wisley RHS Gardens in 1985. Mink are a significant predator in some parts of the London area (Hewlett, no Surrey locality mentioned).

Plumage variations. Bucknill was shown a bird from Haslemere that had a white throat and some white feathers in its wings in 1896. Phillip Crowley had a light buff one from near Croydon. A Moorhen with only the head, belly and flanks black was seen at Godstone in 1955. A pure white Moorhen was seen at Nower Wood, Headley on 1st September 1979.

Coot (Common Coot)   *Fulica atra*

Common breeding resident on lakes and ponds and a winter visitor to reservoirs

Present in Britain in prehistoric times (Harrison and Hollom, 1932). Coots breed in Europe, Asia, Australasia and North Africa. The range has been extending in northern Europe and the number of breeding birds is on the increase. Birds from northern and eastern Europe migrate in winter. Coots breeding in Britain are largely resident but the population is augmented in winter by migrants from other parts of northern Europe. Adults are flightless for a period in summer and moult migrations are known (*MA*). The British population seems to have been stable during most of the 19th and 20th centuries, apart from a decline in parts of Scotland. National breeding numbers in 2001 were at least 70% higher than in 1970.

Early Surrey history. Coots were known, and might have been eaten, in Roman Britain. The remains of two found at an archaeological excavation at Courage's Brewery, Southwark, were dated to Roman times.

19th century. Newman (1849) included Coots as breeding residents in the Godalming district without further comment but they did not breed so commonly in the later 19th century as they do today. Hamilton (1881) wrote of them frequenting Wimbledon Park Lake. Aldridge (1885) said they were rare visitors to the Norwood area. Bucknill thought that the Surrey population may have declined in rural areas but increased in thickly populated areas. He mentioned Broadwater, Forked Pond, Frensham Ponds, Hammer Pond, Hankley Pond [=Hospital Pond?], Hampton Lodge [Cutt Mill], Raike Pond, Royal Pond [the one now on Royal Common?] Tilford Pond [Stockbridge Pond?] and Witley Pond [Witley Park Lake?] as regular sites, with a considerable number always at Leatherhead [Fetcham] Mill Pond and others at Crystal Palace, and Dulwich. Boorman collected eggs at Clandon Common (1903, 1904). There were good numbers in Richmond Park (Mouritz).

20th century. Coots bred, perhaps for the first time, at Virginia Water in 1905, by which year hundreds of Coot were wintering on Staines Reservoirs (Kerr, 1906). Other colonisations since 1900 include Englefield Green (1928) and Battersea Park (1950). Burkhill found 27 nests at Fetcham Mill Pond in 1932. They were mainly winter visitors to Richmond Park in the 1930s. Collenette gave no definite breeding records.

Breeding. Coots were widely distributed breeding birds by 1944, when there were records from Enton, Farncombe, Godalming and Guildford Sewage Farm. They first bred in Battersea Park in 1954. A 1957 survey found 90 nests in the Surrey part of the London area, including 30 at Waddon Ponds, 18 at Fetcham Mill Pond and 11 at Gatton (Homes *et al.*, 1960). A pair bred at the Surrey Docks for the first time in 1975 and there were 12 pairs in 1999. At least 90 breeding pairs were reported in the Surrey part of the London Area in 1983, without a special survey. Coleman (1985) reported 24 pairs at Waddon Ponds in 1986, similar to the number there in the 1990s. Other significant local populations (breeding pairs)

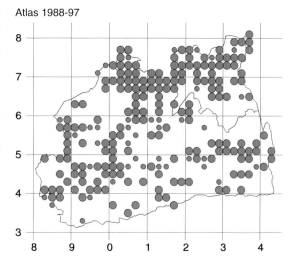

Atlas 1988-97

reported since 1970 are: Ash Vale Gravel Pits (nine), 1978; Badshot Lea (ten), 1975; Barn Elms (eighty-three pairs, over fifty-two broods), 2002; Battersea Park (nine), 1989; Beddington (thirty-two territories), 2001; Dulwich (seven or eight), 1977; Frensham Ponds (twenty-four), 1999; Frimley Gravel Pits (seven), 1977 and 1981, eleven territories in 1972; Holmethorpe (thirteen), 1980; (seven or eight), 1981; Kew Gardens (seven), 1981; Lambeth Reservoir (fifteen), 1993 after recent drainage; Lonsdale Road Reservoir (fifteen), 1977; Papercourt (fifteen), 1977; (nineteen), 1978 and Runfold and Seale Sand Pits (nine), 1980. Coot were listed by Glegg for Staines Common. They are now much more common. At Shepperton Gravel Pits alone, there were 44 nesting attempts in 1985. Ten pairs bred at Perry Oaks Sewage Farm in 1993 and there were 19 broods in 1998 and 34 nests in 1999.

Coots have a preference for larger and more open waters than those used by Moorhens, with the result that the Coot population is smaller and found at fewer sites, being infrequent, for example, at Vann Lake from 1964 to 1996. A pair nested on a boat near Kingston in 1982.

Population size. Coot were found at densities of up to 0.2 territories per ten hectares (about 4,000 territories for the county) in Common Birds Censuses from 1964 to 2002, with a significant upward trend after taking out habitat mix changes in the sample. As with Moorhens, the margin of error in this estimate is wide and this one looks too high. The 1988-97 SBC Atlas survey found Coot in 217 tetrads, including Spelthorne, in the breeding season, suggesting a county population of 500+ pairs. The Breeding Birds Survey 1994-2004 suggests an average of about 900 adults in the breeding season, which compares quite well with 122-225 breeding pairs directly reported from 1994 to 2001 in casual observations. With around 30 territories at Beddington Sewage Farm alone, though, all these figures could be a bit low.

Large counts

Ash Vale Gravel Pits: 260, February 1987 (*HSBBR*)
Badshot Lea: 240, December 1973 (*HSBBR*);
  249, 24th December 2004
Barn Elms: 750, 1976
Beddington Sewage Farm: 448, November 1998;
  591, August 2001
Enton: 186, November 1953
Fetcham Mill Pond: Average 75, December 1969
Frensham: 1,000, September-December 1972;
  1,000, November 1973 (*HSBBR*)

Frimley Gravel Pits: 517, 13th February 1991
Gatton Lake: 200, January 1972
Hedgecourt: 130, January 1947
Holmethorpe Sand Pits: 285, January 1997
Island Barn Reservoir: 500, 16th October 1966
Lonsdale Road Reservoir: 150, 13th January 1980
North Camp Gravel Pits: 104, November 1990
Papercourt Gravel Pits: 463, 27th October 1974
Pen Ponds, Richmond Park: 452, 26th January
  1992

Queen Elizabeth II Reservoir: 363, 17th
   September 2000
Send Gravel Pits: 114, 8th November 1964
Stoke Lake, Guildford: 74, February 1985
Thorpe Water Park: 1,135, January 1992
Tongham Gravel Pit: 220, 7th December 2004
Twynersh Fishing Complex: 324, 5th January
   1997
Waddon Ponds: 141, 12th January 1986
Walton Reservoirs: 1,000, November 1959; 916,

14th October 1984
Wimbledon Park: 50, 19th November 2000
Spelthorne:
King George VI Reservoir: 810, December 1986
Queen Mary Reservoir: 1,000+, 10th September
   1972 (*LBR* for 1973)
Shepperton Gravel Pits: 1,400, December 1981
Staines Reservoirs: 1,353, September 1994
Wraysbury Reservoir: 450, October 1976

Movements and longevity. Recoveries of ringed birds show a continental bird wintering in Surrey:

Ringed	Age		Recovered		Distance/age
Weybridge	Young	8th July 1934	Molesey	September 1934	
Earlswood		27th January 1963	Stadil Fjord, Denmark	17th March 1963	778 km
Buckland	Young	20th July 1982	France	28th December 1982	182 km
Hampton		20th December 1990	near Molesey	6th November 1994	Three years ten months

The longest-lived Coot shown by available records was ringed north of the Thames at Regent's Park on 2nd October 1977 and found freshly dead in Brockwell Park, Lambeth on 6th February 1986. Severe winter weather usually causes extra Coot deaths at the reservoirs. Examples given in the climate section above included twelve at Staines in 1929. Mink predation was noted at Frensham in January 1993 and an adult was taken by a pike at Papercourt in July 1994.

Shooting. There used to be autumn Coot shoots at Frensham. During 1881, over 150 were shot in the first two days. Many were shot on 24th December 1906. Up to 300 would winter on the ponds in the early 1930s, at least until the winter shoots began, but few stayed on to breed. (Shoots were mentioned above in relation to the Haslemere Natural History Society.) Shoots were still taking place at Frensham in the 1950s. Coot were shot to control numbers at Gatton in 1965 and probably in other winters (Coleman, 1991).

Bucknill tasted one and found it to be very fishy - a characteristic not mentioned by current observers.

Plumage variations. A wing from a partially albino Coot was found at Thorpe in April 1971 and given to the British Museum. 'Partial albino' Coots at Staines and Queen Mary Reservoir from late 1989 to early 1991 may all have been the same bird. There was a partial albino at Frimley in December 1991 and January 1992.

Crane (Common Crane)   *Grus grus*
Seven vice-county records
Cranes breed from Scandinavia east to Siberia and there is a resident population in Turkey. They bred in Iron Age Britain. Most European birds winter in France and North Africa. Migrants in Britain are most often seen in October and November. Cranes had bred in East Anglia up to the 1600s and a recolonisation began in Norfolk in 1981. They are presumed to be a lost breeding species in a much wider area of the country. There is some confusion with the Grey Heron, commonly called 'crane' in some counties (Yapp, 1981) and still known as this in some rural parts of East Anglia (*Historical Atlas*). Others have shown that the difference between the two species was well known, at least to bird artists, in medieval times. Yapp mentions more than 60 examples in manuscripts, some of which had been misidentified as Storks by art historians. By contrast, he found illustrations of herons to be much rarer, with a few from Britain and no good examples from continental Europe.

Early Surrey history. Remains of this or an extinct species of crane have been found at a site in the Borough High Street.

It is clear from archaeological evidence that Cranes were known at Southwark in Roman Britain. The remains of two, both dated to 70-100 AD, were found in a natural alluvial channel deposit at 179 Borough High Street. Others from the Roman period were found at Courage's brewery and Winchester Palace. A fifth Southwark specimen was dated to the Middle Ages, 1500-1550 and was at the Fastolf's Palace and Rosary site. A sixth, from Winchester Palace, was dated at 1550-1650. Since Cranes were a popular food item, the exact provenance of these birds must remain somewhat uncertain.

Recent Surrey records do not fit the national migratory pattern, being mainly in the spring:

1966: Frensham Little Pond, one flew over on 16th June (Dr S. G. Kent, *BB, 60:316*).

1968: Newlands Corner, two over on 22nd October (C. K. and Mrs P. O. Dunkley, *BB, 62:466*).

1979: near Horley, two on 4th July (S. Rivers, *BB, 73:504*), influx year.

1987: Thursley Common, one flew over on 30th May (D, J, Eland, S. W. Gale, K. Morgan *et al., BB, 81: 553*).

1995: Thursley/Ockley Commons, flock of 20 northeast on 20th April (M. R. Pankhurst).

2002: Worplesdon, two over Hollow Farm on 8th April (J. Gates).

2003: Thursley/Ockley Commons, one flew over on 16th March (D. J. Brassington).

There is an October 1961 record from Frensham, considered by the BBRC to have been an escape - see Escapes.

Little Bustard   *Tetrax tetrax*
One bird

Breeds from North Africa, Spain and France east to western Siberia and Central Asia. Northern birds move south as far as North Africa in winter. Numbers and range have been declining since the late 19th century.

Surrey. One was shot at Wire Mill, northwest of East Grinstead, in or about 1877, when the species was considerably more common in Europe than it is now. This record, which has not previously been claimed for Surrey in the literature, has a curious history. It was included in a species list that was prepared by H. G. Alexander and published in Knipe's *Tunbridge Wells and Neighbourhood* (H. R. Knipe, 1916). Walpole-Bond included it in *A History of Sussex Birds* (1938). The record was repeated in the next Sussex avifauna (Des Forges and Harber, 1963) and listed for Sussex in the national collations of Evans (1994) and Naylor (1996). Eventually the Sussex writers presumably discovered that Wire Mill is, and always has been, in Surrey rather than Sussex and the record is not mentioned in James (1996).

Oystercatcher (Eurasian Oystercatcher)   *Haematopus ostralegus*
Scarce

Has a scattered coastal and inland breeding distribution from the British Isles east through Russia to Kamchatka. Western European birds move to moulting and wintering grounds after the breeding season, with a return passage from January to April. The *Migration Atlas* shows that Oystercatchers from Iceland and Norway move to Britain after the breeding season. Those found in Surrey are probably mostly from Northern Britain.

In the early part of 19th century, breeding in Britain was confined to coastal areas, but since then inland breeding has become well established in Scotland, northern England and East Anglia. The British population has been expanding for at least 30 years and sightings in Surrey have become more common.

Early Surrey History. Kidd wrote that he had stuffed four from the Godalming district. This would be not later than 1837 (Bucknill). One was killed near Oatlands, Walton-on-Thames not later than 1845 (Yarrell). Another was shot by the Wey, near Guildford on 23rd March 1845 (Newman, 1849) and four days later one was shot below Godalming Wharf (*SALEC*). One was shot at Frensham in early February 1870 and others had been killed there previously. One was shot on the Thames at East Molesey in the autumn of 1872 (Bucknill).

1900 to 1950. There was one at Frensham Little Pond on 10th March 1922. Another was at Frensham on 25th June 1935 (MS note in Shaw). One flying along the Thames at Barn Elms Reservoirs on 30th August 1927 was the first 20th century record for Middlesex (Glegg). Four were at Barn Elms on 30th August 1930 and others on 21st and 23rd August 1931.

The first definite record for Spelthorne was not until 1931, when an Oystercatcher was found at Queen Mary Reservoir on 23rd April (*LN*). One was found at Staines in February 1937 and others in September 1943 and August 1945. One on the frozen Wimbledon Park Lake on 25th January 1942 (not 1941 as in *SEBR*) was the first for January. There was one at Barn Elms on 24th August 1946.

Where found since 1950. Oystercatchers became more common from the 1950s. They were seen at Barn Elms on 22nd May 1950 and 10th August, 1951, establishing the site as a regular one from then onwards. There was one at Guildford Sewage Farm in July 1953. At Frensham, there were single birds on 21st March 1954, 13th August 1961 and 1st August 1962, then on 4th April 1963, 1st September 1963, 8th May 1965, 17th May 1968, 15th September 1968, 20th July 1969 and 28th August 1969. Other sites from 1954-69 included Battersea Park (1964), Beddington Sewage Farm (1955, 1961-62 etc), Bookham (1959), Brooklands (1969), Buckland/Reigate (1966), Crystal Palace (1958), Domewood (1980), Dulwich (1963), East Molesey (1969), Elstead (1962), Gatton (1954, 1960), Hersham (1968), Merstham (1961), Molesey Sewage Farm (1956), Streatham (1957) and Walton Reservoirs (from 1955). About half the records to 1970 were from Barn Elms and Frensham (Parr). Later records for the Spelthorne district include 18 at Perry Oaks Sewage Farm in August 1956 (*BLA*), seven at Queen Mary Reservoir on 10th August 1958 and one at King George VI Reservoir on 16th December 1962.

There was an average of 15 bird months per year in the vice-county from 1970-2000. The newly created Queen Elizabeth II Reservoir drew 75 bird months. Barn Elms (102) was the most important single site. Frensham (34), Frimley Gravel Pits (26), and Walton-on-Thames/Reservoirs (34), were all exceeded by Beddington (65). Other sites, with bird months if more than one, were Ash (two), Ashtead, Barnes, Berrylands (three), Blackfriars/Waterloo (three), Boundstone, Effingham Fish Ponds (two), Egham, Elstead, Epsom (six), Fetcham, Fieldcommon (two), Guildford/Stoke (four), Ham (four), Hammersmith, Hersham (eight), Holmethorpe (fifteen), Island Barn Reservoir (ten), Kew (two), Knaphill (two), Lower Bourne (two), Mitcham, Morden, New Addington, Papercourt (eleven), Richmond, Ripley Sewage Farm, Smallfield (five), South Norwood Country Park, Surbiton, the Surrey Docks (nine), Thorpe, Thursley/Ockley Commons (three), Tilhill (two), Tooting, Vachery, Walton-on-the-Hill, Wandsworth (two), West Ewell, Westminster, Wimbledon Common, Witley and Wrecclesham (three). There was one at Laleham on 9th May 1985. Published records for Spelthorne have since become more frequent and cover all months except January, with an August peak.

There are many later records, including eight at Barn Elms on 28th July 2002, four at Beddington Sewage Farm in July and August 2002, one at Cranleigh on 13th April 2001, two at Frensham on 26th August 2001, four at Island Barn Reservoir on 15th August 2001, and others at Stoke Lake, Unstead Sewage Farm, Wandsworth, Walton Reservoirs and Woking. Eleven records, totalling 24 birds, came from the Walton area reservoirs in 2004.

Calendar. Over 900 bird months from 1970 to 2001 show a weak spring passage from March to May and a strong return passage peaking in August. The first ever November record was from Frensham Great Pond in 1973 and the first for December was from Barn Elms in 1981.

Bird months 1970-2001

	Jan	Feb	Mar	Apr	May	Jun	Jul	Aug	Sep	Oct	Nov	Dec	Total
Vice-county	17	17	36	24	55	21	91	147	20	31	6	20	**485**
Spelthorne	0	10	58	29	69	7	43	162	34	20	3	7	**442**

Large counts

Barn Elms Reservoirs: nine, 19th March 1952 [not 1953 as in Parr and *BLA*]

Beddington Sewage Farm: 11 southwest, 30th August 1997

Spelthorne

Perry Oaks Sewage Farm: 18, August 1956

Movements. Active at night. Night passage has been reported from Crystal Palace, Merstham and Streatham (Parr).

Black-winged Stilt   *Himantopus himantopus*
Five vice-county records and two from Spelthorne

Black-winged Stilts breed in the warmer parts of Eurasia and southern Africa and there are related species in Australia and the Americas. In Britain they are mainly spring migrants to central and southern England, where birds have occasionally bred, first in Nottinghamshire in 1945, and some have wintered or remained all year, as at Titchwell, Norfolk, in the late 1990s.

Surrey. Records do not fit the national pattern, being mainly autumn migrants:

1779:   Frensham: in one of his letters to the ornithologist Daines Barrington, Gilbert White mentions a flock of six *Charadrius himantopus* (the bird being too rare to have an English name at the time), of which five were shot, at Frensham Pond during the last week of April. The Bishop of Winchester's pond-keeper, who was in charge, allowed the sixth to stay alive.

1848:   near Vachery Pond: one was found shot and dead (*SALEC*). It was sold to Stafford by a Guildford dealer for five shillings and was in the Charterhouse Museum in Bucknill's time. It is presumably the bird in the museum in 2001 with Surrey as its provenance.

1955:   Beddington Sewage Farm, one on 17th August, notes in the *LBR*.
        Epsom Sewage Farm, two on 9th September, arrived in the evening.

1968:* Kempton Park, one on 6th July (*BB, 62:470*). Part of this site is not in Spelthorne, so the bird may not have been either.

1973:   Englefield Green: one at Kingswood Hall, Englefield Green on 10th October (S. G. Wilson, *BB, 67:325*).

1984:* Perry Oaks Sewage Farm, two on 8th-9th May (*BB, 78:542, 79:543*) may also not have been in Spelthorne.

*Spelthorne

Avocet (Pied Avocet)   *Recurvirostra avosetta*
Over 110 records to 2005, including around 60 from Spelthorne. Bred in 2006.

Avocets breed on mainly inland waters from Europe east to Siberia and in Africa. Those from the north of their European range, including some of British stock, migrate, and a few go as far as West Africa. Most of the birds wintering in Britain are thought to be of British origin (*MA*). Regular breeding took place along the east coast of Britain in the 18th century but stopped well before 1900, mainly because of persecution. A recolonisation began in the 1940s and is still continuing. A pair bred at Kempton, just beyond the Spelthorne boundary, in 1996.

Early Surrey history. One was shot at Frensham Pond in the winter of 1839 and found dying by a packman named Megenis, who gave it to Stafford (*SALEC*). At about the same time a dying bird was found at Hammer Pond (Bucknill). An adult male Avocet shot at Frensham Great Pond on 5th July 1846 and not mentioned by Bucknill is in the Booth Museum at Brighton, catalogue number 207895. The bird came from the William Borrer collection and was purchased in 1898 (Booth and Griffith, 1927). It was still on display in January 2005 and is the bird mounted as if standing in water in case 378.

After 1900. There were no more records until 1929, when two were found at Frensham on 16th March, followed in 1932 by one at Brooklands Sewage Farm on 13th-16th June. The next was not until 19th May 1955, at Beddington Sewage Farm. The earliest records located for Spelthorne are of one at Perry Oaks Sewage Farm on 8th April 1954 and another there on 23rd September 1956. Twelve at Holmethorpe Sand Pits on 16th March 1969 were mobbed by Great Black-backed Gulls. Avocets were more frequently seen from about this date. The sharp increase in the number of records per decade since the 1970s can be seen in the table.

Number of records by decade to 2005 (incomplete after 2003)

	1900s	1910s	1920s	1930s	1940s	1950s	1960s	1970s	1980s	1990s	2000s	Total
Vice-county	0	0	1	1	0	1	1	2	4	23	16	**49**
Spelthorne	0	0	0	0	0	2	1	4	15	15	7	**44**

Where found. The places at which Avocets have been found, with the number of records, are: Barn Elms (eight), Beddington Sewage Farm (eleven), Brooklands Sewage Farm (one), Frensham (five), Frimley Gravel Pits (one), Hammer Pond (one), Holmethorpe Sand Pits (four), Island Barn Reservoir (one), Queen Elizabeth II Reservoir (four), South Norwood Country Park (two), Stoke Lake (two), Thursley Lake (one), Unstead Sewage Farm (one), Walton Reservoirs (nine), and Wrecclesham Floods (one) and in Spelthorne: Perry Oaks Sewage Farm (seven), Queen Mary Reservoir (one), Shepperton (one), Staines Moor (one) and Staines Reservoirs (thirty-one).

Breeding. A pair fledged four chicks at the Barn Elms London Wetland Centre in 2006 - a remarkable county first for the restructured Barn Elms Reservoirs site. Unfortunately none of the chicks survived, but there may be more success in future years.

Large counts

Frensham Great Pond: 20, 9th November 1992
Holmethorpe: 12, 16th March 1969
Walton Reservoirs: 15, 22nd November 2002

Spelthorne:
Staines Reservoirs: 13, 2nd December 1984; 14, 1st June 1990

Calendar. Avocets have been seen in every month of the year. The largest numbers have appeared as migrants in March and April, with an apparent return passage in November and December. Some of these are probably movements within Britain:

Bird months since 1900

	Jan	Feb	Mar	Apr	May	Jun	Jul	Aug	Sep	Oct	Nov	Dec	Total
Vice-county	0	3	40	39	11	3	2	3	2	2	37	7	**149**
Spelthorne	1	3	19	15	15	21	2	2	1	2	29	20	**130**

Movements and longevity. Evidence for the immigration of European birds is given by the only ringing recovery located, which is of a chick colour-ringed in Germany in 1989 or 1990 and seen at Beddington Sewage Farm, 676 km west, on 28th February 1996.

Behaviour. Avocets are occasionally seen swimming, for example at Frensham on 9th November 1992 and at Staines Reservoirs on 3rd April 1989 and 1st December 1990.

Stone Curlew
Burhinus oedicnemus

Lost breeding species, 28 vice-county records since 1900.

Breeds from Europe east to central and southwest Asia and in North Africa, moving south in winter. The *Historical Atlas* gives a British range covering eastern and southern England west to Dorset and considers that this is as extensive as the distribution had ever been. Signs of a national decline had been evident as early as 1850 and it continued throughout the 20th century, breeding numbers falling by 42% in the 30 years to 1990. They have recently recovered slightly. Migrants come from France, Iberia and West Africa (*MA*). Stone Curlews bred on the North and South Downs until fairly recently. They like open, flinty downland grass for nesting and will also nest on arable land. In Sussex, breeding was last proved in 1981. A small population hangs on in Berkshire. The short grass needed by Stone Curlews can be produced by rabbit grazing. In East Anglia they have nested on land that has been specially ploughed and harrowed.

Early Surrey history. One was killed at Shoelands, near Hampton Lodge, Puttenham in September 1813. Long, to whom this record is due, writing a later note about the specimen, said that they *used to be much more abundant than they are now all along the Hogsback* and that they nested annually in a local field. Stafford had an undated specimen from Compton (*SALEC*). Stone Curlews were known from 'Guildford Downs' (*Letters of Rusticus*, 1837), Chertsey Meads (Meyer, 1842) and Bagshot Heath (about 1850). The foregoing records are all from Bucknill, who gave one later occurrence, at Hankley Common in April 1895. Long's note of a decline at such an early date is remarkable. Jordan (1892) mentioned Stone Curlews at Hackhurst Downs, then sheep pasture. Two pairs were believed to have nested in 1900 (*Zool.*, *1902:308*) and this appears to be the last Surrey breeding record. Parr gives the site as Caterham. Recolonisation is not very likely, but who knows?

Where found. There are 34 subsequent records in the vice-county, with Beddington Sewage Farm and Richmond Park producing most: Barn Elms (1954, 1956), Beddington Sewage Farm (1955, 1957, 1971, 1977, 1979, 1982), Bookham Common (1948), Broadford (1944), Dulwich (1992), Elmers End Sewage Farm (1934), Frimley Gravel Pits (1979), Old Woking Sewage Farm (1988), Oxshott (1959), Pirbright Common (1978), Putney Heath (1969), Queen Elizabeth II Reservoir (1961, 2001), Richmond Park (1924, 1935, 1936, 1937, 1948, 1952, 1953, 1957), Roehampton (1937), the Surrey Docks (1977), Tadworth (1957), Thursley (1995) and Wimbledon Common (1931). There are two records from undisclosed sites. All but one are of single birds. None has been located for Spelthorne.

Calendar. There is a spring peak in April and a rather lower autumn peak in August.

Bird months since 1920

	Jan	Feb	Mar	Apr	May	Jun	Jul	Aug	Sep	Oct	Nov	Dec	Total
Vice-county	0	0	5	13	3	1	3	6	2	2	0	1	**36**

Bucknill mentioned rare occurrences in winter, without details. The one dated winter record that has been located is of a Stone Curlew flying low over the water at Barn Elms Reservoirs on 27th December 1956. Apart from these, the earliest was at Richmond Park on 16th March 1952 and the latest was at Tadworth on 17th October 1957.

Collared/Black-winged Pratincole
Glareola pratincola/nordmanni

Two birds

Whereas Collared Pratincoles are mainly spring migrants to Britain, Black-winged Pratincoles are almost entirely from July to October and in southeast England.

Surrey. One, thought to be a bird of the year, was at Barn Elms Reservoirs on 8th and 11th September 1948 (*BB, 42:221*). Another flew over the downs between Belmont and Banstead on 14th September 1971 (*BB, 65:335*).

Collared Pratincole

Glareola pratincola

Three birds, including one in Spelthorne

Breeds in the warmer parts of Eurasia and in Africa south of the Sahara, where Eurasian birds winter. In Britain, mainly a spring migrant to England, occurring most often in May.

Surrey. The one dated record for our area is in June. Graves mentioned one killed on 'the Eude Waters on the estate of the Duke of Norfolk'. This would have been not later than 1812, the year in which the plate illustrating the species was published (Bucknill). The Eude Waters were, conjecturally, a large pond to the south of Ewood Farm, Newdigate. The Haslemere Educational Museum has a case containing a mounted Collared Pratincole that had been shot on the Portsmouth Road at Wisley in 1858 (Nicholson, 1926). This specimen has been seen and photographed, while in its case. There was a Collared Pratincole at Staines Reservoirs on 19th June 1983 (R. B. Hastings, A. V. Moon and P. Naylor, and *BB, 77:521*).

Little Ringed Plover (Little Plover)

Charadrius dubius

Summer visitor breeding annually in small numbers

Breeds across Europe and Asia, usually by fresh water, moving south to West Africa in winter. A rare vagrant to the British Isles in the 19th century but has since become more common and now breeds. The spread of gravel extraction for the construction industry, the creation of reservoirs and restructuring of sewage farms have assisted colonisation by creating suitable breeding habitat. Little Ringed Plovers prefer actively worked sites with minimal ground cover and near water. They first bred at Tring, Hertfordshire, in 1938 and next at Tring and at Ashford (Middlesex) in 1944. The Ashford site, a group of three gravel pits, was probably just outside the Spelthorne border.

Early Surrey history. In 1945, a pair with three chicks were found at a gravel pit near Shepperton (*BB, 39:12-13*). Two clutches were laid there the following year, but no young are thought to have survived. Two pairs were found on the gravel floor of King George VI Reservoir, then being constructed, in June of that year and three pairs bred on the site in 1947. The first vice-county record was of one at Guildford Sewage Farm on 18th May 1948, with two later in May and one on 10th June.

Breeding. Further breeding was not proved until 1950 when a nest with three eggs was found by E. G. Pedler at a gravel pit near Richmond (presumably one of those on Ham Lands) in 1950 (*BB, 45:62*). P. A. D. Hollom saw two behaving territorially at Walton-on-Thames Sewage Farm on 6th-7th August 1950. Little Ringed Plovers may have bred on semi-flooded, wheat-sown land adjoining an unidentified gravel pit in 1951 and two pairs bred successfully at an unidentified vice-county site in 1952. There was an unsuccessful breeding attempt at Wimbledon Common in 1952 and a pair bred successfully near Guildford in 1953. By 1962 there were 13 pairs in the vice-county. A pair that bred at the Surrey Docks in 1973 was the first to do so anywhere in the LNHS Inner London area. There were up to two territories in Common Birds Censuses at Shepperton Gravel Pits from 1975 to 1980 and breeding was established there in the 1980s, with seven broods in 1983. Fifteen pairs bred at the drained Staines north basin in 1990, which was left unfilled by Thames Water, during a summer drought. Eight pairs bred at Staines Reservoirs during the 1994 drainage. Belsey (2002) includes photographs of a pair breeding on farmland at Laleham.

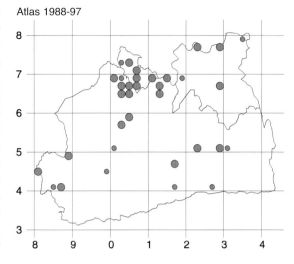

Atlas 1988-97

Duration of occupation. Although one site in northwest Surrey has a record of at least intermittent breeding going back to 1960, most have a much shorter life. Little Ringed Plovers have not bred at Guildford Sewage Farm, one of the first sites to be colonised, since 1962. At Hersham Gravel Pit and the adjacent sewage farm, breeding took place intermittently from 1960 to 1996 but the site is now drained and derelict. Buckland Sand Pits were used from 1974 until 1992 but are now too overgrown. Little Ringed Plovers appeared at the Surrey Docks while they were being redeveloped in 1970, were proved to breed in 1973 and last bred there in 1980, though migrants are still occasionally seen. Frimley Gravel Pits supported several pairs from 1971 until about 1990 but, with excavations long since completed, it has now been abandoned. Little Ringed Plovers appeared at the Stoke Lake site while it was being excavated in 1980 and they nested there in 1981 but the only birds now seen there are occasional passage migrants. A pair bred on temporarily waste ground at Hurst Park in 1994. Another pair bred at Tongham Gravel Pit in 1994 but all suitable nesting areas have now become overgrown. At Barn Elms, where the first pair of Little Ringed Plovers bred in 1980, the conditions created by the restructuring of the site for the new London Wetlands Centre in the late 1990s attracted many more and, although the site has matured, enough habitat has remained to keep it as the most important site in Surrey, with six pairs in 2000, seven in 2001 and 8 pairs (four broods) in 2005. Beddington Sewage Farm has had up to five pairs in recent years. In the vice-county as a whole, the number of territorial pairs has been in the range of five to fifteen, at a somewhat smaller number of sites, for most of the last 40 years, with new sites taking the place of those lost.

Predation. Many nests are lost to predators and in operations at the actively-worked sites that Little Ringed Plovers prefer (*e.g.* Hersham 1979, a building site at Carshalton 1995) or through storms and flooding (*e.g.* Buckland Sand Pits 1983, Old Woking 1994). Carrion Crows are probably the commonest predator but others reported include a Coot (Beddington 1994), a Lesser Black-backed Gull (Buckland, 1992) and a Yellow-legged Gull (Beddington, 1993). At least one clutch was thought to have been taken by a collector at Papercourt in 1976.

Where else found. Migrants at other sites included two at Pen Ponds, Richmond Park on 16th July 1949 and one at Unstead Sewage Farm on 29th April 1956. The first record at Frensham was on 5th May 1961. There were thirteen further Frensham records (17th March to 24th May) by 1979, all single birds apart from two on 3rd May 1974. Sites at which Little Ringed Plovers have been recorded since 1970 include Apps Court Gravel Pit, Ash Vale Gravel Pits, Badshot Lea, Barn Elms, Barwell Court Farm, Beddington Sewage Farm, Berrylands Sewage Works, Bricksbury Hill, Broadford Marsh, Buckland Sand

Pits, Capel, Carshalton, Chertsey, Chobham, Effingham, Farnham Sewage Farm, Fieldcommon, Frensham, Frimley Gravel Pits, Gatwick Airport, Godstone, Guildford Sewage Farm, Hersham, Holmethorpe/Nutfield, Hurst Park, Molesey, Morden, North Camp Gravel Pits, Old Woking, Oxted Sand Pits, Papercourt, Pondover Pit (Lyne), Pyrford Golf Course, Queen Elizabeth II Reservoir, Redlands Gravel Pit (Walton-on-Thames), Ripley Sewage Farm, Runfold and Seale Sand Pits, South Norwood, Stoke Lake, the Surrey Docks, Thorpe, Thursley Common, Tice's Meadow, Tilhill Nurseries, Tongham Gravel Pit, Unstead Sewage Farm, Walton Reservoirs, Watchmoor Park, Wimbledon Common, Wisley Airfield and Wrecclesham Sand Pits. There were 15 at Staines Reservoirs on 9th April 2003. Little Ringed Plovers have attempted to breed at most of these sites at one time or another, but only when the conditions were right.

Calendar. Early and late dates are:

Early		Late	
7th March 1987	North Gatwick	19th October 1969	Guildford Sewage Farm
7th March 2001	Barn Elms		
8th March 1992	Holmethorpe Sand Pits		
9th March 1986	Shepperton, Spelthorne		
9th March 1987	Walton Reservoirs		
11th March 1989	Hersham Gravel Pit		

The chart shows that earlier arrivals in the 1990s coincided with warmer temperatures.

Large counts

Barn Elms: 20, June 1998

Beddington Sewage Farm: 14, 22nd July 1989

Walton Reservoirs: 14, 26th July 1970

Spelthorne:

Perry Oaks Sewage Farm: 56, 11th July 1993

Staines Reservoirs: 25, 7th August 1978

Stanwell Moor Gravel Pits: 25, 18th July 1971

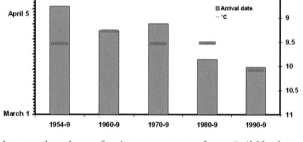

Movements and longevity. Bird ringing has produced one foreign movement, from Guildford to France (480 km) in 1955. An adult ringed in Carmarthenshire on 10th May 1997 was seen at Unstead Sewage Farm on 17th April 1998, the furthest inland movement. A bird recovered at Kempton Park in April 1984, six years and six months after ringing in Hertfordshire, may not have been in Spelthorne. There is no such doubt about a chick ringed at Queen Elizabeth II Reservoir on 24th May 1960 and found dead at Staines on or around 13th April 1964 (BTO).

Ringed Plover   *Charadrius hiaticula*

Common winter visitor and passage migrant, irregular breeding species

Breeds by fresh and salt water in northern Europe east to Siberia and in parts of North America. Winters on European coasts and in Africa south of the Sahara. Those wintering in Britain come from Denmark and southern Scandinavia (*MA*). The British Isles are at the southern end of the Ringed Plover's breeding range. Local declines have been evident in both the 19th and 20th centuries, generally ascribed to disturbance caused by tourist development. Records of occasional breeding at inland sites go back to before 1825. The Wetland Bird Survey shows a national decline in winter numbers. Some 19th century writers used the name Ring-dotterel for the Ringed Plover.

Early Surrey history. Meyer (1842) knew the Ringed Plover from the Thames near Chertsey. A few were shot at Frensham Pond (Waring Kidd in Newman, 1849). A pair in the Charterhouse Collection were killed at Vachery Pond (*SALEC*) but the bird currently held there has Sussex as its provenance. There are a few dated records in Bucknill. They are of two by the Wey between Guildford and Godalming (10th September 1873), one at Redhill (autumn of 1874), one at West Molesey (7th May 1878), some between Redhill and Reigate (autumn of 1878), one on Headley Heath (1883), one at Battle Bridge (about 1884) and one at Frensham Great Pond (25th April 1891 and later). Power heard night migrants over Brixton on 2nd August and 1st September 1876 and on 22nd July 1893.

Breeding. A nest with four eggs was found 300 yards from Frensham Great Pond by H. Bentham on 30th May 1909 (photograph in *BB, 3:416*). The outcome of this attempt, the first recorded for anywhere in Surrey, is not known. A pair summered at Queen Elizabeth II Reservoir when it was under construction in 1961 (Parr). In more recent years, breeding in Surrey has become more frequent as birds have adapted to using stony ground at gravel pits and similar sites. The first successful breeding record, for the LNHS Inner London area as well as for Surrey, was of a pair with a chick at the Surrey Docks on 8th June 1973. A pair raised at least one young there in 1980. Ringed Plovers next bred at Hersham Gravel Pit, where a nest with two young and one egg was found in 1985. Two pairs bred at the nearby Molesey Gravel Pit in 1986, and at Hersham Gravel Pit there were three pairs in 1988, four or five (of which three pairs raised ten young) in 1989 and four in 1990. Two pairs nested successfully in parsnip fields at Lyne in 1989. A nest was predated there in 1990 and a pair bred in 1991. One pair raised three young at Apps Court Gravel Pit in 1991. A pair bred at Thorpe in 1992. In the same year, at an old motorway construction site

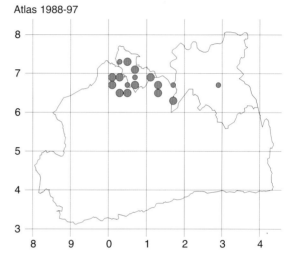

Atlas 1988-97

at junction 11 of the M25, two pairs appeared to be nesting and a pair raised three young there in the following year. A pair raised young at Hersham Gravel Pit in 1999 but no further breeding there is expected as all suitable habitat has now been destroyed.

In Spelthorne, a pair laid eggs at Stanwell Moor Gravel Pits in 1967. A pair bred at Wraysbury Reservoir in 1970 (*LBR* for 1971). A pair with young were seen at Perry Oaks Sewage Farm on 10th June 1978, conjecturally the pair that raised young nearby on London (Heathrow) Airport. Two pairs bred at Perry Oaks in 1981, 1982 and 1983, one pair in 1988, there were two pairs in 1995, four broods were seen in 1996, and a chick in 1998. There were six territories in 1999 but none bred. A pair bred at Queen Mary Gravel Pits in 1984 but at Staines Reservoirs a nest was flooded out when one of the basins was refilled in the same year. In the following year a nest at Queen Mary Gravel Pits was predated but about five pairs bred at Staines Reservoirs and another at Shepperton Gravel Pits. Ten pairs raised 18+ young at Staines North during drainage in 1990 and at least six pairs bred there in 1994.

Migrants. Ringed Plovers were seen at Frensham on 26th August 1901 and at Hedgecourt on 19th August 1911. There was one at Staines Reservoirs on 18th August 1907 (Kerr). Flocks of two to three dozen in May and 25 in August of 1927 at Staines Reservoirs, which had exposed mud at the time, were the largest for many years (Glegg). They became better known as passage migrants elsewhere in the 1930s, when they were regular in spring and autumn at Barn Elms Reservoirs and Brooklands Sewage Farm and were also seen at Beddington, Epsom, Molesey and Walton-on-Thames sewage farms and at Frensham (eight records 1920-54). By 1944 they were being recorded at Guildford Sewage Farm. The maximum at Frensham up to 1979 was nine in May 1969.

Where else found. Other localities at which Ringed Plovers have subsequently been recorded on passage include Abinger cress beds, Addlestone, Banstead, Berrylands Sewage Works, Brooklands Sewage Farm, Croham Hurst Golf Course, Effingham Fish Ponds, Epsom, Esher Sewage Farm, Frimley Gravel Pits, Gatwick, Guildford Sewage Farm, Hersham Gravel Pit and Sewage Farm, Holmethorpe, Hurst Park, Island Barn Reservoir, Lonsdale Road Reservoir, Papercourt Gravel Pits, Queen Elizabeth II Reservoir, Richmond Park, Send, South Norwood Country Park, Stoke Water Meadows, Surbiton, Thorpe, Tice's Meadow, Tuesley Farm (Milford), Unstead Sewage Farm, Walton Gravel Pits and Reservoirs and Wrecclesham. Barn Elms and Beddington each accounted for about a quarter of the 517 bird months from 1994 to 2001, followed by Queen Elizabeth II and Walton Reservoirs.

Calendar. Ringed Plovers may be seen at any time of year but January records are unusual, the most recent up to 2001 being from Thorpe in 1993 and there are clear peaks in May and August.

Bird months 1994-2001 (based on monthly site maxima)

	Jan	Feb	Mar	Apr	May	Jun	Jul	Aug	Sep	Oct	Nov	Dec	Total
Vice-county	0	19	34	57	160	42	25	95	79	3	2	1	**517**

Vice-county November, December and January records include:

November 1994	Beddington	29th December 1999	Milford
9th November 1957	Walton Gravel Pits	January 1993	Thorpe
14th November1997	Beddington	4th and 11th January 1959	Beddington
4th December 1964	Queen Elizabeth II Reservoir	31st January 1958	Guildford

Large counts

Barn Elms: 38, 17th May 1995

Frensham: 9, May 1969

Guildford: 25, 21st May 1959

Walton Reservoirs: 39, May 1992 when drained

Spelthorne

King George VI Reservoir: 28, 25th August 1986

Perry Oaks Sewage Farm: 114, 26th August 1987

Staines Reservoirs: 141, 16th August 1985

Wraysbury Reservoir: 32, 12th September 1995, when drained

Movements and longevity. An adult ringed at Perry Oaks Sewage Farm on 22nd August 1962 was recovered in Greenland on 5th June 1964. The race *C. h. hiaticula* breeds as far north as Greenland as well as in the British Isles.

Tundra Ringed Plover   *Charadrius hiaticula tundrae*

Surrey. A bird with characteristics of this race, which breeds on the tundras of northern Europe, was seen at the Barn Elms London Wetland Centre on 14th May 2001 (R. Kaye) and there were others in May 2005 (*LNHSB*).

Killdeer   *Charadrius vociferus*

One bird

This vociferous, two-banded relative of the Ringed Plover is a common breeding bird on stony ground from North America to Peru, where it winters. In Britain, Killdeers are mainly winter vagrants to English counties, often inland.

Surrey. There was one at Beddington Sewage Farm from 31st January to 1st February 1984 (G. D. J. Messenbird, *BB, 78:544*, in Berkshire before and after).

Kentish Plover
Charadrius alexandrinus

Two vice-county birds, at least nine in Spelthorne

Scattered breeding distribution in Europe, Asia, the Americas and North Africa, moving south in winter. Mainly coastal in Europe buts breeds inland elsewhere. Bred on English coasts from Sussex to Norfolk in the early part of the 19th century but became a target for collectors. This and coastal land use developments reduced the numbers. Regular breeding had ceased by about 1931, with occasional breeding up to the 1970s.

Surrey. The records are:

1878:   near East Molesey, one on the Mole in the spring (Bucknill).

1915:*   Staines Reservoirs, one on 21st April (G. W. Kerr, *LBR* for 1946).

1947:*   The unfilled King George VI Reservoir, one on 3rd September.

1978:*   Staines Reservoirs, one on 1st and 9th April.
           Staines Reservoirs, one on 29th May.

1980:*   Perry Oaks Sewage Farm, one on 1st June.

1981:*   Perry Oaks Sewage Farm, one on 19th May.

1983:*   Staines Reservoirs, on 10th and 22nd April, 16th May and 12th June (at least two different birds).

1984:   Guildford, one at Stoke Water Meadows on 18th April.

1999:*   Perry Oaks Sewage Farm, one on 2nd May.

Spelthorne

Dotterel (Eurasian Dotterel)
Charadrius morinellus

About nine records, five of them from Spelthorne, five in autumn.

Breeds on tundras and mountain ridges from Scotland and the Alps east to Siberia, wintering mainly in the Middle East and North Africa. British breeding birds winter in northwest Africa (*MA*). British Dotterel numbers were falling in the late 19th and early 20th centuries and they stopped breeding in England. Since then, the numbers have tended to vary with the temperature trend, rising in cooler periods.

Surrey. The records are:

1817:   Peckham, five killed on Nunhead Hill in November (Graves, 1811-21). Three of them were sent to Graves as Golden Plovers.

1845:   Hindhead? Two that were bought from a Hindhead innkeeper by Stafford in the spring (*SALEC*), may have been killed in Surrey.

1850:   John Spicer had one which was obtained at Farnham in his collection (*Zool.*, 1854:4367). It was probably one of three shot from a party of five at Frensham around 1850 (Bucknill, 1902).

1884:   Holmwood. The Haslemere Museum has a note of one that flew into telegraph wires at Holmwood Station in or around 1884. This bird, said to be *the true dotterel, of course, not the ring-dotterel* [Ringed Plover] and *in beautiful 'May' plumage*, was said to have later passed to the Charterhouse Museum, though Bucknill made no reference to it.

1955:*   Perry Oaks Sewage Farm, four were seen on 1st August, possibly outside the Spelthorne boundary.

1960:*   Perry Oaks Sewage Farm, one on 3rd April, also possibly outside the Spelthorne boundary.

1977:*   Staines Reservoirs, one on 11th September.

1985:*   Staines Reservoirs, on a drained basin on 29th August.

1992:*   Staines Reservoirs, a party of three flew over on 29th September.

Spelthorne

Dotterel appear on fields in north Hampshire in spring from time to time and it is perhaps surprising that so few have been found in Surrey.

American Golden Plover   *Pluvialis dominica*
One bird, Spelthorne

American Golden Plovers breed on the North American tundra and winter in South America. They are very rare in Britain.

Surrey. There was an adult in partial summer plumage at the partially drained King George VI Reservoir on the evening of 2nd September 1995 (*BB, 89:498*, Moon, 1997).

Pacific Golden Plover   *Pluvialis fulva*
One bird

Pacific Golden Plovers breed in Siberia and Alaska and winter south to Australasia, the Pacific and East Africa. British records are mainly from the north and west, most often in July.

Surrey. One was shot at Epsom Race Course on 12th November 1870 (*BB, 2:150*). It was presented to Stafford by Mr Aubrey, then a clerk at Nine Elms Station as a *Plover* (*like small Golden*) (*SALEC*). The bird came into what is now the Charterhouse Collection, where it was identified by H. L. Popham. It was in the Charterhouse Museum in 2001, where its smaller size and greyish appearance were rather obvious when compared with a Golden Plover mounted near it. This record was not included in the 1883 BOU list or in Saunders (1899) but does appear in the list published in 1915 as the first British record for *Charadrius dominicus fulvus*, the Eastern Golden Plover. American and Pacific Golden Plover species were not separated at the time, but lumped together as two races of the Lesser Golden Plover *Pluvialis (Charadrius) dominicus*. Subsequent authors have generally assigned it to the Pacific race or species, as does the BOU list of 1971.

The Surrey bird constitutes the first British record of either race or species.

Golden Plover (European Golden Plover)   *Pluvialis apricaria*
Increasing winter visitor

Breeds mainly on high altitude moorland and tundras from the British Isles east to Siberia, wintering south to the Mediterranean. A gradual decline in numbers over the past two centuries has become more serious in recent years. In southeast England, Golden Plovers have never been more than a winter visitor and passage migrant. British breeding birds move south in winter. Some from Scandinavia and Russia winter in Britain, mainly in southeast England, and others pass through (*MA*).

Early Surrey history. Plover remains found at Guildford Castle and dated about 1230-1268 were not specifically identified and might have been Grey Plover. Similar remains at Little Pickle, Bletchingley (Poulton *et al.*) were dated to the 16th century. Enormous (but uncounted) flocks visited the Hindhead and Wanborough districts in the winter of 1834/35 (Long in Bucknill). Bucknill gave few other detailed records but mentioned wintering on heaths at Bagshot and Pirbright before disturbance by the military (not later than 1871), a regular wintering flock, often of more than 100 birds, on fields by Epsom Downs and occasional birds on the metropolitan commons. Hamilton (1881) mentioned one shot on Wimbledon Common. The emphasis on heaths and commons is interesting, given that Golden Plovers are now commonest on farmland. Stafford had undated specimens given by contacts in Chiddingfold (*SALEC*). Golden Plovers were common on Staines Moor around 1880.

1900 to 1929. Early 20th century numbers may have been lower. They were only stragglers at Staines

Moore in 1905 (Kerr). Shaw said they were irregular winter visitors to the Haslemere district, citing one at Churt on 11th February 1912. Beadell knew them only as winter visitors in hard weather, his maximum being 40 or 50 in a field. The field had been built over by 1931. Similar numbers were known from Walton Heath up to 1925. Spelthorne records include 20 at Staines Reservoirs on 25th October 1925 (*LN*), and 170 near Stanwell (possibly outside the Spelthorne boundary) on 25th March 1928 (Glegg).

1930-1970. Over the next 40 years, Golden Plovers were found at sites such as Barn Elms Reservoirs (from 1936), Beddington (ten in 1932, 25 in 1935, 1938), Bookham (1970), Brooklands, Croydon Airport (1963, 1966), Ewell (1936), Farnham (1942), Fetcham (1970), Godalming (1937), Godstone (1963), Haslemere (20, 1941), Horley (1945, 1947), Leatherhead (1949), Molesey, Morden (1965, 44 in 1966), Prince's Coverts (1966), Pyrford (1963), Richmond Park (1938, 1949), Smallfield (1944), Thorpe (23 in 1967 and 1969), Thursley (1933 and 1936), Walton Reservoirs (1967) and Wimbledon Common (1938). There were 50 at Frensham on 23rd March 1949. The largest group away from Spelthorne was 100 at Beddington on 24th January 1958. At Staines Moor there were about 100 on 14th February 1938, 200 on 25th January 1950 and 250 on 23rd January 1965.

Since 1970. During the period 1970-1990, Golden Plovers were recorded in every year except 1975, mostly as ones and twos in winter Lapwing flocks or as larger parties flying over. Golden Plovers were scarce at Shepperton in the 1980s. The 1981-84 Winter Atlas Survey showed a decline, flocks being up to a maximum of 50 (Dennis, 1990). Many were seen in rural areas across the county, often with Lapwings such as those on the farmland at Holmethorpe. If flocks in 1974 of 30 over Thursley Common and in 1984 of 40 at Beddington, 100 at Hersham and 60 over Ockley Common are excluded, the total number of birds seen did not exceed about 75 in any year up to 1986. A count of 236 Golden Plover over Tooting in 90 minutes on 10th January 1987 was a 20th century record and there were counts of over 60 at Beddington on the same day and at Epsom later in the year. Numbers were low in the succeeding three years but exceeded 1,000 in 1991, when a movement of about 500 Golden Plover in two hours was seen at Thursley on 6th February, with 101 over Beddington the same day and 180 over Richmond Park on 15th December. Annual numbers were in the 300-1,100 range in 1993-95 and nearly 300 in 1996. There were 316 at Beddington in 1993.

The big flocks arrive. After two more quiet years, there was a striking development in 1999, when a winter flock arrived at Tuesley Farm, Milford in early January and peaked at 726 on the 24th. The flock size has increased since. It reached 3,700 birds in December 2002, a gathering of nationally important size. Numbers usually fall with the onset of harder weather in the New Year. To give this a scale, the Wetland Bird Survey total for Sussex in 2001 peaked in January at 3,480, of which 2,941 were at Chichester Harbour (*Sussex Bird Report*). In the following month there were 1,726 in Sussex and 2,500 at Milford (Soden, 2002). Flock size reached 3,500 in 2003. The source of the Milford birds is not known, but has broadly coincided with an increase in the number wintering on the south coast. Soden thought that some may have been displaced by the flooding of roosting areas elsewhere. Some might have come from a wintering flock on farmland near Odiham in north Hampshire, which held 994 in 1996 or from the December flocks totalling 1,897 between there and the Surrey border in 1994. These flock numbers have recently been smaller (*HSBBR, Hampshire Bird Report*). The birds may not spend the night at Milford, which may be mainly a loafing area from which the birds disperse to feed at night and it is possible that some come to Milford from coastal roosts. All this is, however, speculation.

Large flocks, including one of about 2,800 in 2004, have more recently been seen at Tice's Meadow. Some 500 circling over Compton on 12th March 2001 may have been from Milford.

Calendar. Spring birds may be seen as late as May (*e.g.* Thursley on 8th May 1961, Beddington SF on 12th May 1996) . No May-July records have been located for Spelthorne. Single birds at Papercourt with Lapwings on 25th July 1985 and Ash Vale Gravel Pits on 5th August 1964 were unusual. One at Staines

Reservoir on 16th August 1966 is the first found for August for Spelthorne. Autumn return usually begins in September. One at Brooklands, Weybridge from 2nd April to 10th October 1969 was thought to be an immature bird by C. Ogston.

Golden Plover, northern form — *Pluvialis apricaria 'altifrons'*

Surrey. One at Richmond Park 4th April 1958 had characteristics of the northern form *C. a. 'altifrons'*.

Grey Plover — *Pluvialis squatarola*

Scarce winter visitor

Breeds on arctic tundras and winters on the coasts of every continent except the Antarctic. Those found in Britain come from Russia (*MA*). Grey Plovers became more common in Britain during the 1970s.

Early Surrey history. Newman (1849) listed Grey Plovers as occasional visitors, with a few shot at Godalming. Two that Bucknill knew of in the Charterhouse Museum were said to have been obtained near Guildford (*SCCMS*) but the only bird currently held there has Norfolk as its provenance.

20th century. Two at Barn Elms on 23rd November 1932 (*BB, 26:258*) and one on 11th November 1933 were the first records for the site and the first dated records for Surrey. There were one or two at Brooklands on 26th-30th May 1936 (*BB, 30:346*), four flew over Thursley on 1st October 1938 and two were at Guildford Sewage Farm on 22nd August 1944. The first records at Frensham were on 9th April and 15th May 1967 and in May 1970. Grey Plovers have remained as occasional passage migrants in the Haslemere district. The first Spelthorne record is of six at Staines Reservoirs on 9th April 1922 (Glegg). The next, at the same site, were single birds on 20th December 1930 and 15th November 1931. There was one at Queen Mary Reservoir on 12th December, 1931 and one at Staines Reservoir on 6th June 1934 (*BB, 25:272*). Two at Perry Oaks Sewage Farm on 31st July 1954 were on early return passage.

Where found. There were about 270 vice-county bird months from 1900 to 2000, nearly 240 of them from 1970 onwards. The largest number seen together at any one time was 11 at Beddington on 22nd November 1993. Over a third (98) of the bird months were from Beddington, 40 were from Barn Elms, 28 from Queen Elizabeth II Reservoir, 19 from Walton Reservoirs and 12 from Frensham. The remainder were from Brooklands (two), Capel (two), Chelsham, Epsom (five), Frimley Gravel Pits (three), Grayswood, Guildford (five), Ham Lands, Hersham (two), Horsell (two), Island Barn Reservoir (eight), Molesey Gravel Pit (two), Old Woking (two), Papercourt (three), Pirbright (one), Ripley, Stoke Water Meadows (four), the Surrey Docks, the Thames at Hammersmith (two), Thursley (four), Wandsworth and Worcester Park. There were twice as many bird months (533) from the Spelthorne reservoirs.

From 2000 onward, there have been vice-county records from Barn Elms, Beddington, Island Barn Reservoir, Queen Elizabeth II Reservoir, Richmond Park, Thursley Common and Walton Reservoirs, the largest count being 30 at Beddington on 16th March 2001, a new vice-county maximum. The only larger Spelthorne count was 32 south at Queen Mary Reservoir on 9th August 1980.

Calendar. A third of the vice-county bird months were in May, with a flatter autumn peak from September to November. Only two were in July. One at Barn Elms Reservoirs on 17th September 1972 was the first vice-county September record. One at Papercourt Gravel Pits on 2nd December 1973 was the first vice-county December record.

Bird months 1900-2000

	Jan	Feb	Mar	Apr	May	Jun	Jul	Aug	Sep	Oct	Nov	Dec	Total
Vice-county	24	9	12	10	95	8	2	11	30	22	34	12	**269**
Spelthorne	16	3	12	53	131	25	3	44	46	100	68	32	**533**

Large counts

Barn Elms Reservoirs: seven, 18th September
  1993
Beddington: Sewage Farm: 30, 16th March 2001
Frensham: five on 7th June 1992
Island Barn Reservoir: five, 7th May 1988
Thursley: four flew south, 1st October 1938

Spelthorne

Queen Mary Reservoir: 32, 9th August 1980
Staines Reservoirs: 20, 5th November 1982 when
  the north basin was drained.

Lapwing (Northern Lapwing)   *Vanellus vanellus*
Moderately common breeding resident

A European, Asian and North African breeding species, wintering south to the Mediterranean and Southeast Asia. It was common throughout the British Isles in the 19th century, though declining. The decline has continued, with a fall in breeding numbers of around 40% since 1970 and was still falling in 2005. Adverse factors include increased stocking rates on grassland and the loss of mixed farmland.

Early Surrey history. Lapwing remains found at Guildford Castle were dated to about 1230-1268. Remains found at Winchester Palace, Southwark, were dated at 1440-1550. There were 16th century remains at Little Pickle, Bletchingley (Poulton *et al.*). All were presumably from food items. Graves recorded Lapwings at Reigate Heath in November 1816 (Bucknill) and they nested in thousands in the Godalming area prior to 1849 (Newman). Harting (1866) said that they bred at Chertsey. Aldridge (1885) mentioned flocks flying over the Norwood area but had no breeding records. Bucknill (1900) described Lapwings as being much less common than in former years, citing in evidence a statement by Jesse that it had nested in large numbers in Richmond Park and giving land drainage as a cause. Harting (1866) wrote that he had found eggs in Kempton Park, not definitely inside the present Spelthorne boundary.

After 1900. In Spelthorne, Kerr (1906) reported Lapwings as common and increasing. Boorman collected eggs at Clandon and Send in 1903-07. A nest was found at Shell Wood, Reigate in 1905 (G. T. Winter). Bentham found six clutches in a field near Hedgecourt Pond in April 1906. Many pairs were nesting near Frensham Ponds in 1908 and many at Ockley Common in 1909 and 1913 and at Hankley Common in 1913. Lapwings had stopped breeding at Walton Common, where they had once been numerous, by 1913. Shaw (1921) thought that Lapwings were breeding more freely in the Haslemere district. Lapwings lost ground in the suburbs at an early stage. Power (1910) wrote that they bred at Carshalton but were only passage migrants in the Dulwich area. He had a party of 25 over his Brixton garden on 19th October 1909. Fields used as breeding sites were replaced by houses as the London suburbs spread. They were built over in Mitcham by 1926 and New Malden by 1934. A few pairs were breeding in farm fields around Farleigh up to 1950 and in 1962.

Collenette (1937) knew of no breeding records in Richmond Park later than those mentioned by Jesse in the 1830s. Lapwings nested there again from 1943-46 and in 1948 and 1950 (four pairs) because part of the park was ploughed up but they were lost with its reversion to grass by 1952. Lister had six to eight pairs nesting on 225 acres of mixed arable and pasture farmland near Epsom from 1935 to 1938 and noticed the flocking up in June and July and autumn passage into September which is still a conspicuous feature of Surrey Lapwing movements. At Beddington there were 22 pairs in 1954 and 17 in 1955 (Milne, 1956). Breeding pairs at Unstead fell from about 60 to five over the five years to 1957. Breeding at Epsom stopped when the site was closed and built over. Lapwings bred in central and west Surrey in 1962. Breeding numbers at the Beddington and Guildford sewage farms were being reduced by modernisation by 1970 (Parr). A pair that bred at the Surrey Docks in 1973 provided the first breeding record for Inner London, though Lapwings might have bred there before the docks were built. They bred at Shepperton Gravel Pits in the 1980s, with nine pairs in 1985.

A decline in breeding numbers continued through the 20th century, both nationally and in Surrey. Lapwings were found at territorial densities of up to 0.54 per ten hectares in Common Birds Censuses from 1962 to 2002. There was a significant upward trend but this might not adequately reflect habitat changes. The Blaker Log (1964-96) shows a declining frequency of sightings after 1976. A BTO Lapwing survey showed that the number of Lapwings breeding in England and Wales dropped by an estimated 49% in the 11 years to 1998 (Wilson *et al.* 2001). The Surrey part of the sample 16 tetrads, held 11 pairs in 1987 (Garcia, 1986) and the same 16 tetrads in 1998 found only seven. The sample is small but the direction is the same. The 1982 BTO Breeding Waders of Wet Meadows survey found 83 Lapwing pairs on 14 sites out of 23 that were visited. The same sites were revisited for a further survey in 2001, when only 41 pairs at six sites were found. The pairs were distributed with a striking regional variation:

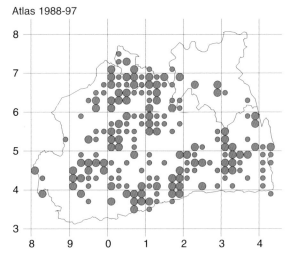

Atlas 1988-97

	1982	2001
Greater London (Beddington)	15	16
Other Surrey excluding Spelthorne	66	25
Spelthorne (Upper Halliford)	2	0

Pairs using dry habitats, gravel pits and heathland were outside the scope of the survey. New habitat at the Barn Elms London Wetland Centre has attracted breeding Lapwings, with 13 breeding pairs and five broods in 2005.

Calendar. Post-breeding dispersal begins in mid June and large flocks appear from late July. Migrant numbers may not have followed the same trend as those of birds breeding. Bucknill mentions autumn and winter flocks 'often of several hundred', around a tenth of those found at sites such as Holmethorpe in the 1990s. Mouritz saw flocks of up to 60 over Richmond Park in November and December 1905. Hundreds seen from the beginning of June on Staines Moor were said to be unusual at this date by Glegg (1935).

Large counts. Much larger numbers were recorded as the century progressed. The wintering flock on fields near Holmethorpe Sand Pits reached 3,500 in January 1994. Maxima at other wintering sites include 4,500 at Tuesley Farm (Milford) in January 1999, 2,300 at Hersham Gravel Pit in January 1999, 2,000 at Papercourt in August 1985, 1,100 at Pyrford in December 1995 (presumably the Papercourt flock) and 1,000 at Enton in January 1984. Habitat changes have reduced numbers in some places. Beddington, which had 1,215 on 17th January 1932, 2,000 at the end of 1953 and 3,000 on 15th January 1955, no longer has such numbers. Guildford had a 1953 maximum of 600 on 18th August, before modernisation. A typical figure for maximum Spelthorne counts of birds on the ground in later years has been 1,000+. There were about 2,000 at Staines Moor on 1st December 1963. Large roosts include 4,000 in January and February 1994 at Staines Reservoirs, roosting in a drained reservoir basin.

Movements. The origin of the birds in autumn and winter flocks is not clear but they are probably a mixture of birds from other parts of Britain and from continental Europe. On 4th March 1970, 10,500 passed over Kingston during a blizzard and 5,800 passed over in 100 minutes at Worcester Park. Some 8,000 flew west at Thursley Common on 6th February 1991. A dawn-to-dusk count at Wraysbury Reservoir on 30th January 1972 found 14,000 going south in a snow-related movement (*LBR* for 1973).

The three foreign ringing recoveries of young, ringed at Beddington, Godalming, Staines and Effingham in May, were from France (February 1965), France (December 1950), East Flanders (November 1951) and Portugal (February 1981) respectively, showing that some Surrey-bred birds winter in continental Europe. A chick that was ringed at Stanwell Moor in May 1963 and recovered in Archangel, old USSR, 2758 km east, in May 1967 may have bred where recovered, supporting the suggestion in the *Migration Atlas* that some British-bred birds migrate with the wrong (continental) flock.

Longevity. Two ringed Lapwings have been found to have lived at least seven years. One was ringed at Runnymede on 17th May 1974 and recovered there on 30th May 1981. The other was ringed as an adult at Ewhurst on 9th September 1961 and recovered 2,212 km east at Smolensk, old USSR in the autumn of 1968.

Plumage variations. A bird with normal head, breast and body plumage but with white, brown-blotched wings was seen at Papercourt in August 1984. There was a leucistic bird, with a mantle and upper wings the colour of milky coffee, at Papercourt in July and August 1992. One with 'piebald colour on mantle and wings' was seen at King George VI Reservoir on 28th July 2001.

Knot (Red Knot) — *Calidris canutus*

Winter visitor and passage migrant (mainly autumn). Over 270 records, of which over 190 are from Spelthorne Breeds mainly on tundras in Greenland, Canada and eastern Siberia. Remains dating from the last glaciation have been found in Britain. Winters mainly on the coasts of Europe, Africa, South America, Australia and New Zealand. Most of those wintering in Britain are from Canada and Greenland and of the race *islandica* (*MA*).

Early Surrey history. The earliest Surrey record is of one shot at 'Pudmoors' [now Pudmore, part of the Thursley/Ockley Common area] a few days before Christmas 1844. It remains the only record from the site. Only three further 19th century occurrences are known, at Broadwater (1852) and West Molesey (spring of 1874 and autumn of 1877).

After 1900. No more were found until 1922, when there were two records of single birds at Frensham Little Pond. One at the Staines Reservoirs south basin on 10th September 1927, when the basin was drained, was the first for the London area as well as for what is now Spelthorne. As the 20th century progressed, Perry Oaks Sewage Farm and Staines Reservoirs became the most frequently visited places, accounting between them for over 80% of the Spelthorne records and over 60% of those for the whole area. Even this conceals the full dominance of the Spelthorne sites, which would be higher if measured by the number of birds. The table shows how the number of records rose sharply in the 1950s and has remained at a high level, peaking in the 1980s and 90s:

Records by decade since 1900

	1900s	1910s	1920s	1930s	1940s	1950s	1960s	1970s	1980s	1990s	2000-05	Total
Vice-county	0	0	2	2	4	14	10	1	7	22	18	**80**
Spelthorne	0	0	1	2	10	31	23	25	52	43	11	**198**

Where found up to 2000. With birds being seen within a short interval of one another at sites such as Staines Reservoirs, figures for the number of records and birds cannot be exact. The summary below gives records by site for 1900 to 2000, single birds unless otherwise stated. Vice-county: *Barn Elms*: 1st-2nd October 1934, 20th December 1938, nine on 22nd December 1938, 27th May 1960, 27th August 1960; 1st-3rd September 1956, 26th January 1963 to 7th February 1963 (one/two), 5th November 1968;

3rd-6th May 1980, 14th March 1986, 29th May 1991 (four), 4th February 1993 (11 north), 15th February 1994, 13th April 1994, 20th September 1995 (two), 13th October 1998; *Barnes*: 9th March 1942 (on mud); *Beddington*: 30th January 1954 to 6th February 1954 (one to three), 2nd February 1956 (23 southwest), 14th-25th January 1959, 10th February 1985, 13th-14th September 1985, 11th January 1987, 19th May 1995 (seven), 26th January 1996, 19th December 1996, 10th August 1999 (three), 1st September 1999, 4th May 2000. 22nd July 2000, 21st October 2000 (two); *Broadwater*: 1852 (two shot, later acquired for Charterhouse Collection); *Enton*: 12th January 1957; *Epsom*: 6th February 1954, 2nd February, 11th February 1956; *Frensham Great Pond*: 4th May 1947, 4th October 1954; *Frensham Little Pond*: 16th May 1922, 7th October 1922, 10th August 1992; *Frimley Gravel Pits*: 4th February 1987 (standing on ice); *Guildford*: 15th April 1956, 9th-10th December 1956, 14th April 1957, 29th August 1960 (two, also one on 30th-31st August 1960); *Henley Park*: 25th February 1947; *Hersham Gravel Pit*: 18th March 1959 (two); *Island Barn Reservoir*: 8th-9th January 1997; *Pudmore*: December 1844; *Queen Elizabeth II Reservoir*: 18th February 1979, 23rd January 1987, 7th May 1999, 23rd August 1999 (presumed from Walton Reservoirs), 20th March 2000, 5th May 2000; *Send Gravel Pits*: 6th August 1966; *Stoke Lake*: 18th December 1995; *Thames at Barn Elms*: 14th February 1994 (on the foreshore); *Thames at Hammersmith*: 3rd February 1963 (two), 14th December 1996 (on the foreshore); *Unstead*: 16th January 1946 (four); 8th February 1954, 4th October 1956; *Walton Reservoirs*: 1st September 1960, 22nd August 1999 (two, and one on the 23rd-24th), 19th March 2000; *West Molesey*: 1874 (female shot in the spring); *Wisley Village*: 23rd August 1968 (50); *Worcester Park*: 22nd March 1963; *Wrecclesham*: 26th January 1996 (on flooded land).

Spelthorne: *Perry Oaks Sewage Farm*, with 57 records, was a major attraction from 1948 to 1993. September was the peak month and no birds were found in February or December. The largest party was 24 on 6th September 1962. A bird on 13th June 1956 was the first in June for the vice-county and for Spelthorne. There was another on 7th May 2000; *Queen Mary Reservoir*: 6th February 1954 (dead), 11th February 1956 (three), 23rd-24th November 1957, 20th September 1959 (and 27th), 4th October 1959, 17th-18th March 1962, 11th November 1962, 5th January 1963, 23rd March 1963 (two), 11th November 1963, 2nd October 1966, 16th May 1971, 9th August 1981 (two northeast), 8th September 1990, 4th September 1993 (four north); *Staines Moor*: 26th March 1951; *Staines Reservoirs*, with 98 records from the first fully dated record for the London area, on 10th September 1927, up to 2000, has been the most favoured site for Knot. Birds have been found in every month except February, with the peak in September. The biggest count was of 13 flying in at dusk on 18th September 1984. *Wraysbury Reservoir*: 19th September 1973, 29th August 1973 (24 south), 2nd September 1984 (11 southwest), 6th-9th September 1995 (five), 24th August 1995, 12th-18th September 1995, 21st September 2000.

Since 2000. There have been at least 20 further vice-county birds from 2001 to mid 2005, including eight at Beddington on 18th September 2001 and 12 at Queen Elizabeth II Reservoir on 29th August 2004. At Staines Reservoirs there were 40 birds on 10th August 2004 (*LNHSB*).

Large counts. A flock of 50 after sunset at Wisley Village on 23rd August 1968 is the largest for the vice-county. The birds were calling as they flew over low. The biggest flock of all was one of 160, seen at King George VI Reservoir in November 1964.

Calendar and movements. As the table of bird months shows, they are mainly of autumn passage migrants, with a rather weak spring passage and a few appearing in winter. The only bird months for June are from Spelthorne:

Bird months 1900-2005

	Jan	Feb	Mar	Apr	May	Jun	Jul	Aug	Sep	Oct	Nov	Dec	Total
Vice-county	13	36	7	4	21	0	1	62	8	8	2	15	**177**
Spelthorne	4	4	8	9	35	9	15	108	177	20	184	18	**591**

Sanderling
Calidris alba

Scarce passage migrant

Breeds on the arctic tundras of Canada, Greenland, Spitzbergen (Svalbard) and Siberia and winters on coasts around the world, south to Tierra del Fuego. Those in Britain may have bred in Canada, Greenland or Siberia (*MA*). Passage migrants tend to come from Greenland and are on their way to Africa, whereas the winter residents are often of Siberian origin (*BWP*). The Wetland Bird Survey shows a national decline in winter numbers.

Early Surrey history. Waring Kidd said that Sanderlings had been shot 'not unfrequently' at Frensham (Newman, 1849). Stafford bought one that had been shot on the Thames near Putney Bridge (*SCCMS*, but Bucknill says two). Two were shot near Farnham a few years before 1854 (Spicer, 1854) and a pair were shot at West Molesey in the spring of 1870 (Bucknill).

After 1900. One at Barn Elms Reservoirs on 6th April 1939 appears to be the first for the site. Sanderlings were seen at Guildford on 14th March and 6th May 1942 and in May 1944. One at Frensham on 2nd May 1960 appears to be the first there since before 1900. It was followed by several more there in 1964 (May), 1966 (May and August) and 1969 (May).

The earliest Spelthorne records are of single birds at Staines Reservoirs on 4th September 1928 and 5th April 1930. There were three at Queen Mary Reservoir on 28th August 1931 and one was seen at the same

Queen Elizabeth II Reservoir　　　*Photo D. M. Harris*

place on 18th September 1931 (Glegg). Another was found at Staines Reservoirs on 24th May 1936. Sanderlings soon became annual passage migrants there, mostly in May.

Where found. The majority of the 268 vice-county bird months from 1900 to 2000 were from Barn Elms (77) and Queen Elizabeth II Reservoir (79). Beddington (27), Frensham Great Pond (27) and Walton Reservoirs (14) are the only other sites in double figures. The other bird months were at Frensham, Frimley Gravel Pits, Gatton (three), Guildford (nine), Holmethorpe (two), Papercourt (three), Richmond Park, Tilhill Nurseries and Walton Gravel Pits. There were at least 25 bird months from 2001 to 2004, coming from Barn Elms, Beddington, Queen Elizabeth II Reservoir and Walton Reservoirs. Sanderling have been far more numerous at the Spelthorne reservoirs, with around 300 bird months up to 1970 alone.

Calendar. Nearly two thirds (168) of the 20th century bird months were in May. The return passage peaked at only 17 in August. Winter records were most frequent in February.

Bird months 1900-2000

	Jan	Feb	Mar	Apr	May	Jun	Jul	Aug	Sep	Oct	Nov	Dec	Total
Vice-county	8	17	2	18	168	4	16	17	15	0	1	2	**268**

One at Barn Elms Reservoirs on 11th June 1987 was the first vice-county June record since 1900. Another at Barn Elms Reservoirs on 30th November 1973 and two there on 2nd December 1973 were the only vice-county records for these months. There are no vice-county records for October but there is at least one for Spelthorne.

Large counts

Frensham Great Pond: eight, 11th May 1969
Queen Elizabeth II Reservoir: eight, 20th May
　1997

Spelthorne

Perry Oaks Sewage Farm: 22, 16th May 1953 (*BLA*).
Staines Reservoirs: 25, 16th May 1994
Wraysbury Reservoir: 22, 16th May 1970

Movements and longevity. An adult ringed at Frensham on 14th August 1966 was recovered in Norfolk, 209 km away, on 17th May 1969.

Little Stint

Calidris minuta

Scarce passage migrant, mainly in September, scarce in spring

Breeds on arctic tundras from Norway east to Siberia, wintering mainly in Africa, and coastal areas of Arabia and India. Those ringed or recovered in Britain have links with Norway, southern Europe and northwest Africa (*MA*).

Early Surrey history. Several were killed at Battersea in 1869 and one of them was in the Charterhouse Museum in Bucknill's time but the bird currently held there has Norfolk as its provenance.

20th century. The next record located is of one seen by Bentham at Frensham Little Pond on 22nd July 1919. There was one at Barn Elms ('one of the reservoirs near Hammersmith Bridge') on 30th September 1930 and another there on 22nd September 1931. During a national influx in 1936, P. A. D. Hollom found one at Brooklands on 14th August 1936, increasing to three on 18th September. In Spelthorne, there was one at Queen Mary Reservoir on 15th and 18th September 1936. Frensham Great Pond saw one on 10th October 1946. A national influx in the autumn of 1953 brought ten to Perry Oaks Sewage Farm on 19th and 20th September.

Where found. Of approximately 382 vice-county bird months from 1900 to 2000, 208 were at Beddington. There have been 58 from Barn Elms, 24 from Queen Elizabeth II Reservoir and 22 from Walton Reservoirs. The remainder were from Ash Vale Gravel Pits, Berrylands Sewage Works (thirteen), Brooklands (eight), Esher, Frensham (nine), Frimley Gravel Pits, Guildford (fourteen), Hersham (five), Holmethorpe (four), Island Barn Reservoir (three), Lonsdale Road Reservoir, Molesey Gravel Pit (three), Molesey Sewage Farm (two), Papercourt Gravel Pits (five), Richmond Park and Thorpe. None have been recorded in February or March. From 1972 to 2000, Little Stints were recorded in every year except 1982. There was a national influx in 1996, which brought record numbers to Surrey.

Calendar. Spring passage is trivial. By far the most have been seen in September.

Bird months 1900-2000

	Jan	Feb	Mar	Apr	May	Jun	Jul	Aug	Sep	Oct	Nov	Dec	Total
Vice-county	1	0	0	2	18	9	15	26	259	43	3	6	**382**

One at Beddington on 15th-17th April 1994 was the first for April. One at Berrylands Sewage Works on 3rd June 1977 was the first for June. One at Hersham on 29th December 1976 was the first for December.

After 2000. Later vice-county records have come from Barn Elms, Beddington, Hersham Gravel Pit, Queen Elizabeth II Reservoir and Walton Reservoirs, with a maximum of five at Beddington on 19th September 2001. There have been numerous records from the Spelthorne reservoirs. One at Staines Reservoirs on 1st January 2002 is the only Spelthorne record located for January.

Large counts. An exceptional national influx in 1996 was reflected in the largest counts:

Berrylands Sewage Works: nine, 21st September 1996

Queen Elizabeth II Reservoir: ten, 1st October 1960

Beddington Sewage Farm: 48, 23rd September 1996

Spelthorne

Perry Oaks Sewage Farm: 39, 10th September 1978

Staines Reservoir: 14+, 28th September 1976

Wraysbury Reservoir: 76, 25th September 1996

Temminck's Stint
Calidris temminckii

Twenty-two vice-county records and about 25 from Spelthorne to 2004.

Breeds from northern Britain and Scandinavia east to northern Siberia, wintering in Africa and southern Asia. Arrived in Britain 10,000 years ago (Thomas, 1999, no evidence given). Ringing has shown British links with Norway, Finland and Spain. In Britain, Temminck's Stints occur most often in May, with a return passage peaking in August and September. Most are found on the east coast but birds are frequently found in inland counties.

Surrey. The records are consistent with the national pattern and are becoming more frequent:

1936: Brooklands, 29th May (first for the London area).

1944: Guildford, one on 23rd-26th August.

1951: Barn Elms Reservoirs, one on 12th and 13th May.

1961: Holmethorpe Sand Pits, one on 4th June.

1965: Barn Elms Reservoirs, one on 5th and 7th September (photograph in the *LBR*).

1980: Richmond Park, one at Pen Ponds on 27th September.

1981: Beddington Sewage Farm, one on 7th May.

1985: Barn Elms Reservoirs, two on 16th May.

1986: Barn Elms Reservoirs, two on 16th May (same date and basin as in 1985).

1988: Hersham Gravel Pit, one on 18th May.

1989: Beddington Sewage Farm, one from 31st May to 4th June.
Hersham Gravel Pit, one on 2nd June.

1990: Beddington Sewage Farm, one on 2nd May.

1991: Barn Elms Reservoirs, one on 30th May.
Beddington Sewage Farm, one on 1st June.

1992: Walton Reservoirs, single birds on 13th, 27th and 28th May (two birds?).

1993: Beddington Sewage Farm, one on 18th-23rd September.

1994: Beddington Sewage Farm, one on 20th May.

1995: Barn Elms Reservoirs, one on 2nd September.

1999: Hersham Gravel Pit, four on 19th May, two next morning, three there in evening, then one still there on the 21st.
Beddington Sewage Farm, one on 29th-31st May.

2003: Beddington Sewage Farm, one on 22nd-24th August.

2004: Beddington Sewage Farm, one on 22nd-25th May 2004.
Beddington Sewage Farm, one calling in flight on 13th August.

There are over twenty records from Spelthorne (single birds unless otherwise indicated): *Perry Oaks Sewage Farm*: 19th September 1954; three on 21st September 1957, 16th-17th May and two on 25th-26th May 1964, two on 15th September 1968, 4th-5th May 1975, 29th August 1975, 10th-15th August 1980, and 29th May 1981, two on 18th May 1987, 19th and 23rd May 1987, 12th and 14th May 1993; *Perry Oaks Sewage Farm* and *King George VI Reservoir*: dates from 9th to 27th September 1955; *River Colne at Staines Moor*: 27th April 1949; *Staines Reservoirs*:16th, 22nd and 31st May 1978, 13th May 1985, two on 26th-28th May 1985, 5th-7th September 1985, 4th May 1988, 6th May

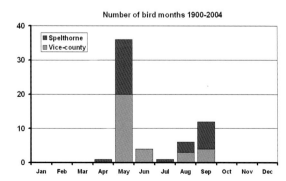

Number of bird months 1900-2004

1992 (also seen at King George VI Reservoir) and 20th May 1992 and 5th July and 23rd-24th August 2004 (*LNHSB*); *Stanwell Moor Gravel Pits*: 28th May 1977.

White-rumped Sandpiper   *Calidris fuscicollis*
Two birds, one of which was in Spelthorne

Breeds in North America and winters in South America. In Britain, White-rumped Sandpipers are almost entirely autumn migrants, peaking in October with occasional winter records and mainly found on the eastern coastal counties. Surrey and Staffordshire were the only inland counties to record the species from 1958 to 1985.

Surrey. There was one at Perry Oaks Sewage Farm from 30th July to 12th August 1984, possibly not in Spelthorne. One at Staines Reservoirs on 18th August 1984 was presumed to be the same bird (R. B. Hastings *et al.*) For both records see *BB*, *78:547, 79:546*. An adult at Walton Reservoirs on 30th August 1995 was found by D. M. Harris (*BB, 89:500*).

Baird's Sandpiper   *Calidris bairdii*
Two birds, both in Spelthorne

Breeds from northeast Siberia east to Greenland and winters in southern South America. British records are nearly all on the autumn migration, peaking in September, with just a few from April to June. Most occurrences are in the southwest, with a few in inland counties. Wintering birds are extremely unusual.

Surrey. There was one at Perry Oaks Sewage Farm on 17th-22nd September 1950 (*BB, 44:252-53*), after a period of strong westerly and south westerly gales in the late summer which also brought a Pectoral Sandpiper and two Sabine's Gulls to the area. This was the first record for Middlesex and the first sight record for Britain, previous birds having been shot. A first-year bird at Staines Reservoirs from 14th October 1982 to 24th April 1983 (G. M. Haig, J. Herbert, G. A. Richards *et al.*, *BB, 76:493, 77:523*), was remarkable in being the first known wintering of the species in the Western Palearctic. The north basin at Staines Reservoirs was drained at the time, leaving a large area of gravel, muddy sand and shallow pools.

Pectoral Sandpiper   *Calidris melanotos*
Thirty-nine records, including 28 from Spelthorne up to 2000, at least two since then

Breeds in the tundras of eastern Siberia and North America, wintering in South America. Birds have been recorded in Britain throughout the year. Most are thought to come from North America, with some coming west from Siberia (*MA*). By far the commonest month of occurrence is September. Although there is a southern and coastal bias to the records, many birds have been found in inland counties. There were significant invasions in 1948, 1950 and 2003. The second of these followed a period of westerly and southwesterly gales.

Surrey. The first for Surrey, Middlesex and the London area, was at Perry Oaks Sewage Farm on 16th-24th September 1950 (*BB, 44:250-51*, to 29th in the *LBR*). Records peaked in the 1980s but began to recover after the 1990s.

Bird months by decade since 1950, incomplete after 2003

	1950s	1960s	1970s	1980s	1990s	2000-06	Total
Vice-county	3	1	0	4	4	6	**18**
Spelthorne	6	6	4	16	3	7	**42**

Where found. Most vice-county records have been at Beddington Sewage Farm. Others have been at Barn Elms, Berrylands Sewage Works, Epsom, Queen Elizabeth II Reservoir, Thursley/Ockley Commons, Unstead Sewage Farm and Walton Reservoirs. A bird found at Beddington on 12th May 1988 was the first spring record for the London area. Among the Spelthorne sites, Perry Oaks Sewage Farm has attracted the most birds.

Calendar. Records fit the pattern rather well, being sharply peaked in September:

Bird months 1950 to 2006

	Jan	Feb	Mar	Apr	May	Jun	Jul	Aug	Sep	Oct	Nov	Dec	Total
Vice-county	0	0	0	0	1	0	1	4	10	2	0	0	**18**
Spelthorne	0	0	0	0	0	0	3	6	29	4	0	0	**42**

Detailed records are below:

Vice-county

Barn Elms: from 4th-12th September 1994; *Beddington*: 17th-27th September 1988 (a juvenile), 12th-14th May 1989, 2nd-6th August 1989, 1st-2nd July 1991, 23rd September 1992, 20th-29th September 1993, 3rd-12th October 2002, 24th September to 1st October 2003, 13th and 15th September 2006; *Berrylands Sewage Works*: 8th September 1984; *Epsom*: from 30th August to 8th September 1952, 19th-24th September 1956 (three dates); *Thursley/Ockley Common (Pudmore)*: 30th August 1964; *Unstead Sewage Farm*: 11th September 2003; *Walton* and *Queen Elizabeth II reservoirs*: 6th-7th September 2003.

Spelthorne

King George VI Reservoir: 2nd September 1995; *Perry Oaks Sewage Farm*: 16th-29th September 1950, 31st August to 10th September 1951, 13th-15th September 1954 (first bird), 20th-21st September 1954 (second bird), 20th-28th September 1958 (*BB, 53:165*), 29th-30th July 1960 (first bird), 21st August 1960 (second bird), 26th August to 3rd September 1960 (third bird) (*BB, 54:185*), 8th-16th September 1962, 19th July 1964; 12th-20th September 1979 (two), 15th-22nd September 1981 (first bird), 26-27th September 1981 (second bird), 16th August 1982, 31st August to 5th September 1982 (*BB, 56:400*), 1st-5th September 1984, 4th-11th September 1988, 20th September 1989, 20th September 1994; *Perry Oaks Sewage Farm* and *Stanwell Moor Gravel Pits*: 1st-9th September 1971; *Staines Reservoirs*: 24th September 1970, 30th September 1982 (first bird), 6th-14th October 1982 (second bird), 7th-12th September 1984 (the Perry Oaks bird), 17th September to 8th October 1984 (first bird), 26th-29th September 1984 (second bird), 21st October 1984 (third bird, juvenile); *Stanwell Moor*: 29th September 1999, 11th-22nd September 2003, also seen at King George VI Reservoir.

Single birds were seen at Staines Reservoirs in August 2004, with two there in September 2004 (*LNHSB*) and one in October (*Bird Watching*). There was another at Staines Reservoirs from 22nd September to 2nd October 2005 (*LNHSB*).

Sharp-tailed Sandpiper   *Calidris acuminata*

One bird, Spelthorne

Breeds on the eastern part of the north Siberian tundra and normally winters in the Pacific Region south of the Equator. Accidental in Europe. Most British birds are seen in August.

Surrey. There was an adult at Staines Reservoirs on 6th August 1976 (R. J. and Mrs S. M. Johns and E. T. Welland, *BB, 70:423*).

Curlew Sandpiper

Calidris ferruginea

Scarce passage migrant

Breeds on the north Siberian tundras, wintering in Africa and on coasts from Arabia east to Australia. A national influx in the autumn of 1953.

Early Surrey history. There are no dated records in Newman (who described it as an occasional visitor to the Godalming district) and none in Bucknill.

20th century. One at Frensham Little Pond on 13th April 1906 (Mouritz) seems to be the first dated record. W. A. Shaw found another there on 16th August 1920. There was one at Brooklands Sewage Farm on 20th September 1931 and two were there on the 22nd. In 1936 there were three on 14th and 16th September. There was one at 'Godalming Sewage Farm' (Unstead?) on 10th November 1937 and another at Pen Ponds, Richmond Park on 23rd October 1938.

In Spelthorne, the first was at Staines South reservoir on 7th September 1927 and there were two more on 10th September, when mud was exposed (Glegg). These birds were the first for the London area since one at Brent Reservoir (not Surrey) in 1873.

Where found. There were 137 vice-county bird months from 1900 to 2001. Almost half of them were from Beddington Sewage Farm, followed by Queen Elizabeth II Reservoir with twelve, Guildford Sewage Farm and Horsell with eleven each and Brooklands Sewage Farm with ten. The remainder were from Barn Elms (four), Berrylands, Elmers End Sewage Farm, Frensham (three), Godalming, Hersham (two), Holmethorpe (three), Papercourt (three), Pen Ponds, Ripley Sewage Farm, Unstead Sewage Farm (two) and Walton Reservoirs (four). There were five times as many records (698) from the Spelthorne reservoirs. After 2001, there were records from Barn Elms in 2002, Beddington Sewage Farm in 2002 and Walton Reservoirs in 2003. There were up to four Curlew Sandpipers at Staines Reservoirs in September 2005 (*LNHSB*).

Calendar. Of 137 vice-county bird months, August and September accounted for 112 and there were none in February, March or December. The 698 in Spelthorne have a very similar distribution.

The single January occurrence is of a Curlew Sandpiper at Unstead Sewage Farm on 16th January 1946. One at Holmethorpe Sand Pits on 24th May 1981 was the first vice-county bird for May. Four at Brooklands Sewage Farm on 2nd June 1939 were the only vice-county June birds ever. The first for June in Spelthorne was at Staines Reservoirs in 1983. One at Frensham Great Pond on 1st November 1963 was a Surrey first for the month, the first for Spelthorne being in 1982.

Bird months 1900-2001

	Jan	Feb	Mar	Apr	May	Jun	Jul	Aug	Sep	Oct	Nov	Dec	Total
Vice-county	1	0	0	3	5	4	3	55	57	7	2	0	**137**
Spelthorne	0	0	0	1	22	5	17	217	344	86	5	1	**698**

Large counts

Beddington Sewage Farm: nine, 20th-21st
  September 1994
Bonsey's Farm, Horsell: eleven, 23rd August 1995
Guildford Sewage Farm: six, 29th August 1960
Queen Elizabeth II Reservoir: nine, 29th August
  1999

Spelthorne
Perry Oaks Sewage Farm: 58, 26th August 1970
Staines Reservoir: 36, 10th September 1985

Purple Sandpiper
Calidris maritima

Nine vice-county records and at least seventeen from Spelthorne

Breeds in Scandinavia and in the arctic regions of Siberia, Canada and Greenland, wintering on the coasts of Europe and North America. Remains dating back to the post-glacial tundra or earlier have been found in Britain. Purple Sandpipers have occasionally bred in Scotland. The Wetland Bird Survey shows a national decline in winter numbers.

In Surrey, Purple Sandpipers have most often been seen in November:

Queen Elizabeth II Reservoir — *Photo D. M. Harris*

1900: Milford, one shot on a pond before 1900 was in the Charterhouse Museum in Shaw's time but the specimen currently held there has Wells as its provenance.

1871: Thames near Molesey, a male shot on 9th January (Bucknill).

1933: Barn Elms Reservoir, one on 2nd November (*BB, 27:209*).

1936:* Staines Reservoirs, one on 29th -30th November (*BB, 30:260, LBR,* first for Middlesex).

1939:* Staines Reservoirs, one on 5th November.

1956: Beddington Sewage Farm, one on 2nd February.

1959:* Queen Mary Reservoir, one on 1st November.

1962:* Staines Reservoirs, one on 13th October. Staines Reservoirs, three on 28th December.

1963:* Queen Mary Reservoir, one on 12th November.

1964:* Queen Mary Reservoir one on 4th November.

1969:* Staines Reservoirs, one on 9th and 11th March.

1970:* Staines Reservoirs, one on 1st-2nd November. Queen Mary Reservoir, one on 7th November.

1970: Thorpe Gravel Pits, one on 30th November.

1972:* Perry Oaks Sewage Farm, one from 18th August to 24th September. One at Staines Reservoirs on 11th September might have been this bird, as might one at Stanwell Moor Gravel Pits on 1st October.

Queen Mary Reservoir, one on 3rd November. This or another on dates to 30th November.

1973:* Staines Reservoirs, one on 30th October.

1974:* Staines Reservoirs, one on 16th November. Queen Mary Reservoir, one on 18th December.

1984: Teddington Lock, one on a rocky islet on 9th-10th September.

1991: Chelsea Reach, one on 7th February. Flew from one side of the river to the other and landed among rocks by the Albert Bridge.

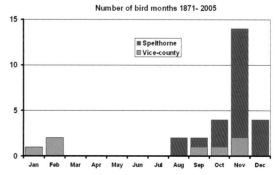
Number of bird months 1871- 2005

Legend: ■ Spelthorne ☐ Vice-county

1991:*   Staines Reservoirs, one on 2nd-4th November.

2003:*   Staines Reservoirs, one on 29th August.

Staines Reservoirs, one on 8th November.

2004:   Queen Elizabeth II Reservoir, one on 25th October (D. M. Harris).

2005:   Island Barn Reservoir, one on 24th December (D. M. Harris, M. Lawford).

*Spelthorne

Dunlin   *Calidris alpina*

Scarce winter visitor and passage migrant

Breeds in the tundra regions of the northern hemisphere and on European moors and wetlands around the Baltic and in the British Isles. Most winter in coastal regions of Europe, North America, the Arabian Gulf, Southeast Asia and the south and west coast of Africa. The race *schinzii* breeds in the British Isles. The majority of those found in Britain outside the breeding season are of the race *alpina*, which breeds from the northern regions of Finland and Scandinavia east to Siberia (*MA*). The lowland population of the British Isles was in decline throughout the 20th century.

Queen Elizabeth II Reservoir   Photo D. M. Harris

Early Surrey history. H. L. Long saw Dunlin at Hampton Lodge, Puttenham in the 1820s (Bucknill) and Meyer (1842) said he had shot them on the Thames in winter. One shot at Battersea was in the Charterhouse Museum in Bucknill's time but the birds currently there have Norfolk/Sussex for provenance. Power heard night migrants in the Dulwich area on 20th April and 12th August, 1876 and saw one going west over his Brixton garden on 8th November 1890. There was one at East Molesey on 10th April 1878, one was caught alive at Witley Station on 4th August 1891 and there were several at Mitcham in the autumn of 1895. Dunlin have been shot at Poynter's, near Cobham and found at Frensham (Bucknill).

1900 to 1970. There were two at Frensham on 3rd September 1905 (*Zool.*, 1905:348) and one was there on 5th August 1906 (Mouritz). Winter records came from Barn Elms and Putney in 1907-08 (*BLA*). Shaw knew of ten local records, mostly at Frensham and there were eleven records at Frensham from 1920-54, where they are still seen on passage from time to time and had been seen in every month of the year by 1980.

There were three at Staines Reservoirs on 9th April 1922 and, during August 1927 when mud was exposed, at least 40 were there Glegg (1935). Four sightings (28th-29th July, August, and December) at Barn Elms in 1925 were among the first of many records for the site. At Queen Mary Reservoir there were three on 4th May 1930. There were up to three on spring and autumn passage at Brooklands Sewage Farm up to 1936. Twenty on the Thames foreshore opposite Chiswick and 32 at Barn Elms in a cold spell in December 1938 were exceptional numbers for the period. Dunlin were seen at Guildford Sewage Farm in April and May and on 24th July 1944. They were often found there in subsequent years. Up to 25 were at Broadmead (Send) and Unstead in 1946. There was a peak of five at Barn Elms on 2nd May 1948. Other sites at which they have occurred include Addington, Ash Vale Gravel Pits, Beddington Sewage Farm, Barn Elms Reservoirs, Cutt Mill, Dorking Sewage Farm, Eagle Pond (Clapham Common),

Enton, Epsom Sewage Farm, Esher Sewage Farm, Farnborough North Gravel Pits, Farnham Sewage Farm, Fetcham Mill Pond, Frensham, Hamm Moor Gravel Pits, Hersham, Holmethorpe, Island Barn Reservoir, Lonsdale Road Reservoir, Molesey Sewage Farm, Papercourt Gravel Pits, Queen Elizabeth II Reservoir, Thorpe, Tice's Meadow, Walton Reservoirs/Gravel Pits and Wimbledon Common.

Since 1970. From 1970 to 2006, Dunlin were seen at many of the wetlands of 1945-69 and at new ones including Addlestone, Apps Court Gravel Pit, Badshot Lea, Berrylands Sewage Works, Chobham Common, Coleford Farm Gravel Pit, Effingham Fish Ponds, Epsom Common, Frimley, Ham Lands, Haslemere, Kew Gardens, Long Ditton, Lyne Sewage Farm, Normandy, Old Woking Sewage Farm, Peasmarsh, Richmond Park, Ripley Sewage Farm, South Norwood Country Park, Stoke Lake, the Surrey Docks, Sydenham Hill, Thursley, Tilhill Nurseries, Tuesley Farm (Milford), and Wrecclesham,

Calendar. The largest numbers have been in winter, with a weak spring and autumn passage. Big winter counts are usually from wet, stony grassland as at Hersham Gravel Pit in 1999 and on the beds of drained reservoirs at Walton-on-Thames in 1991-93 and Staines Reservoirs in 1998 and 2004.

Vice-county bird totals 1994-2001

	Jan	Feb	Mar	Apr	May	Jun	Jul	Aug	Sep	Oct	Nov	Dec	Total
Total	384	290	224	128	205	33	105	157	169	74	210	498	2477
%	15.5	11.7	9.0	5.2	8.3	1.3	4.2	6.3	6.8	3.0	8.5	20.1	100.0

Large counts. The largest counts are relatively recent:

Barn Elms: 24, 15th March 1992

Beddington Sewage Farm: 82, 2nd February 1956

Frensham: total of at least 15 flew west on 30th January 1976

Hersham Gravel Pit: 85, December 1999

Queen Elizabeth II Reservoir: 108, 19th December 1996

Surrey Docks: *c.*70, 11th December 1973

Walton Reservoirs: 162, 11th March 1992

Spelthorne

King George VI Reservoir: 290, November 1991

Perry Oaks Sewage Farm: 142, December 1983

Shepperton Gravel Pits: 60, December 1999

Staines Moor: 70 in December 1995

Staines Reservoirs: 244, November 1998 (when the south basin was drained), 293 on 26th July 2004 (*LNHSB*)

Wraysbury Reservoir: 82 in December 1990

Movements. A Dunlin ringed at East Tilbury on 22nd November 1962 was found dead at Mortlake, 47 km west, on 6th December of the same year.

Northern Dunlin   *Calidris alpina alpina*

Surrey. Subspecific identification is rarely claimed. A bird with characteristics of this race, which may be the commonest race in winter, was at Barn Elms WWT on 15th May 2002 (*London Wetland Centre Bird and Natural History Report 2001 and 2002*) and two more were there in May 2005 (*LNHSB*).

Southern Dunlin   *Calidris alpina schinzii*

Surrey. One with characteristics of this British breeding race was at Barn Elms on 14th and 15th May 2005 (*LNHSB*).

Buff-breasted Sandpiper
Four birds, including three in Spelthorne

Tryngites subruficollis

Breeds on the North American tundra and winters in South America. A few migrating birds reach the British Isles, usually in September and early October and most frequently in the southwest.

Surrey. All the birds were found in September or October:

1953:* Perry Oaks Sewage Farm, one was found by B. A. Richards and L. Baker on 18th October and further dates to 3rd November (*BB, 47:310*). Possibly outside the Spelthorne boundary.

1977:* Staines Reservoirs, one from 14th September to 2nd October (J. Hazell, A. V. Moon and P. Naylor, *BB, 71:501*).

1981:* Perry Oaks Sewage Farm, a juvenile on 12th-25th September (R. B. Hastings, A. V, Moon and P. Naylor, *BB, 75:502*), possibly outside the Spelthorne boundary.

1981: Barn Elms Reservoirs, one on 12th October (P. E. Brown, *BB, 76:495*).

*Spelthorne

Ruff
Scarce passage migrant

Philomachus pugnax

Breeds from England through northern Europe and east to the Bering Strait, wintering mainly in Africa and India. Remains dating back to the post-glacial tundras have been found in Britain. The Ruff were widespread, but local, breeding birds in eastern counties from Northumberland to East Anglia up to the end of the 18th century but persecution and habitat loss wiped them out in most areas by 1900 and everywhere by 1923. Recolonisation began in 1963 (Ouse Washes) and is still continuing.

Early Surrey history. A 'considerable flight' apparently all juveniles, was seen at Godalming on 20th August 1836 (Waring Kidd in Newman, 1849). Several were killed at Broadwater in 1840 (Bucknill). Bucknill thought that at least four from these two occurrences were in the Charterhouse Collection but none of the five currently held have Surrey as their provenance.

1900 to 1970. Glegg gave the first three Spelthorne records as one on 8th September 1928, two on 1st May 1929 and one on 28th August 1931, all from Queen Mary Reservoir. There was one at Brooklands Sewage Farm on 30th July 1934. In 1936 there were two there on 28th March and three on 22nd April. A national influx in the autumn of 1953 brought a maximum of 14 to Perry Oaks Sewage Farm on 23rd August. A major influx began in January 1954, producing a peak of 119 at Perry Oaks on 8th April. The last spring bird was seen on 9th May (*BLA*). Up to 38 (1968) were subsequently seen there annually to 1969. One at Unstead Sewage Farm on 25th-26th March 1956 was the first for the site, as was one at Frensham on 23rd August 1971. There were about 25 at Beddington Sewage Farm on 8th September 1968. There were about 33 bird months in the 1930s, 11 in the 1940s, 110 in the 1950s and 157 in the 1960s.

Where found since 1970. The upward trend continued. The main vice-county sites since 1970 have been Beddington Sewage Farm and the Hersham area. Ruff have also been recorded at Addlestone, Apps Court Farm, Barn Elms, Battersea Park (on the frozen lake, February 1976), Berrylands Sewage Works, Brooklands, Buckland Sand Pits, Effingham Fish Ponds, Epsom Common, Esher Gravel Pit, Fetcham Mill Pond (December 1978), Frensham, Frimley Gravel Pits, Gatwick, Guildford Sewage Farm, Holmethorpe, Island Barn Reservoir, Mitcham Common, Old Woking Sewage Farm, Papercourt Gravel Pits, Pudmore Pond (Thursley), Queen Elizabeth II Reservoir, Richmond Park, Ripley Sewage Farm, the River Thames, the River Wandle, Shalford Meadows, South Norwood Country Park, Stoke D'Abernon, Stoke Water Meadows, the Surrey Docks, Thorpe Water Park, Tilhill Nurseries, Unstead Sewage Farm, Walton Reservoirs and Wrecclesham. There were around 40 bird months annually from 1994 to 2001.

Records since 2000 have come from Barn Elms, Beddington, Hersham, Queen Elizabeth II Reservoir, Unstead Sewage Farm and Walton Reservoirs. In Spelthorne, numbers have been lower since the mid 1970s and double digit counts are now unusual. Eleven flew south at Staines Reservoirs on 31st August 2000. Creation of the right habitat, at Barn Elms perhaps, may yet bring a Surrey breeding record.

Calendar. There is a strong autumn passage in August and September. Ruff often winter, arriving in December, peaking in January and with a spring passage peaking in April. One at Beddington Sewage Farm on 28th June 1981 was apparently the first for June.

Vice-county bird totals 1994-2001

	Jan	Feb	Mar	Apr	May	Jun	Jul	Aug	Sep	Oct	Nov	Dec	Total
Total	23	21	35	36	20	8	16	37	104	10	3	10	323
%	7.1	6.5	10.8	11.1	6.2	2.5	5.0	11.5	32.2	3.1	0.9	3.1	100

Large counts from 1970 onward:

Beddington Sewage Farm: 32, 11th September 1993

Walton Reservoirs: 19, January 1991

Spelthorne

Perry Oaks Sewage Farm: 42, January 1972

Staines Moor: 42, March 1976

Staines Reservoirs: 40, February 1975.

Jack Snipe   *Lymnocryptes minimus*

Scarce winter visitor

Breeds in northern regions from Scandinavia east to Siberia, wintering in the more southerly parts of Europe and from sub-Saharan Africa east to India. Most British-ringed birds recovered abroad are found in France (*MA*). Jack Snipe may have bred in Britain about 10,000 years ago (Thomas, 1999).

Early Surrey history. It is fairly clear from writings of the period that Jack Snipe were a good deal more common in the first half of the 19th century than they were in 1900 or are today. Sites mentioned by Bucknill were Bagshot (not later than 1858), Banstead, Epsom Common, Frensham, Godalming, Guildford, Haslemere, Mitcham, the Mole near Dorking, Nutfield Marsh, Pudmore and Upper Norwood (not later than 1870). Hamilton (1881) found them on Wimbledon Common, but less frequently after the common was drained in 1874.

Where found, 1900 to 1970. Kierton (1909) includes a photograph taken by his brother Cherry of a Jack Snipe feeding in a ditch close to Redhill. Other records for the first half of the 20th century came from Gatton Park (October 1907 and January 1908 (*BLA*)), Weybridge Sewage Farm, (December 1929), Staines Moor, Spelthorne (single birds on 28th February and 6th March 1932), Beddington Sewage Farm, (1st January 1933 etc) and Limpsfield, (one on 3rd February 1934). In 1936 there were records of single birds at the Devil's Jumps, Churt (6th January), Richmond Park (6th October) and Thursley (November). Jack Snipe were found at Beddington and Brooklands sewage farms, Cuddington, Epsom Common and Walton Heath in 1937. Two were flushed at Frensham Little Pond on 15th January 1939 and there were other single birds near Horley in January 1940, at Enton and Ripley in 1942, Fetcham Watercress beds, Guildford Sewage Farm and Leatherhead in 1945. There have since been Jack Snipe at Ash Vale Gravel Pits, Ashtead Park, Barn Elms, Beddington Sewage Farm (14 on 8th October 1951, 57 on 26th February 1956), Bookham Common, Bramley Sewage Farm, Burpham, Camberley Sewage Farm, Dulwich Common, Earlswood Sewage Farm, Elmers End Sewage Farm, Elstead, Enton, Epsom Sewage Farm, Ewell (1965), Ewhurst, Fetcham Mill Pond and Watercress beds, Frimley Gravel Pits, Godstone, Guildford Sewage Farm, Hamm Moor Gravel Pits, Hersham Sewage Farm, Holmethorpe, Horley Sewage Farm, Lonsdale Road Reservoir, Lyne Sewage Farm, Malden Sewage Farm, Molesey Sewage Farm, Ockley Common, Papercourt Gravel Pits, Richmond Park, Send, South Norwood Lake,

Thorpe, Unstead Sewage Farm, Walton Reservoirs, West Molesey, Whitmoor Common and Worcester Park Sewage Farm (12 in 1965).

Since 1970. Vice-county records became more frequent at Frensham, Ockley and Thursley Commons in the 1970s. Other sites since 1970 include Ashtead Common, Badshot Lea, Barn Elms, Barnes, Beddington Sewage Farm, Berrylands Sewage Works, Blackwater Meadows, Bramley Sewage Farm, Broadford, Buckland Sand Pits, Capel, Cheam Park, Chertsey Meads, Chobham Common, Earlswood Sewage Farm, Epsom Common Stew Ponds, Ewell, Farnham Sewage Farm, Fetcham Mill Pond, Frensham, Frimley Gravel Pits, Gatwick, Godalming, Guildford Sewage Farm, Ham Lands, Hamm Moor, Hersham Sewage Farm, Hinchley Wood, Holmethorpe (up to eight, *BHSP*), Horton Country Park, Hurst Green, Island Barn Reservoir, Lyne Old Sewage Farm, Molesey Gravel Pit, Morden Hall Park, Papercourt Gravel Pits, Pirbright Common, Richmond Park, Ripley Sewage Farm, Send Water Meadows, Smallfield, South Norwood, Stoke Water Meadows, Surbiton, the Surrey Docks, Thorpe, Thursley/Ockley Commons, Unstead Sewage Farm, Virginia Water, Walton Reservoirs, Wanborough, Whitmoor Common, Wimbledon Common, and Wrecclesham Floods. Although this site list is fairly long, far fewer Jack Snipe are now being seen than was the case 40 years ago. Most of the more recent records have related to single birds. There are post-2000, records from Barn Elms, Beddington, Berrylands Sewage Works, Fetcham Mill Pond, Hankley Common, Hersham, Holmethorpe, Horton Country Park, Morden Hall Park, Pyrford, South Norwood Country Park, Stoke Lake, Thursley Common, Unstead Sewage Farm, Westend Common/Pirbright Ranges, Wimbledon Common and Worcester Park Sewage Farm, the most being 15 at Beddington on 18th October 2002.

One at Sheepwalk East on 19th April 1985 was said to be a first for Shepperton (*Shepp. BR*). Jack Snipe were recorded in 2000 at Perry Oaks Sewage Farm (January), Shepperton Gravel Pits (February) and Staines Moor (April) (*LBR*) and in March 2002 at Staines Moor (*LNHSB*). Few Spelthorne counts of Jack Snipe since 1970 have exceeded five birds.

Calendar. Extreme dates are:

Arrival		Departure	
14th August 1954	Beddington Sewage Farm	5th May 1979	Hersham Sewage Farm
15th September 1976	Beddington Sewage Farm		

Large counts

Beddington Sewage Farm: 64, 20th November 1955	Frensham Great Pond: ten, 14th March 1973
Earlswood Sewage Farm: 15, December 1962	Hersham Sewage Farm: 11, 28th November 1981
Elmers End Sewage Farm: 47, 13th January 1963	Holmethorpe Sand Pits: eight, March and November 1979
Epsom Sewage Farm: 73, 11th February 1956	Unstead Sewage Farm: up to six, 1958 (CNHS)
Fetcham Mill Pond: 12, 25th March 1962	

Movements and longevity. The only foreign recoveries of birds ringed in Surrey are from France, following the national trend. They are passage migrants. Selected recoveries are:

Ringed	Age		Recovered		Distance/age
Epsom	Adult	7th December 1957	France	3rd January 1958	
Stanwell		15th October 1960	France	24th December 1961	514 km SSW
Leatherhead	Adult	24th October 1959	Hersham	27th October 1962	three years later

Migrant Jack Snipe are sometimes found at dry sites, examples being one flushed from dry bracken on Epsom Common in October 1937, ten on burnt ground at Frensham on 14th April 1973 and six flushed from short heather on Bricksbury Hill on 5th March 2000.

Plumage variations. A very dark bird was shot near Staines in January 1861.

Snipe (*Common Snipe*)   *Gallinago gallinago*
Uncommon breeding resident, winter visitor.

A widely distributed breeding bird of the Americas, Europe east to Siberia and Africa, wintering in breeding areas, in Central America and from sub-Saharan Africa east to Southeast Asia. The British Snipe population is hugely augmented by immigrants from the Baltic and Russia in winter. Some British breeding birds move south to France and Spain (*MA*). The British breeding population came under pressure from land drainage and land use changes in the 19th century. There was a recovery from 1900 to 1940, which has been ascribed to the depressed state of British agriculture and a reduction in shooting (*BWP*) but a steep decline is now in progress. BTO Atlas surveys have shown that the decline was resumed, with a 19% fall in the British population between 1968-72 and 1988-91 (*New Atlas*). There has been some recovery since 1995 (*BTO News 266*). Reductions have been being experienced in other parts of the range (*BWP*).

Early Surrey history. Snipe remains dated at about 1230-1268 and others up to 1600 were found when Bermondsey Abbey, Southwark, was excavated. There were 16th century remains at Little Pickle, Bletchingley (Poulton *et al.*). Since the Snipe was a food item, the provenance of these remains is a little uncertain but it might have been local procurement. Gilbert White wrote in his journal for 30th July 1780 that *Young Snipes were seen at the Bishop of Winchester's table, at Farnham castle, on this day. They have bred on all the moory heaths of this neighbourhood.* They still do, here and there, though the Southwark breeding site mentioned by Graves, on the osier (willow) grounds bordering the Surrey Canal, has for rather long been deserted.

19th century. The Boorman egg collection contains specimens taken at Hindhead in 1869. A few may have bred in Richmond Park before drainage in 1860 or 1861 (Collenette). Phillip Crowley had scores of clutches taken from near Frensham, between 1862 and 1882. Snipe were at one time very common in all the meadows and watercourses around Dorking but had become scarcer by the 1890s (Jordan, 1893). Breeding sites mentioned by Bucknill were Cranleigh, Dorking, Elstead, Epsom Common (1894), near Ewood, Frensham, Godstone, near Hampton Lodge, below Hindhead, Leatherhead, near Lingfield mill pond (until it was drained in the 1880s), Mitcham, near Nutfield Marsh and Wimbledon (1899). As many as twelve nests were found at one locality in 1897. Eggs were taken at Elstead, Gatwick and Tilford in 1899 (Maitland and Turnbull). A flock of 400 at Norwood in 1878 and 1881 is described as 'enormous'. Bucknill and a friend flushed 145 on a two mile stretch of the Mole while fishing in hard weather in 1893. He mentioned some of the large sewage farms as offering the best Snipe shooting and instanced Beddington, where 57 were shot in a day. One flew over Power's Brixton garden during a hard frost on 4th February 1889 was his only local record from 1874 to 1909. A fair number came to the Staines area in hard weather at the end of the 19th century (Kerr, 1906).

20th century breeding. Many Snipe were breeding in the first decades of the 20th century. They nested in large numbers on Ockley and Hankley Commons (Parr) and were found breeding at

Camberley (four eggs) in 1905 and Beddington Sewage Farm in 1910, the first sewage farm breeding record for the London area. The Boorman egg collection contains specimens taken at Send in 1916. Snipe bred on Epsom Common some time between 1914 and 1925, near Cobham in the 1930s, at Epsom Sewage Farm in 1934 and 1957 and at Buckland in 1939. They were present around Limpsfield (1934 and 1935) and were probably widely distributed. Glegg (1935) listed the species for Staines Moor without further comment. There has since been a substantial decline across Surrey.

Two pairs of Snipe bred at Beddington Sewage Farm in 1951, four in 1954, two in 1955 and 1957, four in 1958 and two in 1959 Snipe were drumming at Limpsfield in 1954 and Frensham in 1966 and they bred at Milford in 1962. A nest with eggs was found on Staines Moor in 1954 and four pairs bred in 1955-56. Snipe were proved to have bred in the Thursley/Ockley/Elstead area in 1972 (three pairs), 1977 (five or six pairs), 1992, 1994 (family party 7th August) and 1997. They probably bred there fairly frequently over the period. Snipe bred at Stoke Water Meadows in 1975 (nest and eggs) and probably in other years. There

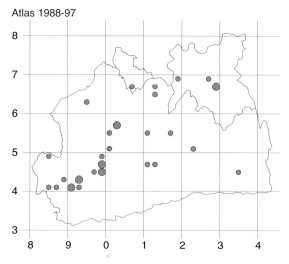

Atlas 1988-97

are no other sites for which proven breeding has been established since 1970, though reports of drumming have come from a number of wetland sites, on wet commonland and in the Mole and Wey valleys.

The 1982 BTO Breeding Waders of Wet Meadows survey found Snipe on six sites out of the 32 that were visited in outer Surrey. The distribution was: SU94 Lammas Lands, Godalming (one present); SU95 Stanford Brook, Woking (one drumming); TQ05 Old Woking (two territories); TQ15 River Mole at Cobham (two present) and Stoke D'Abernon (two present); TQ34 Blindley Heath (one present). Pairs using dry habitats and gravel pits were outside the scope of the survey, missing three drumming birds at Thursley/Ockley Commons. The *London Bird Report* for 1982 indicates that there were none in Greater London or Spelthorne. A repeat of the survey in 2001 found no territorial birds at all. The 1988-97 SBC Atlas survey found Snipe in only 27 tetrads, one of which was in Spelthorne. A few pairs hung on into the 1990s. Drumming or breeding has continued at Beddington up to at least 1997 and one or two can still be found drumming at the Thursley/Ockley Commons and at Stoke Water Meadows.

Migrants. Although declining as breeding birds, for much of the 20th century, Snipe seem to have been recorded as winter visitors and passage migrants in larger numbers than they were before 1900. The main reasons are probably the creation of new habitat on sewage farms where, in the mid 20th century, counts often exceeded the earlier numbers quoted, and the growth of birdwatching. Also few actually counted Snipe flocks before 1900. Immigrants begin arriving in late August and build up to a wintering peak in November or December, after which numbers fall as many birds move further on. Return passage reaches a lower peak in February or March and most migrants have left by early April. Westwood (1961) showed this pattern in weekly counts at Guildford Sewage Farm for the eight years from 1953. A similar pattern was seen at other sites.

There were about 120 at Unstead in November 1947 and 250 in November 1954. Westwood (1961) showed how, from 1954 to 1960, numbers at Guildford Sewage Farm peaked in November with an average count of 430. Very large numbers of Snipe were recorded at Beddington Sewage Farm in the 1950s and 1960s, for example about 1,500 on 11th December 1955 and about 1,000 on 8th December 1968. Exceptional weather conditions brought in an estimated 5,000 birds in December 1962. The days of these large counts now seem to have come to an end with the modernisation or closure of the main sewage farms.

Snipe were regular outside the breeding season at Shepperton in the early 1980s (*Shepp. BR*) and 22 were counted there on 9th February 2000. Snipe are occasionally seen in gardens, *e.g.* at Cranleigh in July 1975, on a freshly watered lawn.

Large counts. The biggest counts go back to the 1950s and 60s:

Addlestone: 37, 23rd March 1995

Ash Vale Gravel Pits: 100, January 1967, 150 prior to 1972 (*HSBBR*)

Badshot Lea: 50+, 18th February 1979

Barn Elms: 91, 24th September 2000

Beddington Sewage Farm: 5,000, December 1962

Bramley Sewage Farm: *c*.100, 3rd January 1971

Brooklands Sewage Farm: 35, 24th August 1936

Chobham Sewage Farm: 35, 31st January 1990

Earlswood Sewage Farm: 300, 30th December 1962

Epsom Sewage Farm: *c*.400, 3rd December 1955

Elmers End Sewage Farm: 500, February 1959

Farnham Sewage Farm: 120, 4th January 1977

Frimley Gravel Pits: 45+, 2nd February 1985

Gatwick Airport: 100, 5th April 1985

Guildford Sewage Farm: 500 on 25th December 1953

Hersham Gravel Pit: 142, December 1997

Hersham Sewage Farm: 100, 24th November 1981

Holmethorpe Sand Pits: 100 on farm fields, 24th November 1994

Hurst Green: 40, 27th March 2001

Lammas Lands: 300, February 1975

Mitcham Common: 200, winter 1947/48

Papercourt Gravel Pits: 150, late 1976

Pyrford: 60, 31st December 1972

Ripley Sewage Farm: 120, 8th December 1974

Send Water Meadows: 300, 21st January 1973

Shalford Meadows: *c*.100, February 1969

Stoke Water Meadows: 110, 27th January 1980

Thorpe: 31, 9th January 2000

Thundry Meadows: 14, 3rd January 1995

Unstead Sewage Farm: 300, 5th January 1970

Walton Reservoirs: 48, February 1995

Wrecclesham Floods: 45, 25th February 1978

Spelthorne:

Perry Oaks Sewage Farm: *c*.250, 4th January 1954

Staines Moor: 150, 25th February 2003

Staines Reservoirs: 350, 30th December 1982, basin drained, Dennis (1990)

Movements and longevity. Snipe ringed in Surrey from October to March have been recovered in Alderney (one, February), Denmark (four, August and October), France (five, November to January, March), Portugal (one, December), Russia (three, May, two in August) and Spain (two, both January). One ringed at Guildford in August 1958 was recovered in Germany in April 1962. The Russian recoveries, from Murmansk (old USSR) in 1965 and Smolensk (old USSR) in 1959 and 1960, suggest breeding localities. The furthest recorded distance travelled is from Earlswood (December 1963) to Murmansk (August 1965), some 2,441 km. The oldest bird was ringed at Hersham on 10th October 1964 and recovered there on 30th November 1969. One was killed by a cat at Farnham in April 1985.

Plumage variations. Bucknill knew of two melanistic birds, one of which was killed at Elstead (*SCCMS*) and the other near Reigate.

Great Snipe   *Gallinago media*

One record.

Breeds from Scandinavia east to Siberia, wintering in Africa. Migrants have been found in Britain in most months, but most frequently from late August to October, almost entirely in eastern coastal counties.

Surrey. H. L. Meyer, in an autumn not later than 1850, flushed two on Chertsey Meads but was unable to shoot them (Meyer in Bucknill). They flew across the Thames, enabling Glegg to claim them for Middlesex (and the present Spelthorne district). This is probably the only record worth claiming for Surrey.

Dowitcher species

Limnodromus griseus/scolopaceus

One before 1900

Most British records of Dowitchers relate to the Long-billed species, which breeds in Alaska and northeast Siberia, wintering south to Guatemala. The Short-billed Dowitcher, *L. griseus*, which breeds in North America, and has a similar breeding range, has never been reliably identified in Surrey.

Surrey. According to Harting (1866, 1889) and *Zool., 1889:416*, a specimen in Frederick Bond's collection had been obtained on the banks of the Thames near Battersea, in or around 1849. The dowitchers were at this time still regarded as one species, and were not split until 1932. Bucknill (1900) listed the bird under the then current name of Red-breasted Snipe *Macrorhampus griseus* and thought it had passed to the Natural History Museum. The Museum did not hold the specimen in 1957-58, when Pitelka examined all its specimens (Pitelka, 1961). Glegg (1935) said it had been sold for two pounds ten shillings (£2.50) at Stevens' on 22nd May 1890. The record is currently graded as Dowitcher species (*Brit. Birds* 54, p.347).

Long-billed Dowitcher

Limnodromus scolopaceus

Two in Spelthorne

The first occurrence was at Staines Reservoirs, where a single bird stayed from 1st-15th October 1977 (I. Archibald, J. Hazell *et al.*, *BB*, *71:503*), to 16th in the *LBR*. There was one of uncertain age at Staines Moor and King George VI Reservoir on 4th-7th October and 24th October to 10th November 1987 and at Perry Oaks Sewage Farm on 8th, 11th and 18th October 1987 (J. A. Hazell, P. Naylor *et al.*, *BB*, *81:558-59*, *LBR*) and 4th November 1987 (*LBR*).

Woodcock (Eurasian Woodcock)

Scolopax rusticola

Locally common breeding resident

Breeds from Europe through central Asia to Japan and in the Himalayas, resident, or wintering south to the Mediterranean, India and Southeast Asia. Many Woodcock that breed in countries round the Baltic, winter in the British Isles or pass through. It is thought that the British breeding population increased during the first half of the 19th century, perhaps because of the spread of woodlands. It may have peaked in the 1880s, when a decline began (*Historical Atlas*). Numbers fell by nearly 90% from 1970 to 2001. The decline may be related to a drying out of woodlands and the maturation of plantations. The preferred habitat is not rare and hence is unprotected (*BTO News 226:4, 9*).

Early Surrey history. Woodcock remains going back to Roman Britain have been found during excavations in the Surrey part of the London area. Two from 18 Union Street, Southwark, were dated at 100-120 AD and one from London Bridge was dated at 120-140. One from Redcross Way and two from Winchester Palace, Southwark were dated at 250-400. Two from the Roman period were found at 15-23 Southwark Street, Southwark. Two others from Winchester Palace were dated at 950-1150. One found at Bermondsey Abbey was dated at 1480-1600. Seven found at Merton Priory were dated at 1230-1300 (two), 1230-1400 (three), 1580-1910 and 1600-1800. Others were found at Chaucer House (1500-1700) and 104 Borough High Street (1666-1800), both Southwark. Woodcock remains found at Guildford Castle were dated at about 1000-1170. Others were from later periods up to 1330. There were 16th century remains at Little Pickle, Bletchingley (Poulton *et al.*). As with other game birds, the exact provenance of all of these is uncertain but they were probably procured locally.

19th century. Young were fledged near Spicer's house at Farnham in 1854. Bucknill thought that the Surrey population had been in decline for most of the century, because of *'building and the reclamation of low-lying grounds'*. Specific breeding localities cited by him were Bagshot Woods (undated), Churt (1896), near Farnham (1853 and 1877), Frimley Park (1860), Godalming (1849 and 1850), Hambledon (*SALEC*), Hampton Lodge at Puttenham (1826), Lingfield (1886), Munstead Heath (Newman, 1849, *SALEC*), St Georges Hill (undated), Streatham (in Yarrell) and Thursley (regular up to the 1880s). Jordan wrote of them nesting near Dorking and on Holmbury Moor. There are other records from Merton (1871) and Farnham (1877).

Fifteen were shot near Haslemere in a single morning in the winter of 1879-80. Bucknill noted Woodcock as winter visitors in varying numbers and mentions *'nine killed in one day by a party of sportsmen, near Guildford, in the winter of 1894, but this is a most unusual bag'*. So it would be today.

1900 to 1940. A pair bred near Leatherhead in 1909 (*BLA*). Woodcock were only winter visitors to the Warlingham district up to the 1920s (Beadell) and to Richmond Park from the 1850s to the 1930s, apart from a few April and May records (Collenette). A pair or two may have bred intermittently in the Farleigh district from the 1930s (Pounds). Woodcock bred near Limpsfield in 1935. They were present on Ranmore Common in May 1939.

Breeding season sites 1941 to 1980. In the period from then until 1980, Woodcock were reported in the breeding season at one time or another from Abinger, Addington, Arbrook Common, Ash Ranges, Ashtead, Bookham Common, Bricksbury Hill, Burgh Heath, Camberley, Caterham, Cranleigh, Crastock (near Woking), Crooksbury Common/Hill, Croydon (Bethlehem Hospital), Cutt Mill, Eashing, East Horsley, Effingham, Elstead, Epsom Common, Esher Common, Fairmile Common, Fairoak Lane Wood, Farleigh, Fetcham Downs, Frensham, Godstone, Haslemere, Headley Heath/Valley, Hindhead, Holmbury St Mary, Holmwood Common, Horsley, Hydon, Juniper Top, Kingswood/ Tadworth, Leatherhead, Leith Hill, Limpsfield Chart, Merrow Down, Mickleham, Norbury Park, Nower Wood, Ockham Common, Olddean Common, Oxshott/Prince's Coverts, Pirbright, Puttenham Common, Ranmore Common, Richmond Park, Seale, Selsdon, South Norwood, Thorpe, Thursley/Ockley/ Royal Commons, Vann Lake, Virginia Water, Walton Heath, West End Common (Esher), Wisley RHS Gardens and Witley Common.

Later Breeding. Breeding records came later from Arbrook Common (1989), Ashtead Common (1990-91), Bagshot Heath/Lightwater Country Park (1997), Bricksbury Hill (1996), Brookwood Heath (1997), Cobbetthill Common (1995), Crooksbury Common (1995), Cuckoo Hill (1997), Elstead (1997), Frensham (1997), Hindhead Commons (1993, 1996), Inval (1985), Limpsfield Chart (at least three roding, 1994), Merrist Wood (1995), Olddean Common (four roding 1993), Pirbright Common (six roding 1994), Puttenham Common (at least five roding 1994, roding 1997), Roke Pond (Witley, 1996), Thursley Common, Vann Lake (1981-86), West End Common (Esher, 1989), and Witley Common (1985). Years are those of published records only. Roding and/or breeding is likely in other years at many of the sites.

Breeding population trend. Woodcock were found at territorial densities of up to 0.62 per ten hectares in Common Birds Censuses from 1969 to 2000, without a significant trend. The only previous quantitative breeding survey appears to be that carried out by R. Blockey in 1934 for the 96 square miles (644 square km) around Haslemere, including parts of Sussex and Hampshire, as referred to in Parr. Blockey counted 228 pairs, over two per square mile. If this density held over the whole of outer Surrey the county population would then have been around 2,000 pairs. Bags of 20 birds in a day were being obtained on large estates in the 1930s (Parr), adding credibility to this estimate. J. J. Bowley thought there were about 30 pairs in the Clandon/Horsley/Ripley/Ockham area in 1973. There were six territories on Witley Common in 2000 and four in 2001.

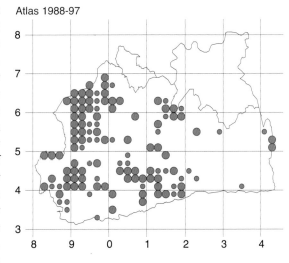

Atlas 1988-97

It is hard to avoid the conclusion Woodcock are now less numerous, even though Surrey is well-wooded and the woodlands have suffered no significant loss. Indeed in some areas, such as the Devil's Punch Bowl at Hindhead, new woods have appeared on what was previously heathland, which will have helped the Woodcock population. Even so, Woodcock were recorded in only 115 tetrads in the 1988-97 SBC Atlas survey. If there has been a big decline, it seems to have occurred before the 1960s, or within sites. BTO Atlas surveys show a 29% drop in the British breeding range between 1968-72 and 1988-91 (*New Atlas*). In Surrey, the range does not seem to have changed much over this period, as a comparison of sites reported in recent years with those in the best three years of the 1960s shows:

Sites 1963	Roding 1966	Sites 1969	Sites 1998	Sites 1999	Sites 2000	Sites 2001
24	17	25	26	15	16	20

Source: Surrey Bird Reports
Sites: present March-July. *Roding:* roding sites.

There are very few published records for Spelthorne. Geen mentioned wintering at a copse near Queen Mary Reservoir. One was seen near Queen Mary Reservoir on 8th, 15th and 22nd April 1978 and there was another at Ferry Lane West in January 1985.

Roding dates. Breeding Woodcock make their display flights (roding) at dawn and dusk from March to July. Extreme dates noted are:

Early
5th March 1939   Horsley Woods (*SEBR*).
6th March 1978   Worplesdon

Late
27th July 1978   Witley Common

Calendar. The breeding birds probably remain in the county but there is a small influx from October to December, during which birds may appear in urban areas as well as on woods, commons and at wetlands such as Holmethorpe Sand Pits.

Large counts. Visible numbers remain small and the winter count of 12 at Chertsey on 8th March 1969 given by Parr does not seem to have been exceeded. There were seven at Hurst Green on 1st January 1983, eight at Kew Gardens in February 1990, 11 at Gatwick Farm, Reigate, on 14th December 1985 and eight at Chelsham in 1997.

Movements and longevity. Proof of immigration is provided by November to January Surrey recoveries of Woodcock ringed in Finland in July and August and Sweden in July. The furthest travelled of these was ringed at Oulu, Finland, on 31st May 1971 and found freshly dead or dying 2 098 km south-west at Dorking on 27th December 1971.

Woodcock have recently featured among the prey items of Peregrines roosting at Guildford Cathedral and nesting at a tower block in Woking. The number (seven at Woking) testifies both to the resourceful-ness of the Peregrines and to the number of local Woodcock. The Woodcock with the greatest known longevity was ringed in Skaraborg, Sweden on 11th July 1963 and found freshly dead or dying at Sutton Green on 27th January 1968.

Behaviour. A Woodcock flushed near Abinger in 1974 carried a chick between its thighs.

Black-tailed Godwit *Limosa limosa*

Scarce passage migrant

Breeds from Iceland east though Europe to Siberia, wintering south to central Africa, India and Australia. Ringing recoveries suggest that most of the birds wintering in Britain are of the race *islandica*, which breeds mainly in Iceland (*MA*). Black-tailed Godwits bred in East Anglia in the 18th century but the conversion of grazing marshes to arable took away most of the habitat. Sporadic breeding continued until 1829 and possibly later. There has been a marked increase in the number breeding in northwest Europe, especially

during the 20th century (*BWP*). In Britain, recolonisation began in the 1930s, with intermit-tent breeding inside and outside its previous range and passage records became much more frequent. The *New Atlas* shows a 37% increase in breeding numbers from 1968-72 to 1988-91. The Wetland Bird Survey shows a national increase in winter numbers from Iceland.

Early Surrey history. Bucknill knew of only two in Surrey, one recorded by Long as killed at Hampton Lodge on 17th August 1823 and the other killed on Epsom Common in the spring of 1895.

20th century. There were seven at the Surrey Docks in 1917 (Macpherson, 1929). The next dated record after 1900 is of one at Brooklands Sewage Farm on 17th-20th August 1932 (Hollom,

Queen Elizabeth II Reservoir   *Photo D. M. Harris*

1935). Up to four were there in the August of 1936 and 1937. There were single birds at Brooklands Sewage Farm on 28th April and 2nd May 1940 and near Wisley on 30th March 1942. There were seven at Guildford Sewage Farm on 5th-7th May 1944 and one there on 5th September. Four on a partly drained reservoir at Lonsdale Road on 19th-23rd August 1945 were apparently the first for the site. In 1947 a flock of thirteen appeared at Elmers End Sewage Farm in March (*BLA*) and there were single birds at Stoke in April, May and August and two there in September. There were single birds at Guildford Sewage Farm on 19th August and at Molesey Sewage Farm on 27th August 1950. One flushed at Pen Ponds on 30th March 1952 landed in deep water and took off again, a first record for the park. There were two at Beddington Sewage Farm in August 1952 and others in 1955-57 and 1959. Single birds were seen at Guildford Sewage Farm in 1950, 1954-56 and 1959. One at Epsom Sewage Farm in 1955 was the first in the district for 60 years and there was another the following year. A Black-tailed Godwit lingered at

Imbham's Farm, Haslemere for about twelve days in August 1957. In the 1960s there were records from Aldershot Camp Sewage Farm (1966), Ash Vale Gravel Pits (1966-67), Barn Elms Reservoirs (1960, 1968), Guildford Sewage Farm (1960, 1966) and Hersham Sewage Farm (1960). In all, there were records of 70-80 birds from 1932 to 1970, over half of them in August (Parr).

In Spelthorne, one at Staines Reservoirs on 14th August 1927 (*LN* for 1928) was the third for the London area. There was another on 24th January 1933 (sixty-three years before the first vice-county record for that month), one on 27th April 1939 and one on 24th April 1949. There were up to two in the district in April and May 1950 and one stayed at Perry Oaks Sewage Farm from 7th October until early December, when it was found shot. There was one at Perry Oaks on 17th July 1951 (*LBR*) and six were there on 10th August 1952 (*LBR*), a year when there were many Spelthorne sightings, and in July 1953 (*LBR*) and April 1954. Black-tailed Godwits became well established migrants in Spelthorne, as elsewhere, during the latter part of the 20th century. There was a striking increase in the vice-county as the decades progressed, with 17 bird months in the 1970s, 62 in the 1980s, 295 in the 1990s and 39 in 2000 alone.

Where found. Nearly half (194) of the 413 bird months from 1970 to 2000 were from Beddington Sewage Farm and another 88 were at Walton Reservoirs. There were 38 from Barn Elms. The remaining bird months were from Ashtead, Berrylands, Capel (four), Frensham (fourteen), Frimley Gravel Pits, Godstone, Guildford Sewage Farm, Hersham, Holmethorpe (five), Old Woking Sewage Farm, Papercourt (fourteen), Pyrford (four), Queen Elizabeth II Reservoir (sixteen), Redhill Aerodrome, Ripley (two), Thursley, Unstead Sewage Farm, Wandsworth and Wrecclesham (three).

Records after 2000 have come from Barn Elms, Beddington, Queen Elizabeth II Reservoir, Thursley and Walton Reservoirs, the largest number being twelve at Barn Elms on 9th July 2001. There were seventeen at Staines Reservoirs on 4th August 2005 (*LNHSB*).

Calendar. Nearly three quarters of the bird months were in July and August return passage, with a small spring peak and one in December and January.

Bird months 1970-2000

	Jan	Feb	Mar	Apr	May	Jun	Jul	Aug	Sep	Oct	Nov	Dec	Total
Vice-county	1	2	9	34	26	21	175	117	21	3	3	1	**413**

Large counts

Barn Elms: 12, 9th July 2001

Beddington Sewage Farm: 14, 29th June 1996; parties of nine and 14 over on 9th July 1996

Brooklands Sewage Farm: four, 10th August 1936

Elmers End Sewage Farm: 13, 15th March 1947

Guildford Sewage Farm: eight, 14th-15th August 1957

Walton Reservoirs: 14, August 1996

Spelthorne – since 1970:

Staines Moor: 16, 11th April 1987

Staines Reservoir: 72 bird days 1st September to 15th October 1977 when drained; 23, 4th August 1994; 49, 4th July 2004 (*LNHSB*)

As migrants, Black-tailed Godwits appear to be much commoner than they were in the 19th century, probably as a reflection of the increase elsewhere in Europe. This is another species that might be tempted to breed at one of the new wetland reserves, such as Barn Elms.

Bar-tailed Godwit   *Limosa lapponica*

Scarce passage migrant

Has a more northern breeding range than the Black-tailed Godwit, running mainly through the low arctic from Finland to Siberia and Alaska. The winter range is more exclusively coastal, round the shores of Europe, Africa, India, Asia and Australia. Birds reaching Britain come from the race *lapponica* and the more eastern race *baueri* (*MA*).

Early Surrey history. Bar-tailed Godwits were apparently rare migrants in Surrey during the 19th century. Graves saw one at Reigate Heath on 16th November 1816. Bucknill was told of one in the Horsham Museum that was said to have been shot at Charlwood. This bird cannot now be traced.

Where found. There were around 89 vice-county records totalling some 408 bird months from 1900 to 2000, none before 1936. Records have become much more frequent in the past 25 years. Most relate to birds flying over but birds, usually one or two together, are sometimes seen on the ground. With 87 bird months, Queen Elizabeth II Reservoir has been the most prolific site, followed by Barn Elms (52), Beddington Sewage Farm (42), Unstead Sewage Farm (33) and Frensham (30).

Other records have come from Berrylands Sewage Works (1976), Brooklands (1936), Capel (1994), Elmers End Sewage Farm (eight in December 1965), Elstead Common (flock of 26 in 1980), Epsom (flock of twenty-four in 1981), Frimley Gravel Pits (1984), Godstone (flock of twenty in 1995), Goldsworth Park (flock of seven in 1999), Hersham Gravel Pit (four), Holmethorpe Sand Pits, Island Barn Reservoir (28, including a flock of twenty-five in 1988), Papercourt Gravel Pits (one in 1989), Pen Ponds (1936), Pewley Hill (seven in 1973), Pudmore pond (1996), South Norwood Country Park (four in 1991), Stoke Lake/Water Meadows (six), the Thames (flock of eight in 1993), Thursley (1976), Unstead Sewage Farm (thirty-three, including a flock of thirty-two in 1996), Walton Reservoirs (seven records, twelve bird months) and Worcester Park (1995). Subsequent records have come from Barn Elms, Beddington, Island Barn Reservoir, Limpsfield Chart, Queen Elizabeth II Reservoir and Walton Reservoirs, the largest number count being flocks of fifteen, five and four over Queen Elizabeth II Reservoir on 7th May 2002 and twenty-one there on 1st May 2004.

There have been at least 110 Spelthorne records up to 2000, beginning with a bird at Staines Reservoirs on 24th January 1933 (Glegg), one at Perry Oaks Sewage Farm on 3rd May 1947, two over Perry Oaks on 8th May 1949 and one at Staines Moor on 27th-29th April 1951. In 1952 there were reports from Perry Oaks (May) and Staines Moor (September) and another Spelthorne bird appeared in 1955. A party of 15-20 visited Queen Mary Reservoir in February 1956. There were up to two in the district in May and September 1957. In 1959, single birds were seen at Perry Oaks (May) and Queen Mary Reservoir (September). They became much more frequent after this date. The more significant counts at the main site, Staines Reservoirs, were on 27th April 1962 (15); 51 bird days from 31st August to 30th September 1975 when drained, with a day maximum of seven; 16 on 26th April 1978; 44 on 30th April 1978; total of 68 bird days in April 1978; about 80 northeast on 26th April 1980 and 25 over on 10th May 1993. There were 38 in two flocks at Staines Reservoirs on 2nd May 2003.

Calendar. Bar-tailed Godwits are principally spring migrants, although they have been seen in every month.

Bird months 1900-2001

	Jan	Feb	Mar	Apr	May	Jun	Jul	Aug	Sep	Oct	Nov	Dec	Total
Vice-county	1	7	0	130	167	0	2	38	53	1	0	9	**408**
Spelthorne	4	21	18	365	132	6	2	35	37	1	2	1	**624**

Large counts

Elstead: 26 northeast, 3rd May 1980

Frensham: 25, 30th April 1978 (flocks of 17 and 8)

Queen Elizabeth II Reservoir: 26 west, 3rd September 1997

Unstead Sewage Farm: 32 east, 2nd May 1996

Spelthorne

Staines Reservoir 80, 26th April 1980; 65, 25th April 1985

A flock of about 80 godwits flying northeast over Staines Reservoirs on 30th April 1971 were thought probably to be of this species, as were 100 over the same place on 10th August 2004 (*LNHSB*).

Whimbrel

Numenius phaeopus

Typically an April/May and August/September annual passage migrant in small numbers.

Whimbrels breed from Iceland and northern Scotland east through the colder parts of northern Europe, Siberia and North America, wintering on coasts of the Americas, Africa, Asia and Australia. They bred in Orkney and Shetland during the 19th century. A population expansion on Shetland in the 1930s led to an extension of the Scottish range and the *New Atlas* showed a continued increase. The European population has remained fairly stable, though it is probably affected by climatic factors (*BWP*). The *Migration Atlas* suggests that birds recorded in southeast England may breed in Iceland, Scotland, Scandinavia or western Russia and that they winter in West Africa and are of the race *phaeopus*.

Early Surrey history. Bucknill mentioned one killed at Cutt Mill in 1833 (Long), one from West Molesey on 8th October 1879, passage over Woking on 14th May 1890, five over Walton Heath on 14th May 1890 and 20-30 on a ploughed field near Epsom race course on 29th September 1894. He regarded Whimbrels as regular migrants. Power gave two spring and five autumn records for the Dulwich area from 1875 to 1900. One shot at Thursley was seen in the Charterhouse Collection by Bucknill but the specimen currently held there is said to be from Norfolk.

After 1900. The 20th century has seen an increase in the recorded numbers, which reflects better observer coverage as well as any real changes.

Where found. There was a Whimbrel at Barn Elms Reservoirs on 10th May 1929, another on 27th May 1933, one over Reigate on 18th August 1934 and one over Thursley in 1936. In Spelthorne, one was heard at Staines Reservoirs on 9th September 1923 and others were there on 3rd May 1925, 2nd August 1927, 12th May 1929 and May and August 1936.

Since then, passage birds have been seen or heard at many places, including Addington (1961, 1963-64), Ashtead (1960), Bagshot Heath (1956), Barn Elms, Barrow Green (25 in 1967), Beddington Sewage Farm (from 1937), Burgh Heath (1977), Burpham (1965), Chelsham (1963), Chessington (1960, 1964), Chilworth (2001), Cranleigh (2001), Crastock (1971), Dorking (1962), Dulwich (1973-74, 1976-77, 1979), East Molesey (1964, 1966-67, 1975), Elstead (1961-62, 1968), Enton (1961, 1964), Epsom (1958), Esher Common, Farnborough North Gravel Pits (1966), Farnham (1968), Frensham, Guildford Sewage Farm, Hankley (1975), Haslemere (1965), Hersham Sewage Farm, Island Barn Reservoir,Kew Gardens (1979), Milford (1969), Newlands Corner (1964), Ockham (1957), Old Coulsdon (1962), Papercourt Gravel Pits (1975), Pirbright (1964), Pyrford (1960), Queen Elizabeth II Reservoir, Reigate (1946), Richmond Park (1950), Sanderstead (1965), Send (1973), South Norwood (1959), Surbiton (1961), Tadworth (1952), Thornton Heath (1952), Thursley/Ockley Commons, Vann Lake (1972), Walton Reservoirs (from 1957), West End Common (1974), West Horsley (two at 22.45 hrs on 25th June 1974) and Woldingham (1963). In Spelthorne, there were six at Staines Reservoirs on 11th May 1946 and one at the unfilled King George VI Reservoir on 8th May 1947. Others were in the district on 19th and 25th April 1953 and from 1954.

Whimbrels became more frequent after the 1970s. New places and notable records since then include: Banstead (6th May 1990), Battersea Park (29th April 1988), Beddington Sewage Farm, (at least seventy-five south on 5th September 1988, eighty-two north, thirty-four east and five others on 8th May 1991), Boundstone (1983), Burpham (2000), Capel (1992, 1994), Chobham (1982), Cranleigh (1985, 1998),

Croham Hurst (1988), Dockenfield (1998), Effingham Fish Ponds (1982), Egham (1997), Farnham (one heard at night on 5th April 1981), Frensham (flock of 30 ENE on 7th May 1991), Frimley Gravel Pits, Godstone (1998), Holmethorpe Sand Pits, Jacobs Well (1994), Jordans Wood (1985), Kingston (1990), New Malden (1995), Normandy (1981), Old Woking Sewage Farm (1995), Puttenham (1990), Queen Elizabeth II Reservoir (25 on 11th May 1995), Riddlesdown (1990, 2000), Shackleford (8th July 1992), Shalford (1993), Shortfield (18 southwest on 18th August 1993), Smallfield (1999-2000), Stoke Lake/Water Meadows (1986, 1993, 1998, 2002), Surbiton (1982), near Thursley (25 northeast on 3rd May 1980, nine on 27th April 1975), Tilford (1981), Tilhill (1985, 1986), Unstead Sewage Farm (2000), Wallington (eight to ten in 1984), Walton Reservoirs, Warlingham (1993, 1997), Wimbledon Common (1985-86), Winterfold (1984, 1999), Witley (1995, 1998), Woking (1982) and Worcester Park (1992). Among the later sightings, there were nine records, totalling 19 birds, at the Walton area reservoirs in 2004. Whimbrels were regular migrants at the Spelthorne reservoirs.

Calendar. Virtually all the spring passage is in April and May. Return passage usually begins around mid July and continues to mid September. There are a few summer records. Early and late dates are:

Early		Late	
4th April 1992	Send	11th October 1961	Enton, heard (R. M. Fry)
5th April 1981	Farnham, heard at night	*Spelthorne*	
7th April 2005	Walton Reservoirs	4th October 1980	Queen Mary Reservoir
9th April 1988	Frimley, two northeast	29th October 1977	Staines Reservoirs
9th April 1985	Papercourt Gravel Pits		
14th April 1950	Pen Ponds		
Spelthorne			
26th March 1994	Staines Reservoirs		
14th April 1984	Queen Mary Reservoir		
14th April 1988	Staines Reservoirs		

Large counts

Barrow Green Sand Pit: 25 west, 22nd August 1967

Beddington Sewage Farm: 75+ south, 5th September 1988; 87 north and 34 east, 8th May 1991

Colley Hill: 50-52 south, 24th August 1946

Dulwich: *c.*50 northwest in two flocks, 18th August 1973

Enton: 22 northeast, 25th April 1961

Epsom Race Course: 20-30, 1894

Frensham: 30 east, 7th May 1991

Guildford Sewage Farm: 35 south, 29th July 1966

Queen Elizabeth II Reservoir: 25, 11th May 1995

near Thursley: 25 northeast, 3rd May 1980

Vann Lake: 28 south, 5th August 1972

Spelthorne

Staines Reservoirs 18, 30th August 1975; 15+24 over, 6th May 1984

Curlew (Eurasian Curlew)   *Numenius arquata*

Scarce, breeding annually

Curlews breed from the British Isles east through Europe to Central Asia, with a range extending further south than that of the Whimbrel. They winter on coasts south to South Africa and east to Japan. The *Migration Atlas* shows that Curlews breeding abroad and found in Britain come mainly from Finland and Scandinavia and that those breeding in Britain tend to move south or west after the breeding season.

At the middle of the 19th century Curlews were known as breeding birds of British moors and uplands in the west and north. In the 1860s the range began an extension into lowland areas, mainly in the north and west. This trend continued into the 20th century and by the 1940s birds were breeding in almost all the eastern counties of England, moving into agricultural habitats such as rough meadows and then, when these were ploughed up during the 1940s, into arable. The expansion seems to have been completed by the 1960s and the *New Atlas* showed a subsequent contraction of range.

Early Surrey history. Remains dated to the 16th century were found at Little Pickle, Bletchingley (Poulton *et al.*). Curlews seem to have been well known as winter visitors to Surrey in the 19th century. They were seen in winter in the Chertsey area prior to 1840 (Meyer). Winter records given by Bucknill included one at Cutt Mill on 10th February 1841, one shot at Thames Ditton on 10th December 1880 and two flying over Walton-on-Thames on 18th January 1892. Passage migrants included several heard over Wray Common after dark on 13th May 1893, a flock of five or six on Epsom Downs in early October 1894, one over Munstead Wood in November of the same year and a November bird on Wimbledon Common, year not given. There are undated references to birds at Frensham (not later than 1845), near Bagshot (not later than 1871), Puttenham (shot, *SALEC*) and the Woking District (well before 1900). Prior to 1880 they sometimes appeared near Thursley, driven by rough weather and one was seen on Clapham Common in 1882 (Bucknill, 1902). Jordan (1892) mentioned them at a mill pond near Box Hill. One shot at Puttenham was seen in the Charterhouse Collection by Bucknill. The specimen currently held there is said to be of unknown origin.

20th century. Power heard night migrants over Brixton during several autumns from 1891 to 1901 and saw a group on filtering ponds near Battersea Park on 14th April 1902. There was one at Chobham Common in October 1900 and a flock was heard over Epsom after dark on 15th April 1902. In Spelthorne, Kerr (1906) reported Curlews flying over on passage. There was one at Staines Reservoirs on 6th January and up to seven were there in August 1924, one in August 1929. Curlews were fairly regularly recorded in the district from this date. Single birds flew over Richmond Park on 7th April 1930 and 2nd April 1933 and other migrants were reported over urban areas from about this time. They also began to be noticed on passage at wetland sites such as Barn Elms (May and August 1934, 25 in August 1936) and Epsom Sewage Farm (October 1934). Pounds gave fifteen records from 1913-48 for the Farleigh district.

Breeding. Surrey was one of the first counties in the southeast to reflect the expansion of the British range. A pair summered at Frensham in 1893 (Bucknill) and breeding was first recorded in 1897 on Chobham Common (*BB*, 2:270). Three eggs were laid. The eggs were the subject of a rigorous authentication procedure devised by Bucknill, which included obtaining a sworn affidavit from the finder, Mr Tice, and examination of the eggs by leading experts of the day. These included Howard Saunders, who confirmed the identification (Haslemere Museum documents LD 9 179). A pair may have bred on Hankley Common in 1912. Regular breeding in Surrey began at least as early as 1913 (*BB*, 12:260-63) on dry heathland (site not disclosed) in west Surrey. Howard Bentham heard a Curlew at Pudmore Pond on 25th May 1913, perhaps the earliest reference to possible breeding in the area. He saw a pair that 'obviously had young' at Thursley/Ockley Commons in June 1921 and from then on they probably tried to breed there in most years. Gosnell collected a clutch of three eggs there on 5th May 1929. The birds were 'much harried' by

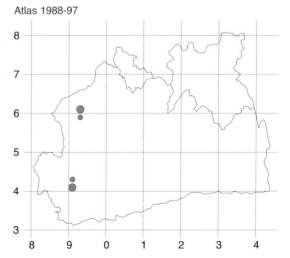

Atlas 1988-97

egg collectors in the 1930s (*SEBR* for 1935). Five nests were found in the Thursley/Elstead area in 1939 and six pairs were thought to be present in 1946. Curlews continued to breed at Chobham Common. Five pairs were present in 1935 and Ludwig Koch made his famous Curlew sound recording there in 1937. At least one other breeding locality existed at about this time - a pair bred at the north end of Bisley Ranges in 1934 and Curlews were seen again there in 1940. The Surrey breeding population peaked at 12-14 pairs in the 1940s. One to three pairs have attempted to breed at Thursley/Ockley Commons in most, if not all, years since 1970 and they have often been successful. Harassment by bird-nesters was mentioned again in 1973. The last breeding attempt at Chobham Common was in the same year. The only other suitable sites are on military lands at Bisley and Pirbright, where they are present from time to time and have bred. Breeding birds currently arrive in southwest Surrey around mid February, a month earlier than the date given by Parr. They leave in July.

Passage and wintering places. Most Curlews away from breeding sites are seen at Barn Elms, Beddington and the Walton-on-Thames area reservoirs. They have become more frequent in recent years. Surrey Bird Report summaries of birds away from breeding sites in the eight years from 1994 to 2001 add up to 357, as shown in the table. Places where Curlews have been recorded on passage or in winter since 1960 include Ashtead, Badshot Lea, Banstead, Barn Elms, Beddington Sewage Farm, Berrylands, Boundstone, Buckland Sand Pits, Burpham, Cheam, Chelsham, Chertsey Meads, Chessington, Chiddingfold, Chilworth, Chobham Common, Churt Common (display in 1983), Colony Bog, Compton, Cranleigh, Cutt Mill, Dulwich, East Horsley, Effingham, Elstead, Enton, Epsom, Farnham Park, Felbridge, Frensham, Frimley Gravel Pits, Guildford Sewage Farm, Ham Common/Lands, Hampton Court, Haslemere, Hersham, Hinchley Wood, Holmethorpe (eight on 27th April 1988, *BHSP*), Island Barn Reservoir, Kew Gardens, Kiln Platt (Shere), Knaphill, Limpsfield Chart, Littleworth Cross, Lucas Green, Milford, Newark Priory, Normandy, Old Woking Sewage Farm, Papercourt Gravel Pits, Pirbright, Puttenham, Pyrford, Queen Elizabeth II Reservoir, Richmond Park, Rowledge, Shalford, South Norwood, Stoke Lake/Water Meadows, Streatham Common, the Surrey Docks (20 over on 12th June 1978), the Thames at Bankside, Thorpe, Unstead Sewage Farm, Vann Lake, Walton Reservoirs, Witley, Woodmansterne, Worcester Park, Worplesdon and Wrecclesham.

Calendar. Numbers away from breeding sites are spread fairly evenly though the winter. They are lowest in May and from September to November. The annual number fell over the period, from a peak of 98 in 1996 to 27 in 2001. Winter records are sometimes associated with cold weather. Harrison (1947) mentioned that Curlews were at Guildford Sewage Farm in the cold spell of February 1948.

Records away from breeding sites, 1994-2001

	Jan	Feb	Mar	Apr	May	Jun	Jul	Aug	Sep	Oct	Nov	Dec	Total
Vice-county	38	26	45	58	15	50	27	32	12	24	5	25	**357**

Large counts

Beddington Sewage Farm: 54, 31st January 1956
Epsom Downs: 19 southwest, 6th December 1969
Ewhurst: *c*.30, 6th December 1962

Wandsworth Common: 50 over, 16th July 1929
Spelthorne:
King George VI Reservoir: 34, 17th August 1952
Staines Reservoirs: 19 NNW, 23rd August 1981

Spotted Redshank   *Tringa erythropus*

Scarce passage migrant

Breeds further north than the Redshank, mainly in wooded tundra east from Norway to eastern Siberia and winters mainly in sub-Saharan Africa and on the shores of India and southeast Asia. Birds ringed in Britain have been recovered as far south as Morocco (*MA*). Small numbers pass through the British Isles on migration and a few usually remain in the west Palearctic. Spotted Redshanks may have bred in post-glacial Britain (Thomas, 1999).

Early Surrey history. One shot at Forked Pond, Thursley in 1855 was seen in the Charterhouse Collection by Bucknill but is not now held there. It had been given to Stafford by Mr R. Greville of Milford.

20th century onward. The next records, both from Frensham were on 5th May 1924 and 1st May 1925 (HNHS, 1955). Howard Bentham and Richard Kearton saw two on a boggy field near Elstead on 27th May 1925 (*BB, 19:214*). There was one at Staines Reservoirs on 23rd September 1928 (*LN* for 1930). There were two at Brooklands in May 1937 and one was at Barn Elms on 1st September 1938. The next was at Lonsdale Road Reservoir on 20th August 1945, followed by one at King George VI Reservoir on 5th September 1947. Records became more frequent up to the 1970s, when they levelled off. They may now be falling back:

Number of bird months by decade

	1900s	1910s	1920s	1930s	1940s	1950s	1960s	1970s	1980s	1990s	2000-03	Total
Vice-county	0	0	4	3	1	15	37	33	59	61	33	**246**
Spelthorne	0	0	1	0	7	33	59	84	58	32	2	**276**

Nearly half the vice-county bird months (101) have been at Beddington Sewage Farm. The only other sites in double figures were Barn Elms (35), Hersham (13), Frensham (11) and Guildford Sewage Farm (11). The remainder were at Ash Vale Gravel Pits (two, 1964 and 1966), Berrylands Sewage Works (23rd-25th April 1988), Brooklands (two, 1937), Buckland Sand Pits (7th September 1985), Capel (four, 11th April 2000), Compton (20th January 1993), Elstead (1925), Epsom Sewage Farm (21st July 1956), Frimley Gravel Pits (26th July 1985), Godstone (seven, 1955, 1979, 1980), Hamm Moor (six, 1964 and 1975), Holmethorpe (six, 1975-76 and 1983-84), Island Barn Reservoir (two, 1976 and 1984), Kew Gardens (1977), Lonsdale Road Reservoir (1945), Lyne Sewage Farm (1962), Papercourt Gravel Pits (four, 1969, 1980, 1984 and 1996), Ripley Sewage Farm (three, 1973 and 1979), South Norwood Country Park (eight, 1991, 1993 and 1998), South Norwood Lake (1989), the Thames at Battersea (1990), Thursley Common (1962), Unstead Sewage Farm (five, 1990 and 1999) and Walton Reservoirs (seven, 1961, 1971, 1984, 1992 and 2002). The only February birds were at Barn Elms on 8th February 1974 and at Holmethorpe Sand Pits on 8th February 1976. There were three at Barn Elms in September 2001. Most of the Spelthorne bird months came from Perry Oaks Sewage Farm and Staines Reservoirs.

After 2001, there were Spotted Redshanks at Barn Elms, Beddington, Queen Elizabeth II Reservoir and Walton Reservoirs, the largest group being 12 at Barn Elms WWT on 7th May 2002. There were single birds at Stanwell Moor in August 2002 and at Staines Reservoirs in September 2003 (*LBR*) and another in the Staines area on 30th August 2005 (*LNHSB*).

Calendar. Spotted Redshanks have been found in every month of the year, with a marked peak in August/September and a much smaller peak in April/May. The only vice-county birds for November were at Beddington on 11th-12th November 1989 and Barn Elms on 20th November 2002.

Bird Months 1900-2003

	Jan	Feb	Mar	Apr	May	Jun	Jul	Aug	Sep	Oct	Nov	Dec	Total
Vice-county	2	2	4	17	32	4	10	86	66	11	9	3	**246**
Spelthorne	1	1	2	18	17	10	8	90	108	17	3	1	**276**

Large counts

Barn Elms: 12, 7th May 2002
Beddington Sewage Farm: at least six, August
  1965; six, August 1986

Spelthorne

King George VI Reservoir: six, 6th September
  1995

Perry Oaks Sewage Farm: seven, 26th-27th
August 1987

Staines Reservoirs: 142 bird days between 9th
August and 4th October 1976, while drained;

maximum of eight on 13th August 1976; 53
bird days autumn 1977, maximum six on
19th September

Redshank (Common Redshank) — *Tringa totanus*

Scarce breeding resident

Breeds from Iceland east through Europe to China and winters south to South Africa and southeast Asia, with an extension of range north in Finland and Scandinavia from the mid 19th century and later elsewhere in Europe. The *Migration Atlas* shows that Redshanks breeding in Iceland and some from countries round the southern Baltic winter in Britain and that some of those breeding in Britain move to other parts of western Europe in winter. The British population had been reduced by land drainage prior to 1850. This was especially drastic in the fens and in southern coastal counties. Later in the century a gradual recolonisation and breeding range extension began. The increase continued through the first part of the 20th century, with an expansion of wet grassland and sewage farms. The ploughing or re-seeding of grassland and further extension of drainage from the 1940s started a decline which still continues.

Early Surrey history. Redshanks were only occasional visitors to Surrey during the 19th century. Graves saw a flock with other waders at Reigate Heath in November 1816. One killed at Hampton (Puttenham) in March a few years before 1829 was said by Long to be the only one he had ever heard of in the neighbourhood. Stafford recorded one at Hammer Ponds in 1849 and another at Elstead. One was shot on Epsom Common in the autumn of 1882 (Bucknill). Others mentioned by Bucknill are one on the Mole on 20th November 1888, one shot at Frensham Pond in September 1893, one at Nutfield Marsh on 28th April 1895, two shot at Mitcham in the autumn of 1895 and some undated references to Frensham. Power's only record for the Dulwich area was of a noisy party going west over Brixton on 8th December 1889. This was during an intense frost. There were two at Staines Reservoirs on 10th July 1907 (Kerr).

Breeding. Redshanks colonised Surrey in the early years of the 20th century, the first breeding being at Beddington in 1910. Howard Bentham found breeding adults at Blindley Heath and Hedgecourt in 1912 and a nest on Itchingwood Common in 1915, having seen single birds there in May 1912 and April 1913. Shaw reported breeding at Frensham in 1917. Redshanks were breeding at Milford from about 1919. There were nine pairs near Elstead in 1921 and they were too numerous to count accurately near Pudmore in 1925 (Parr). Bunyard found a nest and young at an undisclosed locality in 1923. Two pairs bred at Weybridge Sewage Farm in 1929. In Spelthorne, Redshanks were present on or near Staines Moor during the breeding season in some of the years up to 1935 (Glegg) and they bred at Perry Oaks Sewage Farm in 1954.

At Beddington Sewage Farm one pair bred in 1929, two pairs in 1932 and at least four pairs in 1933. They bred there in 1934-35 and fairly regularly in later years. There were six pairs in

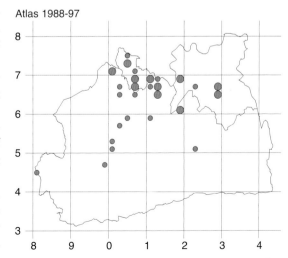

Atlas 1988-97

1954. Two pairs bred at Molesey Sewage Farm in 1930. Redshanks probably bred at Leatherhead Sewage Farm in 1935 (*LBR* 1940).

A few pairs were nesting in west Surrey at about this time (*SEBR* for 1935) and a pair nested near Pudmore in 1939. They were evidently breeding freely in the Guildford area during the 1940s. Harrison (1947), writing about Guildford Sewage Farm, noted that *The first Redshank arrive in early February and numbers increase to about sixty birds in early April, when they spread out along the Wey valley to nest, leaving only a few pairs on the farm, until late June, when adults and young return.* There were up to 15 pairs in Guildford Sewage Farm area in 1956 and 1957. In 1947, two broods were found at Send and three nests were found at Unstead. Redshank bred at Frensham in 1950, Ash Gravel Pits in 1955 and Pudmore in 1956.

Much of the west Surrey population faded early but elsewhere the expansion probably peaked in the 1950s. Known breeding pairs were at Beddington Sewage Farm (nine in 1956, ten in 1958, ten to twelve in 1959), Epsom Sewage Farm (1956, two in 1957), Old Woking Sewage Farm (five or six in 1959), the Peasmarsh area (1950s), Unstead Sewage Farm (three in 1956) and Wisley Common (one in 1959). The Milford colony was of six pairs in 1962.

Redshanks suffered much loss of habitat and feeding area from the 1960s, with the modernisation and closure of sewage farms and the drainage of wet meadows. A few pairs have bred in most years since 1970, most consistently at Beddington Sewage Farm where there have been territorial birds in about twenty of the next 35 years. A pair or two have bred at Berrylands (1986-90), Buckland Sand Pits (1987), Cobham (1970s), Effingham Fish Ponds (1970s), Hersham (intermittently from the mid 1980s), Old Woking/Papercourt Gravel Pits/Ripley Sewage Farm (1970s-1990s), Stoke D'Abernon (1970s), Thorpe (1976), West Molesey (1982-83). The restructuring of Barn Elms and Walton reservoirs in recent years has provided new habitat and Redshanks have started to breed there. The Mole and Wey Valley sites all appear to have been lost, along with most of those at sewage farms. One meadowland site near the Thames was still active in the 1990s. Redshank probably bred at Wraysbury Reservoir in 1970 and at Staines Moor in 1971 (*LBR*).

The 1982 BTO Breeding Waders of Wet Meadows survey found at least seven breeding pairs on four sites out of the 32 that were visited. The distribution was: TQ05 Old Woking (one); TQ07 Runnymede (a pair with four young); TQ15 River Mole at Cobham (two), and Lower Farm, Effingham (one). There were three territories at Beddington Sewage Farm, where one pair is known to have bred. Another pair bred on a reclaimed rubbish tip at Hersham, outside the Survey. Spelthorne results for the 1982 BTO Breeding Birds of Wet Meadows survey are not directly available but the *London Bird Report* for 1982 mentions two pairs breeding at Perry Oaks Sewage Farm and a few non-breeding birds at Staines Moor and Stanwell Gravel Pits from May to July. Overall, including Spelthorne, this was quite a good year, with up to nine pairs breeding. One or two pairs bred at Shepperton in the 1980s (*Shepp BR*). A repeat of the Survey at 23 of the same vice-county sites in 2001 found seven pairs again, this time all at Beddington Sewage Farm. Numbers there have since fallen, with no more than two territories and one brood in 2004. Because of the lack of suitable habitat, the Redshank is now one of Surrey's rarest regularly breeding birds. The London Wetland Centre at Barn Elms is the only significant exception and Redshanks have begun breeding there (two broods in 2005).

Passage and wintering. Migrant and wintering Redshanks are often seen at wetland sites, usually in small numbers. There was one at Barn Elms Reservoirs on 1st December 1923. Collenette knew of four records for Richmond Park, in January, March and August, the first being on 5th August 1928. Other non-breeding sites include Aldershot Camp Sewage Farm (1966), Apps Court Gravel Pit, Beddington Sewage Farm, Bookham, Cheam, Chertsey Meads, Earlswood Sewage Farm (1966), Englefield Green, Epsom Common, Esher, Farnham Sewage Farm, Fetcham Mill Pond, Frensham, Frimley Gravel Pits, Gatwick, Hammer Ponds, Holmethorpe (four on 9th September 1991, *BHSP*), Horsell, Inval, Island

Barn Reservoir, Morden Hall Park, Newark Priory, Pyrford Golf Course, Queen Elizabeth II Reservoir, Send Water Meadows, South Norwood Country Park, Stoke Lake, the Surrey Docks, Thames Ditton, Thursley Common, Tice's Meadow Gravel Pit, Unstead Sewage Farm, Vauxhall, Walton Reservoirs (thirty-one in February 2000), West Horsley, Worcester Park and Wrecclesham Sand Pits and Floods.

Large counts

Barn Elms: 32, 11th September 1992

Beddington Sewage Farm: 124, 27th March 1966

Brooklands Sewage Farm: 53, 14th June 1936 'probably the assembling of locally reared broods'.

Guildford Sewage Farm: 73, 16th April 1950

Hersham Gravel Pit: 20, 3rd January 1999

Island Barn Reservoir: 15, December 1998

Ockley Common: 15, 27th March 1961

Send Marsh: 100, 3rd April 1943

Surrey Docks: 49, 5th January 1974

Unstead Sewage Farm: 38, 25th March 1956

Walton Reservoirs: 42, 31st March 1992 when drained

Wrecclesham: 14, 16th October 1987

Spelthorne

King George VI Reservoir: 19, February 1995

Perry Oaks Sewage Farm: 25, June 1987

Queen Mary Reservoir: 30, December 1976

Staines Moor: 23 adults, 12th June 1999

Staines Reservoir: 80, March 1983

Wraysbury Reservoir: 12, 31st December 1973

Counts in recent years have been lower but there were 16 at Staines Moor on 30th March 2001 and 20 at Staines Reservoirs on 6th April 2002 (*LNHSB*).

Movements and longevity. The furthest travelled and the longest lived among the three available ringing recoveries was of a chick ringed at Stanwell on 20th June 1959 and recovered 135 km and over three years and seven months later at Poole Harbour. The other two were these:

Ringed	Age		Recovered		Distance
Weybridge	Young	16th July 1934	Buckinghamshire, Eton	February 1937	17 km
Kent	Adult	25th January 1970	Queen Mary Reservoir	23rd December 1972	50 km

Marsh Sandpiper *Tringa stagnatilis*

One bird

Breeds from Bulgaria east to Asia, with a winter range from Africa eastwards. Most British records are from May to September and there is a peak in August. The birds are mainly found in Kent and East Anglia, though there have been a few in inland counties.

Surrey. The one bird was found by Jeremy Gates on 4th May 1994. It was feeding on flooded land outside the eastern end of Old Woking Sewage Farm, where it stayed until the 7th (*BB, 88:515*). The bird was seen by many people.

Greenshank (Common Greenshank) *Tringa nebularia*

Scarce passage migrant

Breeds in the northern parts of Europe (including Scotland) and Asia and winters in Africa south of the Sahara, India, southeast Asia and Australia. There is an autumn passage of Greenshank from northeast Europe through southern Britain, probably to winter in Iberia and West Africa (*MA*). The breeding range has been fairly stable historically but may have increased in Scotland, where Greenshanks were first known to have bred around 1830.

Early Surrey history. Greenshanks were rarely found during the 19th century. Kidd's reference to one shot at Hampton Lodge not later than 1837 seems to be the earliest mention of them. One was shot on the Thames near Walton in June not later than 1842 (Meyer). Stafford knew of one from Wonersh in 1850 and another from Elstead in 1885 and one shot (undated) at Peasmarsh. Power heard a Greenshank flying over the Brixton/Dulwich area after dark on 6th September 1880. One was shot on the Blackwater, near Frimley in the winter of 1891 and one was seen at Frensham Little Pond on 11th September 1893. Bucknill gave two undated Frensham records and one of a Greenshank killed at Mitcham in the autumn of 1895 (Bucknill).

20th century. Power again heard a Greenshank after dark over the Brixton/Dulwich area on 18th August 1902. Two were seen at Hedgecourt on 6th October 1906 and one on 30th August 1919. There was one at Barn Elms on 15th August 1925, another was there in 1930, another when mud was exposed during cleaning operations on 3rd April 1932 (*BB*, 25:363) and there were others in May and August 1934. One was at Beddington Sewage Farm on 17th May 1931, one at Brooklands Sewage Farm on 30th May 1931, two there on 11th August 1932 and one found by H. G. Atlee on 18th October 1933 brought the total number of vice-county records up to 21. More were seen there and at Barn Elms in 1936. One flew over Richmond Park on 2nd September 1933 and one was at Epsom Sewage Farm on 27th October 1934. A flurry of records in 1937 brought four birds together over Richmond Park on 1st August, a peak of seven to Brooklands Sewage Farm on 28th August and, on the same day, one over Thursley. There were records from four sites in 1938 and two in 1939, followed by one at Guildford Sewage Farm on 30th April and 1st May 1942, several were there in 1944 and three on 26th August 1950. A Greenshank was seen at Godalming (Unstead?) Sewage Farm on 1st October, 1944.

Greenshanks were found at Staines Reservoirs on 7th and 16th September and 10th and 17th October 1927 and 20th August 1929 (two, *LN*). Up to three were at Staines Reservoirs from 12th August to 8th October 1934 and others were at Staines in May and September 1937, from which date they were seen fairly regularly in Spelthorne.

By 1947, Greenshanks had become regular passage migrants at sewage farms and some other wetland sites. The first 20th century record that has been located for Frensham was not until 1956, when five flew over the Great Pond on 20th August but there were four records there in the 1960s, all in May or August. There was one at Ashtead in 1967.

Since 1970. Greenshanks have become more frequent over the last 30 years or so and bird months were running at over 90 a year from 1995 to 2001. The main places for these have been Beddington Sewage Farm (165), Barn Elms and the Walton-on-Thames/Hersham area reservoirs and gravel pits. Greenshanks are scarce elsewhere. Other places where they have been recorded include Ash Vale Gravel Pits, Berrylands (six on 22nd August 1978), Betchworth, Bookham Common, Brookwood, Buckland Sand Pits, Busbridge, Capel, Cheam, Chessington, Coulsdon, Effingham, Enton, Epsom Common Stew Ponds, Farnham Sewage Farm, Farthing Down, Fetcham Mill Pond, Frensham, Frimley Gravel Pits, Gatwick, Godstone, Guildford Sewage Farm and rubbish dump, Holmethorpe, Kew, Kingston, Leatherhead, Lyne Old Sewage Farm, Milford, Mitcham Common, Morden Hall Park, Ockley Common, Old Woking, Olddean Common, Papercourt Gravel Pits, Puttenham Common, Richmond Park, Ripley Sewage Farm, Sanderstead, Send, Slyfield (Guildford), South Norwood Country Park, Stoke Lake, Surbiton, the Surrey Docks, Sutton, Thorpe, Thursley/Ockley Commons, Tilhill, Tongham Gravel Pit, Unstead Sewage Farm, Waverley Abbey, West Ewell, Wimbledon Common and Park, Windlesham, Witley, Woodmansterne and Wrecclesham.

Vice-county reports from 2000 onward have come from Barn Elms, Beddington, Bookham Common, Busbridge, Effingham, Frensham, Hersham, Island Barn Reservoir, Papercourt, Queen Elizabeth II Reservoir, South Norwood, Thursley, Tice's Meadow, Unstead, Walton Reservoirs, Waverley Abbey, West Ewell and Wrecclesham, the largest numbers being 13 at Beddington on 3rd-4th September 2001 and 16 at Queen Elizabeth II Reservoir on 9th August 2004. There have been others in Spelthorne.

Large counts

Barn Elms: 12, 30th April 1990

Beddington Sewage Farm: 29 juveniles, 23rd August 1987; 38 adults, 22nd July 1987

Island Barn Reservoir: 11, 17th August 1984

Queen Elizabeth II Reservoir: 16, 9th August 2004

Walton Reservoirs: 11, 22nd August 1984

Spelthorne

King George VI Reservoir: 16 southwest, 11th September 1999

Perry Oaks Sewage Farm: 15, 23rd August 1957

Queen Mary Reservoir: 14, August 1975

Staines Moor: 11, 21st August 1977

Staines Reservoirs: 66, 5th September 1985

Wraysbury Reservoir: 13, 26th August 2000

Calendar. The first dated vice-county December record was at Island Barn Reservoir on 1st December 1996. One 'wintered' at Unstead Sewage Farm in 1955/56 (CNHS, 1959). One was recorded at Staines Reservoirs on 18 dates from 5th November to 31st December 1996 and one was at Staines Moor on 1st December 1940. There were two at Thorpe Gravel Pits on 13th January 1968 and one was at Queen Mary Reservoir on 27th January 1977. The one published February record is of a bird that was heard only, flying up the Thames at Barn Elms on 20th February 1999.

Bird totals 1994-2001, from Surrey Bird Reports

	Jan	Feb	Mar	Apr	May	Jun	Jul	Aug	Sep	Oct	Nov	Dec	Total
Vice-county	0	1	0	40	127	4	86	251	189	6	2	1	**707**

Movements and longevity. The one recovery located is of a Greenshank ringed at Perry Oaks Sewage Farm on 8th September 1957 and recovered in France, 503 km away, on 18th October of the same year. Presumably this was a passage migrant from continental Europe. The bird might have been just outside the Spelthorne boundary.

Greater/Lesser Yellowlegs   *Tringa melanoleuca/flavipes*

One bird

Greater and Lesser Yellowlegs breed in northern North America and winter in South America. The Greater Yellowlegs is the scarcer of the two in Britain, where there were no January or February records from 1958 to 1985.

Surrey history. A yellowlegs at Unstead Sewage Farm on 28th January, 11th February and 13th February 1954 was not specifically identified but thought likely to have been the Lesser Yellowlegs which was last seen at Perry Oaks Sewage Farm on 9th December 1953 (*SBR* for 1954, Parr 1972).

Lesser Yellowlegs   *Tringa flavipes*

Five birds, of which four were in Spelthorne

Surrey. The records are:

1953:* Perry Oaks Sewage Farm, one on 30th August 1953 and seen daily until 5th September. It then moved off, probably to Langley, Berkshire, but what was considered the same bird was later seen on five occasions at Staines Moor and finally at Perry Oaks on 9th December (*LBR* for 1953).

1953:* Perry Oaks Sewage Farm, a different bird on 25th-26th September and at Staines Reservoirs on the 26th (F. H. Jones, C. M. Veysey, *et al.*, *BB*, *48:364*).

1984:   Beddington Sewage Farm, an immature bird on 24th-30th September (G. D. J. Messenbird *et al. BB*, *78:551*).

1962:* Perry Oaks Sewage Farm, one on 5th-7th September and at Staines Reservoirs on 9th September (*BB*, *56:400*).

1990:* Staines Reservoirs, an adult from 21st August to 8th September (D. J. Morris *et al.*, *BB*, *84:472*) was seen at Perry Oaks Sewage Farm on 25th August (*LBR*).

*Spelthorne

Solitary Sandpiper   *Tringa solitaria*
One possible bird, Spelthorne

Breeds in northern North America and winters in Central and South America. British records are mostly from July to October and in southern counties, coastal and inland.

Surrey. There was one at Perry Oaks Sewage Farm on 22nd July 1977 (J. Sayers, *BB*, *71:504*, the second British July record), possibly inside the Spelthorne boundary.

Green Sandpiper   *Tringa ochropus*
Passage migrant in small numbers

Breeds mainly in the northern conifer forests from Scandinavia to eastern Siberia. Green Sandpipers may have been in Britain over half a million years ago (Harrison, 1988) and would have recolonised with the return of trees 10,000 years ago (Thomas, 1999). *Migration Atlas* information suggests that most Green Sandpipers found in Britain have bred in the Baltic area, passing through to winter in southern Europe or West Africa.

Early Surrey history. Green Sandpipers are familiar spring and autumn visitors to gravel pits, sewage farms and watercress beds across the county, sometimes wintering. Their Surrey status does not seem to have changed much over the past 200 years. Long saw Green Sandpipers at Hampton Lodge, Puttenham in 1823, 1824, 1825 and 1842 (Bucknill). There were eight at Hammer Pond on 16th September 1845 (Newman, 1849). One was shot near Reigate Heath not later than 1857 (HNHC). Power recorded them from the Brixton/Dulwich area on 11th August 1880, 21st September 1900 and 18th August 1902. Bucknill (1900) said that 'in recent years' they had often been seen along rivers and streams and by the larger ponds and lakes, most frequently in the west and southwest and most often in April, August and September. Sites included Merrow Downs, Newlands Corner, the Tillingbourne near Gomshall not later than 1880 and the Wey below Guildford.

Breeding. Long was told that eggs had been laid during one summer at 'Hatchford' (Bucknill). Blyth noticed that a very young bird shot near Guildford had its primary quill-feathers incompletely developed and concluded that the species bred in Surrey (Yarrell). Jordan (1892) said he had flushed a Green Sandpiper from woodland and thought it might have nested nearby. These accounts are rather speculative. Proof of breeding in Surrey has never been obtained, then or since.

Where found, from 1900. Places where they were later found include: Barn Elms Reservoirs, Beddington Sewage Farm (from 1931), Berrylands Sewage Works (1971), Brooklands Sewage Farm (six on 17th-18th August 1932, 1936-39), Chertsey Weir (1934), Chessington (1952), the Devils Jumps (30th August 1906), Egham (1952), Enton (1942), Epsom Common (1938), Epsom Sewage Farm

(1935, 1939, 1952), Esher Sewage Farm (1952), Farnham Sewage Farm (1971), Fetcham cress beds (1942), Forked Pond (27th August 1906), Frensham (1934 etc), Frimley Gravel Pits (1966, 1971), Guildford Sewage Farm (15/16 on 12th August 1939), Hedgecourt, Hersham Sewage Farm (1952), Holmethorpe (1971), Island Barn Reservoir (1938, 1971), Leatherhead (1938), Mitcham, Molesey, Morden Park (1971), Oxted (most years 1933-40), Papercourt (1971), Richmond Park, Ripley Sewage Farm, Vauxhall (1971), Walton-on-Thames Sewage Farm, Walton Reservoirs, Weybridge Sewage Farm (1929), Wire Mill (1936) and 'Wisley Marshes' (1942-43). By 1946, Green Sandpipers had become known regular passage visitors to wetland sites. In 1954 one summered at Unstead Sewage Farm until 31st October. There were 158 records from 20 localities in 1962, for all months with a peak in August (Parr). Green Sandpipers were reported annually from 1970, usually from 15-20 sites. Barn Elms, Papercourt Gravel Pits and Walton Reservoirs are among the more important places but Green Sandpipers are widely distributed on passage.

A summary of monthly maxima shows an average of about 269 vice-county bird months annually from 1994-2001. Of these, an average of 111 was from Beddington Sewage Farm, including records of 32 there on 3rd August 1999 and the same number in July 2000. Green Sandpipers have continued to be widely reported since 2000, the largest number being 42 at Beddington in July 2002, a new maximum for the site.

In Spelthorne, there was one at Staines Reservoirs on 30th August 1929 and there were six on 10th August 1932. Two on 7th December 1933 made an early winter record. There were others later, including one at Staines Reservoirs on 10th January 1946, one in the Staines area in December 1949, three at Perry Oaks Sewage Farm in January 1969, eight there in August 1970 and a wintering bird there in 1971. Autumn passage numbers increased in the 1990s and were largest at Perry Oaks.

Calendar. Figures in Coleman and Milne (1996) show that Green Sandpipers were present at Beddington Sewage Farm in most or all of the months of every season from 1950/51 to 1996/97, with a steady increase over the period. Peak numbers were in July and August. The 2,299 vice-county bird months from 1994 to 2001 confirm that autumn migration peaks in August and show that wintering numbers are almost level from November to March. There is a modest spring peak in April. May is the month in which Green Sandpipers are least frequently observed.

Summary of monthly totals at all vice-county sites, 1994-2001 from Surrey Bird Reports

Jan	Feb	Mar	Apr	May	Jun	Jul	Aug	Sep	Oct	Nov	Dec	Total
141	131	143	198	29	91	327	464	294	195	157	129	**2,299**

Wintering. One on a stream in southwest Surrey on 25th-27th December 1921 and another near Woking on 26th December of the same year may be the first dated winter records. There were others on 'Wisley Marshes' in January 1942, Island Barn Reservoir in 1946 and Frensham Little Pond in December 1954. Two wintered at Unstead Sewage Farm in 1954-55. Wintering was reported from Beddington in 1965/66, 1966/67 and 1967/68. By 1971 it was not unusual for birds to be recorded somewhere in the county in every month of the year and by 2000 this was the norm. Coleman and Milne show Green Sandpipers at Beddington Sewage Farm annually, with a maximum of 14 in December 1993.

Large counts

Beddington Sewage Farm: 42, 24th July 2002
Berrylands Sewage Works: 10, 22nd August 1986
Guildford Sewage Farm: 20, 31st October 1954
Holmethorpe Sand Pits: 17, 2nd September 1984
Ripley Sewage Farm: 12, 20th August 1979

Walton-on Thames Sewage Farm: 12, 17th
    August 1947
Spelthorne
Perry Oaks Sewage Farm: 29, August 1998
Staines Reservoirs: 20, 17th August 1976

Wood Sandpiper

Tringa glareola

Scarce passage migrant

Breeds from Scandinavia to eastern Siberia. Wood Sandpipers probably colonised Britain with the arrival of trees after the last Ice Age (Thomas, 1999). Those now found in Britain probably come from Finland and Scandinavia and are heading for West Africa (*MA*). Wood Sandpipers bred freely on the Dutch coastal marshes in the 19th century, before they were drained, and bred at least once in northern England. A small Scottish breeding population became established in the late 1950s.

Early Surrey history. Bucknill knew of only a few birds in Surrey. Since then the records, if not the birds, have become rather more common. In Surrey, Wood Sandpipers have for many years been regular passage migrants, mainly in autumn. Meyer illustrated one that had been shot in a gravel pit on Ditton Marsh prior to 1840. Others known to Bucknill were at Wonersh (undated), Eashing (1850), Catteshall (two in spring, 1857), Cranleigh (1859) and the Mole near East Molesey (19th September 1871).

20th century. One at Staines south reservoir on 17th August 1927 and two there on the following day were the first birds for Spelthorne and the first anywhere in the London area since 1900. The reservoir was drained at the time. There was one on the River Colne on 30th July 1933. Wood Sandpipers have been seen in Spelthorne in almost every subsequent year, most often at Perry Oaks Sewage Farm. The influx in 1952 brought peaks of ten in July, 17 in August and two in September and October at Perry Oaks Sewage Farm and there was one at King George VI Reservoir on 24th August.

There were no 20th century vice-county records before 1934, when one was seen at Brooklands Sewage Farm on 15th-16th August. It then became more regular. An autumn influx in 1952 brought one or two to Beddington Sewage Farm in August, September and October, one at Esher Sewage Farm on 10th August and a peak of eight at Guildford Sewage Farm on 27th August.

Where found. Of some 407 bird months up to 2000 in the vice-county, almost half (201) were recorded at Beddington. Another 57 were at Guildford Sewage Farm, all of them in the period 1939-97. The remainder were at Ash Vale Gravel Pits (one), Barn Elms (nineteen, 1955-2000), Berrylands Sewage Works (four), Broadford Marsh (two in 1967), Brooklands Sewage Farm (four, 1934-39), Buckland Sand Pits (1986, 1988), Epsom Common Stew Ponds (five), Epsom Sewage Farm (seven, 1956-57), Esher Sewage Farm (thirteen, 1951-59), Frensham (four, 1986, 1990, 1994), Frimley Gravel Pits (two, 1979, 1981), Gatton (one, 1969), Godstone (one, 1960), Hamm Moor Gravel Pits (one, 1970), Hersham Gravel Pit/Sewage Farm (fourteen), Holmethorpe Sand Pits (eight), Island Barn Reservoir (1957), Mitcham Common (1985), Molesey Sewage Farm (seven, 1950-61), Morden Hall Park (1970), Old Woking Sewage Farm (four, 1994-97), Papercourt Gravel Pits (eleven, 1973-99), Queen Elizabeth II Reservoir (two, 1961), Richmond Park (1976), Ripley Sewage Farm (seven, 1974-82), Send Gravel Pits (1963), Stoke Water Meadows (1991), the Surrey Docks (1978), Thursley Common (nine), Walton Gravel Pits (two, 1956-57), Walton Reservoirs (seven, 1990-95) Walton-on-Thames Sewage Farm (1947), Wimbledon Common (1995 and 1998), Worcester Park Sewage Farm (1962), and Wrecclesham Sand Pits (1999). Sewage farm closure and modernisation has reduced the amount of suitable habitat.

From 2001 onwards, Wood Sandpipers have been seen at Barn Elms, Beddington, Enton, Thursley/Ockley Commons, Unstead, Walton Reservoirs and Wimbledon Common and, in Spelthorne, at Staines Reservoirs and Stanwell Moor. The largest number in the vice-county was three at Barn Elms on 20th August 2001 and the earliest was at Beddington on 24th April 2001.

Calendar. A well-marked autumn passage in August contains nearly half of the records. Spring passage peaks in May and there are no records before 9th April.

Bird months 1900-2000

	Jan	Feb	Mar	Apr	May	Jun	Jul	Aug	Sep	Oct	Nov	Dec	Total
Vice-county	0	0	0	5	71	10	73	190	51	2	3	2	**407**
Spelthorne	0	0	0	3	31	6	60	134	59	6	1	0	**300**

Early and late vice-county dates are:

Large counts. There were 12 at Guildford Sewage Farm on 23rd July 1956, ten at Beddington Sewage Farm on 14th August 1999 and ten at Staines Reservoirs on 22nd August 2004 (*LNHSB*).

Behaviour. One performed a display flight and song at Beddington Sewage Farm 17th May 1989.

Common Sandpiper *Actitis hypoleucos*

Regular passage migrant in small numbers, has bred

Breeds widely across Europe and Asia, wintering mainly in Africa south of the Sahara, India, southeast Asia and Australia. The *Migration Atlas* suggests that birds breeding from northern Britain and Scandinavia pass through southern Britain to winter in southwest Europe and West Africa. A few winter in Britain. British breeding birds are currently found mainly in upland areas, but they had a wider breeding distribution in the 19th century, including lowland areas in Cornwall and parts of southeast England. Numbers have fallen further in the past 30 years.

Early Surrey history. Newman (1849) included Common Sandpipers as passage migrants through the Godalming district. Bucknill said they could be seen on passage along the Mole, the Thames, the Wandle and the Wey and by the larger sheets of water, including Frensham Little Pond.

1900 to 1960. There were large numbers on spring and autumn passage in the Staines area (Kerr, 1906). Power (1910) mentioned fairly frequent spring and autumn passage, giving records from Crystal Palace, Dulwich and Tooting and there were 13 at Staines Reservoirs on 9th September 1922. Glegg (1935) said that peak numbers reached 20 during autumn passage at Staines. Migrants were seen at Epsom Sewage Farm and Gatton in August 1934. Collenette (1937) knew of 48 records for Richmond Park, 19 in April and the remainder from May to September. Common Sandpipers soon became regular passage migrants at the reservoirs and were found at other sites such as Battersea Park (1940, 1942), Camberley (1953), Cutt Mill, Frensham, Guildford Sewage Farm (1944), Hammer Ponds, Hedgecourt (1947), Kew Gardens (January 1940), Mitcham Common (1934), the Thames at Lambeth (1944), Unstead Sewage Farm and Walton-on-Thames Sewage Farm. In 1946, Common Sandpipers were seen at Frensham, Guildford Sewage Farm, Unstead Sewage Farm and Virginia Water (Surrey end, 1946) and from about this time the Common Sandpiper was a frequent migrant at wetland sites.

Later records. By the mid 1990s, about 300 Common Sandpiper bird months were being recorded annually. The highest total (333) was in 2001. Records were widely distributed, but Barn Elms, Beddington, Queen Elizabeth II Reservoir and Walton Reservoirs each had more than 30 in most years and Frensham, Holmethorpe and Island Barn Reservoir could have more than 20. Numbers also appear to have risen in Spelthorne, with up to 50 on autumn passage at Staines Reservoirs and even more at Perry Oaks Sewage Farm, until it was closed. Common Sandpipers have continued to be widely reported, the largest number being a flock of 27 at Frensham Great Pond on 26th August 2002, a record for the site up to that date.

Calendar. There are strong passages in April-May and July-September and up to four bird months annually in each of the winter months.

Monthly totals based on site maxima 1994-2001, from Surrey Bird Reports

	Jan	Feb	Mar	Apr	May	Jun	Jul	Aug	Sep	Oct	Nov	Dec	Total
Vice-county	15	14	13	278	569	41	480	757	262	52	21	16	**2,518**

Wintering. Winter records date back to at least 1914, when two were heard over Wallington on 25th February at 6.30 pm. At Barn Elms Reservoirs, there was one until 13th December 1930 and into 1931 to 27th February at least. Others were at Walton Reservoirs: on 5th, 7th and 18th January 1931, 12th December 1931, 5th and 10th January 1932 (*LN*) and 2nd January 1933 (*LN*) and at Island Barn Reservoirs from October-December 1938. Six at Unstead Sewage Farm on 24th January 1956 stayed into February. Others at Island Barn Reservoir (December 1966/February 1967) Send (December 1966-January 1967), Hersham Sewage Farm and Island Barn Reservoir (December 1968), Thorpe (January to March 1969) and Wisley Sewage Farm (28th December 1976) were examples of possibly wintering birds. There were at least 15 January birds from 1994 to 2001. In Spelthorne, there are published winter records from Queen Mary (1952), Staines Reservoirs (1968/69) and then fairly frequently in the Spelthorne area from 1971.

Breeding. Denham Jordan (1895) found a nest and four young along the Mole. A correspondent of Bucknill's said he had seen a nest and two fledglings a few days old at Frensham Little Pond in 1896. W. A. Shaw thought that Common Sandpipers may have nested at Peper Harow in 1910 and watched a family party of six in Witley Park on 19th July 1911, which the keeper said had nested there. Apart from these three accounts, there is no evidence that Common Sandpipers have ever bred in Surrey, though breeding preliminaries have been seen on a number of occasions. A pair was present in Addlestone from May to August 1969 and display, song flight and distraction activity was observed. A pair were at Thorpe from June to the end of July 1969, making song flights and, at the same site in 1970, a pair were frequently seen defending territory. Display flights were seen at Stoke, Guildford in 1981 and territorial behaviour was seen there in 1987. A pair apparently tried to nest on a man-made island at Lonsdale Road Reservoir in 1982 but gave up after vandals cut the mooring rope.

Large counts

Barn Elms: 30-35, 14th August 1968
Beddington Sewage Farm: 32, 25th July 1987
Frensham Ponds: 47, Great Pond, 5th July 2005 (S. P. Peters)
Guildford Sewage Farm: 18, 20th May 1948 (*BB, 42:314*)
Holmethorpe Sand Pits: 16, 22nd July 1987
Island Barn Reservoir: 20, 18th August 1984
Papercourt Gravel Pits/Ripley Sewage Farm: 19, 3rd August 1978

Queen Elizabeth II Reservoir: 26, 5th August 1999
Richmond Park: 13, 7th September 1934
Thorpe Gravel Pits: 12, 27th July 1966,
Walton Reservoirs: 20, 13th August 1995
Spelthorne
King George VI Reservoir: 30, August 1999
Perry Oaks Sewage Farm: 86, 6th August 1978
Queen Mary Reservoir: 25, 14th August 1975
Staines Reservoirs: *c.*50, 3rd August 1969
Wraysbury Reservoir: 22, July 2000

Movements. The one ringed bird known to have been recovered abroad was an adult ringed at Guildford on 27th April 1960 and recovered in Spain, 1,461 km south, on 20th August in the same year.

Spotted Sandpiper   *Actitis macularius*

One bird

Breeds in North America and winters south to Uruguay. Has occurred in most English counties. Spring passage is in May and June, with a return passage peaking in September.

Surrey. One was found in adult summer plumage at Barn Elms Reservoirs on 16th May 1988 by J. P. P. Wilczur (*BB, 92:578*).

Turnstone (Ruddy Turnstone)   *Arenaria interpres*

Scarce passage migrant

Has a circumpolar breeding distribution on coastal tundras and round the shores of the Baltic and Norway. Not proved to have bred in the British Isles. Wintering birds are found around the coasts of Europe, Africa, the Americas, southern Asia, Australia and New Zealand. The *Migration Atlas* says that most of those wintering in Britain are from Canada, Greenland and Iceland, with a few from Finland and Scandinavia. The Wetland Bird Survey shows a national decline in winter numbers.

Early Surrey history. One killed at Hammer Pond was bought by Stafford from Mr Lillywhite, land-lord of the nearby Half-moon Inn (*SALEC*). Bucknill knew of it in the Charterhouse Museum but the specimen now held there has Norfolk as its provenance. One flew over a garden in Dulwich on 2nd July 1893, possibly from the nearby Belair Lake. Although the date is good for the wild bird, the place is not. It has been suggested that the bird might have been an escape, perhaps from the cages of the collector A. G. Butler, who lived not far away at Penge.

Where found since 1900. A young bird at Queen Mary Reservoir on 20th August 1931 (*BB, 25:134-135*) was the first for the district, followed by one at Staines Reservoir on 24th May 1936. The first few for the vice-county in the 20th century were single birds at Frensham on 20th May 1921 and Barn Elms Reservoir on 16th May 1933, followed in the same year by four at Barn Elms on 3rd September, estab-lishing something of a pattern for the century. There were over 260 vice-county bird months from 1900 to 2001 and the number of birds found has risen considerably since the 1960s.

Bird months by decade 1900-2001

	1900s	1910s	1920s	1930s	1940s	1950s	1960s	1970s	1980s	1990s	2000-01	Total
Vice-county	0	0	1	11	0	28	32	16	39	112	23	**262**
Spelthorne	0	0	0	3	23	101	81	107	141	174	36	**666**

Barn Elms, with 75 bird months over this period, was the most frequented place. Beddington Sewage Farm produced 71 bird months and the remainder were at only nine other places: Brooklands Sewage Farm (30th May 1934 and four on 22nd May 1939); Frensham (14 from 1921 to 1999, maximum three in 1987 and 1989); Frimley Gravel Pits (three, 1985-86 and 1990); Hersham Sewage Farm (two on 21st May 1994); Island Barn Reservoir (nine, including six on 1st May 1958); Papercourt Gravel Pits (24th-25th July 1984); Queen Elizabeth II Reservoir (49, maximum three on any one date); the Surrey Docks (1st May 1978) and Walton Reservoirs (thirty-two, including five on 5th September 2000). There were about 666 Spelthorne bird months over the same period. Nearly half of them (323) came from Staines Reservoirs and 182 from Perry Oaks Sewage Farm. There were 51 from King George VI Reservoir, 58 from Queen Mary Reservoir, two from Stanwell Moor Gravel Pits and 14 from Wraysbury Reservoir.

Records from 2001 onwards have come from Barn Elms, Beddington, Queen Elizabeth II Reservoir, and Walton Reservoirs, the largest number being 11 at Queen Elizabeth II Reservoir on 19th August 2005. There have been at least six records from King George VI Reservoir and eight from Staines Reservoirs since 2000 (*LBR, LNHSB*).

Calendar. In the vice-county, May, with 105 bird months, has been the most frequent month. There have been none in October or November. One seen at Barn Elms on 27th and 30th March 1978 is the only March record. One at Barn Elms Reservoirs on 9th December 1980 was the first for December. In Spelthorne, a third of the bird months were in May and a third in August and there were none in March or November.

Bird months 1900-2001

	Jan	Feb	Mar	Apr	May	Jun	Jul	Aug	Sep	Oct	Nov	Dec	Total
Vice-county	13	3	1	15	105	3	34	43	40	0	0	5	**262**
Spelthorne	2	2	0	49	201	29	77	220	76	9	0	1	**666**

Large counts

Beddington Sewage Farm: ten, 8th September 1993

Queen Elizabeth II Reservoir: eleven, 19th August 2005

Spelthorne

King George VI Reservoir: seven, 4th August 1985

Perry Oaks Sewage Farm: ten, 4th June 1961

Queen Mary Reservoir: eleven, 29th August 1975

Staines Reservoirs: fourteen, 14th August 1991

Wilson's Phalarope   *Phalaropus tricolor*

Two birds, both in Spelthorne

Breeds in North America and winters in South America. British records peak in September, none in winter from 1958 to 1985. Mostly coastal counties but recorded in a number of inland counties.

   Surrey. The first was a juvenile at Staines Reservoirs on 14th-26th September 1983 (A. V. Moon, *LBR for 1986:177-78*; *BB, 77:528,*). There was another juvenile at Staines Reservoirs on 5th-13th September 1997 (T. G. Ball, C and D. K. Lamsdell, D. J. Morris *et al.*, *BB, 91:478*).

Red-necked Phalarope   *Phalaropus lobatus*

Sixteen birds, ten of them in Spelthorne

Another wader with a circumpolar breeding distribution, which in this case is a little further south, to include Scotland, where it has been known to breed since about 1803 (*HA*). The main wintering areas are on the coasts of South Arabia, Peru and the East Indies. It is apparently not known where the Scottish birds winter.

   Surrey. Bucknill knew of a pair shot 'many years ago' near Ash. Dated records are:

1885:   Nutfield Marsh, one shot in about 1885.

1949:*   King George VI Reservoir, one on August 1st and 2nd, the first for Middlesex.

1968:*   Perry Oaks Sewage Farm, one on 10th August.

1987:*   King George VI Reservoir and Staines Reservoirs, one on dates from 17th October to 8th November.

1970:   Godstone Sand Pits, one, possibly two on 16th August.

1983:*   Staines Reservoirs, one on 3rd-4th June.

1988:*   Staines Reservoirs, one on 14th August.

Surrey, 2003   Photo A. V. Moon

1992:* Perry Oaks Sewage Farm, one on 30th July, also at Staines Reservoirs on the 31st,

1993:* Staines Reservoirs, one on 14th-16th September.

1994:* Staines Reservoirs, one from 29th June to 2nd July.

1996:* Stanwell Moor, one on 9th-11th May.

1998:   Unstead Sewage Farm, one on 5th September.

1998:* King George VI Reservoir and Staines Reservoirs, one on 3rd-4th October.

2003:   Queen Elizabeth II Reservoir and Walton Reservoirs, one from 26th September to 3rd October.

*Spelthorne

Grey Phalarope   *Phalaropus fulicarius*
Scarce migrant

Breeds around the arctic regions, penetrating further inland than Red-necked Phalaropes. The main wintering areas are the seas of western South America, West Africa and Namibia. Grey Phalaropes are not known to have bred in the British Isles but may have done so on the tundras of post-glacial Britain. The year 1866 saw a remarkable influx of Grey Phalaropes to Britain. Saunders gave an estimate by J. H. Gurney that, between 20th August and 8th October, upwards of 500 were killed, of which about 250 were in Sussex.

Early Surrey history. The earliest record located is of a female moulting from summer to winter plumage, which was shot on the Thames near Battersea in November 1824, the first for Middlesex as well as for Surrey. The account given in Yarrell (1825) says that the bird was seen by a gardener, who went home, a distance of a mile and a half, to get his gun, came back to find the bird still swimming and feeding near the same spot, and shot it. Yarrell acquired the corpse for his collection. Long found one on a small pond at Hampton Lodge on 14th October 1825 and, in his own words, *it remained quietly while I went for my gun and shot it.*

The next batch of records comes from Morris (2nd edition), as summarised by Bucknill. Meyer killed two on the Thames near Shepperton, one in December 1840 and the other on 2nd December 1841. One was shot on Bagshot millpond on 25th September 1845 and two others were killed in the same neighbourhood. One was picked up near the bridges at Godalming by a Mr Stedman on 30th November 1846 and six others were shot at about the same time at Woking. One was shot on the Wandle at Carshalton in the middle of November 1851.

One was obtained near Farnham not later than 1854 (Spicer). Stafford killed one at Hascombe in 1864 and 'recorded' another at Broadwater, Farncombe in the influx year of 1866. Bucknill mentioned a paper by J. Gurney junior which detailed the Surrey casualties in 1866 as single birds at Farnham, Frensham (on 30th September), Millcourt [Binstead, not in Surrey?], Tilford, and the Thames near Waterloo Bridge (September).

Bucknill noted that 1870 was another great [for the collectors] Phalarope year in which a bird was shot 'on the reservoir at Barnes' at the end of October. The final birds of the century were killed on a brook near Redhill on 16th October 1877, shot near Thursley in an autumn not long before 1880, found dead at Waddon in 1890, shot at West Molesey on 25th October 1891 and picked up dead on a lawn near Dorking in January 1895. One 'occurred' in about 1895 near Frensham. Glegg added one killed on the Thames near Barnes in October 1896 and there are undated 19th century records from near Cranleigh and at Poynter's, near Cobham.

20th century. No more were recorded in the vice-county for over 30 years, the next being one on reservoirs near Hammersmith Bridge (Barn Elms) on 21st-25th September 1930, seen after a gale. This was the first of about thirty vice-county records and thirty-two bird months to 2005. The vice-county and Spelthorne both showed bird month peaks in the 1950s and 1980s:

Bird months by decade 1900-2005

	1900s	1910s	1920s	1930s	1940s	1950s	1960s	1970s	1980s	1990s	2000s	Total
Vice-county	0	0	0	3	1	10	6	2	8	1	1	**32**
Spelthorne	0	0	1	4	3	13	4	4	22	2	1	**54**

Calendar. The great majority of the birds have been in September and October, as this table of bird months shows:

Bird months 1900-2005

	Jan	Feb	Mar	Apr	May	Jun	Jul	Aug	Sep	Oct	Nov	Dec	Total
Vice-county	1	0	0	0	0	0	0	0	7	16	6	2	**32**
Spelthorne	0	0	0	1	1	0	0	3	18	25	4	2	**54**

Details. Detailed records since 1900 are: *Barn Elms Reservoirs* on 20th-25th September 1930, nearby on 9th November 1931 (dead), November 1935, 9th-10th September 1951, 28th November to 15th December 1953 (also seen at *Lonsdale Filter Beds*), 19th-26th October 1959, 8th-12th October 1967, 21st-26th October 1967, 24th-25th September 1981, 16th-18th October 1987; *Beddington Sewage Farm* on 19th-22nd October 1987; *Cutt Mill* on 25th September 1940, 9th-12th October 1958; *Fetcham Mill Pond* on 3rd-6th September 1960 (lame, the earliest autumn record); *Frensham* on 25th October 1950, 25th January 1953 (the only January record), 9th October 1960, 23rd December 1961 (described as a phalarope probably of this species), 16th October 1987 (one flew west, another stayed until next day); *Guildford Sewage Farm* on 18th-21st October 1959, 10th-14th October 1961, *Island Barn Reservoir* on 14th-16th September 1957 (during a national influx), 11th-13th October 1981, 4th-12th November 1989; *Queen Elizabeth II Reservoir* on 18th October 1987, 3rd-10th November 1996; *the Surrey Docks* on 11th-12th September 1974; *Thorpe* on 7th November 1971. All but the 1987 Frensham record were of single birds. Three or four of the 1987 birds were associated with the great gale in October of that year. Later records came from Frensham (16th-21st October 2004), and Walton Reservoirs (13th October 2001).

The first for Spelthorne was not until 1928, when one was seen at *Staines Reservoirs* on 15th August. Others were seen there on 19th August 1930, 16th October 1932 and 2nd December 1934 (Glegg), 21st September 1935 (*LN*), September 1945 (two) and 1st-2nd August 1949. The 1950 invasion brought one to *King George VI Reservoir* on 18th-24th September. There were two at *Staines Reservoirs* on 4th October 1952. The invasion of 1957 brought one to *Queen Mary Reservoir* from 15th-19th September (two on 17th).

Single birds were seen at *King George VI Reservoir* from 24th September to 12th October 1958, 18th October 1959 and 25th-26th November 1961, *Queen Mary Reservoir* on 14th-18th October 1959, 12th October 1960, 1st-3rd September 1969, 24th September 1981 and 8th-11th October 1981, *Staines Reservoirs* on 2nd-3rd and 9th-10th December 1961, 5th-6th November 1970, 16th September 1974, 26th April to 1st May 1981 and 29th September to 1st October 1984 and *Wraysbury Reservoir* on 8th September 1984, with two on the 9th and 10th.

The October 1987 storm brought seven to *King George VI Reservoir*, four staying to the 20th. There were two at *Queen Mary Reservoir* on the 16th with one on the 17th-19th, one at *Staines Moor* on the 17th and two at *Staines Reservoirs* on the 16th and 17th. Subsequent records are of single birds at *King George VI Reservoir* on 4th September 1988, 24th September 1989 and 9th-16th October 2001 and at *Staines Reservoirs* on 9th November 1989 and 30th October 1996.

Skuas   *Stercorarius species*

Surrey. Unidentified skuas were seen at Barn Elms in October 1967 and October 1975, at King George VI Reservoir in October 1999, at Queen Mary Reservoir in October 1975 and August 1989 and at Staines Reservoirs in October 1967, October 1987 and September 1988. There were four at Warlingham in May 1993.

Pomarine Skua
Stercorarius pomarinus

Three vice-county birds and about nine in Spelthorne

Breeds mainly on northern coastal tundras from Russia east to Canada and winters at sea south to southern Africa and Australia. Pomarine Skuas are frequent migrants around British coasts but rare inland.

   Surrey. The first bird found was at Barn Elms:

1970:   Barn Elms Reservoirs, an adult on 25th October, seen by W. Y. N. Roberts.

1972:* Wraysbury Reservoir, one from 30th November to 8th December, killed and ate a Black-headed Gull.

1976:* Queen Mary Reservoir, juveniles on October 19th and 30th. One killed and ate a Black-headed Gull.

1985:* Staines Reservoirs, a rather tame juvenile on 4th-5th October, ate a dead Black-headed gull on the 4th and drowned another in shallow water on the 5th. Seen at Wraysbury Reservoir on the 7th, feeding on the body of a Lesser Black-backed Gull.
     Staines Reservoirs, an immature bird on November 17th.

1985:   Morden, a juvenile was picked up on 20th November and handed to the RSPCA. It died on the following day.

1986:* Queen Mary Reservoir, different juveniles on 3rd-5th and 16th-17th January. A juvenile at Staines Reservoirs on 12th-16th January was probably one of these.

1987:   Frensham Great Pond, a pale-phase adult on October 16th. It was watched for 20 minutes after the great gale of that date.

1987:* Wraysbury Reservoir, a juvenile on 17th October.

1996:* Wraysbury Reservoir, one on 16th November.

Spelthorne

Arctic Skua
Stercorarius parasiticus

At least 40 vice-county records to 2002, many from Spelthorne

Circumpolar breeding distribution, from the Arctic as far south as Scotland. The Scottish population was in decline during the 19th century because of persecution but subsequently increased somewhat until a further decline in the 1990s. Arctic Skuas winter in the North Atlantic and in the coastal waters of Africa, the Americas and Australia.

   Early Surrey history. Arctic Skuas passing through Surrey are likely to be from Scotland and other parts of Northern Europe. A young bird was shot on the Thames near Battersea in September 1824 (Yarrell, 1825). This bird was the first for Middlesex as well as for Surrey. Bucknill has it as a Richardson's Skua, the name usually used for dark-phase birds at the time though it was sometimes used for light-phase birds because the name 'Arctic' was occasionally applied to the Long-tailed Skua (Saunders). One was picked up on Britty Hill, Puttenham in 1840 (Bucknill). The Charterhouse Collection held an undated adult specimen that had been killed at Wonersh (*SALEC*) in Bucknill's time but the specimens now held are of unknown origin.

   Where found. From 1900 to 2002 there were at least 40 records, involving 94 birds, in the vice-county. At least 43 records involving 82 birds have been found for Spelthorne from 1948. One was seen at the Surrey Docks in December 1920 and this, or another, was there for two days in January 1921 (Macpherson, 1929). One, believed to be an immature bird, was at Wimbledon Common on 28th August 1922 and this or another was there on 8th September of the same year (*BLA*). A dark-phase bird was seen by H. A. Craw and C. Hughes at Staines Reservoirs on 24th April 1948, the first for Spelthorne. An immature bird was seen there on 9th October 1949 and this or another on the 14th.

There were no further vice-county records until 1954, since when the records up to 2002, single birds unless otherwise stated and mostly of birds flying over, have been these: *Barn Elms Reservoir*: 9th September 1954, September 1964, 11th September 1971 (and dates to 25th, possibly more than one bird), 14th September 1987 (three), 20th August 1992, 12th September 1994 (four), 15th August 1999, 28th August 2000; *Beddington Sewage Farm*: 18th September 1985 (four), 9th September 1989, 22nd August 1993 (two), 18th May 1995, 22nd August 1999, 4th May 2000 (six), 18th September 2001, 23rd September 2002; *Bricksbury Hill*: 13th September 1998 (two); *Burgh Heath*: 15th April 1980; *Croham Hurst Golf Course*: 16th October 1987 (brought in by the great gale of the night before); *Dulwich Wood*: 18th September 1977; *Ewell*: 13th September 1980 (five over Ruxley Lane); *Frensham Great Pond*: 23rd August 1985; *Hackhurst Downs*: 31st August 1969; *Island Barn Reservoir*: 22nd October 1960, 12th July 1986, 9th May 2001 (two); *Papercourt Gravel Pits*: 22nd September 2002 (two); *Pirbright Common*: 25th May 1998; *Putney*: 6th October 2002 (two); *Queen Elizabeth II Reservoir*:19th-20th August 1998, 16th September 2000 (twenty-one in two parties), 7th October 2000 (three), 10th May 2002; *Richmond Park*: 30th September 1978 (three); *Stoke Lake*: 27th August 1994 (seven); *Thursley Village*: 24th September 1990; *Walton Reservoir*: 4th September 1976, 31st July 2002. The largest party was nineteen at Queen Elizabeth II Reservoir in 2000.

Of the 43 Spelthorne records to 2002, twenty-two have come from Staines Reservoirs, sixteen from Queen Mary Reservoir, three from King George VI Reservoir and one each from Perry Oaks Sewage Farm and Wraysbury Reservoir. On 29th August 1992, five parties totalling twenty-two birds and including two groups of seven flew over Staines Reservoirs.

Calendar. Records peak in September. There are no records for February or March and none in the vice-county for June or November. The peak is even more marked for bird months than it is for the number of records.

Records 1900-2002

	Jan	Feb	Mar	Apr	May	Jun	Jul	Aug	Sep	Oct	Nov	Dec	Total
Vice-county 94	1	0	0	1	5	0	2	10	17	5	0	1	**42**
Spelthorne 82	0	0	0	2	2	1	2	9	21	2	4	0	**43**

Long-tailed Skua *Stercorarius longicaudus*

Seven records, six of them from Spelthorne

Breeds in the circumpolar arctic and further south to Scotland. Those now passing through British waters are thought to winter off southwest Africa (*MA*). Known from Ice Age Britain and may then have bred widely. In Britain, away from breeding areas, they most commonly occur in May, with autumn passage from July to mid November. Most are then found on the east coast, though there are records from most southern inland and coastal counties.

Surrey records were from August to October.

1966:*   Queen Mary Reservoir, one found dead on 26th September (*LBR* for 1966).

1978:*   Wraysbury Reservoir, an immature bird on 30th August (C. D. R. Heard, *BB, 72:525*).

1985:*   Staines Reservoirs, a tame juvenile on 6th-10th September, relocated at Queen Mary Reservoir on the 14th.

1985:   Barn Elms Reservoirs, two, one in summer plumage, drifted over southwest on 8th October (N. P. Senior).

1995:*   Wraysbury Reservoir, a dark-phase juvenile on 30th August.
         King George VI Reservoir, an immature bird on 6th September.

2004:*   Staines Reservoirs, a juvenile on September 9th (*LNHSB*).

*Spelthorne

Great Skua
Stercorarius skua (Catharacta skua)

Nine records to 2002, six of them from Spelthorne

The northern breeding range of the nominate Great Skua *S. s. skua* extends from Iceland to western Russia and south to northern Scotland. South Atlantic and Antarctic races are sometimes split off as separate species. Colonisation of Scotland appears to have taken place during the 18th century. Great Skuas were nearly wiped out there during the 19th century but increased markedly during the 20th. Over half of the world population breeds in northern Scotland (*MA*).

Surrey. Records from 1915 to 2002 are:

1915: Waterloo Bridge, P. E. Bunyard saw two harrying Black-headed Gulls on 14th April 1915. This was the first record for Middlesex as well as Surrey.

1931:* Staines Reservoirs, one on 14th-22nd February.

1975:* Staines Reservoirs, one on 17th November.

1982:* Queen Mary Reservoir, one on 6th September.
Staines Reservoirs, one on 10th September (flew over King George VI Reservoir).

1987:* Wraysbury Reservoir, three on 16th October, after the great overnight gale.

1989:* Queen Mary Reservoir, two on 9th September stayed for an hour.

1998: Beddington Sewage Farm, one spent five minutes on the lake on 28th September (P. R. Alfrey).

1999: Epsom Downs, one was picked up at Langley Vale in late September and taken into care. It was released on the south coast a week later.

Spelthorne

Mediterranean Gull
Larus melanocephalus

Scarce but increasing migrant

Mediterranean Gulls were almost unknown in Britain before 1950. There were only four records, the latest of which was in 1909 (*HA*). At one time a bird from around the Black Sea, a westward extension of the breeding range from the 1950s brought Mediterranean Gulls to many parts of Europe and a few have bred in Britain since 1968, initially in hybrid pairs. Ringing shows movements to and from continental Europe (*MA*).

Early Surrey history. An immature Mediterranean Gull at Barn Elms Reservoir on 19th-20th September 1957 was found by J. Izzard and H. P. Medhurst. It was the first for the London area as well as for Surrey. There are notes in the *LBR* for 1957. An adult at Epsom on 19th February 1967 was followed by a first-winter bird at the Surrey Docks on 15th December 1971. An adult at Staines Reservoirs on 21st September 1965 was the second for the London area. A second-winter bird was at the same site on 2nd December 1967.

There were no more until the appearance of a bird at Stamford Green, Epsom on 25th December 1976 marked the beginning of a remarkable run of records at the same site from W. H. Dady. They related to single birds visiting Stamford Green in winter on around 150 dates and 23 bird months over the following five years, the last being seen in January 1981. Mediterranean Gulls were still quite rare in Surrey at this time. There were only 39 bird months in the 1970s, most of which were at Epsom.

Where later found. Mediterranean Gulls later became more frequent, with 73 bird months in the 1980s, 189 in the 1990s and 49 in 2000-01. The increase was assisted by observers paying more attention to the composition of winter gull flocks. Almost all observations have been of single birds.

Beddington Sewage Farm, with 29 from 1984-1994 and others later, has become the main site followed by the floods at Wrecclesham and tips there when they were active in the 1980s. A dozen or so records from Carshalton Park and Ponds probably have some overlap with the Beddington birds. There have been many seen at Queen Elizabeth II Reservoir since 1995. Other places where the gull has been seen, all with bird months up to 1994 in single figures, are Addlestone, Bankside Reach, Belmont, Barn Elms, Binscombe, Chertsey Meads, Chessington, Egham, Ewell, Farnham Park, Frensham, Gatton Bottom, Goldsworth Park (Woking), Hersham, Holmethorpe, Island Barn Reservoir, Leatherhead (1987), Limpsfield, Merrist Wood, New Addington, Newark Priory, Old Woking, Papercourt Gravel Pits, Shirley (1988), South Norwood Country Park and Lake, Stoke (Guildford), Sunbury Lock, Thames Ditton, Thorpe Water Park, Tongham Gravel Pits, Wandsworth, Wimbledon Common and Park and Walton Reservoirs.

From 2001 onward, Mediterranean Gulls have been seen at Barn Elms, Beddington, Chessington, Frensham, Island Barn Reservoir, Holmethorpe, Normandy, Queen Elizabeth II Reservoir, Seale, South Norwood, Walton Reservoirs and West Ewell, including four at Beddington on 28th February 2002. Mediterranean Gulls are relatively uncommon in Spelthorne, possibly because the district has few suitable feeding sites, but single birds were reported in the *LNHSB* in 2001 (Staines Moor and Stanwell Moor), 2002 (Queen Mary Reservoir) and 2003 (Queen Mary Reservoir). There have been further records to 2005.

Calendar: Mediterranean Gulls have been recorded in every month of the year but only once in June (Beddington Sewage Farm 1986). Surprisingly, there is a minor peak in the following month, July. Of about 360 vice-county bird months, half have been in the first three months of the year.

Approximate bird months 1900-2001

	Jan	Feb	Mar	Apr	May	Jun	Jul	Aug	Sep	Oct	Nov	Dec	Total
Vice-county	62	62	60	6	3	1	35	10	9	25	38	49	**360**
Spelthorne	6	7	5	1	0	1	0	3	3	8	3	7	**44**

Movements. One ringed at Oye Plage, northern France, on 15th June 2000 was recorded in the field at Wraysbury Reservoir, 185 km WNW, on the 24th of the following month.

Little Gull
Larus minutus

Uncommon passage migrant

Most Little Gulls breed in southwest Siberia and Kazakhstan but sporadic breeding has occurred in Europe and North America. Ringing has shown that Little Gulls breeding round the Baltic appear in Britain on passage (*MA*). Up to the early 20th century, Little Gulls were regarded as irregular autumn and winter visitors, mainly seen on the east coast. They became rather more common during the 20th century and large flocks have been found on some of the reservoirs. There have been several breeding attempts in Britain.

Early Surrey history. The Little Gull has the distinction of being one of only two birds on the British list to have been first recorded in Surrey, a single bird having been shot on the Thames near Chelsea prior to 1813 (Montagu, 1813). Chelsea is on the Middlesex bank but the gull was on the waterway between the counties. The bird was obtained by a collector named Plasted, who sent the body to Montagu at his home in Devon for identification.

Four out of a flock of six at Battersea were sent to Stafford by Mr Taylor, Traffic Manager at Nine Elms Station (*SALEC*, *SCCMS*). Unlabelled birds that were probably these and one shot at Walton-on-Thames (*SALEC*) were seen in the Charterhouse Collection by Bucknill and a specimen said to be from Godalming is still held there. Other records in Bucknill are from near Frensham (February 1875), East Molesey (autumn of 1890), Wisley Pond (January 1893) and near Cobham (13th January 1893). One was seen over the Thames at Charing Cross on 15th February 1895, when the river was blocked with ice.

1900 to 1969. Little Gulls were seen at Barn Elms Reservoir on 4th January 1927 (*LN* for 1929) and 1st November 1937 (*BB, 31:238-39*). There was a juvenile at Island Barn Reservoir on 31st December 1938. One was found dead at Frensham on 4th May 1940. The next for the Thames in inner London was not until 1st October 1945 when a Little Gull was seen at Westminster. Later records came from Badshot Lea (1964), Barn Elms (21st July 1947 (*BLA*), 31st January 1948, 1952-54, 1956, 1958, 1961-63, 1965-69), Enton (1957), Epsom Sewage Farm (1955), Frensham (1948, 1951, 1968), Guildford Sewage Farm (1955-56), Island Barn Reservoir (1958), Stoke (28th April 1947), the Thames (Westminster, 1951), Walton Reservoirs (1959, 1964) and Warren Mere (1966).

The first in Spelthorne was an immature bird found by A. Holte McPherson and F. R. Finch at Staines Reservoirs on 6th October 1928. Others were seen at the same site on 20th-21st November 1932, 19th and 20th September 1933 and 13th October 1934. There was an immature at Queen Mary Reservoir on 14th December 1931 (*BB, 25:272*). One there on 29th January and 1st February 1937 was the first for both months. Five at Queen Mary Reservoir on 6th May 1936 made up the largest party for the London area from 1900 to 1956 (*BLA*). There were single birds at Staines Reservoirs in September, October and November 1939, 22nd October 1945, 1948 and January 1950. An adult at King George VI Reservoir on 9th August 1935 was the earliest for the London area since 1900 (*BLA*). In 1951 there were at least three single birds in Spelthorne during the autumn, and again from September to November 1952 and there was one at King George VI Reservoir on 9th August 1953. By that date they were regular migrants in the Spelthorne district.

Where found from 1970. Three reservoirs accounted for most of the 188 vice-county bird months from 1970 to 1988, with 64 from Barn Elms, 40 from Walton Reservoirs and 37 from Island Barn Reservoir. The remaining bird months came from Beddington Sewage Farm (13, including ten on 16th October 1987), Bury Hill Lake, Epsom Common, Frensham (18, including one on 27th July 1983), Frimley Gravel Pits, Long Ditton (19th March 1974), Lonsdale Road Reservoir, Papercourt Gravel Pits (three), Queen Elizabeth Reservoir, Ripley Sewage Farm and the Surrey Docks. One at Barn Elms in May 1984 stayed for three weeks. There were 150 bird days at Island Barn Reservoir in April 1989 and from then on, records became more numerous, with an average of 40 bird days per year from 1994 to 2001. Other sites included Holmethorpe, Shackleford, Southbank (London SE1) and Wrecclesham Floods.

Particularly large passages were noted in Spelthorne in May 1984, October 1987 (mostly storm-driven birds), September 1988, April 1989, September 1993, April 1995 and April 2003. Staines Reservoirs is probably the most important site in Surrey. The largest counts reported since 2000 were in 2003, with 16+ at Walton Reservoirs on 16th April, 17 at Island Barn Reservoir on the 17th and 68 at Staines Reservoirs on the 19th. Dead Little Gulls (not counted in the bird months), have been found at several places, for example at Effingham in January 1984.

Calendar. The vice-county bird months from 1970 to 1988 show a clear autumn passage with a smaller one in April/May. The October 1987 storm brought in at least 49 birds and accounts for the October peak. One at Walton Reservoirs on 15th June 1976 appears to be the first ever for June.

Bird months 1970-1988

	Jan	Feb	Mar	Apr	May	Jun	Jul	Aug	Sep	Oct	Nov	Dec	Total
Vice-county	4	0	1	17	14	1	1	41	33	60	8	8	**188**

Vice-county figures from 1994 to 2001 show a similar picture. In both periods the spring peak was in April but the autumn peak averaged later in the second period. An adult at Holmethorpe Sand Pits on 14th February 1993 is thought to be the first February bird since 1895.

Bird months 1994-2001

	Jan	Feb	Mar	Apr	May	Jun	Jul	Aug	Sep	Oct	Nov	Dec	Total
Vice-county	9	2	13	83	6	2	7	17	35	37	65	49	**325**

Large counts

Barn Elms Reservoirs: 13, 16th October 1987

Beddington Sewage Farm: 23, 3rd November
1997

Holmethorpe Sand Pits: 14, 20th April 1999

Island Barn Reservoir: 19, 12th-13th April 1989

Queen Elizabeth II Reservoir: 30, 6th October
1998

Walton Reservoirs: 16+, 16th April 2003

Spelthorne

King George VI Reservoir: 27, 17th October 1987

Queen Mary Reservoir: 20, 19th August 1975 and
16th October 1987

Staines Reservoirs: 55, 10th November 1969; 186,
29th April 1995

Movements. Oliver (1974) considered that most autumn records for the London area related to birds which were temporarily off-passage and that most migrating Little Gulls would pass through the area unseen, at great height or at night.

Sabine's Gull   *Larus sabini*
Rare

The normal breeding range is from Greenland west to northeast Siberia. Atlantic birds winter off southwest Africa and are presumably the source of most British records. Most are seen in the western approaches and southwest counties. Others travel to the east coast and birds are sometimes found inland, particularly after westerly gales.

Early Surrey history. It was a period of westerly gales that brought 12 Sabine's Gulls to England and Wales in September 1950, including the first two for our area. The earliest of these was an adult found at Staines Reservoir on the 13th, followed by an immature bird on the 18th. Both stayed until the 27th and were seen 'dipping in flight to the surface of the water after the manner of a Black Tern' (*BB*, 44:254-56). A phalarope-like mode of feeding while swimming was also observed. The birds were reported to be indifferent to spectators. *Birds of the London Area* gives the first arrival date as the 11th, rather than the 13th in the *British Birds* account. Associated arrivals included Baird's and Pectoral Sandpipers.

1987. There were no further reports until 1987 when the great gale on the night of October 15th/16th brought many Sabine's Gulls to the London area. Those in Surrey were:

16th October

Beddington Sewage Farm: an adult.

Croham Hurst Golf Course: an adult flying
WNW.

Thames at Hammersmith Bridge: two adults.

Thames at Hungerford Bridge: an adult.

Staines Reservoir: three adults.

Wraysbury Reservoir: one.

17th October

Barn Elms Reservoirs: three adults flew west.

Island Barn Reservoir: four adults, two were still
there on the 24th.

King George VI Reservoir: up to four on 17th,
one until the 20th.

Queen Elizabeth II Reservoir: two adults, also on
18th.

Queen Mary Reservoir: at least three adults and a
juvenile on the 16th, fifth bird on the 17th
and the last three birds on the 20th.

Staines Reservoir: three (from the 16th).

Wraysbury Reservoir: five.

18th October

Frimley Gravel Pits: an immature bird roosted
until the 24th.

Walton Reservoirs: two adults.

20th October

Frensham Great Pond: an adult roosted, also on
the 21st.

22nd October

Long Ditton Filter Beds: an adult until the 24th.

23 October

Perry Oaks Sewage Farm: two adults.

After 1987. There have been two birds since, both in Spelthorne: a juvenile at Wraysbury Reservoir on 14th-16th September 1997 (photograph in the *LBR*) and one of unknown age at King George VI Reservoir on 12th August 2003 (*Bird Watching*).

Bonaparte's Gull   *Larus philadelphia*
One record, Greater London

Breeds in northern North America and winters south to the West Indies. A rare visitor to the British Isles, which has occurred in nearly all months, most frequently in March.

Surrey. A first-winter bird at Barn Elms Reservoirs on 29th January 1983 was found by N. P. Senior among Black-headed Gulls on the filter beds, where it remained for a lengthy period in the afternoon. It eventually flew up to the reservoirs, where it was lost among the gulls that were roosting there (*BB, 77:529*). This was the first British record for an inland county and the first for the London area.

Black-headed Gull   *Larus ridibundus*
Common winter visitor, has bred

Breeds from Newfoundland east through Europe and Asia. Most move south in winter to inland and coastal sites north of the Equator. Many Black-headed Gulls breeding in Scandinavia and the Baltic area move to Britain in winter, as do some breeding in Iceland (*MA*). The European breeding range has been extending since the early 19th century. British breeding numbers are currently fairly stable. The British expansion was initially slowed by land drainage and egg collection and by 1900 Black-headed Gulls were still not breeding in any county adjacent to Surrey except Kent.

Early Surrey history. This is the commonest of the gulls to visit Surrey. Summering birds are found mainly along the Thames. Newman (1849) listed Black-headed Gulls as occasional visitors to the Godalming area but there are no dated records before the spring of 1877, when one flew into telegraph wires between Betchworth and Reigate (Holmesdale Natural History Club in Bucknill). Non-breeding birds were seen in increasing numbers in Surrey from the late 19th century, and roosts became established on the newly-built reservoirs. The trend was initiated by severe weather in winters such as from 1887/88, when Black-headed Gulls reached Putney for the first time, and there were 127 near Waterloo Bridge on 27th February. Frost in 1892/93 brought a further increase and by 1895 a severe February frost brought thousands to the London stretch of the Thames. A fuller history is given in the introductory sections on weather and roosts. Bucknill mentioned records from Wimbledon (1895), Banstead (about the same time), Lambeth Reservoir (May 1896) and Hackbridge (19th July 1896).

20th century. By 1902, Black-headed Gulls were spreading out to feed on fields as far from the Thames as Earlswood. They were, at the time, the commonest gull on Staines Reservoirs (Kerr, 1906). Before 1914, Black-headed Gulls were only winter visitors to any part of Surrey, sometimes arriving as early as August. By 1920 they had become common over Warlingham and they began staying on refuse dumps all day in 1929 (Beadell). There were 3,000 at Beddington Sewage Farm in January 1929 (Parr). Numbers at Brooklands Sewage Farm in 1936 peaked at about 400 on 13th July. They were rarely seen at Chiddingfold in 1935. By 1937, Black-headed Gulls had been seen at Richmond Park in every month except June. They were daytime visitors, roosting at the Staines and Queen Mary Reservoirs. At Vann Lake, Black-headed Gulls were infrequent until about 1975, after which they were commonly seen outside the breeding season (Blaker Log).

Breeding. A breeding colony was established at Perry Oaks Sewage Farm in 1941 or 1942. It had

50-60 nests in 1946 and peaked at 312 in 1948. There were 158 occupied nests in 1950, 240 nests in 1951, 220 nests in 1955, about 150 in 1959, 125 in 1961 (but few young reared), 40 pairs in 1962, five nests in 1963, two in 1964 and none in 1965 (*LBR*). More recently there have been further breeding attempts at Perry Oaks in 1981, 1996, 1998 and 1999 (*LBR*). No young were seen. Several pairs have attempted breeding on the Staines Reservoirs tern rafts from 1997, raising young in 1998 and 1999 (*LBR*). There were at least 14 nests in 2000 and 13 in 2001, though possibly fewer pairs actually bred (*LBR*). Thirty-one pairs were nesting on tern rafts in May 2004 and there were 50 nests on two rafts in the South Reservoir in May 2003 (*LNHSB*). A nest was found at Guildford Sewage Farm in 1956. It was deserted. A pair fledged young at Tice's Meadow in 2007, the first for the vice-county.

Roosts and flylines. Major gull roosts became established. The table shows total Black-headed Gull figures where they have been obtained.

Roost counts December/January/February

	1953	1963	1968	1969	1983	1993	1997	1998
Barn Elms Reservoir	10,000	20,000	24,000	25,000	6,500			
Frensham Great Pond					110	896	1,400	2,000
Island Barn Reservoir	10,000	100	15,000	37,500				
Queen Elizabeth II Reservoir	Not built	92,500	50,000	100,000	79,077	40,201	20,000	19,500
Walton: Knight and Bessborough		1,000	3,300	1,400		6	0	0
Chelsea and Lambeth		100	750	900				
Walton Reservoirs: All	1,000							
Spelthorne								
King George VI Reservoir	900	350	14,300	16,500				
Queen Mary Reservoir	10,250	8,000	15,000	42,000	31,251			
Staines Reservoir	1,000	3,000	7,500	6,000				
Staines + King George VI Reservoirs					1,369			
Wraysbury Reservoir	Not built	Not built	Not built	Not built	601			
Total	**33,150**	**125,050**	**129,850**	**229,300**	**118,908**			

Other roost counts include 20,000 at Wraysbury Reservoir on 23rd November 1979 and 50,000 on 11th December 1988. A roost at Frensham Great Pond was suspected in 1972 and confirmed in 1973, when the January roost count was 1,400 and the year peak was 3,000. Annual maxima for subsequent years have been:

1974-1976 unknown		1983*	*c.* 10,000	1990	3,258	1997	1,400
1977	900	1984	8,000	1991	950	1998	2,000
1978	6,000	1985	6,000	1992	950	1999	2,000
1979	2,500	1986	5,000	1993	2,200	2000	1,920
1980	3,300	1987	4,200	1994	1,550	2001	1,500
1981	2,450	1988	2,000	1995	3,300	2002	890
1982	4,000	1989	2,000	1996	3,000	2003	2,800

* *10,000 of which 5,000 roosted on 18th February 1983.*

S. P. Peters (pers. comm.) has advised that the Frensham gulls, which were mostly Black-headed, fed mainly at rubbish dumps (including Wrecclesham until it closed in the 1990s) and on farm fields in the area whereas those feeding at Tongham and Seale, which are mostly of larger species, probably roost on the Thames Valley reservoirs.

Several other places have been used. Gulls have often rested on fields at Holmethorpe during the day and occasionally, if it was very cold, roosted there overnight on water, when up to 4,000, mainly Black-headed and Herring Gulls with a few Common, may be involved. (S. Gale, pers. comm.). A roost of 3,000 Black-headed Gulls at Holmethorpe Sand Pits on 25th February 1976 occurred at a time when large numbers of gulls were feeding on an adjacent landfill site in Cormongers Lane. Landfill operations have continued in the area. There have been no further reports of roosts in the London and Surrey Bird Reports, but *The Birds of Holmethorpe Sand Pits 1960-1999* refers to birds that used the Biffa Waste Services landfill site to feed and roosted on Mercers Lake and Farm. A few hundred roosted there at the time of the January 2004 BTO roost count. Large numbers of Black-headed Gulls, mostly feeding at Holmethorpe in cold spells include 5,000 on 7th February 1996, 7,000 on 9th January 1997 and 10,000 on 25th December 1981 (*BHSP*). There is sometimes a pre-roost gathering at Gatton. A hundred or so roosted on a barge on the Thames at Hungerford Bridge in September 1979. A few Black-headed Gulls roosted at Frimley Gravel Pits in October 1987.

Large counts away from roosts

Beddington Sewage Farm: 15,000, March 2002

Berrylands Sewage Works: 2,500, December 1974

Enton: *c*.500, 23rd January 1957

Epsom Sewage Farm: 850, 26th February 1958

Hersham Sewage Farm: 1,700, 24th July 1967

Holmethorpe: 10,000, 25th December 1981

Horton Country Park: 2,000, 30th December 1994,

Lyne Sewage Farm: up to 1,000, early 1970,

Papercourt Gravel Pits: 2,200, 25th December 1972

Sandown Park: 2,000, 4th January 1999

Seale/Tongham: 4,000, 13th February 1996

Surrey Docks: 500, 12th December 1977

Thorpe Water Park: 2,000, 24th January 1982

Unstead Sewage Farm: 500, 23rd January 1957

West Horsley: *c*.2,000, 12th January 1974

Wrecclesham rubbish tip and floods: 10,000+, January 1987

Movements. Black-headed Gulls that had been cannon-netted at Gerrards Cross landfill on 20th-21st January 2004 were seen in the following weeks at Beddington Sewage Farm (per J. Allan). Others tagged on the north coast of the Netherlands were seen at Beddington in 2002. Black-headed Gulls that have been ringed in 12 foreign countries during the breeding season are known to have been recovered in Surrey, mostly in the winter months. Countries and numbers are: Czechoslovakia (three), Denmark (seven), Estonia (nine), Finland (eight), Germany (eighteen), Latvia (five), Netherlands (four), Norway (three), Poland (five), Sweden (seven), Switzerland (one) and the old USSR (one). Most have been ringed in June. The ages of the Swiss and old USSR birds have not been located but birds ringed as nestlings have come from the other ten. Adult Black-headed Gulls ringed in Surrey have been recovered from 16 countries, mostly in the breeding season: Belgium (one), Czechoslovakia (three), Denmark (twenty-six), Estonia (nine), Finland (twenty-eight), France (three, September and December), Germany (eight), Israel (one in December), Latvia (six), Lithuania (one), Netherlands (eleven), Norway (three), Poland (three), Spain (one in December), Sweden (sixteen) and the old USSR (four). This suggests where many of our wintering Black-headed Gulls breed.

The distance record was made by one ringed at Wrecclesham on 17th November 1976 and found dead in Israel, a minimum distance of about 3,500 km, on or about 25th December 1980 (BTO). Another, ringed at Wrecclesham on 24th July 1976, was recovered 2,352 km east at Verhnevolzhsky Lakes, Kalinin, old USSR on or about 26th January 1987.

Longevity. A gull ringed at Kempton Park on 4th March 1972 and recovered in the Netherlands 26 years and 3 months later, on 12th June 1998 may not have been ringed in Surrey. There is no such doubt about one ringed at the Guildford refuse tip on 2nd March 1974 and recovered 19 years and four months later, at Magli, Latvia on 17th July 1993. Severe winter weather usually causes extra gull deaths at the reservoirs. Examples given in the climate section above included over 60 at Molesey and Spelthorne reservoirs in 1929 and 65 at Staines in December 1933.

Behaviour. Power watched a flock of 21 catching winged ants over his Brixton garden for a quarter of an hour on 11th September, 1907. Thirty Black-headed Gulls came to an Ashtead garden bird table in December 1970.

Plumage variations. Albinistic and leucistic birds are sometimes seen, as at Barn Elms in 1959, 1962 and 2000, Frensham in 1978, Wraysbury Reservoir in 1985 and 1989, Wrecclesham in 1986, Beddington Sewage Farm in 1992, 1995-96, Queen Elizabeth II Reservoir in 1996 and several years up to 2004, Holmethorpe in 1993 and 1999 and Island Barn Reservoir in 1999.

Ring-billed Gull   *Larus delawarensis*

Seven vice-county birds and one in Spelthorne

Common and increasing in North America, wintering south to Mexico. British records cover all months but have been most frequent from February to March. They have a southwest bias which is more marked than with other American gulls.

Surrey. The records, all of single birds, are these:

1982:* Staines Reservoirs, 28th November (G. M. Haig, *BB, 77:532, LBR for 1984:139-40*).

1985: Barn Elms Reservoirs, one moulting to first-summer plumage on 19th April (R. E. Innes, *BB, 79:553*).

1989: Wrecclesham, an adult in winter plumage on a school playing field on 4th January (S. Abbott).

1995: Barn Elms London Wetland Centre, an adult on 15th January.
       Beddington Sewage Farm, an adult on 6th February.

1996: Tongham Gravel Pit, an adult on 2nd October.

2002: Richmond Park, 9th February.

2003: Barn Elms London Wetland Centre, 9th November.

*Spelthorne

Common Gull (Mew Gull)   *Larus canus*

Moderately common winter visitor and passage migrant

Common Gulls breed in Europe, northern Asia and northwest America, moving to inland and coastal regions north of the equator in winter. Many Common Gulls breeding in Scandinavia and the Baltic area move to Britain in winter, as do some breeding in Iceland (*MA*). In the British Isles, breeding was confined to Scotland and western Ireland up to 1900. Numbers appear to have been fairly stable. There has been a subsequent southward extension of range but, in southeast England, only to coastal areas. Wintering numbers have increased, due to population increases elsewhere, and Common Gulls, like other gulls, have become more common inland.

Early Surrey history. The earliest dated Surrey occurrence seems to be of one shot on the River Mole, near Hampton Court, in the winter of 1831 (Jesse). Meyer thought that Common Gulls were not uncommon and wrote of one at Fairmile Common on 26th December 1836. They were said to have been seen in the Godalming district prior to 1849 (Newman) and several were killed at Godalming (*SALEC*). The next dated record was not until 1888, when an occurrence at Kingston in the third week of March, during the severe frost of that year, was considered noteworthy, as was an appearance with Black-headed Gulls in the frost of early 1895 (Glegg). Bucknill described the Common Gull as a *fairly common and regular visitor to the Thames*, but this was then a very recent development. Gull records in Aldridge (1885) appear vague as to the species involved. Vagrants were found at Bellagio on 23rd November 1890 and on the Wey near Godalming on 10th February 1895. They occasionally appeared at Guildford and Haslemere.

Roosts and flylines. A few were wintering on Staines Reservoirs by 1906 (Kerr, 1906) and numbers had risen by the 1930s. Common Gulls were then well established at winter roosts and they fed in flocks of up to 300 around Epsom (Parr). By 1936, up to 20 or more were visiting Pen Ponds from September to April.

Common Gulls became regular at sewage farms in the 1940s and on recreation and sports grounds soon after. There were about 1,000 on Epsom Downs in January 1943, an exceptional number for the area (Parr). In the 1960s a few were being seen in autumn and winter in central and west Surrey. Roost numbers peaked in 1969, when 7,000 Common Gulls were counted at Island Barn Reservoir, The largest roost since then has been 2,000-3,000 at Queen Elizabeth II Reservoir in December 1989. Roosts of 450-600 birds have been counted from time to time at Walton Reservoirs. These three sites are adjacent and the counts probably overlap. By the 1980s a small winter roost had developed with the Black-headed Gulls at Frensham, apparently drawing on the flock feeding on Wrecclesham rubbish tip. Up to a hundred were roosting in the first quarter of 1984, the largest number recorded was 200+ in November 1987 and current numbers are lower, mostly under 20 since the tip was closed. The biggest roost counts have been in Spelthorne.

Roost counts in Spelthorne

	1953	1958	1963	1968	1969	1973	1983	1993	2000	2004
King George VI Reservoir	1,200	150	1,820	2,100						
Littleton (Queen Mary)	1,750	20,000	8,000	6,000	15,000		4,564			765
Staines Reservoirs			800		2,000					
Wraysbury Reservoir							62			

There has been a striking reduction in roosting numbers since the 1950s. In 1958 the Queen Mary roost held 9,000 birds on 25th January and 20,000 on 8th March (Sage, 1960).

Calendar. There is now a well-marked spring passage in March and April and a few birds hang on into May. Three were at Brooklands Sewage Farm on 28th May 1936 but then, as now, summer records would have been rather uncommon. Very few are present in June and most of these are in the Thames Valley.

Large counts away from roosts

Beddington Sewage Farm: 520, 24th February 1979

Burstow: 300, 8th February 1970

Chelsham: 1,000, 25th February 1998

Compton: 380, November 1989

Holmethorpe: 600, 7th February 1996 and 9th January 1997

Merrist Wood: 422, 28th January 1995

Molesey playing fields: 590, 20th November 1983

Pewley Down: *c.*400, 17th January 1976

Richmond Park: *c.*450, 20th January 1974

Staffhurst: 1,200, 9th January 1998

Stoke: 360 on morning flight, 21st March 1994

Trevereux: 650 west, 8th March 1998

Wrecclesham: 900, February 1986

Movements. Common Gulls that had been ringed in Estonia (one), Germany (two), Netherlands (two), Poland (one) and Sweden (two) during the breeding season have been recovered in Surrey, mostly in the winter months. Adult Common Gulls ringed in Surrey have been recovered from Denmark (one), Finland (four), Germany (two), Norway (one), and Sweden (four). This shows fairly clearly where many of our immigrant wintering Common Gulls breed. One ringed at Storgrundet, Sweden on 30th June 1979 and found dead 1,963 km southwest at Guildford on 24th February 1982 had travelled the furthest.

Longevity. The greatest proven longevity of these birds was of one ringed at the nest in Sweden on 27th June 1950 and recovered at Queen Elizabeth II Reservoir on 20th February 1964, more than 13 years and seven months later. Severe winter weather usually causes extra gull deaths at the reservoirs. Examples given in the weather section of the introduction include nine at Staines in December 1933.

Lesser Black-backed Gull

Larus fuscus

Moderately common passage migrant and winter visitor

Various races breed from Iceland east through northern Europe to Siberia. They winter around European, Mediterranean, Arabian and African coasts and on African lakes. Those from Britain, Iceland and southern Scandinavia mostly move south to winter on the coasts of Iberia and northwest Africa. British numbers increased during most of the 20th century but are now declining. Three races have occurred. The commonest is *L. f. graellsii*, the Western Lesser Black-backed Gull, which breeds in Britain, Iceland and parts of continental Europe from Norway to Portugal. Up to 1900, breeding in the British Isles was mainly confined to the north and west, but since then they have bred more widely and there has been a large increase in the number wintering. Lesser Black-backed Gulls first bred in London north of the Thames in 1982 and about 20 pairs bred on buildings near Billingsgate market in 2000.

Early Surrey history. Lesser Black-backed Gulls are most numerous on autumn passage and some are found in gull roosts. As with other gulls, there are very few dated records before 1888. One was shot at Frensham on 4th May 1826 (Long in Bucknill). One was picked up near Godalming on 20th January 1838, the day of the appalling Murphy's frost, when the temperature dropped to minus 14 degrees Fahrenheit (*SALEC*) and another nearby in 1842 (*SALEC*). There were three at Kingswood, Reigate in 1877. Others, from Guildford and the Thames, are undated.

20th century. One was seen at Frensham on 12th August 1906. Numbers increased and by 1954, up to 300 were roosting at Island Barn Reservoir in November and up to 100 could be found feeding or loafing at sites such as Beddington Sewage Farm, Richmond Park and Shepperton rubbish dump in December. Passage numbers tend to be higher than those of wintering birds. An exceptional passage in 1956 peaked at Island Barn Reservoir with 3,000 on 6th September. At the time, there were still very few records from outer Surrey - only three, (1934, 1950 and 1954) before 1956 at Frensham for example. Nine were at Enton on 19th December 1955.

Lesser Black-backed Gulls are now commonly found in feeding flocks across the county, the largest numbers being on or near rubbish tips such as the one at Seale, on playing fields such at St Paul's School, Addlestone, and on farmland around gravel pits such as Papercourt. The commencement of gravel extraction at Beddington has considerably increased the number resting and feeding. There may be 500 or more at such gatherings but typically a good deal fewer. Numbers are highest in the autumn. A few non-breeding birds are now summering, mainly in the Thames Valley. As with other large gulls, summer records in outer Surrey are rare.

Breeding. The only pair to have attempted breeding in Surrey nested on a Thames barge in 1996. The barge was towed away before the outcome was known. A pair was seen displaying and copulating at Beddington Sewage Farm in 1998 and a pair copulated at Barn Elms London Wetland Centre in 2001.

Roosts and (where indicated) roost flights. As with other gulls, the largest roosts go back to the 1960s:

Capel: roost flight of 1,200, November 1992
Epsom Common: 'thousands' flying over, 4th January 2002.

Island Barn Reservoir: *c.*4,000, 15th October 1960

Queen Elizabeth II Reservoir 1,500-2,500, December 1989

Queen Mary Reservoir, 75,000, 1969; 5,330, January 1983,

Staines Reservoirs: 1,700, 24th August 1975 (reservoir drained)

Wraysbury Reservoir: 4,300, 19th September 1990

Large counts. These are mostly feeding flocks.

Addlestone, St Paul's School: 350, 2nd September 1995

Barn Elms Reservoir: 205, November 2000

Beddington Sewage Farm: 1,155, December 2002.

Broadwater: 80, 14th November 1968

Brooklands Sewage Farm: 4, 18th May 1936

Buckland Sand Pits: 300+, 12th September 1992

Epsom Sewage Farm: 500, 6th October 1962

Hersham: 1,500, 17th and 24th August 1967

Holmethorpe: 550 on 27th March 1997

Lyne Old Sewage Farm: 750, 3rd October 1970

Old Woking Sewage Farm: 330, 11th December 1994

Papercourt Gravel Pits: 450, 13th October 1984

Sandown Park: 1,250-1,500, 6th October 1969 (pre-roost gathering)

Seale Sand Pits: 1,500, 31st December 2002

Thorpe Water Park: 250, 18th October 1981, December 1988

Tongham Gravel Pit: 1,000, Janaury 2002

Walton Reservoirs: 1,612, 17th January 2004

Worcester Park Rubbish Dump: 200+, 11th March 1969

Wrecclesham: 940, September 1979

Western Lesser Black-backed Gull   *Larus fuscus graellsii*

Also known as the British Lesser Black-backed Gull.

Early Surrey history. Rushen (1896) claimed to have seen *L. f. graellsii* on many occasions on the Thames off Blackfriars and Lambeth in 1895, the year of a great frost referred to in the introduction. It was the first indication that Lesser Black-backed Gulls were becoming more common in Surrey, in small numbers. An increase in the number seen outside the breeding season started in the 1920s, when, for example, there were 61 at Barn Elms Reservoirs on 28th August 1927. A. H. Bishop wrote that, from 1930, fairly large numbers began to arrive on the Thames at Barnes in mid June (*BB, 27:219*). Numbers would rise to a peak in September (several hundred on 10th September 1933) and then fall away during October. There were 250 at Barn Elms on 25th October 1932. Although mainly autumn passage migrants at this time, they were seen in every month of the year except February at Barn Elms in 1930 and there were 131 at Staines Reservoirs on 19th May 1934. By this date they had become all-year-round visitors to the Thames in London, recorded annually (Fitter, 1943).

Movements and longevity. Lesser Black-backed Gulls ringed in Belgium (one) and the Netherlands (ten), along with others ringed as chicks on Walney Island and the Farnes, have been recovered in Surrey. Most will be of this race though some Dutch birds may be of intermediate forms (*MA*). The same applies to two ringed as chicks in Vest-Agder, southern Norway and to Surrey-ringed birds recovered in Denmark (one), the Faeroes (two), Iceland (one), the Netherlands (three), the North Sea (two) and Spain (one). There is one recovery from Portugal. One ringed at Guildford on 15th February 1975 and recovered in Iceland later in the same year travelled 1,803 km (1,120 miles), by far the greatest known distance. The longevity record was created by a bird ringed on the Faeroes on 12th August 1963 and recovered over 19 years and seven months later at Queen Mary Reservoir on 3rd April 1983.

Scandinavian Lesser Black-backed Gull   *Larus fuscus fuscus*

No confirmed Surrey records

Also known as the Baltic (Lesser Black-backed) Gull. Breeds in the Baltic and northern Norway. *The Handbook* considered the race as of dubious validity. It was not distinguished from *L. f. intermedius* for recording purposes until rather recently. Identification by field characters is now regarded as unreliable. Proof of its occurrence in Britain depends on ringing records from Sweden and Finland of which only one, ringed as a chick in Finland, has so far been accepted by the BBRC (*Newsacre* 31). No Surrey ringing recoveries of *Larus fuscus* are connected with the northern parts of Finland or Scandinavia.

Continental Lesser Black-backed Gull   *Larus fuscus intermedius*

L. f. intermedius breeds in southern Norway, western Sweden and Denmark. It is the commoner of the two Scandinavian races in Britain.

Early Surrey history. It is likely this is the Scandinavian form that regularly occurs in Surrey, and probably the commonest – see Kehoe (2006). The records below have been published in earlier literature as *L. f. fuscus* but, in the absence of any ringing proof, are best regarded as probably of the current *intermedius*. An adult seen by A. Holte Macpherson on frozen water at Barn Elms Reservoirs on 23rd February 1929 had a mantle that looked jet black and was far darker than the back of some Coots which were near (*BB, 22:329*). This reads like the *L. f. fuscus* of older literature and seems to be the first documented record of *intermedius* for Surrey. Three at Queen Mary Reservoir on 18th January 1930 were the first for Middlesex (Glegg). Later records from the Thames include one near the Tate Gallery on 23rd December 1932, a number at Barnes on 10th September 1933 (Bishop) and one at Millbank on 4th November of the same year (*BB, 27:305*). Others were at Millbank on 18th November 1934 and 24th March 1936 (*BB, 30:368*), at Barnes in 1935 at Barn Elms and Richmond Park in 1937, on the Thames at Hammersmith in 1938 and at Beddington Sewage Farm in 1940. By 1942 they were being seen annually in the Surrey part of the London area though none had been seen in May and only two (on the Thames near Barnes on 30th June 1941), in June. There was one at Guildford Sewage Farm on 3rd August 1945, one at Richmond Park on 4th April 1948 and one at Unstead Sewage Farm on 22nd December 1954. They were later seen at Epsom Sewage Farm (1956), Guildford Sewage Farm (1956), Beddington Sewage Farm (1963), Papercourt (52 on 23rd January 1971), (18 on 22nd October 1972), Ash Vale Gravel Pits (30th December 1974) and Barn Elms Reservoirs (17 on 15th August 1976). At least half of about 750 Lesser Black-backed Gulls at Island Barn Reservoir on 7th October 1973 were said to be of this race, as were about 100 there in the following year and most of a flock of 300 at Wrecclesham on 18th December 1982.

Later reports. The sight records of *L. f. intermedius* that follow are as reported. Identification details have not been seen. A few were seen at the Surrey Docks by Rupert Kaye on 23rd April, 11th-12th May 1997 and on 2nd September and on 5th and 17th December 1998. Others were there in January and March 1999. He reported the race from Barn Elms in May, November and December 2001 and in March and May 2002. M. B. Lancaster found one at Addlestone on 16th June 2000.

Movements. Several Lesser Black-backed Gulls have been ringed in Surrey in winter and recovered in southern Norway in the breeding season. It seems possible that these are *intermedius*:

Ringed		Recovered			Distance
Egham	30th October 1975	Sandnes, Rogaland	Norway	20th June 1979	
Egham	6th November 1975	Kristiansend, Vest-Agder	Norway	29th July 1979	926 km
Wrecclesham	17th November 1976	Bergen, Hordaland,	Norway	26th April 1982	1,078 km
Wrecclesham	4th August 1976	Korssund,	Norway	22nd June 1985	1,172 km
Wrecclesham	23d September 1976	Karmoy, Rogaland	Norway	20th June 1985	962 km
Egham	17th October 1975	Farsund, Vest-Agder	Norway	26th August 1987	876 km

Yellow-legged Gull
Larus michahellis (*Larus argentatus michahellis*)

Scarce, but increasing, migrant

Breeds around French, Spanish and Mediterranean coasts and winters mainly in the regions where it breeds. Now reappearing as a full species in contemporary publications, *Larus cachinnans* was named as the Yellow-legged Herring-Gull in Saunders (1899) and in the BOU list of 1915, where it was a rare bird with only two records (Norfolk, 1886 and Kent, 1904) that could be cited. The current split is the undoing of a later 20th century lumping. There were only six yellow-legged birds, including several 'probables' in *The Handbook*, which grouped the yellow-legged forms under *L. a. omissus*, a name no longer used. A combination of population growth, northward expansion and dispersion now brings many of these birds to Britain.

Surrey. An adult Herring Gull with bright yellow legs was seen by W. J. Darter at Barn Elms Reservoirs on 10th October 1968 and published as *L. a. omissus* (*SBR*). This bird might have been of a race of *L. cachinnans*. Other records of Herring Gulls with yellow legs appeared in Surrey Bird Reports annually from 1977-91, after which they became more numerous and were published separately as *Larus (argentatus) cachinnans* from 1996. Gulls described as having characteristics of *michahellis* were first mentioned in 1982, when they were seen at Barn Elms and the Thames at Westminster on various dates from June to December. There were others at Barn Elms in 1984 and 1986. One was seen at Wrecclesham in 1983, 1984, 1987-90 and at Holmethorpe in 1984. From 1994 onwards, records of birds presumed to be of this form have come from Addlestone, Barn Elms, Beddington Sewage Farm, Chertsey Meads, Frimley Gravel Pits, Hersham, Holmethorpe Sand Pits, Merrist Wood (Worplesdon), Milford, Old Woking Sewage Farm, Papercourt Gravel Pits, Penton Hook Gravel Pit, Seale Sand Pits, Smithwood Common, Stoke Lake, the Surrey Docks, the Thames (various sites from Bankside to Teddington), Thorpe (various sites), Tongham Gravel Pit, the Walton area reservoirs (Island Barn, Queen Elizabeth II and Walton), Wandsworth Park, West Horsley, Wimbledon Park, Windlesham and Wrecclesham. The bird month table shows that, from 1994 to 2001, numbers, reaching 96 in 1995, peaked in 1997 and remained at 100 or more in each subsequent year.

Since 2000, records have come from Addlestone, Barn Elms, Beddington, Island Barn Reservoir, Merrist Wood, Normandy, Papercourt, Reigate Priory, Seale, Shackleford, the Thames, Thorpe, Tice's Meadow, Tongham Gravel Pit, Walton Reservoirs, West Ewell and Woking, the largest number being 19 at Addlestone on 4th October 2001. In Spelthorne, year maxima were eleven at Wraysbury Reservoir in July 2000 and seven at King George VI Reservoir in June 2001 (*LBR*). There were up to 34 at Staines Reservoirs in August 2002.

Calendar. Yellow-legged Gulls are at their scarcest in April and May. An influx begins in July and peaks in August. Wintering birds begin leaving in February.

Vice-county bird months 1994-2001

	Jan	Feb	Mar	Apr	May	Jun	Jul	Aug	Sep	Oct	Nov	Dec	Total
1994	11	9	3	2	0	1	6	17	6	6	6	4	**71**
1995	9	14	4	2	0	1	8	33	1	2	10	12	**96**

	Jan	Feb	Mar	Apr	May	Jun	Jul	Aug	Sep	Oct	Nov	Dec	Total
1996	14	10	4	2	1	0	20	9	16	18	11	9	**114**
1997	16	3	2	1	3	1	30	48	21	16	17	12	**170**
1998	23	5	3	1	3	8	20	26	31	16	12	14	**162**
1999	18	8	4	1	10	5	17	22	20	11	12	9	**137**
2000	10	8	4	2	2	12	7	11	11	14	22	17	**120**
2001	12	4	2	4	3	0	3	3	11	26	14	18	**100**

Large counts

Addlestone: 30, 30th August 1997

Beddington Sewage Farm: 12, 12th January 1999

Chertsey Meads: 13, 25th July 1996

Spelthorne

King George VI Reservoir: 17, July 1986

Queen Mary: 12, August 1992

Staines Reservoir: 97, August 1998

Wraysbury Reservoir: 27, August 1995

Herring Gull

Larus argentatus

Moderately common, mainly in winter, has bred

Races of the Herring Gull breed in North America (*L. a. smithsonianus*), Siberia (*L. a. vegae*), from Armenia to Iran (*armenicus* group) and in Britain and other parts of northern Europe (*argentatus* group). Herring Gulls of the *argentatus* group winter around the coasts of northern Europe and in many inland localities. Many of those breeding in Scandinavia and Russia move south or southwest in winter. Those breeding in Britain, which are of the race *argenteus*, make mainly local movements. The European range has extended since 1900, as it has in Britain. The 20th century has also seen a considerable increase in numbers, in Britain as well as elsewhere. Most of the Herring Gulls found in Surrey are *L. a. argenteus*, but the Scandinavian race *L. a. argentatus* is also known to occur. *L. a. cacchinnans* breeds from the Black Sea east to Kazakhstan and has also been recorded.

Herring Gulls occasionally nest on rooftops. The habit was first observed in southwest England in the 1920s and had reached parts of southeast England by the 1930s. Nests were usually in coastal towns, including Hastings and St Leonards by the 1950s and Eastbourne, Worthing and Brighton by the early 1970s. The increase on rooftops has been accompanied, during the last 40 years, by a 40% overall national decline. Rooftop breeding has spread to inland sites. The first successful breeding in the London area was in Regent's Park in 1963 (*LBR* for 1962). Forty pairs bred at Billingsgate Dock in 2000.

Early Surrey history. Although said to be an occasional visitor to the Godalming district by Newman and Stafford, Bucknill gave no dated references before 1888, when severe weather brought Herring Gulls up the Thames with other gull species. They were frequent along the Thames from 1893. At about this time, Herring Gulls became more common elsewhere, with records from Dorking (in Jordan, 1893a), Dulwich (1894), Epsom Downs and Wisley Heath.

20th century. There was a big flock at Staines Reservoirs on 10th February 1924 (*LN*), which became a major site and, in January 1935, held over a thousand birds. There were 120 at Crystal Palace Fields in February 1925 (Parr). About 40 at Barn Elms on 14th December 1929 was the maximum for the year. Herring Gulls were first seen at Beddington Sewage Farm in 1930 and at Epsom Sewage Farm in 1933. They were only occasional visitors to Limpsfield at about this time and to Richmond Park up to 1936. By the 1960s they were winter visitors to Frensham. Winter numbers have since increased at rubbish tips. In Spelthorne, there were 2,500 at Queen Mary Reservoir on 6th April 1958

Breeding. Although nesting in the London area has been almost entirely north of the Thames, there is a Surrey record from 1983, when one bird was fledged at County Hall, Southbank.

Calendar. Increasing numbers of Herring Gulls are being seen in the summer months, some probably from the roof-top colonies north of the Thames. There were 28 at Queen Elizabeth II Reservoir roost on 3rd June 1998 and 100 at Beddington Sewage Farm on 27th June 2000. A few are seen in southwest Surrey, for example one at Frensham Great Pond on 20th July 1975 and two there on 12th June 1995.

Roosts. Herring Gulls roost in the Thames Valley but disperse widely to feeding sites during the day. About 100 roosted at Barnes in 1931 (Parr) and about 400 were present on 29th January 1966.

Roost counts. December and January roost counts at the reservoirs since the 1950s are shown in the table. Numbers peaked in the cold decade of the 1960s and have since been falling:

	1953	1963	1969	1983	1989	1993	2004
		Dec	Jan	Jan	Dec	Jan	
Barn Elms Reservoir	100	100		3			
Island Barn Reservoir	1,000		2,250				60
Queen Elizabeth II Reservoir		7,000	5,000	2,280	4000-5000	864	5
Walton Reservoir	4,000	200	60			20	160
King George VI Reservoir	2,100		9,300				
Littleton (Queen Mary)	5,500		15,000	1,763			8279
Staines Reservoir	3,000		2,500				
Staines + King George VI				1,664			

In Spelthorne, there were 2,000 at Wraysbury Reservoir on 5th January 1985 and 7,500 on 27th October. There were 1,110 at Island Barn Reservoir on 28th November 2002.

Feeding and loafing

Badshot Lea: 200, 25th January 1985

Barn Elms: 206, 11th November 2001

Beddington Sewage Farm: 3,339, October 2003

River Blackwater: c.500, February 1954 in hard weather (Parr).

Botley Brickyard landfill: 1,200, January and February 1999.

Elmers End Sewage Farm: flocks of 500-600 in January and February 1935-38 (Manser, 1944).

Enton: 110, January 1956

Epsom Sewage Farm: c.500, 24th January 1950

Frensham: 200, 27th December 1985

Holmethorpe refuse tip: 2,000, 9th January 1997

Papercourt Gravel Pits: 468, 14th January 1972

Seale tip/Tongham Gravel Pit: 500, 10th January 1996

Thorpe Water Park: 220, 24th January 1982

Worcester Park Rubbish Dump: c.400, January 1969

Wrecclesham rubbish tip: 1,500, 21st January 1983

Movements. Herring Gulls that had been cannon-netted at Gerrards Cross landfill on 20th/21st January 2004 were seen in the following weeks at Beddington Sewage Farm (per J. Allan). A few ringing recoveries within the UK show movements to and from British locations north to Cleveland. One was found in Guernsey.

Mortality. Severe winter weather usually causes extra gull deaths at the reservoirs. Examples given in the climate section above included four at the Molesey and Spelthorne reservoirs in 1933.

Plumage variations. A first-winter bird with pure white plumage and a black bill visited Wrecclesham rubbish tip in January 1980. Leucistic birds were seen at Wraysbury Reservoir in March 1985 and at Holmethorpe on 20th February 1991 and 11th January 1997.

Scandinavian Herring Gull
Larus argentatus argentatus

Winter visitor

Many of the Herring Gulls wintering in southeast England are of this race (Stanley *et al.*, 1981).

Surrey. It seems likely that many of the wintering gulls in Surrey are of this form.

Movements. One ringed at Queen Mary Reservoir on 4th February 1935, together with all nine of the Herring Gulls ringed at Guildford (seven in January 1974, one in December 1974, one in January 1975) and recovered abroad, were found in Arctic Norway in the breeding season. One recovered at Guildford on 12th December 1973 had been ringed in Arctic Norway. Another, ringed as a nestling in Murmansk, Russia, on 28th June 1985, was found dead at Queen Mary Reservoir, 2,559 km southwest, on 18th December of the same year. One ringed at Guildford on 22nd January 1974 was recovered 2,667 km northeast at Varanger Fiord, Norway on 16th May 1983. Apart from one Caspian Gull, there are no other foreign recoveries of Herring Gulls of any race.

Longevity. The 1975 bird was not recovered until 12 years and four months later, in 1987.

Caspian Gull
Larus argentatus cachinnans

Occasional, mainly in winter

Also known as the Pontic Gull and the Eastern Yellow-legged Gull. Caspian Gulls are migratory and spread widely in winter, some birds moving south or east, perhaps as far as China (*BWP*) while others move west through the Mediterranean and Europe. In recent years it has been established that some of these birds reach the British Isles. The taxonomy is still being discussed. Before the Yellow-legged Gull was advanced again to a full species, the Caspian Gull was regarded as a race of the Herring Gull, which is how it is treated here.

Surrey. The first published Surrey records of birds with characteristics of this race were of single adults on St Paul's School playing fields, Addlestone on 12th August 1997 and 29th December 1998, on the Thames at Wandsworth on 12th September and 10th October and on the Thames at Eel Pie Island on 31st December 1998 to at least January 1999. Later reports were from Addlestone (site as above, up to two in August 1999, others in 2000 and 2001); Barn Elms (many records from 22nd May 1999), Beddington Sewage Farm (many records from 14th February 1999), Eel Pie Island (4th December 2000), Island Barn Reservoir (several from 20th December 1999), Runnymede (11th August 2006), South Norwood Country Park (2nd December 1999), the Thames at Chelsea (29th October 2000), Thorpe Water Park (16th September 2000, 27th January 2001), Walton Reservoirs (21st December 2001) and Wandsworth (26th July, 7th August and 12th September 1999, 20th August and 21st September 2000).

In Spelthorne, gulls showing characteristics of the race included a fourth winter bird at Queen Mary Reservoir on 11th February 2000, a fourth summer bird at Wraysbury Reservoir on 27th July 2000 and a third-summer bird at Staines Reservoirs on 24th March 2003.

The adult at Eel Pie Island from 1988 into January 1999 has been accepted by the BBRC (*BB*, 96:576, A. Pearson *et al.*). Two of the others have not been accepted by the BBRC. Most have not been put to it or are still being considered.

Movements. A fourth-winter Caspian Gull that had been ringed in the Ukraine and given a white wing tag numbered 2H in Germany was identified by its wing tag at Beddington Sewage Farm on 12th January 2002 (J. Allan).

Iceland/Glaucous Gull

Larus glaucoides/hyperboreus

The identification of Glaucous and Iceland Gulls in the London area was not well understood until the analysis by G. T. Kay in 1947 (*BB, 40:369-73*). Older records are therefore subject to qualification.

Surrey. In 1939, birds thought to be Iceland Gulls were seen at Barn Elms Reservoirs on April 15th and at Staines Reservoirs on December 25th. The latter bird was seen again on 14th January 1940. An immature bird at Lonsdale Road Reservoir on 15th December 1941 was thought to be an Iceland, as was a different bird there between 26th December 1941 and 23rd March 1942 and one from the end of 1942 to February 1943. A dark bird thought to be in its third winter was seen in the Lonsdale Road area in November and December 1943. Another Glaucous/ Iceland Gull was reported near Waterloo Bridge on 12th April 1949, a year in which there were several reports in the Barn Elms/Putney area from January to March. A gull at Epsom Sewage Farm in 1954 was initially published as Glaucous but later thought to be Iceland/Glaucous (*SBR* for 1954 and 1955). There was one on the Thames at Chiswick on 26th January 1963, one flew over Kew Gardens on 22nd January 1979 and one was at Stanwell Moor Gravel Pits on 7th December 1986.

Iceland Gull

Larus glaucoides

Scarce winter visitor

Breeds in Greenland and northeast Canada, wintering in and around the North Atlantic and the North Sea. Most British records are around northern shores from November to April (*BWP*). Two Iceland Gulls ringed in Greenland have been recovered in Britain (*MA*).

Early Surrey history. The first gull now believed to be definitely of this species was at Hammersmith Bridge in January 1948 (*BLA*, notes in the *LBR*). It was followed by others at Epsom Sewage Farm from 14th-19th January 1949 (presumably roosting elsewhere) and an immature bird at Barn Elms Reservoirs on 13th and 16th March 1949. There were others in April 1955, seen at Lonsdale Road (11th) and Barn Elms Reservoirs (12th), at Beddington (18th February 1956), Barn Elms Reservoirs (31st March 1962) and the Thames at Chiswick (31st January 1963). An immature bird was seen at King George VI Reservoir on 21st January 1958 and there was one at Charlton Gravel Pits in March 1960.

Since 1970. There were over 30 bird days (seven bird months) in 1984, after severe north-westerly gales. Some thirty of them, probably involving five different birds, came from Wrecclesham from January 6th to February 27th. There were two first-winter birds at Barn Elms Reservoirs on 25th March. A third-summer bird was seen at Wrecclesham on dates from 20th to 26th December. There were eight Spelthorne records from 1983 to 1986.

An adult at Epsom Common on 11th January 1990 was the only vice-county bird from then until 1993 but in January and February 1994 there was another national influx, bringing single Iceland Gulls to Buckland Sand Pits, and Holmethorpe Sand Pits, and two to Stoke Lake. There was another at Beddington Sewage Farm on 27th December of the same year and one in Spelthorne, at Staines Reservoirs, in April. An adult roosting at Queen Elizabeth II Reservoir on 9th November 1996 was the earliest winter bird ever for the vice-county. The second earliest roosted at the same site on 22nd November of the following year and one roosted there in February 1998. One was seen at Holmethorpe on dates from 1st to 9th January 1997 and one flew upriver at Wandsworth on 25th December 1998.

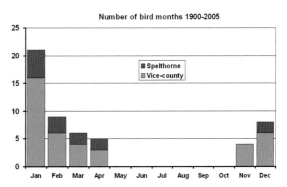

Number of bird months 1900-2005

In 2000, there was an Iceland Gull at Queen Elizabeth II Reservoir on 30th January. Later in the year, sightings of a second-winter bird at Beddington Sewage Farm and Queen Elizabeth II Reservoir in December probably related to the same individual, which roosted at Queen Elizabeth II Reservoir on 5th-6th January 2001. Beddington Sewage Farm held single birds on 29th April and on 26th and 31st December 2001. There were further sightings at Barn Elms in 2003 and 2005, Beddington Sewage Farm in 2005 and Queen Elizabeth II Reservoir in 2002 and 2003. There may have been more Spelthorne birds than this account suggests.

Calendar. The chart shows a marked January peak. Extreme dates are:

Early		Late	
9th November 1996	Queen Elizabeth II Reservoir	31st March 1962	Barn Elms Reservoirs
		29th April 2001	Beddington Sewage Farm

Glaucous Gull   *Larus hyperboreus*

Scarce winter visitor.

Circumpolar breeding distribution, much of it within the Arctic Circle. Winters within and to the south of its breeding range. Birds ringed in Iceland, Bear Island and Norway have been recovered in Britain (*MA*).

Early Surrey history. One was killed at Newark Mill some time before 1900 and sent to Stafford, who catalogued it (SALEC), but Bucknill could not locate the actual specimen.

Since 1900. The next to be seen was not until 1943, when an immature bird on the Thames at Lambeth on 11th December was judged to be of this species (*BB, 38:40*). From then to 2001 there were about 55 reports and 58 bird months for the vice-county and the same number of bird months for Spelthorne. The number of birds involved is probably less because the same individuals are thought sometimes to have been seen at reservoir roosts and at sewage farm or rubbish tip feeding sites. Glaucous Gull records peaked in the 1980s and have since become much scarcer.

Bird months by decade to 2001

	1940s	1950s	1960s	1970s	1980s	1990s	2000s	Total
Vice-county	6	11	2	3	18	11	7	**58**
Spelthorne	0	3	12	7	31	5	0	**58**

Where found. The largest number of vice-county bird months, twelve, has been at *Wrecclesham* sand pit and rubbish tip in the years from 1979 to 1988. *Barn Elms*, with eight bird months, all but one in the period 1947-60, is also one of the most most frequently visited sites. There have been ten at *Beddington Sewage Farm* (15th January 1955, 9th January 1956, 4th February 1956, 9th February 1958, 6th-11th March 1999, 5th April 1999, 21st-25th February 2000, 27th December 2000, January/February 2001) and *Queen Elizabeth II Reservoir* has had eight (24th February 1991, 7th January 1995, 8th-12th February 1996, 8th March 1999, 22nd-24th February 2000, January 2001, January 2002, January 2003). The remainder of the Glaucous Gulls were at *Barn Elms* (November 1984), *Epsom* (7th April 1958), *Frensham Great Pond* (roosted 24th February 1981), *Holmethorpe Sand Pits* (26th December 1991, 23rd-24th January 1997, seen over Redhill Station on 25th January 1997), *Island Barn Reservoir* (8th November 1984, 28th December 2000, February 2004), *Mitcham Common* rubbish tip (10th March 1955), *Molesey Sewage Farm* (13th January 1963), *Papercourt Gravel Pits* and landfill (27th December 1972, 13th November 1981, 22nd January 1994), *Runfold* (10th January 1984), *Seale Sand Pits* (7th December 1979), *Stoke Water Meadows* (3rd October 1992), the *Thames at Barnes/Lambeth* (11th December 1943, 23rd February 1947, 17th January 1948, 5th April 1954), *Thorpe Water Park* (16th

November 1980), *Wimbledon Common* (13th January 1986) and *Walton Reservoirs* (9th February 1993, 4th March 2000).

An immature gull at Staines Reservoirs from 9th-14th February 1934 was judged to be a Glaucous Gull by the observers and appeared in Glegg (1935) and *BLA*. In 1952 there were others at Staines Reservoirs on 6th February and Perry Oaks Sewage Farm on 1st April. The Spelthorne dates range from 2nd November (Staines Reservoirs 1986) to 27th May (Queen Mary Reservoir 1966).

Recent occurrences include Barn Elms (November 2005), Beddington Sewage Farm (dates from 26th January to 11th March and 5th April 2001), January 2003 and February 2004), Island Barn Reservoir (February 2003 and February 2004), Queen Elizabeth II Reservoir (January 2001, January 2002 and January 2003) and Seale (January 2003). These places are not very far apart and the same gull may be seen at more than one of them. For example the January 2001 bird was seen at Beddington and Queen Elizabeth II Reservoir. None of the gulls have roosted at Beddington but they might have done at these or other reservoir sites in Surrey.

Calendar. Most Glaucous Gulls are seen from December to February, peaking in January:

Bird months 1900-2001

	Jan	Feb	Mar	Apr	May	Jun	Jul	Aug	Sep	Oct	Nov	Dec	Total
Vice-county	18	14	5	5	0	0	0	0	0	1	5	10	**58**
Spelthorne	15	11	7	3	1	0	0	0	0	0	8	10	**55**

Extreme dates are:

Early	**Late**
Stoke Water Meadows: 3rd October 1992	Barn Elms: 20th April 1960
	Queen Mary Reservoir: 27th May 1966

Great Black-backed Gull   *Larus marinus*
Moderately common winter visitor

Breeds around the North Atlantic and the coasts of Scandinavia, wintering in the same regions. Northern populations are migratory but those in the British Isles make mainly local movements. Many Norwegian breeding birds and some from Iceland and Russia winter in Britain. Great Black-backed Gulls bred in the Thames estuary up to the 1840s but shooting wiped out these and other British colonies later in the century. There has been a substantial increase in British breeding numbers over the past 100 years.

Early Surrey history. One killed at Putney in severe weather during February 1841 was the first for Middlesex as well as for Surrey. It is the bird figured in Yarrell. The illustration is the work of Yarrell's friend Mr Broderip and is reproduced here. The Charterhouse Collection included an undated specimen found in a stubble field near Milford (*SALEC*) in Bucknill's time but the two currently held there are said to have come from Norfolk. One flew over the Thames at Lambeth in 1879. Records from the Thames after the 1895 frost include one at Temple Gardens on 5th November 1895, three at Blackfriars Bridge on 4th February 1896. One found dead on the county border near Limpsfield on 25th November 1893 might not have been in Surrey.

20th century. Parr mentioned one at Limpsfield Common in 1904. From about this time the national increase began to be reflected in the increased numbers seen in Surrey. There were seven adults flying over the Thames at Westminster on 14th April 1924, after a gale (*LN*), and there were other Thames sightings in October and December 1925. One was at Barn Elms Reservoirs on dates from September to November 1926. The first at Staines Reservoirs was from 30th August to 23rd September 1929 after which year they began to appear regularly in the Spelthorne district. Great Black-backed Gulls were at Ewell and Limpsfield in 1936 but were not seen at Beddington Sewage Farm until 1947. There were single birds at Epsom Sewage Farm and Mitcham Common on 17th September 1948 (LBR). The first at Frensham (apart from a claim in 1906) and the Farleigh district were not until 1951. Up to eight were seen at Unstead Sewage Farm in the 1950s (CNHS, 1959). Places away from the Reservoirs after 1960 include Earlswood Sewage Farm, Gatton and Richmond Park. They have since been seen annually, usually in numbers. Great Black-backed Gulls are still relatively uncommon in outer Surrey but have been seen at the Seale Tip, Tongham Gravel Pit and other sites in recent years, with up to 75 at Tongham.

Roosts. Up to 2,450 roosted at Walton Reservoirs in 1968 and 1,500 at Queen Elizabeth II Reservoir in 1969 but numbers have since fallen considerably, to fewer than 200 at the end of the 1990s and just seven in the January 2004 count.

Selected roost counts

	1953 Jan	1963 Dec	1968 Dec	1969 Jan	1983 Jan	1993 Jan	1999	2000	2004 Jan
Barn Elms Reservoir		100	10		3				
Island Barn Reservoir			100	250					1
Queen Elizabeth II Reservoir		500	500	1,500	188	200	150	74	7
Walton Reservoirs	350	650	2,450			200			37
King George VI Reservoir		500	260	300					
Queen Mary Reservoir		500	200	300	23				44
Staines Reservoir		950	200	100	86				

Large counts. These include some roosts. Numbers peaked in the 1960s:

Brooklands: *c.*120, 29th December 1966

Egham: 100 on a rubbish dump, December 1956

Epsom Downs: 100+, 9th March and 2nd September 1979

Epsom Sewage Farm: 70, 16th February 1957

Frimley Gravel Pits: 100+, 22nd December 1972

Holmethorpe Sand Pits: 400, 25th December 1981

Island Barn Reservoir: 300, 30th November 1957, 2nd January 1976

Queen Elizabeth II Reservoir: 2,000, 30th December 1962

Wrecclesham: 250, 21st January 1983

Spelthorne

Perry Oaks Sewage Farm: 160, 14th December 1975

Queen Mary Reservoir: 75 roosting, 30th December 1989

Staines Reservoirs: 151, 15th November 2002

Wraysbury Reservoir: 650+, 23rd December 1983

Food. When Great Black-backed Gulls are seen feeding, they are usually at rubbish tips but one was seen to catch a ten inch long flat-fish in the Thames at Waterloo on 10th September 1979.

Movement and longevity. Most of the ringing information derives from work in the 1950s and 60s, when six young raised in the Great Ainov Islands, old USSR and one from Murmansk were found in Surrey, at Barn Elms, Queen Elizabeth II and Walton Reservoirs. There have also been contacts with Denmark, Norway and the Shetlands. An adult ringed at Guildford on 25th January 1975 was recovered at Murmansk, which is some 2,626 km northeast, in June 1981. Its longevity, at least six years four months, is the greatest located.

Kittiwake (Black-legged Kittiwake) *Rissa tridactyla*
Scarce winter visitor

Kittiwakes breed on coasts around the North Atlantic and the North Sea and in Arctic and sub-Arctic regions east to Alaska. They winter in the breeding area and adjacent waters. The British population changed little in the 19th century but extended its range and increased markedly in the 20th. Russian, Norwegian and British birds tend to move southwest after the breeding season, so those seen in Surrey might be from any of these sources. Storm-driven birds have appeared in 'wrecks' across the country in some years.

Early Surrey history. One was taken alive on the Thames near Esher on 19th January 1837 and another nearby on 22nd February. One was shot on a pond near Wandsworth Common around February 1851 and in February 1869 two more were shot on Chertsey Common and one at Putney. Aldridge (1885) said that he had seen up to four on the Thames at Battersea but gave no details to substantiate the observations. Specimens were found near Godalming (*SALEC*). Single Kittiwakes were picked up exhausted at Gatton and dead in Molesey Lock in about January 1890 and there were three at Dulwich in 1893 (Bucknill). There is an undated record from Epsom Common. Kittiwakes were becoming more frequent in the Thames Valley by 1900, for example along the Thames from Waterloo to Putney (Dixon, 1909).

1900 to 1970. No more were found until 1921, when there was one at Frensham in November. In 1926 there was one on the Thames near Putney on 21st March. A dead bird found at Staines Reservoirs on 18th March 1926 was the first for the district (Glegg). There were two at the same site on 7th December 1929 and a dead bird was found there on the 16th of the same month. Another was on the Thames above Barnes Bridge on 18th January 1928. A corpse was found at Queen Mary Reservoir on 18th January 1930.

Island Barn Reservoir   *Photo D. M. Harris*

There was a first-winter bird at Staines Reservoir on 7th December 1930. In 1936 an adult was at Queen Mary Reservoir on 13th November, an immature bird on the 21st and a dead adult at Staines on the 22nd. One appeared at Staines on 7th February 1937 at the end of a national influx of divers and grebes. The first records for Richmond Park were of an immature bird on 28th February 1937 and an adult on 8th January 1940. There were two adults at Ham Gravel Pits on 15th June 1941 and single birds at Frensham on 22nd October 1939 and 3rd April 1948. One flew over Haslemere in November 1954. The 1950s brought larger numbers. There were fifteen among other gulls over Barn Elms on 24th December 1954. A storm which caused a national wreck of Kittiwakes in February/March 1957, the first for the British Isles, brought one bird to South Norwood Lake on 15th-20th February. In Spelthorne, one was found dead at Queen Mary Reservoir on 17th February. Three parties totalling *c.*116 birds flew over Fetcham Mill Pond on 22nd February 1959. In the 1960s, Kittiwakes were seen annually, mostly from December to May but with a few birds in June and August.

Kittiwakes have been seen more frequently since then and the number of birds involved has been much increased by substantial movements in March 1986 (124 west at Barn Elms on the 25th), and January 1993 (238 west at Barn Elms and 70-80 WSW at Mortlake on the 25th, brought in by North Sea gales). Even larger weather-related movements in February 1999 brought westward movements of 337 at Queen Elizabeth II Reservoir and 120 at Beddington Sewage Farm on the 7th and 370 at Beddington on the 17th. As the table shows, the surge in sightings after the 1940s was sustained for at least 60 years. Overall, there were about 256 records and 1,981 vice-county bird months from 1900 to 2001.

1900s	1910s	1920s	1930s	1940s	1950s	1960s	1970s	1980s	1990s	2000-01	Total
0	0	3	2	4	24	27	20	55	102	19	**256**

Where found. Barn Elms (60 records, 468 bird months) and Beddington (48 records, 560 bird months) are the largest contributors. Other records have come from Ashtead (1960), Battersea Park (two records in 1993), Brooklands (1968, 1994), Capel (1992), Chobham Common (party of 13 in November 1995), Fetcham Mill Pond (1959), Frensham (seventeen records, twenty-three bird months, six on 17th January 1955), Frimley Gravel Pits and Blackwater (five records), Godstone Bay Pond (1999), Hamm Gravel Pits (1941), Haslemere (1954), Hersham Gravel Pit (2001), Holmethorpe (seven records 1989-96, 29 bird months), Island Barn Reservoir (eight records 1957-2001), Kew Gardens (sixty-five on 2nd January 1979, one in 1983), Lambeth (1964), Papercourt Gravel Pits (four records of single birds), Queen Elizabeth II Reservoir (twenty records totalling 366 bird months), Richmond (1993), Richmond Park (four records of single birds), Seale Sand Pits /rubbish tip/Tongham Gravel Pit (1980, 1995), Shirley Hills (1962), South Norwood Country Park and Lake (1957, 1991, 1994, 2000), Southbank (1953, 1997), Stoke Lake (five records), the Surrey Docks (1995, 1998), Sutton, the Thames (25 records Kew to Bankside), Thorpe Water Park (1990), Thursley Common (1995), Tongham Gravel Pit (1997), Unstead Sewage Farm (50-60 southwest on 22nd February 1999), Vann Lake (1966-67), Walton Gravel Pits (1955), Walton Reservoirs (fifteen records, 24 bird months) and Wrecclesham (five records 1984-94). Since 2001 there have been Kittiwakes at Bankside Reach, Barn Elms, Beddington, Esher, Frensham, Hedgecourt, Island Barn Reservoir, Queen Elizabeth II Reservoir, Stoke Lake, Walton Reservoirs and Wrecclesham, the most being groups of thirty-four, one and two in an hour at Queen Elizabeth II Reservoir on 29th January 2003.

There have been rather fewer Kittiwakes, or possibly there has been less intensive recording, in Spelthorne with only about 491 bird months counted from 1900 to 2001. Kittiwakes were seen at all the reservoirs, most often at Staines where the larger numbers included 33 on 28th April 1985, 55 on 10th November 1968 and about 120 soaring high on 25th January 1993.

Calendar. January and February account for four-fifths of the vice-county bird months and a third of those in Spelthorne. June and July have the fewest. The first vice-county July records were at Beddington and Barn Elms in 1994 and Beddington in 1996.

Bird months 1900-2001

	Jan	Feb	Mar	Apr	May	Jun	Jul	Aug	Sep	Oct	Nov	Dec	Total
Vice-county	428	1,141	196	38	41	7	4	12	13	8	45	48	**1,981**
Spelthorne	133	34	68	76	54	4	5	13	17	6	75	6	**491**

Large counts

Beddington Sewage Farm: 124 flew over during the day, 25 March 1986

Queen Elizabeth II Reservoir: 337 west including parties of 113, 76 and 58, 7th February 1999

Spelthorne

Staines Reservoirs: *c*.120, 25th January 1993

Movements and longevity. A young Kittiwake ringed in East Lothian on 4th July 1958 was recovered at Dorking, 549 km south, on 19th November 1959.

Sooty Tern
One bird, Spelthorne

Onychoprion fuscata (*Sterna fuscata*)

Sooty Terns are wanderers from tropical and sub-tropical islands around the world, wintering at sea. Of the dozen or so British records from 1955 to 2001, two were in inland counties, one in Northamptonshire and the other at Staines. Dates ran from April to October.

Surrey. There was an immature bird at Staines Reservoirs on 18th August 1971 (G. D. Elcombe and L. E. Pritchard, *BB*, 65:337). Apparently this was the only British record of a Sooty Tern younger than first summer up to 1991 (*LBR* for 1991).

Little Tern
Scarce passage migrant

Sternula albifrons (*Sterna albifrons*)

Little Terns have a more southerly breeding distribution than Common Terns. Britain is at the northern edge of their range, which extends around the world. American and Japanese birds are sometimes split off as the Least Tern *S. antillarum*, which has been found in Britain. European birds winter mainly round the coasts of Africa. Numbers breeding in Britain were reduced by beach disturbance and other habitat changes in the 19th century and, after a recovery into the 1930s, have declined again in spite of increased protection. Little Terns are also declining in other parts of their European range.

Early Surrey history. There are several undated 19th century references, including a statement by Kidd in Newman (1849), that they had occasionally been shot at Frensham. Three were shot at one of the ponds on Puttenham Heath on 25th August 1894, one was shot at Frensham in 1895 and two were shot on a pond at Ashtead on 18th August 1899 (Bucknill). A local specimen once in the Charterhouse Collection is no longer held there. There were two on the Thames at Petersham on 28th August 1895 (Glegg).

1900 to 1950. Little Terns were seen at Hedgecourt (5th May 1906, 6th October 1906 (two), 13th October 1906), Frensham (5th August 1908, 13th July 1909 (two), 16th October 1920, 27th April 1930, 24th and 26th October 1932) and Putney (11th August 1911). Three adults and one immature bird at Staines Reservoirs on 22nd September 1925 comprise the first record for Spelthorne. There were two at Staines Reservoirs on 8th August 1929 and one there on 19th October 1934. At Barn Elms Reservoirs, Little Terns were seen on 6th August 1926 (one), 24th May 1930 (two), 7th May 1931(one) and 1st October 1932 (one). There was one at Walton Reservoirs on 19th September 1927 . One flew down the Thames at Hammersmith on 2nd May 1946 (*BLA*). There were three at Guildford on 5th June 1948. In Spelthorne, one was found at Queen Mary Reservoir on 26th August 1931 (Glegg) and another was there on 21st May 1937.

Where found since 1950. There have been over 450 bird months over the whole period up to 2001, well over half of them from the Spelthorne reservoirs. A long-dead Little Tern was found at Walton Reservoirs in January 1962. Of the 135 vice-county live bird months since 1950, most were from Barn Elms (31) and Queen Elizabeth II Reservoir (34). The other places, with their bird months, were Badshot Lea (one), Beddington Sewage Farm (seventeen), Frensham (nine), Hersham Gravel Pit (two), Holmethorpe Pits (five), Island Barn Reservoir (seven), Papercourt Gravel Pits (four), South Norwood (two), the Thames (two), Thorpe (one), Walton-on-Thames/Reservoirs (sixteen) and the Wey at Wisley (two).

Little Terns have been seen after 2001 at Barn Elms on 23rd April 2002 , 26th April 2002 (three) and 1st May 2005 (London Wetland Centre), Frensham on 9th July 2004 and 23rd July 2005, Queen Elizabeth II Reservoir on 9th August 2001 (three) and 13th October 2001, 19th May 2002 (three), 3rd May 2004 (three), 27th July 2004 and 6th August 2004 and in Spelthorne at Staines Reservoirs (2001, 2002, 2003).

Calendar. All the live birds have been in the period April to October, with peaks in May and August.

Bird months 1900-2001

	Jan	Feb	Mar	Apr	May	Jun	Jul	Aug	Sep	Oct	Nov	Dec	Total
Vice-county	0	0	0	16	66	14	9	25	27	24	0	0	**181**
Spelthorne	0	0	0	32	55	19	6	77	66	15	0	0	**270**

Early and late dates are:

Early
Beddington Sewage Farm: 16th April 1996
Spelthorne
Staines Reservoirs: 9th April 1999

Late
Frensham Great Pond: 26th October 1932
Spelthorne
Queen Mary Reservoir: 26th October 1934

Large counts. The largest count located is of thirty-three:

Barn Elms Reservoirs: thirteen, 27th January 1931; ten, 21st September 1955; Queen Elizabeth II Reservoir: parties of three, twelve, five and one, 3rd May 1997, 20 of the birds before 6 am.

Spelthorne
King George VI Reservoir: ten, 3rd October 1954
Queen Mary Reservoir: thirty-three, 20th August 1987
Staines Reservoirs: eleven, 3rd September 1954

Gull-billed Tern   *Gelochelidon nilotica*

One bird

A mainly southern species with a station in Denmark. European birds winter south of the Sahara. British records run from March to November, with peaks in May and July. Most come from southeast England. A pair bred in Essex in 1949 and 1950.

Surrey. One found at Barn Elms Reservoir on 26th July 1980 by T. J. Lawrence (*BB, 74:475*) was the first record for an inland county and the only one up to 1996.

Caspian Tern   *Hydroprogne caspia*

Three birds

Breeds in the Baltic and on warmer coasts from the Black Sea south and east to southern Africa, Australia and North America. European birds mostly winter in West Africa. There is an eastern bias to the British records, suggesting a Baltic origin. Dates run from March to November, with a June-August peak in which the three records for our area have occurred.

Surrey. One flew over Staines Reservoirs on 29th July 1979 (M. J. Rogers, *BB, 73:513*) and another on 11th August 1982 (A. V. Moon and P. Naylor, *BB, 76:501*). Robin Stride found one on a sand spit at Papercourt on 9th August 1984 (J. Beck, T. M. J. Doran, R. Stride *et al.*, *BB, 78:558*).

Whiskered Tern   *Chlidonias hybrida*

Four birds, all Spelthorne

Breeds from southwest Europe through Asia and in parts of Africa and Australia. European birds winter south of the Sahara. British records are mainly from southern inland and coastal counties, peaking in May and June, with a much smaller autumn peak in September.

Surrey. Records fit this pattern rather well:

1961:* Staines Reservoirs, one on 24th and 25th June (R. J. Johns, M. Nobbs, D. Putman *et al.*, *BB*, *55:575*) was the first for the London area.

1964:* King George VI Reservoir, one on 22nd-24th June (K. Barrett, D. Putman, D. I. M. Wallace *et al.*, *BB, 58:363*).

1977:* Staines Reservoirs, one on 17th August (R. J. and Mrs S. M. Johns *et al.*, *BB, 71:508*).

2005:* King George VI and Staines reservoirs, a second-summer bird from 22nd-25th May (A. Moon *et al.*, *Birding World 221* including a photo, *BB, 100:53*).

*Spelthorne

Black Tern   *Chlidonias niger*
Moderately common passage migrant

Breeds in fresh water habitats from Europe east to Siberia and in Africa, Asia, North America and Australia. Black Terns might have bred in Britain in prehistoric times. Most European birds winter on inland waters in Africa. Black Terns bred in East Anglia and elsewhere in the 18th and early 19th century and continued to breed in Kent as late as the 1880s. Breeding is said to have taken place again in 1966 (Ouse Washes, *Historical Atlas*) and since then there have been several other British records.

Early Surrey history. There is no evidence that Black Terns ever bred in Surrey, but they were known (and shot) as migrants from at least September 1823, when Long noted that one out of a party of three was killed at Hampton Lodge, Puttenham (Bucknill). Other casualties included two more from the same place in 1840, three from there in 1841 (two of which are probably the ones still to be seen in the Charterhouse Collection) and six, also in 1841, from Vachery Pond (*SCCMS*). Meyer shot two near Weybridge on 10th August 1842 and another, out of a party of 20, nearby on 12th May 1842. Two more were shot at Chertsey in May 1849 and they were often shot at Frensham (Bucknill). They became less frequent in later years, probably reflecting the decline in breeding numbers elsewhere. Subsequent records in Bucknill are from near Horsley (25th May 1859), Earlswood Pond (September 1875), the Thames at Hampton (12th May 1877), Frensham (about 1885), Gatton (a few years prior to 1890), Windlesham (about the same time) and Shalford (first week of November 1895).

1900 to 1945. The rather few records from 1900 to 1945 include Frensham on 31st July 1910 (H. Bentham), six there on 15th August 1910 (*BB, 4:223*) and a record on 2nd August 1914 (Shaw). There were five at Staines Reservoirs on 9th September 1923 and two immature birds there on 21st August 1926 and many were there in 1929. Black Terns were at Queen Mary Reservoir in May 1927 and on 1st May 1929 and there were 21 at Staines Reservoirs on 7th September 1927. Black Terns were regular at these sites from the 1930s. Back in the vice-county, there were others at Walton Reservoirs on 6th September 1929 and 23rd September 1935, two at Brooklands on 27th May 1936, eight at Mitcham on 26th April 1937, two at Walton Reservoirs on 27th August 1938, and a late bird at Island Barn Reservoir on 19th November 1938. There were up to twelve at Barn Elms in the 1930s, with the maximum on 29th August 1933.

1946 to 1970. There was an exceptional passage of Black Terns in May 1946, which brought up to sixteen at Frensham between the 3rd and 9th (*BB, 40:25*), a maximum of ten to Barn Elms on the 25th, one to Enton on the 21st, and six to Hedgecourt on the 12th-14th. Another large national passage in 1948 was recorded at Barn Elms Reservoirs with a maximum of 30 on 21st May and Guildford with a maximum of ten on 18th May. Much larger numbers were seen at Frensham. The Charterhouse Natural History Society claimed 200 on 20th May (CNHS, 1959). The HNHS published a smaller, but still substantial and possibly more reliable maximum of 50 on 21st May (HNHS, 1955). In 1949 the May influx was less marked, with maximums of two at Barn Elms (*LBR*), five at Frensham, two at Guildford and, in Spelthorne, fifteen at Staines Reservoirs (*BB, 43:178*). There was one at Walton Gravel Pit on 18th June

(*LBR*). Passage was strong in May 1950, with birds at Barn Elms Reservoirs (peak of 40), Frensham (peak of 30), Gatton and Richmond Park. Waves of Black Tern arrivals have been correlated with periods of warm weather in the Bay of Biscay and northeasterly winds in the Channel, as mentioned in the weather section of the introduction. Similar conditions in 1954 brought unusual numbers to Britain and to Surrey. The year 1963 saw an exceptional autumn passage, with 77 records in August and 54 in September and a maximum of 38 birds at Barn Elms on 30th August. Other sites at which Black Terns were recorded up to 1970 include Broadwater, Enton, Esher Sewage Farm, Frensham Great Pond, Godstone, Island Barn Reservoir (now a regular site), Moat Pond and Papercourt/Send.

Spelthorne. The national influx in 1948 produced a maximum of 25 at Staines Reservoirs on 22nd May. The maximum there in the 1949 influx was 15+ on 15th May. In 1950 the spring passage was stronger, with a peak of 121 on 16th May at Staines and a few at Shepperton. There was a peak of 21 at Staines on return passage in 1954 and about 150 at Queen Mary Reservoir on 27th August 1958. A strong national influx in May 1959 included a movement of at least 151 birds across Island Barn and Staines reservoirs on 23rd May and 39 at Staines Reservoirs on the 24th. There were 127 at Staines Reservoirs in a heavy passage on 13th May 1961 and 190 on 5th August 1969. Around 30 have been seen on a June day at Staines Reservoirs (*e.g.* in 1969).

Since 1970, Black Terns have appeared annually, usually in small numbers and most frequently at Barn Elms, Frensham and the reservoirs at Walton-on-Thames. Other sites where Black Terns have occurred since 1970 include Badshot Lea, Battersea Park, Beddington Sewage Farm, Brooklands, Chertsey Reservoir, Dulwich, Effingham, Enton, Farnham, Frimley Gravel Pits, Gatton, Hedgecourt, Holmethorpe, Papercourt Gravel Pits, Richmond Park, Stoke Lake, the Thames, Tongham Gravel Pit, Unstead Sewage Farm, Wentworth Lake and Wimbledon Park.

There was a strong autumn passage in 1974, with 62 at Papercourt Gravel Pits on 15th September. The most substantial influx was in the autumn of 1992. The first wave brought 265 to Barn Elms on 6th September and a flock of 216 passed through on the 13th. There had been a huge passage at Dungeness (Kent) on the 11th (*BB, 100:241*). Large numbers passed through Spelthorne, as detailed below and there were more records than usual from elsewhere. About 164 birds passed through in the autumn of 1994. The spring of 2000, with around 56 birds, was above average but the autumn was poor. The largest number reported after 2000 was 17 at Barn Elms on 13th October 2001. Black Terns have been seen at Barn Elms, Beddington, Frensham, Queen Elizabeth II Reservoir, Walton Reservoirs and other sites up to 2006.

Spelthorne. A large movement on 15th September 1974 brought 182 Black Terns to Staines and King George VI reservoirs and 138 to Wraysbury Reservoir, a record total for the area. There were 100+ at Queen Mary Reservoir on 14th August 1985 and 170 at Staines Reservoirs on 19th August 1989. The 6th September 1992 influx brought a maximum of 140 to Staines. Later movements included 46 at Staines Reservoirs on 7th May 2000 (*LBR*), 85 at King George VI Reservoir in August 2001 (LBR) and 67 at Queen Mary Reservoir on 2nd September 2004 (*LNHSB*).

Large reservoir counts

Barn Elms: 265, 6th September 1992

Queen Mary: *c.*159 in 1958

Walton: 71, 15th September 1974

Staines: 170, 19th August 1989

Spelthorne

Wraysbury: 138, 15th September 1974

King George VI: 85, August 2001

Calendar. Return passage usually gets under way in August but migrants were present from 29th July (Beddington) in 1955. Early and late dates are:

Early		Late	
11th April 1914	Mitcham	4th November 2001	Queen Elizabeth II Reservoir
11th April 1979	Frensham Great Pond	15th November 1967	Frensham (Clark, 1984)
12th April 1971	Wentworth Lake	19th November 1938	Island Barn Reservoir (*LBR*)
Spelthorne		*Spelthorne*	
10th April 1960	Staines Reservoirs	4th November 2001	King George VI Reservoir
		5th November 1939	Staines Reservoirs
		24th November 1968	Queen Mary Reservoir

White-winged Black Tern (White-winged Tern)   *Chlidonias leucopterus*

Four vice-county records, 16 from Spelthorne

Breeds from central and eastern Europe across to China. Western birds winter in Africa south of the Sahara. Most British records are from eastern and southern coastal counties but they have also come from almost all of the counties inland. There is a marked spring passage, peaking in May and June. The return passage is much larger, reaching a maximum in August.

Surrey. The records for our area show the same pattern:

1961:* Queen Mary Reservoir, a summer adult on 13th May (C. Hughes, G. D. Moore *et al. BB, 55:575*) was the first for the London area. This or another was at Staines Reservoirs on the following day (R. S. Brown *et al., BB, 55:575*).

1964:* Staines Reservoirs, one on 16th-23rd August (*BB, 58:362*).
King George VI Reservoir, a juvenile on 13th September (*BB, 58:362*).

1966:* Queen Mary Reservoir, an immature bird on 27th August (*BB, 60:321*).

1967:* Staines Reservoirs, one on 2nd-8th September (*BB, 61:345*).

1968:* Staines Reservoirs, an immature bird on 12th-13th August (A. Goddard, R. J. Johns, C. Westwood *et al., BB, 62:472*, dates given as 13th-14th in the *LBR*).

1970:* Queen Mary Reservoir, two on 3rd May (F. R. Cannings, K. J. and Mrs A. Herber *et al., BB, 64:354*).
Queen Mary Reservoir, an immature bird on 25th August (G. Walker, *BB, 64:354*).
Queen Mary Reservoir, one on 9th September (Mr and Mrs J. A. Bailey, *BB, 65:351*)

1974:* Queen Mary Reservoir, an immature bird on 9th September (M. J. Rogers, *BB, 68:321*).

1975:* Queen Mary Reservoir, an immature bird on 8th August (M. J. Rogers, *BB, 69:381*).

1977:* Staines Reservoirs, an immature bird on 23rd August (J. Hazell, *BB, 71:509*). Probably the same bird at Queen Mary Reservoir from 24th August to 4th September (J. Hazell, M. J. Rogers, *BB, 71:509*).
Queen Mary Reservoir, a second immature bird on 25th August (Dr D. B. Jones, R. J. Johns, *BB, 71:509*).
Queen Mary Reservoir, a third immature bird on 10th-12th September (P. Clement, P. R. Colston, *BB, 71:509*).

1978:* Queen Mary Reservoir, an adult and a juvenile on 19th August (M. J. Rogers *et al.,BB, 72:528*).

1994: Barn Elms Reservoirs, a juvenile for four hours on 25th September (F. J. Maroevic, S. J. Spooner *et al., BB, 59:508*).

1995:* Staines Reservoirs, a juvenile on 18th August (*BB, 89:508*, 19th not 18th in the *LBR*).

1995: Frimley Gravel Pits, a juvenile flying southwest on 9th September (S. Abbott, *BB, 89:508*), had been seen at Camp Farm Gravel Pit, Hampshire on the previous day and was relocated at Fleet Pond, Hampshire.

2004:   Barn Elms London Wetland Centre ('Barnes' in *BB*), a juvenile on 18th August (R. Kaye, *BB*, *100:53*).

Queen Elizabeth II Reservoir, a juvenile on 6th September (D. M. Harris, *BB, 98:663*).

*Spelthorne

Sandwich Tern   *Sterna sandvicensis* (*Thalasseus sandvicensis*)
Scarce passage migrant

Sandwich Terns have a scattered breeding distribution on the eastern coast of the Americas and from the British Isles to the Caspian Sea. European birds winter south to southern Africa. In the 19th century, the British range contracted due to persecution which terminated breeding in southeast England, but most of the 20th century saw a recovery, now apparently reversed. Most British colonies are on nature reserves. Some other parts of northern and western Europe have experienced increases since 1900.

Early Surrey history. A specimen shot at Frensham in 1837 (*SALEC*) and another of about the same date from Hampton Lodge were in the Charterhouse Collection in Bucknill's time but neither is now held there. There are no other definite 19th century records.

Since 1900. From 1900 to 2001 there were about 915 bird months in the vice-county and over 700 in Spelthorne. The number of bird months has been increasing over the decades:

Bird months by decade

	1900s	1910s	1920s	1930s	1940s	1950s	1960s	1970s	1980s	1990s	2000-01	Total
Vice-county	0	1	2	6	58	22	98	152	170	241	165	**915**

Sandwich Terns remained scarce in the early 20th century. One seen in the Haslemere district on 11th July 1914 (Shaw) might not have been in Surrey. Two seen over the Thames at Barnes on 28th August 1926 comprised the first dated record for Middlesex (Glegg). There were two at Barn Elms Reservoirs on 4th August 1931 and two flew west along the Thames at Hammersmith on 5th October 1937. There was

Island Barn Reservoir   *Photo D. M. Harris*

one at Frensham on 17th September 1947 and 4th September 1949 and four were there on 29th April 1948. From the 1940s onward, Sandwich Terns were seen much more frequently.

One at Queen Mary Reservoir on 20th August 1931 (*LN*) was the first in the 20th century for Spelthorne. There were three at Staines Reservoirs on 3rd May 1933. Single birds were seen at Staines Moor on 1st October 1933 and at Staines Reservoirs on 19th and 28th October and 4th November 1934 (Glegg).

Where found. By far the most important vice-county site has been Barn Elms, with more than a third of the bird months, 367. The next biggest figures have been from Beddington Sewage Farm, with 106, Queen Elizabeth II Reservoir, with 75 and the Thames, with 70. Other places, with their bird months if more than five, were Badshot Lea, Battersea Park, Berrylands Sewage Works (fifteen), Brockham, Chertsey (thirty-two), Chessington, Chipstead, Chobham Common, Enton, Epsom Sewage Farm, Frensham (fifty), Frimley Gravel Pits (fourteen), Godstone, Great Bookham, Guildford, Ham Gravel Pits, Haslemere, Holmethorpe Sand Pits (thirteen), Island Barn Reservoir (thirteen), Kew Gardens, New Malden, Papercourt Gravel Pits (thirty-eight), Richmond Park (seven), Shirley (thirty), South Norwood (six), Stoke Lake, the Surrey Docks, Sutton Water Works, Thorpe Gravel Pits, Walton Reservoirs (thirty-seven), Wimbledon and Wrecclesham. The Spelthorne birds were mostly from Queen Mary and Staines reservoirs.

From 2001 onward, Sandwich Terns were seen at Barn Elms, Beddington, Enton, Island Barn Reservoir, Kingston, Queen Elizabeth II Reservoir (including fourteen birds in 2004), South Norwood, Stoke Lake and Walton Reservoirs. A flock of over fifty flew round Barn Elms for several minutes on 29th September 2001 but did not land. Earlier in the day there had been nine at Queen Elizabeth II Reservoir, and 16 were counted there a day later. There were eight at Staines Reservoirs on 9th September 2004 (*LNHSB*).

Large counts

Barn Elms Reservoirs/London Wetland Centre:
 *c.*90, 15th September 1968, a day of very
 heavy rain;: 52-57, 29th September 2001
Chertsey 30+ flew over, 13th September 1973
Shirley: 30+ flew over, 14th September 1974,
 seen by street lighting

Spelthorne

Staines Reservoirs: *c.*20, 12th September 1950
Queen Mary Reservoir: 40+, 30th August 1975

Calendar. Spring passage peaks in April. The much larger autumn passage peaks in September.

Bird months 1900-2001

	Jan	Feb	Mar	Apr	May	Jun	Jul	Aug	Sep	Oct	Nov	Dec	Total
Vice-county	0	0	6	64	46	16	33	129	578	41	0	0	**913**
Spelthorne	0	0	1	50	41	15	16	154	390	50	0	0	**717**

Early and late dates are:

Early

21st March 1996 Holmethorpe Sand Pits
23rd March 1996 Queen Elizabeth Reservoir
31st March 2003 Barn Elms Reservoirs
2nd April 1995 Barn Elms Reservoirs
2nd April 2004 Queen Elizabeth II Reservoir (AR)

Late

19th October 1934 Staines (*BLA*)
27th October 1989 Berrylands Sewage Works
4th November 1934 Staines (*BLA*)

Common Tern
Sterna hirundo

Common passage migrant, now breeding annually

Breeds in North America, Europe, Asia and North Africa and winters south to South America, South Africa and Australia. British birds winter mainly in African waters. Identification problems made British numbers hard to estimate before 1900, but they are thought to have been declining through persecution, reflecting a decline in other parts of its range. They did much better in the 20th century, benefiting from protection and the creation of new gravel pits. Inland breeding has been encouraged by the provision of rafts.

Early Surrey history. Graves mentioned nearly two dozen on the Grand Surrey Canal early in 1812. Long shot a pair at Hampton Lodge in October 1822 and Meyer shot one on the Thames at Chertsey Weir on 6th October 1846 (Bucknill). Kidd wrote that they had frequently been shot at Frensham (Newman, 1849). Later there were single Common Terns at Wisley Pond (Boldermere?) on 15th July 1865, at Epsom on 24th April 1879 and at Gatton in the summer of 1879 (where flocks were said to sometimes occur after storms), together with some undated references to West Surrey localities (Bucknill). Power saw one on the Thames at Battersea Park in August 1882. He had also seen Common Terns at Barnes and Kew but gave no dates. Stafford had undated specimens from Catteshall and Enton (*SALEC*).

1900 to 1950. Common Terns were occasional at Frensham in the early 20th century, with records on 5th August 1912 and 8th June 1913 (H. Bentham) and two there on 8th October 1920 (Shaw). Other sites where they were found in the 1930s included Barn Elms Reservoirs (30-36 on 4th October 1930,

25 on 23rd August 1935) and Brooklands (1937). Unusual numbers of Common and Arctic Terns came to Britain in April 1947 and a flock of 14 was seen at Frensham on the 28th. Six at Queen Mary Reservoir on 7th May 1927 were the first located for Spelthorne. There were reports from Staines Reservoirs, including 21 on 1st August 1927, 28 on 16th August 1929 and 50 on 22nd August 1935. At Queen Mary Reservoir there were 30 on 26th August 1931.

Since 1950. Numbers seen on migration increased greatly, reflecting higher population levels elsewhere and they may have peaked in the 1950s, with up to 500 at Staines Reservoirs on 23rd August 1950 and 304 there on 28th April 1952. At King George VI Reservoir there were 226 on 21st August 1950. Migrant Common Terns still occur on many waters, sometimes in parties of 20 or more but usually of one or two birds only. At Beddington Sewage Farm, 24 flew southwest on 26th August 1989.

Breeding. *Vice-county*. The first suggestion of possible breeding in the vice-county occurred in 1969, when two Common Terns were thought to have attempted to set up territory at Thorpe Gravel Pits, two being seen there on 8th and 15th June. Breeding definitely took place there in 1976, when Frank Blackburn photographed a nest with two young on 21st July. The young flew from the site on 21st September. A nest was flooded there in the following year and one was predated in 1978. Although fledged young often visited Papercourt in the years that followed, the next proven breeding was at Queen Elizabeth II Reservoir in 1985. Common Terns first bred at Barn Elms in 1989, at Lonsdale Road Reservoir in 1991, at Stoke Lake in 1993, at the Surrey Docks in 1997 and at Frimley Gravel Pits in 2000 and 2001. A pair bred at the Surrey Docks (Canada Water) in 2000, with two pairs in 2001. A new raft at Unstead Sewage Farm has attracted a breeding pair since 2001. At Frensham, a tern raft was provided in 2002 but it was not used until 2004, when one pair bred. A pair prospected a newly cleared island at

Enton in 2003. They were seen mating but did not stay. A pair bred at Hedgecourt in 2003. Two broods were reared at Boldermere in 2004, on a raft that had been provided in May of that year and two pairs bred there in 2005. The terns took up residence on the raft within two weeks of its provision (Surrey Wildlife Trust). On 19th July 2006, a pair with two chicks was seen on an island in a sand pit at Holmethorpe.

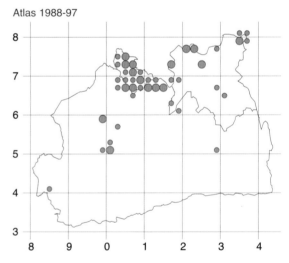

Atlas 1988-97

Breeding at Lonsdale Road, where a raft has been provided, has continued, with success in 2000 and 2002. Three pairs of Common Terns bred at the redeveloped London Wetland Centre at Barn Elms, where a new raft was provided, from 2002 to 2005. The Queen Elizabeth II Reservoir colony has continued to thrive, at least up to 2004, sometimes with around 20 pairs though often with many failures. The rafts at Stoke Lake are being used by one or two pairs annually, with variable success. Common Terns are now well established at these and other sites across the vice-county. Breeding and juvenile terns will feed on adjacent rivers, ponds and pits, for example those at Stoke Lake visit Papercourt Gravel Pits. Juvenile birds have been seen at Frensham.

Spelthorne. A pair nested at Queen Mary Reservoir in 1958. Eggs were laid but the nest was predated. This was the first breeding record for the London area. There was 'an unconfirmed report' of attempted breeding at Shepperton in 1967 (*LBR*). Two pairs each reared three young in the Staines area in 1970 (*LBR*). One or two pairs bred at Queen Mary Reservoir on an industrial raft until this was removed in 1982 (Geen). A pair bred at Shepperton Gravel Pits in 1986, using a raft that had been provided in 1985.

A second pair bred there on a pontoon in the same year. The first published breeding record for Wraysbury Reservoir was for 1993. Breeding on rafts at Staines Reservoirs is well-established, with 58 pairs at the south basin in 2000 and 61 pairs in 2001. A pair bred on a new raft at Shepperton Gravel Pits (Sheepwalk) in 2005 (Surrey Wildlife Trust).

Large counts. This list excludes parties published as being of mixed Common and Arctic Terns without separate counts. There may still be Arctic Terns in some of the migrant flocks.

Barn Elms Reservoirs: 175 southwest, 20 August 1992

Beddington Sewage Farm: 71 southwest, 20th August 1987;

Frensham: 42, 1st May 1979

Holmethorpe: 33, 20th April 1999

Island Barn Reservoir: 78, 6th August 1996

Papercourt: 19, 6th May 1980

Queen Elizabeth II Reservoir: 69, 27th July 2001
Spelthorne

Staines Reservoirs: 155, May 1996 (BTO)

Queen Mary Reservoir: 110, 6th August 2003

Calendar. The main passages are April/May and August/September. There have been no definite Common Terns in the vice-county in November. Early and late dates are:

Early		**Late**	
24th March 2005	Stoke Lake (S. Chastell)	21st October 1974	Barn Elms Reservoirs
26th March 1968	Staines Reservoirs	16th December 1925	Tooting Bec Common:
29th March 1989	Frensham		two on the ground, exhausted, (*BB, 19:256*)

The chart shows some correlation with temperature, which may also be connected with the expansion of breeding:

Movements and longevity. A Common Tern ringed at Lymington on 26th July 1959 and found dead at Runfold, 72 km northeast, on 8th May 1966 was easily the longest lived and furthest travelled among the few ringing recoveries located. One ringed at Kempton Park (though probably

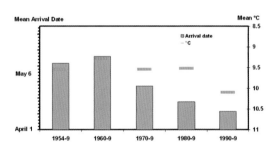

not in Spelthorne) on 12th July 1975 was recovered in Portugal on or about 2nd October 1978. Another, ringed as a nestling at Stoke Lake on 10th June 2002, was recovered at Wisley on 7th August 2005.

Common/Arctic Tern   *Sterna hirundo/paradisaea*

There are a few significant Surrey records where the exact species could not be determined.

Large counts

Barn Elms Reservoirs: c.90, 15th September 1968; 184, 5th September 1982

Battersea Park: 385 upriver, 26th August 1989

Beddington Sewage Farm: 150-200 northwest, 17th August 1989

Frensham: 49, 1st May 1979, of which seven thought to be Arctic (at least twelve in HNHS 1980)

Walton Reservoirs: 20, 3rd May 1991
Spelthorne

King George VI Reservoir: 226, 21st August 1950

Queen Mary Reservoir: 134, 20th August 1989

Staines Reservoirs: up to 500, 23rd August 1950; 304, 28th April 1952; 220, 20th August 1989

Calendar. Early and late dates are:

Early		Late	
4th March 1974	Staines Reservoirs: 20, the earliest for either species	12th November 1967	Frensham
		22nd November 1970	Frensham
8th April 1961	Barn Elms Reservoirs	17th December 1925	West Norwood: *c*.twelve flew over, (*BTO Guide* 15, *BB, 19:256*)
12th April 1979	Frensham, one		
		24th November 1968	Queen Mary Reservoir, two

Roseate Tern   *Sterna dougallii*

Twelve records, eight of them from Spelthorne

Roseate Terns have a scattered breeding range around the world, from North and Central America through the British Isles to East Africa, Asia and Australia. The British colonies are at the north of its range and winter mainly in West African coastal waters. Most British and Irish colonies were wiped out by persecution in the 19th century. There was a marked increase up until the 1960s, since when there has been a large decline.

Surrey records are from about 1873 to 2005. They reflect the national increase up to the 1960s and the subsequent decline:

1873: Vachery Pond. The Charterhouse Collection once included a Roseate Tern killed at Vachery Pond in about 1873 (*SALEC*) and brought to Stafford by a servant of Mr Thornton of Baynards Park (*SCCMS*) but the specimen is no longer held there. Jordan (1894) wrote that the bird had been shot at Frensham but gave no details.

1953:* Perry Oaks Sewage Farm, 6th May, notes by W. H. Dady and D. A. Preston in the *LBR*.

1960:* King George VI Reservoir, two east on 12th May.

1961: Barn Elms Reservoirs, two on 18th July.

1963: Barn Elms Reservoirs, one on July 24th, seen in flight and at rest.

1967:* Queen Mary Reservoir, one on 6th September.

1968:* Staines Reservoirs, one on 17th May.

1969:* Staines Reservoirs, one on 6th May.

1970:* Staines Reservoirs, one on 11th May.

1971: Frensham Great Pond, one on 7th May, watched for over two hours.

2002:* Staines Reservoirs, one on 3rd June.

2005: Queen Elizabeth II Reservoir, one on 19th-20th May, found by D. M. Harris.

*Spelthorne

Arctic Tern   *Sterna paradisaea*

Scarce passage migrant

Arctic Terns have a circumpolar breeding distribution, more northerly than that of the Common Tern and Britain is at the southern end of their range. In common with some other southern populations, breeding numbers have declined in recent years. Their migratory movements are among the most remarkable of all birds, extending as far south as the Antarctic pack ice. The *Migration Atlas* shows that birds breeding in Finland and Scandinavia pass through Britain.

Early Surrey history. Arctic Terns appeared in some numbers on the Thames in 1843 (Bucknill). There is a record in Meyer of a young bird shot in company with a Common Tern on the Thames at Chertsey Weir on 6th October 1846. These two records are the first for Middlesex as well as for Surrey (Glegg). Booth (E. T. Booth, whose collection is in the Booth Museum presumably) informed Bucknill that a young specimen in the Natural History Museum at South Kensington was labelled *Croydon* and presented by a Colonel Irby.

1900 to 1970. There were two at Barn Elms in September 1926. One found dead at Staines Reservoirs on 1st September 1935 (*BB, 29:186*) appears to be the first record for the site and only the second for Middlesex. Live birds were seen there on 26th and 28th September and 1st October and there was another there on 9th September 1936. There was one on 10th October 1937 (the latest London area date up to 1956). Unusual numbers of Common and Arctic Terns came to Britain in April 1947 (*BB, 41:167-73*). Surrey Arctic Tern records came from Barn Elms (up to *c*.20), Earlswood Common (one), Frensham (up to nine from the 23rd, the first for the Haslemere district) and Guildford Sewage Farm and one at Perry Oaks Sewage Farm on 3rd May. Later Frensham records came in 1948 (seven on 21st May) and 1956. Autumn records were infrequent up to 1970. Parr could only find three from 1950-70 (1956, 1960 and 1970).

Since 1970. The number of migrant Arctic Terns counted has risen considerably since the 1970s, as may be seen from the table.

Bird months by decade since 1970

	1970s	1980s	1990s	2000-01	Total
Vice-county	36	95	328	99	**558**
Spelthorne	31	681	375	29	**1,116**

There were major influxes in 1981, when up to 130 were present at Staines Reservoirs in late April and early May, and in 1982 when there were 140 at Staines Reservoirs on 29th April.

Where found. The migrants have been concentrated on a small number of places. In the vice-county from 1970 to 2001, only five places, Barn Elms (126), Beddington Sewage Farm (63), Frensham (66), Island Barn Reservoir (153) and Queen Elizabeth II Reservoir (67) accounted for four-fifths of the 558 bird months. The other places where Arctic Terns were seen, with the number of bird months if more than five, were Badshot Lea, Battersea Park, Frimley Gravel Pits (seven), Hersham Gravel Pit, Holmethorpe Sand Pits (six), Longside Lake, Papercourt Gravel Pits, Richmond Park, South Norwood Country Park, Stoke Lake, the Thames (seventeen) and Walton Reservoirs (twenty- nine). They were even more concentrated in Spelthorne, where Staines Reservoirs accounted for 78% of the bird months, the others being from the King George VI, Queen Mary and Wraysbury reservoirs.

Records after 2000 have come from Barn Elms, Beddington, Frensham, Island Barn Reservoir, Papercourt, Queen Elizabeth II Reservoir, Walton-on-Thames and Wandsworth. The largest number was 19 at Frensham on 13th May 2001. There were 38 at Staines Reservoirs on 4th May 2005.

Calendar. Passage peaks are in April and September:

Bird months 1970-2001

	Jan	Feb	Mar	Apr	May	Jun	Jul	Aug	Sep	Oct	Nov	Dec	Total
Vice-county	0	0	0	215	182	12	11	41	79	17	1	0	**558**
Spelthorne	0	0	0	493	317	9	18	96	171	12	0	0	**1,116**

Nine at Island Barn Reservoir on 1st June 1989 made up the first vice-county June record. One at Frensham Great Pond on 27th June 1990 was the second. Two at Barn Elms Reservoirs on 10th August 1975 were the first for August since at least 1900. One at Hersham Gravel Pit on 7th November 1982 was the first for November. Early and late vice-county dates are:

Early		Late	
7th April 2000	Walton Reservoirs	11th October 1999	Frensham
7th April 2003	Island Barn Reservoir	31st October 1982	Hersham Gravel Pit
10th April 1996	Island Barn Reservoir	7th November 1982	Hersham Gravel Pit
10th April 2003	Island Barn Reservoir		

The earliest located Spelthorne date since 1970 is 5th April 2003 and the latest is 29th October 1981, both from Staines.

Large counts. There was an exceptionally large count in 1982:

Barn Elms Reservoirs: *c.*20, 26th April 1947

Beddington Sewage Farm: 27, 24th April 1995, briefly after heavy shower

Frensham: 12, 1st May 1979 (HNHS 1980)

Queen Elizabeth II Reservoir: 25, 29th April, 1995

Spelthorne

Queen Mary Reservoir: 60, 10th September 1981

Staines Reservoirs: 140, 29th April 1982

Auk species

An auk seen at Hammersmith on 5th October 1948 was not specifically identified (*BLA*). One on the Thames at London Bridge 10th September 1971 was a Guillemot or a Razorbill. One on the Thames between Twickenham and Chiswick on 4th October 1987 was possibly the Guillemot seen at Hammersmith Bridge.

Guillemot (Common Guillemot) *Uria aalge*

Rare

Races of the Guillemot breed in Scotland (*aalge*), other parts of the British Isles (*albionis*) and on coasts around the North Atlantic and the North Sea (*MA*). There are other races in California and the North Pacific. All winter at sea in the regions where they breed. Storm-driven birds may appear inland. Breeding numbers in Britain were fairly stable in the 19th century but have since declined, due to habitat disturbance, oil pollution and probably the over-fishing of sand eels.

Early Surrey records. T. Edmonston saw one fly over London Bridge and settle on the Thames under Cannon Street Railway Bridge in the second week of November 1879, after a night of storms (Green, 1893), apparently the first record for Middlesex. Most, if not all the Surrey birds have been brought in by storms. An undated specimen from Milford (*SALEC*) was in the Charterhouse Collection in Bucknill's time but the specimen currently held is of unknown origin.

1900 to 1985. Only a few were seen in this period. They included two on the Thames above London Bridge on 7th November 1930 (*BB, 24:197*); one exhausted in a garden at Limpsfield on 14th January 1934 after a night of storms; one on the Thames between Westminster and Lambeth Bridges on 8th October 1955; an immature bird at Queen Elizabeth II Reservoir on 16th September 1973; one on the Thames at Vauxhall on 22nd October 1980 and one at Wandsworth Bridge and the Thames at Barn Elms on 16th-17th January 1982. In 1983, one and sometimes two in winter plumage were seen on the Thames, from Putney to Chiswick from 19th February to 17th March, one in summer plumage was at Teddington Lock on 21st-24th February and there was one at Staines Reservoirs on 9th March.

The 1986 invasion. One on the Thames at Barnes Bridge from December 1985 was the herald for a major invasion in 1986, brought in by strong northeast winds. This began with one on the Thames at Westminster on 26th January and up to five new birds on the Thames from Kew to Putney on 14th-21st February. One flew low over Beddington Sewage Farm on 15th February 1986 and on the same day there were two on the Thames at Barnes. Next came single birds at Stoke Lock, Guildford on 16th-17th February and on the Thames at Battersea on 21st February. Many were counted on the Thames between Kew and Putney from 26th February to 27th March 1986, when the last one, at Kew, was seen. These included 28 moving up the Thames on 1st March 1986 (one at Grosvenor Bridge, 18 at London Bridge, nine at Waterloo Bridge). Nine were counted between Kew and Wandsworth and two at Teddington Lock on this date. There were 11 between Ham Lands and Wandsworth on 2nd March and others were seen on the Thames on 2nd-5th March (Kingston) and 27th March (Kew). It is not clear how much double counting is involved, but clearly there were at least 18 birds on the Thames and there might have been over 30.

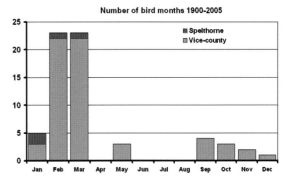

A few were found elsewhere, including one found at Dorking on 2nd March, one under a bramble bush at Ham Common on the same day and one picked up at Wimbledon in March. One at Queen Mary Reservoir on 15th February 1986 might have been the Guillemot found dead there on the 22nd.

1987 onward. Nine more have been seen since: one on the Thames at Hammersmith Bridge on 4th October 1987; one on the Thames, Richmond-Kew on 13th September 1991 and at Teddington on the 14th September (*SBR*); one flew over Beddington Sewage Farm on 30th September 1998 and one was found shortly afterwards at the nearby Roundshaw estate, Wallington and taken into care. It was later released at Winchelsea. There was one at the Surrey Docks on 22nd May 2001, one on the Thames at Putney on 6th September 2003 and there were two at the Millennium Bridge on 25th May 2005 (*Birding World*). In Spelthorne, one was found dead at Queen Mary Reservoir on 25th January 1987 and there was one in summer plumage at Wraysbury Reservoir on 18th-19th January, also in 1987.

Razorbill   *Alca torda*

About eighteen records, of which four were from Spelthorne

Razorbills have a more restricted breeding range than Guillemots, running from Maine to western Russia and south to Scandinavia and Britain. Like Guillemots, and for the same reasons, population levels have declined.

Surrey. Razorbills are rare, usually storm-driven, birds in Surrey. They are most often seen in the autumn, but sometimes in spring. Bucknill knew of five birds, all in outer Surrey. Since 1900, all have been elsewhere.

Single birds from Cranleigh and Shalford were in the Charterhouse Collection in Bucknill's time. (Those currently in the Charterhouse Collection in 2002 were of unknown origin.) One shot at Vachery Pond, Cranleigh was in the Stafford Collection (*SCCMS*) but not sold to Charterhouse.

Others are:

1831:   Cobham, one on a pond at Pains Hill (Jesse).

1894:   Thames at Rotherhythe. Cook (1894) said he had received large numbers for preservation after severe weather and inferred that they had been taken on the Thames at Rotherhithe.

1895:   Surrey. One in a ploughed field, presumed to be in Surrey, '*sitting up like a rabbit in one of the furrows, no doubt lost in wonder as to where he had got to*'. It twice bit a boy who tried to pick it up, and was killed with a kick (Jordan, 1894).

1911:   Blackfriars Bridge, five on 29th November, after more than a fortnight of wet and stormy weather (A. K. Collett).

1934:*   Queen Mary Reservoir, a remarkable party of sixteen on 22nd October. Four days later they were all dead. They were found to be infested with a fluke *Cotylarus platycephalus* (*BB*, 28:188, 245).

1935: Thames, one swam upstream during the Boat Race, between two motor boats, on 6th April (Professor Warmington).

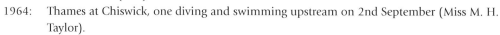

Number of bird months 1900-2003

1936: Chiswick Bridge, one on 13th May.

1938: Thames above Richmond, one on 22nd October (F. Dutton).

1948: Westminster and Lambeth Bridges, seven on 5th October (W. G. Teagle).

1960: Westminster Bridge, one flew over on 18th October (*LBR*).

1964: Thames at Chiswick, one diving and swimming upstream on 2nd September (Miss M. H. Taylor).

1966:* Staines Moor, one on the River Colne, 19th-24th October.

1973:* Queen Mary Reservoir, one on 22nd October (*LBR* for 1974), also on 13th and 27th (Geen).

1983:* Wraysbury Reservoir, one on 6th February.

1983: Thames at Wapping, one picked up by the River Police on 9th February. Since Wapping is on the north bank of the Thames, the bird might arguably never have been in Surrey.

Spelthorne

Black Guillemot

Cepphus grylle

Three undated before 1900

An auk with a circumpolar distribution on Arctic and North Atlantic coasts. Remains from Devon and Derbyshire dating from late in the last Ice Age (Harrison, 1988) suggest that Black Guillemots may have occurred in our own area at the time.

Surrey. The first definite evidence is Stafford's note of one in winter plumage at Lambeth, killed by being jammed between two pieces of floating timber (*SALEC, SCCMS*). This bird was seen in the Charterhouse Collection by Bucknill, but does not seem to be there now. Two others, from Cranleigh and Guildford, were mentioned in Stafford's private notes. Bucknill saw the notes but could not locate the specimens or any other details about them.

Little Auk

Alle alle

At least twenty-seven records since 1900 and eleven earlier

An arctic breeding species, wintering at sea. Recorded in southern Britain towards the end of the last Ice Age (Harrison, 1988). Birds of the race *polaris*, from Franz Josef Land, have been found in Scotland (*MA*).

Early Surrey history. Little Auks are most often seen in Surrey after winter gales. Bucknill knew of at least eleven birds before 1900. One found near Haslemere (not in Surrey?) was given to the Charterhouse collection. Another in the Stafford collection, found at Cranleigh (*SALEC*), was held by Bucknill.

Dated records before 1900 are:

1860: near Guildford, one captured alive in a chalk pit in February. It refused food and died two days later (*Zool.*, 1861:7438).

1870: Witley, one captured alive in a pond in March (*The Field*, 1870 p. 352).

1883: Chertsey, close to Chertsey Lock, one shot on 8th December, also in Glegg (1935) as the first for Middlesex.

1890:   Godstone, an exhausted bird on 2nd December. It weighed 3½ ounces (100 grams) against a normal 250 grams. (*Zool., 1891:397* in Bucknill).

1892:   Compton, one found in the winter of 1892/93.

1895:   In the severe weather of early 1895, a national wreck brought at least four to Surrey. Bucknill saw three of them, from Down Place, Guildford on 23rd January, Sutton Park on the 25th, and Woking on the 25th. There was another at St George's Hill later in the year.

Since 1900 there have been thirteen records from the vice-county and 16 from Spelthorne:

Vice-county

1900:   Nunhead, one caught alive on 23rd March (Bucknill).

1912:   Dormansland, one at the Ford Manor estate on 2nd February, part of a national wreck.

1930:   Lambeth Reservoir, one on 1st January (national wreck in December 1929).

1967:   Barn Elms Reservoirs, one on 20th November.

1970:   Walton Reservoirs, one on 24th October.

1984:   Barn Elms Reservoirs, one flew low over the allotments on 15th February.

1985:   Woking, one found dead on 14th November.

1988:   Streatham, one found dead on a doorstep at 6 am on 3rd January.

1995:   Frensham and Woking, one at Frensham Little Pond and one on the Basingstoke Canal at Woking on 4th November, during a national wreck.

1997:   Caterham, one found alive in a garden in early October (*LBR*).

1999:   Pirbright, one picked up dead by the roadside on 15th November.

2003:   Haslemere, one on 4th November, died in care.

Spelthorne

King George VI Reservoir: single birds on 23rd October 1955 (found dead on the 29th), 10th January 1957 and 25th-27th November 1977. One was found dead at King George VI Reservoir in February 1950.

Staines Reservoirs: one found by Donald Gunn on 28th November stayed until 6th December 1928 (when it died), one before 31st October, one on 31st October and two on 31st December 1929, one from 13th-16th November 1932 and 10th October 1934, two

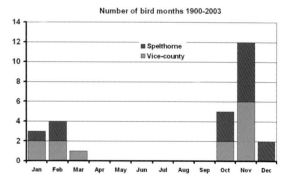

Number of bird months 1900-2003

■ Spelthorne
□ Vice-county

on 9th November 1957 (at King George VI Reservoir on the following day), one on 1st November 1959, one on 24th November 1969, one on 30th October 1974 (also seen on King George VI Reservoir) and two on 24th November 1974.

Wraysbury Reservoir: one on 9th February 1983.

Calendar. All Surrey records are from October to March, with a peak in November, when many birds are moving south.

Puffin (Atlantic Puffin)   *Fratercula arctica*

Thirty-two records since 1900 and at least seven earlier

Breeds on coasts around the North Atlantic and the North Sea and east to Novaya Zemlya, wintering at sea. British breeding numbers seem to have been declining throughout the 19th and 20th centuries for reasons similar to those affecting other auks.

Early Surrey history. George Graves said that, at about the end of May 1812, one was taken on the Thames near Chelsea, and kept alive for some days (Graves in Glegg, 1935). This was the first for Surrey and Middlesex. There were specimens from Hascombe Pond, Witley and a pond at Hydons Ball in the Stafford collection (*SALEC, SCCMS*, no dates, but probably after 1849). The Charterhouse Collection recently held Puffins with Surrey and Godalming as provenances and may have been two of these. One was caught near Reigate in the autumn of 1890. *BRP* for 1949 mentions one at Kew Gardens in 1891. One was picked up alive on a Surrey moor in 1893 (Jordan, 1895). Shaw referred to one picked up on the Hog's Back but gave no date.

Since 1900:

1905: Thames at Hammersmith Bridge, one on 8th October (Becher, 1905).

1909: near Croydon, one shot on 29th October, found in a field.
Banstead, one in a garden on 1st November. Caught with difficulty, given to a zoo.

1911: Thames between Hammersmith and Barnes, one on 4th October (Hope, 1911).

1923: Cobham, one captured on 28th October.

1934: Banstead, one picked up alive on 20th October and given to a zoo.

1938: near Milford, one picked up exhausted on 16th February and released later on Thursley Hammer Pond.

1944: Thames at Chiswick Eyot, an immature bird on 3rd January.
Selsdon Wood, a female was picked up dead on 19th February.

1946: Merrow, a juvenile female was found alive on 5th October. It was chloroformed, and the skin was sent to the British Museum.

1947: Barn Elms Reservoirs, a juvenile was found dead on 10th December.

1949: Surrey Docks, one found oiled on 7th November. It was cleaned and taken to the London Zoo.

1953: Headley, an immature bird was found in a garden on 12th April. It was identified at the Natural History Museum (*LBR*)

1955: Barn Elms Reservoirs, one seen on 23rd and 25th September and 18th October, possibly the same bird.
London SE1, one found outside the Union Jack Club, Waterloo Road on 15th October. It was taken to London Zoo.

1955:* Staines Reservoirs, an immature bird on 2nd, 23rd and 25th October.

1956:* Staines Reservoirs, an immature bird on 12th September.
King George VI Reservoir, an immature bird on 7th October.

1957:* Queen Mary Reservoir, one on 17th September.
Perry Oaks Sewage Farm, one on 5th October.

1958: Thames at Westminster, an immature bird on 13th November.

1959: Albert Bridge, an adult was found on the bridge on 20th October and later released at Hastings (*LBR*).

1961: Shirley, one found in a garden, exhausted on 2nd November.
Thames at Putney Bridge, one on 8th November.

1963: Thames at Westminster, a dead Puffin floating on 25th February.

1967: Ewell Court Park, one flying west on 3rd July.

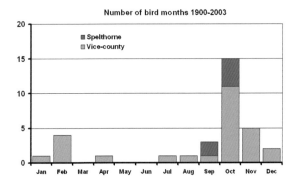

Number of bird months 1900–2003

Merstham, one on 19th October 1967. It died a few days later.

Thames at Barn Elms, one swimming on 22nd October.

1976: Thames at Barnes, one swimming on 14th December.

1985: Between Ranmore and Westhumble, one picked up on 31st August. It died under treatment.

1989:* Wraysbury Reservoir, one on 24th October.

1991: Thames at Richmond, one picked up on 8th February. It was taken into care but later died.

*Spelthorne

Pallas's Sandgrouse   *Syrrhaptes paradoxus*

A few in rare irruptions, has nested

Breeds from Central Asia to Manchuria, wintering further south. Most British records have come from periodic irruptions, which were on a major scale in the 19th century, but are now much smaller. There was an irruption in 1863. The 1888 irruption was on a spectacular scale. Some 1,500 to 2,000 were estimated for Scotland alone and there were many breeding attempts across Britain. A special Act of Parliament was passed to protect the birds but it did not come into effect until February 1889, by which time most had been shot, succumbed to the weather, or moved on.

Surrey history. Two were seen *on a heath, at no great distance from the camp at Aldershot* on 26th May 1863 and one of them was shot. Nine were seen near the camp at around the same time and one of these was shot (Murray A. Matthews in *Zool. 1863:8683-84*). The *Zoologist* note is entitled *Pallas' Sand Grouse in Hampshire,* but Matthews lived in Weston-super-Mare and may not have been too familiar with the local county boundary. Clark (*Birds of Hampshire*) writes that *at least one was obtained near Aldershot* in 1863. Stafford's private notes mentioned a third bird shot at Aldershot. Some or all of these Aldershot birds may have been in Hampshire but it seems possible that the heath of 26th May was part of the military land in Surrey, northeast of Aldershot. Another Pallas's Sand Grouse was shot at Horsley and three more at Wonersh, two of which were eaten (Bucknill).

The 1888 irruption brought larger numbers. A flock of about a dozen was seen near Staines Moor on 19th June 1888 (Glegg). About six were shot near Horsley by a labourer. Five of them were eaten and a sixth was stuffed (*The Field 23rd June 1888 p.901*). This one was later seen by Bucknill, who thought that all six might have come from a party of 30 or 40 seen in Hampshire, flying towards Aldershot, on 20th May. A flock of eleven flew over Wimbledon Common towards Richmond Park on 16th June and might have been those seen a few days later near Staines Moor (about 12 on 19th June 1988, *Zool., 1889:227*). Seven were seen by the largest pond on Royal Common (exact date not known). The final dated record of the year was of four in a field near Chobham Common on 5th December, two of which were shot (*The Field, 1st January 1889*). One was shot at Shirley at the end of February 1889 in the belief that it was a dove (*Zool., 1889:227, The Field 23rd February 1889 p.260*) and another was seen on a lawn in Godalming on 1st March of that year. The 1888-89 occurrences can all be found in Bucknill, but the final, and perhaps most surprising event of the invasion, is not. The Stafford Collection catalogue manuscript contains this note: *Nested at Puttenham in 1889 but the eggs were taken.*

Three were seen at Holmwood on 28th June 1908 (*BB, 2:98*), part of a national influx (*The Handbook*). There have been none since. The Holmesdale Natural History Club museum holds a specimen of unknown provenance.

Feral Rock Dove (Rock Pigeon)

Columba livia

Widely naturalised in built-up areas

The native range runs from western Europe to North Africa and India. Feral Rock Doves are descendants of domesticated birds and are found throughout the world, away from polar regions. Colonies inhabited the old St Paul's Cathedral at the end of the 14th century (Fitter, 1956) and have been increasing and spreading since at least the late 19th century (*Historical Atlas*). Cramp and Tomlins (1966) used information from a study in Bloomsbury to conclude numbers had increased from 1950 to 1965 and that feral pigeons were as numerous as House Sparrows by the end of the period. They and other authors have questioned the use of culling as a population control measure, pointing to food supply as being the main factor limiting numbers. Breeding numbers have shown little change since 1994.

Early Surrey history. There is no evidence that wild birds have ever bred in Surrey but feral birds were known in the Godalming district before 1849. Bucknill cites several examples of apparently feral populations at places such as Claremont Park and Esher Place (Meyer) and in a ruined building at Cobham Park (1868).

1900 to 1960. The main stronghold of the feral birds was initially in the more heavily built-up part of London, including a large portion of metropolitan Surrey (Parr). Numbers are largely determined by available food supply and nest sites. Food associated with the many horses used for transport in the early 20th century have gone but feral pigeons are expert foragers and are often fed well by residents and visitors. There is virtually no quantitative information about the number or distribution of feral pigeons in the Surrey part of the London area before 1968. Cramp and Teagle (1952) mentioned them nesting under bridges and feeding on the mud of the Thames foreshore and both of these activities may still be observed.

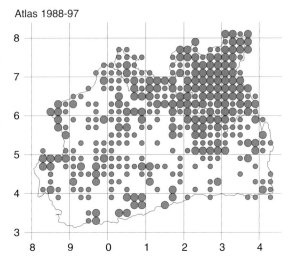

Atlas 1988-97

Trend since 1960. Of the 231 tetrads in northeast Surrey, 49% were found to hold territories in the 1968-72 Atlas survey and 75% in the 1988-97 Atlas, a substantial growth. The more limited coverage of the Common Birds Census showed further significant growth from 1989 to 2000. The part played in this increase by better coverage is unclear.

Number of Northeast Surrey tetrads with feral Rock Doves present in the breeding season

10 km square	TQ05	06	07	15	16	17	25	26	27	35	36	37	38	45	Total
Number of tetrads	1	16	15	16	25	10	25	25	20	25	22	17	4	10	**231**
Present 1968-72	0	11	2	2	15	4	11	15	16	9	8	16	4	1	**114**
Present 1988-97	1	12	15	7	22	8	23	25	19	17	22	16	4	5	**196**

Nesting. Nestlings can be seen as early as mid February (Guildford Railway Station, 1988) and as late as 31st December (a Guildford car park, 1991).

Population size. The fieldwork of 1981-84 for the *Winter Atlas* provided the first county-wide measure of the abundance of feral Rock Doves. Some 896 were counted by field workers, half of them in SU94 and probably a small fraction of the total:

Square	84	93	94	95	96	03	04	05	06	07	14	15	16	24	25	26	27	34	35	36	37	Total
Count	0	50	475	23	10	40	30	2	84	0	0	40	23	2	63	0	0	30	24	0	0	**896**

In Spelthorne, winter counts of up to 250+ were made in fields in 1982-83 (some not in the Atlas figures), with similar numbers up to 1986. The Common Birds Census picked up territories of feral birds from 1989 and numbers since then have shown a significant rise. County population estimates for recent years of about 33,000 adults (Breeding Birds Survey) and 9,000 territories (Common Birds Census) are of the same order, and make them more numerous than Stock Doves and Collared Doves. There was a cull at Gatwick Airport in 2002.

Large counts. In the decades following the *Winter Atlas*, the larger feeding flocks have included 400 at Barn Elms in September 2001, 260 at Battersea Park (TQ27) in 1991, 400 at Eashing (SU94) in December 1991, 1,000 at Henley Wood (Chelsham, TQ35) on 16th December 1998, 500 on the Hog's Back (SU94) in 1998, 550 at Papercourt Gravel Pits (TQ05) on 2nd January 1993, 300 at Pyrford (TQ05) in 1987, 750 at Rushett Farm, (Epsom, TQ16) on 17th October 1997, 300 at South Norwood Country Park on 27th September 2002 and 600 at Woodmansterne (TQ26) on 23rd August 1983.

Plumage variations. Domesticated Rock Doves of many varieties, including pure white ones, have long been kept in pigeon lofts and dovecotes and are often seen in urban and rural Surrey. Eric Parker described an escaped bird of the Archangel variety that took up home with him (Parker, 1954).

Stock Dove (Stock Pigeon) *Columba oenas*

Moderately common breeding resident

Breeds from Britain and Spain east to Central Asia and winters mainly in the southern and western part of its breeding range. Did not breed in northern or western Britain at the beginning of the 19th century. Numbers have increased in Britain and other parts of western Europe. National breeding numbers are thought to have increased by about 90% since 1970. Large autumn flocks might include drift migrants from other parts of Europe, possibly travelling with Woodpigeons (*MA*).

Early Surrey history. Stock Doves were local, but not uncommon, breeding birds in Surrey before 1900. Jesse (1838) said that some pairs of 'Rock-pigeons', (taken by Collenette to mean Stock Doves) nested in holes in old oak pollards in Richmond Park and that the keepers there always took the young, which they said were excellent eating. Bucknill noted Stock Doves as breeding in the parks at Ashtead, Betchworth, Gatton, Norbury, Peper Harow and elsewhere, at Puttenham Common and on many of the western heaths, where they occasionally nested in rabbit burrows. He did not mention any large flocks.

Breeding 1900 to the 1970s. The Boorman egg collection includes the species, taken at Cobham (Painshill) in 1903. Stock Doves were still breeding in Richmond Park in 1905 (Mouritz). Power (1910) did not think that Stock Doves had bred in the Dulwich area but occasionally saw probable migrants. Gosnell collected eggs at Woking in 1914. Stock Doves were fairly common in the Farleigh district

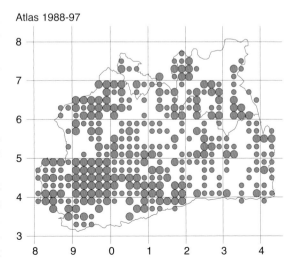

Atlas 1988-97

from 1904 to 1925, with flocks of up to 20 and a number of known breeding sites. A flock of 80 was seen there in February 1941. There are no records in Kerr but Glegg said that Stock Doves were at Stanwell Place before 1936.

Stock Doves bred at Ashtead, Banstead, Beddington Park, Gatton, Ham Common, Oatlands Park, Petersham and Richmond Park in the 1920s and 30s. They bred in the Warlingham district in the 1930s (Beadell) and near Limpsfield in 1935. Several pairs attempted to breed in Battersea Park in 1950 and the first successful breeding was in 1952. There were four pairs at Beddington Sewage Farm in 1955 (Milne, 1956). A decline probably associated with pesticide residues took place from the late 1950s but was halted by 1970 (Parr). Stock Doves bred at Ashtead (1969), Epsom Common (1969), Frensham (1967), Gatton (1969), Kew Gardens (1949-56), Nonsuch Park (1967), Oxshott (1969), Pickhurst (1972), Richmond Park (most years 1938-76), Stoke D'Abernon (at least nine pairs, 1969) and they were present in the breeding season at other sites during the period. Two pairs were on Staines Moor in 1964, where Stock Doves had declined, and there were four pairs in 1967. Stock Doves bred at Shepperton in 1970.

Trend since the 1970s. Numbers seems to have increased since the 1970s. Although the number of vice-county areas from which Stock Doves have been reported each year has generally been 20-40, the Common Birds Census shows a significant increase in numbers from 1970 to 2000, after allowing for changes in the proportion of woodland in the sample, and there is definite Atlas evidence of growth in northeast Surrey. Of the 231 tetrads in the northeast, 40% were found to hold territories in the 1968-72 Atlas survey and 50% in the 1988-97 Atlas. In the south, Stock Doves were rarely recorded at Vann Lake before the late 1970s, when they became regular in the breeding season.

Population size. The Winter Atlas found partial survey counts and estimates totalling 768 birds in 1981-84, suggesting a minimum size for winter population. Common Birds Census numbers suggest an average population of about 2,700 territories and probably more at the end of the period. Grossed-up Breeding Birds Survey information for 1994-2004 suggests a summer population of 2,500-2,600 adults. If Surrey held a proportionate share of the British breeding population as given by the *New Atlas*, the population would be around 1,700 territories, or 0.9 per square km. These figures span the likely population size. The birds are thinly scattered. Bookham Common held at least five territories in 2004 (A. D. Prowse) but most of the west Surrey Commons have fewer than this. Turf Hill, with 16-20 pairs, is very much an exception. Stock Doves are scarce in urban areas but one or two were at the Surrey Docks in May 1975 and there were others in 1998 and 1999. There was one on Battersea Park on 31st July 1989 and others were found in September 1993 and April 1997. The 2003 BTO Spring Migration Watch produced seventeen Spelthorne reports of up to five birds.

Large counts. Stock Doves flock up in winter and, as Parr remarked, often associate with Woodpigeons. Early in the 20th century a flock of 50 birds was a large one, but as the population increased the flocks became larger. About 100 at Richmond Park on 9th March 1935 was a big number for the period. Winter numbers rose further in the 1940s. There were 100 at Lower Kingswood on 27th December 1941, 200 at Tandridge on 30th December 1943 and 300 on Epsom Downs on 9th December 1945 (Parr). Winter flocks of up to 100 are now not uncommon outside the breeding season. Some of the wintering birds might have come with immigrant Woodpigeons. Flocks of 100 or more have been seen at various places throughout the period. There were 104 at Stanwell Moor on 15th March 2000. Larger counts are:

Artington: 185, 11th October 1998

Beddington Sewage Farm: 135, 8th February 2002

near Brockham: 180, 8th March 1981

Capel: 110, 22nd September 1992

Clandon Downs: over 400, 26th October 1974

Downside: 153, 8th November 1978

Eashing Farm: 140, 5th March 1992

Frensham: 115, 7th December 1984

Headley: 100-200, 5th April 1987

Holmethorpe Sand Pits: 310+, 18th March 1992
Horley: 100, 18th March 2000
Limpsfield Chart: 120, 7th March 1993
Merrist Wood: 140+, 7th February 1993
Mizen's Farm, Horsell: 200, 29th November 1997
Molesey Heath: 200+, 10th February 1986
Old Woking Sewage Farm: 162, 4th November 1997
Oxshott: 200+, 1st April 1983
Slyfield: *c*.200, 5th January 1975

Sutton Place: 250, 1st January 1970
Tuesley Farm, Milford: 167, 16th March 2000
Wanborough: 250, 8th November 1965
West End Common, Esher: 230, 8th February 2002
Spelthorne
There were about 300 on the site of a new reservoir at Staines on 10th October 1937 and about 200 at Perry Oaks Sewage Farm in May and June 1953.

Movements and longevity. There are few observations of visible passage, but 72 flying northeast at Thursley Common on 8th January 1977 might have been part of a local movement. Only one foreign ringing recovery has been located, a nestling ringed at Thorpe Water Park on 10th July 1994 and found freshly dead in northern France on or about 12th January 1999. This was thought to be only the sixth recovery from France. The distance, 340 km, is a Surrey record. The bird's age, at least four years and six months, is a Surrey longevity record, albeit well short of the nine years plus recorded elsewhere by the BTO. Another long-lived bird was ringed at Ottershaw on 14th August 1984 and found dead at Worplesdon on 24th January 1989.

Woodpigeon (Common Wood Pigeon)   *Columba palumbus*
Common breeding resident

Woodpigeons have a rather more extensive breeding and winter range than Stock Doves do, reaching central Siberia. Some continental Woodpigeons are strongly migratory. Woodpigeons were breeding in wooded areas throughout Britain in the first half of the 19th century and increased in numbers in subsequent years despite heavy local culling. They are thought to have increased by at least 90% since 1970. Tame birds have been found in towns with feral Rock Doves since at least the final years of the 19th century. There are an estimated 60 breeding birds per square km in the eastern lowlands of England and Wales (Wilson, 2001a).

Early Surrey history. Remains found at 15-23 Southwark Street, Southwark were dated to Roman Britain. Three other sets of remains, from Merton Priory, were dated at 1150-1200, 1380-1500 and 1480-1550 AD. One from Bermondsey Abbey, Southwark, was put at 1480-1600. Some or all of these might have been from birds bought in for the table but they may have been procured locally, or wild.

Woodpigeons joined crows in pillaging cabbage crops in the Godalming area during the severe winter of 1813/14. They bred abundantly in the late 19th century, being found for example at Norwood in the 1880s (Aldridge) and in the then private Brockwell Park (Hudson) and at Putney (Hamilton) by 1881. They had established themselves in a semi-domesticated state in the metropolis before 1900 (Bucknill).

Since 1900. The Boorman egg collection includes that of Woodpigeon, taken at Burhill in 1905. Woodpigeons were common in Richmond Park (Mouritz, 1905) and resident in considerable numbers in the Dulwich area in 1910 (Power). They were very common in the Staines district (Kerr, 1906). Woodpigeons later moved into the Surrey part of central London where they have nested in and on buildings, for example, on a girder inside Waterloo Station in 1954 and behind a coat of arms on the Royal Festival Hall in 1957. The Winter Atlas found partial survey counts and estimates totalling 6,995 birds in 1981-84, nine for every Stock Dove. Woodpigeons are common in the Spelthorne area with recorded counts of up to 60 in spring and probably many more.

Recent trend. There is not much evidence of change in numbers since 1970. Common Birds Census figures are not significant and Atlas penetration of northeast Surrey, already at 98% in 1968-71, had little room for further advance. The biggest movements are mostly recent but the biggest counts are older.

Population size. Grossed-up Breeding Birds Survey information for 1994-2004 suggests a minimum summer county population of about 50,000 individuals (25 per square km). If Wilson's 60 breeding birds per square km were representative of Surrey it would give a current population of about 123,000 adults.

Territory counts. By way of comparison, there were 15 pairs at Beddington Sewage Farm in 1954 and 1955 (Milne, 1956), equivalent to about 25 breeding birds per square km. Some areas have much higher densities. Rowhill Copse, had 40 territories in its 55 acres in 1997 (180 per square km). The Common Birds Census, which under-represented Woodpigeons, showed no significant change since 1970. Much larger numbers have been counted after the breeding season, for example at Ewhurst in October/November 1969, when numbers in the area peaked at 20,000 on November 11th.

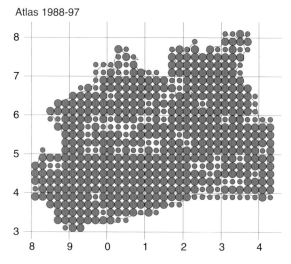

Atlas 1988-97

Nesting. Woodpigeons sometimes nest very early. A nest with two young was found at Godalming on 15th January 1874 (Bucknill) and another in Surrey on 28th January 1923. One was incubating eggs on Leith Hill on 5th January 1988. A young bird was fledged at East Horsley on 23rd February 1969 (Parr). Recently-fledged young were seen at Addlestone on 17th December 1994.

Song. Eric Parker heard one singing at 12.30 am on 1st October 1950 (Parker, 1954).

Large counts and feeding flocks.

Addlestone: up to 5,000 on *brassicae* in January 1963

Battersea Park: 6,000+ on the evening of 14th January 1962

Beddlestead Valley: 1,000 feeding on young rape, 9th March 2002

Clock Barn Farm: 3,000+, 12th January 2003

Ewhurst: 20,000+, 11th November 1969

Gatton Park: *c.*20,000 during hard weather (*The Field, 8th December 1877* in Bucknill)

Leatherhead: 12,000, mid January 1930.

Richmond Park: 4,000, January 1935, feeding mainly on acorns.

West Horsley: 5,000, 4th January 1988

West Horsley/Ripley/Ockham/East Clandon: *c.*20,000, October to December 1973

Witley Common: 1,000, 25th November 1979

Spelthorne

Shepperton: *c.*1,000 feeding, 6th December 1986.

Roosts. Woodpigeons roost in small numbers in woods and copses across Surrey. Large roost counts are uncommon but 2,000 roosted at Richmond Park in December 1938.

Movements. Apparent autumn migratory movements of large size have often been noted in Surrey, typically in October or November. Watching from Staines Moor on 7th December 1929, Glegg saw thousands move south across the Thames against a south-westerly gale. Other large movements include:

Barn Elms: 7,000 south, 4th November 2000; 14,000 southwest, 28th October 2002; 11,800 southwest, 4th November 2002

Berrylands Sewage Works: 15,000 southwest in

55 minutes, 5th November 1989

Frensham: 14,566 south, 3rd November 2002

Guildford: 10,000 southwest, 7th November 1999.

Holmethorpe: 5,500 southeast, 15th November 1995

Lambeth: *c.*6,000 flew over in four flocks, 27th November 1964

Leatherhead: 5,000, 6th February 1977

Milford: *c.*15,000 flew over in 20 minutes, November 1971.

New Malden: 10,000 NNE in five minutes, 30th November 1971

Ottershaw: 65,000 SSE between 0700 and 0930 hrs, 5th November 1995 (R. A. Denyer)

Papercourt Gravel Pits: 4,216 southwest, 31st October 2004

Salfords: 8,000 east in 40 minutes, 15th November 1989

Slyfield: 5,000 west in an hour, 31st December 1978.

Thursley Common: movements on six dates, 4th-19th November 1995 totalled 26,000; flocks totalling 13,000 moved mostly south in a total of four and a half hours on 21st-24th October 1997

Trevereux: 4,800 southwest, 7th November 2003

Unstead Sewage Farm: 19,959 southwest, 7th November 1999

Walton Reservoirs: 8,880 south, 7th November 1999

Weybridge: 4,000-5,000 southeast, 9th November 1961

Although it is sometimes supposed that these movements involve immigrant birds, definite evidence has been hard to find (Ash *et al.*, 1956). Three Surrey Woodpigeons ringed in the summer and recovered in France in the winter, were proof of at least limited outward migration or dispersion in autumn. A Woodpigeon ringed at Mitcham Common on 24th June 1984 was recovered in Calvados, France, 260 km south, on 15th November 1988. A nestling ringed at Elmers End Sewage Farm on 4th June 1961 was killed at Riaillé, France, 439 km south, on 11th November of the same year. The furthest travelled was a nestling ringed at Ottershaw on 15th August 1975 and killed at Finistère, 470 km southwest, on 3rd December of the same year.

Longevity. The greatest longevity located is of a nestling ringed at Lower Morden on 8th April 1969 and found dead three km away on 30th March 1979, almost ten years later. An adult, ringed north of the Thames at St James's Park on 24th May 1955, was found freshly dead at Leigh on 13th September 1964. Woodpigeon Diphtheria has been found in Surrey (*BB, 2:70, SBR* for 1960).

Plumage variations. Bucknill mentioned a nearly white bird near Richmond in 1864. One at Chilworth in 1995 had a normally-coloured head and neck but a creamy-yellow body.

Collared Dove (Eurasian Collared Dove)   *Streptopelia decaocto*
Common breeding resident

Collared Doves expanded their range west from India but bred no further west than the Balkans until about 1930, when a further expansion of range started. The first British breeding record was from Norfolk in 1952. Breeding numbers are thought to have increased by over 300% since 1970. Ringing results show some exchange between Britain and nearby parts of continental Europe (*MA*).

 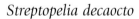

The reasons for such a rapid colonisation are not well understood, but are potentially important in a number of conservation debates. For example, it may have been triggered by a genetic change. This does not seem to have been proved, but could be of relevance in the more general context of the opportunities and risks of genetic modifications to plants and animals. There was evidently an ecological niche waiting to be filled, since no species, except possibly for Turtle Doves in some of the more mature gardens, appear to have been disadvantaged by the Collared Dove's arrival. Collared Doves have been found breeding in every month of the year. Whatever the reasons, there may, as with Ring-necked Parakeet discussed below, be something

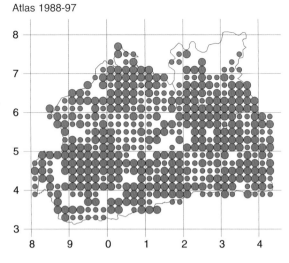

Atlas 1988-97

useful to be learned about how to help declining species. Of course, some will disagree, and argue that the population dynamics of the two are very different from that of most declining residents.

Early Surrey history. The first Surrey Collared Dove was found feeding in a chicken run at Gomshall from 15th April to 13th May 1956 (*BB, 50:270-71*). Collared Doves first bred at Shamley Green in 1960. In late 1961 and early 1962 a flock of twelve was seen on a Carshalton smallholding. Pairs nested unsuccessfully at Banstead and successfully at Cheam in 1964 (*LBR*). Winter flocks of about 150 were found at two localities in 1966.

Trend since 1964. The *LBR* for 1967 listed 28 pairs at 14 Surrey localities. Collared Doves reached Hindhead in 1964 and were first known to breed there in 1971. They were resident at Vann Lake from 1975. Collared Doves were reported from Staines in 1964 and by 1967 the breeding density in Staines was estimated at about six pairs per half mile of road (*LBR*). They first bred at Littleton and Shepperton in 1968 (*LBR*).

By the time of the 1968-72 LNHS Atlas survey, Collared Doves were found in 52% of 231 northeast Surrey tetrads, including Spelthorne, in the London area. A comparison of the 1968-72 and 1988-97 Atlas surveys shows a 46% increase in the number of tetrads where the species was present:

Number of Northeast Surrey area tetrads with Collared Doves present in the breeding season

10 km square	05	06	07	15	16	17	25	26	27	35	36	37	38	45	Total
Number of tetrads	1	16	15	16	25	10	25	25	20	25	22	17	4	10	**231**
Present 1968-72	0	15	12	3	19	3	19	15	1	16	13	0	0	3	**119**
Present 1988-97	1	16	12	12	22	3	22	25	5	24	20	4	0	8	**174**

Where now found. Today, Collared Doves breed in almost all occupied parts of the county, in towns, villages and on farms. As the breeding distribution map shows, they had not fully penetrated the extreme northeast, which is heavily built up, by 1997 although there were single birds in Battersea Park on 17th May 1985, 16th September 1986 and a few subsequently and one was found at the Surrey Docks on 19th April 1999. Nor are they found far away from human habitations. Garden conifers are a preferred nest site. TV aerials make good song posts. Bird tables and stockyards provide an ample food supply.

Population size. The Winter Atlas found partial survey counts and estimates totalling 376 birds in 1981-84, one for every two Stock Doves. Collared Doves were first picked up by the Common Birds Census in 1967. The censuses provide a county estimate of about 10,000 territories for 2000, which compares with a Breeding Birds Survey estimate of about 10,000 adults.

Large counts. Clandon and West Horsley counts from the 1970s remain the highest on record:

Clandon: 800-900 on farmland, October to December 1973, not all in one flock

Lower Hammer Farm, West Horsley: 400, February 1973

Tongham: *c.*200, September 1984.

Spelthorne

Queen Mary Reservoir: 100+, 21st September 1974

Shepperton: 47, 19th November 1984 (*Shepp. BR*). Well-reported in Spelthorne in the spring of 2003.

Movements and longevity. A Collared Dove that was ringed at Ekeren, Belgium on 6th March 1967 and recovered at Reigate three months later remains the only published Surrey recovery involving another country. One ringed at Worplesdon on 9th July 1978 was found dead at Guildford on 25th May 1984, over five years and ten months later. Collared Doves were found dying of the pigeon canker *Trichomoniasis* at Sanderstead in 1969 and 1971.

Plumage variations. 'Partial albinos' have been reported.

Turtle Dove (European Turtle Dove)   *Streptopelia turtur*

Moderately common but declining summer visitor, breeding annually

A summer migrant to Europe (including most of England) and western Asia, wintering in sub-Saharan Africa. British breeding birds winter in West Africa. England is on the northwest edge of the breeding range, which was confined to southern counties in the early 19th century, but has since extended north and west. The expansion continued into the 20th century but by the 1960s a decline was becoming apparent. The decline has continued, with a national fall of nearly 80% from 1970 to 2001 following the intensification of farming methods. Tall, overgrown hedges, a favourite nest site, have been cut down and weed seeds, the main food in the 1960s, are no longer freely available in farm fields (Browne and Aebischer, 2003). There may also be a problem in the wintering area.

Early Surrey history. Turtle Doves were in the Godalming district in 1849 and bred commonly across the county in the late 19th century. Hamilton (1881) found them on Wimbledon Common. Stafford received one from a farmer at Unstead (*SALEC*). Aldridge (1885) had seen the bird once in the Norwood area, at Crystal Palace Lake. Flocks of up to 30 could be seen among cereal crops (Jordan, 1894). The Holmesdale Natural History Club Museum has a nest taken at Redhill in 1890.

1900 to 1960. Boorman collected eggs at East Clandon in 1902. Bucknill said that Turtle Doves bred at Dulwich Wood and Wandsworth. They were very common along the Thames Valley at Staines (Kerr, 1906). In Richmond Park they were numerous at the turn of the century (Mouritz, 1905). Collenette, writing in 1937, thought that at least one pair nested there annually. Power (1910) saw Turtle Doves occasionally and thought they bred in Dulwich and Sydenham Woods. They were recorded at Woking in 1915 (Maitland and Turnbull). Macpherson (1929) gave an undated reference to Battersea Park. A flock of fifteen at Stanwell on 16th July 1932 was the largest known for Middlesex up to 1935 (Glegg). Turtle Doves bred in the Warlingham district (Beadell, 1932). Cherry Kearton would get eight or nine coming to food in his Kenley garden during the 1930s. Turtle Doves bred at least once at Addlestone, Ashtead Common, Bookham, Box Hill, Carshalton Downs, Cheam Warren, Epsom Common, Fetcham, Godstone, Ham Common, Richmond Park, St George's Hill and Stoke D'Abernon between 1919 and 1938. About 35 Turtle Doves were on the bed of the unfilled King George VI Reservoir in August 1947.

Trend since 1960. Nowadays, Turtle Doves are not garden birds, even on large estates, and their place seems to have been taken by their Collared cousins. In east Surrey, where there were up to four pairs on Limpsfield Common in the 1930s, there were none in 1999. Turtle Doves bred throughout the Farleigh district up to 1950 but are now very scarce. Six pairs bred at Brooklands in 1961 and three pairs at Thorpe in 1966. There were up to five territories on Bookham Common in the 1960s and eight in 1971. The habitat remains good and held six pairs in 2000 but there were none in 2004.

At the time of the 1968-72 Atlas survey, Turtle Doves were still found in 53% of 231 northeast Surrey tetrads, including Spelthorne, in the London area. A comparison of the 1968-72 LNHS and 1988-97 SBC Atlas surveys shows a 75% fall in the number of tetrads where the species was present.

Number of Northeast Surrey tetrads with Turtle Doves in the breeding season

10 km square	05	06	07	15	16	17	25	26	27	35	36	37	38	45	Total
Number of tetrads	1	16	15	16	25	10	25	25	20	25	22	17	4	10	**231**
Present 1968-72	1	14	8	16	16	1	23	7	0	21	7	0	0	8	**122**
Present 1988-97	1	4	2	6	3	0	2	5	0	6	1	0	0	0	**30**

Turtle Doves summered at Vann Lake from 1964 to 1977, after which they were rarely recorded (Blaker Log). The Common Birds Census suggests that a 1970 county total of over 3,000 territories had been all but wiped out by 2000, consistent with a Breeding Birds Survey estimate of under 150 pairs. Some 28 territories were reported to the Surrey Bird Club for 2001, a partial count more consistent with the Breeding Birds Survey figure. There were a few at Shepperton in the 1980s (*Shepp. BRs*), by which time they had become much scarcer around Queen Mary Reservoir (Geen). Ten flew over the Queen Mary Gravel Pits on 6th May 1989. An autumn migrant was present at Stanwell Moor on 17th September 2002.

Where recently found. Grossed-up Breeding Birds Survey information for 1994-2004 suggests a summer county population of less than 140 individuals. Scrub on Bookham Common, Hankley Common (thirty territories in 2000) and Thursley Common (five pairs in 2000) and the hedges found in southeast Surrey are examples of the remaining good Turtle Dove habitat in Surrey, though numbers are falling. Other recent sites are Backside Common (Wood Street, 1997), Baynards (2000), Blackheath (2001), Broadstreet Common (five territories, 2001), Capel (2004), Chiddingfold (2002), Crooksbury Common (2001), Effingham Fish Ponds (2002), Frensham Little Pond (2000), Headley Heath

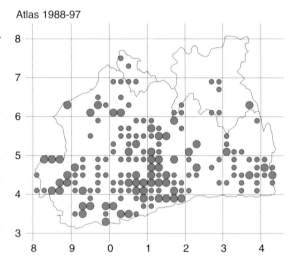

Atlas 1988-97

(2002), Hindhead Commons (2000), Hurst Green (2002),Limpsfield Chart (2002), Netley Heath (2003), Papercourt Gravel Pits (2000), Royal Common (2003), Sydney Wood (2001), Thursley Common (annual), Tugley Wood (2002), Unstead Sewage Farm (2001) and Winterfold (2003).

Nesting. Two nests made partly or all with plastic-covered copper wire were found on Bookham Common in 1967.

Calendar. Turtle Doves arrived towards the end of April and left early in October in Bucknill's day. The average arrival date in the London area south of the Thames from 1929 to 1939 was 11th April.
Other early and late dates are:

Early

4th April 1961	Elstead (SBC archive)
12th April 1966	Thorpe
18th April 1981	Queen Mary Reservoir (Geen)

Late

18th October 1977   Staines Reservoirs

23rd October 1907   one in Power's Brixton garden on 18th-23rd October 1907, finally killed by a cat

10th November 1956   Enton

23rd November 1969   Beddington Sewage Farm (apparently injured)

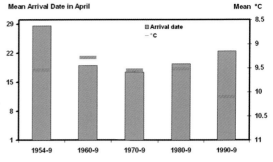

The arrivals chart shows little association between average date and temperature, probably because declining numbers have driven it.

Wintering. One was seen at Addington from January to late March 1985.

Large counts. The largest count on record remains the gathering of 234 in a garden off the Hog's Back, undated but apparently in the 1930s, which was referred to by Parr and can be found in Parker (1941, p.71). Other large counts, none more recent than 1979, are:

Chelsham: 90, 1963

Epsom Sewage Farm: 100, 18th August 1956

Hog's Back: 50-100, 30th June 1935 (*SEBR*)

Limpsfield: 50+, 1st September 1935

Ockham: 100+, 7th August 1962

Old Lyne Sewage Farm: 55, 21st July 1968

Tilhill Nurseries: 140, 1st July 1979

Movements and longevity. There have been three overseas recoveries of Surrey-ringed birds, all of them from Spain. The first was an adult ringed at Thorpe on 23rd September 1976 and recovered 1,118 km southwest, eight years later. The second was a nestling recovered in June 1979, nine months after being ringed in Ottershaw. The third was an adult ringed at Witley Common on 6th June 1981 and found freshly dead, also 1,118 km SSW, on or about 1st September 1984. A Turtle Dove ringed at Pilgrim's Fort, Caterham on 8th July 1981 and retrapped there on 4th June 1990 was remarkable both for its age of over eight years ten months and for its site fidelity.

Ring-necked Parakeet (Rose-ringed Parakeet)   *Psittacula krameri*
Local breeding resident

In their native range, Ring-necked Parakeets breed from sub-Saharan Africa north and east to India and are resident. They occur in huge numbers in India, where roosting flights over Indian cities such as Agra are a common sight at sunset. Most breed in lowland areas, though related species live higher up in the foothills of the Himalayas. They nest at the great wetland reserve of Bharatpur, a reminder that in Europe they seem to prefer sites near water, often in poplars. There are now small Ring-necked Parakeet colonies scattered across Europe and the parakeets roost, for example, in poplars by the Rhine. Ring-necked Parakeets have become familiar birds in many parts of southern Britain. Small parties shoot across the sky like little green rockets, uttering harsh *keer-keer* cries, with their long tails trailing and their short wings raked, a marvel and sometimes a puzzle to those who see them. The *Historical Atlas* mentions pairs breeding in 1855 (Norfolk), 1930 (Essex) and 1931 (Northamptonshire). Butler (2002) discussed the then current British range.

In India, Ring-necked Parakeets are said to be a pest in grain fields, descending on the crops in huge numbers. When they first started expanding in Britain, there were fears that they could be a serious agricultural pest here too (*e.g.* Hawkes, *Sussex Life*, April 1978). This has not so far occurred, though British birds are known to feed on many different nuts and fruits and they have certainly done local damage.

An important food in Britain, though not in India, is peanuts, generously provided in garden feeders. Pithon and Dytham (1999) reported twelve London Area nests at natural sites and found an average of 0.8 fledglings per nest. Of 175 nest boxes set up in southeast England, only one was occupied by a mature pair, suggesting that natural cavities are not a limiting resource. The successful colonisation of southern Britain, from escaped and/or released stock, has been a striking and surprising event. Inexperienced observers who do not expect to find birds of the parrot family in London suburbs sometimes take them for other, superficially similar, species such as the Long-tailed Skua and the Bee-eater. Other hole-nesters, such as the woodpeckers and Stock Doves, Little Owls and Starlings, might have been dispossessed by them and, being powerful birds with stout beaks, the parakeets might often have done so but the evidence is lacking. Starlings are in decline even in areas where there are no parakeets and the cause is probably connected with grassland management.

As with the Collared Dove, the success of the Ring-necked Parakeet owes nothing to conservation efforts but something to the exploitation of an ecological niche. A factor that helps them is the lack of major competitors or natural enemies (apart possibly from squirrels). This seems worth studying. It may be a problem for those concerned about the introduction of an alien species to the British scene but it also presents an opportunity. Why not see what we can learn from the success of these bold, colourful and attractive birds? We may find new ways of helping native species that have fallen on hard times.

Early Surrey history. The archives of the Holmesdale Natural History Club include a reference to birds seen and shot by the stationmaster of Dorking in 1857, so Surrey escapes are nothing new. Three birds that were shot were acquired by the Holmesdale Museum, but they are no longer held there. Green parakeets were seen in Brixton in 1984, 1894, 1897 and 1899. They were larger than a Budgerigar, with a cry like 'caak'and having a very Cuckoo-like flight. Single birds were seen in Dulwich Park in 1893 and 1894 (Power, 1910). These might have been Ring-necked, as also suggested by Chandler, (2003).

After 1900. Nothing else seems to have been listed in the county until 1969, when small numbers of Ring-necked Parakeets were seen in the Croydon/Shirley area. A family party of unknown origin was seen at Southfleet, Kent, in the same year. There are many suggestions for the origin of the recent stock. For example, in about 1970, the owner of a pet shop in Fordbridge Road, Sunbury-on-Thames said that Ring-necked Parakeets had escaped from the shop through an open window. 'Several years later' there were many Ring-necked Parakeets in the area (A. James, pers. comm.). Belsey (2002) favours a widely-circulated story that the first birds were a few that got out of a cage at Shepperton Studios, although the suggestion that the film being made was *The African Queen*, dating from 1952, seems unlikely to be the source. Birds trapped in 1987 by the Runnymede Ringing Group were identified as belonging to the Indian race *P. k. borealis*, location unstated. (*SBR*). D. Butler and D. Griffin confirmed *borealis* by measurements at Molesey in 2001.

Breeding. Feral birds were seen in the Claygate/Esher area from late 1970. Pairs bred in the wild in this area and near Croydon in 1971. Lever (1987) mentions breeding at 'Langley Park' (Bromley, Kent) in 1971. Hudson (1974) provides a few notes on the early history of this colonisation and there is more information in Lever (1979). The *New Atlas* shows birds in five of the Surrey ten km squares. Ring-necked Parakeets were recorded at Queen Mary Reservoir in 1976 (Geen). A dead bird, not fully fledged, was found at Kew in 1977 (*SBR* for 1978). A few were seen at Shepperton in 1981.

Surrey Nestling   *Photo D. Griffin*

In west Surrey, one flew over Crooksbury Common on 2nd September 1983 and others were seen at Chiddingfold in 1984 and Farnham and Camberley in 1985 (*HSBBR*). In the years up to 1993 the numbers in Surrey increased only slowly with no more than three breeding pairs reported in any one year and with maximum flock numbers well down into two figures. Pairs bred at Beddington Park from 1982 to 1985 and in 1987 and 1988, at Shepperton in 1985, at Hersham in 1986, at Dorking in 1987, at Croydon in 1988, at Staines Moor in 1990 and at Betchworth and Ham House in 1992. They were thought to be breeding in the area of the Shepperton Studios in 1982 and at Queen Mary Gravel Pits in 1985.

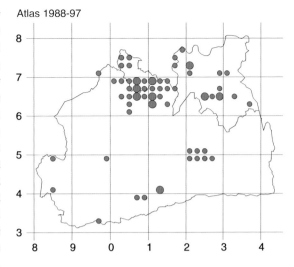

Atlas 1988-97

For a bird so conspicuous at its roosts, the number of breeding reports is still rather low, currently in the region of 20-30 per annum if territorial birds are included. Breeding season reports are most frequent from Chertsey Meads and other Thames Valley locations. Even in Richmond Park, where flocks are common in winter, they may be absent in May and June. Breeding records have come from a few other sites. A pair bred at Laleham Park in 2001. Ring-necked Parakeets have proved themselves capable of surviving the harsher winters of the 1970s and 1980s and may, like Woodlarks and Dartford Warblers, have had a boost from the milder winters of recent years. The latest available Breeding Birds Survey, for 2004, suggested a county breeding season population of over 4,000 adults, so many territorial birds are probably going unreported.

Nests. Natural nests are hard to find or monitor because they tend to be high up and, in Surrey, few in number. Nest sites reported include in Ash, Black Poplar, Copper Beech, Chestnut, Oak, and Willow trees and in old Green Woodpecker holes.

Roosts. The preference in Surrey is for waterside roost sites, especially along the Thames. Most of the roosts have been in the Thames Valley and the Mole Valley up to Reigate and Redhill. Ring-necked Parakeets are still infrequent in the south and west of the county. The biggest roosts are found after the breeding season and many of the flylines seem to originate outside the county, north of the Thames or west of Egham. This suggests that many of the roosting birds breed outside the county. There are now several Surrey roosts. The largest has been at Elmbridge, in poplars at Esher Rugby Club. A roost of 540 at Reigate (Butler, *British Birds* July 2002) was counted at 900+ on 2nd January 2007 (D. Washington, *SurreyBirders*). A roost at Shepperton contained 230 birds on 22nd December 1992. The Elmbridge roost has been counted fairly regularly. The annual maxima up to 2002 showed a sharply rising trend:

Annual maxima at the Elmbridge roost (including Esher Rugby Club)

	1994	1995	1996	1997	1998	1999	2000	2001	2002
Maximum	697	770	1,120	1,507	1,704	2,500	2,999	3,080	3,650
Month	Dec	Dec	Oct	Sep	Dec	Nov	Oct	Feb	Nov

Numbers continued to increase and 6,918 were counted leaving the roost at Esher Rugby Club on 24th August 2003 (D. M. Harris). From time to time the roost site has changed by a mile or so. There was an abrupt change in the late summer of 2006, when the parakeets again deserted the roost. They apparently moved to trees in the Staines area. By early 2007, many had moved back again (D. M. Harris, *SurreyBirders*). When at Elmbridge the parakeets would arrive at dusk in parties of 20 or more, sometimes

Poplars at Esher Rugby Club. In the late 1990s these trees became the roosting place of an immense gathering of Ring-necked Parakeets, later of over 6,500 birds.

John Davis

100, just as the light was getting too poor for good photographs. The arrival took about 45 minutes. It was an astonishing sight - more birds than you might see at a good Amazonian salt lick.

Calendar. The same information averaged by months shows much lower numbers in the summer:

Monthly averages at Elmbridge 1994-2002 (no count in July)

	Jan	Feb	Mar	Apr	May	Jun	Jul	Aug	Sep	Oct	Nov	Dec
Average	1,201	1,169	1,009	305	4	200	–	110	936	1,473	1,986	944

Food. Very little information has been published about what the birds have been eating in Surrey, except that they readily come to peanut bags, sunflower hearts and other bird food in gardens. One ate a pear in about ten minutes at Barn Elms in 1977. Apples are a favoured food. Ring-necked Parakeets were seen feeding on Crab Apples with Woodpigeons at Egham on 17th December 1994 and 20th April 1995, in a garden feeding on windfall apples at Molesey on 25th November 1997 and eating apples in an apple tree at Reigate on 3rd October 1996. They have been seen feeding on various nuts and seeds, including fallen Sweet Chestnuts at Weybridge and Sycamore seeds at Island Barn Reservoir on 24th September 1997. A pre-roost gathering was seen feeding on Ash at Reigate on 8th December 1996. Others were on Weeping Willow buds at the River Crane (Spelthorne) in 2003 and 2004. There were 94 on an Indian Bean Tree at Englefield Green on 5th December 2004, feeding. (David Ross).

There seems little likelihood of the Ring-necked Parakeet becoming a widespread agricultural pest in Surrey but the population is on the rise and there has been some local damage, for example to vineyards and to fruit trees in gardens.

Movements. Most of the Ring-necked Parakeets ringed so far have been trapped in a garden at East Molesey, where they have been attracted by nut feeders. Up to the end of 2006, 295 Ring-necked Parakeets had been ringed and there had been 33 retraps. A pair raised young in a Copper Beech in the front garden there in 2001, 2002 and 2006.

Movements are usually local:

Ringed			Recovered			Distance
Walton-on-Thames	Surrey	10th October 1996	East Molesey	Surrey	12th April 1999	3 km
East Molesey	Surrey	19th May 2001	East Molesey	Surrey	15th June 2006	0 km
East Molesey	Surrey	21st July 2002	East Molesey	Surrey	10th June 2005	0 km
Merton Park	Surrey	3rd September 2003	East Molesey	Surrey	29th December 2003	12 km
East Molesey	Surrey	20th July 2005	Hersham	Surrey	6th January 2006	5 km

Longevity. Winter food supply, rather than the British climate, is probably the main factor limiting Ring-necked Parakeet numbers. They can probably live to a great age. The greatest longevity proved for the Surrey birds was of one ringed at Laleham on 8th January 1995 and recovered at Heston, Greater London well over eight years later on 9th May 2003 (*Runnymede Ringing Group Newsletter* 292).

Cuckoo (Common Cuckoo)   *Cuculus canorus*

Moderately common summer visitor, breeding annually

Breeds in Europe, Asia and North Africa, wintering in southeast Asia and in Africa south of the Equator. The world population seems to have been stable from 1800 to the 1950s, since when there has been a decrease in the British Isles (especially the north and west) and in other parts of northern Europe. Concern about the decline in Britain is growing. Cuckoos breeding in Britain are believed to winter in Africa but there is only one recovery (in Cameroon) to indicate where (MA).

Early Surrey history. Gilbert White recorded Cuckoos when visiting South Lambeth on 8th May 1785 and 9th June 1791. Aldridge had seen fledged young being fed by Dunnocks in Battersea Park. The Holmesdale Natural History Club Museum has a case containing Cuckoos eggs and young from Colley Hill (skin, 1880), Reigate Heath (Pied Wagtail nest, 1882), Walton Heath ((Dunnock nest, (1880), Willow Warbler nest, (1864) and Yellowhammer nest, (1867)), and Wray Common (skin, 1862). In the Staines area, Cuckoos frequently laid eggs in Sedge and Reed Warbler nests (Kerr, 1906).

1900 to 1965. Eggs collected by Boorman at Clandon Common (1902, 1908), Ockham (1908-10), Ripley (1902, 1904), Send (1902, 1905, 1909, 1915) and West Horsley (1907) and by D. A. Collings (Worplesdon, 1903) are in the Haslemere Museum. Cuckoos were fairly numerous in Richmond Park in 1905 (Mouritz) and quite common around Dulwich up to 1910 (Power). Although they bred again at Dulwich in 1935 and at Mitcham Gravel Pit in 1938 and summered on Streatham Common in 1949 (*BLA*), Cuckoos no longer normally breed in these areas.

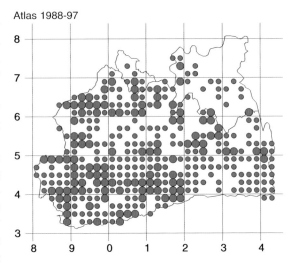

Atlas 1988-97

Trends since 1965. Cuckoos bred at Perry Oaks Sewage Farm in 1970. They had become very scarce at Queen Mary by the 1980s (Geen) and are perhaps still diminishing in Spelthorne - only one was found in the 2003 BTO Spring Migration Watch. There may have been a contraction of range in the London area. Cuckoos last bred on Wimbledon Common in 1987 (Wills and Kettle, 1997, *Birds of Wimbledon Common and Putney Heath*, 2005). They were breeding in Richmond Park up to at least 1975 (*BRP*) but were not breeding there by 1997 (Hewlett). A comparison of the 1968-72 LNHS and 1988-97 SBC Atlas surveys shows a fall of a sixth in the number of tetrads where Cuckoos were present, from 48.% to 40%.

Number of Northeast Surrey tetrads with Cuckoos present in the breeding season

10 km square TQ05	06	07	15	16	17	25	26	27	35	36	37	38	45	Total
Number of tetrads	1	16	15	16	25	10	25	25	20	25	22	17	4	10	**231**
Present 1968-72	1	12	8	13	18	3	18	3	2	18	7	1	0	6	**110**
Present 1988-97	0	13	3	10	14	2	15	9	3	13	6	0	0	4	**92**

Taking the county as a whole, though, indicators are somewhat contradictory. The number of reported sites has tended to increase over the last 30 years:

Number of vice-county sites reported 1973-2001

Year	1973	1974	1975	1976	1985	1986	1987	1988	1989	1990		
Number	50	35	25	25	40	42	40	34	38	24		
Year	1991	1992	1993	1994	1995	1996	1997	1998	1999	2000	2001	2002
Number	28	20	38	36	46	50	62	59	54	53	44	49

This, and the contrary lower percentage of LNHS tetrads occupied, will include observer coverage effects. The Common Birds Census shows a significant decline of about 44% from 1970 to 2000 but will be affected by a changing mix in habitats. Cuckoos are still fairly common in the more rural districts, especially on heathland. Migrants are sometimes seen in places where they do not breed. A male was caught and ringed at the Surrey Docks on 4th May 1982.

Population size. The Common Birds Census results suggest a county population of about 2,000 territories towards the end of the period. The Breeding Birds Census figures are more pessimistic, suggesting a current summer population of about 1,100 adults.

Hosts noted in Surrey by Bucknill were the Skylark, Swallow, Tree Pipit, Meadow Pipit (common), Yellow Wagtail, Pied Wagtail (locally common), Dunnock (common, and still one of the most frequently reported hosts), Robin (common), Blackbird, Song Thrush, Sedge Warbler, Reed Warbler, Blackcap, Dartford Warbler, Wood Warbler, Chiffchaff, Willow Warbler, Spotted Flycatcher, Red-backed Shrike, Chaffinch, Greenfinch, Linnet, Yellow Hammer, Cirl Bunting and Reed Bunting. Parr added Wren (!), Nightingale, Stonechat, Whitethroat and Starling.

Meadow Pipits, where they can be found, are regular hosts, though a study at Frensham suggested that the Cuckoo eggs, which are laid early, are mainly taken by Carrion Crows for their young so that few young Cuckoos are fledged (HNHS, 1980). Bunyard obtained seven eggs from the same female, all in Whitethroat's nests, in Surrey during the 1914-18 war (Cole and Trobe). Bucknill (1928) described a female Cuckoo removing eggs from a nest at West End Common, Esher and flying off with them (as described by Edgar Chance). A Cuckoo was seen carrying an egg at Frensham on 26th April 1981.

Calendar. During the last quarter of the 19th century, Cuckoos normally arrived in southern counties between 10th and 14th April (*Historical Atlas*). Aldridge said they were not uncommon in the Norwood District from about 15th April. The average arrival date in the London area south of the Thames from 1929 to 1939 was 11th April. Extreme dates are:

Early

20th February 1953	Farnham (*BB, 48:512*)
9th March 2000	Bagmoor Common
27th March 1983	Beddington Sewage Farm
1st April 1965	Haslemere and Grayswood
1st April 1974	West Horsley

Late

21st October 1972	Frensham Common
23rd October 1983	Thursley Common
25th October 1994	South Norwood
26th November 1946	Lambeth: one flew across the Thames (*BB, 40:181*)

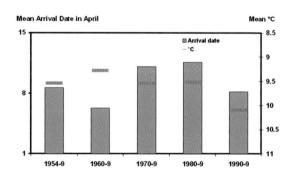

The chart shows some association with temperature, particularly in recent years when arrivals became earlier in the warmest decade.

Movements. Three Surrey-ringed Cuckoos have been recovered in France. One of them, ringed at Beddington Sewage Farm on 13th September 1959 and recovered near Les Sables d'Olonne, France on 20th October 1959, had travelled the furthest, 553 km.

Longevity. A Cuckoo ringed at Frensham on 5th June 1977 was found freshly dead at Le Havre on or about 27th August 1985. This does not meet the BTO standards for a national longevity record but is a notable recovery for Surrey. A Cuckoo ringed at Beddington Sewage Farm on 5th August 1957 was found dead at Stockport, Cheshire on 27th June 1961, over three years and ten months later. A Cuckoo being raised by a pair of Reed Warblers at Shepperton Gravel Pits in 1986 was killed by a cat (*Shepp. BR*).

Plumage variations. Hepatic (liver-coloured) Cuckoos are occasionally reported, *e.g.* Frensham and Richmond Park (1972), Pirbright Common (1977). Bucknill knew of none.

Yellow-billed Cuckoo
Coccyzus americanus

One record, Outer Surrey

Breeds in the Americas and moves south in winter. British records run from September to December, with a peak in October. From 1958 to 1985, all the 24 British records were from southern and eastern coastal counties. Over a third of the birds found since 1958 are known to have died in Britain.

Surrey. The one Surrey record is of a bird picked up in a moribund or stunned condition from a platform at Oxted Station at about 10.30 am on 17th October 1991 by an unknown observer, who took it to a pet shop opposite the station. The owner of the shop telephoned Elitta Fell, who collected the bird, took it to her home on the county border at Moorhouse and alerted Philip Jones, who ringed it. The bird was fed and at about 1.30 pm was released in the garden, where it dived into a bush and was not seen again (details from Elitta Fell and K. C. Osborne, pers. comm.). Photographs by Philip Jones appeared in the 1991 London and Surrey Bird Reports. This was only the third inland record for Britain (*BB*, 85:532).

Barn Owl
Tyto alba

Scarce breeding resident

Barn Owls are among the most widely distributed birds in the world, breeding in every continent except Antarctica. European birds are largely resident, with some dispersal after fledging. The nominate race *T. a. alba* breeds in Britain south to France and the Canary Islands. Agricultural and other changes have caused a gradual reduction in the size of the British breeding population since the 19th century. National numbers are now thought to be stable.

Early Surrey history. Newman took three owlets and three eggs from a nest that he found between Munstead and Hascombe Lane in 1822. Another nest was found at Tooting in the 1830s. Barn Owls were said to be common breeders in rural districts at the end of the 19th century (Bucknill), but were evidently less so near London. They were very uncommon in the Norwood district (Aldridge, 1885). Hamilton (1881) saw them twice in his garden at Putney Hill but had no other records. They were found at Witley Park not later than 1884 (*SALEC*) and at Belair, Dulwich in or before 1900 (Bucknill). Power (1910) had only one record for the Dulwich area from 1875 to 1909. No Spelthorne records are given by Kerr or Glegg.

1900 to 1970. There was a Barn Owl in Richmond Park on 8th April 1906 and it might have bred there (Collenette). Breeding records came from Ashtead (1935), Banstead (1933, 1954), near

Beddington Sewage Farm (1954-55, 1957, 1958, two pairs in 1969), Bookham (eggs collected by Douglas, 1926), Capel (1938), Caterham (1902-12, SBC archive), Chipstead (1933, 1939), Clapham Common (1923 *BLA*), Elstead (1967), Esher (1966), Ewhurst (1966), Farleigh (before 1952), Horsley (1968), Norwood Junction (1961), Ockley (1971), Oxted (by 1920, Parr), Pyrford (three pairs, 1957), Richmond Park (1960s), South Croydon (1912), Thorpe (1947), Wanborough (1965), Warren Barn Farm (Beadell, 1932) and Weybridge (1961).

National Barn Owl Surveys carried out in 1932 (Blaker, 1934) and 1982-85 produced Surrey estimates of 132 and 34 pairs, respectively (Shawyer, 1987). There was a national decline associated with toxic chemicals in the 1960s (Parslow, 1967). No information about Surrey or any subsequent recovery has been located. Surveys carried out in 1967 improved coverage and produced breeding pairs at Beddington, Richmond Park and three other sites. There were sightings from eleven other vice-county localities including Epsom Common, Esher, Ewell, Mickleham and Prince's Coverts (Montier, 1968; Parr, 1972). Two at Kempton Park on 24th March 1963 (*SBR*) and other records from the Kempton area in 1969 (*LBR*) might at times have been in the Spelthorne area and would be the earliest located for it. One was found dead at Staines Reservoirs on 31st October 1970.

Where found since 1970. As shown in the table, the level of Barn Owl reporting increased from 1970 to 2001.

Vice-county sites (all year) and known breeding pairs 1970-2002

Year	1970	1971	1972	1973	1974	1975	1976	1977	1978	1979	1980	1981	1982
Sites	16	16	11	22	14	7	11	7	3	11	4	8	9
Pairs	2	2	2	1	2	2	2	2	1	3	2	1	0
Year	**1983**	**1984**	**1985**	**1986**	**1987**	**1988**	**1989**	**1990**	**1991**	**1992**	**1993**	**1994**	**1995**
Sites	17	3	13	8	9	3	9	15+	11+	9+	*c.*13	9	16
Pairs	7+	0	4	0	4	0	4	10+	3	7	3	2	4
Year	**1996**	**1997**	**1998**	**1999**	**2000**	**2001**	**2002**						
Sites	19	23	18	21	10	6	9						
Pairs	7	7	7	8	5	4	1						

One seen in Richmond Park for much of 1988 is thought to have been from a pair reared and released by the Superintendent of Bushy Park. Single birds were seen at Laleham in 1971 and Perry Oaks Sewage Farm in 1972 and 1973. A pair bred at Perry Oaks in 1978. Later records came from King George VI Reservoir (1981), Laleham (1984) and Perry Oaks (1993) and Stanwell Moor (2002, *LNHSB*). Barn Owls were seen at over 20 sites after 2000, at eight of them during the breeding season. Several pairs bred.

Nests. Suitable nest sites are a critical constraint on Barn Owl numbers in Surrey and Sussex. A nest box project carried out by J. Baldwin and P. Maynard in the two counties has achieved breeding success at ten sites in south Surrey and nest box sites now account for the majority of breeding Barn Owls currently reported. The same is true for Sussex (*Sussex Bird Report* for 1998). Breeding Barn Owls are thought to be considerably under-recorded, but the improvement in sites and pairs that is

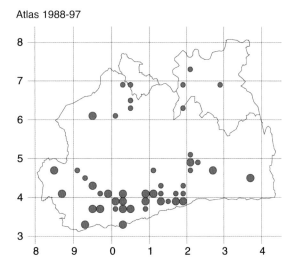

Atlas 1988-97

shown in the table must reflect the success of conservation efforts. The Breeding Birds Survey and Common Birds Census provide little information about this crepuscular bird.

Movements and longevity. An early ringing result, of a young Barn Owl ringed at Coulsdon in June 1912 and recovered two miles away in December 1913, is probably typical of most Barn Owl movements, but other recoveries show that some of them fly considerable distances within the UK. One ringed at Dunsfold on 6th July 1975 was recovered 350 km north in East Yorkshire on 23rd March 1979. Another, ringed in Dorset on 5th June 1983, was recovered 135 km ENE at Send on 20th March 1984. The greatest known longevity was shown by a young Barn Owl ringed at Capel on 22nd July 1990, which was recovered over four years and one month later at Ranmore on 15th September 1994.

Dark-breasted Barn Owl   *Tyto alba guttata*

T. a. guttata breeds in central Europe and is occasionally found in Britain. The 1971 BOU list mentions 50 or more records, mainly October to December and chiefly in southeast England from Sussex to Norfolk. A dark-breasted bird was found in a brood from a light-breasted pair in Devon in 2003, possibly due to hybridisation of one of the recent ancestors with a dark-breasted bird, or as an abnormal colouration. (French, *BB, 99:210-11*).

Surrey. Walpole-Bond (1938) mentioned a bird captured at Newdigate on 15th November 1905. The record was included in *A History of Sussex Birds* but seems actually to be a Surrey record and it fits the pattern well. Palmer (2000) says that the first British record was from Kent in 1937 (*BB, 43:54*), but the Newdigate bird, for what it is worth, pre-dates it.

Little Owl   *Athene noctua*

Moderately common breeding resident

Breeding range extends through the temperate regions of Europe and Asia and from North Africa to the Persian Gulf. Introduced to Britain from 1843 (Yorkshire) but introductions were not successful until releases from about 1874, in Kent, where breeding was first proved in 1879 (Lever, 1977). The British population grew rapidly until 1930 but is currently declining, as it is in other parts of Europe. Habitat changes are thought to be the main reason. Changes in farming methods have led to a decline in prey items such as small birds, small mammals and large insects.

Early Surrey history. Little Owls are birds of open parkland, farming and riverside country with mature, scattered trees. They are often active during the day. They were occasionally reported in Surrey in the years before their successful introduction and were generally presumed to be escapes. Edwards (1758) mentioned a bird which came down one of the chimneys of the house of Peter Theobald, in Lambeth and thought it might be a native species, because it was the second such record that he knew of, the other being from St Catherine's parish, on the Middlesex side of the river near Tower Bridge. These records found their way into the works of other authors including Yarrell. Bucknill thought they must be escapes. One caught near Lambeth Palace not later than 1884 (*SALEC*) was in the Charterhouse Collection in Bucknill's time. The collection still recently included a

Little Owl in 2001 but its provenance was given as Norfolk. Harting (1866) mentions a sight record of one flying at Kempton Park, which might have been in Spelthorne.

Colonisation. Little Owls are thought to have spread into the county from Kent. A pair seen by Miss C. M. Acland at Coulsdon in June 1900 were at a probable nest site. Two pairs nested on an estate near Horley in 1907, (*BB, 1:340*) and this was the first definite breeding in Surrey. Little Owls were established at Chipstead, the Godstone valley and Oxted by 1910 (*BLA*) and there were five pairs in Titsey Park in 1911. A pair nested at Hamsey Green in 1915, after which they became more common in the Warlingham area (Beadell). Eggs were collected at Ripley in 1920 (Boorman) and at Claremont in 1920 and 1926 and Frensham in 1931 (Maitland and Turnbull). Little Owls had been recorded in Richmond Park by 1921 and were breeding there by 1924. There was one in Battersea Park at the end of October 1923 (Macpherson). The report of the Little Owl Food Enquiry of 1936-37 (Hibbert-Ware, 1938) included some observations from Surrey, relating to 1936 or 1937: Camberley, none in the district; Limpsfield and Lingfield, four nests in a circle of 1¼ mile radius, total of five nests in 1936; Old Woking, one pair bred.

By the 1950s, Little Owls were nesting at Beddington Sewage Farm (three pairs), Charterhouse, Dulwich (1950), Kew Gardens and Peper Harow Park. Breeding was reported from 20 widely scattered areas in 1965-69 and a pair bred in Battersea Cemetery in 1969 (Parr). There were seven or eight terri-

tories in Richmond Park in 1967. The *LBR* for 1969 mentions 18 breeding season localities in the LNHS part of Surrey.

Trends since 1970. Little Owls were present in at least seven Spelthorne tetrads in the 1968-72 LNHS Atlas survey and fledged young were seen at Laleham in 1985 (*Shepp. BR*). There were at least three breeding tetrads in the 1988-97 SBC Atlas survey. The number of sites from which Little Owls have been reported in the whole county has risen from up to 35 in the 1970s to 50 or so in recent years. The Common Birds Census shows a significant increase over the same period. These figures seem to be at variance with the national trend.

A comparison of the northeast Surrey Atlas

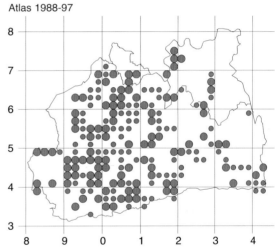

Atlas 1988-97

results shows a fall of a third in the number of tetrads where Little Owls were present, from 29% to 19%, possibly related to local habitat changes, and gives a better reflection of the national picture:

Number of northeast Surrey tetrads with Little Owls present in the breeding season

10 km square	TQ05	06	07	15	16	17	25	26	27	35	36	37	38	45	Total
Number of tetrads	1	16	15	16	25	10	25	25	20	25	22	17	4	10	**231**
Present 1968-72	0	10	7	6	11	4	10	7	1	4	2	2	0	3	**67**
Present 1988-97	1	9	0	7	9	3	5	7	1	3	0	0	0	0	**45**

Population size. Although Little Owls are often active during the day they can, like other owls, be picked up rather erratically in population studies, for which current estimates are 110 adults (Breeding Birds Survey) and about 1,000 territories (Common Birds Census).

Food. Prey species are not often recorded in Surrey but they include juvenile Starlings (Chessington, 1965) and field voles (Richmond Park, 1967). The most exhaustive Surrey list seems to be that in Hibbert–Ware, which includes Rabbit, rat species, mouse species, vole species, shrew species, Mole,

Starling, Blackbird, Song Thrush, frog species and various invertebrates from five nests at Limpsfield and one at Old Woking.

Movements and longevity. Movements are mainly over short distances but one of 95 km has been recorded. This bird had a life of well over four years. There are no foreign ringing recoveries.

Ringed		Age		Recovered				Distance
Thorpe	Surrey	Young	30th June 1947	near Wells		Somerset	April 1952	95 km
Ottershaw	Surrey	Nestling	2nd June 1991	Mayford, Woking	Surrey		21st May 1995	8 km

Tawny Owl   *Strix aluco*
Moderately common breeding resident

Breeds from Europe east to Korea. The British population was reduced by persecution in the 19th century but increased substantially after the Bird Protection Acts were passed. Numbers continued to increase until the 1930s but then stabilised and there was a decline in the last 30 years of the 20th century.

Early Surrey history. Scattered references show that they have long been present in what is now Greater London. Gilbert White heard an owl hooting at Vauxhall on 14th March 1778. Bucknill mentioned that Graves noted breeding on Dulwich Common in 1811, that Blyth said they nested at Wimbledon Park in the 1830s and that Jesse included them for Richmond Park not later than 1836. Tawny Owls were evidently not common breeding birds in the last quarter of the 19th century. Bucknill regarded them as *a fairly common resident in the rural districts* and *undoubtedly . . . more abundant* than the Long-eared Owl, an interesting comment on the status of both species. Few would compare the abundance of the two today.

1900 to 1965. Dixon (1909) said that Tawny Owls bred at Kew and Wimbledon. They were numerous in Richmond Park by 1905 (Mouritz) and Collenette (1937) thought there were two or three pairs there. They were increasing around Godalming by 1906 (Dalgliesh). Power did not record them for the Dulwich area until 1906, and then again in 1908, when a friend heard one calling on the borders of Mitcham Common. The abundance and range of Tawny Owls in Surrey increased in the first half of the 20th century, breeding in Battersea Park and becoming the commonest owl in all parts of the county. Prest (1955) found no evidence of a change in Surrey over the period 1953-63 in spite of a national decline from the late 1950s, associated with pesticide residues.

Where found since 1966. A survey in 1967 found 28 known breeding pairs and 42 others that may have bred. A dozen or so of the pairs were in Richmond Park, so the total could have been a considerable underestimate (Parr). During the 1968-72 Atlas Survey, Tawny Owls were found in 156 of the 231 northeast Surrey tetrads. Nine territories were found on Bookham Common in 1968, a site mostly contained in a single tetrad. Tawny Owls were breeding in Spelthorne in 1968-72 (Atlas), holding territory in 1979 (Common Birds Census), present at Shepperton (*Shepp. BRs*) and breeding at Queen Mary Reservoir (Geen) in the 1980s and breeding in Spelthorne in 1988-97 (Atlas).

Tawny Owls were only found in 84 of the northeast Surrey tetrads in the 1988-97 SBC Atlas survey. The reduction is thought to be due mainly to poorer nocturnal coverage, especially in the 54 London area marginal squares where only the Surrey portion was included, of which seven were reported occupied. Tawny Owls were recorded at Vann Lake in almost every month from 1964 to 1995 (Blaker Log).

Population size. The Common Birds Census does not show any significant change since 1970, suggesting a population of about 900 territories at the end of the period, a good many more than the national average of .07 per square km, but the census was not too reliable for this nocturnal woodland species. Very few were found by the Breeding Birds Survey. The Surrey Bird Club was informed of 23-35 breeding season localities for each of the years 1995 to 2001, likely to be a small fraction of the breeding birds. Tawny Owls were found in 246 of the 575 Surrey tetrads in the 1988-97 Atlas survey.

Food. Food depends on local prey availability. Pellets collected by Rawlence in Richmond Park in 1938 contained the remains of the Brown Rat, Long-tailed Field Mouse and Short-tailed Vole and Burying Beetle (*Birds of the Royal Parks*). Species identified in pellets by Beven (1967) were mostly mammals (including Water Voles and Brown Rats) on Bookham Common and at Holmethorpe, mostly Brown Rats at Earlswood and mostly birds (61% by weight) in Richmond Park. Pellets he collected at Esher in 1972 contained the remains of three fish, 32 frogs, 22 voles, and 13 rats and mice, two shrews, two Starlings, four Blackbirds, ten House Sparrows, a Dunnock and various insects. In suburban Morden, the pellets included the remains of many earthworms, as well as birds and mammals.

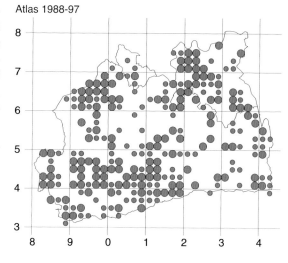

Atlas 1988-97

Movements and longevity. There is no evidence of more than local movements. A Tawny Owl ringed as a nestling at Banstead on 7th May 1910 and recovered near Coulsdon on 29th January 1912 was typical. The furthest recorded travel was by a young bird ringed at West Byfleet on 4th May 1996 and recovered 14 km away at Guildford on 30th May 1997. One ringed at Capel on 14th May 1977 and recovered there almost 16 years later, on 7th May 1993, showed considerable longevity.

Behaviour. Tawny Owls sometimes call in broad daylight. M. Wemys heard one at midday on 31st December 2000 on Headley Heath when snow was on the ground and one was heard calling in bright sunshine at midday in July 2003 at Elstead. Ring-necked Parakeets (*e.g.* May 2001) are among the species that have been seen mobbing them.

Long-eared Owl   *Asio otus*

Scarce winter visitor and irregular breeding species

More widely distributed than Tawny Owls, being found in North America and North Africa as well as Europe and Asia. Numbers fluctuate with the prey population. Long-eared Owls are migratory in northern Europe and many Scandinavian birds winter in the British Isles. The British breeding population has greatly reduced since 1900. Sometimes nests on the ground.

Early Surrey history. One shot on Dulwich Common in the spring of 1815 was used by Graves as the model for a plate in his book. Newman (1849) included Long-eared Owls without comment as resident natives in the Godalming district. Spicer (1854) mentioned a specimen from the Farnham district. Bucknill described them as *quite a rarity* in most parts of Surrey but thought that a few probably nested each year. Records that he gave included birds at Ashtead Oaks (1893), Bagshot Woods, Cheam, Chessington, Cranleigh, Farnham (29th May 1829), Gatton, Leith Hill, Weybridge (in firs) and Woodmansterne (a young bird). One shot on Hydons Ball (*SALEC*) in 1871 was in the Charterhouse Collection in Bucknill's time and is presumably the bird still in the collection with Surrey as its provenance in 2001.

Breeding up to 1900. Long-eared Owls nested at a Godalming heath in 1840. Phillip Crowley had several clutches from Churt, taken in the 1860s. Bucknill gave eight later breeding records, of a nest at Witley in 1863, from which a nestling was taken and reared, a nest with five eggs on Reigate Hill on 28th

March 1874, a partially fledged bird captured near Box Hill on 5th June 1876, a nest with eggs near Churt in 1881 and a nest in about 1882 at Thursley, where Long-eared Owls occasionally bred. They nested near Reigate in 1890 and near Mickleham (nest with two young taken) in 1898. A pair at Chobham in about 1897 were probably nesting. Saunders said he knew of eight broods in a single, unidentified, Surrey fir plantation – a statement that looks surprising, even for the period.

Breeding after 1900. In the first decade of the 20th century, nests were found in Claremont Woods (1904, *Zool.*, 1904:265), and another at Dorking and Titsey (*BLA*). Bentham

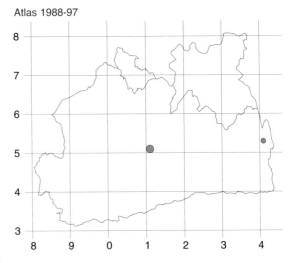

Atlas 1988-97

heard seven calling along a one mile stretch of road between Waverley and Farnham on 5th August 1911 (Bentham in the *SBR* for 1965, Parr). Long-eared Owls apparently bred in Richmond Park from 1924 to 1927 and perhaps earlier (Collenette). They bred much less frequently as the century progressed. A pair bred at Coulsdon in 1934. A nest found by F. V. Blackburn near Stonehill, Chobham in 1948 was later robbed (Parr). A fledged family was found in Titsey Wood on 29th April 1957. A gamekeeper found a nest with three young in a rabbit hole in the roots of a thorn tree in central Surrey in 1975 (*SBR*, location not disclosed). There was a pair with fledged young in a conifer plantation at Netley Heath on 24th May 1977. Four young were found at the same spot on the next day and the young were last seen on 6th June. Two juveniles (one seen) were calling in mixed coniferous and deciduous woodland at Albury Bottom, Chobham Common on 20th June 1977. The Atlas survey found evidence for breeding in one 10 km square in 1989. A Long-eared Owl was heard giving barking calls in March 1992 and an alarm call was heard at another site on May 18th of the same year. No suggestions of breeding have been located since, at least up to 2004.

Other places where found since 1900. Returning to those records from 1900 which are of presence rather than breeding, Beadell gave undated records from Bushy Bank and Lumberline Wood, Warlingham. There were single birds at Kew Gardens on 12th December 1939 and at Reigate on 10th April 1940 (*LBR*). One at Perry Oaks Sewage Farm in November 1947 and January 1948 was the first for Middlesex since 1871 (*LBR*) and may have been in Spelthorne.

Others were at *Ashtead Common* (January 1980, June 2004), *Barn Elms* (November 1934), *Beddington Park* (February/March 1986), *Beddington Sewage Farm* (November 1993 to January 1994, December 1994 to April 1995 with a maximum of seven on 8th March, December 1996, January, March and December 1997, February 2005), *Berrylands Sewage Works* (December 1986), *Bookham Common* (1979, 1985, 1992), *Chelsham* (October 1998), *Chipstead* (22nd February 1951), *Churt* (April 1954, HNHS 1968), *Earlswood* (January 1987), *Effingham* (May 1989), *Epsom Common* (March 1976), *Esher* (13th May 1950), *Farnham Park* (Carron Pond - single birds February-April 1995, March-April 2000), *Frensham Little Pond* (January 1989), *Gatton* (April 1976), *Hackhurst Downs* (August 1961), *Ham Lands* (November 1986, April 1987, March 1988, April 1989, October 1989 (two), November 1990 to March 1991, another March 1991), *Headley Heath* (December 1983, SBR for 1984), *Holmethorpe Sand Pits* (November-December 1990, March-April 1992), *Horley* (up to two in March 2000), *Leith Hill* (May 1953), *Limpsfield Chart* (November 1997), *Littleworth Common* (November 1983), *M3/M25 junction* (dead, March 1986), *Mitcham Common* (1st December 1978 (three), November 1986, November 1989, November 1990), *Molesey Heath* (two), January-March 1987), *New Haw* (July 1997), *Petersham* (20th February 1966), near *Ripley* (dead on the

A3, March 1991), *Sanderstead* (April 1969), *South Norwood Country Park* (2002), *Streatham* (dead, September 1972), *Thursley* (May 1939 HNHS 1955, May 1994), *Walton Heath* (March 1954), *Weybridge* (January 1962, November 1982), *Whiteley Village* (Hersham, March 1979). There were two at *Queen Mary Gravel Pits* from 16th November to 31st December 1991. The two at Ham Lands on 31st October 1989 were the first for October.

Roosts. Those found at winter roosts in Surrey are presumably mainly from Scandinavia. Bucknill does not mention any winter roosts but it is possible that these were at least as frequent a hundred years ago as they are now. This would be consistent with the Scandinavian populations not having experienced the same population decline as that in Britain. Roosts are rarely reoccupied. Well documented roosts are only those at Beddington (1986, 1992/93, 1993/94), Bookham (1979 (up to eight), 1985, 1992, 1997), Epsom Common (1976), Ham Lands (1990/91), Holmethorpe (1987, 1990), Molesey Heath (1987), Send (1992), and Weybridge (November 1982, first November record). One roosted at Heathrow Terminal 4 on 26th October 1999. The old Spelthorne border passes through the site. Roost trees have included Blackthorn, Hawthorn and Willow.

Food. Some 180 pellets collected on Thursley Common in 1942 were found to contain the remains of 132 small mammals, six birds, six frogs and nine beetles. Prey items in pellets at Bookham Common in 1979 included 43 Field Voles, 23 Wood Mice, ten Bank Voles, a Long-eared Bat, one thrush species, a Wren, two Starlings and four Dunnocks (Beven, 1980).

Movements and longevity. A Long-eared Owl ringed as a nestling near Ellmaki, Finland on 9th June 1978 was found dead near Haslemere, some 2,010 km southwest and possibly not in Surrey, on or around January 1982 (BTO).

Short-eared Owl   *Asio flammeus*

Scarce winter visitor

Breeds across Europe, Asia and the Americas, moving south as far as Africa and India in winter. Some Finnish and Scandinavian birds reach the British Isles. In Britain, Short-eared Owls bred mainly in East Anglia and the north during the 19th century but were becoming fewer. They have bred in Kent and Sussex. Numbers in Britain fluctuate with the prey population, but fell between the 1968-72 and 1988-91 Atlases.

Early Surrey history. Bones dated not later than 1650 were a surprising find at the excavation of Oatlands Palace (Cohen). Short-eared Owls are mentioned by Blyth, Newman, Jordan (*A Son of the Marshes*) and other 19th century writers, usually without any specific records. H. L. Long shot one on Puttenham Common on 4th December 1824 (Bucknill), the earliest with a date. Spicer (1854) mentioned a specimen from the Farnham district in his collection. Other records in Bucknill include Cheam (about 1881), Chipstead (autumn of 1889), near Cobham (August 1893), Godalming (1873), Headley Common and Walton Heath. A bird currently in the Charterhouse Collection with Surrey as its provenance is presumably one of the local specimens seen there by Bucknill.

Where found since 1900. Bunyard recorded one on a Surrey common from 12th March to 15th April 1916 (*BB, 17:204*). One in the Haslemere district on 13th March 1920 might not have been in Surrey. One was seen over South Croydon on October 28th, 1934. Up to five roosted under gorse bushes on Walton Heath from 12th February to 25th March 1939. One flew south at Churt on 1st October 1946. Beddington Sewage Farm became a significant site for Short-eared Owls when up to four were found there in the winter of 1946/47 and up to eight in the 1950s. Up to three were on the adjacent Mitcham Common in the winters of 1952/53 and 1953/54. There was one at Walton Gravel Pits in the winter of 1946/47 and one at at Bookham Common on 12th November 1950. Single birds at Perry Oaks

Sewage Farm (20th April) and King George VI Reservoir (8th October) in 1955 (*LBR*) are the earliest records located for Spelthorne. There were up to six in the Staines area from November 1958 to mid March 1959.

Short-eared Owls were seen at Perry Oaks Sewage Farm, Queen Mary Reservoir, Shepperton and Staines Moor in the 1970s. There were up to 15 at Perry Oaks and seven at Staines Moor in late 1978. The number of vice-county bird months peaked in the 1970s and 1980s. There are now, possibly for climatic reasons, rather fewer.

Bird months by decade 1900 2001

	1900s	1910s	1920s	1930s	1940s	1950s	1960s	1970s	1980s	1990s	2000-01	Total
Vice-county	0	2	0	10	6	71	14	120	116	83	11	**433**
Spelthorne	0	0	0	0	0	23	6	46	39	9	1	**124**

Of the 433 vice-county months, 226 came from Beddington Sewage Farm and the nearby Mitcham Common. There were 56 from the Hersham/Walton-on-Thames area and 18 each from Barn Elms and Richmond Park. Short-eared Owls are much scarcer on the western heaths. Thursley/Ockley/Elstead Commons, with 16 bird months, was the most frequent site. Other places where Short-eared Owls have been seen include Banstead, Berrylands, Bisley, Bletchingley, Bookham Common, Bramley Sewage Farm, Chertsey, Chessington, Chobham Common, Croydon Airport, Epsom, Esher, Farleigh, Farnham Park, Farthing Downs, Frensham/Churt, Frimley Gravel Pits, Gatwick, Godalming, Godstone, Guildford (Artington, Stoke, Guildford Sewage Farm), Ham Lands, Holmethorpe, Holmwood, Langshott, Leatherhead, Lonsdale Road Reservoir, Olddean Common (November 1989, not October as in the *SBR*), Pirbright, Raynes Park, Sanderstead, Send/Ripley/Papercourt/Old Woking/Pyrford, South Norwood, the Surrey Docks, Sutton, Wallington, Walton Heath, Wimbledon Common, Wisley Common, Witley Common, Woodmansterne and Worcester Park. There were single birds at Laleham Farm and Queen Mary Reservoir on 13th April 1985 and at Sheepwalk East on 12th January 1986 (Geen, *Shepp. BR*).

Short-eared Owls were seen after 2000 at Barn Elms (2001, 2002, 2004, 2005), Beddington (2001, 2002, 2004), Chelsham (2001), Island Barn Reservoir (2004), Papercourt (2004), Pirbright (2001), Queen Elizabeth II Reservoir (2001, 2002, 2004), South Norwood Country Park (2002), Thursley/Ockley Commons (2001), and Worplesdon (2002), all but one in September - November, the other in March. Staines Moor and the adjacent reservoirs can still attract a few in winter, the largest available recent count being four in December 2002 (*LNHSB*).

Calendar. The main arrival is in October/November and most are gone by the end of April. Extreme vice-county dates are 22nd July 1964 (Chertsey) and 30th May 1992 (Thursley).

Bird months 1900-2001

	Jan	Feb	Mar	Apr	May	Jun	Jul	Aug	Sep	Oct	Nov	Dec	Total
Vice-county	61	51	48	29	11	0	1	4	13	66	88	61	**433**
Spelthorne	19	13	14	13	3	0	0	2	3	11	23	23	**124**

Large counts are all from Beddington:
Beddington Sewage Farm: up to eight, January 1959
Beddington Sewage Farm: ten in the winter of 1970/71 (Parr)
Beddington Sewage Farm: up to 12, 22nd October 1978 to the end of the year

Food. Prey species identified by Bentham in pellets from Walton Heath in 1939 were mainly birds, including Skylark, Blackbird, Song Thrush and Starling but voles are thought usually to be the main food (Parr).

Nightjar (European Nightjar)   *Caprimulgus europaeus*

Locally common summer visitor breeding annually

Nightjars breed from Europe and North Africa east to Central Asia. Most of the world's Nightjars probably winter in eastern and southern Africa but there is not enough ringing evidence to indicate the winter location of British breeding birds (*MA*). The earliest British record goes back to 998 AD. Nightjars presumably benefited from the spread of heathland before and after this date. More recently, young conifer plantations have been an important British habitat. A widespread fall in breeding numbers across the European range was first noticed in the late 19th century and has continued since. Heathland conservation measures can arrest or reverse the decline. In Britain the decline has slowed and there have been recent increases.

Early Surrey history. Nightjars presumably moved into Surrey with the development of the heathlands in Bronze Age times. Bucknill mentioned an early reference in a manuscript note on an interleaved copy of Merrett's *Pinax Rerum Naturalium Brittanicum &c.*, held at the British Museum. The book was published in 1666. The note, in 'very old-fashioned characters', against the page says *In Surrey Eud'gar or Eudninggar*, (*i.e.* 'Eve-jar or Evening-jar), evidently local names for the bird at the time.

19th century. H. L. Long wrote about Nightjars in 1815. Graves said that they were abundant at Sydenham Common in about 1821 (Glegg, 1938). Mr J. H. Belfridge saw three or four on the wing at once at Laleham (Spelthorne), hawking over the river at dusk (Harting, 1866). Blyth found Nightjars at Dulwich and Meyer found them at Claremont (Bucknill). 'Pudmoors' [Thursley/Ockley Commons] was a favourite area for Nightjars, which were plentiful on every heathy district around Godalming in the first half on the 19th century. Stafford shot 47 in a very short space of time on Highdown [Hydon] Heath (Newman, 1849). Hamilton (1881) mentioned seeing up to three Nightjars at a time on Wimbledon Common. Nightjars remained common, especially on the western heaths, until the end of the century. M. Burr said they were very common around Bellagio and Warlingham (*Zool., 1890:144*). Bucknill listed Barnes Common, Coombe Woods, Dulwich, Richmond Park and Streatham Common among the places where they had been found nesting, with references going back to 1852. He put a reduction in the Surrey Nightjar range down to the building of houses on heathland, an early reference to a critical factor. Power (1910) said that Nightjars bred at Shirley Wood and had several records of Nightjars over his Brixton garden, including single birds on 3rd September 1879, 15th September 1892 and 28th August 1895.

1900-1950. The Haslemere Museum has eggs collected by Boorman at Albury (Netherne Wood, 1907), Clandon Common (1906, 1907), Pyrford Rough (1907), Send (Stringham's Copse, 1906) and Wisley Common (1906) and by D. Edwards at Bramley (Selhurst Common, 1902). A nest with young was found in the Godalming district in 1905. Nightjars were numerous on Holmbury Hill and Peaslake Common in 1906. They bred regularly in enclosures at Richmond Park (Mouritz, 1905,) and were 'very common' in 1909. They gradually declined there, and were down to one pair in 1927, two in 1928 and 1929 and one (in Isabella Plantation) in 1930. Breeding was not proved again (Collenette, 1937). Nightjars were lost from Kew Gardens and Wimbledon Common by 1918 (*BLA*). A pair nested at Warlingham in 1919. Eggs were collected at Cutt Mill in 1913, Frensham in 1934 and Oxshott in 1904 (Maitland and Turnbull).

Later territorial sites reported were Arbrook Common (1935-37), Bookham Common (1924-26, 1930, bred 1934), Burgh Heath (1933), Epsom Common (1934-37), Esher Common (1935-37), Ham

Common (present 1932), Headley Heath (1933, 1935-37), Limpsfield (1930, one pair bred 1935-36), Oxshott (1930), Walton Heath (1933, two pairs 1935, 1939) and northwest Surrey (scarce in 1935). Heath fires destroyed many nests in 1938. Nightjars were still breeding at Farleigh Commons and Limpsfield in 1945 and they nested again in Richmond Park in 1950, where the nest was bulldozed (*BLA*).

After 1950. In the 1950s, Nightjars nested on Hankley Common, Mousehill Down, Puttenham Common and Thursley/Ockley Commons and were present on Frensham Common, Hydon Heath and Royal Common. The 1957-58 Nightjar Enquiry (Stafford, 1962) gave no statistics but indicated a decline in Surrey and the UK. Nightjars were in territory on Bookham Common from 1957 to 1959. They were breeding at Holmbury Hill, Limpsfield Chart, Oxted and Wisley/Ockham Commons at the end of the 1960s (Parr) and were churring at Albury Warren in 1969 and Headley Heath in 1970. Areas cleared of woodland may be colonised within about five years. Examples in Parr are Prince's Coverts (cleared late 1940s) and Netley Heath (cleared mid 1960s).

The main sites are currently the military lands of Bisley, Pirbright and West End commons, on which live ammunition is used in training activities. It should be appreciated that a full count at these sites needs considerable care, organisation and effort, not always possible to achieve even with national surveys. A BTO survey in 1981 found 174 territories in Surrey and the total was estimated at 200-250 pairs (Sage, 1982). The survey showed an almost complete desertion of sites within the LNHS part of the county, where there had been up to 44 birds from 1953 to 1980. A further Surrey survey in 1992 (Evans, 1993a) found 144 churring males but did not cover the Bisley, Pirbright and West End military commons despite arrangements having been made to include them.

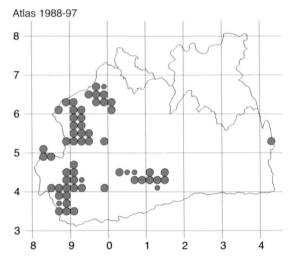

Atlas 1988-97

Where found since 1994. Coverage generally has been rather more systematic since 1994, mainly due to the efforts of David Cary and John Clark. The more recent figures show a population which has probably remained in the 200-250 pair range and the recovery of lost northeast Surrey sites at Headley Heath and Limpsfield Chart.

Recent Nightjar Territory Counts in West Surrey

	1994	1995	1996	1997	1998	1999	2000	2001	2002	2003	2004	2005	2006
Bagshot Heath/													
Lightwater Country Park		1	2	3	2	2	1	1	1		0		
Bourne Wood								1					
Brentmoor Heath/													
Turf Hill		2	1	2	2	3	1	1	1	3	2		
Brookwood Heath/													
Pirbright Common			4	4	3	3	3	5	3	4			
Bullswater Common			1							1			
Chobham/Sunningdale/													
Wentworth			8		13	20				19	63		
Churt Common	1	3	4	4	4	4		3		2			

	1994	1995	1996	1997	1998	1999	2000	2001	2002	2003	2004	2005	2006
Crooksbury Common		4						3			3		4
Donkey Town							1	1					
Frensham Common	3	8	8	9	12	10	10	7		10	11	11	13
Furze Farm, Bisley							3	3					
Hankley Common		4	15	15	16	18	19	20	15	18	18	19	13
Hindhead	1	7	1	6	4	5	5	6	5	3	7	9	7
Horsell Common					7	6	5	4	3	9	13	6	
Lightwater Country Park (from 2000)							1	1		1	1		
Lower Puttenham Common			1	1	3	3	2		3	2	3		
Lucas Green										4	1	1	
Mare Hill				1	1	1	1	1	0	2	1	0	0
Mytchett Place			4	3	2	1		2			11		
Ockham Common											1		
Olddean Common		2		4	6	6				9	14		11
Pirbright Common/ Ash Ranges			44	14		65	3	1	1	47	53		
Puttenham Common			3	2	1	2	2	1	2	2			2
Royal/Bagmoor Commons											6		
Sheet's Heath					1	2	1	2	1	1	1		
Stanford/Cobbetthill Commons											2		
Thursley/Ockley/ Elstead Commons		13	4	5				5	14	3	26		
Un-named									1	1			
West End Common/ Pirbright Ranges						34	40	45	31	29	32		35
West Heath, Pirbright											1		
White Hill/Test Track									1				
Whitmoor Common			4							1	1		5
Witley Common			6	4	4	5	5	3	4	4	4	5	3
Total	**5**	**44**	**97**	**80**	**82**	**190**	**105**	**117**	**91**	**168**	**284**	**50**	**93**

From counts organised by John Clark. Italics indicate incomplete count. Blanks indicate no count.

Blackheath, not included in these figures, is an old site that had two or three pairs in 2002. There have been a few Nightjar territories in other areas, such as Farnham Park in 1994 and along the Greensand hills and North Downs east of Guildford. Tree clearance at the RSPB's new Farnham Heath reserve has begun to attract Nightjars.

Late nesting. A very late nest at Lightwater holding two live young on 30th September 1995 was found predated on the following day. Another late nest was found in 2005. Two young about eight days old were in the nest on 2nd September. The young were nearly ready to fledge on the 9th but the nest was found predated by a fox on the 11th (both accounts from R. A. Denyer).

Migration. Migrants are sometimes found at sites where they do not breed, such as a headless female at Shepperton (Queen Mary Reservoir) on 7th July 1983, one near Charlton village on 5th September 1992 and one at Queen Mary Gravel Pits on 6th September 1997. A Nightjar was seen at Battersea on 4th June 2005 (*Bird Watching*). Perhaps the strangest occurrence was of a male Nightjar that set up a territory based on a street tree at Teddington from 30th May to 17th June 2006. It churred, flew about and displayed on most evenings, landing on houses, cars, street furniture and the road (*LNHSB*). Many humans were attracted but no feathered mate.

Calendar. The average arrival date in the London area south of the Thames from 1929 to 1939 was 12th May. Extreme arrival and departure dates are:

Early		**Late**	
12th April 1949	Hydon Heath (HNHS 1955)	5th October 1920	Court Wood, Addington
15th April 1908	Surrey (*The Handbook*)	16th October 1994	Frensham Little Pond
16th April 1909	Surrey (*The Handbook*)	19th October 1974	Hackhurst Downs

The chart shows that arrival dates since the 1950s have broadly followed temperature trends. They got later in the colder 1960s and have become earlier in the succeeding warmer decade.

Movements and longevity. Two Surrey-ringed Nightjars have been recovered in France, presumably on their way to their unknown African wintering grounds. One of the birds, ringed at West End, Bisley on 22nd July 1991 and recovered at Cherre, Marne et Loire on 15th May 1998, had travelled 404 km. The other was ringed at Horsell on 10th August 1972 and found dead at Villegardin, 430 km southeast on or about 29th September of the same year. A nestling ringed at Worksop, Nottinghamshire,

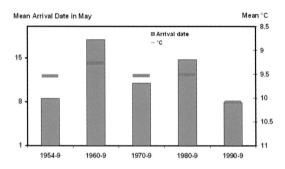

on 20th June 1997 was recovered at Whitmoor Common, 218 km south, on 26th May 1999. The oldest known Nightjar was ringed as a young bird at Bramshill, Hampshire on 4th July 1987 and recovered at Chobham Common over nine years and eleven months later on 30th June 1997.

Behaviour. At Ashtead in 1965, a Nightjar was seen churring while hovering with its tail displayed, evidently an uncommon action but mentioned in *BWP*. Nightjars are occasionally active during daylight hours, *e.g.* one wing-clapping at Headley on 29th June 1947. One was churring at mid-day in strong sunlight at Thursley Common on 31st May 1968 and there are several more recent records of daytime churring. One at Hackhurst Downs on 19th October 1974 was being mobbed in daylight. A daytime photograph of one roosting at Holmethorpe on 19th May 1997 is in the London and Surrey Bird Reports for that year.

Common Nighthawk   *Chordeiles minor*

One record, Greater London

Breeds in North America and winters in South America. All but one of 18 British records from 1958 to 1999 were from Cheshire or further south, 12 being from the Scillies. Dates ranged from September to October. There were two in inland counties, one in Nottinghamshire and the other in Surrey.

Surrey. The Surrey bird was an adult male. It was found in a weak condition at Barnes Common on 23rd October 1984 by a dog walker, whose dog flushed it. He took the bird to Putney RSPCA, where it was identified as a Nightjar (M. J. Cowlard, Inspector A. Foxcroft (RSPCA) *et al.*, *BB*, *78:562*). It died on 28th October and was put into a freezer. M. J. Cowlard came to collect it for a possible skin specimen on 9th November. He realised that the bird was a Nighthawk and took it to B. A. Marsh, who agreed the identification. The corpse was sent away to be mounted and has been retained by B. A. Marsh A posed photograph (taken after mounting) is in the London and Surrey Bird Reports for 1984. This was the first record of an American landbird in the London Area, though not the first in Surrey.

Swift   *Apus apus*

Common summer visitor, breeding annually

Swifts breed in Europe, Asia and North Africa and winter in Africa, mostly south of the Equator. No substantial changes in numbers or range are known in the 19th or 20th centuries. In Britain at least, a large increase in the number of buildings would have assisted earlier expansion but a change to tidier structures has tended to reduce suitable habitat in recent years, reflected in a fall in breeding numbers since 1994. In the more northerly parts of their range Swifts quite commonly make use of trees for roosting and as nest sites. A number of Scandinavian examples are detailed in Roger and Fosse (2001), together with details of much rarer cases from other parts of Europe and from Russia.

Early Surrey history. In a letter of 26th September 1774, Gilbert White wrote of the Swifts that *haunt some of the churches in The Borough* and *frequented the Tower* [of London] *playing and feeding over the river just below the bridge* (*Natural History of Selbourne*). He made a number of observations on Swifts in what is now south London and the suburbs, including 'a cloud of Swifts' over Clapham on 4th July 1786, many near Kingston on 7th July 1786 and many at Cobham, Kingston and Wansworth [*sic*, Wandsworth?] on 15th June 1787.

19th century. Swifts were listed as summer visitors to the Godalming area by Newman (1849). They bred commonly in Surrey from 1875 to 1900 (*Historical Atlas*). Swifts were frequent at the South Norwood and Crystal Palace lakes (Aldridge) and over Wimbledon Common (Hamilton) in the 1880s and they nested in Dulwich up to 1892.

After 1900. Swifts nested in the Crystal Palace district until around 1910 (Power). They were breeding at Putney and Tooting around this date (Dixon in *BLA*) and were common in the Staines District (Kerr, 1906). Eggs collected at Tithe Barn, Ripley (1907, 1908) are in the Boorman collection at the Haslemere Museum. Breeding pairs in the Surrey part of the London area from 1930 to 1965 include: Norwood, 40-50 in 1938; Putney, one in 1938; Richmond, three or more in 1938. They were breeding at Dulwich in 1941, Clapham in 1949 and 1963, Streatham and Tooting in 1949, Wandsworth in 1949 and 1963, Barnes and Putney in the 1950s and Balham in 1963 (Gooders, 1968). This is a similar penetration of the London suburbs to that of 1900, but numbers were severely reduced by rising air pollution. The reduction of air pollution in London which followed the Clean Air Act of 1956 brought feeding flocks of Swifts back to areas like Lambeth and Southwark. In the more rural parts of Surrey, Swifts were widely reported. There were about 15 pairs at Charterhouse in the 1950s and, from then until the end of the period, Swifts frequented the centres of the older towns such as Dorking, Guildford and Weybridge, where they often bred. They were seen every year from 1964 to 1996 at Vann Lake.

Tree nesting and roosting. A pair nested in a hole near the top of a large elm tree at Woodcock Hall Farm, Thorpe in 1953. The hole was about nine inches long and two inches wide and two young were reared in it (*SBR* for 1986, Mercer Bolds pers. comm.). A Swift roosted in an elm at West Ewell on 1st August 1956 (*LBR*).

Trend since 1970. Of the 231 tetrads in northeast Surrey, 87% were found to hold territories in the 1968-72 Atlas survey and this rose to 96 % in the 1988-97 Atlas. Although breeding reports are still infrequent in the Surrey part of Inner London, Swift are now being reported throughout the area in summer.

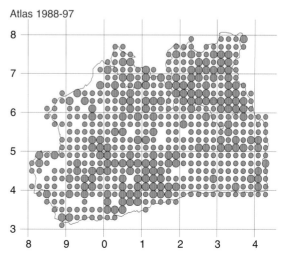

Atlas 1988-97

Population size. The Breeding Birds Survey provides a current summer population estimate of about 15,000 adults. It is difficult to assess how this relates to the breeding population size but it looks a bit high, perhaps because Swifts may range over extensive areas to feed. On the other hand, only two territories have ever been found by the Surrey Common Birds Census, which included very little of their typically urban habitat. If Surrey held a proportionate share of the British breeding population as given by the *New Atlas*, the population would be nearer to 600 territories, or 0.3 per square km. Swifts were found in 525 of the 575 Surrey tetrads in the 1988-97 SBC Atlas survey.

Calendar. Bucknill said that Swifts arrived in May. The latest date known to him was 9th October (*The Field*, 15th October 1887). Glegg (1935) gave the average arrival date in Middlesex for 35 (non-consecutive) years as 1st May. The average arrival date in the London area south of the Thames from 1929 to 1939 was 22nd April and the average departure date was 16th September. The arrivals chart shows that Glegg's date is about ten days later than the average for Surrey since the 1950s, as well as showing some recent correlation between mean temperature and arrival date.

Early and late arrival dates are:

Early

4th April 1997	Crystal Palace Park
8th April 2001	Barn Elms
10th April 1935	Staines Reservoirs
13th April 1988	Hankley Common
13th April 1996	Unstead and Walton Reservoirs
15th April 1995	Beddington Sewage Farm
16th April 1936	Virginia Water
16th April 1968	Beddington Sewage Farm
16th April 1968	Send
16th April 1968	Sutton
Spelthorne	
21st April 1915	Staines Reservoir

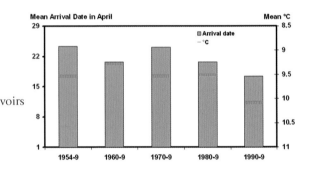

Late

14th October 1944	Frensham	11th November 1994	Chobham
19th October 1956	Sutton	14th November 1972	Chertsey
7th November 1970	near Povey Cross, latest for vice-county 1900-70	28th November 1997	Sutton
		29th November 1994	Shalford
8th November 1984	Thorpe	*Spelthorne*	
9th November 1976	Pebble Combe	8th October 1960	Queen Mary Reservoir, latest there up to 1988.
9th November 1984	Wrecclesham		

Large counts

Barn Elms Reservoirs: 3,000, 25th June 1966
Beddington Sewage Farm: 3,000, 22nd May 1994
Fetcham: 800-1,000, 28th May 1938 (*LBR*)
Frensham: 5,000-6,000, 12th June 1991
Guildford Sewage Farm: 1,500, 23rd July 1958
Walton Reservoirs: 2,000, 16th-17th May 1970

Spelthorne
Staines Reservoirs: 5,000+, 6th May 1962 and 1st May 1968; 5,000, 19th June 1977. The largest available counts since 1999 have been *c*.1,000 in May 2001 and 2003(*LNHSB*).

Movements. Many of the Swifts feeding at Beddington Sewage Farm probably breed not far away in the south and southwest suburbs of London (Hutson *et al.*, 1971, based on ringing results). Visible migration observations include about 100 in an hour at Thorpe on 13th August 1966, 400 in two hours at Burgh Heath on 1st August 1967, 50-60 per minute at Farnham on 11th August 1968 (Parr), a rate of

3,000 per hour (no duration) at Staines Reservoirs on 28th April 1962 (G. H. Gush), 1,200 per hour for 2½ hours at Hersham Sewage Farm on 6th May 1962 and 1,500 in one hour at West Ewell on 31st July 1966 (*LBR*). The winter range and the migratory journey are well illustrated by information from Surrey, heavily dependent on work done at Beddington Sewage Farm from 1957 to 1983. The table is arranged broadly by the distance of the recovery point, separately for autumn and spring:

Ringed			Recovered in autumn			Distance
Kempton Park	13th June	1980	Dunkirk, France	15th August	1984	
Beddington Sewage Farm	May	1965	Perpignon, France	23rd August	1965	
Beddington Sewage Farm	19th June	1983	Castres, Tarn, France	11th August	1986	883 km
West Ewell	27th July	1957	Guipuzcoa, Spain	17th August	1958	1,200 km
Beddington Sewage Farm	28th June	1959	Rasueros, Avila, Spain	8th August	1960	
Beddington Sewage Farm	11th June	1961	Valencia, Spain	20th August	1961	
Beddington Sewage Farm	23rd June	1968	Villasmartin, Cadiz, Spain	*c.*19th August	1968	
Mitcham	9th July	1962	El Kelaa, Marrakesh, Morocco 22nd	September	1969	
Beddington Sewage Farm	2nd July	1972	Tafrant, Taounate, Morocco	August	1986	1,905 km
Queen Mary Reservoir	25th May	1974	Kalumba, Kasai, Congo/ Zaire	27th November	1975	
Epsom	22nd July	1960	near Lilongwe, Malawi	17th January	1966	7,981 km
			Recovered in spring			
Beddington Sewage Farm	13th July	1957	Saurat, Arriege, France	3rd May	1961	
Beddington Sewage Farm	4th July	1962	Pas de Calais, France	17th May	1970	
Beddington Sewage Farm	24th July	1966	Hautes-Pyrénées, France	16th May	1972	
Walton Reservoirs	17th May	1970	Octevillesurmer, France	1st May	1972	
Barn Elms Reservoirs	18th June	1964	Tata, Morocco	*c.*20th May	1969	
Beddington Sewage Farm	28th June	1964	Oujda, Morocco	30th April	1974	
Beddington Sewage Farm	13th July	1957	near Kole, Congo/Zaire	*c.*6th April	1960	
Beddington Sewage Farm	26th July	1970	Due, Kinshasa, Congo/ Zaire	15th May	1972	6,449 km
Beddington Sewage Farm	29th July	1965	Idiofa, Kinshasa, Congo/ Zaire	4th April	1968	6,546 km

Longevity. The most long-lived bird found was ringed at Egham on 4th July 1970 and recovered over 16 years and eleven months later, in Yorkshire on 26th June 1987.

Plumage variations. A white-bodied bird with normal head, wings and tail was seen at Frensham in 1977-79. One with white on the outer tail, lower back and lower belly was seen at Beddington on 1st May 2000. There were partial albinos at Barn Elms (mottled) in May and June 2001, Island Barn Reservoir on 5th April 2002, Staines Reservoirs on 20th May 1990 and Walton Reservoirs on 28th April 2002.

Swift species
Apus sp.

A few very late swifts were not described well enough to rule out other species such as the Pallid Swift *Apus pallidus*. Most are included in the Swift account, but one at New Malden on 9th December 1984 came at a time when there were reports of Pallid Swifts elsewhere.

Alpine Swift

Apus melba

Twelve records to 2005, including three from Spelthorne

Alpine Swifts breed in Africa and from southern Europe east to India. European birds winter in Africa. This is a typical southern overshoot species, with most British records in the spring and a lesser peak in September and October. The majority occur in southern and eastern coastal counties but there is a scatter of records further inland.

Surrey matches the pattern quite well:

1834:   Garratt Copper Mills, a description of one seen on the River Wandle with Swifts on 30th April was given to E. Blyth, who took his gun and went to look for it. The bird had gone, but he went back several times to find what turned out to be three or four, all out of range (Bucknill). This remains the only claim of a multiple sighting.

1841:   Chobham, one was shot in August and later acquired by Frederick Bond (*Zool., 1889,415-16,* Harting, 1889). It subsequently passed to the Booth Museum in Brighton, where it was still on display in January 2005, in one of two cases numbered 361 (361a in Booth and Griffith, 1927).

1895:*   Staines, one with other swifts on 19th May (Glegg, *Zool., 1906:232*).

1951:   Ash Vale, one 25th April (*BB, 45:330*).

1967:   Beddington Sewage Farm, one seen three times on 18th June, among *c.*1,500 Swifts (P. R. Colston, *BB, 71:510*).

1975:*   Staines Reservoirs, one on 19th September (V. R. Leclercq, W. McCubbin et al., *BB, 69:342*)

1977:*   Staines Reservoirs, one on 25th August (R. J. Johns, *BB, 71:510*).

1983:   Barn Elms Reservoirs, one on 24th-26th April (D. J. Booth, R. B. Hastings, N. P. Senior (*BB, 77:539, 87:176 plate 52*).

1989:   Croham Hurst Golf Course, one flew over on 12th August (P. Holt, *BB, 83:470*).

2000:   Richmond Park, one present for at least ten minutes at Pen Ponds on 27th May (S. Czapski, *BB, 94:482*).

2004:   Barn Elms London Wetland Centre, one on 17th October (R. Green, R. Kaye, *BB, 98:664*).

2005:   Walton Reservoirs, one on 30th April (S. J. Spooner, *BB, 100:57*).

Spelthorne

Kingfisher (Common Kingfisher)

Alcedo atthis

Moderately common breeding resident

Breeds in suitable habitats across Europe and Asia. Birds in the northeast of the range move south or west in winter to get away from frozen water but most British birds make only local movements. A few Kingfishers ringed in Britain during the breeding season have been recovered on the continent (*MA*).

Hard winters have been the main factor governing numbers across its range. The British Kingfisher population was reduced by persecution for various purposes in the 19th century. Charlotte Smith, cited in Yarrell (1845), wrote that dead Kingfishers would be hung from cottage ceilings in the belief that, although indoors, they would turn to point their beaks into the direction of the wind prevailing outside. Smith (1887) repeated this for early 19th century Wiltshire. Kingfishers were popular with collectors and were used to decorate hats. Water pollution has affected the number in Britain during the 20th century, but its adverse effects have been broadly offset by conservation and protection measures.

Early Surrey history. Among the earlier records, Blyth (1833) said that they bred at Tooting, Hamilton (1881) had one in his Putney garden, Aldridge knew of one caught at South Norwood on 16th June 1882 and there was one in Richmond Park on 25th August 1889 (*Zool.*, *1889:435*). Localities mentioned by Bucknill included Balham (bred 1879), the Mole above Cobham, Epsom, Lingfield, Pen Ponds, the Pipp Brook near Dorking, the Tillingbourne at Abinger and Shere, the Wey between Guildford and Godalming and, in the west, Cutt Mill, Forked Pond, Frensham Ponds and Hammer Pond. He mentioned reports of growing scarcity and thought that Kingfishers may have declined, but said that they were still present at the sites where he was used to finding them. As a sign of the rehabilitation he wrote of *many persons who are pleased with its appearance and who like to have it about their residences*.

1900 to 1960. Eggs in the Boorman collection at the Haslemere Museum came from Ripley (1905, 1906) and West Molesey (1904). Mouritz (1905) listed Kingfishers as visitors to Richmond Park and Bentham saw one at Oxted in January 1906. Kerr (1906) wrote that there were never less than a dozen nests along the Thames between Penton Hook (Laleham) and Romney Lock (Windsor). Presumably some of these were in Spelthorne. Power saw Kingfishers occasionally in Dulwich Park from 1898 to 1910. Kingfishers bred at Barn Elms around 1924 (*BLA*). Later records are somewhat sparse until the start of the Surrey Bird Report in 1957.

After 1960. Numbers were greatly reduced by the severe winter of 1962/63 but made a rapid recovery in many parts of the county. Meadows (1972) showed that, in the London area, the number of adults recorded in the breeding season on and south of the River Thames was cut to two in 1963 but was back to 26 by 1965 and had stabilised close to this level by 1968. Habitat was lost when the banks of part of the Mole at Hersham and Molesey were concreted after the 1968 floods. Kingfishers were breeding at Vann Lake in the 1960s (Blaker Log) and at Frensham in most years in the 1970s (HNHS, 1980). Numbers in the county were cut back again by the 1981/82 winter but soon recovered. Of the 231 tetrads in northeast Surrey, 16% were found to hold territories in the 1968-72 Atlas survey and 24% in the 1988-97 Atlas. There has been a substantial increase from the 1990s, associated with a run of mild winters. The increase is apparent in the table showing the number of sites reported sine 1960.

Number of vice-county sites reported and pairs proved breeding from 1960 to 2001

Year	60	61	65	66	67	68	69	70	71	72	73	74	75	76
Sites	18	20+	n/a	40+	46	n/a	n/a	n/a	n/a	n/a	n/a	n/a	n/a	n/a
Bred	4	5	6	2	15	6	14	12	3	1	6	8	8	9

Year	77	78	79	80	81	82	83	84	85	86	87	88	89	90
Sites	n/a	n/a	29	49	41	30	45	40	40	50	38	40	37	50
Bred	1	1	4	9	n/a	13	n/a	6	3	n/a	8	7	6	11

Year	91	92	93	94	95	96	97	98	99	2000	2001	2002
Sites	19*	20*	27*	42	83	59	61	75	74	65	65	60
Bred	6	4	2	n/a	n/a	n/a	n/a	n/a	n/a	n/a	n/a	n/a

*Breeding season only

A pair were seen at a nest hole at Queen Mary Reservoir in 1966. Kingfishers bred at Queen Mary Gravel Pits in the 1980s, Shepperton in 1969, 1976, 1984, at least two pairs in 1985-86 and at Stanwell

Moor Gravel Pits in 1972. They are still present in Spelthorne during the breeding season. Elsewhere, Kingfishers are very thinly represented in population surveys, with no significant trend. Kingfishers are occasionally seen in the Surrey part of Inner London, e.g. on a jetty at Battersea in March 2002.

Population size. Grossed-up Breeding Birds Survey information for 1994-2004 averages only 35 adults. This may look low given the number of sites, but if Surrey held a proportionate share of the British breeding population as given by the *New Atlas*, the population would only be about 30 territories. Kingfishers were found in 151 tetrads during the 1988-97 SBC Atlas Survey but this was over a period of nine years.

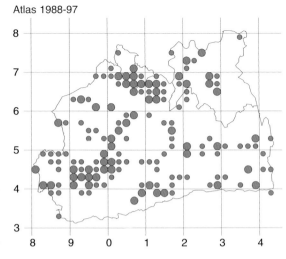

Atlas 1988-97

Nest sites. Although Kingfishers typically nest in burrows that they excavate in river banks, they will use man-made cavities. At Hackbridge in 2001, a pair bred in an artificial bank designed for Kingfishers for the first time since it was built in the winter of 1995/96. In the same year, a pair bred in a culvert at Carshalton (D. A. Colman).

Large count. Nine Kingfishers at Thorpe Water Park on 10th September 2000 was an unusual number.

Movement and Longevity. Kingfishers ringed as juveniles in Surrey have been recovered in Kent, Oxfordshire and Suffolk and on the Isle of Wight. One ringed at Queen Mary Reservoir on 27th July 1986 and recovered 124 km northeast at Bury St Edmunds, Suffolk on 17th October 1986 is the furthest-travelled. One ringed at Yeoveney, Berkshire on 7th July 1984 and found sick after hitting glass at Chertsey on 16th December 1986, over two years and five months later (BTO), is the oldest for which details have been located. The bird was subsequently released.

Bee-eater (European Bee-eater) *Merops apiaster*
Ten records, including two from Spelthorne

Southern birds, with a breeding range similar to that of Alpine Swifts, and moving south in winter. There is a small resident population in South Africa. Although Bee-eaters are now mainly vagrants to Britain, they may have bred regularly in some of the warmer periods of the last 5,000 years. The southern overshoot pattern of current British records is well marked and peaks in May, with occurrences mainly in southern and eastern coastal counties. A few pairs are known to have bred, mostly in southern Britain, the first being in 1920. A nest was predated in 2005.

Surrey:

1830: Godalming, one shot in a garden in Church Street, probably in 1830 (*Letters of Rusticus* in Yarrell (1845) and Bucknill).

1869: Walton-on-Thames. A widely published record of one "feeding upon yew berries" in a large garden at Oatlands, in late (November?) 1869 (*Zool., 1870:2027*) would not get through today's records committees without more corroboration. Berries are occasionally eaten by Bee-eaters in African winter quarters (*BWP*).

1958: Beddington Park and Sewage Farm, an adult flew over on 5th August (B. S. Milne, *BB, 53:167*).

1963:*   Staines Reservoirs, one on 30th April (Dr. A. D. Prowse, *BB, 59:300*).

1967:*   Staines, one on 19th-20th July (H. Axell, D. Mower, *BB, 61:333*).

1986:   Milford, one on 11th May (Dr E. F. J. Garcia, *BB, 84:479*).

1993:   Streatham, one flew over on 22nd June.

1995:   Guildford, one flew over Bellfields on 8th May.

1997:   Nore Hill, four flew northwest on 16th June, after a national influx in May.

1999:   Richmond Park, six flew north at Pen Ponds on 9th June.

*Spelthorne

Roller (European Roller) *Coracias garrulus*

Four, including one in Spelthorne

Breeds in southern Europe and as far east as southwest Siberia and winters in Africa. Most British birds occur on spring passage, peaking in June. Autumn passage peaks at the end of September. Records are well scattered, with an east coast bias.

Surrey:

1959:   Oxshott, one on 23rd-29th May (D. Parr, *BB, 53:421*).

1959:*   Staines Reservoirs, one on 26th September (E. E. Green, *BB, 53:421*).

1970:   Chobham Common, one on 17th-20th June (J. A. Lucas, T. Otley, C. C. White *et al.,BB, 64:357*).

1978:   Gatwick Airport, one a mile north on 29th May (J. G. Harrison *BB, 72:530*).

*Spelthorne

Hoopoe *Upupa epops*

Scarce migrant, has bred

Typical southern overshoots which, like Bee-eaters, have occasionally stayed to breed in southern Britain. Four pairs bred in 1977, the last to do so until 1996. The normal breeding range extends from southern and central Europe east to China. European birds winter in Africa. Spring passage in Britain peaks in April, with a smaller autumn peak. Some birds are long-stayers. Some have wintered.

Early Surrey history. There are three 18th century records. One is in Edwards (1743-51) and may not have been in Surrey, see Other Published Records. The next is of one shot *on the vast heath called Hind-head in Sussex* by Dr John Hill (Hill, 1752). Presumably this bird was actually in Surrey. Latham mentioned one killed in Surrey in September 1783.

Graves mentioned a remarkable flock of fourteen at Blackheath. He gave no date but it was probably in the summer of 1810 (Bucknill). Blyth knew of a pair at Tooting in the summer of 1831 and a pair at Mitcham Common a few years later (Bucknill). Richard Sturt shot one at Frensham in the summer of 1838 (Newman, 1849). Spicer (1854) mentioned one from Farnham in his collection and this or another from Farnham was alluded to by Bridger (*Zool. 1862:8283*). Several were shot between the years 1850 and 1860, one of which was at Claygate in July 1859. One was shot at Barnes Common on 28th April 1854 (*Zool., 1854:4329*) and another was shot at Esher in the summer of 1855 (Bucknill). Later records from Bucknill, 1900, 1902 and other sources include Dulwich (26th April 1859), Guildford (1862), Streatham Common (one shot, another seen, 1865), Wimbledon Common (7th November 1873, Hamilton, 1881), Tandridge (16th August 1879), Epsom Common (about 1882), Witley (spring of 1883), Bury Hill, Dorking (about 1885), Holmwood Common (11th October 1885), Streatham (27th April 1888), near Oxted (26th June 1892, *Zool., 1892:269*), Camberley (11th November 1893),

Shackleford (7th September 1894), near Horsell (summer of 1895) and Epsom Common (1898). There is a pre-1902 record from Sunningdale railway station. One from Godalming (Busbridge, *SALEC*) that Bucknill saw in the Charterhouse Collection is no longer there.

After 1900. There was one at Reigate on 22nd June 1901 (*Zool.*) and one in Richmond Park on 1st May 1902 (Collenette). Others were at Haslemere in 1915 (HNHS 1921), Hurtmore in April 1920 (HNHS 1921) and Limpsfield in the spring of 1926 (*LN* for1932). The next Hoopoe located dates from 1941, when one visited a Thursley garden in September. After this date, published vice-county sightings became much more frequent, with birds in at least 55 of the 62 years from 1944 to 2005. There were four in 1968, when there was a large national influx and five in 1971, another influx year.

Bird months by decade, 1900-2005

	1900s	1910s	1920s	1930s	1940s	1950s	1960s	1970s	1980s	1990s	2000s	Total
Vice-county	2	0	1	0	16	31	17	36	22	18	4	**147**
Spelthorne	0	0	0	0	1	2	1	1	1	0	0	**6**

Where found. Hoopoes have been seen at the A3 at Guildford and Ripley, Abinger Common, Abinger Roughs, Albury Heath, Beddington Sewage Farm, Berrylands Sewage Works, Blackheath, Bookham Common, Broadstreet Common, Brook, Camberley, Capel, Carshalton, Cheam, Chiddingfold, Chipstead (four), Dockenfield, Dorking (two), Dormansland, Dunsfold, Earlswood, East Croydon (two), Elstead, Epsom, Epsom Sewage Farm, Ewhurst, Farnham, Frensham (eight), Frimley Gravel Pits (three), Gadbrook, Godstone, Gomshall, Guildford (four), Hankley (two), Haslemere (three), Hinchley Wood, Hindhead, Horne, Holmethorpe Sand Pits, Hurtmore, Kenley, Kingston, Kingswood, Kingswood Warren, Leatherhead, Lightwater Country Park, Limpsfield, Mayford, Merstham, Merton, Ockham, Oxted (three), Raynes Park, Redhill, Reigate (two), Reigate Heath Golf Course, Richmond Park (four), Sanderstead (two), Seale, Shirley Park (Croydon), Streatham, Surbiton Golf Course, the Surrey Docks, Sutton, Thorpe, Thursley Common and village and Ockley Common (six), Tilford, Tolworth, Virginia Water, Walton-on-the-Hill, West End (Woking), West Molesey, Weybridge (two), Wimbledon Common (two), Windlesham, Windsor Great Park, Witley Common and Woldingham (two).

Breeding. The earliest breeding record comes from Dorking, where a pair nested in the hollow of a tree in an orchard in 1841 (*Zool., 1844:564*). The eggs were taken. A pair nested in a Leatherhead garden and fledged the young, not later than 1875 (both records from Bucknill). It was more than 100 years until the next known breeding, which was of two young raised at Thursley in 1977, a year when three other pairs bred in Britain.

Calendar. Overall, there were at least 145 bird months from 1900 to 2005. They cover all months of the year with a peak in April and May.

Bird months 1900-2005*

	Jan	Feb	Mar	Apr	May	Jun	Jul	Aug	Sep	Oct	Nov	Dec	Total
Vice-county	2	2	12	34	36	15	9	7	12	7	8	3	**147**
Spelthorne	0	0	1	2	1	1	0	1	0	0	0	0	**6**

*Incomplete after 2001 and probably earlier for Spelthorne

These totals exclude two undated records and include four May and four June bird months from the pair that bred in 1977. There is a wide scatter of places. Even the most frequent of them, Frensham, has had only eight. Many of the birds have been seen in gardens. In Spelthorne, a Hoopoe at Queen Mary Reservoir on 29th March 1947 is the earliest spring migrant located for the district. Others in Spelthorne were on 18th April 1952, 8th August 1954, 14th April 1965, 25th June 1972 (Queen Mary Reservoir, Geen) and 3rd May 1987.

Wintering. Hoopoes have been seen in winter at Wimbledon Common (7th November 1873), Frimley Gravel Pits (21st November 1971), Frensham and Tilford (18th October to 5th December 1973), Raynes Park (11th November 1981), West Molesey (3rd November 1983), Frensham Little Pond (12th December 1988 to 13th April 1989) and Gomshall (October 1994 to 5th March 1995).

Large counts. The fourteen at Blackheath mentioned by Graves remains the largest flock, presuming that it was the Surrey Blackheath. Four at Oxted in April 1949 (*BLA*) had previously been put in square brackets as uncertain (*LBR* for 1949).

Food. Not much has been published about food in Surrey but Hoopoes feed mainly on grassy ground, probing with their long bills. One was eating ants on a lawn at Chipstead on 30th July 1948.

Wryneck (Eurasian Wryneck)   *Jynx torquilla*

Scarce passage migrant, no longer breeds

A summer migrant to Europe and Asia, wintering from Africa south of the Sahara to southeast Asia, south of the breeding range. Migrant birds from Scandinavia pass through Britain. A decline in the British range was first noticed around 1830 and continued through the 19th and 20th centuries. The decline has been experienced in other European countries. Climatic factors have been suggested as a reason, though no firm evidence has been obtained.

Early Surrey history. Wrynecks were in the Godalming district prior to 1849. They were said to breed commonly in the vice-county from 1875 to 1900 (*Historical Atlas*), though they had already become scarce in the Norwood District (Aldridge, 1885). Hamilton (1881) listed Wrynecks for Putney Heath and Wimbledon Common. Power (1910) knew of only two records for Brixton. He heard them every year in Dulwich but thought they did not stay to breed. Wrynecks were, even so, still common summer visitors to Surrey in 1900 (Bucknill).

Where found, 1900 to 1960. Dixon (1909) added Barnes, Banstead, Battersea Park, Croydon, Epsom, Esher, Kew Gardens, Kingston, Richmond, Sydenham and Tooting to the localities where they had been found in the Surrey part of the London area. In the Staines area, Wrynecks were commonly seen perching on fences and hedges in spring (Kerr, 1906).

In rural Surrey an empty nest was found at Gatwick in 1901 (Maitland and Turnbull). Eggs collected by Boorman at East Clandon (1905), Ockham (1905, 1909), Send (1906, 1909) and by an unnamed collector at West Molesey in 1908 are in the Haslemere Museum. A Wryneck was seen at Eashing on 7th April 1906 (Mouritz, 1907) and Wrynecks were abundant at Milford and Witley at about this time. They bred at Mitcham up to 1905, at Morden in 1910 and at Upper Norwood and Croydon in 1913-14 (*BLA*). A pair nested at Caterham in 1914-1915 and 1921. Eric Parker heard one calling at Chilworth in 1915 (Parker, 1947). A nest hole was found on an LNHS field meeting at Warlingham in May 1919, where Wrynecks were lost by 1932 but seen again in 1938. Five clutches totalling 36 eggs were taken at Woking in 1915-16 (Maitland and Turnbull). Bunyard thought that Wrynecks had become comparatively rare by 1923 but they were said to be increasing around Epsom at about this time. Wrynecks last bred at Ashtead and Epsom in 1936 (*BLA*). A pair bred in a nest box near Woldingham from 1922 to 1927 and at Worms Heath from 1929 to 1931. They were fairly common at Limpsfield in 1930. There was a pair there in 1935 and one on Limpsfield Common in 1938. In all there were about ten pairs in the Godstone/Limpsfield/Oxted area but none bred there after 1949 (*BLA*).

Wrynecks could be found at Chelsham, Halliloo Wood (Warlingham), Slynes Green and near Warren Barn (Beadell, 1932). In Richmond Park, they bred until 1920 but after that date the only definite reports were of single birds calling in the springs of 1927, 1929, 1931, 1935 and 1937 (Collenette). They bred in Cherry Kearton's garden at Kenley in the late 1930s and at Kenley in 1940. A pair bred in a nest box near

Woldingham from 1937-42 and 1944-45. There were Wrynecks in the Frensham/Tilford area from 1953 to 1958 and from 1964 to 1966 and they may have bred. A pair did breed near Truxford in 1956.

Others were breeding or were present in the breeding season at Ashtead (1935, bred in a nest box 1936, 1937, two pairs 1938), Banstead (1934, 1937), Bookham Common (1934, 1936-37, 1942), Croham Hurst (1937), Englefield Green (1946), Epsom Common (1935), Epsom Sewage Farm (1936), Ewell (1938), Frensham (1953, 1954), Guildford (1944), Kenley Common (1939), Kew Gardens (1934), Leith Hill (1944), Limpsfield (1936, 1938-39, 1941-43), Milford (1944), Purley (1933, 1944), South Croydon (1949), Tadworth (up to six pairs, present 1938, none in 1954), Thursley (several local pairs, 1934, one seen 1940), and Walton Heath. One of the last sites was at Chipstead where Wrynecks bred until 1960 (Parr).

Final breeding. Eight eggs were laid in a garden nest box in June 1964 but the nest was deserted, because of heavy rain or a cat. In 1966 a nest was built in a natural hole in an apple tree in a former orchard. Young were fledged and apparently taken by a predator. Another pair made a nest. Reports of breeding in the 1968-72 Atlas period seem to be based on the statement in Parr that a pair bred at Warlingham in 1968. Unfortunately no observer or other details can be located for this. A Wryneck investigating tree holes at Holmethorpe on 2nd June 1968 may be the one said to have probably bred at Holmethorpe Sand Pits in the 1968-72 Atlas period (Hewlett). A pair probably breeding at Park Downs, Banstead in this period (Hewlett) might be connected with one seen at Park Farm, Banstead on 25th August 1972. There were several reports of single birds or pairs holding territory in later years, some of which would have met the 1988-91 Atlas definition of breeding but at only one of these, in northwest Surrey in 1984, was breeding actually proved.

Nesting. Wrynecks were known as prolific egg-layers. Bucknill mentioned a clutch of 62 eggs obtained by the abstraction of the eggs as they were laid. At Limpsfield in 1930, a bird that had been visiting a garden to feed on ants was seen to remove eggs from a nest box which was being used by a pair of Great Tits. The Wrynecks fledged young from the box on 11th July of that year (Robbins, 1931). A nest box at Limpsfield or Oxted was used in seventeen consecutive years (*BLA*).

Where found. As with Hoopoes, reports are widely scattered and few sites are favoured more than once. The most consistent feature is the frequency of sightings in gardens, particularly in the autumn, where they will be conspicuous even to those who are not regular birdwatchers.

Spelthorne. No breeding records have been located for Spelthorne but birds were found at Staines on 6th May 1936 and at Queen Mary Reservoir on 25th September 1969. There were at least seven from 1970 to 1993, all in autumn, at Queen Mary Reservoir/Gravel Pits on 27th August 1973, 28th and 30th August 1976, 13th and 25th September 1976 and 23rd September 1981; Shepperton on 2nd September 1980; and Staines Moor/Reservoirs on 31st August 1976 and 12th September 1993.

Calendar. Spring passage peaks in May and return passage peaks in September:

Bird months 1970-2005

	Jan	Feb	Mar	Apr	May	Jun	Jul	Aug	Sep	Oct	Nov	Dec	Total
Vice-county	0	0	1	6	14	7	0	14	33	3	0	0	**78**

The average arrival date in the London area south of the Thames from 1929 to 1939 was 8th April. Early and late dates are:

Early		**Late**	
12th March 1911	Surrey, *The Handbook*	3 October 1931	Tadworth
28th March 1938	Ashtead	5th October 1976	Chiddingfold, killed by a cat
28th March 1972	West Surrey	6th October 1979	Pirbright Common
31st March 1923	Shalford Common.	13th October 1967	Ashtead
31st March 1957	Richmond Park	14th October 1972	Fetcham.

Food. Wrynecks feed on ants, particularly the Yellow Meadow Ant *Lasius flavus*, which is a grassland species, more common in downland areas. Peal (1968) linked the Wryneck's British decline in the 70 years to 1939 to a reduction in the amount of grazing and a deterioration in the grassland stock. Chalk grasslands in Surrey have been reduced by the spread of arable farming and scrub. Yellow Meadow Ants are still common in Surrey, so this cannot be enough to explain the decline on its own. It might, however, explain why so many records of autumn migrants come from gardens, since Black Garden Ants *Lasius niger* and Yellow Meadow Ants are often found in and around garden lawns.

Movements. Seven vice-county records in the autumn of 1976 reflected a big influx of autumn migrants (*Ringing and Migration 1:231*). The number of migrant bird months is falling, from 34 in the 1970s to 15 in the 1980s, 14 in the 1990s and one in 2000. Later records have come from Croydon (2004), Dunsfold (2002), New Malden (2003), Newdigate (2004), Salfords (2003), Thursley Common (2002) and Wishmoor Bottom (2001). One was photographed in a Reigate garden on 24th April 2006 (*Bird Watching*). The only ringing recovery located is of an adult Wryneck trapped at Limpsfield on 10th June 1920 and found there again on 9th June 1921 (*BB, 15:112*).

Green Woodpecker   *Picus viridis*
Common breeding resident

Green Woodpeckers are resident in Europe and parts of the Middle East. They may have arrived in post-glacial Britain with the appearance of trees but records only go back to the 8th century. Their range extended in Britain and Scandinavia during the 20th century. Breeding numbers in the UK are affected by the severity of winters. British numbers fell back a little between the 1968-72 and 1988-91 BTO Atlases overall but were stable in southeast England. They are thought to have more than doubled since 1970. No overseas recoveries are mentioned in the *Migration Atlas*.

Early Surrey history. Gilbert White recorded a Green Woodpecker at Vauxhall on 14th March 1778. Newman (1849) listed Green Woodpeckers for the Godalming district. Hamilton 'saw the Green Woodpecker pretty frequently' during his morning ride on the lower part of Wimbledon Common in 1872. Bucknill described the birds as the most abundant of the Surrey woodpeckers, common in rural parts of Surrey and occurring near London in such places as Dulwich, Richmond Park and Wimbledon Common. There are no Spelthorne records in Kerr or Glegg.

1900 to 1970. Boorman collected eggs at Camberley, Cobham, West Horsley and Wisley from 1903-1908. Power (1910) found Green Woodpeckers to be rare in the Dulwich area, with only two records, at Dulwich Park, in the springs of 1905 and 1906. Eggs were collected at Chobham in 1920, Oxshott in 1914 and Woking in 1915 (Maitland and Turnbull). Beadell (1932) wrote that they had much increased around Warlingham since the 1914-18 war. Collenette (1937) estimated four or five pairs in Richmond Park and they were the commonest of the woodpeckers there in 1948. As ground-feeding birds, Green Woodpeckers were badly affected by the severe winter of 1962/63. They were present in six of about eighteen Common Birds Census areas during the 1960s, with a total of 28 territory years (Parr), many fewer than those of the Great Spotted Woodpeckers. Recovery took around ten years.

Trend since 1970. A reduction in numbers at Chobham Common after the 1976 heath fire was thought to be due to the destruction of ant colonies (*SBR* for 1977). Numbers were back to the 1975 level in 1978. The Winter Atlas found partial survey counts and estimates totalling 58 birds in 1981-84, making them the second commonest of the woodpeckers. The Common Birds Census showed that the number of territories may have nearly trebled from 1970 to 2000. Of the 231 tetrads in northeast Surrey, 63% were found to hold territories in the 1968-72 Atlas survey and 66% in the 1988-97 Atlas.

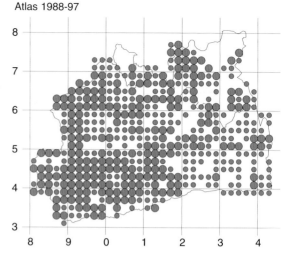

Atlas 1988-97

Population size. Green Woodpeckers were found in an average of 67.5% of the Breeding Birds Survey squares in 1994-2001, about the same as for the Great Spotted, suggesting a relative and absolute increase. They were reported from 89 sites in the year 2000 breeding season. At Vann Lake, Green Woodpeckers were found in almost every month of every year from 1964 to 1996. The Common Birds Census suggested an estimated 9,000 territories by the end of the period. This level is well above the possibly more reliable Breeding Birds Survey end-period estimate of about 2,700 individuals. If Surrey held a proportionate share of the British breeding population as given by the *New Atlas*, the population would be only 200 pairs.

Local counts. There were 18 territories at Chobham Common in 1999, ten in the Chilworth area in 2000, 12 at Frensham Common in 1998 and 2005 and 30 at Hankley Common in 2001, 2002 and 2003. Wimbledon Common and Putney Heath held at least 25 pairs in 2005 (*The Birds of Wimbledon Common and Putney Heath 2005*). Green Woodpeckers are rare in Inner London. One wintering in Battersea Park in 1995/96 was exceptional, as was one at the Surrey Docks in the autumn of 1998. There were 20 at Holmethorpe Sand Pits on 25th November 2004 (S. W. Gale). In Spelthorne, Green Woodpeckers bred at Ferry Lane Gravel Pit 'in former years' and were still present in the breeding season (*Shepperton Bird Report* for 1986). They were breeding at Queen Mary Reservoir in the 1980s (Geen).

Food. Ants are the main food. Green Woodpeckers are significant predators on Wood Ants *Formica rufa* on the Surrey heaths, burrowing into the large, mounded nests (J. Pontin, pers. comm.). They will feed on fallen apples when the ground is frozen. One ate elderberries at Farnham in October 1997.

Movement and longevity. Green Woodpeckers ringed at Queen Mary Reservoir in 1997 were recovered at Effingham in 1998 and Worcester Park in 2001, both locations being 17 km distant. A first-year bird was ringed at Egham on 1st August 1970 and recovered near Chertsey on 9th August 1985, 15 years later, a national longevity record. Three were killed by motor vehicles near Unstead Sewage Farm in 1998.

Great Spotted Woodpecker

Dendrocopus major (*Picoides major*)

Common breeding resident

Resident across Europe and Asia. British records go back to the end of the last Ice Age and they may have arrived with the oaks. There have been withdrawals and recolonisations over their more recent range as, for example, in northern Britain. These are sometimes ascribed to forestry changes. The *Migration Atlas* shows only one overseas recovery of a British-ringed bird. UK breeding numbers are thought to have more than doubled from 1966 to 1999 (*BBWC*).

Early Surrey history. H. L. Long wrote in 1824 that there were generally one or two Great Spotted Woodpeckers around Hampton Lodge, and that he had killed specimens in March and August

(Bucknill). Jesse (1835-36) had a note for Richmond Park. Meyer (1842) mentioned a nest near Claremont. They were listed without comment as breeding residents in the Godalming district by Newman (1849). References given by Bucknill for the latter part of the 19th century are few and rather scattered, coming from Ashtead Park (can usually be seen), Chilworth (*The Field*, 1893), Churt (eggs taken in 1860 and 1863), Dulwich (*Zool.*, 1858), Epsom, Gatton (nesting annually), Hurtwood, near Leith Hill, Malden, Peper Harow (nest in 1888), near Stoke Lock (nest, 1879), Virginia Water, Walton-on-Thames (*Zool.*, 1893), Waverley, Wimbledon (very rare around 1895) and Witley. There are no Spelthorne records in Kerr or Glegg.

1900 to 1970. A nest was found at Oxshott in 1904 (Maitland and Turnbull). Power (1910) thought that Great Spotted Woodpeckers were rare in the Dulwich area, with single records in 1876, 1905, 1906 and 'this year'. Mouritz (1905) had only two records for Richmond Park but Collenette (1937) estimated six or seven pairs there. Beadell (1932) wrote that they had much increased around Warlingham since the Great War. They were the commonest of the woodpeckers in the Haslemere district in 1934 and, in the Surrey part of the London area, they had reached Battersea Park by the 1950s. They were present in nine Common Birds Census areas during the 1960s, with a total of 54 territory years (Parr).

Trend since 1970. Numbers have increased since the 1970s. In the 1980s, Great Spotted Woodpeckers were scarce but resident at Shepperton and known to have bred at least once (*Shepp. BR 1982-86*). Two pairs were breeding at Queen Mary Reservoir in the 1980s (Geen). The Winter Atlas found partial survey counts and estimates totalling 87 birds in 1981-84, making them the commonest of the woodpeckers. At Vann Lake, Great Spotted Woodpeckers were found in almost every month of every year from 1964 to 1996. Of the 231 tetrads in northeast Surrey, 62% were found to hold territories in the 1968-72 Atlas survey and 66% in the 1988-97 Atlas. The Common Birds Census shows a very large and significant increase from 1970 to 2000, finishing up to four times higher.

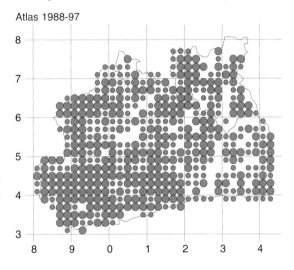

Atlas 1988-97

Population size. An estimated 12,000 territories at the end of the period is implied by the Common Birds Census. This probably derives from the over-representation of woodland (the Breeding Birds Survey suggests something about 2,700 adults) but there is no doubt that this is the commonest of the Surrey woodpeckers. Great Spotted Woodpeckers were reported from 98 sites in the year 2000 breeding season.

Local counts. There were at least 28 territories at Bookham Common in 2003 (A. D. Prowse), 17 on Chobham Common in 1999 (J. M. Clark), 18 at Frensham in 2005 (S. P. Peters) and 20 at Hankley Common in 2003 (J. A. Little). W. Attridge and D. M. Gyngell ringed 24 at Oakdale Farm, Weare Street in 2001. Wimbledon Common and Putney Heath held about 50 pairs in 2005 (*The Birds of Wimbledon Common and Putney Heath 2005*). Great Spotted Woodpeckers are still infrequent in Inner London, but one flew over Westminster Bridge in 1983. There was one in Battersea Park outside the breeding season in 1985, 1986 and 1987, juveniles were seen there in 1991 and birds were seen again in 1994. Others were at the Surrey Docks in 1992 and 1998.

Drumming. Great Spotted Woodpeckers are active in establishing territories from December onward. For example, drumming was heard at Bisley on 11th December 1991, at Elstead in late December 2006 and at Island Barn Reservoir and Painshill Park in January 2000.

Food. While Great Spotted Woodpeckers normally search tree bark for invertebrates, they sometimes feed on the ground. One was seen catching ants at Farnham in August 1980. They come readily to peanuts and fat at feeding stations.

Movements and longevity. Movements have been more significant than those of Green Woodpeckers, the furthest being 123 km, covered by a bird ringed at Queen Mary Reservoir on 14th March 1987 and recovered less then two months later, at Bradford-on-Avon, Wiltshire, on May 2nd. A Great Spotted Woodpecker ringed at Englefield Green on 8th April 1973 was recovered locally in November 1980, over seven years and six months later.

Lesser Spotted Woodpecker — *Dendrocopus minor* (Picoides minor)

Once common, now much less so.

Resident across Europe, North Africa and Asia. First recorded from Britain towards the end of the last glaciation and currently absent from Scotland and parts of northern England. There are no British ringing recoveries involving foreign countries (*MA*).

The British range does not seem to have changed significantly for most of the period from 1800 but there has been a decline in numbers of over 60% since the 1970s, possibly due to competition with Great Spotted Woodpeckers and less small-diameter dead wood (Fuller *et al.* 2005). Habitat changes through Dutch Elm Disease and more intensive woodland management have also been suggested as reasons for the national decline. Lesser Spotted Woodpeckers mainly use habitats which are too common to attract special conservation measures and which may have developed an undetected problem (*BTO News 226:4, 9*). There is as yet little hard evidence to support any of these speculations.

Early Surrey history. Blyth, writing in the 1830s, said that Lesser Spotted Woodpeckers were very rare near Tooting but more numerous in the fir woods beyond Croydon. They were found at Crooksbury Hill, Eashing, Peper Harrow and other localities in the Godalming area in the 1830s (Newman, 1837) and listed as breeding and resident in the Godalming district without further comment by Newman (1849). Harting (1866) described them as being not uncommon at Kew. Other localities mentioned by Bucknill included Ashtead, Cheam, Chilworth (*The Field*, 1893), Chobham, Dulwich (fairly plentiful in 1854, present 1894), Egham (nest 1881), near Epsom, Ewell, Gatton, Guildford, Headley, Hurtwood (around 1896), Malden, Nutfield, near Reigate, Richmond Park, Sidlow (nest 1901), Weybridge (nest 1895), Wimbledon, Witley (common in fir woods), and Wray Park. Bucknill thought that Lesser Spotted Woodpeckers might have had a wider distribution in Surrey than that of Great Spotted Woodpeckers. There are no Spelthorne records in Kerr or Glegg.

1900 to 1960. Power (1910) found Lesser Spotted Woodpeckers to be the commonest of the woodpeckers in the Dulwich area, with about two pairs resident, though becoming rarer every year. Mouritz (1905) said they were commoner than the Great Spotted in Richmond Park, where Collenette (1937) estimated two or three pairs of Lesser Spotted and the *LBR* for 1967 mentioned seven pairs, again outnumbering the Great Spotted. They also appear to have been the commoner of the two in the Epsom area in 1969 (*LBR*). Lesser Spotted Woodpeckers bred at Mitcham (1939) and in Richmond Park (1939 and most/all years 1948-77). Beadell (1932) wrote that they were scarce around Warlingham. Pounds (1952) said they were the scarcest of the woodpeckers in the Farleigh district. They were present in four Common Birds Census areas during the 1960s, with a total of 15 territory years (Parr).

Trend since 1970. Of the 231 tetrads in northeast Surrey, 78% were found to hold territories in the 1968-72 Atlas survey but only 61% in the 1988-97 Atlas. The Common Birds Census suggests a fall in the number of territories of 80% from 1970 to 2000. The table shows the number of sites reported annually has held up better, but there is no doubt that Lesser Spotted Woodpeckers are now much less common than Great Spotted Woodpeckers. While this is partly due to the increase in the Great Spotted, it also reflects a decline in the Lesser Spotted in the second half of the 20th century. The number of sites from which Lesser Spotted Woodpeckers were reported peaked in the 1970s, while those of the Green and Great Spotted Woodpeckers are still on the rise. The Winter Atlas found partial survey counts and estimates totalling only 29 birds in 1981-84, making them the least common of the woodpeckers. At Vann Lake, Lesser Spotted Woodpeckers became scarcer after 1975 and were not recorded at all after 1988.

Number of vice-county sites reported and number of proved breeding sites from 1960

Year	1960	1961	1966	1967	1968	1970	1971	1972	1973	1974	1975
Sites	19	17	n/a	n/a	n/a	n/a	n/a	n/a	n/a	n/a	n/a
Breeding sites	n/a	n/a	4	0	3	6	3	3	4	3	6
Year	1976	1977	1979	1980	1981	1983	1984	1985	1986	1987	1988
Sites	n/a	n/a	36	32	40	30+	48	55	50	45	27
Breeding sites	6	6	3	2	2	1	1	6	n/a	n/a	4
Year	1989	1990	1992	1993	1994	1996	1997	1998	1999	2000	2001
Sites	35	42	21*	22*	30*	30*	27*	27*	40*	30*	19*
Breeding sites	7	6	n/a	n/a	n/a	n/a	n/a	n/a	n/a	n/a	n/a

Breeding season only. 39 others outside the breeding season in 1998, 24 in 1999, 20 in 2000, 23 in 2001

Where found. Typical habitats in the Wey Valley have been wooded slopes below Charterhouse (1950s) and riverside woods at Stoke, Guildford (1970s). There were six pairs on Wimbledon Common in 1985, up to five pairs bred in Richmond Park in 1990 and there were four territories at Frensham in 1991. There was a pair at Shepperton in the 2000 breeding season. Records came from Battersea Park outside the breeding season in 1985, 1989, 1991 and 1997. Lesser Spotted Woodpeckers were present in the breeding season at Shepperton in 1970 but were said to be declining at Queen Mary Gravel Pits in 1986. They were the scarcest of the woodpeckers at Shepperton in the 1980s, with no breeding records in the *Shepperton Bird Reports* for 1982-86, but were still present in Spelthorne in the breeding season in 2000. Lesser Spotted Woodpeckers have now become very scarce in many parts of Surrey. Even so, A. D. Prowse knew of four territories on Bookham Common in 2003.

Population size. The Common Birds Census suggests a final population level of around 200 pairs. The Breeding Birds Survey suggests only 50 adults, which seems too low. The birds are canopy feeders and hard to see.

Movements and longevity. Two Surrey ringing recoveries have been located, both from the BTO. One ringed in South London on 29th December 1969 was recovered 7 km west on 4th March 1971. The other was ringed at Wood Street, Guildford on 6th August 1982 and found freshly dead in the same place on the following day. Surrey bird reports since 1977 have mentioned a longevity of three years and eight months but no details are available.

Plumage variations. A partially albinistic bird was reported from Kingston Vale in 1965.

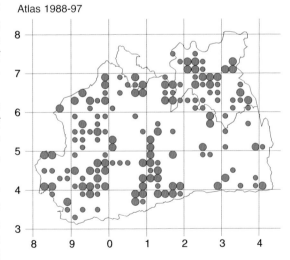

Atlas 1988-97

Short-toed Lark

(Greater Short-toed Lark)

Calandrella brachydactyla

(*Calandrella cinerea*)

Three birds, including two in Spelthorne

Breeds from Iberia and northwest Africa east to Manchuria. European birds mostly winter in Africa. A less obvious southern overshoot species in Britain, with a small peak in May and a larger one at the end of September. Most records are from southern and eastern coastal counties. From 1958 to 1985 all the inland county records were in the spring. These included three for our area.

Surrey. One at Staines Moor on 8th-16th June 1960 (J. Cox, R. J. Johns, M. Nobbs *et al.*, *BB, 54:189*), was a first record for the London area. One at Beddington Sewage Farm on 24th April 1966 (P. J. M. Morgan, Dr A. D. Prowse, *BB, 66:323*) was the second. A third, at Wraysbury Reservoir on 29th-30th April 1985 (C. D. R. Heard, *BB, 79:561*), also 1st May 1985 was thought to belong to one of the southern reddish forms, probably *C. c. brachydactyla* (*LBR*).

Crested Lark

Galerida cristata

One record

A widespread breeding species throughout continental Europe south to Africa and as far east as Korea. It is perhaps surprising that British records have been so few, less than 20. The European birds are mainly resident, which must be the reason for its rarity. Nearly all occurrences have been in southern Britain.

Surrey. Monica Curtis saw two Crested Larks feeding on mud and gravel exposed at low tide on the bank of the Thames between Hammersmith Bridge and Chiswick Eyot on 8th March 1947, during a spell of cold weather. She watched them from the towpath for ten minutes, noting that they were not shy, that they had very noticeable crests and other details confirmed the identification (*BB, 41:345*). Some references, *e.g.* Naylor (1996), show this as a Middlesex record, presumably because that is where Hammersmith and Chiswick are. The towpath is, however, on the Surrey bank and that is where the birds presumably were, since they were said to be tame, implying that they were close to the observer. The original reference in the *London Bird Report* for 1947 shows them as being in Surrey.

This was the first record for the London area, the first from an inland county and, per Naylor, the eleventh for the British Isles.

Woodlark (Wood Lark)

Lullula arborea

Locally common breeding resident

Currently breeds in Europe, North Africa and the Middle East and would have benefited, in Britain and elsewhere, from the spread of heathland. Woodlark remains dating back to the last glaciation have been found in Britain. Many northern birds move south in winter but remain in Europe. Some British coastal records might involve continental migrants (*MA*). Resident birds are affected by the severity of the winter weather. They are also affected by habitat changes such as the burning of heathlands (which helps them). Population levels have fallen over much of the European range. The British range contracted during the 19th century. Numbers have increased in recent years but some parts of the British range of the 1950s have yet to be recolonised. There were an estimated 3,085 pairs in 2006 (*BTO News 270*).

Early Surrey history. Woodlarks were abundant in 1840 (Meyer, 1842). Newman (1849) listed them as breeding and resident in the Godalming area. Hamilton (1881) wrote that they were occasional on Wimbledon Common. Jordan (1893) knew them well and wrote of *one gravelly hollow … sunk in the hillside facing direct to the south* as a favourite nest site. They were much less common near London, being for example rare at Tooting in 1836. Power (1910) found one on waste land near Tulse Hill on 16th September 1887, his only record for the Dulwich area since 1875. Woodlarks must have been savaged by the severity of some of the winters in the 1880s and 1890s and they had become extremely local by the end of the century. Bucknill had seen eggs from Ashtead and Godalming (no date) and knew of nests taken near Kingston in 1884 and at Byfleet on 24th June 1894. He had seen Woodlarks at Caterham and near Shere and had notes of them from Betchworth, Cheam, Clandon and elsewhere.

1900-1945. The first half of the 20th century saw a somewhat erratic increase. A nest and eggs at Camberley in 1905 was destroyed by moles (Maitland and Turnbull). There was one at Brook on 8th May 1906, a year when song was recorded in Richmond Park (Mouritz, 1907). Eggs were taken from Selsdon Park at about this time. A slow recovery was evidently under way, but Woodlarks were hit hard by the winter of 1916/17. Breeding was not proved again on the southwest Surrey commons until Bunyard located a nest in 1919 (*BB, 13:226-228*), though he had heard song earlier. Walpole-Bond (1938) dated a marked recolonisation of Sussex to 1919. By 1923 a pair or two could again be found in most suitable localities in Surrey (Bunyard, 1924). Eggs were collected at Chobham Common and Woking in 1923 (Maitland and Turnbull). Woodlarks did not breed within 20 miles of St Paul's Cathedral until 1924 (Harrison, 1961), when Colthrup reported a nest on a northeast Surrey heath, after finding a pair in June of the previous year (Colthrup, *BB, 18:192*). He found eight breeding pairs there in 1925. Dallas (1928) described birds summering in the Box Hill area in 1926 and he provided photographs of a nest found there in 1927. Woodlarks bred there in 1936. They were well known autumn visitors to Wimbledon Common in the 1920s and they bred in 1925 and 1926 (*BLA*). Records in Collenette (1937) and *BRP* show that breeding was attempted in Richmond Park, usually successfully, from 1924 to at least 1936. Woodlarks were locally quite common in west Surrey in 1935 (*SEBR*). Gosnell collected clutches at Churt (1935), Hindhead (1936, 1938, 1939), and Thursley (1936-1937). The cold winter of 1939/40, followed by those of the early 1940s reduced the number and range of Woodlarks in Surrey and accelerated a decline that had already started. They were lost to Box Hill, Richmond Park and the rest of the Surrey part of the London area, where they were not seen again until 1944. Woodlarks were present at Hydons Ball in the autumn of 1941 but were not seen again until they nested there in 1944 (Parker, 1947).

Since 1945. Woodlarks bred in Richmond Park from 1945 to at least 1962 (*BRP*). They became quite numerous there and 33-35 individuals were counted on 2nd September 1950 (B. A. Marsh, pers. comm.). Woodlarks were also breeding on Ham Common (*BLA*) and Putney Heath (Parr) by 1950. The British population continued to increase with checks during severe winters and, by the 1950s, Woodlarks were found (or refound) on downland sites. Two pairs on the southern slopes from Box Hill to below Walton Heath in 1958 were fewer than usual (Collenette, in archive). Numbers fell back again by 1961 and although Surrey numbers are now high, the downland sites have yet to be reoccupied. 1961 records of one at Queen Mary Reservoir on 14th April and two over King George VI Reservoir on 25th November are the earliest located for Spelthorne. Others were seen at Stanwell Moor in December 1969 and January 1970.

Population size. The earliest reasonably comprehensive county population estimate is for 1969, when there were 14 pairs on the western heaths. Since then, figures have been published annually in the *Surrey Bird Report*. Numbers fluctuated between six and 25 pairs from 1969 to 1977. The figures vary a good deal in coverage, those for the later years being more complete. None of them is based on a thorough survey of the whole county. In 1977 Woodlarks returned to two areas burnt by the fires of 1976, where they had been absent for some years but numbers fell again after harsh weather and prolonged snow cover in early 1982. The Winter Atlas found partial survey counts and estimates totalling 59 birds in 1981-84, nearly all of them in SU84 and TQ06 and a surprisingly high total. There was a full survey of the western heaths in 1986, organised by the BTO. It found 40 territories and the county total was estimated as 55-60 (*SBR*). A full analysis was not published until ten years later (Sitters *et al.* 1996) and no separate Surrey results were given in it. A 1988 survey covered the west Surrey heathlands and was sponsored by the Royal Society for the Protection of Birds. It found 40-42 territories. Surrey results were included in the *Surrey Bird Report* for 1988.

A national survey of breeding Woodlarks was jointly organised by the BTO, English Nature and the Royal Society for the Protection of Birds in 1997. The Surrey part of the survey was set up by John Clark and John Eyre, with assistance from the Surrey Bird Club. The survey was intended to cover all sites known to have held Woodlarks in the previous 30-40 years, with additional coverage of all suitable habitat around the main population centres to determine how far birds were moving from traditional sites. Observers were asked to make three visits during the period March to June, noting the number of singing males and additional territories and mapping all the information. They then estimated the number of territories on the basis of these observations. Large sites were divided into 1 km squares, separate figures being obtained for each. Survey work on the larger sites was especially arduous and access was restricted by range practice on some

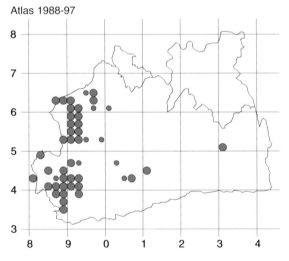

Atlas 1988-97

of the military land. John (J. M.) Clark made ten visits to the Ash/Cleygate/Pirbright Commons military complex, mostly at Easter, May Day and Whitsun. Sites were classified by land use category and territories by habitat type.

The survey was the most thorough study of Woodlarks ever carried out in Surrey. The number of territories was estimated at 160-171, which is the largest figure on record up to that date. The addition of a few territories found after the survey was completed brought the total up to a maximum of 177.

More regular West Surrey counts organised by John Clark provide a fuller picture for the years from 1994, as shown in the table overleaf.

In 2000 there were at least 160 territories in Surrey after allowing for incomplete coumts. This was 11% of an estimated UK total of 1,429 spread across nine counties (Ogilvie *et al.*, 2002), the same percentage as in the census year of 1997. Numbers appear to have been maintained or increased after 2000, with more territories at Bourne Woods (four in 2006), Puttenham Common (seven in 2006) and Thursley/Ockley Commons (nine in 2006). The first full count for some years found 26 territories at Westend Common/Pirbright Ranges. A serious fire at Thursley after the breeding season in 2006 has produced a lot more Woodlark habitat. Woodlarks are set for a further increase in breeding numbers provided that the present climate trend continues. They have yet to recolonise downland sites and

Recent Woodlark Territory Counts in West Surrey *(includes incomplete counts)*

	1994	1995	1996	1997	1998	1999	2000	2001	2002	2003	2004	2005	2006
Avalon Fruit Farm, Churt			1										
Bagmoor Common				1								1	1
Bagshot Heath			2	1	2	1		1					
Bourne Wood				1	1	1	2	3	3	4			4
Brentmoor Heath	2		1	1	2	3	2	2	2			4	2
Brookwood Cemetery													4
Brookwood Heath			2	1	1	1	1	1	1			1	1
Bullswater Common					1	2	1	1	1		1	1	1
Chobham/Sunningdale /Wentworth			1	5	7	8				8	2	8	12
Churt Common	1	1	2	3	4	4	1						4
Crooksbury Common	2	1	6	6	3	2	4	6	2		2	2	2
Frensham Common	5	5	5	6	6	9	8	9	9	8	7	8	8
Furze Farm, Bisley								1					1
Hampton Nursery				2	1								
Hankley Common	9	12	15	24	29	25	30	24	25	25	22	26	21
Hindhead	2	2	8	6	5	5	5	5	7	5	3	8	9
Horsell Common					1		2	1					
Lightwater Country Park							1						
Mare Hill, Witley				1	1	1	2	1	1			1	1
Milford Common				1									1
Mytchett Place			1	2	2	2	3	1	1				
Old Dean Common	8	9	8	6	18	9	7	8	7	8	7	10	17
Pirbright Common/ Ash Ranges	18	21	13	25	12	28	32	19	25	15	14	19	37
Puttenham Common	2		2	3	4	5	6	6	8	6	6	nc	7
Rodborough Common				1									
Royal Common													1
Sands Golf Course			1										
Shackleford													1
Sheet's Heath					1	1	1	1		1			1
Stanford/Cobbetthill Commons							2	1				1	
Tankersford Common													1
Thursley/Ockley/ Elstead Commons	15	17	15	15	12	4	5	5	10	8	8	6	9
Tilford Common													1
Tilhill Nurseries		3	3	3	3	3	3	3	3	5	6	5	6
Turf Hill							1			1			
West End Common/ Pirbright Ranges	14	12	2	28	13	5	11	8	7	7	26	23	24
West Heath, Pirbright													1
Whitmoor Common			1		1	1							1
Whitmore Vale				1	1	1		1					
Wisley/Ockham Commons													2
Witley Common	–	1	1	2	4	5	3	2	5	5	3	6	4
Total counted	**78**	**84**	**90**	**145***	**135**	**126**	**133**	**110**	**118**	**105**	**107**	**130**	**185**

From counts organised by John Clark. This table excludes a few pairs along the Greensand Hills and the North Downs.

* 160-171 including all of Surrey

heathlands in northeast Surrey, so the 1997 numbers may still be below the peak of the 1950s. The abandonment of downland and farmland sites is not confined to Surrey. Sitters *et al*. point out that the same thing has happened in other counties in spite of a strong increase in numbers.

Local counts. Figures for individual sites reveal marked changes. L. J. Raynsford found a minimum of 11 pairs on an area of 1,500 x 500 yards (18 per square km) on Witley Common in 1958 (Parr (1972), SBC archive). This compares with between one and six territories on the whole common since 1994. Habitat changes have played a part. Wisley Common held at least two breeding pairs in 1959. It has been only recently recolonised after being divided into four pieces by the A3/M25 junction.

Autumn and winter. Woodlarks begin to sing again in September, after the breeding season is over. They flock up in autumn. Some Woodlarks remain in the breeding area throughout the winter, provided that the weather is mild. Dallas found a winter party of six on Mickleham Downs in the early 1920s. There were up to 26 at Thursley from October to December in 1962 and a flock of 35 was found at Thursley on 28th September 1993 (*HSBBR*). Up to 20 were at Tilhill Nurseries, adjacent to Frensham Common, in December 1977 and again in the following winter. Others leave and are probably the birds which are sometimes seen on farmland. Farmland flocks include 22 on market garden land at Elstead in the autumn of 1966, 25 on Elstead fields in 1970, 16 at Red House Farm, Elstead in early 1989 and 24 on stubble at Merrist Wood Agricultural College on 7th February 1993. Places where dispersing or migrating birds have been seen include Addlestone (1930), Selsdon (April 1930) and Walton Reservoirs (January 1970). There have been occurrences in Spelthorne, including at Queen Mary Reservoir in August 1974 (Geen) and September 1995 and at Staines Reservoirs in October 1992 and November 1998. Five flew south over the Surrey Docks on 9th October 1998 and others flew over Barn Elms on 17th and 31st October 2002. Some of these birds were probably of Surrey origin but others might have been on passage, possibly including members of the more migratory East Anglian population. Woodlarks return to the commons early, most taking up territory in February and March, and some have been heard singing as early as January.

Habitat. Woodlarks need light, well-drained soils for successful breeding and these are found in the four types of habitat which have been used in Surrey. Heathlands in west Surrey and on the hills and commons of the Weald currently provide most of the sites in the county. Forestry plantations and tree nurseries are also used. Smaller populations have been found on chalk downland in the past. Heaths such as those at Ashtead, Epsom and Wimbledon, which are on the much younger Thames Valley gravels and sands, have also from time to time supported breeding Woodlarks, but most no longer do so. Woodlarks breed on light arable farmland, as at Tilhill Nursery. Burnt ground was first identified as an important habitat by Venables (1937).

The 1997 survey showed the dominance of heathland in the current breeding season distribution, which can be seen from the summary in the Habitats table. A comparison with the national 1986 survey shows that the interpretation of this information needs some caution. Over 90% of the Breckland population and 60% of the Suffolk coast birds were in young forestry habitats, which are very modestly represented in Surrey. The high score for military training sites in Surrey reflects a common habitat preference among Woodlarks and soldiers, as much as the protection afforded by keeping the public out.

Habitats used for 127 of the Territories in 1997

Habitat Type	Territories	Habitat Type	Territories
Bracken-dominated heath	3	Broad-leaved woodland	1
Grass-dominated heath	11	Conifer woodland	3
Heather-dominated heath*	82	Conifer plantation	4
Bare ground – burnt	14	Mixed woodland	1
Bare ground – natural	4	Total	**127**
Cleared woodland	4		

* Mainly Ministry of Defence land

The preference of Surrey Woodlarks for heather-dominated heaths suggests that conservation activities which are aimed at encouraging heather cover may increase the population density, provided that bare earth and open rides are retained and that more heather is not at the expense of other valuable habitat types. From the point of view of the birds, there may be much less difference between heathland and young forestry plantations than we humans might suppose. East Anglian Woodlarks, like those in Surrey, may just be using the suitable habitat which is locally most abundant, rather than preferring one to the other. This could be a useful subject for further study.

Winter weather. Harrison (1961) drew attention to a broad correlation between the mean annual temperature at Kew and Woodlark numbers in the London area. Surrey numbers are known to have fallen after severe winters in 1938/39 and 1962/63 and they probably did after others including those of 1928/29, 1939/40, 1940/41, 1941/42 and 1946/47. A gradual temperature rise, which peaked in 1949 and then fell to 1956, roughly coincided with a rise in breeding Woodlark numbers to a peak in 1950, followed by a decline. They fell again after harsh winter weather in early 1981. The rise in Surrey numbers since the 1980s has coincided with generally milder winters and rising average annual temperatures. However, as other writers have pointed out, there are many things about the population dynamics of Woodlarks that are not well understood. There is, for example, not a lot of information about where the birds go after the breeding season. Sitters suggested that the East Anglian birds might migrate to southwest France, where the majority of Dutch birds overwinter, but there is no evidence that Surrey birds do.

Longevity. A Woodlark colour-ringed in a West Surrey nest on 18th April 1988 was found nesting at the same site on 17th April 1993, a national longevity record (per A. Davis, BTO website).

Skylark (Sky Lark)   *Alauda arvensis*
Common, but reduced breeding resident

Breeds throughout Europe and northern Asia, northern birds moving as far south as North Africa and the Middle East after the breeding season. Many migrants winter in western Europe. Foreign-ringed birds from France northeast to the Baltic have been found in Britain, confirming visible migration evidence of a British passage of continental birds, though the pattern is far from clear. There are introduced populations in Australasia and Canada. Skylarks were in southern Britain during warmer stages of the last Ice Age. In the post-glacial period their range would have been restricted by the spread of trees but later, with the introduction of arable farming, they increased and spread. Skylarks were widespread and common in Britain during the 19th century. Many were trapped for sale as songbirds or shot for eating. Declines became apparent in Britain and other parts of its European range in the late 20th century. *BWP* distinguishes two races breeding in Britain - *scotica* in northern areas and *arvensis* elsewhere. Most British breeders move only short distances.

Early Surrey history. References are rather few. The first of note is an awesome description by Newman of the plight of Skylarks in the Godalming district during the winter of 1813-14: *'the most remarkable feature of that terrible winter – as regards birds – was the number of Skylarks that it actually starved to death. They wandered around in flocks, from field to field, from garden to garden till they became mere bags of bones, and sometimes of a morning you might find them frozen to the surface of the ground: and when we drove up the survivors, how forlorn was their look, how weak their flight … how different in all respects from the happy Skylark of the summer'*. A pioneer bird census found eight pairs in Wray Park around 1880 (Crossfield). Aldridge recorded song at South Norwood Hill in the 1880s, though the bird was becoming less common as London spread outwards.

1900 to 1970. In the Staines area, Skylarks were common residents and winter visitors (Kerr, 1906). Power (1910) said that a few still bred in Dulwich Meadows. Eggs collected by Boorman at Ripley (1902,

1910) and Send (1902-05, 1907, 1909-10, 1918) are in the Haslemere Museum. Skylarks were resident on Clapham, Tooting and Wandsworth Commons and on Peckham Rye in the 1920s (*BLA*). They were numerous in Richmond Park in 1905 (Mouritz) and probably bred there throughout the 20th century, with other records in the 1930s and 40s. They bred annually from 1951 to 1976 (*BRP*) and from 1995 to 2004 (Birds of Richmond Park 1995-2004). Gosnell collected a Skylark clutch at Frensham in 1935.

The decline since 1970. Skylarks continued to prosper in Surrey until the last quarter of the 20th century. The Winter Atlas found partial survey counts and estimates totalling 1,726 birds in 1981-84, about twice the number of Meadow Pipits. Of the 231 tetrads in northeast Surrey, 73% were found to hold territories in the 1968-72 Atlas survey but only 49% in the 1988-97 Atlas. The Common Birds Census showed that territories on farmland , which averaged 13.3 per square km in 1961-69, averaged 2.8 in 1990-1999, a fall of nearly 80%. Local counts tell a somewhat varied story. At Vann Lake, Skylarks were recorded annually in the breeding season up to 1978, but not after (Blaker Log). There were six pairs at Wimbledon Common in 1983 but none bred in 2004 or 2005. Large numbers bred on farmland at Shepperton in the 1980s. There were 177 at Sheepwalk Gravel Pit on 2nd March 1986. Some heathland, such as Hankley Common, (18 territories in 2004) and Chobham Common (14 territories in 1999) still holds good numbers but the combined population at Frensham and Thursley crashed from 21 to a single territory from 1995 to 2004. Skylarks are also doing well on some farmland. There were 20 territories at Tuesley Farm, Milford, in 2001.

Various reasons for the decline have been suggested including a switch from spring to autumn-sown cereals, an intensification of grassland management and a heavier use of insecticides. Mortality outside the breeding season has increased and loss of winter stubbles appears to be an important contributory factor (Chamberlain and Crick, 1999). The fall is not confined to farmland. The Common Agricultural Policy has recently had some positive effects with the creation of set-aside fields, where the farmer is paid for keeping the land out of use. This can create a good nesting habitat. Linseed, a subsidised crop, is unharvested in some years, attracting winter flocks of finches and larks.

Local factors have played a part. At Beddington Sewage Farm, which held 14 pairs in 1954 (Milne, 1956), there was only one territory in 1999 after prolonged management regime changes. Skylarks bred on the north side of Stoke Park, Guildford until the site was redeveloped as a sports centre in 1993. Skylarks bred or held territory at the Surrey Docks from at least 1971 until 1991, after which redevelopment removed the last suitable habitat. At least eight pairs bred there in 1977 and five in 1984.

Current population size. The Common Birds Census suggests a county population of about 1,000 territories in 2000. The Breeding Bird Survey suggests a current breeding season population of 3,000-4,000 adults, quite a good match.

Large counts. The largest counts date back to the 1970s:

Alderstead Heath: 400, 27th December 1992
Beddington Sewage Farm: 900-1,000, 19th
    January 1936; 3.000, 28th January 1940;
    *c.*1,000, 15th January 1955; *c.*3,000, 23rd and
    25th January 1963; *c.*5,000, 8th March 1970
Chelsham: *c.*300 feeding on young rape, 30th
    December 2000
Earlswood: *c.*1,000 roosting in grass tussocks,
    18th January 1966.

Epsom Sewage Farm: flock of *c.*150, 26th
    February 1955
Holmethorpe Sand Pits: 400 feeding, 27th
    January 1979
Old Woking: 2,000-3,000 feeding, part of a
    January 1979 movement
Rushett Farm: 300, 21st January 1991
Unstead Sewage Farm: 100, 22nd February 1956

Movements. Power knew Skylarks as prominent autumn migrants. He watched them fly south over his garden for nearly an hour on the 16th December 1874 and saw many flocks of up to 70 birds passing over in the Octobers of 1888, 1891 and 1892. On 28th November 1890, a few days into a ferocious frost, he counted roughly a thousand passing over his Brixton garden in the course of 20 minutes. More were seen in 'arctic' weather in mid February 1895. The largest movement of all was on 13th-26th October 1902.

Some 3,000 birds at Beddington Sewage Farm on 28th January 1940 came after heavy snow in the coldest part of the 1939/40 winter (Fitter, 1941). Large numbers appeared at Beddington and Epsom sewage farms in January 1955 and 141 flew southwest at Barn Elms on 20th February. Beddington Sewage Farm again held exceptional numbers in the icy January of 1963 and in March 1970. Cold weather movements of about 1,000 were seen at Epsom Sewage Farm on 27th October 1956, at Addington and Leatherhead on 31st December 1961 and at Staines on 7th January 1970 and there were about 2,000 at Shirley on 1st January 1962. Smaller movements recorded include 313 south over Ockley Common on 10th October 1976 (Clark, 1984).

There were very large movements across Surrey in January 1979, including 5,000 south over Epsom, 600 southwest at Frensham and about 1,000 over Queen Mary Reservoir on the 1st and, at Wrecclesham, 1,000 south on the 23rd and 2,300 southwest on the following day, when 1,350 were also seen flying west at

Atlas 1988-97

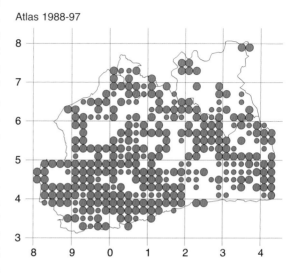

the Surrey Docks. There were 2,000-3,000 in an uncut cornfield at Old Woking on the 6th. Later movements include 1,534 southwest at Frensham on 12th December 1981 and 143 west at Barn Elms on 11th November 2001.

There is no doubt that recent numbers have been historically low, at least since the 1970s. Figures for earlier years are less complete and there may be some long term ups and downs. The largest flock on record was of about 5,000 at Beddington Sewage Farm on 8th March 1970, just before the current decline began.

Longevity. An adult Skylark ringed at Zandvoort, the Netherlands on 16th February 1970 was recovered nearly three years later and 370 km west, at Lower Pyrford on 27th January 1973.

Skylarks and the Arts. Skylarks have long been able to strike a response in the world of the arts. The composer Ralph Vaughan Williams, who lived for most of his life in Surrey and was a student at Charterhouse, is said to have been inspired to write his 1914 publication *The Lark Ascending*, in which a soaring violin takes the part of the bird, by song heard near Crooksbury Common and by a poem, *The Lark Ascending*, published by George Meredith when he was living at Box Hill. A few lines easily confirm the identification:

> He rises and begins to round,
> He drops the silver chain of sound,
> Of many links without a break,
> In chirrup, whistle, slur and shake,
> All intervolved . . .

Shore Lark (Horned Lark)   *Eremophila alpestris*

At least five vice-county records and three from Spelthorne

Breeds in the northern fringe of Europe and Asia and across much of North America. Also found on mountains from North Africa through Europe to Asia, with a station in the Andes. Shore Larks were present in southern Britain during the last glaciation and may have bred (Harrison, 1988). In later years they were sporadic winter visitors to Britain until an invasion in 1879, since when they have been more common. Most, if not all, are thought to come from Scandinavia or Western Russia (*MA*). Shore Larks have bred in Scotland.

Surrey. Bucknill mentioned two Shore Larks - one then in the Charterhouse Collection (though not there now), which had been shot on Merrow Downs (*SALEC*), and one in his own collection, bought at the Stafford Collection sale and from 'Surrey', possibly the same bird. Dated occurrences are:

1961:   Queen Elizabeth II Reservoir, three, 28th October, when the reservoir was under construction.

1971:*   Wraysbury Reservoir, one from 22nd December to 1st April 1972 (*LBR* for 1972).

1979:   Barn Elms Reservoirs, one flew over on 1st January.

1980:*   Queen Mary Reservoir, one flew over on 25th October.

1983:   Barn Elms Reservoirs, one on 12th November.

1985:   Barn Elms Reservoirs, an adult from 29th September to 8th October.

1996:*   Queen Mary Reservoir, one briefly on 16th November.

*Spelthorne

Sand Martin   *Riparia riparia*

Locally common summer visitor, breeding annually

Breeds across Europe, Asia and North America. European birds winter in Africa south of the Sahara. The range seems to have been stable since 1900, but population decreases have been noted in parts of western Europe. A crash of at least two-thirds in the British population between the 1968 and 1969 breeding seasons was ascribed to drought in the main wintering area, the Sahel region of West Africa. Since then, numbers have recovered. British breeders winter in Africa south of the Sahara (*MA*).

Early Surrey history. In a letter written in 1675 or 1676 and included in John Aubrey's *Natural History and Antiquities of Surrey*, John Evelyn mentioned that Sand Martins (*Trogladytic Martines*) nested in sandy banks around Albury. They were still nesting there when Bucknill wrote. One factor assisting their survival in Surrey may be their ability to exploit new habitats. Natural sites, such as river banks and sand cliffs, are now extremely rare but the loss has been balanced by an increase in the number of sand pits and other man-made habitats. Sand Martins were known in the Godalming district by 1849. The *Historical Atlas* gives Sand Martins as breeding commonly in Surrey from 1875 to 1900 but specific sites are hard to locate. Bucknill gave none apart from Albury, though he said they bred in sand pits and railway cuttings. They were only passage migrants at Wimbledon (Hamilton, 1881) and in the Dulwich area, with an early date of 10th April (Power, 1910). Sand Martins did not breed in the Staines area when Kerr wrote, in 1906, but they were seen daily in summer.

Breeding. Nearly all Surrey nesting sites since 1900 have been man-made, mostly in sand pits. There was a colony at Send Sand Pits around 1900. The Haslemere Museum holds eggs collected from this site in 1901, 1903 and 1904. Sand Martins nested in various sand pits around Send for most, if not all, of the rest of the 20th century. Sand Martins bred at Coombe Warren, Wimbledon (Mouritz, 1905) and there was a new colony near Barrow Green in 1906. Fitter (1940) gave details of colonies in the London area from 1900 to 1940, many of them even then no longer in existence. Those in Surrey included Barn Elms, a Beddington sand pit, Brooklands, near Earlsfield Station, Ham Gravel Pits, Mitcham Junction, Moorhouse, near Nutfield, Oxted (Coney Hill), Reigate (three sites), Tilburstow Hill, Waddon and a Weybridge sand pit. One of the longer-lived colonies, on Limpsfield Common, was new in 1906, was active in 1934 and had about five pairs in 1937 but none in 1940 or 1999. Elsewhere in the county there were colonies at Oxshott (new in 1906), Englefield Green, (1934) and Frith Hill (Godalming, 1939). A colony between the two ponds at Frensham was active in 1934 but was later destroyed by tank practice (HNHS, 1955).

Trend since 1970. Of the 231 tetrads in northeast Surrey, 23% were found to hold territories in the 1968-72 Atlas survey but only 16% in the 1988-97 Atlas. The Common Birds Census did not cover Sand Martin sites and there is no other good measure of change. Colonies often depend on the state of work at the sand pits and can die out if conditions change.

Nest sites. The only natural site in Middlesex that was known to Glegg (and the only one out of 75 colonies known to the writers of *BLA*) was in a sandy bank of the Thames at Shepperton, where many nested. The *Shepperton Bird Reports* for the 1980s show that Sand Martins were nesting at Ferry Lane West (36 holes in a newly exposed bank in 1985), Laleham Farm Gravel Pit (over 100 holes in 1985), Littleton Lane East (old site, overgrown when there were three or four holes in 1986), Littleton Lane West (30 holes in 1983) and Sheepwalk East (150 holes in 1983).

Sand Martins nested in the dry drainpipes of a railway embankment at Clapham Junction around 1902 (*BLA*), an early example of such a nest site. Drain pipe colonies existed at Earlsfield for a few years up to 1944, a drain hole was used at Godalming in 1960. A small colony bred in drainage pipes at Kingston from 1970 to at least 1972. Four pairs used drainage holes in a concrete river wall at Berrylands Sewage Works in 1967, 1972-74, 1993-94 and probably in other years. At Walton-on-Thames in 2001, 54 pairs nested in a special bank that had been built as part of reservoir restructuring. The provision of artificial nesting tunnels at Barn Elms WWT has built on this experience to create a new colony. Twenty-five pairs raised 33 broods in them in 2005.

Sand Martins nested in waste chalk pits at Leatherhead Water Works in the 1970s. They take readily to steep-sided piles of excavated soil, as near Stoke Lake in 1981 and from 1993 to 1998 in spoil heaps made during the construction of Pyrford Golf Course, but these sites are sometimes quickly destroyed. At Beddington Sewage Farm, Sand Martins nested in gravel diggings, on a temporarily exposed sand bank and in holes in an effluent channel, from 1999-2003.

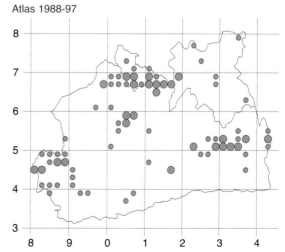

Atlas 1988-97

Population size. The most comprehensive breeding population figures published were those in Nau (1961) for Caterham, Redhill, Reigate and Westerham and in Weller and Weller (1962) for the south. Nau found 300 holes at Caterham, 550 at Redhill and Reigate and 40 at Westerham. Weller and Weller found 1,400 pairs in the Farnham area, a total of 300 pairs at two colonies in Dorking, 60 pairs at Gomshall Station and 50 each at Albury and Shamley Green. These figures exclude large colonies at Betchworth and Buckland and some elsewhere. The total is, even so, larger than any published in recent years. A vice-county total of 840 pairs was estimated for 1978. Published counts for 1982 totalled 825, with perhaps 200-300 at uncounted sites. The 1994-2004 Breeding Bird Survey suggests a breeding season population of 1,000-1,500 adults.

Colonies reported since 1970:

Addlestone, Moated Farm: 1996

Berrylands Sewage Works: 1970-2000, 15-16 pairs in 1977

Buckland/Buckland Sand Pits: 1974-1996, 142 pairs in 1989

Chertsey Gravel Pit: 1996

Chessington: 1984, five pairs

Dorking: 1973 last record

Fieldcommon: 1986, 60 pairs

Godstone area: 1996 latest, 50 pairs in 1986

Guildford: St Catherine's 1973

Hamm Moor: 1970, 98 holes

Hersham Gravel Pit: up to 1989 when 50+ pairs; 'Molesey Gravel Pit': 1989, 60-80 pairs

Hogsmill at Kingston: to 1997 at least, up to 15 pairs,

Holmethorpe Sand Pits: throughout, 180 pairs in the 1980s

Leatherhead: 1970-72, 80 holes in 1971

Limpsfield: 1970

Long Ditton: 1980s, 1990s up to six pairs

Lyne, Trumps Farm: 1994-95, 240-260 holes in 1994

Moorhouse: 1996, possibly throughout

Oxted: 1996, possibly throughout

Papercourt: to at least 1997, 200-300 pairs in 1997

Pyrford Golf Course: since 1993, 30 holes in 1995

Runfold/Seale: throughout, 515 holes at two sites in 1982

Surbiton, Seething Wells: occasional

Stoke, Guildford: 80 holes, all destroyed, in 1981

Thorpe: probably throughout, 120 pairs 1992

Virginia Water, Pondover Pit: 1970-71, 105 pairs in 1970

Walton-on-Thames, Apps Court: 1984-97, 150-200 in 1990

Walton-on-Thames – Chelsea and Lambeth Reservoirs: 54 nest holes in 2002, 69 in 2003

Weybridge – River Wey: up to ten pairs in 1991

Wisley: 1970-91, 12 holes in 1970

Wrecclesham Sand Pits: up to 25 holes, 2000-2002

Spelthorne

Shepperton: 36 pairs in 1985

Calendar. Bucknill said that Sand Martins normally arrived around 8th April. Glegg (1935) gave the average arrival date in Middlesex for 23 (non-consecutive) years as 19th April. The average arrival date in the London area south of the Thames from 1929 to 1939 was 3rd April. The arrivals chart shows that Glegg's date is about a month later than the average for Surrey since the 1950s, as well as showing the correlation between mean temperature and arrival date. Currently, autumn flocks begin to collect from mid July. October birds include one at Papercourt Gravel Pits on 22nd October 1972, ten at Beddington Sewage Farm on 24th October 1990, a juvenile at Godalming on 27th October 1959, one at Beddington Sewage Farm on 30th October 1932 and there

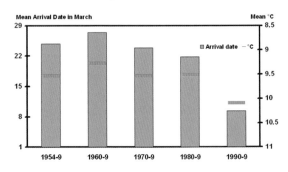

have been a few in November. A Sand Martin at Walton Reservoirs on 14th-15th December 2000 was the first for December and the latest on record for Surrey. A sign of climate change? Maybe not, since one perched on a chimney at Egham on 2nd January 1948 (*BB, 42:186*). Other early and late dates are:

Early		Late	
3rd March 1994	Elstead	3rd November 1977:	Holmethorpe Sand Pits
3rd March 1998	Unstead Sewage Farm	6th November 1949:	Staines reservoirs
5th March 2003	Beddington Sewage Farm	14th-15th December 2000:	Walton Reservoirs
6th March 1997	Frensham Little Pond		
8th March 1995	Holmethorpe Sand Pits		
9th March 1992	Apps Court Sand Pit		

Large counts and movements. The biggest counts are more than 30 years old.

Beddington Sewage Farm: 800, 25th September 1999

Frensham: 800, 24th July 1977; roost of 300, 20th October 1962 (Parr); 1,000+ on 25th April 1989

Holmethorpe Sand Pits: 2,000-3,000, June/July 1967

Queen Elizabeth II Reservoir: 1,500, 17th July 1995

Thorpe Gravel Pits: 800, 5th and 12th September 1965

Spelthorne

King George VI Reservoir: *c*.1,000, 1st April 1966

Perry Oaks Sewage Farm: passage of at least 4,000, 6th August 1958

Queen Mary Reservoir: 7,000, 12th August 1967

Staines Reservoirs: *c*.8,000, 11th August 1966; 5,000 SSW, 20th August 1968; *c*.1,000, 18th April 1970; 2,000-3,000; 9th August 1980

Returning Sand Martins may not go back to their natal colony. Also, wandering juveniles of continental origin may be found at British colonies as early as late July (*Ringing and Migration* 2:192), so Sand Martins at around this time can present problems of origin. One of unknown hatch locality was ringed at a Virginia Water colony on 20th July 1975 and controlled at a colony at Herongen, Germany, where it may have been breeding, on 16th July 1976 (*Ringing and Migration 1:232*). The bird was seen again at or near Herongen in the Augusts of 1977 and 1978.

Movements. European recoveries of Sand Martins ringed in Surrey have come from Belgium (three), France (eight), Germany (four), Luxemburg (one) and Spain (nine). Three ringed in France and one ringed in the Netherlands have been recovered in Surrey. There are six African recoveries:

Ringed				Recovered			Distance
Wrecclesham	Surrey	27th July	1962	Figuig	Morocco	2nd May 1963	
Godstone	Surrey	5th August	1966	Missour	Morocco	13th April 1967	
Farnham	Surrey	7th August	1966	Le Kef	Tunisia	24th April 1967	
Farnham	Surrey	8th July	1989	Fleuve	Senegal	9th March 1991	4,108 km
Virginia Water	Surrey	9th June	1989	Fleuve	Senegal	11th March 1991	4,133 km
Fleuve	Senegal	2nd January	1992	Queen Mary Reservoir	Surrey	6th June 1993	4,138 km

Longevity. Three Sand Martins are known to have lived at least five years, the longest lived being one ringed at Lydd, Kent on 16th July 1968 and recovered at Virginia Water on 22nd July 1973.

Plumage variations. A cinnamon-coloured bird was seen at Brooklands Sewage Farm on 2nd August 1929, a leucistic bird at King George VI Reservoir on 31st August 1981 and an albino at Walton Reservoirs on 7th July 1995.

Swallow (Barn Swallow)

Moderately common summer visitor, breeding annually

Hirundo rustica

Breeds across Europe, North Africa, Asia and North America. Virtually all winter south of the breeding range. British birds winter in Southern Africa as far south as the Cape. Swallows were present in southern Britain half a million years ago but it may not have been until much later, with forest clearance and the spread of buildings, that they became at all common (Harrison, 1988). Numbers and range in Britain have been fairly stable since 1800, with an increase since 1970. Swallows from North Sea and Baltic countries have been found in Britain (*MA*).

Early Surrey history. Gilbert White wrote of the *myriads of the Swallow kind* seen annually at Sunbury in the autumn (*Natural History of Selbourne, Letter X, 1767*, referring to a period about ten years earlier). He saw a Swallow at Ripley on 4th April 1778 and recorded others feeding young at William Curtis's botanic garden in Lambeth on 27th June 1780.

Jesse (1832-35) described Swallows feeding over the Thames in autumn and they were listed for the Godalming district by Newman in 1849. Swallows were common in the late 19th century. They nested at Battersea in 1884 and in Battersea Park around 1896.

Since 1900. Kerr (1906) described Swallows as common in the Staines area. Boorman collected eggs at Ockham, Ripley and Send between 1902 and 1910. Dixon (1909) said they bred at Barnes, Streatham and Tooting. Eggs were collected at Flutters Hill, Chobham in 1916 (Maitland and Turnbull). Pairs bred at West Dulwich in 1928 and Camberwell in 1945 (*BLA*). They often bred at Ham House from 1950 to 1976, but less often in Richmond Park (*BRP*). At Wimbledon Common, they bred up to 1981 or 1982 but are now only passage migrants (Hewlett). A pair bred under the gang plank of a launch on the Thames at Teddington in 1986 (*LBR*). Swallows bred at Beddington Sewage Farm in 1989, the first for many years (*LBR*). Swallows were breeding in the Shepperton area in 1983-86. The 2003 BTO Spring Migration Watch in Spelthorne picked up counts of up to 70 birds.

Trend since 1970. Of the 231 tetrads in northeast Surrey, 81% were found to hold territories in the 1968-72 Atlas survey but only 64% in the 1988-97 Atlas. The Common Birds Census shows a large and significant increase not entirely consistent with other evidence. Some of the largest movements have been in recent years but these birds have probably not bred in Surrey.

Population size. Common Birds Census densities have risen significantly since 1970. Virtually all the territories were on farmland. The sample size is small, and may not be representative of all farmland in Surrey. The 1994-2004 Breeding Bird Survey suggests a breeding season population of about 3,000 adults. The Common Birds Census suggests rather more, between 4,000 and 8,000 territories. If Surrey held a proportionate share of the British breeding population as given by the *New Atlas*, the population would be about 4,000 territories, or 2 per square km, which is surprisingly close.

Nesting. Young may be seen as early as mid May (*e.g.* Brooklands, 1966).

Calendar. Aldridge (1885) wrote that Swallows arrived in March in the Norwood district. Bucknill said they normally arrived around 8th April. Glegg (1935) gave the average arrival date in Middlesex for 56 (non-consecutive) years as 14th April. The average arrival date in the London area south of the Thames from

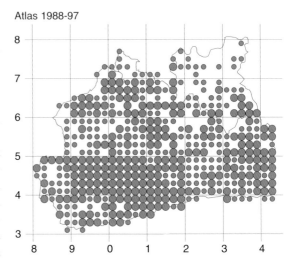

Atlas 1988-97

1929 to 1939 was 6th April. The chart shows that Glegg's date is at least three weeks later than the average for Surrey since the 1950s, as well as showing the correlation between mean temperature and arrival date. The average final date in the London area south of the Thames from 1929 to 1939 was 5th November. Bucknill knew of November and December records.

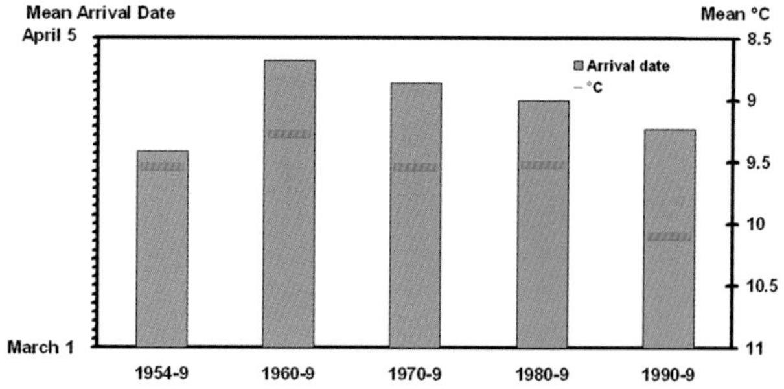

More recent extreme dates are:

Early

3rd March 1956   Guildford Sewage Farm
16th March 1977   Gatton
19th March 1961   Frensham Great Pond
19th March 1990   Frensham Great Pond
19th March 2000   Barn Elms Reservoirs
Spelthorne
31st March 1972   Queen Mary Reservoir (Geen)

Late

22nd November 1981 Beddington Sewage Farm
23rd November 1961   Molesey
28th November 1998   Unstead Sewage Farm
4th December 1949   Godstone
9th December 1970   Thorpe
Spelthorne
21st November 1970   Queen Mary Reservoir
      (Geen)

Large counts (probably includes some roosts)

Epsom Downs: 500+, 18th September 1979
Frensham Great Pond: 500, 22nd September 1985
Grayswood: flock of *c*.1,000, 29th August 1975
Guildford Sewage Farm: *c*.500, 5th July 1966 (Parr)

Guildford Sewage Farm: *c*.800, 28th August 1968
Tadworth: 500, 19th August 1970
Unstead Sewage Farm: 500+, 13th August 1973.
Vachery: 500, 18th April 1964

Current numbers are lower but there were 200 at Wraysbury Reservoir on 19th September 2000 and 200 at Staines Reservoirs on 8th October 2001.

Roosts. There were 5,000 in a reedbed at Epsom Sewage Farm on 7th September 1955. About 1,000 roosted at a small Elstead pond on 18th September 1967. A roost was established at a dry *Typha* bed at Unstead Sewage Farm in 1998. Numbers built up from 500 on 31st August and peaked at 4,000 on 4th September, with 1,000 on the following day.

Movements. Visible migration is most obvious in September and there was an exceptionally heavy passage in September 1999. Large movements include:

Richmond Park: 1,000-1,200 per hour southwest, 26th August and 9th September 1957 (Parr)
Hersham Sewage Farm: *c*.1,400 in two hours, 21st July 1962
Worcester Park Sewage Farm: 1,400 southeast in two hours, 19th September 1969
Pebble Combe: 2,000 in two hours, 16th September 1973
Capel: 1,200 south, 20th September 1994
Milford: 2,200 south, 25th September 1999
Morden Hall Park: 1,500 west, 25th September 1999

Beddington Sewage Farm: 3,040 west, 26th September 1999
Farthing Down: over 5,000 an hour, 26th September 1999
Queen Elizabeth II Reservoir: 1,250 southwest, 26th September 1999
South Norwood Lake: 2,200 west, 26th September 1999
Unstead Sewage Farm: 7,500 south, 26th September 1999

European ringing recoveries have come from France (seven), Italy (one), the Netherlands (two), the Republic of Ireland (three) and Spain (three). These are the ones found for Africa, all but one before 1977:

Ringed			Recovered				Distance
Weybridge	21st August	1972	Ksar Mellaha	Morocco	c.21st June	1976	
Chertsey	6th August	1976	Victoria	Cameroon	c.5th November	1976	
Capel	22nd August	1993	Donga, Mantung	Cameroon	16th April	1994	
Ewhurst	11th September	1962	southwest of Kimberley	South Africa	17th November	1962	
Ewhurst	22nd August	1968	Thabazimbi, Transvaal	South Africa	13th November	1968	
Lyne	24th June	1972	Penvaan, Natal	South Africa	1st February	1973	
Cobham	20th June	1970	Hofmeyer	South Africa	December	1970	9,590 km
Kempton Park	14th August	1971	Port Elizabeth	South Africa	25th January	1972	9,827 km

Longevity. One ringed in the nest at Thorpe on 8th August 1982 and recovered at Thorpe on 13th October 1987 showed site fidelity as well as being the oldest bird found by ringing. Cricket was a hazard for 19th century Swallows. One was killed by a ball bowled by Fred Caesar to Lord Winternon at Godalming in 1849 or 1850. Other similar deaths (probably not in Surrey) are cited by Bucknill.

Plumage variations. Bucknill mentioned a pied specimen shot at East Molesey in May, 1872. There was a leucistic bird at Beddington Sewage Farm on 28th September 1993.

House Martin *Delichon urbicum* (*Delichon urbica*)

Common summer visitor, breeding annually

Breeds across Europe and Asia and winters south of the breeding range, in Africa south of the Sahara and in southeast Asia. The British population seems to have been stable, at least up to the end of the 1980s, in spite of 19th century perceived competition for nest sites from a rising population of House Sparrows (sadly not now a problem). Since the 1980s numbers have fluctuated and are currently rising. Numbers have fluctuated in other parts of the European range. In Britain, nest sites on cliffs and in caves had been largely replaced by artificial structures such as buildings, by the 19th century, though they were still occasionally used.

Surrey has no natural cliffs or caves suitable for House Martins, so that the entire breeding population is in some way dependent on human activities. The House Martin is one of the species which has responded markedly to changes in the quality of London's air.

Early Surrey history. House Martins were well known as urban breeding birds during the 18th century. One of Gilbert White's correspondents saw one going in and out of a nest in The Borough, Bermondsey on 23rd October 1767 (*Natural History of Selbourne, Letter X* to Daines Barrington) and he had seen them himself by 1773 (Letter XIV). On 5th June 1782 his brother Thomas nailed several large scallop shells on the eaves of his South Lambeth house to see if House Martins would nest in them and, within half an hour, several pairs had settled on them and begun building. Air pollution later killed off the airborne insect population and drove House Martins out of the Surrey part of central London though they held on in the inner suburbs. William Cobbett described House Martins as being 'in abundance' over farm land between Reigate and Crawley on 5th May 1823 (Parker, 1952). House Martins were abundant at Wimbledon (Hamilton, 1881). Aldridge (1885) mentioned nests at Norwood and Power (1910) knew of nests in Balham, Dulwich and Tooting. Eggs were collected at Shackleford in 1893 (Maitland and Turnbull).

1900 to 1950. There is not much detailed information about the first half of the 20th century but House Martins appear to have bred in most of the county. House Martins were common in the Staines area (Kerr, 1906). Boorman collected eggs from Ockham, Send (1902, 1903) and West Clandon (1903). There were about 70 at Oxted Mill early in the century (Parr).

Since 1950. The Clean Air Act of 1956 led to a gradual recolonisation of central London. Censuses in two 1 km squares at Barnes in 1949 and 1974 showed an increase from 17 to 28 nests as part of a larger and more general London area increase (Strangeman, 1977). There were colonies at Mitcham and New Malden in 1939 (*LBR*) and Streatham and Tooting in 1965 (Parr). House Martins have been breeding in Richmond Park since 1964 (*BRP*). A 1968 survey found 405 nests at Alfold, Bramley, Chilworth, Cranleigh, Dunsfold, and Ewhurst (Parr).

Trend since 1970. Of the 231 tetrads in northeast Surrey, 88% were found to hold territories in the 1968-72 Atlas survey and 86% in the 1988-97 Atlas, very little change. House Martins rarely registered in the Common Birds Census areas.

Local studies. House Martins were breeding freely in residential areas at Shepperton in the 1980s. They bred at Swan Street SE1 in 1980, apparently the first Surrey Inner London breeding record for many years. There were up to 16 nests at Burgess Park and 12 at Rotherhithe Station in 1991. A study of active House Martin nests at East Molesey by David Griffin found 155 in 1995 and 180 in 1996 but since then there was been a substantial fall, with 124 in 2000, 122 in 2001, 114 in 2002, 116 in 2003, 127 in 2004, 116 in 2005 and only 95 in 2006. Nesting was being discouraged by some householders, who had streamers hanging from their eaves. There were about 40 nests at

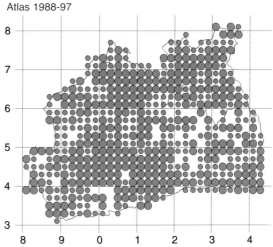

Atlas 1988-97

Garsons/Winterhouse Farm, Esher in 2000-2002. Quite large numbers of nests are sometimes found on individual buildings, for example 50-70 on the Memorial Gates at Polesden Lacey in 1969-70 and 26 nests on Barclays Bank, Cobham in 1973. Twenty pairs raised 83 young on a house at Thorpe in 1995 (H. M. Bolds).

Population size. The 1994-2004 Breeding Birds Survey suggests a breeding season population of at least 6,000 adults. If Surrey held a proportionate share of the British breeding population as given by the *New Atlas*, the population would be less than 3,000 territories, or 1.3 per square km, a very similar figure.

Nest sites. Cliff-like nest sites have been recorded from time to time. J. D. Salmon found House Martins nesting in chalk quarries at Guildford and Wanborough. At the Wanborough site he found 150 nests attached to the face of the chalk under projecting ledges. The nests were made of powdered chalk with the occasional belt of darker material and were hard to see against the rock (Newman, 1849). Frohawk noticed a House Martin's nest next to a wasp nest on the gardener's house at Wisley, both nests being occupied (Frohawk, 1891).

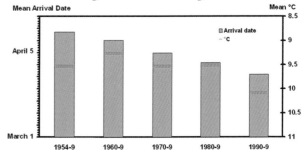

Calendar. Glegg (1935) gave the average arrival date in Middlesex for 35 (non-consecutive) years as 23rd April. The average arrival date in the London area south of the Thames from 1929 to 1939 was 10th April. The chart shows that Glegg's date is nearly three weeks later than the average for Surrey since the 1950s, as well as showing the correlation between mean temperature and arrival date.

The average final date in the London area south of the Thames from 1929 to 1939 was 28th October. Geen gave extreme dates at Queen Mary Reservoir of 13th April 1974 and 6th November 1976. Dates for the county are:

Early		Late	
12th March 1979	Carshalton Beeches	8th November 1902	Dulwich Park (Power).
19th March 1938	Surrey (*The Field, 26th March 1938* in *LBR*)	28th November 1926	Staines town (*LN*).
		2nd December 1963	South Nutfield
23rd March 1992	Betchworth	4th December 1962	Milford
23rd March 1988	Frensham Great Pond	7th December 1975	Tongham
24th March 1995	Hurst Park, Molesey	12th December 1974	New Addington
26th March 1997	New Haw		
27th March 1959	Guildford Sewage Farm		

Large counts. In the autumn there are often large flocks of House Martins at the reservoirs and many are on the move, passing across open country without much of a pause, unless grounded by bad weather. These are some examples:

Barn Elms: 1,650, 30th September 2001

Battersea Park: 1,000, 17th September 1989

Beddington Sewage Farm: several thousand, 16th October 1938 after strong winds earlier in October; 2,000, 30th September 1988; 5,000, 24th September 1995

Capel: 1,800, 25th September 1992

Mizen's Farm, Horsell: 1,000, 19th September 2002

Thursley: 4,000+, 14th September 2000

Unstead Sewage Farm: 3,000, 20th and 22nd September 2000

Walton Reservoirs: *c*.1,000, 6th-7th September 2000

Witley: 5,000-6,000 brought down by heavy rain, 19th September 1990

Spelthorne

Staines Reservoirs: 2,000, 10th September 1983; 5,000, 10th September 1995

Wraysbury Reservoir: 2,500, 24th September 1984; 3,000, 2nd September 1995

The largest available recent counts are 1,000+ at Wraysbury on 16th September 2000 (*LBR*) and at Staines Reservoirs on 25th September 2004 (*LNHSB*).

Visible migration is most obvious in the autumn, some of the larger counts being these:

Beddington Sewage Farm: 5,000 southeast in small flocks, 24th September 1995; 2,000 through, 2nd October 1995

Chilworth: 1,000+ south, 1st and 8th October 2000

Hersham Sewage Farm: 1,500 per hour for two hours on 21st July 1962

Holmethorpe Sand Pits: 2,185 southwest, 9th October 1999

Leatherhead: *c*.2,000 pushed south by rain, 29th September 1960 (*BLA*).

Richmond Park: 2,000 through, 26th September 1999

South Norwood Lake: 2,350 WSW at 12.25-

12.58, 30th September 2001

Stoke Lake: 700 southwest in five minutes, 25th September 1995

Tadworth/Walton Downs: 3,000 ESE on 23rd and 24th September 1977

Unstead Sewage Farm: 3,000 south, 26th September 1999

Witley: Several thousand southwest, 14th September 1987; a similar number west, 18th September 2000

Spelthorne

Staines Reservoirs: 2,000 west in two hours, 1st October 1968

Movements. There are European recoveries from France (two) and Spain (two). There are also three African recoveries, but none from the presumed West African wintering area.

Ringed			Recovered				Distance
Polesden Lacey	28th July	1972	Berkine, Taza	Morocco	6th June	1974	1,965 km
Farnham Sewage Farm	9th October	1981	Taourirt	Morocco	22nd November	1981	1,874 km
Aldhurst Farm, Capel	5th September	1993	Khemisti	Algeria	15th September	1993	2,103 km

Longevity. The greatest fully documented age established by ringing is of a House Martin ringed at Hersham on 4th May 1963 and recovered there five years later, on 5th May 1968. There is also an unpublished record longevity of six years (per Richard A. Denyer).

Parasites. A juvenile trapped at Beddington Sewage Farm on 2nd July 1972 carried 36 louse flies *Sterepteryx hirundinis* and a flea.

Plumage variations. Bucknill had seen one or two pure white birds. Another was killed at Cranleigh. Pounds mentioned an albino at Godstone (1921). There were two in the Hampton/Sunbury area in 1945. A 'complete albino' nested at Blindley Heath in 1976 and one was seen at Barn Elms WWT on 16th August 1999. Leucistic birds were seen at Barn Elms, Beddington and Kingston Vale in 1979, at Queen Mary Reservoir in 1986, and at Burgess Park in 1992.

Red-rumped Swallow *Cecropis daurica* (*Hirundo daurica*)

Six birds, including three in Spelthorne

Another migratory southern species, breeding from Iberia and Africa east to Japan, with European birds wintering in Africa. British records are mainly in eastern and southern coastal counties. They peak in May, with a smaller autumn passage to mid November.

Surrey. The records for our area are all of single birds in April or May:

1973:* Staines Reservoirs on 17th May (R. J. Johns, *BB, 69:361*).

1996:* Staines Reservoirs for 40 minutes on 6th May (M. Holt, *BB, 90:491*).

1997: Stoke Lake, found by J. Gates on 6th May (*BB, 91:498*). It was seen again on the 7th, 11th and 12th.

1999: Beddington Sewage Farm, flew east at 0815 hrs on 16th May (G. D. J. Messenbird, *BB, 93:546*).

2003: Beddington Sewage Farm on 28th April (*BB, 97:591*).

2003:* Staines Reservoirs on 28th April (R. E. Innes, F. J. Maroevic *et al.*, *BB, 98 667*).

*Spelthorne

Richard's Pipit *Anthus richardii* (*Anthus novaeseelandiae*)

At least six birds, including two in Spelthorne

The breeding range runs from Siberia east to Mongolia and also includes Africa and New Zealand. Northern birds winter in India and Asia. In Britain, almost entirely autumn migrants, peaking in October and appearing mainly in eastern and southern coastal counties. There are records from a number of inland counties, mainly in the south.

Surrey. In 1837 the British Museum obtained a specimen which was stated to have come from Bermondsey (Yarrell). This might be one of the two said to have been caught near London in that year by Gould and might be the possible Tooting Common bird mentioned by Blyth (1836). Three of the six dated records for our area are for April:

1956:* Staines Reservoirs, one on 10th and 21st April.

1958:   Beddington Sewage Farm, one on 17th-18th April (J, Cook, H. P. Medhurst, B. Milne, *BB*, *53:171*), notes in the *LBR* for 1958.

1958:* King George VI Reservoir, one on 30th April (Mrs V. A. Gillham, *BB*, *53:171*).

1970:   Beddington Sewage Farm, two on 23rd October, one on 25th and 26th (*BB*, *64:362*).

1986:* Staines Reservoirs, one on 26th September.

1994:   Barn Elms Reservoirs, one on 26th September, during a national influx.

*Spelthorne

Tawny Pipit   *Anthus campestris*

Seven records, including four from Spelthorne

Southern and eastern breeding range from Africa and Iberia east to Mongolia, northern birds wintering in Africa and Saudi Arabia. Most of those found in Britain are on autumn passage, which peaks at the end of September. Spring passage is lighter and less peaked, running from March to June. The majority of the birds are found in southern and eastern coastal counties.

Surrey. Two in spring, five in autumn:

1954:* Perry Oaks Sewage Farm, one on 17th October (*LBR* for 1955).

1963:* Perry Oaks Sewage Farm, an immature bird on 15th September (to 18th in the *LBR*). Perry Oaks Sewage Farm, an adult on 22nd September (*BB*, *57:275*).

1975:   Pirbright (Cleygate Common), one on 23rd March (one of only two spring records from inland counties from 1958 to 1985).

1989:   Beddington Sewage Farm, an adult from 30th September to 2nd October.

1990:* King George VI and Staines reservoirs, one on 3rd and 4th May.

1992:   Beddington Sewage Farm, two first-winter birds on 6th September.

*Spelthorne (the three Perry Oaks birds may have been outside the boundary)

Tree Pipit   *Anthus trivialis*

Locally common summer visitor, breeding annually

Breeds in Europe and Asia and winters south of its breeding range. European birds winter in Africa south of the Sahara, others in India. Tree Pipits were common over much of England and Wales during the 19th century and their range extended into most of Scotland before 1900. They remained common across Britain for much of the 20th century but breeding numbers fell by over 60% from 1970 to 2001. In Britain this may be due to fewer young conifers and less woodland management (Fuller *et al.*, 2005). Tree Pipits need a tree at least 15 feet high for a song post (Venables, 1937). Declines have been recorded in other parts of western Europe.

Surrey. Breeding Tree Pipits are now almost exclusively confined to heathland with scattered trees, where they nest on the ground. Migrants are sometimes found well away from these areas, for example over Battersea Park in April 1945 and at the Surrey Docks in 1977.

Early Surrey history. They were mentioned as summer visitors to the Godalming district without further comment by Newman (1849). Hamilton (1881) listed them for Putney Heath and Wimbledon Common. They were common summer visitors in or around 1884 (*SALEC*) and 1900 (Bucknill (1900), but evidently less so in Spelthorne. Kerr (1906) said he had found only one Staines area nest in twelve years.

1900 to the 1960s. Dixon (1909) mentioned Tree Pipits as breeding at Streatham and Norwood where they were later pushed out by housing development. They were never common in the Dulwich district (Power). Further out, eggs collected by Boorman at Newlands Corner (1910), Ockham (1905,

1906, 1909), Send (1908, 1909), Send Gravel Pits (1907, 1909, 1910) and Wisley Common (1907, 1908) are in the Haslemere Museum. An LNHS field meeting found eight nests at Warlingham on 25th May 1919, more than would be found today. Eggs were collected at Woking in the 1920s (SBC archive) and at Chobham Common in 1921 and 1927. Tree Pipits were still plentiful on downland around Warlingham at about this time (Beadell, 1932). There were up to four pairs at Limpsfield Common in the 1930s. Eggs were collected at Epsom Common in 1934. Tree Pipits were common around Haslemere in that year. One that flew over Battersea Park on 21st April 1945 was very unusual for the inner suburbs.

In Richmond Park, Tree Pipits were summer visitors, breeding in the bracken and commoner than Meadow Pipits (Mouritz, 1905), with fifteen singing males in 1935 (Collenette, *BRP*), and they were there until at least the late 1960s, but since then there have been only occasional birds in territory. Up to twelve pairs bred on Bookham Common before 1940, numbers falling with the growth of scrub (Parr). Eggs were collected there in 1923 and 1949. Eggs were collected at Hindhead in 1947.

Early Surrey Bird Reports had nothing to say about the breeding season distribution of Tree Pipits, beyond noting them as common summer visitors and that they may have been increasing. The first published information came in 1963, when Tree Pipits were said to be well reported, with about 50 pairs around Dorking, ten singing at Esher Common, seven singing at Headley Heath, 12 pairs at Holt Wood and six singing at Thursley Common. Tree Pipits were reported from 27 sites in 1966 and 30 in 1969.

Change in numbers since 1970. A 1985-87 survey in Palmer (1988) shows a contraction of range in northeast Surrey compared with that in the 1968-72 Atlas. This was confirmed in the 1988-97 SBC Atlas survey, where only nine tetrads were found to be occupied in the LNHS area, compared with 61 in 1968-72. Most of the sites along the North Downs, from Ranmore and Boxhill north and east to Epsom and Reigate seem to have been lost and numbers at Headley Heath are much reduced. It is more difficult to say what has happened in the remainder of Surrey. There is little overall change in the number of Tree Pipit sites in the Surrey Bird Reports, as the table shows. Admittedly these must be incomplete, given the 61 Atlas tetrads in northeast Surrey alone.

Number of sites, where given in Surrey Bird Reports, 1966-2001

Year	1966	1967	1968	1969	1970	1971	1972	1973	1974	1975	1976	1977	1979	1980
Sites	27	27	22	30	19L	15	19	26	27	19	19	12	20	16
Year	1981	1982	1983	1984	1985	1987	1988	1989	1990	1993	1994	1995	1996	1997
Sites	18	17	19	20	25	14	11	35	26	14	25	17	22	30
Year	1998	1999	2000	2001										
Sites	29	30	20	28										

L – London area only

No Tree Pipit territories were found at Common Birds Census sites after 1985, probably because heathlands were phased out of the census. One or two pairs bred at Staines Reservoirs in 1968, where they now appear as migrants only. Numbers have held up well on most of the heathlands. Forty singing males were found on Hankley Common and ten on Thursley/Ockley Commons in 1978 and numbers were thought not to have declined over the previous 20 years.

Where found since 1994. Annual figures for the main sites, where available, are these:

Territories on heathlands 1994 to 2004

	1994	1995	1996	1997	1998	1999	2000	2001	2002	2003	2004
Crooksbury Common	2	8	4	4	6	7	6	7	4	5	3
Frensham Common	17	15	12	10	13	16	15	18	12	14	13
Hankley Common	18	15	22	18	27	28	43	41	23	22	15
Hindhead	9	8	12	11	10	10	12	16	14	13	13

	1994	1995	1996	1997	1998	1999	2000	2001	2002	2003	2004
Olddean Common			13	18	21	21	18	33			14
Pirbright Common/ Ash Ranges		67		85		94	67	90	62		
Thursley/Ockley/ Elstead Commons	22	22	19	12	14	14	10	21	11	13	10
West End Common/ Pirbright Ranges		54		53				57			20

From counts organised by John Clark. Table omits incomplete counts.

Other places where Tree Pipits have held territory since 1994 include Bagmoor Common, Bagshot Heath, Bisley, Blackheath, Botany Bay, Bourne Woods, Brentmoor Heath, Bricksbury Hill, Brookwood, Bullswater Common, Capel, Chelsham, Churt Common, Cobbetthill Common, Farley Heath, Hascombe, Holmbury Hill, Horsell Common, Leith Hill, Limpsfield Chart, Mare Hill (Witley), Milford Common, Mytchett Place, Netley Heath, Pitch Hill, Richmond Park, Walton Heath, White Downs, Whitmoor Common, Whitmore Vale, Wimbledon Common, Winterfold and Witley Common.

Population size. The 1994-2004 Breeding Birds Survey suggests a breeding season population of at least 200 adults, rather short of the likely total. There are no comprehensive estimates of total numbers before 1994 but since then there has been an increase:

Atlas 1988-97

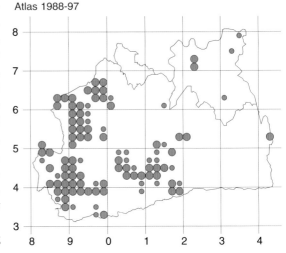

Vice-county territories 1994-2001

Year	1994	1995	1996	1997	1998	1999	2000	2001
Pairs	220	249	185	265	265	341	308	335

Calendar. The average arrival date in the London area south of the Thames from 1929 to 1939 was 3rd April. Early and late dates are:

First

10th March 1995	Thursley Common
12th March 1994	Stoke Lake, Guildford
15th March 1983	Thursley
16th March 1993	Capel
20th March 1977	Ashtead Common

Last

18th October 1998	Beddington Sewage Farm
19th October 1993	Capel
19th October 2001	Barn Elms
26th October 2003	Wimbledon Common
30th October 1984	Tilhill

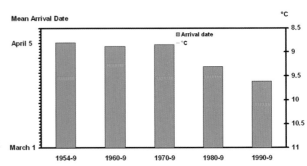

The chart shows that Tree Pipit arrival dates have tended to reflect climate change since the 1950s.

Counts at non-breeding sites include one at Bermondsey on 22nd May 1996, a total of nine migrants at Stoke Lake during the period 3rd-18th September 1995 and a total of 14 at Beddington in September/October 1998.

Movements and longevity. There are no recoveries of Surrey-ringed birds from the African wintering areas, but two young ringed in Surrey and recovered in Portugal indicate the route. One of these was ringed at Haslemere on 29th June 1962 and recovered 1,362 km south in Beira Litoral on 20th September 1962. The other was ringed at Ash on 30th May 1974 and recovered over 15 months later and a similar distance south at Beira Baixa on 8th September 1975. One ringed in France on 21st August 1999 and recovered at Brookwood on 2nd June 2000 is thought to be only the fourth ever foreign-ringed Tree Pipit to be found in Britain.

A Tree Pipit ringed as a nestling at Chelsham on 5th August 1963 was found dead two km away on 24th July 1966 (BTO). Adders will prey on Tree Pipit nests (see the *SBR* for 1973). Predation of singing males by Kestrels has been blamed for a reduction of the breeding population at Banstead Downs (*SBR* for 1980). In 1976, most of the Tree Pipit nests at Chobham were lost to fire. Tree Pipits at Thursley were singing in the centre of the fire area of that year only a few days after the burn.

Meadow Pipit   *Anthus pratensis*

Moderately common resident and winter visitor, breeding annually

Breeds in Greenland, Iceland and northern Europe, most wintering in western Europe and south as far as North Africa and the Middle East. As breeding birds, Meadow Pipits are typical of upland moors and grasslands, using lowland habitats of a similar type where they exist. Numbers and range seem to have been fairly stable from 1800 to the 1970s, though there have been decreases due to habitat changes. Numbers have declined by perhaps a third since then.

Surrey. Although Meadow Pipits are now mainly found on heathland, they will breed in rough grass where it is suitable, as it used to be in several places around Guildford in the 1970s. The grassy banks of reservoirs have proved to be very acceptable. The grass has to be six inches or more long, and rather coarse. A good deal of the rough grassland in Surrey has been lost since 1900, to housing up to the 1940s, and later to scrub with the cessation of grazing and for recreational use as in Stoke Park, Guildford and on Merrow Downs.

Early Surrey history. Newman listed Meadow Pipits for the Godalming district without comment in 1849. Hamilton (1881) listed them for Putney Heath and for Wimbledon Common but did not mention breeding. In Surrey they were said to be common residents in 1900 (*Historical Atlas*), at least locally. Bucknill remarked that numbers were *reinforced in spring by a considerable addition to its numbers from the south*, a curious comment for a bird which is currently best known as a winter visitor and passage migrant rather than a spring arrival. In the Staines area there were large numbers in winter but none in the summer (Kerr, 1906).

1900 to 1940. The Boorman egg collection in the Haslemere Museum includes a Meadow Pipit egg and nest from Send (1902). Meadow Pipits bred at Betchworth in 1905 (G. T. Winter). They were still breeding on Mitcham Common in 1909 but in reduced numbers because of increased recreational use of the area (Power). Eggs were collected at Chobham Common in 1920-21 and Meadow Pipits bred on Wandsworth Common in the 1920s (*BLA*). Mouritz (1905) said they were rather uncommon in Richmond Park, and essentially winter visitors, though a few pairs were breeding there by the 1930s (Collenette) and breeding continued into the 1990s. Meadow Pipits were only winter visitors to the Warlingham district (Beadell, 1932). Several pairs nested near Frensham and one or two at Thursley in 1934, much the same numbers as can be found there today. 'Many pairs' were said to be at Frensham in

1935, when there were a few pairs at Thursley and one or two at Hindhead (*SEBR*). H. T. Gosnell collected seven clutches containing Cuckoo eggs at Frensham in 1932-34 (SBC archive).

1941 to 1960s. In the 1950s, Meadow Pipits were breeding on Streatham Common and on Elmers End and other sewage farms (*BLA*). A 1957 census found 39+ pairs in the Surrey part of the London area: Arbrook Common one, Banstead Downs about seven, Embercourt one, Epsom Downs three, Headley Heath fourteen, Hook one, near Island Barn Reservoir one, Nutfield one or more, Prince's Coverts one of more, Reigate Heath one, Richmond Park one, Walton Heath four and Wimbledon Common three (Homes *et al.*, 1960). The Surrey population probably reached a 20th century peak in the 1960s. Of four nests found on Hankley Common in 1960, three held Cuckoo eggs. P. G. Davis found fifty nests at Frensham in 1968, of which six contained Cuckoos.

1970 to 2000. The Winter Atlas found partial survey counts and estimates totalling 950 birds in 1981-84, a figure which would have included many non-breeding birds. The decline in breeding numbers in Surrey is probably greater than the 3.2% recorded for Britain as a whole between the 1968-72 and 1988-91 BTO Atlas surveys. Good figures are available from 1994 but a baseline for the 1970s is hard to construct from the rather scrappy nature of the information for the 1970s and 80s. Of the 231 tetrads in northeast Surrey, 35% were found to hold territories in the 1968-72 Atlas survey but only 21% in the 1988-97 Atlas. The last territory to be picked up by the Common Birds Census was in 1985. Most Meadow Pipits were on Banstead Downs, on Chobham, Epsom, Frensham and Hankley Commons and at Walton Reservoirs. Only one was ever found on farmland. The census covers the main sites in its later years so it is not a good guide. The 1982 BTO Breeding Waders of Wet Meadows survey included the Meadow Pipit as an additional species but again coverage of the preferred habitat was poor. Wetness is not the feature that draws Meadow Pipits to their main Surrey breeding sites. Birds were found at Old Woking, Run Common and Whitmoor Common, but there were none at the other 29 outer Surrey sites that were visited. The table of territorial pairs at currently important sites shows a significant decline only at Frensham and Pirbright. Heathland restoration at Walton Heath has increased numbers:

Territorial pairs at the main sites

	1970s		1980s		1990s		2000-04		2004
	Highest count		**Highest count**		**Highest count**		**Highest count**		**Count**
Chobham Common/Sunningdale					1999	34	2004	28	28
Churt Common					1994	1	2000	6	0
Frensham Common	1978/79	14+	1984	12	1996	4	2002	2	0
Hankley Common	1979	19	1981	27	1999	35	2002	32	15
Pirbright Commons			1985	6	1999	9	2002	2	0
Thursley/Ockley Commons			1982	7	1994	7	2002	7	7
Walton Heath			1989	3	1999	20	2004	17	17
Whitmoor Common					1996	1	2003	4	3
Total						**111**		**98**	**70**

There has been a widespread loss of the remaining breeding Meadow Pipits at downland and London area sites, nearly all of which are now deserted. Of the places where 39 pairs were found in 1957, only Molesey Heath (near Island Barn Reservoir), Richmond Park, Walton Heath and Wimbledon Common have any now. Meadow Pipits bred at the Surrey Docks in 1977, the first breeding record for any part of Inner London. Three pairs bred there in 1984 but none now do so. Twenty-seven nests were examined at Frensham in 1978 and 1979 as part of the Cuckoo study referred to in the Cuckoo account above. There were 16 territories at Banstead Downs in 1980. Some of the breeding counts in the late 1990s have been among the highest on record. In part this is because of better coverage but there seems to have been a genuine increase at some of the larger sites, including Chobham and Hankley commons. Heathland restoration on Walton Heath was followed in 1999 by an increase to 20 territories.

In Spelthorne, Meadow Pipits were present in the breeding season at Staines Reservoir in 1971 and resident in the Shepperton area in the 1980s, with at least nine breeding pairs in 1986. Single pairs were at the doomed Perry Oaks Sewage Farm in 1999 and 2000. There were three pairs at Staines Moor in 2003. Meadow Pipits were still breeding at Shepperton in 2002 but the site had been disturbed by the Shepperton Bypass and none were seen there in the following year (Belsey).

Population size. The Breeding Birds Survey suggests that on average there were about 120 adult Meadow Pipits in the 1994-2004 breeding seasons. This is not very far away from the number of territorial pairs found in survey work on the western heaths.

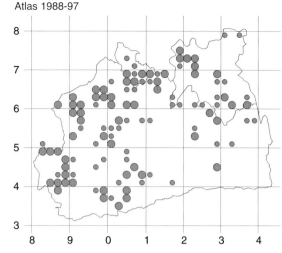

Atlas 1988-97

Large counts

Abinger Cress Beds: *c*.100, January and February 1974

Barn Elms: 85+, 29th March 1976; 574 (passage?), 3rd October 2001

Beddington Sewage Farm: 2,000, 27th March 1960

Bramley Sewage Farm: 75-100, 12th November 1972

Bricksbury/Beacon Hill: 100, 28th September 1979

Capel: up to 550 in fields, 22nd-26th September 1990

Earlswood Sewage Farm: 250, 1st January 1965

Effingham Fish Ponds: 180, 29th March 1984

Frensham: 160, 10th October 1982

Hankley Common: 200, 17th October 1998

Holmethorpe: 220, 2nd October 1994

Lammas Lands, Godalming: 150+, 22nd March 1979

Papercourt Gravel Pits: *c*.150, 22nd October 1972

Pirbright Commons: *c*.300, 30th September 1980; 253, 14th November 1981

Ripley Sewage Farm: *c*.120, 23rd March 1974; 120+, 13th October 1974

The Surrey Docks: *c*.150, 28th December 1976

Thursley/Ockley Commons: 300, 11th October 1992

Tuesley Farm, Milford: 500, 17th September 2000

Unstead Sewage Farm: 200, 10th February 1986

Walton Heath: 150+, 5th March 1977

Worcester Park allotments: 170, 19th September 1969

Spelthorne

Perry Oaks Sewage Farm: 150, 28th December 1980

Staines Moor: 140, 17th September 2002 (*LNHSB*).

Roosts. At least 120 roosted on the Pirbright Commons in November 1980. There were 100+ roosting in heather at Frensham on 28th September 1981. Winter roosts of around 300 birds built up at Pudmore in the early 1990s (*HSBBR*), but current numbers there are lower. At Stoke Lake, 96 roosted on 12th March 1996. A roost at Winterfold peaked at 150+ on 13th February 2001.

Movements. The breeding population is supplemented by winter immigrants and passage migrants. The main passage times are March and October. Autumn flocks of up to 50 were seen at the Surrey Docks in 1971. Flocks of a hundred or more can be found on the western heaths with smaller numbers at sites such as Richmond Park where there were, for example, about 40 on 21st October 2000. Numbers may be much larger. At least 2,000 were present at or over Beddington Sewage Farm on 27th March 1960 during a period of northwest movement elsewhere. There were flocks of up to 150 at the Surrey Docks in the winters of the 1970s. Also at this time, Meadow Pipits were seen at Vann Lake in February and March (Blaker Log). Visible passage is best observed in March, September and October. Examples of movements are:

Barn Elms: 574 SSW, 3rd October 2001

Beddington Sewage Farm: 2,000, 27th March 1960; 435, 26th September 1992; 1,400 flew over, 17th-18th March 1995

Bricksbury Hill: 120 north in two hours, 19th March 1983

Nore Hill, Chelsham: c.300 south, 1st October 2000

Thursley/Ockley Commons: 200 south in 90 minutes, 23rd September 1993

Stoke Lake: 436 southwest, 26th September 1992

Worcester Park Sewage Farm: 220 south 7-9 am, 16th September 1970

Meadow Pipits ringed in Surrey in the breeding season have been recovered in Portugal (January) and Spain (January and November), showing that some, at least, of the local breeding birds winter further south. The most remarkable foreign recovery is of a bird ringed at Wisley on 2nd November 1986 and recovered in Iceland, 2,098 km northwest on 19th May 1988, a dramatic illustration of winter immigration.

Longevity. A Meadow Pipit ringed at Hersham on 7th November 1964 and recovered there over five years later, on 30th November 1969 had the greatest age that has been determined by ringing.

Plumage variations. A bird with a white face and streaking on its forewings and upper breast was at Frensham in March 1994.

Red-throated Pipit   *Anthus cervinus*

Eight birds, including one in Spelthorne

An arctic and subarctic breeding species with a range that runs from Norway to Siberia and western Alaska. European birds winter mainly in Africa. There are well-marked spring and autumn passages, peaking in May and October respectively, and with a strong south and east coast bias. Inland records were rare up to 1985.

Surrey:

1964:* Staines Reservoirs, one on 17th-18th April (J. B. Cox, *BB, 58:367*), the first for the London area.

1988: Barn Elms Reservoirs, a male on 13th May (R. B. Hastings and J. P. P Wilczur, *BB, 82:539*). Well coloured, present for about an hour.

1992: Barn Elms Reservoirs, one in winter plumage on 28th September (R. B. Hastings *et al.*, *BB, 86:504*),

1994: Barn Elms Reservoirs, one on 14th October (N. P. Senior, *BB, 89:513*),

1995: Beddington Sewage Farm, one on 2nd November (S. J. Aspinall, *BB, 89:513*),

1996: Beddington Sewage Farm, one on 7th-12th October (J. Allan *et al.*, *BB, 90:493*, from 6th in the *LBR*, earlier still in the *BBR*, identified on the 7th),

1998: Beddington Sewage Farm, one flew over on 3rd October (J. Allan, G. D. J. Messenbird and A. Pearson, *BB, 92:587*),

2000: Beddington Sewage Farm, one on 15th October (D. Eland, N. Gardner and G. D. J. Messenbird, *BB, 94:485*),

*Spelthorne

Rock Pipit
Anthus petrosus

Scarce winter visitor and passage migrant

Rock Pipits breed around the coasts of northwest Europe from the Bay of Biscay to northwest Russia. No major changes in range or number have been located. Most British birds are of the race *A. p. petrosus* and are mainly resident or dispersive but some northern birds move south (*MA*). There is a separate race in the Outer Hebrides. Finnish, Russian and Scandinavian birds are of the race *A. p. littoralis* and move south and west in winter. There has been some extension of range. Rock/Water Pipit records have been ignored in what follows.

Early Surrey history. In Surrey, Rock Pipits are most often seen on passage in October and November, with smaller numbers in March. Some of the early reports, particularly those from sewage farms, might relate to the Water Pipit, which was treated as a race of the Rock Pipit until 1986. The first vice-county birds were in 1928, when there was one at Beddington Sewage Farm on 8th December 1928 (Bentham) and one undated at Barn Elms (*LN*). One at Staines Reservoirs on 6th January 1924 (*LN*) appears to be the first for the district, followed by single birds at Staines on 22nd September 1925 and 18th February 1927 and in 1928.

1930 to 1970. Rock Pipits were seen at *Barn Elms* (28th December 1930, 20th February 1932, October 1932 (up to six), 1937 (two) and 1946-50, 1952, 1954-55, 1957-63, 1966-70), *Beddington* (1955-56, 1958, 1961, 1963-70), *Epsom Sewage Farm* (1955-56, 1958), *Esher Sewage Farm* (1957), *Frensham* (1953, 1970), *Hersham Sewage Farm* (1970), *Holmethorpe* (1960, 1962-63), *Island Barn Reservoir* (two on 22nd October 1938 and later records) and at *Walton Reservoirs* (24th December 1930 and in 1956, 1958-59, 1963, 1966-70). Occasional sites up to 1970 included Leatherhead (1959), Molesey Sewage Farm (1959), Richmond Park (1949) and the Thames opposite Chiswick (1939) and at Mortlake (1940). Single birds were at Staines Reservoirs in 1938 and 1952. There was one at Queen Mary Reservoir on 7th October 1936 and one at Perry Oaks Sewage Farm on 13th March 1949. Later records in the Spelthorne district came in October-November 1953, 1954-58, March 1957, April 1958, September to December 1959, October-November 1964, March and October 1965 and from 1966 onwards.

Where found since 1970. Rock Pipits have been found since 1970 at Barn Elms, Beddington Sewage Farm, Berrylands Sewage Works, Capel, Frensham Great Pond, Frimley Gravel Pits, Hersham Sewage Farm, Holmethorpe, Island Barn Reservoir, Papercourt Gravel Pits, Queen Elizabeth II Reservoir, South Norwood Country Park, Stoke Lake (1989, 1999), Surbiton Sewage Works, the Surrey Docks, the Thames foreshore at Tower Bridge (1994), Unstead Sewage Farm, Walton Reservoirs and Wandsworth Park. They have been seen in Spelthorne at King George VI Reservoir, Perry Oaks Sewage Farm, Queen Mary Reservoir, Staines Moor, Staines Reservoirs and Wraysbury Reservoir.

Calendar. Arrival and departure dates are:

Early arrivals		Late departures	
8th August 1976	Frensham	11th April 1984	Barn Elms
10th September 1958	Epsom Sewage Farm	17th April 1958	Hersham Sewage Farm
17th September 1971	Surrey Docks	18th April 1958	Beddington Sewage Farm
17th September 1992	Barn Elms Reservoirs	18th April 1971	Barn Elms Reservoirs
		19th April 1994	Barn Elms Reservoirs
		24th April 1972	Frensham Great Pond

Large counts. Most parties are of up to four birds, but some are larger:

Barn Elms Reservoirs: thirteen, 18th October 1981

King George VI Reservoir: eight, 27th September 2002.

Barn Elms towpath: twelve, 9th January 1968

Staines Reservoirs: ten, 12th October 1975

Movements and longevity. One ringed at Bramley on 1st February 1976 was recovered at Eastleigh, Hampshire, 54 km WSW on 25th November 1978 (BTO). No other ringing recovery has been located.

Scandinavian Rock Pipit
Winter visitor and passage migrant

Anthus petrosus littoralis

Identification difficulties appear to have masked the true status of the race, which normally does not attain its distinctively-coloured underparts until the spring. It is now thought, from ringing evidence, that a large proportion of the Rock Pipits wintering in southeast England belong to the race *littoralis* (*BTO News* 226:24).

Surrey. Presumably this is true of those appearing in Surrey, where Rock Pipits are absent in the breeding season. Indeed *littoralis* may be the normal wintering form, although until recently this race of the Rock Pipit was thought to be a rare visitor, mostly identified in autumn and spring. Birds thought to be of the race were seen in 18 of the vice-county years from 1900 to 2001 and annually from 1990. Few Spelthorne records have been published.

A Rock Pipit with characteristics of the race was caught and ringed at Stoke Lake on 23rd March 1995 and thought to have been present all winter. It returned to Stoke Lake on 24th October and remained until 29th March 1996 (J. Gates).

The others are all, so far as is known, sight records of untrapped birds (one except where stated) with characters of the race. They are:

1966:	Beddington Sewage Farm, 15th-16th March (A. D. Prowse pers. comm., Parr)
1967:	Beddington Sewage Farm, 5th April (A D Prowse pers comm., Parr)
1982:	Barn Elms Reservoirs, 12th April
1983:	Barn Elms Reservoirs, 6th-11th April
1985:	Barn Elms Reservoirs, 20th March
1987:	Beddington Sewage Farm, March Barn Elms Reservoirs, 2nd and 27th April
1988:	Barn Elms Reservoirs, 13th and 28th March
1990:*	Staines Reservoirs, 13th March
1990:	Beddington Sewage Farm, 16th-17th March
1991:	Beddington Sewage Farm, 12th-19th January Barn Elms Reservoirs, 29th March
1991:*	Queen Mary Reservoir, 8th March
1992:	Beddington Sewage Farm, 21st March, 29th March (two), 5th April Walton Reservoirs, 25th March
1993:	Beddington Sewage Farm, 9th March, 14th March (two), 24th March Barn Elms Reservoirs, 31st March
1994:	Walton Reservoirs, 4th April

1995:	Barn Elms Reservoirs, 13th-14th March Beddington Sewage Farm, 16th-18th March
1996:	Old Woking Sewage Farm, 10th February, 3rd March Holmethorpe Sand Pits, 3rd-23rd March Beddington Sewage Farm, dates from 5th March to 4th April, two on 27th March Barn Elms, 31st March Queen Elizabeth II Reservoir/Walton Reservoirs, 2nd to 9th April
1997:	Beddington Sewage Farm, March Queen Elizabeth II Reservoir, 31st March Barn Elms Reservoirs, 12th-15th April Walton Reservoirs, 5th October (two)

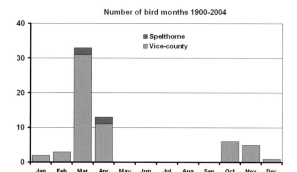

Number of bird months 1900-2004

1998: Beddington Sewage Farm, 23rd February, 16th March
Queen Elizabeth II Reservoir, 8th March
Island Barn Reservoir, 17th March (two)

1999: Barn Elms Reservoirs, 15th April (two), 16th October (two)

2000: Beddington Sewage Farm, 17th-18th March
Hersham Gravel Pit, 17th March

Barn Elms London Wetland Centre, 3rd November (four)
Queen Elizabeth II Reservoir, 20th October

2001: Barn Elms London Wetland Centre, March

2004: Beddington Sewage Farm, 16th March

2004:* Staines Reservoirs, 18th April (*LNHSB*)

* Spelthorne

Water Pipit

Anthus spinoletta

Scarce winter visitor

Breeds in mountains from southern Europe east to Siberia. Many birds from central and southern Europe (but not the Alps) winter further north and it is presumably some of these that reach the British Isles. Not much seems to be known about range or population trends.

Early Surrey history. The first for the vice-county was found at a sewage farm near Woking (Old Woking Sewage Farm?) by D. Goodwin on 11th December 1949 (*BB, 43:294*). Single birds at Smart's Heath on 24th March 1951 and at Beddington Sewage Farm on 3rd April 1955 were followed by others at Beddington in 1956-59. One at Staines Reservoirs on 15th October 1949 (W. H. D. Wince, notes in *LBR*) appears to be the first for the district, and for Surrey. There were others at King George VI Reservoir in the Octobers of 1952 and 1954 and at Staines Moor on 3rd April 1954, followed by further Spelthorne birds in 1955, 1957 and 1959.

1960s. Beddington was to become one of the two best sites for Water Pipits in the London area during the 1960s (Osborne, 1971). Water Pipits were also seen at Abinger Cress beds, Barn Elms, Earlswood Sewage Farm, Guildford Sewage Farm, Holmethorpe Sand Pits, Island Barn Reservoir, Queen Elizabeth II Reservoir, Ripley Sewage Farm, Thursley/Ockley Commons and Unstead Sewage Farm. There were five Spelthorne records, including March and November, in 1970. Geen mentioned nine Queen Mary Reservoir records up to 1973 but thought that some of them might have been Scandinavian Rock Pipits.

1970 onward. Other places, with the year of first record and selected large counts, are:

Ash Vale Gravel Pits 1974, four in 1975
Bramley Sewage Farm 1971
Bricksbury Hill 1978 (*HSBBR*)
Buckland Sand Pits 1986
Capel 1992
Farley Heath Cress Beds 1973
Farnham Sewage Farm 1976 (four)
Frimley Gravel Pits 1971
Guildford – St Catherine's 1999

Hersham Sewage Farm 1969, seven or more in 1981
Hersham Gravel Pit 1985
Horley Sewage Farm 1984
Lammas Lands, Godalming 1977
Millmead, Guildford 1976
Ockham Mill 1983
Old Woking Sewage Farm 1979
Papercourt Gravel Pits 1972

Ripley 1969, six in 1977 and 1985
South Norwood Country Park 1992
Stoke Water Meadows 1974
Walton Reservoirs 1981

Wisley Sewage Farm 1980
Worcester Park Sewage Farm 2001
Wrecclesham Floods 1984

Stoke Water Meadows was an important place for Water Pipits from at least the 1970s to the 1990s. A combination of factors produces the short grass on wet ground with shallow ditches favoured by wintering birds. A paper by Jeremy Gates (Gates, 1993) shows how the birds normally arrived in mid October and that numbers fell to a low in November or December and then rose to a much higher peak in March or April.

Beddington Sewage Farm was the main site for much of the period, with at least nine in 1970, 14+ in April 1971, about 20 on 28th November 1971 and 11 in February 1994. Unstead Sewage Farm was a significant site in the 1970s, with at least six in 1973 and it still hosts a bird or two. Water Pipits have been seen from the 1970s in Spelthorne at King George VI Reservoir, Perry Oaks Sewage Farm, Staines Reservoirs, Stanwell Moor Gravel Pits and Wraysbury Reservoir. Numbers across Surrey have been at a low level in recent years, with only single birds at any site in 2000 and a maximum of five at Staines Moor in 2001. One or two were seen at Barn Elms London Wetland Centre in 2005.

Calendar. Water Pipits begin arriving in October and leave by early May:

First of autumn		Last of spring	
1st October 1990	Beddington Sewage Farm	2nd May 1959	Barn Elms Reservoirs
1st October 1990	Unstead Sewage Farm	2nd May 2000	Staines Moor
7th October 1980	Barn Elms Reservoirs		
7th October 1983	Barn Elms Reservoirs		
7th October 2002	Barn Elms London Wetland Centre		

Large counts. Stoke Water Meadows: 17, 23rd March 1991; Beddington Sewage Farm: about 20, 28th November 1971.

Movements and longevity. Only two British-ringed Water Pipits have been recovered away from the ringing site (*MA*). One of these, also the longest lived for Surrey, is below. The other was ringed outside Surrey and recovered in the Netherlands. The Stoke recovery below shows site fidelity.

Ringed			Recovered			Distance	Age
Bramley	1st February	1966	Hampshire	25th November	1978	60 km	12 years 9 months
Stoke, Guildford	14th March	1993	Stoke, Guildford	26th March	1997		4 years 0 months

Yellow Wagtail

Motacilla flava

Moderately common passage migrant, breeding annually until the end of the 1990s

Races of Yellow Wagtail breed from Europe and North Africa east through Asia to Alaska. They winter in Africa south of the Sahara and in India and southern Asia. The race normally found in Britain is *M. f. flavissima*, which winters in Africa south of the Sahara. There has been a contraction of range in France and Germany. The British range has been contracting since the 1930s, mainly due to land drainage and a reduction in the amount of suitable grassland. Breeding numbers fell by a further 60% from 1970 to 2001. Preferred nesting habitats are generally near open areas with bare soil for foraging (Hewson and Vickery, 2003).

Surrey. There has been a similar contraction of range in Surrey although, curiously, the breeding population retreated to more urban environments, such as waste ground in the Surrey part of Inner London and finally to the sewage farm at Beddington.

Early Surrey history. Yellow Wagtails were apparently quite common in the early 19th century, breeding in heather and wet meadows. Newman listed them for the Godalming district. Meyer (1842) said they *abounded upon the islands of the Thames*. Bucknill cited other places where they had bred, including Chobham, Frensham, Reigate, Richmond Park and on the Wey from Weybridge to Godalming but described them overall as uncommon breeding birds. There were six pairs on Wimbledon Common in 1902, and at least two pairs nested (*Zool., 1902:313*). Power (1910) could find only thirteen records for the Dulwich area, none of them of breeding. Then, as now, spring and autumn migratory movements were observed. Yellow Wagtails bred along the river in the Staines area and there were many autumn migrants (Kerr, 1906).

Later breeding. Six pairs bred at Frensham in 1907 (Parr) and they continued to breed there until about 1919. Boorman collected eggs at Ripley (1906, 1908) and Send (1902, 1903, 1907). Yellow Wagtails bred in Richmond Park until 1912 but there were no definite breeding records after that date (Collenette). There were three pairs at Horsell Common in 1914 (SBC archive). Eggs were collected at Chobham Common and Old Woking in 1919 (Maitland and Turnbull). Since then, Yellow Wagtails have been very thinly distributed in the county and in the later years they were almost totally dependent on sewage farms and derelict urban land. They bred at Barn Elms from 1909 at least intermittently to 1954 (four pairs) and at Elmers End Sewage Farm from 1935 to the 1950s. They also bred at Mitcham Common (1928), Epsom Sewage Farm (1929), Brooklands Sewage Farm (1933, 1936 and 1939), Esher Common (1934-35) and Walton Reservoirs (1938, 1946). Two pairs bred in southwest Surrey in 1936.

Eggs were taken at Peasmarsh in 1938. Pairs bred near the Wey at Guildford and at Godalming [=Unstead?] Sewage Farm in 1944 and at Guildford Sewage Farm and Shalford in 1946. There were four pairs at Stoke Water Meadows in 1947. The Guildford colonies were extinct by 1959, as were the colonies at Barn Elms and Frensham. The Unstead Sewage Farm colony was active in 1952 and died out when long grass was cut down in 1956. The others are now extinct for reasons which are not entirely clear – change in the habitat does not seem to have been a factor.

In 1957, all but five of the 42 or so known pairs were on sewage farms and four of the others were at a gravel pit. Common Birds

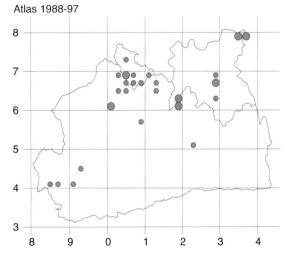

Atlas 1988-97

Census territories were found at Wey Manor farm in 1962 and Walton Reservoirs in 1973. Colonies that were discovered after the 1950s and have since died out were at Thorpe (a pair in 1968, six pairs in 1970) and on waste ground at Vauxhall in 1968 and 1970 - the first to breed in any part of Inner London (Cornelius, 1971). A pair bred successfully at Nine Elms (Vauxhall) in 1979. The 1982 BTO Breeding Waders of Wet Meadows survey included the Yellow Wagtail as an additional species. It found only one bird, at Runnymede on 5th May, in the 32 outer Surrey sites that were visited. The London and Surrey Bird Reports for the same year gave breeding records of one pair at Beddington Sewage Farm and five to ten pairs at the Surrey Docks. Yellow Wagtails bred at the Surrey Docks from 1987 until 1991, when further site development kept them away.

At Beddington Sewage Farm, where the history of the colony goes back to at least 1909, they bred until 1997. An excellent account of this colony is given by Milne *et al*. Up to ten pairs were recorded as breeding in the 1930s and there might have been more, since observations were limited to what could be seen from Mile Road, then a public right of way across the site. Ten pairs were recorded in 1944. There were 18-22 pairs from 1950 to 1955, rising to 35 by 1958 and there were still 20 pairs in 1970. Numbers then dropped sharply to ten pairs in 1971 and 1972. Numbers have since ranged up to a maximum of nine (1996), at least partly reflecting the habitat changes outlined earlier. There were two pairs in 1997 and they have not bred since. Gravel extraction and the cessation of grazing are thought to be the main factors.

In Spelthorne, about ten pairs bred at Staines Reservoirs in 1946 (*LBR*) and three pairs bred there in 1994, during a period of drainage (Hewlett). Pairs bred at Queen Mary Reservoir and Shepperton Gravel Pits in 1982 (*LBR*) and a few pairs bred annually at Shepperton in 1983-86 (*Shepp. BR*). In 2000, there were six territories at the doomed Perry Oaks Sewage Farm, where Yellow Wagtails had bred for many years.

Calendar. The average arrival date in the London area south of the Thames from 1929 to 1939 was 14th April. Spring passage peaks in late April, as shown in the table. Return passage peaks in early September.

Total vice-county bird days 1994-2001

Month	Mar		Apr		May		Jul		Aug		Sep		Oct	
Date	1-15	16-31	1-15	16-30	1-15	16-31	1-15	16-31	1-15	16-31	1-15	16-30	1-15	16-31
Number	1	5	226	434	175	39	8	17	56	277	629	474	57	3

Annual numbers varied from 481 in 1995 down to 191 in 1999.

Since 1970, migrants away from breeding localities have been seen at over 80 places across the county. Lingering migrants include one at Barn Elms Reservoirs on 22nd November 1929, one at Perry Oaks Sewage Farm on 11th and 12th November 1950 and a male watched through a window near Haslemere on 12th December 1953. A male at Beddington Sewage Farm from 9th November 1956 to 22nd March 1957 was the first known to winter in Britain. Two years later one first seen at Beddington on 29th November 1959 was joined by a second in January and at least one of them stayed on until 5th March.

Others at the same site were a male from 27th November 1960 to 26th March 1961 and a first-winter bird from 4th December 1984 to 2nd January 1985. Late birds have become less frequent in recent years but there was one at Shepperton on 19th November 2005 (H. W. Evans). The arrivals chart shows some connection with temperature, arrival dates being later in the colder springs of the 1960s.

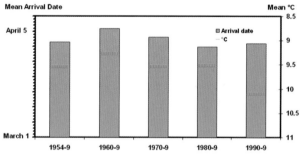

Large counts. Declining numbers are well illustrated by the big counts and roosts of earlier years:

Barn Elms Reservoirs: 100+, 28th August 1926, 70+, 25th April 1989

Beddington Sewage Farm: 120, autumn of 1937 (Milne *et al.*), 60-65 roosted in September 1989, 95 there on 16th September 1990

Capel: 21, 11th August 1991

Frensham: 26, 2nd May 1960

Frimley Gravel Pits: 27+, 24th April 1989

Holmethorpe Sand Pits: 35, 3rd May 1980

Queen Elizabeth II Reservoir: 31, 31st August 1996

Thorpe Gravel Pits: 110 roosting, 5th September 1965

Walton Sewage Farm: *c.*70 roosting, 14th September 1947

Walton Reservoirs: 32, 19th September 1996

Spelthorne

King George VI Reservoir: 400, 29th April 1951

Queen Mary Reservoir: 60, 30th August 1986 (Geen)

Staines Reservoirs: *c.*500, 23rd August 1946; 78, 6th September 1986

Wraysbury Reservoir: 80, 9th September 1995

Current numbers are much lower. The 2001 maximum at King George VI Reservoir was 55 on 8th September (*LBR*). The largest available recent count is of 80 at Staines Moor on 10th September 2002.

Movements and longevity. Yellow Wagtails ringed in Surrey have been recovered in France (two) and Portugal (three). There are two relevant African recoveries. One ringed at Kempton Reservoirs in 1970 and recovered in Morocco seems not to have been a Surrey bird, but there is no doubt about the other. It was ringed at Thorpe on 30th August 1965 and recovered on its probable wintering ground in Senegal, 4,325 km south, on 1st December of the same year. A Yellow Wagtail ringed at Beddington on 7th September 1958 and recovered at Ashford, Middlesex over three years and ten months later, on 18th July 1962 shows the greatest proven longevity.

Plumage variations. The Beddington study showed that birds resembling other races also occurred there. Some at least might be natural variants within the *flavissima* population. The origin of these birds is uncertain. Birds with characteristics of the race *flava* were paired with *flavissima* mates at Beddington Sewage Farm in 1966, 1969 and 1970 (Parr). Their offspring might then have been *flava* x *flavissima* hybrids, a form found along the Belgian and French Channel coast and known as the Channel Wagtail (Dubois, 2007). There was a white-headed bird at Beddington Sewage Farm on 15th May 1959 and a leucistic bird at Barn Elms Reservoirs on 9th April 1987.

Blue-headed Wagtail   *Motacilla flava flava*

Scarce summer visitor and passage migrant

Breeds in much of western Europe and east to the Urals. Early records for this race have been treated with caution, especially if in months later than June. Some might, at any time of year, be variants of M. *f. beema* (Sykes's Wagtail).

Early Surrey history. There were three in a woodland glade bordering Wimbledon Common on 2nd June 1890 (Bucknill). Birds with characteristics of the race were reported in a flooded meadow near Staines in June 1903. At Frensham there were single birds on 13th May and 5th August 1906 (Mouritz, 1907). Single birds were seen at Barn Elms on 18th April 1936 and 12th May 1936, and at Beddington Sewage Farm in May and June 1937, with three there in May 1940. In Spelthorne there were birds at Staines Reservoirs in 1926 and 1938.

Where found since 1940. Many records in the 1950s were described as variant wagtails, but birds with characteristics of Blue-headed Wagtails were reported from Barn Elms Reservoirs (1948, 1956, 1962, 1969, 1973, 1978-79, 1981, 1983-89, 1991, 1993, 1995-97, 1999-2002), Beddington Sewage Farm (1950-52, 1957, 1962-64, 1966-72, 1976-82, 1984, 1986-89, 1992-93, 1995-96, 1998), Frimley Gravel Pits (1988), Hersham Gravel Pit (1999), Hersham Sewage Farm (1958, 1962), Holmethorpe Sand Pits (1991, 1999), Island Barn Reservoir (1958, 2002, 2004), Old Woking Sewage Farm (1994), Queen Elizabeth II Reservoir (1996), Ripley Sewage Farm (1980), Send (1965), South Norwood Country Park (1991, 1997), Stoke Lake (1991, 1995), the Surrey Docks (1972), Thorpe (1967), Unstead Sewage Farm (1997, 1999), Walton Reservoirs (1997), Weybridge (1967) and Witley (2002).

In Spelthorne, later records came from King George VI Reservoir in 1947 and 1998, Perry Oaks Sewage Farm in 1949, 1988, 1990, 1993-94, 1996 and 1999, Queen Mary Reservoir in 1985, Staines Moor in 1949 and 1979, Staines Reservoirs in 1978, 1979, 1983, 1988, 1993, 1995-96 and 2000, Stanwell Cemetery in 1983 and Wraysbury Reservoir in 1984 and 1986.

Breeding. At Beddington Sewage Farm, a '*flava*-type' male bred in 1955 (Milne *et al.*). In 1966 a male with characteristics of the race was at Beddington Sewage Farm from June to August and probably bred with a female Yellow Wagtail. There were similar events at Thorpe in 1967, Beddington Sewage Farm from 1969 to 1972 and 1978 and Perry Oaks Sewage Farm (outcome unknown) in 1996. A female with characteristics of this race bred with a male *flavissima* at Barn Elms in 1978 and Beddington Sewage Farm in 1990.

Calendar. Early and late dates include:

Early		Late	
3rd April 1981	Barn Elms Reservoirs	6th October 1958	Hersham Sewage Farm
9th April 1996	Beddington Sewage Farm		
10th April 1995	Beddington Sewage Farm		
12th April 1988	Beddington Sewage Farm		

Black-headed Wagtail   *Motacilla flava feldegg*

One possible

Breeds from Montenegro to southern Ukraine. Very few accepted for Britain.

Surrey. There are no foreign ringing recoveries to support the occurrence of this race in Surrey, but a male at Beddington Sewage Farm on 7th-28th June 1970 with characteristics of this race paired with a female *M. f. flavissima*. This has not apparently been put to the BBRC.

Grey-headed Wagtail   *Motacilla flava thunbergi*

Possibly thirteen birds

Breeds from Norway east to Siberia.

Surrey. There have been at least 11 reports of birds with characteristics of the race, none of which are thought to have been examined in the hand or confirmed by ringing:

1962:   Beddington Sewage Farm, one on 19th April.
1968:   Barn Elms Reservoir, a male on 6th May.
1973:* Perry Oaks Sewage Farm, one on 19th May.
1984:   Barn Elms Reservoirs, one on 10th May.
        Effingham Ponds, one on 29th May.
1986:   Beddington Sewage Farm, one on 1st May.
1991:   Beddington Sewage Farm, a male on 3rd-6th May, a second on 28th May and a third on 1st June.
1991:* Staines Reservoirs, one on 2nd June.
1993:* Staines Reservoirs, a male on 9th-11th September.
1994:   Beddington Sewage Farm, two males on 8th May.

* Spelthorne

Sykes's Wagtail   *Motacilla flava beema*

Possibly at least eight birds

Breeds in Siberia and central Asia. Found breeding in southeast England as early as 1935 (Milne, 1959).

Surrey. There are no recoveries of foreign-ringed nestlings to support the occurrence of this race in Surrey, but birds with characteristics of Sykes's Wagtail are found from time to time, possibly arising from the variability of *M. f. flava*, *M. f. flavissima* or hybridisation. Eight males were found breeding at Beddington Sewage Farm in 1957. In 1993, a male resembling *beema* but probably a hybrid was paired with a *flavissima* female at Perry Oaks Sewage Farm and was seen feeding young.

Others are:

1948:* Staines Moor, one on 7th-30th May
1973: Barn Elms Reservoirs, a male on 10th June.
1989: Barn Elms Reservoirs on 23-25th April (*LBR*).
1991: Beddington, five in April and May,
1993: Beddington Sewage Farm, one on 1st May.
1995: Beddington Sewage Farm, two on 15th April (*BBR, LBR*).
1996: Beddington Sewage Farm, one on 26th April (*BBR, LBR*).
1997: Beddington Sewage Farm, one on 18th April.

* *Spelthorne*

Movements. One of the 1957 birds had been ringed as a juvenile Yellow Wagtail at Beddington Sewage farm on 21st July 1956. It was retrapped as an adult male resembling Sykes's Wagtail at Beddington on 6th July 1957 and recovered near Ovar, Beira Litoral, Portugal on or about 15th September 1958.

Spanish Wagtail *Motacilla flava iberiae*

Not proved to have been found in Britain.

Surrey. A bird resembling this race at Walton Reservoirs on 12th April 1970 and others at Barn Elms on 17th and 19th May 1973 and 12th May 2004, were presumably not *iberiae* but variants of other races.

Ashy-headed Wagtail *Motacilla flava cinereocapilla*

Several resembling this race but none proved by ringing.

Breeds in southern Europe and North Africa. A rare visitor to Britain.

Surrey. There are no foreign ringing recoveries to support the occurrence of this race in Surrey but birds resembling it are sometimes seen. A male with characteristics of *cinereocapilla* was tending young in a nest at Perry Oaks Sewage Farm in May and June 1959. It was not mated to any hen bird (B. A. Marsh, A. Quinn, J. Shepperd *et al., BB, 53:427*). Other birds with characteristics of the race were seen at Beddington Sewage Farm on 19th-22nd May 1976, Unstead Sewage Farm on 3rd-4th May 1991 and at Hersham Gravel Pit on 20th May 1999.

Citrine Wagtail *Motacilla citreola*

One bird

Breeds in Russia and Central Asia and winters in India and further east. In Britain they are almost entirely autumn migrants to coastal counties, from mid August to October.

Surrey. The one record is remarkable for being so far inland but otherwise fits the pattern. It was of a juvenile bird at Beddington Sewage Farm on 24th-28th August 1993 (A. Greensmith, J. S. Walsh *et al., BB, 88:530*, photographs in *BB, LBR* and *SBR*).

Grey Wagtail
Moderately common breeding resident

Motacilla cinerea

Breeds across Europe and northwest Africa, with a separate population in northern Asia. Most British birds are resident but more northern and eastern populations are migratory, wintering from Europe and Africa east to southern Asia. The European range has been expanding since at least 1850. In Britain, where Grey Wagtails were previously birds of the north and west, the expansion consisted of the colonisation of southeast England. In the 1830s, Grey Wagtails were winter visitors to the counties around London, though they may once have bred at or near Penge Common, probably across the border in Kent (Yarrell, 1845). Breeding in Kent was first proved in 1885. Numbers have fallen by perhaps a third since the 1970s but currently seem to be recovering. A few British-ringed birds have been found on the continent.

Early Surrey history. Blyth (1836) knew Grey Wagtails only as rare winter visitors to Tooting, but Meyer (1842) said they were fairly common in winter along the banks of the Thames. They were known as winter visitors to the Godalming area by Newman (1849) and to Richmond Park (Mouritz, 1905). Other records are given by Bucknill for Dulwich (early spring), Gatton, Gomshall Common, Horsell (summer), Nutfield Marsh (winter), Reigate (winter from 1868), on the Mole (*sic*, Wey presumably meant) near Slyfield and on the Wey. They were occasional in the Dulwich area from the 1870s (Power) and known as autumn migrants and winter visitors to the Staines district (Kerr, 1906).

Breeding was not proved for Surrey until 1893, when a nest with four eggs, partially incubated but deserted, was found on Wimbledon Common on 15th April. The eggs were taken and two more were laid. A nest with five eggs was found on Barnes Common on 10th June 1898. These too were taken. Bucknill gives more detail. The Barnes nest is presumably the one referred to by Dixon (1909) as coming from Barnes about a dozen years previously.

Where breeding 1900 to 1969. Other nests or young were found near Farnham in 1901, in southeast Surrey in 1906 and 1909-11, at Elstead in 1908, on the Wey near Elstead on 14th May 1911 and at Godstone in 1912. Bentham found a nest containing five young at Leigh Mill on 24th April 1920. Grey Wagtails bred at Pyrford in 1921. Blockey reported 30 nest sites in the western Weald in 1937, many presumably in Surrey.

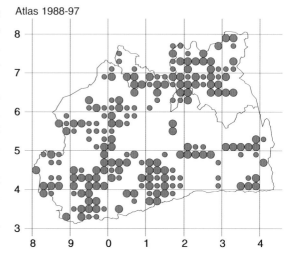

Atlas 1988-97

Expansion continued through the 20th century. Breeding localities mentioned from 1933 up to the early 1950s include Beddington and Epsom sewage farms, Fetcham, the River Wandle at Morden Hall and Watermeads (Mitcham). There were seven territories on the Tillingbourne in 1955 and in 1961 the county population was estimated at 35 pairs (Parr). There was a set-back after the hard winter of 1962/63, followed by a recovery. Grey Wagtails bred at Littleton in 1969.

Since 1970. Breeding sites per ten km were estimated at 3.6 for the Eden, 8.3 for the Hogsmill, 6.1 for the Mole and 4.8 for the Wey in 1979-81 (Palmer, 1982). There were eight pairs along the River Wandle from Waddon Ponds to Morden in 1998. Grey Wagtails were present in the breeding season at Shepperton in 1979-80. An adult and juvenile were there in 1985 and at Queen Mary Gravel Pits in 1989-90. Grey Wagtails are now well established at dams, locks and similar sites in Surrey, from Inner London sites such as Battersea Park (1990 and 1995) and St Saviour's Creek, Southwark (1992 and 1994) out to the many artificial water structures in rural Surrey.

The Winter Atlas found partial survey counts and estimates totalling 71 birds in 1981-84, which probably included some winter immigrants. The table shows that reported breeding numbers have changed little since 1970. This probably reflects improvement in observer cover as well as underlying change.

Number of vice-county breeding season sites reported to the Surrey Bird Club since 1970

1970	1971	1972	1973	1974	1975	1976	1977	1978	1979	1980	1981	1982	1983	1984	1985
18	24	30	29	40	42	38	29	32	18	24	34	28	26	32	34

1986	1987	1988	1989	1990	1991	1992	1993	1994	1995	1996	1997	1998	1999	2000	2001
32	28	21	54	38	29	22	20	28	38	32	38	43	31	43	40

Of the 231 tetrads in northeast Surrey, 20% were found to hold territories in the 1968-72 Atlas survey and 33% in the 1988-97 Atlas, a more encouraging indication of growth.

Population size. A grossed-up Breeding Birds Survey average of 130 birds (perhaps 65 pairs) from 1994 to 2004 fits fairly well with these figures. Grey Wagtails were present in 210 tetrads (including Spelthorne) in the 1988-97 SBC Atlas survey. If Surrey held a proportionate share of the British breeding population as given by the *New Atlas*, the population would be nearer to 250 territories, or 0.1 per square km.

Nest sites. Grey Wagtails often nest at or near locks and sometimes nest in other artificial structures. Examples include a clump of ferns in a broken rain-water pipe on a railway viaduct (Vauxhall 1975) and a railway embankment retaining wall (Hinchley Wood 1976).

Large counts

Beddington Sewage Farm: 20, 22nd January, 21st October and 17th December 1961

Guildford Sewage Farm: 13, 28th August 1996

Hersham Gravel Pit: 12, 19th September 1989

Hurst Green: Up to 12 roosting on a small island, early 2000

Unstead Sewage Farm: 22, 19th January 1997; 25, 24th January 1998

Spelthorne

Staines Reservoirs: 11, December 1983. About 10, 11th October 2003 (*LNHSB*)

Movements. The Surrey Grey Wagtail population is augmented in winter by immigrants from northern Britain. Three recoveries of ringed birds illustrate this. A Grey Wagtail ringed at Kirby Lonsdale, Cumbria on 11th May 1985 was recovered at Lightwater, 344 km south, on 19th October 1985. Another, ringed at Wisley Sewage Farm on 24th November 1996, was found at Catterick, 348 km north, on 29th May 1997 (BTO). The third, found at Dulwich on 11th October 1994, had been colour-ringed at Arbroath, 590 km (367 miles) north in April 1992, the furthest known distance travelled. The incidence of large counts, at its height from October to January, also suggests winter immigration.

Longevity. A Grey Wagtail ringed at Ripley on 29th December 1968 and recovered there over seven years later, on 1st January 1976 had the greatest age established by ringing.

Pied/White Wagtail

Motacilla alba

Moderately common breeding resident

Pied Wagtails breed in the British Isles, where they are mainly resident, and they breed, or have bred, in a few scattered locations from the Netherlands and North Africa east to Syria. In Britain, where they had been stable in population and range, apart from some regional fluctuations, since at least 1800, numbers have increased substantially since 1970. Other races of *M. alba* form the White Wagtail group and breed from Iceland across Europe to Asia and Alaska.

Pied Wagtail

Motacilla alba yarrellii

Early Surrey history. Pied Wagtails were common at Wimbledon (Hamilton) and bred in Battersea Park (Hudson) and in Richmond Park. Bucknill said that they bred throughout the rural parts of the county and in most of the south London parks. Aldridge knew them only as uncommon summer visitors to the Norwood district. They were resident in the Staines area (Kerr, 1906).

Since 1900. Boorman collected eggs at Clandon, Ockham, Ripley and Send between 1902 and 1911. Power confirmed that Pied Wagtails bred in Dulwich Park and summered on Tooting Common. They were common at Richmond Park around 1900 (Mouritz, 1905) and 'hundreds' were seen there, flying towards Mortlake on 15th March 1913. Pied Wagtails have nested in the park since at least the 1930s. Large gatherings include 150 on 1st December 1937. Pied Wagtails appear to have been only passage migrants at Barn Elms and Beddington Sewage Farm at about this time. Sewage farms later attracted breeding Pied Wagtails. Ten to twenty pairs bred at Hersham Sewage Farm in the early 1960s (Parr). Of 19 nests at Farnham Sewage Farm in 1978, 12 were successful. The Winter Atlas found partial survey counts and estimates totalling 1,157 birds in 1981-84, compared with only 71 Grey Wagtails.

Colonisation of the Surrey part of Inner London began with a pair feeding young in Archbishops Park in 1967 (*SBR*). Pied Wagtails bred at the Surrey Docks from 1974, with five to ten pairs in 1990. At least one pair bred there as late as 1997 (Hewlett). A pair nested at Allied Brewery Warehouses, Nine Elms, in 1979 and there were others at Battersea Power Station and Battersea Park in 1985. Pied Wagtails have been resident in the Shepperton area since at least the 1980s and no doubt much longer.

Trend since 1970. Of the 231 tetrads in northeast Surrey, 83% were found to hold territories in the 1968-72 Atlas survey but only 69% in the 1988-97 Atlas. The Common Birds Census showed no significant change over this period.

Population size. As in Bucknill's day, Pied Wagtails are now common around buildings, farms and water bodies in the more rural areas, recorded, for example, at Vann Lake in almost every month from 1964 to 1996 (Blaker Log). Common Birds Census figures suggest between 2,000

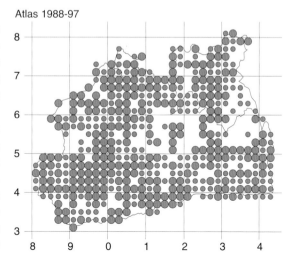

Atlas 1988-97

and 3,000 territories. The 1994-2004 Breeding Birds Survey suggests a breeding season population of over 2,000 adults. If Surrey held a proportionate share of the British breeding population as given by the *New Atlas*, the population would be about 2,200 territories, or one per square km. Roost numbers below suggest that these may be considerable underestimates unless they include winter immigrants. The Winter Atlas, with its limited coverage, found partial survey counts and estimates totalling 1,157 birds in 1981-84, suggesting a minimum size for winter population.

Nest sites. A pair fed three juveniles on a barge moored at Westminster in 1973. A nest at Lyne in June 1974 contained ten young, nine of which were reared. A pair bred on the roof of County Hall SE1 in 1984. A duck nest box was used at Buckland Sand Pits in 1988. A pair that bred under the Royal Box on the Centre Court at Wimbledon in 1990 often activated the magic-eye call equipment, which caused some amusement among the spectators but distracted the players. Nests on working or mobile machines are occasionally reported. In 1974 a pair nested and incubated at Salfords in the engine compartment of a van used every weekday. The van was taken off the road when the young were hatched and they all fledged. Belsey (2002) mentions a pair with young in a nest under the seat of a tractor. The adults fed them while the tractor driver ploughed the fields. Two pairs used tractors (one of which was in daily use) in 1994.

Roosts. Pied Wagtails roost communally in autumn and winter, favouring urban areas. Roost sites have been in riverside Alders (Stoke 1971), Bamboos (Virginia Water, 130, October 1956), Bulrushes, in greenhouses (Milford July-September 1973 etc, Cranleigh 1985), gum trees (*Eucalyptus*, Frimley 1979), Plane trees (Richmond 1991), Reeds (Godstone 1974, 1984), Rhododendrons (Haslemere 1971), Silver Maples (Redhill shopping centre), roofs, including a Guildford hospital (1994) and a heated swimming pool at Tandridge (2000).

Large counts and roosts. Large roosts build up towards the end of the year, often in town centres where they may be taking advantage of the additional warmth but also in bushes and trees elsewhere. Commercial greenhouses have at times attracted large numbers. Among the larger roosts, flights and counts have been:

Roosts

Balham: 150, 11th February 1937

Barn Elms Reservoirs: 250-300, October 1952

Beddington Sewage Farm: 250, December 1989

Berrylands Sewage Works: 200+, winter of 1980

Black Pond, Esher Common: well over 100, 15th November 1936; 129, 15th September 1937; roost still in use in 1945.

Croydon town centre: 550, 16th January 2002

Dunsfold: 300 in Bulrushes, 29th December 1974; 300+, January 1975

Epsom High Street: 200, 10th October 2001

Gatwick: 200 in bushes, 30th November 1986

near Godstone: 400-600, September 1972

Guildford: 200, Royal Surrey County Hospital, 15th January 2001

Hamm Moor: *c*.300, 22nd October 1969

Oxshott Brickworks: 617, 10th February 1962

Papercourt: up to 300 in reeds and bushes, July-September 1975

Redhill Town Centre: 400 in Silver Maples, 1986; 450, 4th December 1995

Richmond Park: 'usual roost' of at least 300, 24th September 1970

Silvermere: 300-350 in reeds, late 1967

Sutton High Street: 150 roosting, 31st January 2002

Thornton Heath: up to *c*.300 in street trees, August-October 1949 and August 1950, mostly from Beddington Sewage Farm: 293 were seen leaving on 4th September 1949 (*LBR*)

University of Surrey: 200 in December 1994

Unstead Sewage Farm: 327 flying to a roost near the sewage farm, 9th January 2000.

Woking: 200 in Goldsworth Road, 27th November 1994; 420 in the town centre, 24th December 1998

Counts not described as roosts

Beddington Sewage Farm: 300 in January 1989

Capel: over 700, 2nd October 1992, flock put up by Sparrowhawk

Cranleigh: up to 200 in greenhouses, November and December 1985. In 1988, at the same site, L. G. Weller caught and ringed 700 and released them at Ewhurst.

Dorking Sewage Farm: 250, March 1965

Epsom Sewage Farm: up to 600, December 1955; *c.*300, 1st October 1955 (Parr)

Frensham: 200, 6th September 1970

Frimley Gravel Pits: 200+, 5th November 1972

Godalming: *c.*250, pre-roost gathering, December 1979

Guildford Sewage Farm: 200, 2nd November 1967

Hersham Sewage Farm: *c.*300, 10th April 1970, included a few White Wagtails

Hurst Green: over 200, October 1993; 425, 2nd November 1995

Milford: 300+ on roofs and in greenhouses and 200 outside the greenhouses during a thunderstorm at Hurst Farm, 15th September 1973

Ripley Sewage Farm: 200+, 22nd September 1974

Shalford Park: 200+ juveniles, July-September 1977

near West Horsley: *c.*200 on farmland, 2nd February 1974

Spelthorne

Perry Oaks Sewage Farm: 'several hundred', 12th December 1976

Queen Mary Gravel Pits: 300, 23rd December 1975

Feeding. Sewage farms have often been used as feeding areas by large numbers of Pied Wagtails. There were about 180 at Berrylands Sewage Works on 14th August 1960 and about 120 juveniles at Beddington Sewage Farm on 3rd August, 1969. They are frequent on sludge and sprinklers at sewage farms and on watercress beds (Abinger 1974). They form small flocks on newly ploughed fields and on crops including carrots (Frensham 1974), kale grazed by sheep (Moorhouse 2000), reseeded grass (Frensham 1977) and fields treated with sludge (near Box Hill 1979).

Movements and longevity. Most Pied Wagtails are resident but six ringed in Surrey have been found in France and one in Portugal. An early and interesting French example was of the one ringed during the 1914-18 war at Limpsfield on 19th May 1916 and recovered in the Gironde, France in March 1917. A Pied Wagtail ringed as an adult at Ewhurst on 25th September 1962 and recovered in Portugal on about 7th February 1963 had travelled further, at 1,191 km. A Pied Wagtail ringed at Queen Mary Reservoir on 7th August 1971 was recovered at Sunbury on 14th March 1978, when over six years and five months old. Surrey Bird Reports since 1988 have mentioned an age of eight years nine months but no supporting details have been located.

Plumage variations. An apparent albino was reported from near Ockham Common in 1965. 'Semi-albino' birds were in Burgess Park in 1992 and Brunswick Park SE5 in 1994.

White Wagtail   *Motacilla alba alba*

Uncommon passage migrant

Breeds in Europe (including Iceland), east to the Urals and Asia Minor. A few pairs breed in the UK (Ogilvie *et al.*, 2002). Many of the northern birds are migratory and winter in southern

Europe and Africa south to the equator. Other races breed further east. The population is thought to have been stable, apart from regional fluctuations. Pied and White Wagtails are easiest to distinguish in spring.

Surrey. White Wagtails are sometimes claimed for the autumn, when they must occur, but in the absence of detail about the sightings, most of them have been ignored for the purposes of this account.

Early Surrey history. Blyth (1936) said he had shot White Wagtails two or three times in the summer months, but had not kept any specimens because he thought they were just plumage variations of the Pied Wagtail. Perhaps they were, because summer records are uncommon. The first definite record is of one shot in spring plumage at Broadwater, Farncombe by J. P. Stafford (*SALEC*) and seen in the Charterhouse Collection by Bucknill. A bird in autumn plumage, also said to be of this race and from Broadwater, was in the collection at the time, but neither bird is there now. Kerr (1906) had no definite records for the Staines area. There were single birds at Barnes on 18th April 1925, in April and May 1927 and in 1929 and another was in Richmond Park on 22nd-25th April 1927.

Where later found, up to 1969. There are later records from Addington (1967), Barn Elms, Battersea Park (1955, 1957), Beddington Sewage Farm, Byfleet (1959), Dulwich (1956-58), Earlsfield (1963), Earlswood Sewage Farm (1960), Elmers End Sewage Farm (1936-37), Epsom Sewage Farm (1955-56), Esher (1945, 1957), Ewell (1934, 1962), Fetcham (1955, 1960), Frensham, Godstone (1960), Gomshall (1940), Guildford Sewage Farm (four on 22nd March 1945), Ham Gravel Pits (1948), Haslemere (8th March 1946), Hersham Sewage Farm (1955, 1958-59, 1961), Holmethorpe (1960), Island Barn Reservoir (1932, 1958-59), Lonsdale Road Reservoir (1937, 1955), Queen Elizabeth II Reservoir (1961), Reigate (1932), Richmond Park, Sutton (1931), Unstead Sewage Farm (1935), Walton Reservoirs, Wandsworth Common (1964), Wimbledon Common (1965) and Wisley Common (1959). In April 1931 there were three at Queen Mary Reservoir on the 23rd, one was there on the 28th and there was one at Staines Reservoirs on the 26th (*LN*). There was one at Staines on 31st January 1937 (*LBR*).

Where found since 1970. Since 1970 there have been records from Barn Elms (most years), Battersea Park, Beddington Park, Beddington Sewage Farm (most years), Belair Park (Dulwich), Burstow Sewage Farm, Capel, Cranleigh (one ringed in a Pied Wagtail roost on 3rd October 1988), Dormansland, Effingham Fish Ponds, Farleigh, Farnham Sewage Farm, Frensham (most years), Frimley Gravel Pits, Gatwick Airport, Guildford Sewage Farm 1970, Guildford, Hedgecourt, Hersham Gravel Pit, Hersham Sewage Farm, Hogsmill Riverside Open Space, Holmethorpe Sand Pits (most years), Holmwood Sewage Works, Island Barn Reservoir, Long Ditton, Merrist Wood, Mizen's Farm (Horsell), Motspur Park Sewage Farm, New Addington, Oxted, Papercourt Gravel Pits, Pondover Pit, Queen Elizabeth II Reservoir, Reigate Heath, Richmond Park, Ripley Sewage Farm, Send Water Meadows, South Norwood, Stoke Lake, the Surrey Docks, the Thames at the National Theatre and Wandsworth, Thursley (3rd June 1972), Tilhill, Trevereux (Limpsfield), Tuesley Farm (Milford), Unstead Sewage Farm, Walton Reservoirs, Warlingham, Wimbledon Common, Wisley Golf Course and Wrecclesham. Spelthorne sites include King George VI Reservoir, Perry Oaks Sewage Farm, Queen Mary Reservoir, Shepperton Gravel Pits, Staines Moor, Staines Reservoirs (most years), Stanwell Moor and Wraysbury Reservoir. In the spring of 2000 there were over 50 bird days across Spelthorne, with a maximum of ten at Staines Reservoirs on 18th April.

Calendar. The average arrival date in the London area south of the Thames from 1929 to 1939 was 8th April. More recent early and late dates are:

Large counts. There were at least eight at Barn Elms Reservoirs on 21st April 1978 and 21 on 25th April 1989. At Staines Reservoirs there was a spring peak of ten on 18th April 2000.

Waxwing (Bohemian Waxwing)   *Bombycilla garrulus*

Irruptive winter visitor

Breeds in the northern conifer forests of Europe across to west Siberia (*B. g. garrulus*), central and west Siberia (*B. g. centralasiae*) and North America (*B. g. pallidiceps*). Most move south to more temperate areas in winter. They are prone to irruptions, the timing of which depends on population size and the availability of food. Most of those arriving in Britain come from Finland, Russia and Scandinavia (*MA*).

Early Surrey history. Waxwing years were well known in Surrey during the 19th century, from as early as 1803 when Graves (1811-21) mentioned a number shot in the neighbourhood of Camberwell around Christmas time, one of which he used as a model for his illustration of the species. This was presumably an invasion year, since Bewick mentioned several taken in Northumberland and Durham in 1790, 1791 and 1803. Yarrell mentions 1810, 1820, 1822, 1828, 1830, 1831, 1834 and 1835 as being further invasion years, mainly affecting northern Britain. Surrey records of several shot at Tooting in the winter of 1831/32 (possibly an error for 1830/31, Bucknill), one at Godalming in 1832 and a pair at Claremont in January 1837 do not fit these years very well. There was one in 1846 and on 17th January 1847 near Chertsey.

A big irruption occurred in the winter of 1849/50, when the *Zoologist* for 1850 detailed 586 killed in different parts of Great Britain. One was killed at the border of Peper Harow Park (*SALEC*) in the winter of 1849 and another at Wimbledon in the second week of January, 1850. One recorded in *The Zoologist* as being shot at Hambledon on 9th February 1849 and another obtained near Farnham before 1854 were thought by Bucknill to have been 1850 birds. National irruptions in 1866-67 and 1872-73 left no definite Surrey records. There was a Waxwing at Windlesham in 1886. One was shot at an Epsom brickfield in November 1892.

20th century irruptions. During the 20th century there were significant national irruptions in the winters of 1903/04, 1913/14, 1921/22, 1931/32, 1936/37, 1943/44, 1946/47, 1949/50, 1959/60, 1965/66, 1970/71 and 1995/96. Beadell saw one in the Warlingham area in the winter of 1910/11. One at Roehampton on 25th January and another at Dorking on 27th March 1914 were part of the invasion of that year.

1921 to 1960. The influx from November 1921 mainly affected northern Britain (Kearton and Bentham, 1925) but two at Woodham in January 1922 were presumably part of it. Invasions in the 1930s seem not to have reached Surrey but up to 17 birds were seen at Banstead (four, *LBR*) and Surbiton in early 1944, during the 1943/44 invasion (Parr). There was a very large national influx in the winter of 1946/47. In Surrey, birds were seen at Ashtead, Barnes Bridge, Brixton (18, 29th March), Cutt Mill, Effingham (up to 35, December/January), Guildford, Haslemere (at least four, January), Horsley, Malden (up to fifteen), Mitcham, New Malden (about twelve), Redhill (about six, 1st March), Richmond Park (two, 1st December), Shirley, Surbiton (up to seven, February and March), Unstead and Wimbledon Common (about six, 8th April). There were two at Staines on 1st February. A smaller influx in 1948 produced flocks at Whyteleafe Hill in January and Englefield Green on 2nd March. In the winter of 1949/50 the first birds appeared in December, at Croydon, New Malden and Wimbledon followed, in 1950, with birds at Farnham, Guildford, Long Ditton and Woking in January, Teddington in February and Ashtead up to 4th April. In early 1957, there was one at Cutt Mill, up to 19 were at Esher Common and there were six at New Malden. An influx in 1959 brought 20 to Bookham and smaller numbers elsewhere, including single birds at Queen Mary Reservoir on 8th February 1959 and 17th January 1960.

1961 to 1971. The major invasion in 1965/66 began in Surrey with one at Oxshott on 19th October 1965 and the last seen was at Burgh Heath on 1st May 1966. The invasion peaked in the second half of December 1965, when a total of 380 were recorded (*SBR* for 1965). Waxwings were seen at 15 localities in northeast Surrey, including 17 at Tadworth (the largest number). Elsewhere they were widely recorded, with birds seen at Camberley, Cranleigh, Dorking, Ewhurst, Farnham, Godalming, North Holmwood, Outwood, Weybridge, Woking, Wrecclesham and other localities.

A smaller invasion in 1970/71 began in December 1970 and involved under 100 birds in total, the most being 40 at Woking in April 1971 and up to 35 at Limpsfield Chart in December 1970. There were smaller numbers at ten or so other localities, mostly in northeast Surrey up to early April and one was found dead at Queen Mary Reservoir on 30th January 1971 (Geen).

1972 to 1994. There were single birds at Frensham Great Pond on 1st December 1972, Mitcham on 29th December 1973 and Purley on 10th November 1974, two at Virginia Water on 6th January 1975, two at Knaphill in December 1975 and two at Worcester Park on 20th-21st February 1976. Single birds were at Knaphill on 19th-21st February 1976, Purley on 16th January 1977, Raynes Park on 19th February 1979 and Southfields, Wimbledon from 6th February to 3rd March 1982. There were two at Headley from 7th-12th February 1981 and two at Goldsworth Park, Woking from 1st-18th February 1987, when they were joined by a third bird to 7th March. In 1988, one was seen from a train near Lambeth Palace on 9th November and two were seen from a Leatherhead office window on 9th December. There were two at Oxted (the Godstone birds?) on 6th February 1989, two at East Molesey on 11th-13th February 1989 and two in Godstone from 14th February to 1st March 1989, when they were joined by a third bird, all staying until the 18th. There were two at Addington on 13th December 1989 and one flew over Queen Mary Gravel Pits on 17th February 1991. There were three at Ham Lands on 27th December 1991, four at South Norwood Country Park on 28th December 1991 and two at Sainsburys, Cobham on 7th-31st March 1992.

1995 to 2003. The winter of 1995/96 saw the largest influx to Britain since that of 1965/66 and brought about 250 Waxwings to Surrey. The first in Surrey was at Banstead on 20th January 1996. Subsequent records, chronologically, with numbers in brackets if more than one, were: Carshalton 27th January; Tooting 27th January (two); Ewhurst 29th-30th January (three), 3rd-4th February; Streatham 31st January; Charlwood 4th February; Cranleigh 5th February; Beddington Sewage Farm 6th February; Epsom 6th February (six), 23rd March (fifteen); Capel 10th February (two); Guildford 22nd February (six); Walton-on-Thames 24th February (fourteen); Horley early March; Camberley 1st-4th March (thirteen); Onslow Village, Guildford 8th March (thirteen), maximum 19th March (twenty-five), last 26th March (thirteen); Ash Vale 14th-15th March (twenty); Tongham 14th March (seven); Dorking 20th-26th March (thirty-five); Hinchley Wood 5th-26th April (up to twenty); Tolworth 11th-12th April (twelve); Knight's Garden Centre, between Godstone and Oxted 13th-17th April (up to fifteen); Pirbright 14th April (eighteen) and the University of Surrey 16th April (seven to ten) and 17th April (nine).

There were single birds at Beddington Sewage Farm on 12th January 1999 and Roundshaw Downs on 31st December 2000. Many were seen in early 2001 (maximum 27 at Wisley RHS on 23rd February and Virginia Water on 25th March) and a few were seen in early 2003.

2004-2006. There was one at Lingfield in February 2004. A huge influx that began in October 2004 brought Waxwings to the county by the early months of 2005. Around 70 of the available reports totalled over 4,200 birds and included flocks of over 100 at Badshot Lea, Farnham, Guildford, Horley and Virginia Water and other flocks at Barn Elms, Elstead, Frimley, Milford, Mytchett, Send, Woking and elsewhere. Most birds were west from Guildford. The last was on 18th April. The actual number of birds involved, allowing for multiple reporting, is impossible to say, but there seem to have been separate flocks of 100+ at Farnham, Horley and Guildford in January and February as well as many smaller elsewhere. The 2004 irruption brought at least 100 to Staines town centre in January 2005 with smaller numbers into March. A few were seen at Epsom and Putney in January 2006.

Movements and longevity. Although the whole Surrey history of the Waxwings is one of movement, the origin of the birds that have been seen here is mainly conjectural. The *Migration Atlas* says there was only one British pre-1979 recovery, involving the Netherlands, presumably the adult ringed at Arnheim, Haarlem on 19th November 1970 and recovered at Woking on 6th January 1971 (*SBR* for 1971). A bird in the late 2004 influx was ringed at Inverurie, Grampian Region on 30th October and controlled at Egham, 661 km south, on 1st March 2005.

Dipper (White-throated Dipper) *Cinclus cinclus*

Nine records, including one from Spelthorne

Dippers breed from Europe and North Africa east to Central Asia. Typically birds of upland streams, they can be found breeding at sea level in parts of their range, for example in Wales. The race which breeds in most of Britain is *C. c. gularis*. Most British breeders make only local movements. The Irish Dipper *C. c. hibernicus* breeds in parts of Scotland. Dippers did not breed in any of the counties adjacent to Surrey in the early 19th century, since when there has been a contraction of range and number, apparently still continuing. Dippers found in southeast England are probably of the north European Black-bellied race *C. c. cinclus*.

Early Surrey history. Graves (1811-21) said that the species had been found in Surrey but gave no details. Meyer (1842) said he had seen a Dipper *sat motionless upon a lump of dried clay close by the waterside* by the River Mole at Claremont. One was shot by an Unstead farmer at some time after 1849 (SALEC). It was in the Charterhouse Collection in Shaw's time but is no longer held there. Shaw (1921) wrote that he had seen one which had been shot at Peper Harow some 40 years previously. Yarrell (1845) has a record for Spelthorne: *The nearest spot in which I have heard of a Dipper being seen [in the counties around] was at a water-mill tail at Wyrardisbury [Wraysbury], on the Colne, about two or three hundred yards above the place at which it falls into the Thames, just below Bell Weir*. Records in *Epsom College Natural History Society Reports No 2 (1890)* and *No 19 (5th May 1907)* for the Staines area might be satisfactory but no supporting details are available.

Dated records are:

1895:   Mickleham, one shot on the Mole by Mr Young, the Sutton taxidermist, in the autumn.
1915:   between Leatherhead and Cobham, one on the Mole on 28th March, during very cold weather (*BB, 8:292*).
1926:   Leatherhead Railway Bridge, one on the Mole on 3rd May (*BB, 20:107*).
1965:   Leigh Mill Pond, one trapped and ringed on 13th April.

None of the birds has been identified at sub-specific level to admit, or eliminate, occurrences of the Black-bellied race *Cinclus c. cinclus*, or indeed of the Irish Dipper.

Wren (Winter Wren) *Troglodytes troglodytes*

Abundant breeding resident

Wrens breed in temperate regions of Europe, Asia and North America. Many northern birds move south within these regions in winter. Most British birds are sedentary but some travel substantially longer distances. A few continental breeders have been found in southern Britain. No substantial British range changes are known, but the population level is strongly affected by the severity of winters. Breeding numbers showed a strong increase from 1970 to 2001.

Early Surrey history. Wrens in the Godalming district by 1849 are the earliest located in print. They were common garden birds at Norwood in the 1880s (Aldridge). Bucknill described them as common and gave Dulwich as a place near London where they were very common. They were abundant in Richmond Park at the time. In the Staines area they were very plentiful (Kerr, 1906).

Since 1900. Power said they were no longer breeding in Camberwell but still breeding in Dulwich in 1909. Eggs were collected at Cobham, Ockham and Send (1903-09) and at both Bookham and Frensham in 1939. They have bred in Battersea Park since at least 1952, when two broods were reared. Numbers increased to at least 20 territories in 1987 and 1988, 20 pairs raised about 40 young in 1989 and 22 pairs raised 32 young in 1990. At Vann Lake, Wrens were found in every month of every year from 1964 to late 1996 (Blaker Log). Selected nests/nesting, pairs/territories and singing males since 1970 are:

Banstead Wood: 16 singing in 1980, 14 in 1987

Barn Elms London Wetland Centre: 36 territories in 2003

Barnes Common: 58 territories in 1999

Beddington Sewage Farm: 56 territories in 1993, 67 territories in 1994, 90 territories in 1995, 48 in 1996, 28 in 1997, 47 in 1998, 68 territories in 1999, 57 territories in 2000, 60 territories in 2004 (154 per square km)

Bookham Common: 60 territories in 2002

Burgess Park: 10 territories in 1992, five singing in 1998

Cannon Hill Common: 13 territories in 1997, 15 territories in 1999, 22 territories in 2001

Coombe Hill Wood: 17 territories in 1997

Frensham: 50 singing in July 1985, 65 singing on 4th April 1988, 40 singing in 1990, 39 in 1991, 43 in 1992, 50 in 1993, 34 in 1994, 41 in 1995, 26 in 1996, 27 in 1997, 31 in 1998, 32 territories in 1999, 28 territories in 2000. A full survey by S. P. Peters in 2004 found 76 territories

Frimley Gravel Pits: 13 singing in 25 hectares in 1980

Headley Heath: 30 singing on 28th April 1983, 43 singing on 6th May 1985, nine singing in 1986, 26 singing on 24th April 1988

Holmethorpe: 12 pairs bred in 1990

Hyde Copse, Churt: 16 territories in 11.5 hectares of scrub in 1980

Lonsdale Road Reservoir: six or more territories 1996, 18 singing in 1999

Merrist Wood: 22 territories in 1995

Molesey Heath: 28 territories in 2004

Morden Hall Park: 80 territories in 1997, 90 in 1998, 70 territories in 1999, 75 territories in 2000

Nonsuch Park: *c*.20 pairs nested in 1972

Nunhead Cemetery: 58 territories in 1997

Pickhurst: 14 pairs nested in 1972, 11 territories in 1980

Reigate Priory: 21 territories in 1997

Richmond Park: nine singing in 1999

Surrey Docks: 3 territories in 1976, 28 territories 1999

Tolworth Court Farm: 31 territories in 1995

Unstead Sewage Farm: 42 territories in 1998, 31 territories in 2000

West End Common, Esher: 20 territories in 2003, 23 in 2004

Three miles of River Wey: 100+ territories in 1975

Wey Valley at Moor Park: 43 territories in 116 hectares of farmland in 1980

Spelthorne

The commonest song bird at Littleton Lakes in 1986, with a probable 16 territories (*Shepp. BR*)

Nesting. Bucknill mentioned nesting in the first week of January. At Farnham Sewage Farm there was a nest with young on 5th September 1978. One fed Blue Tit nestlings and removed their faecal sacs at Farnham in 1981. House Martin nest boxes have been used at Compton (1979) and East Horsley (1979) and an old House Martin's nest at Esher (1994).

Hard winters and the trend. The severe winter of 1962/63 reduced the number of territories in

Common Birds Census areas from forty to four. The winter of 1978-79 reduced Common Birds Census numbers by over 20% and that of 1995/96 reduced them by 35%. Even so, the underlying trend since 1970 has been firmly upwards, numbers more than doubling over the period.

Population size. The Winter Atlas found partial survey counts and estimates totalling 402 birds in 1981-84, not many but comparable to the number of another small bird, the Goldcrest. The 1994-2004 Breeding Birds Survey suggests an average breeding season population of at least 19,000 adults and might be a considerable underestimate. The Common Birds Census density would imply about

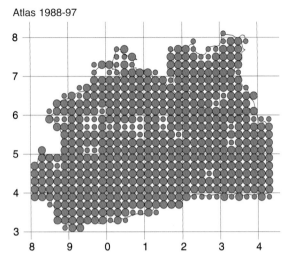

Atlas 1988-97

160,000 territories, a density of about eighty per square km at the end of the period. This is well above the 25 per square km found nationally in the *New Atlas*. Wrens were the commonest of the birds on ten Common Birds Census plots in 1990-1994, making up 16% of the total. They were found in over 94% of the 231 northeast Surrey tetrads in both Atlas surveys.

Movements and longevity. Some Wrens make more than local movements. A juvenile ringed at Grimston Woods, East Yorkshire, on 19th July 1975 was found dead 267 km south at Esher on 10th February 1976. A Wren ringed at TQ0468 (Chertsey) on 13th November 1965 and recovered there over four years and three months later, on 3rd March 1970, is the oldest that has been located. Surrey Bird Reports since 1977 have mentioned an age of six years but no supporting details have been located.

Dunnock (Hedge Accentor)   *Prunella modularis*

Common breeding resident

Breeds in Europe across to western Russia. Northern and eastern birds winter south to southern Europe and the Middle East. Dunnocks breeding in Britain are mainly sedentary. Birds of the Finnish and Scandinavian race *modularis* migrate southwest in autumn and some are found in Britain. Some 19th century extension of range in Scotland and more recently in Sweden. The British population, like most others in western Europe, is stable or increasing. Nineteenth century writers noticed that they moved into urban areas as hard weather approached. The *Historical Atlas* suggests that the spread of human habitations is likely to have improved the habitat and led to an increase in numbers in the late 1800s. There was a fall in numbers of about a third since 1970 to the 1990s, possibly due to canopy closure following less woodland management and increased browsing pressure from deer (Fuller *et al.*, 2005). More recent numbers have been increasing again.

Early Surrey history. Gilbert White recorded a Dunnock singing at South Lambeth on 19th February 1782. Newman noted Dunnocks for the Godalming district in 1849. They were to be found in every Norwood garden throughout the year (Aldridge) and present on Wimbledon Common (Hamilton) in the 1880s. Kerr (1906) noted them as resident in the Staines area. Bucknill noted the Dunnock *keeps largely to the neighbourhood of dwelling houses*. He knew of nesting in early January.

1900 to 1970. Mouritz (1905) found Dunnocks to be common in Richmond Park, where they bred throughout the 20th century, with 47 pairs in 1952. Boorman collected eggs at Ockham, Ripley and Send from 1902-1910. The 1916/17 winter cut numbers back and they were still well below the 1916 level in 1923 (Bunyard). There is little quantitative information for this period. Even the hard winter of 1962/63 had little effect on numbers and Dunnocks were the fourth commonest species in the Common Birds Censuses of the 1960s (Parr).

Since 1970. The Common Birds Census shows a firm downward trend, with Surrey numbers falling by about a third from 1970 to 2000, but the trend is less obvious at some individual sites. For example at Epsom Common, the number of territories varied erratically between two and eight from 1973 to 1987. Other sites, such as Eastern Wood on Bookham Common, clearly follow the national trend. Numbers increased somewhat at Park Farm, Chessington, from 1988 to 2000.

Nesting. Three pairs each raised three broods in a garden at Godalming in 1971 and Dunnocks are still very much garden birds. A pair nested in glasshouse carnations at Hurst Farm, Milford in 1976.

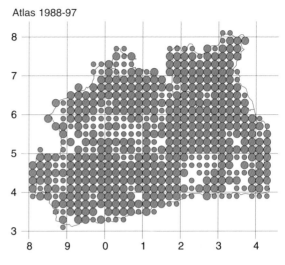

Atlas 1988-97

Population size. The Winter Atlas found partial survey counts and estimates totalling 368 birds in 1981-84, not many, but similar to the number of Wrens. The 1994-2004 Breeding Birds Survey suggests an average breeding season population of at least 6,000 adults and may be a considerable underestimate.

The Common Birds Census suggests a current 26,000 pairs. If Surrey held a proportionate share of the British breeding population as given by the *New Atlas*, the population would be nearer to 14,000 territories, or seven per square km.

Local territory counts. Dunnocks have been well established in Inner London for many years. Eight pairs bred on Wandsworth Common in 1964 (*BRP*). Dunnocks bred at Lambeth in 1966 and there were eight to ten singing in Battersea Park in 1967. Single pairs bred at the Surrey Docks in 1973 and 1974. More recently Dunnocks have bred in bushy places at Southbank (Osborne, 1997). Burgess Park held three territories in 1992. The number of pairs in Battersea Park varied from about ten to 30 from 1987 to 2000. Other breeding counts from the late 20th century onward include:

Barn Elms London Wetland Centre: 19 territories in 2003

Beddington Sewage Farm: 24 territories in 2003

Bookham Common: 37 territories in 2002 (95 per square km)

Elmbridge Leisure Centre: 18 territories in 1999

Frensham: 30 singing in 1995, 37 in 2000, 46 in 2005

Morden Hall Park: 30 territories in 1997, 25 in 1998, 20 in 2001

Nunhead Cemetery: six territories in 1997

Unstead Sewage Farm: 14 territories in 1997, 29 in 1998, 21 in 2000

Wimbledon Common: 65 territories in 1997

Spelthorne

Littleton Lakes: possible nine pairs in 1986

Perry Oaks Sewage Farm: three territories in 1999

Selected large counts

Battersea Park: *c*.50 in February and November 1990

Beddington Sewage Farm: 27 on 24th January 1982

Elmers End Sewage Farm: 34 on 5th October 1986

Thorpe: over 120 ringed between 1st October and 16th November 1970

Spelthorne

Queen Mary Reservoir: 70 ringed in September 1976

Movements and longevity. Autumn influxes have sometimes been noted, for example by Power, who mentioned parties of three or four passing from tree to tree in October. He noticed an October influx to parks and gardens in South London, including Kennington Park in 1904. During an influx at Dulwich in October 1957, I. R. Beames noticed parties of four to fourteen flying west across a road and a golf course and through a wood. No recent observations of this type have been located. A Dunnock ringed at Bradwell, Essex on 25th August 1961 and recovered at Newdigate on 2nd April 1962 had travelled the furthest, at 103 km (65 miles). The oldest known Dunnock was ringed at Kempton Park on 12th January 1974 and recovered at Sunbury over eight years and six months later on 13th July 1982. Another was ringed at Mitcham Common on 8th May 1983 and recovered there on 4th August 1991. One found dead in 1967 was infected with salmonellosis. Four nestlings died of pneumonia at Esher in 1971.

Behaviour. Night song has occasionally been recorded. A Dunnock swallowed hailstones at Frimley Green in March 1977.

Plumage variations. Bucknill mentioned occasional albino and pied birds. An almost wholly white bird was at Frensham Vale in 1974. There was a white-headed bird at Beddington Sewage Farm in 1981. One, possibly two albinos were at Oxted in 1997.

Alpine Accentor *Prunella collaris*

Two birds, before 1900

Breeds from the Pyrenees east to Japan and is at most an altitudinal migrant. The 13 British appearances from 1958 to 2000 were all in coastal counties, mostly in southern England and in all months except February and September.

Surrey. Neither of the Surrey records is fully dated and both are unusual in being inland. An Alpine Accentor was killed at Milford by a boy in the winter of 1841 (SALEC) while it was hopping about on a heap of stones by the road. The bird was in the Charterhouse Collection in Bucknill's time but is not now there. Surrey was not one of the counties listed in the BOU 1883 list but the county appeared in the list of 1915, presumably for this record.

Arthur G. Butler, a prominent collector of the period, provided an account of the second bird. '*I caught a specimen in my garden at Penge about the year 1883. At the time I did not know what to make of it: and, not being aware of its rarity, I never recorded the capture: indeed I supposed then that it might be only an unusually large, brownish and somewhat aberrant variety of the Hedge-Sparrow: it was evidently a young bird, as the white throat-patch was barely indicated. So far as I can remember, I caught this bird in September; I know that it was just when the bird-catchers were bringing Linnets and Goldfinches for sale. The bird was abominably wild, knocked itself about in a cage, finally got a growth over one eye, and died in such poor condition that I never thought of preserving the skin: had I then known its value, I should have saved it in proof of my statement, and certainly kept it when alive in a large cage by itself; whereas it had two Hedge-Accentors as companions; the latter, by the side of their rare relative, looked insignificant, much as a Song Thrush by the side of a Missel-Thrush … In a cage this bird runs like a Chaffinch, or like the Hedge-Accentor, and although I did not see it before it entered my box-trap, I do not hesitate to affirm that I am certain it ran (as well as hopped) in my garden.*' This account is in *British Birds with their Nests and Eggs*, Tegetmeier, Cordeaux, Aplin *et al.* (1896-98), which was mainly written by Butler and illustrated by Frowhawk, and was located by J. J. Bowley. Although lacking in exact detail, it seems plausible and is worthy of inclusion, not least for its vivid nature. Butler, who was living at 10 Avington Grove, Penge (just within the vice-county boundary) at the time of the 1881 census, was then a 36 year old Assistant Keeper in a Zoological Department.

Robin (European Robin)   *Erithacus rubecula*

Abundant breeding resident

Breeds from Europe and North Africa east to Siberia. Northern and eastern birds winter south to North Africa and the Middle East and some pass through Britain on migration. The British race *melophilus* is largely sedentary. Its population increased by around 40% from 1970 to 2001.

Early Surrey history. The earliest reference located for Surrey relates to the Godalming District in the early 19th century. At the end of the century, Robins were very plentiful in Dulwich (Power), the Norwood district (Aldridge) and Richmond Park (Mouritz). Hamilton (1881) listed them for Wimbledon Common. They were common in the Staines area (Kerr, 1906).

1900 to 1969. Robins seem to have been common and widespread throughout the period. Boorman collected many eggs at Ripley and Send from 1902 to 1912. Gosnell collected eggs at Frensham in 1936. Robins bred in the garden of Lambeth Palace in 1950 (*BLA*) and at Battersea Park in 1966-67.

Breeding counts since 1970 include:

Barnes Common: 26 territories in 1999

Battersea Park: bred 1971 (*LBR*), where they increased to 18-23 pairs in 1988-94 (Hewlett)

Beddington Sewage Farm: 19 territories in 1994, 14 in 1995, 16 in 1996, 14 in 1997, 15 in 1998, 26 in 1999, 21 in 2000, 29 in 2001, 17 in 2004

Bookham Common: 79 territories in 2002 (203 per square km)

Cannon Hill Common: 12 pairs in 1999, 15 in 2000, 20 in 2001

Frensham: 30 singing males in 1981, 22 in 1990, 20 in 1991 and 1992, 17 in 1994, 20 in 1995, 27 in 1996, 24 in 1997, 19 in 1998 and 1999, 26 in 2000, 15 in 2001. In a full survey, S. P. Peters counted 52 territories in 2005.

Hankley Common: 2002 *c.*30 pairs, increasing

Headley Heath: 34 singing males on 22nd April

1984, 42 on 6th May 1985, 20 on 14th June 1986, 14 pairs in 1987

Lonsdale Road Reservoir: three pairs in 1994, nine singing males in 1999

Morden Hall Park: 25 territories in 1997, 38 in 1998, 32 in 1999, 35 in 2000, 38 in 2001

Nunhead Cemetery: 42 territories in 1997

Reigate Priory: 19 pairs in 1996, 14 in 1997

Rowhill Copse: 62 territories in 1997

Sixty Acre Wood, Surbiton: 23 pairs in 1987

Surrey Docks: about ten pairs bred in 1990, five territories in 1999

Unstead Sewage Farm: 25 territories in 1998, 40 in 2000

West End Common, Esher: 11 territories in 1994, 32 in 2004

Whitmoor Common: 23+ pairs in 1999

Witley Common: *c.*25 territories in 1979

Robins were widely reported, in Spelthorne and elsewhere, during the 2003 BTO Spring Migration Watch.

Nesting. A nest was built in a Christmas wreath on a door at Roehampton in December 2006. Four eggs were reported to have hatched in late January (*The Times*, 5th February 2007). Young were out of the nest on 22nd March at Thorpe in 1974, much nearer to the normal date.

Rising Trend. Of the 231 tetrads in northeast Surrey, 94% were found to hold territories in the 1968-72 Atlas survey and 98 % in the 1988-97 Atlas. The Common Birds Census shows a significant overall increase, with numbers at least doubling from 1970 to 2000, more than the national trend.

Territory counts. Territories in selected Common Birds Census areas from 1994 to 2000 were:

	Square km	1994	1995	1996	1997	1997	1998	1999	2000
Arbrook Common	0.34	40	38	35	36	36	25	29	29
Ashtead Common	0.22	46	45	41	40	40	33	36	44
Barwell Court Farm	0.80	22	27	32	20	20	18	26	30
Bookham Common*	0.39	34	48	43	44		n/a	n/a	n/a
Broadstreet Common*	0.41	34	30	43	43		n/a	n/a	n/a

Nower Wood	0.30	24	20	22	18	18	22	30	33
Park Farm	0.74	26	31	25	17	17	29	27	34
Sugden Road	0.08	16	20	16	18	18	14	18	17
Total	**3.28**	**242**	**259**	**257**	**236**	**149**	**141**	**166**	**187**

*No census after 1997

Population size. The Winter Atlas found partial survey counts and estimates totalling 703 birds in 1981-84. The 1994-2004 Breeding Birds Survey suggests a breeding season population of at least 20,000 adults but this could be much too low. The Common Birds Census suggests that at the end of the period, there might have been 160,000 territories or 80 per square km. Robins were the first or second commonest birds in Common Birds Censuses from 1962 to 1994. They remain common throughout Surrey, benefiting from the extensive woodlands. If Surrey held a proportionate share of the British breeding population as given by the *New Atlas*, the population would be only 30,000 territories.

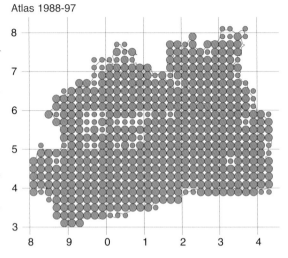

Atlas 1988-97

Large counts

Bowlhead Green: 64 counted in six hours, 31st January 1982

Caterham: ten round a bird table, 11th November 1983

Frensham: 56, 19th September 1993

Holmethorpe Sand Pits: 40, 18th September 1999

Kew Gardens: 25 counted in 80 minutes, 30th September 1986

Reigate Priory: 42, October 1993, 47, April 1996

Food. Robins are familiar at feeding stations, taking a variety of foods, sometimes from nut bags.

Movements. One ringed at Epsom Downs on 17th July 1982 was recovered three km away on 12th May 1989. There are European recoveries from France (three), Germany (one) and Switzerland. The last of these, ringed at Ewhurst on 31st July 1966 and recovered at Klosters, Switzerland on 18th April 1969, had covered 889 km and was the first British-ringed Robin to have been recovered from the country.

Longevity. A Robin ringed in Wiltshire on 27th September 1981 and recovered over eight years and six months later, at Farnham on 11th April 1990, had the greatest longevity located. One died of fowl cholera (*Pasteurellosis aviseptica*) at Esher in 1970.

Plumage variations. Bucknill knew of some pied specimens. A buff-coloured bird was reported at Limpsfield in February 1922 (*BB, 15:216*). A white-headed female was at Horsell for three years to 1970. There was a xanthocroistic (blond-coloured) Robin at Hurst Green in 1979 and a 'partial albino' at Stoke Lake in 1994.

Continental Robin   *Erithacus rubecula rubecula*

Robins of the continental race *rubecula* are strongly migratory in Finland and Scandinavia. Many of its members pass through the British Isles. Two or three birds showing characteristics of the race were seen at Beddington Sewage Farm on 30th October 1992 (J. P. Allan). There are no Surrey recoveries of *E. r. rubecula* nestlings ringed abroad to support their presence in Surrey but some of the European recoveries of autumn-ringed Surrey birds fit the pattern.

Nightingale (Common Nightingale)   *Luscinia megarhynchos*

Locally common summer visitor, breeding annually

Breeds from southern England through southern Europe to central Asia and winters in sub-Saharan Africa. Declining over much of its European range. Some continental birds may pass through Britain (*MA*). Numbers in Britain were held back by persecution during the 19th century and have since declined for other reasons. Fuller *et al.* suggest that deer browsing and canopy closure following less woodland management may have been factors.

Early Surrey history. The song of the Nightingale has made it a well known Surrey bird since at least the time when Nicholas of Guildford wrote, or may have written, the medieval poem *The Owl and the Nightingale*. Nicholas was using the bird as one party in an allegorical debate but real birds appear in the diaries of Samuel Pepys, who heard Nightingale song at a concert given at Vauxhall. This was then a pleasure garden in the country, to which Londoners travelled by boat from the north bank of the Thames.

It says something for their numbers in the first half of the 19th century, that there were enough to make economic exploitation worthwhile. To quote *The Letters of Rusticus*: *Every year, directly the Nightingales arrive, we have the London bird-catchers down here with their traps and meal-worms, and a great proportion of the earliest arrivals are conveyed to town.* Sydenham was reckoned to be a good place to hear them sing in the 1820s. In the 1840s they were abundant in Dulwich Wood and on the site later used for the Crystal Palace (Fitter, 1949). Elmers End was a reliable spot in the 1880s (Aldridge). Yarrell (1845) wrote that Surrey Nightingales were thought to be the finest songsters of their species and that professional bird catchers went into Surrey woods to collect them. The birds could, with judicious management, be kept singing for three months or more. Others were not so lucky. Jefferies (1886) described the trade, which involved luring the birds to traps baited with meal-worms, tying the wings of those that were caught and caged to stop them beating themselves to death against the wires, and darkening the cages with coverings of paper. Light was gradually let in and after two weeks, if the bird survived that long, the wings would be untied. Jefferies said that seventy percent of the birds died within a week of being caught. Those that survived were worth 30 shillings (£1.50).

Bucknill recorded that, in his own school days, the youth of Godalming used to offer dozens of Nightingale eggs to the boys of Charterhouse School for threepence each, or five for a shilling (5p). What they did with the eggs, and how they were identified, is not recorded. The price was similar to that for Dartford Warbler eggs which, at about the same time, fetched a shilling a clutch.

In spite of the pressure from collectors, Nightingales were still widely distributed in Surrey at the end of the 19th century and could still be found well into the London suburbs. Harting knew them at Kew (*Zool., 1886:243*). Bucknill mentions them being at Balham, Battersea Park, Clapham Park, Dulwich, Norwood (1873), Richmond Park, Tooting Bec Common and at Wimbledon Common (where Hamilton (1881) wrote that they were already rare and Fitter said they had been much reduced by the cutting of cover). Nightingales bred at Reigate Hill in 1872. They were particularly numerous around Slyfield Manor House, near Cobham in 1893 (Kearton, 1911). Bucknill mentioned Ashtead Park and Richmond Park (where they were mainly outside the park walls, and not common, according to Mouritz) as reliable places to hear them and Ashtead and Epsom Commons as holding many birds. Bucknill shot a migrant in an Epsom garden on 18th September 1894, a fairly late date.

1900 to 1950. Laurence Housman provided poetic support for the presence of Nightingales at Battersea in 1901:

> The missel-thrush with throat of glea,
> And nightingales at Battersea!
> *Annus Mirabilis (1902)*

There were large numbers in the Staines area in 1906, but fewer than formerly (Kerr, 1906) - this might relate to birds outside Surrey. The 20th century saw a decline which, in Surrey, continued into the 1999 Nightingale census organised by the BTO. Habitat changes, especially a reduction in coppiced woodland and the thinning of the lowest scrub layer, are thought to be factors in the decline. The Nightingale, like the Lesser Spotted Woodpecker, lives in a widespread and unprotected habitat (*BTO News* 226:4). By observation, the maturing of scrub in some of its traditional Surrey sites, such as Witley Common and at Truxford, has resulted in good habitat becoming overgrown and unsuitable.

Information about the first half of the 20th century is rather fragmentary. A pair held territory at Sanderstead in 1903-04. Eggs were collected at Shackleford in 1904 (Maitland and Turnbull). Boorman collected eggs at Bramley (Selhurst Common, 1902), East Clandon (1909), Ockham (1909), Ripley (1902) and Send (1902). Nightingales were heard at Addington and Grayswood in April 1906. A national survey carried out around 1910 found Nightingales to be 'regular and numerous' in Surrey (Ticehurst and Jourdain, 1911). They were common in southern England 'above all in Surrey' according to Hudson (1921). The Richmond Park population started to decline around 1910 and had gone by 1930. Bentham found many Nightingales at Itchingwood Common in 1912 and at Brockham and Holmwood Common in 1918. Nightingales were nesting at Pyrford in 1926 and in the Holmesdale area in 1928. Song was heard at Norwood in 1929. Beadell (1932) reported many nests in the Warlingham/Chelsham area. Hollom surveyed six square miles west from Addlestone on 9th-23rd May 1933 and found 26 singing birds, one per 148 acres (1.7 per square km). Apart from Addlestone itself, the area was then mainly one of small woods, rough copses, pasture, nurseries and parkland, without gorse or thorn (*BB, 28:81-82*). At Englefield Green the Nightingales, which had been numerous before the clearance of woods in the 1914-18 war, were only slowly returning by 1934. On Limpsfield Common there were three pairs in 1938, but none in 1940.

Other sites, not necessarily of breeding birds, were at Anstead Brook (eggs collected 1949), Bookham, (1934, 1938), Cheam Warren (1937), Chiddingfold (1935-37), Churt (1938), Claygate (1950), Coulsdon (1950), Croham Hurst (before 1950), Englefield Green (1934, much less common than before 1914 due to tree clearance), Epsom/Epsom Downs/Banstead(1934, 1935, 1937), Farleigh (Freelands Wood up to 1928), Godstone (1950), Ham Common (1937 and 1942, two pairs in 1943), Hambledon (1938, 1945), Haslemere (1934-36), Leatherhead (1950), the Limpsfield district (1934), Wandsworth Common (1950) and Wimbledon Common (bred 1950). There is no further information earlier than 1945, when good numbers were reported at Englefield Green and in southwest Surrey.

1950 to 1969. Rather more information came to hand with the establishment of the *Surrey Bird Report*. Numbers below relate to birds singing. Taking the largest counts, this gives 211 territories at 93 sites.

1970 to 1975. The Surrey Bird Club began a countywide census of Nightingales in 1970 and completed it in 1971. The work in 1970 found 167 territories at 44 sites. The further work in 1971 found 22 more territories at 11 sites where none were found in 1970, suggesting a minimum population of about 200 pairs, and possibly 300 if allowance is made for under-recording (Wheatley, 1973b).

1976 to 1980. The BTO organised national censuses of Nightingales in 1976 and 1980. The Surrey Bird Club achieved almost full coverage for the vice-county in both of these. The national results for 1976 were apparently lost by the BTO and never published but the Surrey information for both years is available. The surveys revealed further declines, to 115 territories at 48 sites in 1976 and 103 territories at 57 sites in 1980 (Wheatley, 1980). There were no records from Vann Lake, where Nightingales had been attracted by the planting of hawthorns after 1975.

1999. The overall decline has continued. The 1999 census found 87 territories.

The pattern of the decline since 1957 is shown by the table. A noteworthy feature within the decline from the 1950s to the 1976 and 1980 censuses is the relative stability of the range, after the contraction earlier in the century. Four 10 km squares (SU85, SU96, TQ36 and TQ45) lost their birds and two (TQ17, TQ23) gained them. Only for TQ36 were the numbers more than marginal. The collapse on Witley and other commons in SU94 is particularly striking.

Summary of the 1957-1999 territories by 10 km square

Square	SU84	SU85	SU86	SU93	SU94	SU95	SU96	TQ03	TQ04	TQ05	TQ06	TQ13	TQ14	TQ15
1957-69	6	1	1	16	27	11	2	8	11	11	5	6	7	24
1970-71	12	2	0	13	38	12	0	39	21	1	1	5	16	14
1976-80	12	0	0	18	40	6	2	24	9	1	4	5	8	15
1999	0	0	0	13	5	5	0	17	3	1	2	0	1	18

Square	TQ16	TQ17	TQ23	TQ24	TQ25	TQ26	TQ27	TQ33	TQ34	TQ35	TQ36	TQ44	TQ45	All
1957-69	23	0	0	10	4	1	1	3	5	16	9	0	3	**211**
1970-71	11	0	0	1	1	0	0	0	3	8	0	0	0	**198**
1976-80	10	1	1	5	1	0	0	0	7	5	0	0	0	**174**
1999	1	0	0	6	0	0	0	0	12	1	0	1	1	**87**

Losses have been severe in some of the other large colonies. Newlands Corner in TQ04 was once one of the best places in Surrey to hear Nightingales. They sang from the hawthorns on the crest of the downs, at the edge of the grassy southern slope, and they used some of the scattered hawthorns among the grass. Today there are no Nightingales and the full reasons are none too obvious. Huge numbers of people now use the area for recreational purposes but this may not be solely to blame. Something about the scrub may have changed, and perhaps the food sources as well. The scrub has probably become too mature, without the bramble understorey that Nightingales need for nesting. Nightingales used to breed in similar sites on other parts of the North Downs but there too they have been lost. Wilson (2001) found that Nightingales prefer thickets with a dense canopy cover and bare ground in the centre. These are vulnerable to disturbance in heavily used areas like Newlands Corner.

Where found since 1999. More recent records, some possibly of migrants, have come from Barnes Common, Beddington, Blindley Heath, Bookham Common, Broadstreet Common, Capel, Chiddingfold, Coulsdon, Cranleigh, Crowhurst, Effingham, Elstead, Guildford, Ham Lands, Hambledon, Haslemere, Horton Country Park, Merle Common, Milford Common, Morden Hall Park, Parkgate, Purley, Shere, Smallfield, South Norwood, Stoke Lake, Sydney Wood, Thursley, Tugley Wood, Wallington, Weatherhill Common and Witley Common. There are a few places where numbers have been growing since the 1980 census. Bookham Common (TQ15) is the best example. Prowse (1999) showed how scrub management at Bookham Common, which in recent years has held the largest colony in Surrey (12 singing in 1999) has helped to increase the numbers. Even here though, there were only five territories in 2003.

Spelthorne. Migrants or possibly breeding birds were recorded at the Spelthorne reservoirs in 1931, 1932 and 1933. Nightingales were present in the breeding season at Laleham and Shepperton in the early 1930s, an area which has now been deserted. Single birds were trapped at Queen Mary Reservoir on 26th April 1975, 7th August 1976, 12th July 1980 and at Queen Mary Gravel Pits on 15th July, 18th July and 8th August 1981, 30th July 1983, 20th July and 4th September 1985, 15th August 1987 and 2nd August 1988.

One was singing at Queen Mary Gravel Pits on 2nd May 1987. Single birds were at Shortwood Common on 10th July 1998 and Staines Moor on 16th July 2002. One at Queen Mary Reservoir on 4th September 1985 was a late bird.

Song. Nightingales have a short song period, from their arrival in late April to about mid June in most years. Hollom found that song was most reliable between 11 pm and 2 am. One singing at Stave Hill, Surrey Docks on 20th April and 5th May 1998 was the first Inner London song since 1985 (Hewlett). One was singing at Holmethorpe Sand Pits in May 1998, the only record for the site since at least 1960. Eric Parker, the Surrey naturalist, left a fine poem about the Nightingale in his private papers (Parker, 1987).

Population size. If even half of the vice-county had enjoyed the same density of Nightingales as found in Hollom's Addlestone study, the 1933 vice-county population would have been 1,640 pairs, nearly 20 times the current number. Nightingales have not been recorded in Common Birds Censuses well enough to establish a trend. The 1994-2004 Breeding Birds Survey results imply less than ten adults in the breeding season which, given the 1999 census results, is clearly too low, not surprisingly for a skulking bird with such a short song period.

Calendar. Some very late 19th century records are from Godalming, where Nightingales were seen in October and November before 1849 and heard on 12th December 1823 or 1824 (Newman in Bucknill). Although these might seem questionable, winter records as late as 20th December (Suffolk) are listed in Hudson (1973) and Nightingales are known to sing occasionally in winter quarters. Bucknill gave an average arrival date of 14th April, derived from about three hundred Surrey records which extended over many years. This is slightly earlier than in the 1990s, when the population level was much lower. The average arrival date in the London area south of the Thames from 1929 to 1939 was 18th April. Early and late dates since 1900 are:

Early

22nd March 1903   Ashtead

26th March 1908   Barnes Common

5th April 2000   Capel

Late

13th September 1962 Shirley

4th September 1985   Moor Park (*SBR* for 1994)

24th September 1960 Addington (SBC archive)

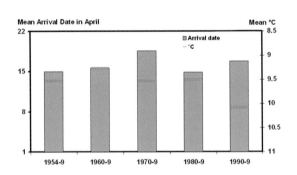

The chart shows that there has been little correlation between arrival dates and temperature over the past 50 years.

Movements and longevity. There are no overseas ringing recoveries from Surrey. One ringed just over the county border at Gospel Green, Sussex in 1970 (*SBR* for 1971) was recovered in Spain in September of the same year. Other recoveries show mostly local movements:

Ringed				Recovered			Distance
Pyrford	Young	14 June	1926	Leatherhead	20 August	1929	
Frensham	Young	8 June	1976	Hampshire	3 August	1976	43 km
*Witley Common		20 June	1979	Witley Common	8 June	1984	
Hampshire	Young	8 June	1980	Witley Common	6 June	1981	
Beddington Sewage Farm	3	August	1997	Beddington Sewage Farm	13 June	1999	

*The greatest longevity, over four years and eleven months, and shown by a local recovery.

Details of surveys

1957 to 1969. Sites, with maxima where available and grouped by 10 km square were: *SU84*: near Farnham Sewage Farm (1, 1966), Frensham (5, 1964), Seale; *SU85*: Frimley (1, 1964); *SU86*: Camberley (1, 1965); *SU93*: (Prestwick Lane 10, 1964,), Sleepy Hollow (1, 1969), Wormley (5, 1967); *SU94*: Busbridge (2, 1963), Elstead (1961), Godalming/Busbridge (2, 1960, 1963), Hydestile (1965), Puttenham (1, 1969), Rodsall (1, 1960), Shackleford (2, 1960), Thursley/Ockley (4, 1965), Warren Hill (3, 1960), Winkworth (1, 1969), Witley/Rodborough (9, 1968, 1969); *SU95*: Ash Green (3, 1967), Henley Park (1, 1969), Smart's Heath (1, 1966, 1967), Wanborough (5, 1966),

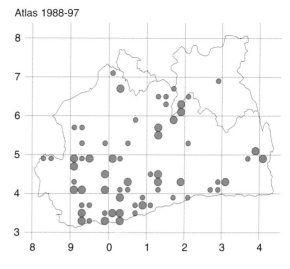

Atlas 1988-97

Whitmoor Common (1, 1969); *SU96*: Deepcut (1, 1961), Pondover Pit (1969); *TQ03*: Alfold (7, 1969), Cranleigh (1960); *TQ04*: Bramley (1, 1969), Ewhurst, Merrow Downs (1, 1967), Netley Heath (1, 1964), Newlands Corner (6, 1963), Shamley Green ; *TQ05*: Clandon Downs (1, 1969), East Clandon Common (6, 1962), East Horsley (1, 1961), Merrow Downs (1, 1969), Ripley (1, 1962), Wisley Common (1); *TQ06*: Byfleet (1, 1961), St George's Hill (2, 1961), Wey Manor Farm (2, 1962); *TQ13*: Exfold Wood (1, 1965), near Bonet's Farm (1, 1965), Vann Lake (4, 1966, 1968) ; *TQ14*: Abinger Roughs (2, 1965), Forest Green (1, 1969), Green Copse (1, 1963), Hackhurst Downs (1), Holmwood Common (1, 1968), Newdigate (1, 1963); *TQ15*: Ashtead Common (12, 1960; 8-10, 1964), Banks/Bookham Commons (2, 1964; 5, 1968), East Horsley, Effingham Common (1, 1969), Fetcham Downs (2, 1963; 1, 1964), Headley Heath (1), Mickleham (1, 1957, 1969), Stoke D'Abernon (1959); *TQ16*: Ashtead (2), Chessington, Epsom Common (3, 1965), Esher/West End (3, 1965), Prince's Coverts (6-7, 1964; 9, 1965; 12, 1968), Surbiton (1, 1967); *TQ24*: Charlwood (5, 1968), Earlswood (1) Reigate (4, 1966); *TQ25*: Chipstead (1, 1964), Epsom Downs (1, 1964), Park Downs (1968), Reigate Hill (1968); *TQ26*: Coulsdon (1, 1960), *TQ27*: Wimbledon Common (1, 1965, 1967); *TQ33*: Felbridge (3, 1962); *TQ34*: Bransland Wood (1, 1963), South Nutfield (2, 1965), Weatherhill Common (2, 1965); *TQ35*: Barrow Green (1, 1966), Bletchingley (5, 1958), Caterham (1), Godstone (3, 1964), North Park Farm (1, 1958), Tilburstow Hill (2, 1960), Warlingham (1), Whitehill Roughets (1, 1957), Woldingham (1, 1964); *TQ36*: Farleigh/Addington (6, 1957), Kings Wood (1, 1960, 1963), Selsdon Wood (2, 1960); *TQ45*: Itchingwood Common (1961), Limpsfield Common (1962), Tatsfield (1, 1957, 1966).

1970 to 1975. Results for the 55 sites, grouped by 10 km square and for 1970 unless otherwise stated, were: *SU84*: Frensham (4, 1970; 11, 1971), Truxford (1, 1971); *SU85*: Frimley (2, 1971); *SU93*: (all sites, 13), Grayswood (2, 1971), High Street Green (2, 1971); *SU94*: Godalming (1+), Godalming-Guildford towpath (1, 1971), Oxenford (1), Puttenham Common (6), Thursley/Ockley (1, 1970; 3, 1971), Witley/Rodborough Commons (26), *SU95*: Ash (2, 1971), Broadstreet Common (1), Henley Park/Lake (2), Merrist Wood (1), Pirbright (3), Wanborough (2), Whitmoor Common (1); *TQ03*: Alfold/Dunsfold (28), Cranleigh (2), Lower Canfold Wood (7, 1971), Vachery (2); *TQ04*: Albury Downs/Newlands Corner (6), Albury Park (1, 1971), Brooklands area (1+), Chantries (2), Merrow Downs (4), Netley Heath (5), Run Common (1, 1971), Shamley Green (2); *TQ05*: Merrow Downs (1); *TQ13*: Vann Lake (5); *TQ14*: Forest Green (1), Hackhurst Downs (3, 1970; 6, 1971), Holmwood Common (2), Leith Hill (1), Ranmore (2), Redlands, Weare Street (2), Westcott Rifle Range (2); *TQ15*: Ashtead Common/Forest (1), Bookham Common (5), East Horsley (1+), Effingham Common (3), Headley (2), Mickleham (2);

TQ16: Ashtead Common/Forest (1, 1971), Prince's Coverts (10); TQ24: Brookside Farm, Reigate (1); TQ25: Gatton (1); TQ34: Ashen Plantation (1, 1971), Bransland Wood (1, 1971), Weatherhill Common (1, 1971); TQ35: Barrow Green (1), Black Bushes (1), Little Hawke/Woldingham (1), North Park Farm/Gravelly Hill (2), Warlingham (1), Whitehill Roughets (2).

1976 to 1980. The 1976 and 1980 results, grouped by 10 km square, were: *SU84*: Claypit Wood (-, 2), Farnham (-, 2), Frensham Common (2, 5), Hankley/Truxford (1, -), Seale (-, 1), Tilford (1, -); *SU93*: Botany Bay (-, 2), Combe Lane farm (-, 1), Durfold Wood (-, 1), Enticknaps Copse (-, 1), Holloways Heath (1, -), Oldlands (-, 1), Pockford Harbour (-, 1), Prest Wood (-, 3), Rampingdown Copse (-, 1), Sandhills (-, 1), Stroud Wood (3, -), Tugley Wood (-, 1), White Beech Copse (-, 1); *SU94*: Puttenham (2, -), Rodsall (1, -), Shackleford (1, -), Thursley/Ockley (-, 1), Wanborough (2, -), Wildfield Copse (2, -), Witley/Rodborough Commons (31, 30); *SU95*: Broadstreet Common (1, -), Wood Street Common (-, 3), Worplesdon (-, 1), Wyke Common (1, -); *SU96*: Chobham (2, 1); TQ03: Dunsfold (11, 1), Ewhurst Place (-, 1), Howicks (-, 1), Lakers Green (-, 2), Little Rickhurst Copse (-, 1), Nanhurst (-, 1), Nymet (-, 1), Oldhouse (1, -), Park Hatch (-, 1), Pickenswood Copse (-, 2), Sachelhill Lane, Alfold (-, 1), Tickner's Heath (-, 1); TQ04: Ewhurst Place (2, -), Hackhurst Downs (1, -), Run Common (1, -), Scotland Farm (-, 1), St Martha's (3, -), Strood Common (-, 1); TQ05: Effingham (1, -); TQ06: Brooklands (-, 1), Egham (-, 1), Woodham (1 or 2, -); TQ13: Ewhurst Green (2, -), Exfold/Somersbury (1, -), Knoll Farm (1, -), Smokejack Farm (-, 1); TQ14: Betchworth (1, -), Gadbrook (1, -), Green's Farm (1, -), Holmwood Common (-, 1), North Breache (-, 1), Waterlands, Jordans (3, -); TQ15: Ashtead Common (2, -), Bookham Commons (6, 5), Effingham Common (3, 1), Headley (2, -), Horns Hill (1, -), Knott Park (1, -); TQ16: Claremont (-, 1), Ditton Common (-, 1), Epsom Common (2, -), Prince's Coverts (4, 4), West End (-, 1), Weston Green (-, 1); TQ17: Petersham (1, -); TQ23: Russ Hill (1, -); TQ24: Bunce Common (1, -), Brookside Farm (1, -), Horley (-, 2), Wray's Farm (-, 1); TQ25: Epsom Downs (-, 1); TQ34: Bransland Wood (1, -), Bridges Wood (-, 1), Hornecourt Hill (-, 1), Thunderfield Castle (-, 1), Weatherhill (2, 3); TQ35: Barrow Green/Little Hawks (2, -), Farthing Down (1, -), Marden Park (1, -), North Park Farm (1, -).

1999. The 87 territories found, grouped by 10 km square, were: *SU93*: Birch Copse (1), Canterbury Rew (2), Duns Copse (1), Durfold Wood (2), Fisherlane Wood (1), Oaken Wood (4), Tugley Wood (2); *SU94*: Milford Common (4), Potter's Hill (1); *SU95*: Broadstreet Common/Wood Street (5); TQ03: Aldermoor Copse area (3), Furzefield Wood (2), Hammer Lane (3), Pollingford Manor (1), Sidney Wood (8); TQ04: Alderbrook (1), Mansfield Park (2); TQ05: Horsell Moor (1); TQ06: Brooklands (1), Chertsey Meads (1); TQ14: Hatchland Copse/Capel (1); TQ15: Banks Common (3), Bookham Common (12), Effingham Fish Ponds (1), Headley Heath (1), White Hill/Headley Heath (1); TQ16: Ditton Common (1); TQ24: Mulberry Farm old brick works (1), Parkgate old brick works (3), Reffolds Copse (2); TQ34: Blindley Heath (4), Crowhurst Lane End (1), Hangdog Wood (1), Hookstile Gully/Blindley Heath (6); TQ35: Little Common Lane/White Post (1), TQ44: Foyle Farm/Merle Common (1); TQ45: Hurst Green (1).

Bluethroat   *Luscinia svecica*

Ten birds, including one in Spelthorne

Red-spotted Bluethroats breed in the northern conifer forests and tundras from Scandinavia east to Siberia and Alaska. The White-spotted form has a more southerly distribution from central Europe east to the Ukraine. Bluethroats were not recorded from Britain until 1826, though Thomas (1999) suggests that they may have been common in the marshy scrub that followed the last glaciation. A few Bluethroats have bred in Britain. Some European Bluethroats winter in Spain, others move south to the African Sahel (*MA*). British occurrences are mainly from southern and eastern coastal counties but many birds have been found further inland. There is a well-defined peak in May with a broader and smaller autumn peak in September. There were no July records from 1958 to 1985.

Race not determined:

1862:   Banstead. Mr Young, a Sutton taxidermist and birdcatcher, told Bucknill that he had seen a *blue-throated redstart in* Castle Bottom, Banstead in September. Bucknill included this as the Red-spotted form, but gave no further description.

1963:   Beddington, one on 22nd September.

1976:   Beddington Sewage Farm, a first-year male trapped on 10th October.

Red-spotted Bluethroat *Luscinia svecica svecica*

1862:   Wandsworth, a male said to have been killed in May (*SALEC*), was at one time in the Charterhouse Collection.

1977:* One trapped at Perry Oaks Sewage Farm on 12th September.

1982:   One at Tadworth on 20th May, died soon afterwards.

*Spelthorne

White-spotted Bluethroat *Luscinia svecica cyanecula*

There was a male in full breeding plumage, said to have been killed at Guildford Castle (*SALEC*), in the Charterhouse Collection in 2001. It was undated. The vague provenance may be why it was not included by the authors of *The Handbook* and why, as Bucknill put it, the bird 'escaped the notice of the compilers of the Standard works on English Ornithology'.

1965:   Ewhurst, a first-year bird was trapped on 30th August.

1997:   Beddington Sewage Farm, a first-year male was trapped at Beddington Sewage Farm on 3rd August and retrapped there on 13th June 1999. It was heard singing then, after starting its post-nuptial moult, was trapped again on 4th July and was last seen on the 10th. The *Migration Atlas* gives two other examples with up to five years between ringing and recovery, indicating regular passage.

2004:   Barn Elms London Wetland Centre, a bird believed to be of this race was seen from 30th April to 3rd May by many observers (*Bird Watching*).

2006:   Frensham Great Pond, a male in the reeds on 29th April.

Black Redstart *Phoenicurus ochruros*

Scarce breeding summer visitor and passage migrant, occasionally wintering.

Black Redstarts breed from Britain south to North Africa and east to Central Asia. The breeding range has extended in northwest Europe, including Britain and Scandinavia. The *Migration Atlas* shows no British-ringed recoveries south of Iberia. Birds from the range as a whole winter south as far as the Horn of Africa and India. In Britain, remains dating back to the last glaciation have been found. Black Redstarts were rare during the first half of the 19th century, known mainly from southern counties. The first British breeding record came from Durham in 1845. Regular breeding began in Sussex in 1923. A gradual increase in numbers, possibly assisted by better identification techniques, brought the first London area breeding record at the derelict Wembley Exhibition site in 1926. Bomb damage in London during the 1939-45 war created more habitat and numbers continued to rise into the 1950s. The British breeding population seems to have peaked in 1988-91, when the BTO Atlas survey showed a 51.5% increase over the Atlas of 1968-72 but it is currently declining under pressure from the reclamation of derelict land.

On the continent Black Redstarts often breed in houses and gardens. It remains to be seen whether the British birds, possibly assisted by a warmer climate, will prove able to adapt to the change.

Early Surrey history. The earliest Surrey records all refer to wintering or passage birds, reflecting the Black Redstart's 19th century national status. A male was shot near Haslemere in or around 1830 and Kidd shot a female at Godalming in November in or around 1838 (both from Bucknill, 1902). Stafford had one that was killed at Ockford Road, Godalming in 1855 by a boy with a stone, when the ground was snow-covered (*SALEC*). Another was seen between Godalming and Guildford on Christmas Day 1873, a third was at Milford at about the same time. A female was shot near Rowledge Vicarage on 7th November 1882. Bucknill mentions a specimen in the Natural History Museum which is said to have come from Wimbledon Common.

Migrants from 1900. A female seen at Thornton Heath (Surrey) on 21st October 1910 was the first record for the London area. The skin of this bird was one of a collection exhibited to the LNHS by a Mr Horn in 1919 (LNHS 1919). There was a male at Caterham on 25th September 1912 and another near Bugg Hill Farm, in November 1916. In 1922, there were males at Tadworth on 19th-25th March and on 20th May. There was one at Brooklands Sewage Farm on 22nd March 1931. Another was at Mortlake from 18th December 1932 into January 1933 and there was a male at Barn Elms on 30th November 1935. In 1936, one was found at Frensham Little Pond on 28th March and another at The Devil's Jumps on 10th November (HNHS, 1955). Spelthorne records include a female at Queen Mary Reservoir on 6th November 1935 and one at Staines Reservoirs on December 30th, 1936.

Where found since 1956. Most of the migrants have been seen at places in the London area such as Barn Elms, Battersea, Beddington, Croydon and the Surrey Docks, and at Walton-on-Thames and in the Spelthorne area at gravel pits and reservoirs. Migrants became more frequent on the commons of south-west Surrey in the 1960s, perhaps as the results of the establishment of a small breeding population in the London area. Places where they have been seen include Ashtead, Badshot Lea, Birtley Green, Bisley, Bletchingley, Bricksbury Hill, Brooklands, Buckland, Camberley, Capel, Caterham, Chessington, Coldharbour, Compton, Dorking, Elmers End Sewage Farm, Enton, Epsom Sewage Farm, Frensham, Frimley Gravel Pits, Gatwick, Guildford, Godalming, Godstone, Hankley Common, Haslemere, Henley Park Ranges, Hersham, Hinchley Wood, Hindhead, Holmethorpe, Hurst Green, Kew Gardens, Kingston, Kingswood, Leatherhead, Lightwater, Limpsfield, Morden Hall Park, New Addington, New Haw, Nore Hill, Ockley, Olddean Common, Old Woking Sewage Farm, Papercourt, Pirbright Commons, Purley, Raynes Park, Redhill, Reigate, Richmond Park, Sanderstead, Seale, Shirley Hills, South Norwood, St Martha's, Sunbury Lock, Surbiton, Sutton, Thorpe, Thursley, Unstead Sewage Farm, Vann Lake, Wisley, Woking and Wrecclesham.

More recent migrants have been at Barn Elms (2001, 2003, 2005), Berrylands (2003), Capel (2004), Charlwood (2002), Cranleigh (2004/05), Frimley (2004), Gatwick (2002), Guildford (2001-03), Island Barn (2001-02, 2004), Milford (2003), Peaslake (2001), Queen Elizabeth II Reservoir (2001-02), Raynes Park (2001), Redhill (2004), South Norwood (2002-03), Trevereux (2001), Unstead Sewage Farm (2002), Walton-on-Thames (2001-03), Wandsworth (2002), Waterloo Bridge (song, 2001) and Witley (2001, 2003). There were others at King George VI Reservoir and Staines Reservoirs in 2000. Winter records from Staines Reservoirs included November 2003.

There has been a striking increase in the number of migrant Black Redstarts seen since the 1960s:

Number of bird months (excluding breeding birds) by decade

	1900s	1910s	1920s	1930s	1940s	1950s	1960s	1970s	1980s	1990s	2000-01	Total
Vice-county	1	4	1	24	31	36	40	108	113	147	29	534

Breeding. The main needs for successful breeding are a cavity for the nest, a high song post and a fairly extensive area of waste ground which supports plenty of ants and other insects (Fitter, 1956). The first breeding records were from a bombed building at Wandsworth in 1941 and 1942, when a nest with young was found. One singing at the Surrey docks on 9th June 1943 was a forerunner of later breeding pairs there. Since then pairs have been found with some regularity at sites along the old London waterfronts and less frequently on industrial and commercial buildings elsewhere. There were at least four nests at the Surrey Docks in 1972. A pair were found feeding fledged young among ruined buildings by Croydon Airport on 10th July 1944.

Power stations have been a favoured site. At the power station adjacent to Beddington Sewage Farm, Black Redstarts first bred in 1949, were present in 1950, bred in 1952 and had four breeding pairs in 1956 and three in 1957 and 1958, one singing male in 1959, bred in 1961, probably 1962, bred 1963 and 1964. A pair bred at Fairfields Hall, Croydon in 1965. Two pairs probably bred in the Beddington/Croydon area in 1970 (*LBR*). Three males held territory on a building site at Peckham in 1969 but breeding was not established (*LBR* for 1970).

Breeding has been rare outside the London area. It was suspected at the Guildford cathedral construction site in 1948 and 1950 and was proved in central Guildford close to the telephone exchange, which was used as a song post, in 1989. Young were raised at Horley in 1967. A pair bred at Elmers End Sewage Farm in 1968. Pairs bred at Chertsey in 1993 and Redhill in 1996.

Breeding and territorial sites 1970-2001

	1970	1971	1972	1973	1974	1975	1976	1977	1978	1979	1980	1981	1982	1983
Bred	1	1	7	2	4	2	2	5	5	3	6	2	0	0
Present	4	0	0	1	2	1	0	1	3	0	3	0	0	2
Singing	2	6	1	4	1	6	9	0	8	4	1	0	0	5
All	**7**	**7**	**8**	**7**	**7**	**9**	**11**	**6**	**16**	**7**	**10**	**2**	**0**	**7**

	1984	85	86	87	88	89	90	91	92	93	94	95	96	97
Bred	0	3	2	3	4	2	3	1	0	1	2	1	3	1
Present	0	1	2	3	3	2	2	2	0	1	5	0	0	2
Singing	8	3	4	7	3	4	2	2	2	4	1	3	1	1
All	**8**	**7**	**8**	**13**	**10**	**8**	**7**	**5**	**2**	**6**	**8**	**4**	**4**	**4**

	98	99	2000	2001
Bred	0	0	1	1
Present	2	0	0	0
Singing	1	1	1	1
All	**3**	**1**	**2**	**2**

Bred – breeding pairs. Present – bird(s) present, no song, breeding not proved. Singing – singing male holding territory.

The breeding population rose to a peak in 1978 and has subsequently experienced an erratic decline, probably linked to the loss of suitable nest sites in Inner London. Successful breeding requires the continued existence of tall industrial buildings with adjacent areas of rough ground. Old sites of this type are being redeveloped in many parts of Surrey. A once sizeable population among old buildings from the Thames to Battersea was down to a pair or two in the late 1990s after many of the old sites had been redeveloped. The 1988-97 SBC Atlas

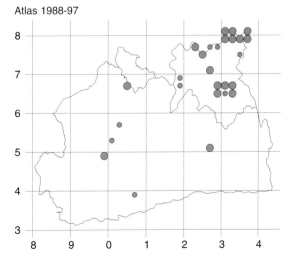

Atlas 1988-97

survey gives a somewhat optimistic summary of the current distribution. In 2000 and 2001 the only proven breeding was from single pairs at a government DERA site on the north side of Chobham Common. Pairs bred at Battersea and Battersea Power Station in 2002 and there was a singing male at Battersea in 2003.

Calendar. The table shows a spring passage mainly in March and April and a return passage peaking in October and November, with a few birds remaining to winter. It is not known if wintering birds are from the breeding population or winter visitors from other areas.

Bird months for migrants 1900-2001

	Jan	Feb	Mar	Apr	May	Jun	Jul	Aug	Sep	Oct	Nov	Dec	Total
Vice-county	30	25	92	121	29	6	7	11	13	97	70	33	**534**
Spelthorne	12	11	10	4	2	0	0	1	1	8	11	11	**71**

Movements and longevity. The only available ringing information is of a Black Redstart ringed at Barn Elms Reservoirs on 29th April 1992 and recovered 238 km north in Yorkshire on 14th May of the same year.

Redstart (Common Redstart) — *Phoenicurus phoenicurus*
Locally common summer visitor, breeding annually

Redstarts have a more northern range than Black Redstarts, and are woodland birds, wintering in sub-Saharan and central Africa. Most foreign recoveries of British-ringed birds are from France and Iberia (*MA*). The range in the British Isles appears to have extended north and west during the 19th century. Britain is one of a number of European countries to have experienced a decline during the 20th century, though there was some recovery in the closing years.

Early Surrey history. Gilbert White heard a Redstart singing at South Lambeth on 26th April 1785 and 20th May 1787. Newman (1849) listed Redstarts for the Godalming district. Hamilton (1881) recorded the species from the Wimbledon Common/Putney Heath area. Bucknill gave undated records from Battersea Park, Beddington, Betchworth Park, Carshalton, Caterham, Chobham, Godalming, Godstone, hills near Gomshall, Leith Hill, Reigate, Richmond Park, Streatham Common, Sutton, Weybridge, Wimbledon Common, Witley, Woking and Wray Common. He knew of nests on Ashtead Common (eight eggs in 1893) and Epsom Common. His comment that Redstarts *cannot be properly described as an abundant species in any part of Surrey, though in some places it is fairly common* is quite a good summary of the current distribution, apart from a withdrawal from the northeast. Kerr's 1906 comment that Redstarts were becoming rarer around Staines but had never been plentiful there remains true.

1900 to 1969. Boorman found a nest at Wisley in 1907. There was an early bird at East Dulwich on 28th March 1909 (*BB, 4:308*). Redstarts were numerous at Richmond Park in 1904-05 (Mouritz, 1905). Bentham thought there were twelve pairs there in 1908. Collenette found about 25 pairs in 1935 of which about 20 bred. There were only ten pairs in the park in 1948 (*LBR*) and about nine pairs in 1953 (*BLA*). Power (1910) knew Redstarts as migrants at Dulwich and Tooting and said they bred in Shirley Woods. They were still breeding in the Shirley Hills in the 1950s (*BLA*). Beadell (1930) said they were only passage migrants at Warlingham. They bred at Addington in 1929, 1942-43 and 1945-46 and at Wisley in 1930. Three pairs bred at Limpsfield in 1946. In the Haslemere district, Redstarts became scarcer during the 1930s but then increased again up to the 1960s. Breeding season localities across Surrey in the 1950s and 60s include Addlestone, Ashtead Woods, Bagshot Heath, Chobham Common, Crooksbury Common, Elstead (Royal Common), Esher Common, Felbridge, Frensham, Hindhead, Hurtwood, Hydon's Ball, Leith Hill, Limpsfield Chart, Olddean Common, Pitch Hill, Thursley, Wisley and Ockham commons and Wisley RHS Gardens.

Breeding since 1970. A very large contraction of range has taken place in the 231 tetrads of northeast Surrey, where only four occupied tetrads were found in the 1988-97 SBC Atlas survey, compared with 22 in 1968-72. The Common Birds Census, which lacked regular cover of Redstart sites, did not pick up any territories after 1981.

Population size. There are currently around 110 pairs on the western heaths, with Hankley, Pirbright/Ash Ranges, Thursley/Ockley and Westend/Pirbright Ranges accounting for most of them, as shown in the table.

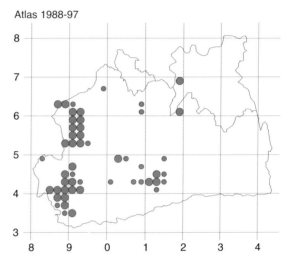

Atlas 1988-97

Territorial birds on the western heaths, 1994-2004

	1994	1995	1996	1997	1998	1999	2000	2001	2002	2003	2004
Crooksbury Common	2	3	1	4	4	3	2	1	2	2	2
Frensham Common	5	7	8	7	9	9	9	9	9	7	7
Hankley Common	5	13	7	9	8	10	14	16	17	18	21
Hindhead Commons	0	1	3	4	4	4	3	2	2	2	4
Mytchett Place				3	4	9			2		
Olddean Common			6	6	11	9	5	8			5
Pirbright Common/											
Ash Ranges	18	20	17	16	16	28	26		25		
Thursley/Ockley/											
Elstead Commons	16	19	18	15	15	13	11	15	19	16	19
West End Common/											
Pirbright Ranges				19						20	26
Witley Common				2		4	4	4	6	5	3

From counts organised by John Clark. Table omits incomplete counts.

Intermittent reports from Bourne Woods, Brentmoor Heath, Brookwood Heath, Chobham, Churt, Frensham, Hindhead, Puttenham, Winterfold and Witley suggest that these may hold another 15-20 pairs.

Nesting. A nest at Pirbright was taken over by Great Tits, who built their own nest over the clutch, in 1972. Nest sites include a squirrel's drey (Pirbright 1975).

Calendar. In the late 19th century, a typical arrival date was the middle of April (Saunders, 1899). Glegg (1935) gave the average arrival date in Middlesex for 33 (non-consecutive) years as 15th April. The average arrival date in the London area south of the Thames from 1929 to 1939 was 8th April. The chart shows that Glegg's date is about the same as the current average for Surrey and earlier than in the 1950s and 1960s, as well as showing the correlation between mean temperature and arrival date.

Extreme dates:

Early		Late	
14th March 2000	Beddington Sewage Farm	29th October 1973	Milford
20th March 1937	Surrey (*Handbook*)	29th October 1977	Milford
20th March 1961	Frensham	1st November 1966	Dulwich, caught by a cat
22nd March 1973	Richmond Park	19th December 1970	Perry Oaks Sewage Farm

The arrival dates chart shows an association between spring temperatures and arrival dates, the average date being latest in the cold 1960s.

Movements and longevity. Migrants are sometimes found at non-breeding sites. Examples are Wimbledon Common (25th-26th May 1980), Tooting (10th May 1983), Clapham (1st August 1985), the Surrey Docks (16th April 1996), Battersea Park (23rd August 1997) and Barn Elms London Wetland Centre (April 2005). Redstarts are rare migrants at Holmethorpe, with only seven records from 1960 to 1999 (*BHSP*). There are Spelthorne records from Queen Mary Gravel Pits and Reservoir, Staines Moor/Stanwell Moor (two singing on 14th April 2000), Staines Reservoirs and Wraysbury Reservoir.

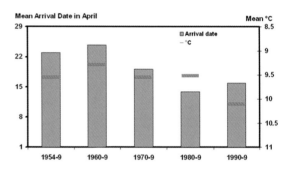

Redstarts ringed at Ewhurst on 27th September 1965 and 8th September 1968 were recovered respectively in Portugal on 1st November 1965 and Spain on 12th April 1970. There is one African recovery, of a young Redstart ringed at Witley Common on 14th June 1982 and recovered 2,185 km south in the same year, at Safi, Morocco on or about 15th October. A young Redstart ringed at Egham on 12th June 1991 was recovered over three years later at Rushmoor on 20th June 1994.

Whinchat   *Saxicola rubetra*

Moderately common passage migrant, formerly bred

Breeds in Europe and western Russia, wintering in sub-Saharan and Central Africa. Most foreign recoveries of British-ringed birds are from France and Iberia. A continental origin is likely for many autumn migrants to the south and east (*MA*). The number and range seem to have been stable in Britain during the 19th and early 20th centuries, since when there has been a decline, which has also been experienced in other European countries.

Early Surrey history. Whinchats bred on Wandsworth Common in the early 19th century (Glegg, 1938) and were listed for the Godalming district by Newman (1849). The Holmesdale Natural History Club Museum has a nest collected at Redhill in 1874. Hamilton (1881) recorded the Whinchat from the

Wimbledon Common/ Putney Heath area. Bucknill said it was common in suitable localities. Favoured habitats were gorse, rough ground and meadowland. He gave no indication of any population change and mentioned breeding at Dulwich, Streatham and Wimbledon Common. Power (1910) thought that Whinchats had probably bred on Mitcham Common before 1874, before golfers disturbed the area. He recorded migrants at Clapham Common (1887 and 1888) and Tooting Common (1897).

1900 to 1950. Whinchats seem to have been well-established in 1900 but the Surrey range contracted substantially during the early and mid 20th century. Whinchats bred in Richmond Park (Mouritz, 1905) and three or four pairs usually bred until 1940, when the site was turned over to military training. Howard Bentham recorded breeding on the Thursley/Ockley Commons in 1908, 1913 (four nests in about three acres of Ockley Common), 1915 and 1920-21 (SBC archive). Three pairs bred at Walton Heath in 1914 and five in 1915 (Bentham, SBC archive). Others bred at Churt Common (Boorman egg collection, 1900), at Effingham Common in 1914 and at Royal Common in 1919 (Bentham, SBC archive). Whinchats bred annually in rough grass in the Butler's Dene Valley, Woldingham, but lost habitat to building development there (Beadell, 1932). Other breeding records for the period up to the 1960s were from Bookham Common (1934), Epsom Common (1934-35, 1939), Island Barn Reservoir (two pairs 1938), a west Surrey Heath (1947), and Walton Reservoirs (1938). Bentham heard of a nest on Ashtead Common in 1939 (SBC archive). In Spelthorne, Whinchats bred round the edge of the reservoirs (Kerr (1906), *LN* for 1933). There were two pairs in 1946, three or four pairs in 1948 and ten pairs in 1949.

1951 to 1980. At Walton Gravel Pits, Whinchats bred in 1951, 1952, 1953 and 1955 and were present in 1956 and 1957. The West End, Bisley and Pirbright Commons do not seem to have been much explored in the first half of the century but there were four pairs at Bisley Common in 1952, at least one pair raised young in 1967 and 1969 and there was one territory in 1972. Whinchats bred at Royal Common in 1957 and 1958. Two pairs bred at Pirbright in 1973 and one in 1974 and a pair bred at West End, Bisley in 1976. Whinchats bred on the Thursley/Ockley Commons up to 1974, with at least one pair in 1957, 1958, 1959 and 1960, one in 1964, two in 1967 and one in 1969. They bred there from 1971 to 1974 and the last definite breeding anywhere in Surrey was at Ockley Common in 1980, when one pair raised young. Whinchats were well established round the Spelthorne reservoirs in the 1950s. There were five pairs at King George VI Reservoir in 1955. Two pairs bred in 1962 and 1966. Whinchats have only been passage migrants in Spelthorne since then.

As with the Lesser Spotted Woodpecker and some other species, the BTO sees dependence on a widespread and unprotected habitat (*Bird Study 226:4*) as being a factor in the decline. This is clearly true of the suburban sites mentioned by Bucknill but does not explain why Whinchats no longer breed on Thursley Common, or other heathland sites where there has been little obvious change and a good deal of protection.

Since 1980. A family party including four juveniles at Hersham Gravel Pit in August 1989 (*LBR*) suggested local breeding. The largest numbers available since 2000 are eleven at Nore Hill, Chelsham on 5th September 2002 and, from the *LNHSB*, 11 in Spelthorne on 10th September 2002.

Calendar. In the late 19th century the typical arrival date for southern England was rather before the middle of April and its departure in early October (Saunders, 1899). Bucknill (1900) said they arrived in Surrey in mid April and left in September. The average arrival date in the London area south of the Thames from 1929 to 1939 was 18th April. Glegg (1935) gave the average arrival date in Middlesex for 27 (non-consecutive) years as 22nd April. The chart shows that this is a few days later than the average for Surrey since the 1950s. The main arrival is in the second half of April, with a return passage peaking in the first half of September:

Half-month totals of birds in the vice-county, 1994 to 2004

	Apr		May		Jul		Aug		Sep		Oct	
	1-15	16-30	1-15	16-31	1-15	16-31	1-15	16-31	1-15	16-30	1-15	16-31
1994		22	14	1			5	54	91	39	5	
1995		18	14	4			4	35	95	34	1	
1996		21	4	2			1	39	58	20	6	
1997		20	20	1			4	32	28	29	2	3
1998	1	20	12	1		2	9	48	67	22	6	2
1999		1	5	1			1	43	25	37	11	1
2000		6	2		1	0	2	41	36	10	9	
2001		6	9	5				40	39	15	9	
Total	**1**	**114**	**80**	**15**	**1**	**2**	**26**	**332**	**439**	**206**	**49**	**6**

Early and late dates are:

Early		Late	
9th March 1930	Addington	27th November 1982	Fairoaks
10th March 2003	Barn Elms London Wetland Centre	12th December 1999	Beddington Sewage Farm
13th March 1905	near Chobham (*BB, 12:279*)	20th December 1998	Staines Reservoirs
19th March 1993	Woodmansterne (*LBR*)	26th December 1934	Elmers End Sewage Farm (*BLA*)
27th March 1989	Wimbledon Common		

The chart shows the arrival dates have tended to reflect mean spring temperatures, being earlier now than they were in the colder 1960s.

Large counts. The largest one-day counts were made over 25 years ago:
Beddington Sewage Farm: 31, 24th August 1980
Beddington Sewage Farm: 23, 9th September 1955
Capel: 97 on autumn passage, 1992
Epsom Downs: 37 bird days, autumn 1978
Just north of Gatwick: 40, 4th April 1967
Richmond Park: 13+, 26th April 1969

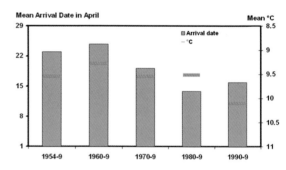

Movements and longevity. A Whinchat ringed at Beddington Sewage Farm on 12th August 1968 was recovered 1,079 km south at Montanana, Zaragoza, Spain on 26th September 1969. This is the furthest travelled and longest lived Whinchat located. The only other Whinchat recovery traced was ringed in the nest at King George VI Reservoir on 8th June 1958 and found dead at Byfleet on 12th August of the same year (BTO).

Stonechat   *Saxicola torquata*

Locally common breeding resident

Stonechats have an unusual breeding distribution which extends across Europe and Asia and includes most of Africa (including Madagascar) outside the desert regions. They are complete or partial migrants over much of their range. Many northern European birds move south, some as far as North Africa. Most foreign recoveries of British-ringed birds are from France and Iberia (*MA*). Autumn migrants to or

through Britain include a few from other regions east to western Siberia. The British population seems to have been stable during the 19th century but has declined, at least until the 1970s, as it has in some other European countries. Loss of habitat has presumably been the main reason. Milder winters have benefited British breeding numbers, which may have at least doubled since 1994 (BTO).

Early Surrey history. Newman (1849) listed Stonechats for the Godalming district. The Holmesdale Natural History Club Museum has a nest taken at Reigate Heath in 1873. Hamilton (1881) recorded the Stonechat from the Wimbledon Common/Putney Heath area. Bucknill described Stonechats as much less common than Whinchats and mainly summer visitors. He gave Banstead Common, Epsom Common, Headley Heath, Mitcham Common and Reigate Heath as specific breeding localities, adding that Stonechats were found on most of the large furze commons of the county. There was one on Wandsworth Common not later than 1889.

Where found 1900 to 1929. The main breeding season habitat in Surrey is open heathland with scattered gorse. Gorse provides the nest sites. Encroachment by Silver Birch can drive the birds out fairly quickly. L. J. Raynsford has shown that, in Surrey at least, they will not tolerate more than about 50 saplings per acre (per 2.5 hectares)(Magee, 1965). Fires can destroy heather, gorse, birch and nests alike and leave a clear site for future scrub invasion. Power gave only two records - a road casualty at Tooting on 14th April 1900 and three at Mitcham Common on 26th April 1904. Boorman collected eggs at Churt in 1900 and at Wisley Common in 1908. There were at least four pairs at Limpsfield in 1906. Bucknill found many pairs at Thursley in 1907, Frensham in 1911 and Elstead in 1913 (Parr). In Spelthorne, Stonechats were wintering and nesting irregularly at Staines Reservoirs, with three families reared in 1906 (Kerr). Stonechats were wiped out in Surrey by the harsh winter of 1916/17 and came back only slowly, still being scarce in 1919. Weather was probably the main factor affecting numbers in Richmond Park, where Mouritz (1905) said that Stonechats were uncommon. In the years up to 1937, numbers varied from none to at least four, increasing in the 1930s. Eggs were collected at Woking in 1923 and Chobham in 1924 (Maitland and Turnbull) and at Wisley Common in 1924 (Boorman). Stonechats at one time bred regularly at Worms Heath but stopped before 1931 (Beadell).

1930s. Stonechats were clearly quite widespread in the 1930s. They had nested 'in recent years' at Bookham Common, Epsom Common and Sewage Farm, Molesey, near Riddlesdown, Walton Heath, Warlingham and Weybridge Sewage Farm (*LN* for 1933). Stonechats bred at Banstead Downs (1933), Banstead Heath (1933), Bookham Common (1933, 1934, 1939), Burgh Heath (1933), Epsom Common (up to ten pairs in the 1930s), Epsom Downs (1933, 1939), Headley Heath (1933), Mitcham Common (1933, 1934, 1937, 1939), Richmond Park (1933, 1938, 1943), Tadworth (1931), Walton Heath (1933, 1939) and Wimbledon Common (1933, 1937, 1939). Ten pairs nested on a west Surrey heath in 1934, they were abundant in northwest Surrey in 1935 and they were found at Smithwood Common some time before 1941 (Watson). They were nesting there and near Queen Mary Reservoir in the early 1930s.

1940 to 1969. The cold winters of the 1940s severely reduced the population but there was a good recovery by 1961, when L. J. Raynsford organised the first countywide census, which produced single pairs on Esher Common, Headley Heath, Redlands (Dorking) and Worms Heath and 37 pairs in West Surrey. The West Surrey pairs were at Ash-Pirbright (eight), Bagshot area (three), Blackheath (two), Chobham Common (four), Hindhead/Frensham (four) and Milford-Tilford (sixteen) (Parr). Numbers were reduced again by the 1962/63 winter but had recovered to at least 30 pairs by 1969.

1970-2000. Of the 231 tetrads in northeast Surrey, seven were found to hold territories in the 1968-72 Atlas survey and eight in the 1988-97 Atlas, a marginal growth. Stonechats bred again in Richmond Park from the 1970s up to 2005. Elsewhere there has been a marked increase in numbers since 1969, helped by milder winters. The table shows pairs found in the vice-county from 1972 to 1986.

1972	1973	1974	1975	1976	1977	1978	1979	1980	1981	1982	1983	1984	1985	1986
40-41	52	56	n/a	85	20	27	60	55	46	39	33	100	169	195

Stonechats were not common in Spelthorne after 1970. A few were in the Shepperton area from 1983-86, there were four at Staines in the winter of 1983, a female was there on 29th October 1988 and there were others outside the breeding season at Perry Oaks Sewage Farm and elsewhere through the 1990s into the 21st century. There were twelve at Staines Moor on 28th October 2002.

Current population size. The Surrey breeding population is still largely confined to heathlands, the area of which has been much reduced since the beginning of the 20th century, but it has continued to grow strongly.

Territories on heathlands 1994-2004

	1994	1995	1996	1997	1998	1999	2000	2001	2002	2003	2004
Bagshot Heath/Lightwater	3	1	4	2	4	2	0				0
Brentmoor Heath/Turf Hill	3	2	3	5	4	5	3	3	2	1	2
Brookwood Heath/ Pirbright Common					2	4	2	2	1	1	
Chobham Common			7		47	46				31	40
Churt Common	4	4	4	7	5	5	4				
Crooksbury Common	3	7	3	2	4	4	4	4	3	4	1
Frensham Common	17	21	14	11	16	17	23	21	19	20	21
Hankley Common	10	15	14	15	14	26	33	30	35	48	36
Hindhead Commons	4	8	7	9	8	7	6	8	9	8	7
Horsell Common					2	3	3	3	5	5	3
Olddean Common (Surrey)	7	8	6	9	13	16	6	8			10
Pirbright Common/ Ash Ranges	48	62	26	33	27	49	41	44	29	27	35
Thursley/Ockley/ Elstead Commons	31	45	33	21	28		16	22	20	28	34
West End Common/ Pirbright Ranges	23	48		14		31		34		10	12
Witley Common		1	1	2	3	3	4	4	3	4	4

From counts organised by John Clark. Table omits incomplete counts.

A few pairs have bred from time to time at other sites since 1994, including Bisley, Blackheath, Bourne Woods, Bullswater Common, Lightwater Country Park, Mytchett Place, Puttenham Common, Richmond Park, Sheet's Heath, Stanford/Cobbetthill Commons, Turf Hill, Walton Downs, Whitmoor Common, Whitmore Vale and Wrecclesham. In Spelthorne, Belsey found a pair nesting on Halliford Common in the early 1990s. Allowing 20 pairs for these, and taking the largest of the counts for each place in the table, the recent county population is likely to have been well over 300 pairs in good years.

Calendar. Spring passage begins in February and continues through March. Return passage may begin as early as July and peaks in September or October. There were 12 in Richmond Park on 9th October 1998 and ten there on 5th November 1992 and 12th November 1999. Most Stonechats leave the heaths in winter, though a few are usually to be found at Frensham, Thursley and other breeding sites if the winter is not too severe. The remainder disperse to parks (notably Richmond Park), sewage farms, gravel pits and riverside marshes in Surrey and to milder localities on the coast and abroad. The movement abroad reduces the effect of severe winters on the breeding population. The number of wintering birds is less than a quarter of the breeding population - 34 birds at 15 sites in January and February 1996, 22 at 11 sites in 1997, 51 at 20 sites in 1998, 35 at 15 sites in 1999, 53 at 22 sites in 2000. In the last two months of 2001, a total of 66 birds were reported from 25 sites, most of them away from the western heaths.

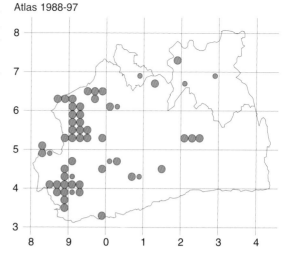

Atlas 1988-97

Movements. Ringing returns show movements between Surrey and Algeria, Morocco and Spain. The furthest travelled bird was ringed as a young bird at Frensham on 30th April 1988 and recovered 2,022 km south at Casablanca, Morocco on about 3rd August 1990. The Algerian recovery was in 1993.

Longevity. The longest life span located is of a Stonechat ringed in Hampshire on 9th May 1995 and recovered over three years later, at Olddean Common on 31st May 1998.

Wheatear (Northern Wheatear)   *Oenanthe oenanthe*
Moderately common passage migrant, formerly bred

Wheatears breed in North Africa and in temperate and Arctic regions of Europe, Asia, North America and Greenland. All, apart from some resident North African birds, winter in sub-Saharan and Central Africa. Most foreign recoveries of British-ringed birds are from France, Iberia and northwest Africa (*MA*). Wheatears bred in most parts of Britain during the 19th century. No great population changes appear to be on record in Britain until a decrease began in the 1930s and continued through the rest of the century. The decrease has been experienced in other parts of Europe. Nests are in crevices and rabbit holes.

Early Surrey history. Wheatears have a long association with the county. John Evelyn's letter quoted in the Sand Martin account also mentioned that Wheatears were to be found on the Downs between Dorking and Guildford. Wheatears were a much-prized food item at this time. They were still on the downs when Bucknill wrote. At the beginning of the 19th century, Wheatears were known around Battersea and Peckham (Graves, 1811-21). They were uncommon passage migrants at Tooting around 1836. A pair nested in a pit by the railway at Croydon in 1874 and 1875, one or two pairs nested every year on Purley Downs around 1878 and a pair nested on Reigate Heath in 1886 (Thomas, 2001). Hamilton (1881) recorded Wheatears from the Wimbledon Common/Putney Heath area. Bucknill gave a record for 1894 or earlier from Dulwich and mentioned breeding at Banstead Heath, Box Hill, Burwood Common, Chertsey Heath, Epsom Downs and Common, Headley Heath, Leith Hill, Reigate

Heath, Walton Heath and the West Surrey Hills. Power (1910) knew Wheatears as occasional migrants at Mitcham Common.

Breeding since 1900. Pairs nested near Addington in 1902 and at Caterham in 1908 and 1917 (Pounds). A specimen in the Boorman egg collection at the Haslemere Museum is said to have been taken in 1905 at East Clandon, a surprising site but possibly on the downland. At least one pair bred in Richmond Park from 1904 to 1908, after which there were no definite breeding records to 1935 at least (Collenette). Eight pairs nested around Frensham Ponds in 1909 (Parr) and at least one pair on Thursley Common in 1914. Birds nested at Epsom and Purley in 1912, on Walton Heath in 1914 and at Caterham in 1917 (*BLA*). Breeding continued on Park Downs up to 1930 (Parr). About eight pairs nested in the Haslemere district in 1934 (*SEBR*) but it is not known how many of these were in Surrey. In 1935 a few pairs in northwest Surrey stayed until June.

Years of decline. The national decrease which began in the 1930s was also experienced in Surrey, with very few later breeding pairs found. Wheatears bred at Kettlebury Hill, Hankley Common in 1939 (*SEBR* for 1940). They bred at Upper Warlingham in 1949,(*BLA*), Richmond Park in 1955 and Frensham in 1961. A pair and three apparently recently fledged young were seen at Hankley Common on 15th June 1969 but they were not seen again on a later visit. A pair bred at Pirbright in 1970 (Clark, 1984). A pair reared two young at Hankley Common in 1977. In 1978, young were seen being fed in a nest at Hankley Common on 11th June but fledging was not confirmed. A nest was predated by humans, the eggs taken, in northwest Surrey in 1982.

Territory was held on Walton Heath in 1941 and a pair may have bred there. At Holmethorpe a nest was abandoned in 1970. There were juveniles at Staines Reservoirs in June and July 1978 and Perry Oaks in July 1981. Hewlett suggested that they may have fledged locally. More recent attempts have been unsuccessful. There were two breeding attempts in 2000. A pair took up territory at Beddington Sewage Farm, but moved away. Another pair seem to have built a nest on a North Downs golf course, using the crevices in a stack of turfs as a nest site. This was destroyed by a predator. The latter example shows the habitat required, rough ground with short turf and holes – rabbit burrows, buried ammunition boxes, rock crevices or something of that kind. A second requirement is for plenty of insect food.

Calendar. Spring passage begins in February or March. The table shows that it peaks in late April and continues into early June. Return passage begins in late July or August, peaks in late August and continues into early November. Fewer are recorded in autumn than in spring. Kerr (1906) referred to 'recent' occurrences at the Staines area reservoirs, where they were also seen in the 1920s and 30s. Wheatears are still widespread as spring and autumn migrants, found on park, farm, heath and downland throughout Surrey. No less than 156 were recorded at 12 sites on 22nd April 1998. Bucknill said that few arrival dates were earlier than 30th March. The average arrival date in the London area south of the Thames from 1929 to 1939 was 23rd March.

Half-month totals of birds in the vice-county 1994-2001

	Mar		Apr		May		June	Jul		Aug		Sep		Oct		Nov
Date	1-15	16-31	1-15	16-30	1-15	16-31	1-15	1-15	16-31	1-15	16-31	1-15	16-30	1-15	16-31	1-15
1994	3	50	89	79	15	2										
1995	4	44	92	93	20	3										
1996		73	56	138	30	5	1		5	4	25	8	6	7	1	
1997	3	18	21	95	17	2	2		3	8	16	42	4	4		
1998	1	40	23	204	49	3				13	45	25	8	10	4	1
1999	1	14	54	47	27	3	1			7	30	13	23	8	1	
2000	3	10	63	50	23					14	24	27	26	22	2	
2001	1	53	9	24	17	8	2		1	10	29	22	9	5	3	
Total	16	302	407	730	198	26	6	0	9	56	169	137	76	56	11	1

Source: Surrey Bird Reports

Early and late dates are:

Early

24th February 1943	near Horley (*SEBR*)
27th February 1994	Frensham Common
4th March 1982	Papercourt
4th March 1992	Beddington Sewage Farm
5th March 1978	Tatsfield

Late

13th November 1983	Barn Elms Reservoirs
14th November 1961	Tolworth
22nd November 1959	Mitcham Common
24th November 1963	Elmers End Sewage Farm

There was a female or immature bird at Walton Reservoirs on 28th December 1990 and in January 1991. The arrivals chart shows that spring arrivals were later in the colder decades since the 1950s and were earliest in the 1990s.

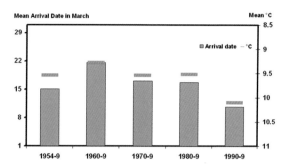

Large counts of migrants.

Barn Elms: 23, 3rd April 1986; 18, 3rd April 1995

Beddington Sewage Farm: 87, 2nd May 1955; 35, 2nd April 1985

Brooklands: 20, 9th April 1970

Epsom Common: 25 on ploughed part, 27th August 1944 (*LBR*)

Frensham: 20-30, 5th April 1922

Horley: 58, 24th March 1967

Nore Hill, Chelsham: 59, 22nd April 1998

Ockley Common: 15, 2nd April 1986

Richmond Park: 46, 22nd April 1998

Stoke Lake: 13, 3rd April 1986,

Surrey Docks: 16, 21st April 1975

Spelthorne

Perry Oaks Sewage Farm: 20, 26th August 1969

Staines Moor: 22 on 30th March 1987

Staines Reservoir: 20, 3rd April 1994

Significant counts since 2000 include 14 at Barn Elms on 3rd May 2002 and ten at Queen Elizabeth II Reservoir on 3rd May 2002.

Movements and longevity. The furthest travelled bird was ringed in Estonia on 5th July 1976 and recovered in the same year 1,807 km southwest, at Salfords on September 22nd. A Wheatear ringed at Beddington Sewage Farm on 30th April 1972 was trapped at Fair Isle on 24th April 1975 over two years and eleven months later, a longevity record for Surrey.

Greenland Wheatear

Oenanthe oenanthe leucorhoa

Scarce passage migrant

Breeds in Greenland, Iceland and northeast Canada and winters in Africa, with other races.

Surrey. There are no ringing recoveries to prove that this race has occurred in Surrey but there are many sight records. A few birds have been caught and measured by ringers and these offer the most reliable evidence. Power mentions a male *of the larger race* at Mitcham Common on 6th April 1904. Others that have been seen include: *Barn Elms Reservoirs*: 16th May 1930, 9th May 1980, 2nd May 1983, 19th May 1984, 11th and 19th May 1985, 13th May 1988, six on 2nd May 1989, two on 5th May 1989, 16th May 1989, two in May 1990, 9th May 1991, at least two in May 1991, 26th May 1991, 30th April 1992, 21st April 1993, 29th May 1994, 28th September 1994, two on 2nd and 8th May 1995, 18th May 1995, 27th May 1996, 8th May 2000, 26th September 2001, 1st and 3rd May 2002; *Beddington Sewage Farm*: 8th May 1938, 3rd-7th June 1984, 20th April 1988, 25th May 1988, three on 20th April 1993, 4th May 1997, 22nd

April 2000; *Bookham Common*: 1934; *Capel*: a female was ringed on 5th May 1992, 24th September 1992, 5th May 1993, another ringed there on 28th April 1994; *Chessington*: 4th May 1970; *Chilworth*: 1st November 1998; *Chobham Common*: 9th May 1999, 29th April 2000, three on 29th April 2001; *Elmers End Sewage Farm*: April 1936, 1937; *Epsom Downs*: 27th September 1930, 4th September 1932, 30th April 1985; *Epsom Sewage Farm*: 1956; *Frensham*: 16th May 1927, three on 5th May 1977, 14th May 1991; *Ham Lands*: 8th May 1990; *Hankley Common*: 6th-7th September 2004; *Hersham Gravel Pit*: female on 16th May 2001; near *Horley*: 1946; *Horsell*: 13th October 1996, three on 26th April 1997, 6th and 13th May 1997, 6th-7th September 1997, two on 29th August 1998, one ringed 28th October 2001; *Milford*: two on 10th October 2002; *Morden Hall Park*: 11th May 1996; *Olddean Common*: 2nd-3rd May 1999, two on 28th April 2001; *Purley*: August 1929; *Queen Elizabeth II Reservoir*: 1st October 2000, 12th April 2005; *South Norwood Country Park*: 23rd May 1991; *Stoke Water Meadows*: 23rd May 1997, 5th October 1998, female ringed 15th May 2001, two on 22nd April 2002; *Thursley Common*: 1956; *Walton Heath*: 2nd and 3rd May 1998, 27th April 2000; *Walton Reservoirs*: 27th April 1992, 20th May 1996; *West End Common*: pair at Folly Bog on 24th April 2000; *Worplesdon*: 20th September 1999; *Unstead Sewage Farm*: 24th September 1999 and in Spelthorne: *Perry Oaks*: two on 4th May 1992; *Queen Mary Reservoir*: several up to 1988 (Geen), 14th October 1989 (two), 27th April 1996; *Queen Mary Gravel Pits*: 14th May 1991; *Shepperton Gravel Pits*: 31st May 1991 and *Wraysbury Reservoir*: a pair on 9th September 1988.

Calendar. Over half of the birds have been seen in May:

Bird months 1900-2002

	Apr	May	Jun	Jul	Aug	Sep	Oct	Nov	Total
Vice-county	19	56	2	0	2	6	6	1	**92**

Desert Wheatear
Oenanthe deserti

One bird

With a breeding range from North Africa east through the southern Caucasus to Mongolia, this is an unlikely bird to have been found in Surrey. The normal wintering range runs from the Sahara to Pakistan. Most records are from eastern and southern coastal counties. They have mainly been from September to January, peaking in November, with a few in March, April and June.

Surrey. The one record appears to be the first for an inland county. A first-summer male was found at Barn Elms Reservoirs on 13th April 1989 by B. P. Aris (*BB, 84:483, LBR* for 1989:136-37, photographs in *BB, 82:431*) It stayed until the following day. The bird was very active, feeding on the ground and catching insects, often within a few feet of observers. It was the first for the London area as well as for Surrey.

Siberian Thrush
Zoothera sibirica

One, before 1900

Breeds from Siberia east to Japan and wintering from India to Indonesia. There were seven accepted British records up to 1985, all in the period from September to December. None of these is from Surrey. A male was reported from Alice Holt Forest, just over the border, on the 28th December 1976 but this is not now accepted (*BB, 85:538*).

Surrey. An unlikely visitor to Surrey. Bucknill gave one record, of a bird bought from a dealer by the 19th century collector Frederick Bond, who thought it was a melanistic Redwing. The bird was said to have been shot between Guildford and Godalming in the winter of 1860/61. It was later identified as a Siberian Thrush by Edward Blyth, who had been curator of the Calcutta Museum for 22 years prior to 1864 and was an expert on oriental birds. Gould illustrated the specimen, which he said was a female and shot by a Mr Drewitt at St Catherine's Hill, near Guildford (on the road to Godalming) at the beginning of February 1855, during the Crimean War and in a winter of exceptional severity (Gould 1862-73), so there is a discrepancy between the accounts. According to Saunders, the specimen was bequeathed by Bond to the British Museum. There are accounts in *The Field* 24th September 1870:277, *Zool., 1889:415* and Saunders (1899). Saunders thought that the evidence was not strong enough.

The BOU (1883 and 1915 lists) and the authors of *The Handbook* (citing Saunders), thought that there was insufficient evidence to substantiate the record, which was also not included in Witherby's 1941 Checklist or in the 1952 or 1971 BOU lists. Dymond *et al.* (1988) omit it. Naylor (1996) puts it in square brackets, citing only Saunders and *BOU 1915*. It is not included in the running tallies of the BBRC annual reports (most recently published in 1995).

It remains quite possible that this is a good record, despite doubt about the date, and that it is the first British record. In the lengthy note appended to Andrew, Nelder and Hawkes (1955), the editors of British Birds, while not accepting the record, said that the rejection seemed to date from the comment in Saunders (1899). (This is not correct since the same reason for rejection was given by the BOU in 1883). They went on to say that the identification has never been in doubt and they produced more evidence in a statement by Gurney that Bond obtained the bird from '*Mr Smither of Farnham in Surrey, near the place where it is believed to have been killed by a Mr Drewett in February 1885 [sic, presumed a misprint for 1855 by the British Birds editors]. Smither was a retired gamekeeper* [therefore not a dealer in the ordinary sense], *and Gould gives him a high character in his article on the Dartford Warbler'*. They thought that fraud was unlikely, since the bird was originally believed to be a Redwing, that the date must have been 1855 as stated by Gould, who had mentioned the Crimean War, and that the 1860/61 winter was probably when Bond acquired the bird from Smither, not the time when it was shot. Smither himself, to give another twist to the tale, has a name very like the 'man named Smithers, a bird-stuffer of Churt' who scoured the western heaths for Dartford Warblers, supplied Gould with specimens and paid boys a shilling for every clutch they could provide (Hudson, 1915).

Thanks are due to P. A. D. Hollom (pers. comm.) for providing more information about the background to this record, some of which may not have been known to Saunders or others who have assessed it. As regards the date, he drew attention to an account of the bird in volume 2 of H. E. Dresser's eight volume History of the Birds of Europe (1871-81), first published in 1876, wherein it is stated that '*It has been once obtained in Great Britain. A specimen sent to Mr. Bond as a variety of the Redwing, having been obtained between Guildford and Godalming in the winter of 1860-61. This bird I have examined; and it is certainly referable to the present species'*. Since there appears to have been no formal evaluation of the record subsequent to the unfavourable analysis of 1955, it is included here as part of the systematic list.

Ring Ouzel   *Turdus torquatus*

Scarce passage migrant

Breeds in Europe and the Middle East and winters south to North Africa. Most birds of the British and northern race *T. t. torquatus* winter in southern Spain and northwest Africa. The British population was stable in the 19th century, and extended to occasional breeding in lowland areas of southeast England (the latter not accepted by Shrubb). A decline became apparent across Britain and Ireland and in Sweden in the 20th century. Climatic factors might be partly responsible. Intolerance of human disturbance has been put forward as another factor. Ring Ouzels have given way to Blackbirds in some upland areas of Britain.

Early Surrey History. Hindhead seems to have been the last stronghold of breeding Ring Ouzels in Surrey. Long shot one at Hampton Lodge, Puttenham on 18th April 1827 and made a marginal note in his copy of Bewick that *they are every year on Hindhead where they breed* (Bucknill). It is not clear when or why the site was abandoned. The *Historical Atlas* says that they were driven off the Surrey Hills when the land was ploughed up or built on. This may have been true in other localities, but Hindhead was not ploughed and any building was rather later. The spread of tree cover could provide a reason, but the Devil's Punch Bowl was then largely devoid of trees.

Other early records are of several at Tooting in Michaelmas Week, 1833, one trapped at South Lambeth and a small flock on Wimbledon Common in October before 1843 (Yarrell). Single birds or small flocks were seen at Aldershot (Hampshire?) on 8th September 1844 (*Zool., 1844:445*), Esher in August, 1849 (one shot in August, *Zool., 1849:2567*), Peckham on 22nd October 1850, Dorking in 1857 (Holmesdale Natural History Club), Guildford in April 1857, Woking on 16th April 1873, Shalford in October 1878, Gomshall in the Spring of 1879, Chilworth in October 1880, near Wimbledon in the Springs of 1883 and 1884, Hindhead in 1888, Headley Heath on 26th September 1889, Puttenham Common in September 1890, near Leith Hill on 25th September 1894, Banstead Downs in 1896 and Reigate Hill in the autumn of 1899 (Bucknill). There are undated 19th century references to birds at other localities.

1900 to 1950. One was near Stanwell on 1st April 1907 (Kerr). On the downland of the Farleigh district, Ring Ouzels were seen in 1902, 1904, 1910, 1912-13, 1915, 1926-27, 1930-31, 1937 and 1947. There was one in Richmond Park on 10th September 1905 (Mouritz, 1906) and one in December 1909 (Collenette). The next that have been located were from near Addington Lodge Farm on 22nd March, Wimbledon Common on 2nd April, and Walton Heath on 14th September, all in 1930. Other records are from: Warlingham on 26th April 1931 (Beadell); Surbiton (1934), Headley (1935), Guildford (1944, 1947) and Walton Heath (1946, 1951). Another at Wimbledon Common on 2nd April, 1945 was only the 12th for the whole of the London area since 1924.

1951 to 1970. Records became more frequent from about this time, from places which included Addington (1956), Banstead (1959, 1967), Barn Elms (1955), Beddington Sewage Farm (1955, 1957-58, 1960, 1965-67, 1970), Caterham (1966), Chessington (1965, 1970), Chobham (1962), Croydon Airport (1963), Curley Hill (1956), Dulwich (1953-54, 1961), Enton (1953), Epsom (1959), Ewell (1966), Farleigh (1951), Farthing Down (1965-66), Frensham (1964, 1968), Haslemere (1961), Headley Heath (1961, 1965), Hindhead (1954, 1972), New Addington (1961), Putney (1969), Richmond Park (1951, 1959, 1963, 1965, 1968), Rodborough (before 1959), South Norwood (1954), Walton Heath (1951, 1954-55, 1960-61), Wey Manor Farm (1970), Woking (1969, in a garden), Woldingham (1965). From 1960-69 there were 18 spring and 18 autumn records (Parr).

In Spelthorne, a male frequented King George VI Reservoir and Staines Moor from 1st January to 20th April 1955 and another remained at Queen Mary Reservoir from January to 30th March 1959. Other migrants from March onwards were at King George VI Reservoir in 1956 and 1957; Queen Mary Reservoir in 1966, 1968; Staines Reservoirs in 1969 (13th February to 26th March).

Where found 1970 to 2000. Later records came from Beddington Sewage Farm, Belmont Downs, Capel, Chobham Common, Ockley Common, Richmond Park, Thursley, Tolworth, Walton Reservoirs and many other places. In Spelthorne, Ring Ouzels were found at King George VI Reservoir (1989, 1994, 1997, 1998 (up to five)); Perry Oaks Sewage Farm (1970, 1973); Queen Mary Reservoir (1972 (Geen), 1975, 1977 (Geen), 1980); Staines Moor (1985, 1988, 1995); Staines Reservoirs (1977, 1987, 1989, 2000); Stanwell Moor (1999) and Upper Halliford Green (1987).

Since 2000. Later records include Barn Elms (28th April 2001, dates from 25th March to 2nd November 2005), Beddington (1st-4th October 2001, 14th November 2001, 13th October 2002), Capel (9th October 2004), Devil's Punch Bowl (October 2005), Dunsfold (4th November 2001), Effingham

Fish Ponds (19th April 2003), Hollow Farm, Worplesdon (19th-24th October 2003); Headley Heath (20th October 2005), Holmbury Hill (17th April 2001), Island Barn Reservoir (29th October 2005), Kingston (25th January to 26th March 2001), Papercourt Gravel Pits (20th April 2006), Pirbright Common (30th April 2001), Queen Elizabeth II Reservoir (1st April 2002), Stoke Lake (31st October 2001), Thursley (14th October 2001 and 21st April 2007), Tongham Gravel Pit (16th October 2002) and Winterfold (17th April 2001). Spelthorne records include one at Stanwell Moor on 17th April 2004, one at King George VI Reservoir on 1st-3rd May 2004 and single birds at Staines Moor on19th April 2003 (*LBR*) and 18th-26th October 2005 (*LNHSB*).

Calendar. The table shows that spring passage begins in March and peaks in late April. Return passage begins in August and peaks in early October. Fewer birds are seen in autumn than in spring.

Half-month totals of vice-county birds 1970-2000

	Mar		Apr		May		Aug		Sep		Oct		Nov	
	1-15	16-31	1-15	16-30	1-15	16-31	1-15	16-31	1-15	16-30	1-15	16-31	1-15	16-30
Total	3	10	56	120	15	0	0	1	6	15	38	24	5	0

Early and late dates:

Early		Late	
6th March 1977	Epsom Common	15th-16th November 1983	Beacon Hill, Hindhead
12th March 1990	Ham Lands		
12th March 1995	Barn Elms	2nd-17th November 1999	Hindhead
22nd March 1981	New Cross	23rd November 1986	Barn Elms Reservoirs
22nd March 1981	Pirbright Common	December 1909	Richmond Park
23rd March 1977	Epsom Common	9th December 2000	Staines Reservoirs

A first-winter male stayed at Kingston from 25th January to 26th March 2001.

Large counts. Ten at Walton Heath on 8th October 1951 was the maximum from 1900 to 1970. There were about 30 at Warlingham on 27th April 1974 during a national influx (June Reports and Spring Summary, *BB, 67:403*)

Alpine Ring Ouzel *Turdus torquatus alpestris*
One record
Breeds in the mountains of central and southern Europe.

A male was seen at Epsom from January to 17th February 1975. A few feet of cine film seen by D. Parr showed that the bird had the characteristics of this race.

Blackbird (Common Blackbird) *Turdus merula*
Abundant breeding resident
Blackbirds breed in Europe, the Middle East, North Africa and southern Asia through to China, with introductions elsewhere. Northern birds move south within the breeding range in winter, many of them reaching Britain. Blackbirds breeding in Britain are largely sedentary but they are joined by migrants from the Low Countries, Finland and Scandinavia in autumn and winter. Blackbirds were common across rural Britain in the late 19th century. Their numbers had increased from about 1850, when they began spreading out from woodlands into urban areas. The spread, and a further colonisation of Scotland, continued through the first half of the 20th century. The *Historical Atlas* says that in Britain the Blackbird became the dominant species, in relation to the Song Thrush, during the 1939-45 war.

Blackbirds also moved into newly afforested upland areas. Numbers have fallen nationally in recent years.

Early Surrey history. Archaeologists have found Blackbird remains dating from Roman Britain at two sites in Southwark. Of three sets found at 104, Borough High Street, one was dated at 50-100 AD and another at 70-80 AD. Other remains, from the Roman period, were at what is now an escalator shaft at London Bridge. Remains dated to 1230-1350 AD were found at Merton Priory.

Blackbirds were in the Godalming district in 1849. Blackbirds and Song Thrushes were both common in the Norwood district in the 1880s (Aldridge). The two were equally common at Wray Park in 1881 (Crossfield) and in South London in 1909 (Power). Bucknill noted that the spread into urban areas was well advanced in Surrey by 1900, and that it *penetrates the thickly populated districts in greater numbers than the thrush*. He described the Blackbird as the commonest thrush. Kerr (1906) rated it as common in the Staines area. Boorman's Send area egg collection (1903-18) for the Blackbird was larger than that for the Song Thrush.

Since 1950. Blackbirds bred in the garden of Lambeth Palace in 1950 (*BLA*) and were well established in the Surrey part of Inner London by the 1970s, with breeding pairs at County Hall, the Festival Hall and the Surrey Docks. The Winter Atlas found partial survey counts and estimates totalling 1,917 birds in 1981-84, one for every four Fieldfares. Local territory counts include 29 at Ashtead Common, 30 at Beddington Sewage Farm and 25 at Morden Hall Park in 2001. There were seven or eight pairs at Littleton Lakes in 1986.

Population size. The Common Birds Census showed no significant change in the number of Blackbird territories from 1970 to 2000 and suggested a county population of about 95,000 pairs. This is much larger than a Breeding Bird Survey estimate of about 34,000 adults, which was probably on the low side. If Surrey held a proportionate share of the British breeding population as given by the *New Atlas*, the population would be about 32,000 territories, or sixteen per square km. The Blackbird was the fourth commonest species to have been ringed in Surrey and the fourth commonest species in Common Birds Censuses from 1995 to 2000, perhaps reflecting the amount of woodland in the county. A measure of Blackbird success compared with that of Song Thrushes is given by the ratios of Blackbirds to Song Thrushes in Common Birds Censuses in each five-year period since 1965, shown in the table.

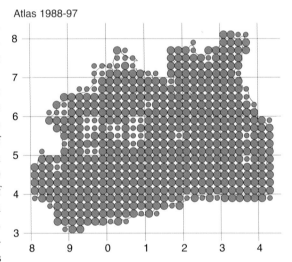

Atlas 1988-97

Average ratio of Blackbirds to Song Thrushes from Common Birds Censuses, by quinquennium

1961-65	1966-70	1971-75	1976-80	1981-85	1986-90	1991-95	1996-2000
2.81	2.64	2.72	3.56	3.69	4.20	3.63	4.28

Breeding. Blackbirds may breed early in a mild winter. A nest with three fresh eggs was found in Norwood on New Year's Day, 1866 (Bucknill). A nest with five eggs was found at Thorpe Water Park in January 1983. A three-week old bird was being fed at Elstead on 5th February 1989. There was a fledgling at Leatherhead on 15th February 2000. A nest containing eight eggs was found at Pickhurst in 1972. Song is sometimes heard in December.

Food. Unusual items noted include a bumble bee (Virginia Water 1975) and a frog that was dismembered and fed to young at Compton in 1976.

Large counts and Movements. Autumn flocks of around 100 birds were often reported in the 1960s and 1970s, when the winters were harsher than they were in the 1950s or in later decades. At least 500 roosted in hawthorns at Walton Reservoirs, where there had been a heavy crop of haws, in late 1968 and 200 were there in November 1970. There were 244 in Kew Gardens during December 1983. These birds probably included immigrants. Current autumn influxes are usually under 50. Forty or fifty moving south at Beddington Sewage Farm on 20th October 1995 constituted a rare example of observed visible migration. There were about 50 at Staines Reservoirs on 17th and 20th November 2000. Counts of up to 20 were made in the Spelthorne area during the 2003 BTO Spring Migration Watch.

Blackbirds ringed in Surrey in winter have been recovered in the breeding season (taken as March to August) in nine countries: Belgium (two), Denmark (one), Finland (two), France (two), Germany (five), Norway (one), Spain (one), Sweden (seven) and the Netherlands (six). Three Blackbirds ringed as young in Belgium have been recovered in Surrey. These recoveries confirm winter immigration from the Baltic and from or through Germany and the Low Countries. One Blackbird ringed as a young bird in Surrey was recovered from Brest, France in January 1949, showing that some British-bred birds also disperse abroad. The furthest travelled was ringed in Ewhurst on 29th November 1968 and recovered 1,979 km northeast, at Rahikkala, Finland on 19th August 1969.

Longevity. The longest-lived of the ringed birds was trapped at Ewell on 8th October 1967 and recovered at Walton-on-the-Hill on about 2nd March 1979. A dead bird found at Sanderstead in 1969 was infected with Pasteurellosis (rabbit flu)and Aspergillus (a fungus).

Plumage variations. Albino and partially albino birds (usually males) are seen from time to time but their breeding success may be poorer, at least for completely white birds. Bucknill knew of a male bird that had many white feathers. It bred twice in 1894 and once in 1895 and 1896, all in the same Epsom garden, after which it was found dead. Power saw one with a symmetrical grey mantle in Dulwich in 1892. Cherry Kearton made notes of a white-headed male in his garden at Kenley during the 1930s. The bird was unsuccessful in finding a mate, but subsequently took on a fostering role, assisting with feeding the young when the male of a breeding pair was lost. One at Brooklands from 1973 to 1975 moulted in stages through two autumns to an all-white plumage. It exhibited territorial behaviour but did not find a mate. Pure white birds with yellow bills, presumed male, are uncommon. One was at Stoke Water Meadows from January 1970 to May 1971. There was another at Weybridge in March 1972. A pure white bird was seen at Oxted in March and April 1973. Another was at Surbiton in 1977 and 1978 and was trapped at Ashtead in 1979.

Fieldfare
Common winter visitor

Turdus pilaris

Breeds from northern Europe east to western Siberia. Fieldfares have bred in Scotland since 1967 and southeast England (mainly Kent) since 1972. Fieldfares migrate southwest in autumn, many of them to or through the British Isles.

Surrey. Fieldfares are conspicuous in winter, feeding on pastures and they are fond of fallen apples in gardens and orchards. There are large winter roosts, often in bushy places near water, as at Pudmore on Thursley Common. A few birds have been seen in May, June and July but no evidence of breeding has been found.

Early Surrey history. Newman (1849) listed Fieldfares as winter visitors to the Godalming district. They were winter visitors to the Norwood district, in small numbers, in the 1880s (Aldridge) and to the Dulwich area from 1874 to 1909, where they were mainly recorded on autumn passage (Power). Hudson (1898) wrote of many at Dulwich, Richmond and Wimbledon in the winters of 1895/96 and 1896/97.

Since 1900. Fieldfares became considerably more numerous in the 20th century, reflecting the expansion of their European range. They were regular winter visitors to Richmond Park from at least 1909 (Collenette, 1937) and common in winter in the Staines area (Kerr, 1906). Flocks of several hundred birds were seen at Chobham Common and Walton Heath in 1934. The period 1945-1980 produced the highest roost and feeding counts of the century, to some extent for climatic reasons. The Winter Atlas found partial survey counts and estimates totalling 7,859 birds in 1981-84, making it the commonest of the thrushes, not surprising for such a conspicuous bird.

An onset of hard weather in December is sometimes accompanied by large westward movements of Fieldfares. There were up to 3,000 in Yews at Norbury Park on 15th December 1946. The harsh weather of February 1947 brought some 2,500 to Beddington. 'Thousands' flew north over Frensham on 12th December 1953. About 1,500 flew southwest over Sutton on 6th November 1961 and in the December of that year about 1,000 flew over Addington in hard weather. On 26th October 1974, at least 5,000 flew west at Clandon Downs in seven hours. Smaller movements were seen in the 1990s but 1,500 flew west at Beddington Sewage Farm on 1st November 1998 and 1,000 flew west over Unstead Sewage Farm on the following day. There were 500 at Queen Mary Reservoir in February 1976. Flocks of up to about 138 were seen in the Shepperton area in 1982-86. Numbers have remained lower in recent years, but 1,270 flew WNW over Barn Elms on 10th November 2001. There were 350+ at Staines Reservoirs on 10th February 2003 (*LNHSB*) and the Thursley Common roost was active in late 2006.

Other large counts

Avalon Apple Orchard, Churt: *c*.5,000, 26th January 1979

Beddington Sewage Farm: 2,000, 19th January 1969

Dockenfield: 1,000, 7th February 1979

near Farnham Sewage Farm: 2,000, 1971 (*HSBBR*)

Mitcham: 1,500-2,000, 12th December 1955

Shere: 5,000+, 21st February 1969 on ploughed fields

Stoke D'Abernon, 1,000, 2nd April 1969 (Parr)

Staines Moor: 1,000 on 15th April 1977

Roosts

Clandon Downs: *c*.2,000, 28th December 1973

Frensham Little Pond: *c*.500, December 1962

Papercourt Gravel Pits: roost in 2001

Pirbright: 211 roosting in heather, 2nd March 1980; 580 in the heather, 7th February 1982; 270, 11th November 1984 (*HSBBR*)

Thursley/Ockley Commons: 220, 20th December 1993; 300, 1st November 1995 and 1st November 1997

West Horsley: *c*.3,000, 22nd February 1974

Wisley Common: 900 in sallows, 29th November 1958

Woodhatch: 1,500 in an orchard, 18th February 1969

Calendar. There were 14 at Weybridge on 7th September 1891 (Bucknill), an early arrival date for the period. The average arrival date in the London area south of the Thames from 1929 to 1939 was 29th October. Arrivals are now earlier, vice-county averages for the last 30 years of the 20th century being 27th, 29th and 30th of September for the successive decades. Bucknill knew of departure dates up to the third week of April but was inclined to doubt a claim by Blyth that they were near Tooting until the second week of May. There have been a number of subsequent mid May occurrences, including one at Beddington Sewage Farm on 15th May 1968, two at Barnes Common on 18th May 1984 and one at Epsom Common on 23rd May 1976. One stayed at Beddington Sewage Farm from 17th May to 16th August 1959, apparently the first summer record for the London area. There have been a few other summer records, including one at Wimbledon Common on 25th June 1978, one at Beddington Park on 2nd July 1969, three, one possibly a juvenile, south of Bramley on 8th July 1979 and one at Wimbledon Common on 8th August 1994. The table shows an arrival and passage migrant peak in November.

Monthly count totals 1994-2001

Year	Jan	Feb	Mar	Apr	May	Jun	Jul	Aug	Sep	Oct	Nov	Dec	Total
1994	1,150	490	1,860	255				1	3	815	1,010	360	**5,944**
1995	335	390	835	390	1					360	500	680	**3,491**
1996	3,375	3,210	2,290	675					3	1,050	2,350	730	**13,683**
1997	655	581	345	10						1,723	2,781	1,789	**7,884**
1998	1,618	1,255	635	18				1	3	768	6,074	1,483	**11,855**
1999	2,688	2,095	769	80						559	1,438	1,207	**8,836**
2000	2,114	1,802	630	315					1	34	3,191	1,617	**9,704**
2001	2,210	1,328	1,160	179						488	3,447	484	**9,296**
	14,145	**11,151**	**8,524**	**1,922**	**1**	**0**	**0**	**2**	**10**	**5,797**	**20,791**	**8,350**	**70,693**

Source: Surrey Bird Reports

Movement and longevity. The furthest travelled was ringed at Godstone on 24th March 1967 and recovered 2,093 km northeast at Kiuruvesi Finland in July 1969. There is one other Finnish recovery, along with one each from Italy and France and five from Norway. It may be significant that there have been no Finnish or Russian recoveries since 1969, which was during the period when large flocks were more common. A Fieldfare ringed at Godstone on 6th February 1954 was recovered just over six years and two months later, at Rybatchiy (Kaliningrad) in the then USSR.

Behaviour. One at Sutton Green on 27th April 1973 became agitated when a Cuckoo called nearby. It flew into a tree, adopted a food-begging posture and called loudly. It flew off when the Cuckoo stopped calling.

Song Thrush — *Turdus philomelos*

Common breeding resident

Breeds from Europe to Siberia. Northern birds move south as far as North Africa and the Middle East. The British race is *T. p. clarkei*. Many British breeders are sedentary but some winter in France or Iberia. A few Belgian and Dutch birds winter in Britain (*MA*). There are introduced populations in Australasia. Remains dating back half a million years have been found in Britain. In the 19th century, numbers in Britain remained broadly stable apart from fluctuations caused by severe winters. A decline became apparent by the 1940s and continued until the end of the century with a fall of around 50% from 1970 to the 1990s, with a recent partial recovery. Song Thrushes like to forage in damp places and these are in decline (Peach *et al.*). Canopy closure arising from less woodland management may have been a factor (Fuller *et al.*, 2005). Slug pellets in gardens are toxic to Song Thrushes and may have affected their numbers.

Early Surrey history. Song Thrushes were in the Godalming District in 1849 (Newman) and bred abundantly in the vice-county from 1875 to 1900 (Bucknill and *Historical Atlas*). They were common breeders in the Norwood district during the 1880s (Aldridge).

Breeding since 1900. Song Thrushes were breeding in Brixton and Dulwich in 1909 (Power) and were common in the Staines area around 1906 (Kerr). There were 64 pairs in Kew Gardens in 1951. Song Thrushes were well-established in the Surrey part of Inner London by the 1960s. Two pairs bred at Lambeth Palace in 1966. Since then there has been a decline. At Battersea Park, there were up to sixteen pairs in 1967 (*LBR*) and an average of 30 in 1974-80, 13 pairs in 1987, 18 in 1988 and falling to under five in 1996 (Osborne, 1997). Elsewhere in Greater London, ten territories at Cannon Hill Common in 1988 fell to three in 1997 (Kettle, 1998).

These reductions did not always reflect those in more rural parts of Surrey. As noted by Hewlett, a strong population remains on Wimbledon Common, with 46 singing males in 1996, 43 in 1998 and 61 in 1999. At Vann Lake, Song Thrushes were present all the year round from 1964 to mid 1996 (Blaker Log). Among 21st century territory counts there were 11 at Limpsfield Chart, ten at Morden Hall Park and 11 at Unstead Sewage Farm in 2001 and 21 territories on Bookham Common in 2003. In Spelthorne, four pairs bred at Littleton Lakes in 1986 and Song Thrushes were well reported in the 2003 BTO Spring Migration Watch.

Population Size. The Winter Atlas found partial survey counts and estimates totalling 455 birds in 1981-84, one for every four Blackbirds. The Common Birds Census shows significant declines of about 85% on farmland and 40% in woodland from 1970 to 2000 and an estimated 20,000 pairs at the end of the period. The 1994-2004 Breeding Birds Survey suggests a recent breeding season population of 7,000 or more adults. This may be too low but it is only a fifth of the number of Blackbirds in the same survey. It is consistent with the Winter Atlas finding and a striking change from the position a century earlier. The increasing dominance of Blackbirds is shown in a table in the Blackbird account above.

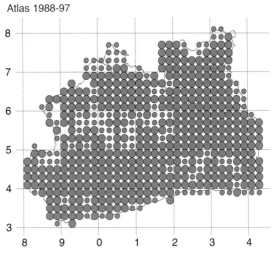

Atlas 1988-97

Song and nesting. Kearton heard one start to sing at midnight on 3rd June 1893, just as the moon was rising, while he was staying near Cobham and thought it had mistaken the moon for sunrise. A nest with eggs was found near Hindhead on 15th December 1953 during a mild spell. Song is sometimes heard in December (Oxted 1983, Guildford and Milford 1985).

Large counts

Battersea Park: 50+, 24th November 1990

Beddington Sewage Farm: 150, 9th January 1960; 150, 25th November 1961; 200, 6th January 1963; 75, 1st January 1994

Capel: 55+, 31st October 1993

Limpsfield Chart: 44 northwest in 70 minutes in October 1998

Lyne Old Sewage Farm: 65, 8th November 1970

Movements. Some residents move south in winter. Immigrant Thrushes arrive in the autumn and seem to have been most numerous in the colder weather of the 1960s. At Walton Heath, 156 were seen flying south on 26th September 1964. Large autumn movements around Queen Mary Reservoir were common in the 1970s but were on a much reduced scale by 1988 (Geen).

Foreign ringing recoveries have come from Belgium (one), Finland (one), France (thirteen), Germany (ten), the Netherlands (four), Portugal (two) and Spain (five). Three of them where apparently winter immigrants. These were: the Belgian bird, ringed at Elmers End Sewage Farm on 18th December 1960 and recovered at Hainault on 3rd June 1961; the long distance traveller ringed at Bramley on 26th December 1973 and recovered 1,624 km (1,009 miles) northeast on the Aland Islands, Finland on 15th July 1976 and one of the Dutch birds, ringed at Queen Mary Reservoir on 20th September 1999 and found dead in the Netherlands on 29th May 2002. All three could have been of the continental race *philomelos*, see below. One of the Portuguese recoveries, of a Song Thrush ringed in June and recovered in Portugal in December, together with at least two of the Spanish recoveries, ringed in the breeding season as young and recovered in October and December, are evidently British-born birds emigrating for the winter. Most of the others were ringed in Surrey outside the breeding season and recovered further south in the winter and could therefore have been passage migrants.

Longevity. The oldest known Song Thrush was ringed at Streatham Common on 8th January 1981 and found dead there on 7th October 1991, a national as well as Surrey longevity record.

Plumage variations. A melanistic bird was seen at Ash Vale on 18th March 1973. A leucistic bird was seen at Leatherhead in January, February and December 1975 and an albino at Oxted in January 1985.

Continental Song Thrush   *Turdus philomelos philomelos*

One was trapped at Thorpe on 7th December 1969. An adult ringed at Elmers End Sewage Farm in December 1960 and recovered in Belgium in June 1961 and another ringed at Bramley in December 1973 and recovered in Finland in July 1976 also seem likely to have been of this race, which might be commoner than these few records suggest. There are occasional reports of possible birds seen but not trapped.

Redwing   *Turdus iliacus*

Common winter visitor

Another bird with British records going back to the last glaciation. Currently breeds from Iceland through northern Europe to eastern Siberia, wintering south to the Mediterranean and North Africa. Numbers have increased in Finland, Iceland, Russia and Sweden. Small numbers have bred in Britain since 1925, from Scotland as far south as Kent. Redwings that bred from Norway to Russia just east of the Urals have been found in Britain. Some move on southwest to Iberia. Icelandic Redwings of the race *coburni* have been found in Scotland and Ireland (*MA*).

Early Surrey history. Redwings are conspicuous autumn migrants in Surrey, marking the turn of the seasons in a dramatic way when the first birds are heard flying over after dark on October evenings. They were commoner than Fieldfares in the Dulwich area from 1875 to 1909 (Power), where the largest flock recorded was up to 400 on a meadow near Denmark Hill on 1st November 1880. Aldridge wrote that they arrived in the Norwood district during October and noted that they were among the first casualties of severe winter weather.

Since 1900. A good number usually wintered in the Staines district (Kerr, 1906). There were about 125 at Richmond Park on 4th March 1934, about 500 at Epsom Sewage farm on 3rd February 1940 and about 400 at Holmwood on 1st April 1945. The cold winters of 1946/47 and 1962/63 brought much larger numbers to Beddington Sewage farm. The Winter Atlas found partial survey counts and estimates totalling 5,465 birds in 1981-84, nearly three for every Blackbird. In Spelthorne, 250 were feeding on a berry crop at Queen Mary Reservoir on 1st January 1979 and there were 400 on 4th October 1980. There was a small roost in the 1980s. Flocks of up to about 60 were in the Shepperton area in 1982-86 and counts of up to 58 in the 2003 BTO Spring Migration Watch.

Song. Good song was reported from Surrey by Bentham, Hollom (March 1967, 6th April 1968) by Mr and Mrs White (Parr), by J. J. Bowley at East Horsley in March 1972, by R. B. Hastings at Barnes Common on 24th March 1984 and by Steve Fowles at Riddlesdown on 12th March 2003 (per G. M. Cook). No evidence of breeding has been obtained.

Calendar. The largest numbers are usually seen in October. These probably include birds passing through as well as those wintering. The average arrival date in the London area south of the Thames from 1929 to 1939 was 12th October but the table shows that they now arrive earlier. There are a few summer records (all months) from Surrey, including one at Littleworth Common on 8th June 1978, one in Richmond Park from 10th June to 10th July 1976, one at Richmond Park on 19th August 1972 and one with an old injury and unable to fly on Wimbledon Common on 19th August 1950. The table shows how numbers vary from month to month.

Monthly count totals 1994-2001

Year	Jan	Feb	Mar	Apr	May	Jun	Jul	Aug	Sep	Oct	Nov	Dec	Total
1994	2,800	2,270	1,460	26					9	1,070	1,330	500	**9,465**
1995	480	970	670	8					1	6,600	1,520	2,060	**12,309**
1996	10,610	8,220	5,410	1,225	1				18	2,495	995	985	**29,959**
1997	2,432	1,586	533	8					7	31,405	495	660	**37,126**
1998	1,439	901	1,123	3					3	14,227	8,715	2,341	**28,752**
1999	3,317	2,169	1,155	14	1				2	3,646	360	1,413	**12,077**
2000	2,348	1,618	910	30					9	1,666	14,564	997	**22,142**
2001	2,191	620	731	27		1		1	32	5,268	2,233	1,120	**12,224**
Total	**25,617**	**18,354**	**11,992**	**1,341**	**2**	**1**	**0**	**1**	**81**	**66,377**	**30,212**	**10,076**	**164,054**

Edward Blyth saw 30 or 40 lingering at Tooting until the end of the first week of May, 1833 (Bucknill). Other extreme records include:

Early arrivals

22nd & 25th August 2001	Farnham Park
6th September 1833	Tooting (Blyth in Bucknill)
12th September 1973	Esher
12th September 1998	Unstead Sewage Farm
14th September 1984	Tilhill
14th September 1975	Tadworth

Late departures

5th May 1949	Frensham, one freshly dead
8th May 1969	Haslemere, c.20
9th May 1984	Effingham Ponds
11th May 1969	Beddington Sewage Farm
11th May 1996	Wimbledon Common
13th May 1991	Frensham
18th May 1991	Chobham Common
6th June 2001	Farnham Park

Large counts. The largest counts date back many years and were made in colder decades:

Beddington Sewage Farm: c.2,000, 8th February 1947; c.5,000, 8th January 1963

Epsom Sewage Farm: 1,000 flew over, 27th October 1956

near Farnham Sewage Farm: up to 1,000, late 1971

Mitcham Common area: 1,500-2,000, 12th December 1955 (*LBR*).

Thursley: 1,500, 15th October 1993, 1,600 west, 22nd October 1995

Roosts

Addington: c.2,500 December 1962

Ash Vale Gravel Pits: 60, 6th February 1977

Badshot Lea: 100, 22nd February 1977
Broadstreet Common: 300, 1958, as earlier years
Caterham: *c*.4,000 in hawthorns, 19th December 1962
Coulsdon: *c*.3,000 in scrub, 30th December 1976
Headley Heath: 3,500, 1st November 1980
West Horsley: up to 1,000: February/March 1974
Wisley Common: 300 in sallows, 29th November 1958

Selected large movements. The largest observed movements are generally westerly, in October or November:

Beddington: 15,000 west, 12th October 1997
Bookham Common: *c*.5,000 southwest, 9th November 1952 in just under five hours
Clandon Downs: 10,000+ west, 0600-1300 hrs, 25th October 1974
Englefield Green: 3,000 west, 15th October 1972
Headley Heath: 4,000 west, 15th October 1963
Stoke Lake: 2,725 northwest, 22nd October 1995
Thorpe: 3,500-4,500, dawn to mid-day, 12th October 1969
Unstead Sewage Farm: 5,255 west, 12th October 1997; 7,033 west, 20th October 1998
West Ewell: 2,356 west, 9th October 2004; 1,346 southwest on the following day
Spelthorne
Queen Mary Gravel Pits: 1,000+ west, 24th October 1981

Movements and destinations. Redwings recovered in Finland in May 1972 and May 1977 and probably those recovered in Georgia (old USSR) in March 1959 and December 1980 give an indication of the origin of wintering birds. Recoveries in the breeding season in Belgium, Finland and Germany, of birds which had been ringed in Surrey in the winter suggest immigration or passage. Of others ringed in Surrey in the autumn and winter, ten were recovered in winter in France, three in Spain, two in Italy and one each in Portugal and Sardinia, suggesting that they were birds passing through Surrey or not visiting Surrey at all in other winters. The Redwing ringed at Epsom on 25th January 1958 and recovered in Georgia, 3,337 km southeast, on 19th March 1959 had probably travelled furthest. Another Georgian bird, ringed at Kempton Park in January 1980 and recovered in December 1980, travelled slightly further (3,387 km) but may not have been in Surrey.

Longevity. The greatest longevity found was of a bird ringed at TQ1257 (Cobham) on 29th October 1966 and recovered in France over three years and four months later, on 7th March 1970. A longevity record of four years has appeared in Surrey Bird Reports since 1977 but no details of it have been traced.

Plumage Variations. A bird with white feathers in its crown, back and tail is mentioned by Bucknill. There was a partial albino at Walton Heath on 12th December 1971.

Icelandic Redwing *Turdus iliacus coburni*
Rare winter visitor
The Icelandic race winters in Scotland, Ireland, western France and Iberia. None has been ringed in Iceland and recovered in England or Wales (*MA*).

Surrey. Two have been claimed. One at Wisley Common 15th January 1967 was trapped and ringed (Parr). One was trapped at Queen Mary Gravel Pits on 5th March 1983. The *Migration Atlas* says there are no English recoveries of Icelandic-ringed birds but both of these have been identified by competent ringers.

Mistle Thrush

Common breeding resident

Turdus viscivorus

Breeds from Europe, North Africa and the Middle East, east to Siberia. Northern birds migrate but mostly winter within the breeding range. The vast majority of those breeding in Britain are sedentary but a few have been recovered from Belgium or France. Visible migration from the continent has been observed (*MA*).

Remains dating back to the last glaciation have been found in Britain. An expansion of British range is known to have begun at the end of the 18th century and continued through the 19th, by which time it had colonised Ireland and was common almost everywhere except in the Scottish islands. Numbers increased further up to at least the 1950s but have fallen by about a third since the 1970s.

Early Surrey history. Mistle Thrushes were breeding in the Godalming district early in 19th century (Newman, 1849) and the Norwood district in the 1880s (Aldridge). Jordan knew them from the Surrey Hills. Bucknill said they were generally distributed in rural areas and bred in smaller numbers at sites closer to London, such as Dulwich, Richmond Park, Streatham Common and, following Hamilton (1881), Wimbledon Common (all sites which are still occupied). He did not mention any change in status, but remarked that numbers were increased in autumn by arrivals from the continent. Kerr (1906) said they had recently increased in the Staines district.

Since 1900. Eggs were taken at Farnham in 1904 (Blackburne collection), at Chobham in 1903-4 and Woking in 1915 (Maitland and Turnbull) and at Clandon, Guildford and Send from 1903-12 (Boorman). The winter of 1916/17 drastically reduced the population, which had not fully recovered by 1923. The birds were not much affected by the 1962/63 winter (Common Birds Census, Parr).

Mistle Thrush numbers probably increased with the national trend up to 1970 and the Common Birds Censuses showed an increase in the 1960s (Parr). In the Surrey part of Inner London, Mistle Thrushes had colonised the larger open spaces by the 1950s. They have bred at Battersea Park since before 1950 (Nicholson, 1995), at Lambeth in 1950 (*BLA*) and in 1966, 1968 and 1970, in Southwark in 1970 (*LBR*) and no doubt there and elsewhere in other years. The Winter Atlas found partial survey counts and estimates totalling 301 birds in 1981-84, rather fewer than the number of Song Thrushes. Wimbledon Common held 29 territories in 1985 and 20-25 in 2005. At Vann Lake, Mistle Thrushes were found all the year round from 1964 to 1996 (Blaker Log). They were common breeding residents at Shepperton in the 1980s (*Shepperton Bird Reports*). More recently there has been a decline in Battersea Park (Hewlett), but a pair bred at Beddington Sewage Farm, apparently for the first time, in 2000. They usually breed in the adjacent Beddington Park.

Trend since 1970. Of the 231 tetrads in northeast Surrey, 94% were found to hold territories in the 1968-72 Atlas survey but only 84% in the 1988-97 Atlas. The Common Birds Census has suggested a significant rise of about 50% on farmland and a significant fall of about 50% in woodland since 1970, within a fairly steady level of about two to four territories per square km overall. This is a rather puzzling result and may reflect on the representativeness of the samples.

Population size. The overall population estimate for the end of the period is about 8,000 territories from Common Birds Census, which might be too high. It compares with an

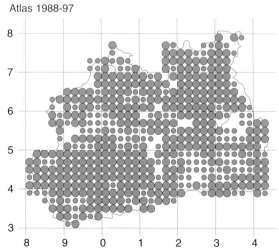

Atlas 1988-97

estimate based on the Breeding Birds Survey of about 3,000 birds. If Surrey held a proportionate share of the British breeding population as given by the *New Atlas*, the population would be about 1,700 territories, or 0.8 per square km.

Large counts. The biggest counts are over 50 years old. They were in winter and may have been immigrants and they have not been repeated. Most autumn and winter flocks reported since 1970 had been of 50 or fewer birds. Those over the past decade have rarely exceeded 30, exceptions including 36 at Frensham Great Pond on 19th August 2001 and 38 at Nore Hill, Chelsham on 6th September 2001. Earlier counts include:

Banstead Wood: 50 juveniles, 11th June 1955 (Parr)

Beddington Sewage Farm: 89, 26th June 1932

near Caterham: 150, 3rd August 1919

Cobham: 141 on sports fields, 24th July 1954

Effingham: 50+, 26th September 1971, feeding on yew berries

Frensham: *c.*100 in pines, 6th October 1936

Mickleham Downs: *c.*250, 10th October 1937, feeding on Yew berries (*BLA*)

Ranmore Common: 100, 2nd January 1972

Selsdon: 1,000, 6th December 1942 (*BLA*, no source given)

South Croydon: 400, 22nd January 1946 (*BLA*)

Movements. Small influxes have sometimes been noted in September and October, usually as an increase of up to 50 or so birds at a particular site. Records of visible movement include 200 southwest at Epsom Downs on 22nd January 1979, 200+ southwest at Tadworth on 23rd December 1979 and 100+ southeast at Walton Heath on 8th March 1982. There is little evidence of the origin of these birds. No Surrey recoveries of birds ringed abroad have been located, so there is no firm evidence to support the supposition that winter numbers are augmented by foreign immigrants, though observations (*e.g.* in Parr) suggest that this might be so. Three winter ringing recoveries in France of young ringed in Surrey (latest 1963) are the only foreign ones that have been located. They illustrate a dispersive or migratory tendency among at least some British birds.

Longevity. The longest lived bird was ringed at Weybridge on 24th December 1964 and recovered there over seven years and seven months later on 6th August 1972. The furthest travelled was ringed at Haslemere on 3rd August 1962 and recovered 510 km south, at Olonne-sur-mer, France on 2nd February 1963. Another was ringed at Ewhurst on 5th May 1952 and recovered 230 km southeast at Hermanville, France in January 1953. All three French recoveries date from a period when large flocks were more common.

Plumage variations. A partial albino was seen at Milford (Bucknill, 1902) and there was a leucistic bird at Merton in 1984.

Behaviour. Mistle Thrushes have taken well to suburban life. The lone thrush in the middle of the playing field is likely to be one. Belsey (2002) includes a photograph of a nest in a traffic light at Staines.

American Robin   *Turdus migratorius*

Three, latest 2006

Breeds in North America, wintering south to Guatemala. The 22 records from 1958 to 2001 were scattered across the British Isles. Most were from October to February but there were a few in spring. Surrey has had more than its share of the birds, which are rarest in inland counties.

Surrey. There was one at Wick Pond, Windsor Great Park from 12th February to 5th March 1966 (M. Parker, D. M. Putman, C. M. Veysey *et al.*, BB, *61:363*). A first-winter bird in poor condition visited a Haslemere garden on 12th October 1984, where it was seen by Miss R. Ritchie and Miss V. Z. Walmisley and subsequently killed by a Magpie (BB, *78:573*). The most surprising was one seen by a handful of birders at Peckham on 27th and 28th March 2006, having previously been reported to the RSPB by Fiona

Hill, who saw it in her garden, and photographed by Ian Skelton (photographs in *Birding World* and *Bird Watching*). The bird, which had apparently been in the area since mid January, flew off strongly at dawn on the 28th and was not seen again.

There was an attempted introduction near Guildford by Lord Northcliffe in about 1910 (*The Handbook*, Saunders 1991: 170).

Cetti's Warbler   *Cettia cetti*

About 20 occurrences including three in Spelthorne

Cetti's Warblers are sedentary or partial migrants in western Europe. From a base in Asia Minor, they began a range expansion across Europe which brought them to Britain in 1961. Breeding began in Kent in 1972.

Surrey. Records mostly relate to long-staying winter visitors, though spring or summer territories have been held on a few occasions:

1978:   Bookham Common, one from 7th May to 24th July singing, found by R. C. Price.

1979:   Bookham Common, one on 13th and 26th May and 7th July.
        Holmethorpe, one from 28th August to 5th September and in November, then in January and February 1980 set a pattern for wintering birds.

1980:* Queen Mary Reservoir, a juvenile that was trapped on 12th July remained in the area until at least 13th September and was the first for Middlesex as well as Spelthorne.

1981:* Shepperton Gravel Pits, one singing on 23rd May and 12th July.

1984:   Epsom Great Stew Pond, one on 23rd October.

1987:   Frensham Little Pond, one singing on 27th September. This or another was later recorded at the Great Pond on dates from 18th to 29th October. It might have been the bird at Frensham Little Pond on 14th and 28th February and 20th March 1988.

1988:   Frensham Little Pond, one singing from 15th December to 5th April 1989.

1989:   Frensham Little Pond, one singing on 24th September.

1990:   Frensham, one singing on 7th August.

1991:   Frensham Little Pond, a male from 11th November to 5th December and at the Great Pond on dates from 27th December until at least 1st April 1992.

1992:   Frensham Great Pond, one from 28th September to 29th March 1993.

1996:   Hurst Green, a male from 26th April to 28th June.

1996:* Queen Mary Reservoir, one trapped on 28th September.

1997:   Walton Reservoirs, a male from 3rd November to 10th March 1998 in the drained and over-grown Lambeth basin, went undetected for long periods.

1998:   Stoke Lake, a female was trapped and ringed on 5th May.

1999:   Frensham Little Pond, one, thought to be a female since it did not sing, from 11th November to 5th February 2000.

2002:   Barn Elms London Wetland Centre, one from 30th November, joined by a second bird on 29th December, both staying into the following year. One was heard calling on dates to 17th May 2003.
        Beddington Sewage Farm, one on 5th April.

2003:   Barn Elms London Wetland Centre, one from 7th September to 1st April 2004, two on 30th November.
        Frensham Great Pond, one on 28th-29th October.
        Unstead Sewage Farm, one on dates from 20th October to 9th November and in February 2004 *Bird Watching*).

2004: Frensham Great Pond, one on 16th-24th October, 25th December and January-March 2005.
Barn Elms London Wetland Centre, one on dates from 10th October, remaining into 2005 (*Bird Watching, London Wetland Centre*).

2005: Frensham Great Pond, one from 4th November to 6th December.
Unstead Sewage Farm, one on dates from from 9th November to 21st December.

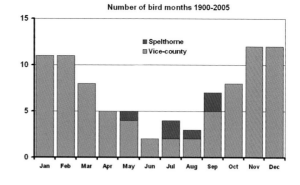

Number of bird months 1900-2005
■ Spelthorne
□ Vice-county

*Spelthorne

Barn Elms has newly planted and extensive beds of reeds. Bookham Common is wet commonland on clay. The site was among bushes beside a small stream, without *Phragmites* reeds. A few hundred square yards were in use in a total site of about 1.5 square miles (10 square km). There was no evidence of a second bird or of breeding. Frensham Ponds have large stands of *Phragmites* and some scrub round their margins. Records from there all relate to single birds, normally in the *Phragmites* and often located by brief bursts of song.

Movements. The bird trapped at Queen Mary Reservoir on 28th September 1996 had been ringed at Totten (Hampshire) on 16th August 1995 and was controlled at Wraysbury Gravel Pit (Berkshire) on 6th July 1996.

Grasshopper Warbler (Common Grasshopper Warbler)   *Locustella naevia*
Once bred, now only a scarce passage migrant

Breeds from Europe east to Siberia and winters south of the breeding range. Western birds are thought to winter in West Africa south of the Sahara but information is rather limited. There was a decline in Britain of at least 50% between the two Atlases. *BWP* suggests that numbers are increasing in parts of western Europe and now stable in Britain, where new forestry planting has provided sites which offset losses on heaths and commons. Recent Breeding Birds Census figures show an increase.

Early Surrey history. Breeding Grasshopper Warblers were uncommon but widely distributed on heaths and commons in 19th century Surrey. They bred on Streatham Common and near Tooting in 1833. Meyer mentioned Ditton Marsh and Claremont. W. Stafford shot one at Hampton Lodge (*SALEC*). The Holmesdale Natural History Club Museum has a nest taken near Reigate in 1872. They nested at Tooting and Redhill in 1880 (Bucknill, 1902) but were rare visitors to Wimbledon Common (Hamilton, 1881). Bucknill listed nearly 20 central and west Surrey sites where they bred towards the end of the 19th century. There were many along the river at Staines (Kerr, 1906).

Vice-county breeding 1900 to 1970. Grasshopper Warblers had gone from the Dulwich area by 1910 according to Power, who had a migrant in his Brixton garden on 30th July 1894. They were very plentiful in 1919 (*BB, 13:228*) and widely distributed on west Surrey commons in 1934 (*SEBR*). Later, following a decline, there was an upsurge in the 1960s. In 1969, over 44 singing males were reported from at least 32 areas in addition to at least 22 proven breeding pairs.

Breeding sites included: *Ashtead Common*: three pairs 1934, 10-15 pairs 1935, present 1936, 1938-39, breeding in the 1950s, five+ pairs 1969; *Banstead Downs*: 1969; *Bookham Common*: one on Bank's

Common, 12th May 1928, one on 12th May 1929, a nest in 1930, three pairs in May 1933, at least 20 birds in July 1934, young 1936, present 1938-40, possibly a pair in 1942, breeding in the 1950s, six singing in 1969; *Bramley*: 1945; *Chobham Common*: 1969; *Dunsfold*: five singing in 1969; *Epsom Common*: four or five pairs in 1934, 12 singing in 1937, 15-20 pairs in 1938, a nest in 1940, four pairs in 1948; *Esher Common*: 1936; *Ewhurst*: 1969; *Frensham*: 1970, *Littleworth Common*: heard in 1937; *Oxshott*: Prince's Coverts four to ten pairs in 1957-70; *Smallfield*: three pairs in 1939; *Thorpe/Virginia Water*: five pairs in 1969; *Thursley Common*: 1908; *Walton Heath*: present in 1937-39 and near *Wonersh*: 1940. Nest sites at *Thursley Common* were burnt out in 1956. Pounds (1952) had no definite breeding records for the *Farleigh* district. 1970 was the peak year, with a total of at least 140 singing birds in 47 localities, following 44 singing in the previous year and 66 in the year following. The peak year for the Grasshopper Warbler in the Common Birds Census was also 1970, when 19 territories were found.

There were migrant Grasshopper Warblers at Beddington Sewage Farm (1957, one summered in 1969), Burpham (1970), Clandon Downs (1970), Cutt Mill (4th August 1906), Dulwich (1942), Eashing (one singing in 1956), East Horsley (1969), Epsom Common (1927), Epsom Sewage Farm (1957), Farleigh (1947-48), Godalming (8th July 1944), Highcombe Bottom (1970), near Hindhead (two on 28th August 1906), Merrow Downs (1970), Old Coulsdon (1949), Peasmarsh (1970), Riddlesdown (1938), Shirley (1946), Stoke Park (1970), Unstead (1970), Vann Lake (1966-73), Warlingham (Beadell had one record), Weybridge Sewage Farm (21st April 1929) and Wisley (3rd May 1906).

Vice-county breeding since 1970. Breeding numbers, measured by territorial birds, held up in the 10 to 20 range until 1972 and climbed back to 38 in 1983 but this was followed by a collapse, the highest subsequent figure being six in 1985. Of the 231 tetrads in northeast Surrey, forty-five (19%) were found to hold territories in the 1968-72 Atlas survey but only eight (3%) in the 1988-97 Atlas. Breeding and territorial localities in this period included: Ashtead Common (1972-5, 1977-87), Banstead Downs (1979), Baynards (1999), Beddington Sewage Farm (1982, 1996), Berrylands (1997), Bookham Common (1972-5, 1985, 1996, 1997), Broadstreet Common (1975), Capel (1992, 1996), Caterham (1982), Chaldon (1977), Chobham Common (1975, 1980), Eashing (1975), Effingham (1974, 1981, 1986), Epsom Common (1975-80, 1982-3, 1986, 1988-9), Frensham (1988, 1990, 1994), Hackhurst Downs (1975), Hankley Common (1974-5), Hersham Gravel Pit, Holmethorpe (1977, 1979, 1991), Horsell Common (1977), Horton Country Park (1990, 1995, 1997, 1999), Hurtwood (1983), Jordan's Wood (1985), Lightwater (1975), Merrow Downs (1978), Moor Park (Farnham, 1981), Netley Heath (1974), Ockham Mill (1997), Park Downs (1979), Pewley Down (1982), Pirbright Commons (1978, 1982, 1990, 1996), Send (1985-7), Stoke D'Abernon (1972), Stoke Water Meadows (1985), the Surrey Docks (1975), Thursley Common (1994), Unstead Sewage Farm (1991), Vann Lake (1973, failed), West End Common (1991), Warlingham (1995), Wimbledon Common (1985), Wisley Common (1974), Woldingham (1998) and Worplesdon (1995). Breeding was last proved at Woldingham in 1998. None were located in the Common Birds Census after 1986. At Ashtead Common, habitat loss due to scrub encroachment has been mentioned as a factor in the decline (*LBR* for 1985) but many other lost sites have changed very little.

Since 2000, migrant Grasshopper Warblers have been found at Bookham Common (2001), Frensham Common (2004), Island Barn Reservoir (2004), Papercourt (2004), Penton Hook (2004), Roundshaw Downs (2002), Stoke Lake (2001), Thursley (2001) and Unstead Sewage Farm (2001).

Spelthorne records include 20th-21st April 1929 and other passage migrants later. There were single birds at Queen Mary Reservoir on 4th May 1952 and Staines Moor on 27th April 1977 and three were singing at King George VI Reservoir on 19th April 1997.

Calendar. The average arrival date in the London area south of the Thames from 1929 to 1939 was 24th April, about a week later than the more recent dates in the chart. Early and late dates are:

Early

3rd April 1970	Reigate Heath
5th April 1974	Ashtead Common
7th April 1969	Esher Common
10th April 1988	Wimbledon Common

Late

30th September 1969	Ashtead Common
3rd October 1982	Chobham Common
8th October 1992	Thursley Common
17th October 1993	Ockley Common

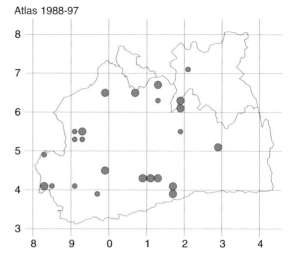

Movements. Autumn passage through Surrey is far heavier than might appear from the few published records. Tape-luring in an intensive study of a field of grasses, rushes and thistles at Worplesdon in August and September 2005 resulted in the trapping of two adults and 16 juveniles (J. Gates). A nestling ringed at Virginia Water on 6th June 1972 and found dead there in mid July (BTO) is the only ringing recovery located.

There has been no relationship between arrival dates and temperatures, possibly because of the big rise and fall in breeding numbers over the period.

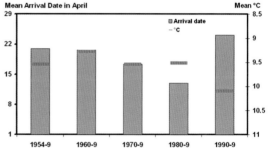

Mean Arrival Date in April   Mean °C

Aquatic Warbler   *Acrocephalus paludicola*

Six definite records, including two from Spelthorne, three more from Perry Oaks Sewage Farm

Aquatic Warblers breed from Germany and Italy east to Hungary and Siberia. They winter in Africa. Birds ringed as nestlings in Poland have been recovered in Britain. The Aquatic Warbler is almost entirely an autumn migrant in Britain, peaking in August and appearing most frequently in southern coastal counties.

Surrey. Records for our area fit the national pattern very well:

1924:* Staines Reservoirs, one on 6th August, seen by D. Gunn (Glegg, 1935).

1951:* Perry Oaks Sewage Farm, one on 25th-26th August (*BB, 45:416*).

1955:* Perry Oaks Sewage Farm, one in a thicket of *Artemisia* and *Heracleum* by the Duke of Northumberland's River on 29th July (*BB, 48:514*). The river is outside the Spelthorne boundary (as the boundary then lay) for most of its traverse of the area and both of the Perry Oaks birds may have been outside it.

1959: Beddington Sewage Farm, one trapped on 20th September (J. Cooke, P. J. Morgan and R. C. Righelato, *BB, 53:424*).

1965: Beddington Sewage Farm, one on 17th August (P. J. Wilson, *BB, 59:294*).

1965:* Perry Oaks Sewage Farm, one, possibly not in Spelthorne, on 30th August (*BB, 61:361*).

1966:* Queen Mary Reservoir, one on 20th-21st August (*BB, 60:325*). Other dates given for this bird are 24th August (Hardwick and Self, 1992) and 7th September (*LN* for 1924, p.37).

1972: Badshot Lea, one on 21st-22nd September (J. M. Clark, *BB, 73:522*).

1977: Surrey Docks, one on 23rd and 24th September, the first for Inner London. (R. E. Alderton, *BB*, 71:519-20)

Spelthorne

Sedge Warbler   *Acrocephalus schoenobaenus*

Locally common summer visitor, breeding annually

Breeds in Europe and western Asia and winters in Africa south of the Sahara, ranging almost as far as the Cape. African recoveries of British-ringed birds are all from the west (*MA*). In Britain, Sedge Warblers were widespread and common through the 19th century and most of the 20th. Habitat requirements differ from those of the Reed Warbler, including more bushes and scrub and less solid stands of *Phragmites*. National breeding numbers in 2001 were similar to those in 1970.

Early Surrey history. Newman listed Sedge Warblers for the Godalming district in 1849. Yarrell, though not specifically mentioning Surrey, wrote that *the marshy banks of the Thames, on either side of the river where beds or willows or reeds abound, are well stocked with the bird.* Bucknill found Sedge Warblers to be common by rivers, streams and ponds and said that in the Surrey part of the London area they nested at Dulwich Park, Richmond, Wimbledon Park and similar places and that they were very common in the Mole and Wey valleys. Sedge Warblers were breeding in the Staines district by 1906 (Kerr).

1900 to 1950. A nest was collected by Boorman at Send in 1902. A bird was recorded from Oxted on 5th May 1906 (*Zool., 1906:100*). Between 1900 and 1936, Sedge Warblers nested at Beddington (1932), Dulwich Park (1901), Elmers End Sewage Farm (1936), Epsom Sewage Farm (1929, lost about 1938), Esher (Black Pond, 1933), Frensham Great and Little Ponds (about 1933), Godstone (1904), Ham Gravel Pit (1934), Nutfield Marsh (1902), Old Malden (1933), Oxted (1907-12), the Reigate area (Brocklehurst and Sidlow, 1905), Send (eggs collected by Boorman, 1902), Thorpe (1907), Weybridge (1929) and Wire Mill (1907). Sedge Warblers were occasional at Richmond Park, up to the 1930s, recorded from 1906 (7th May) but not proved to breed. A few pairs nested at Guildford Sewage Farm in 1944-45. When Frensham Ponds were refilled after having been drained during the 1939-45 war it was Sedge Warblers that first moved into the bushes and scrub on the site, which is now dominated by large Reed Warbler colonies in well-established reedbeds. They did the same on the sites of drained ponds in Richmond Park in 1945 and 1946. *Spelthorne*: in the early 1930s Sedge Warblers colonised the bush-covered banks of Staines Reservoirs.

1950 to 1970. Losses of suitable habitat, particularly along rivers, have been to some extent offset, in Surrey, by the creation of gravel pits. Breeding sites identified in the 1950s and 60s included Addlestone (Mill Pond, 'New Lines' [Lyne?] Pond), Barn Elms, Beddington Sewage Farm, Berrylands Sewage Farm, Brooklands, Chertsey Meads Sewage Farm, Cutt Mill, Eashing, Enton, Frensham Ponds, Frimley Gravel Pits, Gatton, Gatwick, Godalming, Hamm Moor Gravel Pits, Hersham Sewage Farm and Gravel Pits, Leatherhead, Mitcham, Molesey Sewage Farm, the River Wey from Guildford to Godalming, Stoke Water Meadows, Sutton Park (Guildford), Thorpe Gravel Pits and Unstead Sewage Farm. There were thought to be less than 30 pairs in the vice-county in 1969 and around 20 in the Guildford area in 1970 (Parr).

Since 1970. Sedge Warblers bred or held territory at some time or other at over 70 sites in the years from 1970 to 2000. This compares with the 54 tetrads in which they were found in the 1988-97 SBC Atlas survey and suggests that the atlas cover was reasonably thorough. There has been a decline in northeast Surrey. Of its 231 tetrads, 38 were found to hold territories in the 1968-72 Atlas survey and 31 in the 1988-97 Atlas. The 1982 BTO Breeding Waders of Wet Meadows survey included the Sedge Warbler as an additional species. Site visits to 32 areas produced three birds at Stoke Water Meadows, Guildford, two territories at Old Woking and two birds at Runnymede. The London and Surrey Bird Reports for 1982 make it clear that most of the breeding Sedge Warblers were not in wet meadows. Beddington Sewage

Farm alone had up to 16 singing males. In Spelthorne, there were territories at Staines Moor in 1976 and Staines Reservoirs in 1978. Shepperton Gravel Pits had two pairs in 1979 and one pair in 1980. They bred in 1984 and 1986 (*Shepp. BR*). Perry Oaks Sewage Farm held 11 territories in 1999.

Population size. Overall, the breeding strength has increased since the 1960s. In 2000 the largest colony, at Beddington, was bigger than that in the Guildford area in 1969 and the number of pairs/singing males reported in the vice-county in 2000, some 68, is more than double the county total for 1969 estimated by Parr. Sedge Warbler habitat was poorly represented in the Common Birds Census and no territories were recorded after 1981. Numbers are dependent on the available habitat at a relatively small number of sites. On the plus side, the creation of new reedbeds and scrub at Barn Elms WWT had brought the number of territories to a record high of 17 by 2002. A count of 19+ singing males at Buckland Sand Pits in 1985 (I. Dodd, J. Newland) is one of the largest on record for any site. Beddington Sewage Farm, the main site, is undergoing rapid adverse change. Eighteen Sedge Warblers were trapped

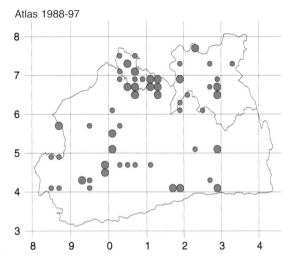

Atlas 1988-97

there in 1986. The number of territories rose from 20 in 1995 to 28 in 1999 and then crashed from 25 in 2000 to nine in 2004. There were 15 singing males at Stoke Water Meadows in 2000 and 44 juveniles were ringed there in 2002. Some 26 singing Sedge Warblers were counted at Papercourt Gravel Pits and Broadmead on 2nd May 2004. Sedge Warblers no longer breed at Frensham.

Sedge Warblers do well in bushy sites, such as Molesey Heath and the main marsh at Stoke Water Meadows. At Queen Mary Reservoir the digging of the gravel pits created new temporary habitat and four pairs bred in 1980, but were soon lost. Reed Warblers took over as the habitat matured. There were ten pairs at Stanwell Moor in 2001. Sedge Warblers use reedbeds in Ireland, where Reed Warblers are absent.

Calendar. The average arrival date in the London area south of the Thames from 1929 to 1939 was 18th April. Glegg (1935) gave the average arrival date in Middlesex for sixteen (non-consecutive) years as 28th April. The chart shows that this is about two weeks later than the average for Surrey since the 1950s, as well as showing the correlation between mean temperature and arrival date. Average arrival dates became later in the colder 1960s and have since become earlier.

Early and late dates are:

Early

23rd March 1975 Eashing
23rd March 1992 South Norwood Country Park
27th March 1993 Berrylands Sewage Works
28th March 1989 Ham Lands

Late

14th October 1906 Hedgecourt
15th October 1994 Stoke
18th October 2001 Barn Elms London Wetland
  Centre
22nd October 1969 Hamm Moor, Weybridge
26th October 1986 Berrylands Sewage Works

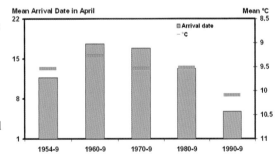

Large counts include about 70 at Hersham Sewage Farm on 2nd September 1961 (Parr).

Movements. Presumed migrants at sites unsuitable for breeding include birds at Banstead Downs in 1988, Battersea Park, May and August 1986 and one singing in chalk scrub at Brockham on 9th June 1970, one singing from a rose bed at the Royal Surrey Hospital, Guildford on 12th May 1993 and one singing in gorse at Thursley Common on 10th May 1991. One at Nore Hill (800 feet) on 13th August 2000 was unusually high (for Surrey). Sedge Warblers occasionally appear in gardens on passage. Birds singing in early May are sometimes only passing through. Four Sedge Warblers ringed in Surrey have been recovered in France and one each in Belgium and Portugal. The Portuguese bird was ringed at Effingham on 18th July 1981 and recovered 1,607 km southwest, at Baixo Alentejo on 22nd August of the same year. One ringed in the Republic of Ireland on 28th July 1985 was recovered in the same year at Buckland on 21st August.

Longevity. A Sedge Warbler ringed in the nest at Stoke Water Meadows on 2nd June 1999 and recovered there over five years and one month later, on 4th July 2004 had the greatest known longevity.

Marsh Warbler   *Acrocephalus palustris*

Fifteen vice-county records up to 2001, has bred

Breeds from Europe to western Russia and winters in eastern Africa from Uganda southward. Has declined in the western part of the range, including Britain since 1950, but there has been some expansion from Scandinavia east to St Petersburg (Leningrad).

. **Surrey**. Marsh Warblers were first proved to breed in Surrey in 1907, when two nests, each containing four eggs, were found in a bed of willows, nettles and other rank vegetation at Thorpe (Kerr, 1907, 1908). Mouritz knew of these nests and it is presumed that these are the two that Shaw (1921) gives him as a reference for, although they are not in the Haslemere district. No reference to them has been located in a Mouritz publication, but he was probably personally known to Shaw and may have told him about them. There were no further records for over 50 years:

1958:   Gatton Park, two birds were present from 23rd June, one of which was initially identified by its song. Behaviour suggesting the feeding of young was seen on 11th July. A bird thought to be a juvenile was seen (H. Bentham). The birds were last seen on 31st July. They bred, according to the *LBR* and *BLA*.

1961:   Guildford Sewage Farm, a male stayed for about a fortnight during the breeding season (R. K. Murton, N. J. Westwood).

1966:   Walton Reservoirs, one trapped on 9th July.

1980:   Hamm Moor Gravel Pits, one singing on 2nd July.

1989:   Ottershaw, one on 2nd-13th September, trapped, photograph in the *SBR*.

1993:   South Norwood Country Park, a singing male on 9th-25th June, probably in the Kent part of the park.

1994:   Beddington Sewage Farm, a singing male from 22nd May to 19th June.

1995:   Lambeth Reservoir, a singing male on 8th-10th June.
        Beddington Sewage Farm, a male from 31st May. A second singing male on 21st-30th June, both singing at once, an adult seen in July, and a juvenile on the 30th. Adult not seen feeding young.

1998:   Stoke Water Meadows, a singing male on 22nd-23rd June.

1999:   South Norwood Lake, a singing male in rank vegetation near the lake on 13th June.

2000:   Beddington Sewage Farm, a singing male on 10th-16th June.

2001:   Barn Elms, a singing male from 25th May and two adults with a juvenile were seen there on 9th July. These were assumed to have bred locally.

Reed Warbler (Eurasian Reed Warbler)   *Acrocephalus scirpaceus*

Locally common summer visitor, breeding annually

Breeds from Europe and North Africa east to Central Asia and winters in sub-Saharan and Central Africa. The European race *scirpaceus* winters in Africa from Nigeria to the Congo basin. Migrants from Eastern Europe and Scandinavia pass through Britain (*MA*). The range has extended northwest in Scandinavia and northwest Russia since the mid 19th century and has fluctuated in Britain. UK breeding numbers are thought to have more than doubled since 1970.

Early Surrey history. Yarrell (1845) wrote that Reed Warblers could be found in Surrey within a few miles of London. This is possibly a reference to a statement in Meyer (1842), cited by Bucknill, that Reed Warblers were *in tolerable abundance* on the borders of the Thames and *nesting on the Abbey River within the town of Chertsey*. They had been found at Battersea by 1833 (Glegg, 1938). Power said they nested in Battersea Park up to 1895. Bucknill regarded them as rather scarce and local in Surrey. Places which he mentioned include Chertsey, Godalming (1873), Milford, the Mole from Betchworth to Cobham, Richmond, near Stoke Lock (nesting) and Virginia Water. There were colonies along the river banks in the Staines area (Kerr, 1906).

1900 to 1969. Eggs that Boorman collected by the River Wey at Send (1905, 1910, 1911, 1913) are in the Haslemere Museum. There were six pairs of Reed Warblers at Godstone in 1933, where they had bred since 1907. Other breeding sites recorded up to the 1950s included Albury, Beddington (at least two pairs, 1935), Frensham Great Pond (1930s), Godstone (1935), Kew (1914 and 1917), Leigh Mill, Richmond Park (from 1951, apparently a new colonisation), the Thames at Thorpe (1907), Vachery and Wire Mill. The small pond at Barn Elms Reservoirs had breeding Reed Warblers from the early 1950s (*BLA*). Reed Warblers were in the Abinger area in 1953.

Since 1970. In the 1970s, there were colonies at Abinger, Albury, Barn Elms, Frensham, Gatton, Gomshall, Guildford Sewage Farm, Hamm Moor, Papercourt Gravel Pits, Richmond Park, Silvermere Lake, Thorpe Gravel Pits and Wire Mill (Parr). In Spelthorne, Queen Mary Gravel Pits had ten singing males in 1980, twelve in 1981 and eight later in the 1980s. Shepperton Gravel Pits had several pairs in the 1980s, one pair bred at Ferry Lane and five or six pairs were at Littleton Lakes in 1986. There were singing males on Staines Moor in 1976 and 1981.

Trend. Of the 231 tetrads in northeast Surrey, 10% were found to hold territories in the 1968-72 Atlas survey and 18% in the 1988-97 Atlas and there has been further growth. Numbers are currently at a high level in the county as a whole but rather localised. Reed Warbler habitat was poorly represented in the Common Birds Census and no territories were recorded after 1983.

Population size. There were about 100 territories in 1998, rising to 240 in 2001. As with Sedge Warblers, habitat changes can produce sharp changes in population levels. The creation of new reedbeds whether accidental, fol-

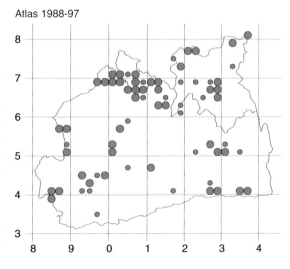

Atlas 1988-97

lowing drainage as in the case of Lambeth Reservoir in the mid 1990s or deliberate, as at Barn Elms from about 1999, will rapidly attract a large additional population. There were 121 territories at Barn Elms in 2004. Gravel extraction can quickly destroy habitat, as at Beddington Sewage Farm and Lambeth

Reservoir in the late 1990s. At Beddington, the population surged forward again, with 29 territories in 2001 but there were only ten in 2004.

Territory counts. Other recent counts include seven singing at Ash Vale Gravel Pits in 2003, two at Black Pond, Esher in 2003, one at Broadmead, Send in 2004, 36 at Frensham in 2003 and 33 there in 2004, 15 at Frimley Gravel Pits in 2002, at least two at Hedgecourt in 2003, two at Morden Hall Park in 2001, at least ten singing at Papercourt in 2002, 18 at Stoke Lake in 2002 and at least three at Wire Mill in 2003.

Nesting. While the largest colonies are in reedbeds, other sites are sometimes used. Bulrushes are not uncommon and a colony at Papercourt Gravel Pits in the 1970s was in a dense *Salix* bed.

Song. Wandering birds sometimes sing in places well away from water (*e.g.* gardens at Farnham in 1986, Godalming in 1989, Guildford in 1978 and Roehampton in 1988). One sang in birch woods at Newdigate in 1970 and another sang from birch scrub at Pirbright Common on 25th June 1981. One at Esher in 1981 sang well away from any water. One sang from shrubs at a road junction in London SE1 in 1983.

Calendar. The average arrival date in the London area south of the Thames from 1929 to 1939 was 29th April. This is at least a week later than the average since the 1980s, as shown in the chart.

Early and late dates are:

Early

7th April 1995	Lonsdale Road Reservoir
7th April 2001	Frensham Great Pond
7th April 2002	Frensham Great Pond
8th April 1997	Frensham Great Pond

Late

1st November 2003	Barn Elms London Wetland Centre
6th November 1938	Mitcham
10th November 1984	Ripley Sewage Farm, blind in one eye, very active
26th November 2002	Island Barn Reservoir

Mean Arrival Date in April — Mean °C

Spelthorne. Early and late dates for Queen Mary Reservoir up to 1988 were 22nd April 1987 and 17th November 1984 (Geen).

Movements and longevity. European recoveries of birds ringed in Surrey have been made in France (three), Spain (three) and Portugal (one). Two birds ringed in France have been recovered in Spelthorne. There are two links with Africa. A Reed Warbler ringed in Senegal on 9th April 1992 was recovered in Spelthorne on 31st May 1994, 4,138 km north. Another, ringed further south, in the Gambia on 4th March 2001, was recovered at Queen Mary Reservoir, 4,341 km north, on 4th June 2002. A Reed Warbler ringed at Queen Mary Reservoir was recovered over nine years and eleven months later at the same site, the county longevity record (R. A. Denyer). Another, ringed at Wraysbury Gravel Pit on 23rd August 1986, was recovered over six years and ten months later at nearby Queen Mary Reservoir on 10th July 1993.

Great Reed Warbler   *Acrocephalus arundinaceus*

Four vice-county records

The breeding range covers most of continental Europe east to Central Asia and extends south to northwest Africa. The European range has expanded in the north and east but has decreased in some other parts of Europe since 1900. The birds winter in southeast Asia and in Africa south of the Sahara. British records come mostly from the south and east coastal counties and are most frequent in spring.

Surrey. The 20th and 21st century records are from Frensham:

1858:   Godalming, one was shot by J. P. Stafford at Ockford Pond in the spring (Bucknill, *BB*, *1:84*, *SALEC*, season not given). It was in the Charterhouse Collection when Bucknill wrote but is not there now. The record was only the third for Britain, the first being in 1847.

1965:   Frensham Great Pond, one on 7th-19th June, trapped on the 11th (P. G. Davis, *BB*, *59:294*). Present from the 5th in HNHS 1968.

1966:   Frensham Great Pond, one from 29th May to 6th June, trapped (P. G. Davis, *BB*, *60:324*).

2002:   Frensham Little Pond, one from 18th May to 12th June, song recorded (S. P. Peters, *BB*, *96:593*).

Icterine Warbler   *Hippolais icterina*
Three, one of them from Spelthorne

Icterine Warblers breed from northeast France and Scandinavia east to Siberia and Iran and winter in Africa south of the Sahara. Bred in Scotland in 1992 (Mead). The Scandinavian population has increased. In Britain, they are most frequent on autumn passage, peaking at the end of August and heavily concentrated in eastern and southern coastal counties. Spring birds occur mainly in May and June, in eastern coastal counties.

Surrey. One at Staines Reservoirs on 9th August 1965 was the first for the London area ('JBC', *LBR* for 1966).

The second was a singing male at Seears Park, Cheam on 10th June 1983 (S. J. Holdsworth). Another was seen at Abinger on 13th September 1987, field notes in the *SBR*.

Icterine/Melodious Warbler   *Hippolais icterina/polyglotta*

Two, not identified to species, one at Queen Mary Reservoir on 18th September 1984 and the other at Richmond Park on 10th October 1991.

Melodious Warbler   *Hippolais polyglotta*
Three, two of them in Greater London

Melodious Warblers have a more southern and western distribution than Icterines, both as breeding birds and in their British distribution. The breeding range covers south and west Europe, from their northernmost station in the Netherlands to Iberia in the west and the Adriatic in the east, with a winter range further south in Africa. The breeding range has extended in several countries since 1900. British records are mainly from southern coastal counties and are much more frequent in autumn, peaking in August and September, than in the spring.

Surrey. There were no spring records from inland counties from 1958 to 1985, making two of the Surrey records rather unusual. One on Croham Hurst Golf Course from 30th April to 2nd May 1987 was seen and heard singing on the evening of 30th April and the identification was confirmed on the following day (P. Holt, J. A. Lindsell *et al.*). One at Barn Elms Reservoirs on 5th May 1990 soon moved onto the allotments nearby (R. B. Hastings). There was one at Papercourt Gravel Pits on 13th-15th October 1991 (J. Bryant).

Blackcap
Sylvia atricapilla

Common summer visitor, breeding annually, scarce winter visitor

Breeds in North Africa and in Europe east to western Siberia and winters in western Europe and in Africa south to Malawi. The vast majority of the Blackcaps that breed in Britain winter in Iberia or northwest Africa. Winter recoveries of Blackcaps in Britain are predominantly of birds breeding on the near Continent (*MA*). The population has increased in much of western Europe since 1960, with small extensions of range in the British Isles, where breeding numbers are thought to have more than doubled since 1970. The *New Atlas* put the British population at 580,000 in 1988-91.

Early Surrey history. Blackcaps were in the Godalming district by 1849 (Newman). The *Historical Atlas* describes Blackcaps as uncommon breeders in the vice-county from 1875 to 1900. This may be, but Harting (1866) quotes Mr Shirley Hibbard as saying that '*At Dulwich, Hornsey, Kensington, and St John's Wood, the Blackcap may be heard every season, soon after the last days of March, but it makes its way only into such of the more urban districts as enclose within their boundaries much rural scenery.*' Aldridge (1885) put the arrival in the Norwood district as late as early May.

Bucknill describes them as more numerous in Surrey than the Garden Warbler and, in respect of Dulwich, quotes a correspondent (Teesdale) as saying that they were the second commonest of the summer visitors to Dulwich Wood the commonest being Willow Warblers. He quotes the author of an 1869 paper who said that they had often been recorded from Battersea Park, and Blyth, who wrote that they were 'excessively common' in the neighbourhood of London. Breeding sites that Bucknill mentioned include Norwood, Roehampton and, following Hamilton (1881), Wimbledon Common. They were numerous in Richmond Park (Mouritz). All this has a modern ring, as the map below shows. Blackcaps are still to be found at both Battersea Park and Dulwich, as well as at many other sites in the Surrey part of the London area. Blackcaps were sparsely distributed in the Staines district (Kerr, 1906).

1900 to the 1960s. Little extra is known about Blackcaps in the early part of the 20th century. Eggs were collected near Peper Harow in 1901 and 1918, at Ockham, Ripley and Send from 1902 to 1910 and at Woking in 1920 and 1922. There were 13 song posts on Bookham Common in 1943, more than the number of those of Garden Warblers (Carrington *et al.*, 1944). There is some evidence that they were then less common than Garden Warblers elsewhere, at least in the more rural areas (Parr) but by the 1960s they were at least as common.

Where found since 1960. Blackcaps are now found in most areas of woodland where there is an understorey of brambles and shrubs. Of the 231 tetrads in northeast Surrey, 82% were found to hold territories in the 1968-72 Atlas survey but only 78% in the 1988-97 Atlas. Most other evidence, though, points to a growth in numbers. They summered at Vann Lake in almost all years from 1964 to 1996 (Blaker Log). They have bred at Battersea Park from 1985 at least and they have colonised the newly created woodland at the Surrey Docks, where two pairs bred in 1990. Blackcaps have also moved into Burgess and Southwark Parks, near Clapham Junction (Hewlett). They now breed at the restructured Barn Elms London Wetland Centre, where there were ten pairs in 2005. In the Shepperton area there were at least four territories in 1983, three in 1984, about seven territories in 1985 and about eight in 1986 (*Shepp. BRs*). There were counts of up to seven on the 2003 BTO Spring Migration Watch.

Territory counts. Breeding season counts include *Bookham Common*: 49 territories in 1997, 28 on 96 acres (39 hectares) in 2004; *Frensham Ponds*: eight territories in 1994, 16 in 2005; *Wimbledon Common*:

45 territories in 1983, 58 in 1984, 63 in 1985, 70 in 1989, 89 in 1995; *Wimbledon Common and Putney Heath*: 100 pairs in 2005.

Population size. The Breeding Birds Survey from 1994 to 2004 grosses up to about 4,500 adults. The Common Birds Census shows a significant and very large increase from 1970 to 2000. It over-represents the key habitat, which is woodland, where Blackcaps show a fivefold increase. If Surrey held a proportionate share of the UK population as given by the *New Atlas*, the population would be nearer to 4,200 pairs, or two per square km, which looks more plausible. There is no doubt about there being a large increase in the number of Blackcaps, which are now widely distributed in all but the most densely built up parts of the county.

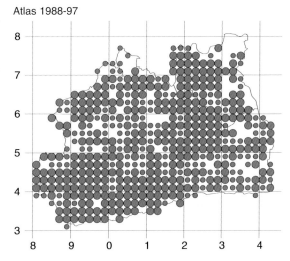
Atlas 1988-97

Calendar. Power (1910) gave an earliest date for first song of 9th April and a late date for song of 24th October in the Dulwich area. Glegg gave the average Middlesex arrival date over 38 (non-consecutive) years as 17th April. The average arrival date in the London area south of the Thames from 1929 to 1939 was 10th April. Fledged young have been recorded as early as 12th May (Epsom Stew Ponds, 1982).

Wintering. Harting and Bucknill both knew that Blackcaps occasionally wintered. Harting quotes no Spelthorne records but Bucknill cites Morris for one seen at Dorking in December. The first two 20th century winter records were at Haslemere on 12th February to 20th March 1937 (*SEBR*) and at Leatherhead on 25th December 1959 (the first December record), after which they were seen in Surrey in most winters. Numbers have been increasing and in early 1996 a total of 103 birds (52 males, 22 females and 29 unsexed) were found at 74 places between January and mid March. There were at least nine at Banstead and 22 in and around Croydon. The Croydon RSPB Group found Blackcaps in 21 gardens in January 2001 alone. The number of birds involved in this total was probably rather fewer. Glegg (1935) had no winter records for any part of Middlesex but there were winter records from Queen Mary Reservoir, where birds were often trapped in November and December (Geen) and in Staines and Stanwell Moor in 1971. There are also winter records at Shepperton in 1984 and 1985. The wintering birds are likely to be of European origin. One sang at Kew on 17th December 1983. Song heard in February (*e.g.* Weybridge 25th February 1975, Purley 1976, Wallington 28th February 1983) is presumably from wintering birds.

Large counts of probable passage migrants include 30 at Holmethorpe on 2nd September 1995 and 40 at Morden Hall Park on 8th May 1996.

Food. Winter food notes include asparagus seeds, berries of *Cotoneaster bacillaris*, bird seed, black sunflower seeds, bread, Christmas pudding, fat, holly, honeysuckle (the most frequently reported item), ivy, pastry mix, peanut butter and *Pyracantha*. Other things eaten include apple, grape and the fruits of Stinking Iris *Iris foetida*. Eight fed on elder berries at Unstead Sewage Farm on 27th August 1998.

Movements and longevity. There have been continental European recoveries from France (six), the Netherlands (one), Sardinia (one) and Spain (nine). African recoveries have come from Algeria (five) and Morocco (seven). The furthest travelled of these birds was ringed at Betchworth on 9th August 1980 and recovered 2,103 km south, at Oued-Zem, Morocco on 12th April 1983. These cover the main wintering areas. A Blackcap ringed at Caterham on 7th July 1981 and recovered there over nine years and ten months later, on 10th May 1991 was remarkable for both longevity and site fidelity.

Garden Warbler
Locally common summer visitor, breeding annually

Sylvia borin

Breeds from Europe east to central Siberia and winters in Africa south of the Sahara. Most foreign recoveries of British-ringed Garden Warblers are from France and Iberia. Some of the Garden Warblers that breed in Scandinavia and elsewhere in Europe pass through Britain (*MA*). It seems likely that the British population was broadly stable during the 19th and 20th centuries.

Early Surrey history. Garden Warblers were in the Godalming district by 1849 (Newman). Bucknill noted them as present in suburban localities such as Dulwich Wood (two or three pairs, (Power)), Richmond, Tooting (1830s) and, following Hamilton (1881), Wimbledon, and thought them less numerous than Blackcaps. There were many in spring, in the Staines district, but few stayed to nest (Kerr, 1906).

1900 to 1970. Eggs were collected near Elstead in 1901 (Maitland and Turnbull) and at Clandon, Ockham, Send and Wisley from 1907 to 1909 (Boorman collection). Mouritz (1905) thought them much less common than Blackcaps in Richmond Park. Other localities mentioned early in the 20th century included Addington, Elstead, Leigh Mill, Leith Hill, Ockley, Selsdon Woods and Wonersh (Parr). A nest was found at South Park in 1905 (G. T. Winter). Garden Warblers were breeding at Frensham in the 1930s and Gosnell collected eggs there. Three pairs were on the southern edge of Banstead Downs in 1934. There were five song posts on Bookham Common in 1943 (Carrington *et al.*, 1944). Breeding sites reported during the 1950s and 60s included Ashtead, Banstead, Dulwich Wood, Farleigh, Ham Common, Headley, Leatherhead, Prince's Coverts, Reigate, Richmond Park, Thorpe, Vann Lake and Wimbledon Common and there were no doubt many more.

Since 1970. The later distribution has been much the same. Extra sites named included Archbishop's Park, Southwark (1988), Thorpe parish (six pairs 1970) and Walton Heath (1970). The Common Birds Census showed a significant increase of around 50% from 1970 to 2000. This increase differs markedly from the Atlas Results for the Surrey part of the London area. Here the number of occupied tetrads fell from 173 in 1968-72 to 91 in 1988-97 and showed, at the least, a substantial loss of ground in northeast Surrey. Trends vary greatly from place to place. At Bookham Common there were at least ten territories in 1973 but 24 in 2003. The increase there has coincided with that of the local Turtle Doves and Nightingales, which are also birds of bushy places. This is probably due to habitat change. The same may be true at other places which have experienced significant increases or decreases.

Population size. Population estimates for the end of the 20th century of about 8,000 territories (grossed up from the Common Birds Census) and 600 adults (from the Breeding Birds Survey) might span the true figure. The Breeding Birds Survey suggests that there are three times as many Whitethroats as Garden Warblers. Garden Warblers may be harder to pick up in a transect survey. The actual number of territories reported to the Surrey Bird Club in recent years is typically over 150. If Surrey held a proportionate share of the UK population as given by the *New Atlas*, the population would be nearer to 1,400 pairs which may be the best estimate.

Other territory counts. Among the larger populations at the end of the period were 24 territories on the 0.24 square km plains area of

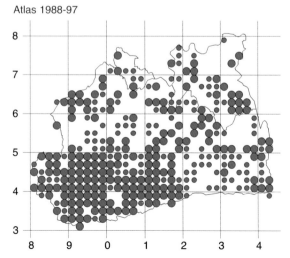

Atlas 1988-97

Bookham Common in 2003, 12 at Frensham in 2003 and ten at Unstead Sewage Farm in 2000. At Wimbledon Common there were five territories in 1990, 14 in 2002 and 24 in 2005. In Spelthorne, Garden Warblers bred along Littleton Lane in 1983 and 1986 but were scarce in the Shepperton district (*Geen, Shepperton Bird Reports* 1983-86).

Calendar. Power (1910) gave an earliest date of 2nd May for song in Dulwich Wood. Glegg (1935) gave the average arrival date in Middlesex for twelve (non-consecutive) years as 28th April. The chart shows that this is over a week later than the average for Surrey since the 1950s, as well as showing the correlation between mean temperature and arrival date. The average arrival date in the London area south of the Thames from 1929 to 1939 was 18th April.

Subsequent early and late dates are:

Early

27th March 1954	Epsom Common
10th April 2000	East Molesey
11th April 1943	Haslemere (Clark, 1984)
12th April 1964	Frensham
12th April 1993	Frensham

Late

10th October 1990	Mitcham Common
14th October 1965	Ewhurst
17th October 1992	Beddington Sewage Farm
18th October 1991	South Norwood Country Park
5th November 1988	Queen Mary Gravel Pits

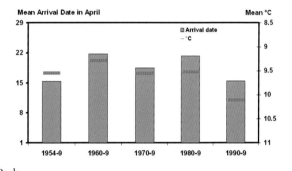

Large counts. Falls of migrants include about 50 at Thorpe in August 1970 and about 30 at Bookham Common on 6th May 1972.

Food. Berries, such as honeysuckle, are among the autumn and winter foods. Other berries eaten include *Euonymus* (Guildford, 1987) and Ivy (Ockley, 22nd April 1987).

Movements and longevity. The only continental European recovery is from Norway but there are two from Morocco. One of these was of a bird ringed at Kempton Park, possibly not in Surrey, on 27th August 1988 and recovered 1,853 km south on 23rd April 1989. The other was ringed at Witley Common on 11th June 1988 and recovered at Boulemane, 1,997 km south, on or about 2nd July 1989. Wintering grounds are further south. The longest-lived Garden Warbler for which details are available was colour-ringed at Witley Common on 30th May 1981 and seen there again on 24th June 1987.

Barred Warbler

Sylvia nisoria

One bird

Barred Warblers are typical of scarce east coast migrants, breeding from Scandinavia and Germany east to Iran and Central Asia and wintering in East Africa. The Scandinavian range has extended since 1960. The great majority of British records are in the autumn, peaking from late August into September and coming from eastern coastal counties, with most of the others from the south. Very few have been found further inland.

Surrey. The one record, of a first-winter bird found by D. P. Boyle in Richmond Park on 21st September 1985 and present from 8.45-9 am, was on a typical date. It was feeding on hawthorn berries and was calling until inadvertently disturbed.

Devil's Punch Bowl (south) – panorama. Grazing by cattle was introduced in 1994 and has been successful in extending the heather cover. The beech glade in another plate is on the left of the painting. Two Ring Ouzels stayed for three days in October 2005.
           John Davis

John Davis
Devil's Punchbowl 4ᵏ November '98

Lesser Whitethroat
Sylvia curruca

Moderately common summer visitor, breeding annually

Breeds from southern Britain and eastern France east to Siberia and winters south of the breeding range from Nigeria east to India. British birds are thought to take a broadly southeast route, mainly wintering in northeast Africa. The Lesser Whitethroat was added to the British list in the late 18th century, when it was found in Buckinghamshire. Numbers changed little overall from 1970 to 2001 apart from falling at the end of the period. Lesser Whitethroats were much less affected by the Sahel drought of 1968/69 than were Whitethroats, because of their more eastern wintering range. The *New Atlas* put the British population at 80,000 territories, mostly in the southern half of England.

Early Surrey history. Lesser Whitethroats appear to have been fairly common in Surrey during the 19th century though, as now, less so than the Whitethroat. Newman (1849) listed them for the Godalming district. Bucknill described them as frequent in suburban districts and as *abundant, especially on migration* at Dulwich, *very plentiful* at Richmond (in 1871) and *noticed*, but *not common* at Wimbledon. He said that they were more abundant than the Whitethroat in some places. Power (1910) said that Lesser Whitethroats nested in the larger gardens of Brixton and Camberwell up to 1894, but that these gardens were fast disappearing. Lesser Whitethroats bred in Battersea Park (Hudson, 1898). The Holmesdale Natural History Club Museum has a nest taken on Wray Common in 1898. Lesser Whitethroats were breeding in the Staines district at about this time (Kerr, 1906).

1900 to 1969. Mouritz (1905) had only three records for Richmond Park and Lesser Whitethroats remained scarce there up to the 1930s. Boorman collected eggs at Clandon, Ockham, Ripley and Send from 1902 to 1909. Lesser Whitethroats bred at Hedgecourt in 1914, at Woking, where eggs were collected in 1915 and 1919, at Tooting Common in 1926 and at Ham Common and a garden at Sheen (both 1939). In the Haslemere district, in the early 1930s, Lesser Whitethroats were mainly found in hedgerows on the Weald Clay. They were abundant on Ashtead and Epsom Commons in 1936 and Bentham found twelve nests on Ashtead Common in 1939 (Parr). They bred at Mitcham Common in 1941, Wandsworth Common in 1942 and Streatham Common in 1950. Lesser Whitethroats were more common than Whitethroats around Horley in 1945. Pounds (1952) found Lesser Whitethroats breeding locally in the Farleigh District. Later probable breeding sites were Barnes Common (1956), Enton (1953-54, 1956-67), Frensham Great Pond (1956), Hurtmore (1954), Inval (1979), Mitcham Common (1956), Oxshott (1956), Reigate Heath (1956), Richmond Park (1956), South Norwood Lake (1956), West Ewell (1956) and Witley Common (1956). These scattered reports suggest that Lesser Whitethroats were widely, if thinly, distributed across Surrey in the period.

Trend since 1970. Numbers seem to have fallen back since 1970. In the Surrey part of the LNHS area, the numbers of occupied tetrads was 120 in the 1968-72 Atlas survey, compared with 91 in the 1988-97 SBC Atlas survey. Other information suggests a rising trend. The table shows that the number of reported sites has risen somewhat since the 1970s, possibly due to greater observer effort:

Number of vice-county Lesser Whitethroat sites reported to the Surrey Bird Club

1972	1973	1974	1975	1976	1977	1978	1979	1980	1983	1985	1986
19	21	c.30	20	21	29	26	21	30	20	41	40

1987	1992	1993	1994	1995	1996	1997	1998	1999	2000	2001
33	17	18	24	32	39	36	29	32	34	25

The Common Birds Census showed a significant but erratic increase of about 80% from 1970 to 2000, which is more than is shown in the table. Lesser Whitethroats bred at Beddington Sewage Farm in 1970 and at Vann Lake in 1977, for the first time on record at each site. They bred at Kew Gardens in 1982 for the first time on record and were found at the Surrey Docks in the 1990s, where one pair probably bred in 1995 and there was a single territory in 1999. Lesser Whitethroats remain thinly distributed and associated more with hedges and scrub than with heathland.

Lesser Whitethroats were scarce summer visitors to Shepperton in the 1980s and remain so today. Two pairs bred at the Littleton Lakes in 1986 and five pairs bred at Queen Mary Reservoir in 1988.

Other territory counts. At Ashtead Common, the largest number of territories was five, in 1994 and 2000. Numbers have remained steady at Bookham Common, where there were five territories in 1970, four in 2001 and five in 2004. Ten or more territories in the Hurst Green area in 2003 and four singing at Smallfield in 2000 suggest that currently the largest area population is in the southeast of Surrey. Most areas reported no more than two territories.

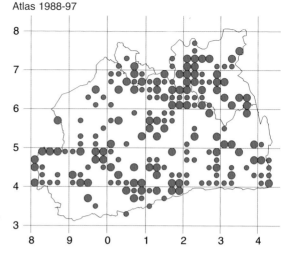

Atlas 1988-97

Population size. The 1994-2004 Breeding Birds Survey suggests a breeding season population of 100-150 adults, which seems too low given the number of reported sites and has a wide margin of error. The Common Birds Census suggested about 3,000 territories for 2000, about 1.5 per square km. If the Surrey density were similar to that of farmland in the national figures, about one territory per square km, the county would hold about 2,000 pairs. If Surrey held a proportionate share of the UK population as given by the *New Atlas*, the population would be nearer to 1,000 pairs.

Calendar. The average arrival date in the London area south of the Thames from 1929 to 1939 was 21st April. Geen gave early and late dates for Queen Mary Reservoir to 1988 as 21st April 1984 and 19th November 1983. The arrivals chart suggests a weak relationship with temperature in that the recent spring dates are earlier than in the colder 1960s. Extreme dates are:

Early

26th February to 4th March 1995	Stoke Lock
2nd April 1956	Mitcham
10th April 1956	Papercourt
13th April 1989	Ham Lands
13th April 1996	Hackhurst Downs

Late

4th October 1994	Beddington Sewage Farm
4th October 1986	Beddington Sewage Farm
6th October 2001	Beddington Sewage Farm
14th October 1991	Barn Elms Reservoirs

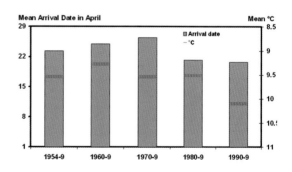

Large counts. A dawn fall brought 15 or more to Papercourt Gravel Pits on 21st August 1975.

Movements. Surrey ringing recoveries are consistent with a southeastern routing:

Ringed			Recovered				Distance
Near Staines	11th August	1979	Schiers	Switzerland	5th May	1981	886 km
Thorpe	7th August	1971	Pian de Borno	Italy	14th September	1971	994 km
*Kempton Park	17th May	1986	Safita	Syria	1st March	1987	3,466 km
Queen Mary Reservoir	15th August	1985	Chhim	Lebanon	c.5th April	1986	3,519 km
Queen Mary Gravel Pits	5th May	1979	Bir El Abd, North Sinai, Egypt		6th November	1980	3,564 km

* Possibly not in Surrey

Longevity. The longest lived of the ringing recoveries was ringed at Staines Reservoirs on 27th June 1987 and recovered over four years and ten months later, at the nearby Wraysbury Reservoir on 16th May 1992.

Whitethroat (Common Whitethroat) — *Sylvia communis*
Common summer visitor, breeding annually

Breeds in North Africa and from Europe east to Siberia, wintering in Africa south of the Sahara. Most foreign recoveries of British-ringed Whitethroats are from France and Iberia. Few Whitethroats breeding abroad seem to pass through Britain (*MA*). Common summer visitors to all parts of Britain except northern Scotland during the 19th century, they would have lost some ground to the spread of towns. The British population remained broadly stable for much of the 20th century, with the notable exception of the crash caused by the drought in the Sahel area of West Africa, believed to be its main wintering area, in the winter of 1968/69, which reduced the numbers by 77% in 1969. Numbers have fallen over the past 30 years. The *New Atlas* put the British population at 660,000 territories in 1988-91.

Island Barn Reservoir   *Photo D. M. Harris*

Early Surrey history. Whitethroats were in the Godalming district in 1849 (Newman). Hamilton (1881) noted Whitethroats from the Wimbledon Common/Putney Heath area. Aldridge (1885) found them common in Norwood. Bucknill said that they were very abundant, found even in suburbs such as Dulwich. They were common in the Staines district (Kerr, 1906).

1900 to 1968. In Richmond Park they were initially numerous (Mouritz, 1905) but less so in the 1930s. Eggs were collected at Newlands Corner, Ockham, Ripley, Send and Wisley from 1902 to 1909 (Boorman), at Woking in 1915 (Maitland and Turnbull) at Frensham in 1933 and 1936 and at Fetcham in 1935. Whitethroats bred on Tooting Bec Common up to 1928. In the Surrey part of the London area they were breeding at Dulwich Wood (*LBR* for 1949) and at Mitcham Common, Streatham Common and Wimbledon Common in the 1950s (*BLA*). With about fifteen males, they were the most abundant warbler at Richmond Park in 1951 (*BRP*).

Changes since 1968. Following the 1968-69 drought in their main wintering area, the Sahel zone of Africa, just south of the Sahara Desert, the 1969 Surrey Whitethroat population was down by 75% on Ashtead Common, 100% in Ashtead Woods, 31% on Bookham Common, 100% at Shirley Hills and 80% in the Thorpe/Chertsey/Weybridge area. At Sanderstead, where there had been 17 territories in 1968, there were only two in 1973. Whitethroats were scarce summer visitors to Shepperton in the 1980s, where breeding was not proved in 1983-86. They were much scarcer than Lesser Whitethroats at Queen Mary Reservoir in the 1980s (Geen).

There was a gradual recovery in the county as a whole but numbers fell again in 1991. Although they rose back to a peak in the late 1990s, the table shows that some heathland counts are again showing a downward trend. The Common Birds Census for 1970-2000 does not show a significant overall increase or any significant change on farmland, but there was a significant fall of about 60% in woodland and a significant rise from almost none to around 15 territories per square km in other habitats. This very mixed picture is supported by other evidence away from farms and woodland.

Where found since 1970. A singing male at the Surrey Docks in 1971 did not breed but Whitethroats bred there in 1981, 1990 and 1991 after the creation of scrub. The establishment of territories on waste ground in Bermondsey (1977 and 1998) and in Burgess Park, London SE5 (1998) is another indication of the rising Inner London Whitethroat population in the 1990s. Wills and Kettle (1997) reported a striking increase on Wimbledon Common, from six territories in 1993 to 19 in 1996, since when there has been a further increase to 36 (including Putney Heath) in 2005 (*The Birds of Wimbledon Common and*

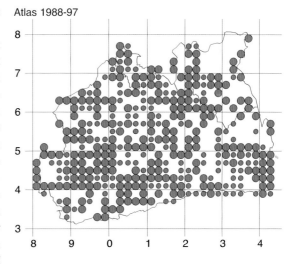

Atlas 1988-97

Putney Heath 2005). A pair bred at Beddington Sewage Farm in 1970 and the increase there following habitat changes has been even more remarkable, with 104 territories in 1996. Numbers subsequently fell to 99 territories in 1998 and to 72 in 2004.

There have been colonies along the North Downs, including 25 pairs at Headley Heath in 1973. There were 13 Spelthorne reports in the 2003 BTO Spring Migration Watch. Whitethroats are more numerous on bushy commons than on some of the heathland.

The western heaths have been thoroughly surveyed since 1994:

Territory counts on the western heaths 1994-2004

	1994	1995	1996	1997	1998	1999	2000	2001	2002	2003	2004
Chobham Common/ Sunningdale Golf Course					6	12					16
Frensham Common	1	1	2	0	0	0	2	2	1	0	2
Hankley Common			7	4	5	4	10	6	6	6	7
Hindhead Commons		5	3	4	3	5	6	4	4	2	
Olddean Common (Surrey)	4	6	10	7	4	7					12
Pirbright Common/ Ash Ranges		42		63		58	77	63			
Thursley/Ockley/ Elstead Commons	13	18	25	26	22	15	15	28	16	11	13
West End Common/ Pirbright Ranges		8		16		15		19			
Witley Common	1				1	2	2	2	7	4	10

From counts organised by John Clark. Table omits incomplete counts.

Other territory counts. At Beddington Sewage Farm there were 56 territories in 2003. There were 36 territories on Bookham Common in 2002 (92 per square km) and 11 at Broadstreet Common in 1996, more than on the much larger Hankley Common. Molesey Heath, which is now not heath but grass and scrub, held 26 territories in 2004. There were 30 singing males at South Norwood Country Park in 2002. Pirbright Commons, a much larger area than any of these, held 77 territories in 2000 and Thursley's population reached a high of 28 territories in the following year.

Population. The 1994-2004 Breeding Birds Survey grosses up to a breeding season population of about 2,000 adults. This compares quite well with the 400-500 territories being reported by observers in recent years but is probably too low. Common Birds Census suggests a population density which looks implausibly high for the county as a whole but if Surrey held a proportionate share of the UK population as given by the *New Atlas*, the population would be nearer to 5,000 pairs, or 2.5 per square km, which may be a closer estimate.

Calendar. Bucknill said that Whitethroats arrived early in the first week of April, much the same as in the 1990s. The average arrival date in the London area south of the Thames from 1929 to 1939 was 15th April. Early and late dates given by Geen for Queen Mary Reservoir are 16th April 1977 and 21st September 1974. Elsewhere, early and late dates are:

1st April 1943	Almshouse Common, Haslemere (Clark, 1984)
1st April 1956	Dunsfold
2nd April 2000	Molesey Gravel Pit
6th April 1961	Gatton
22nd October 1963	Ewhurst
17th December 2001	Island Barn Reservoir

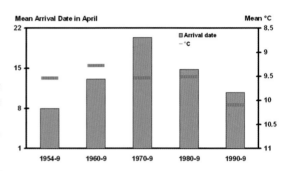

The arrivals date chart shows how those Whitethroats that returned to Surrey after the Sahel drought did so much later than usual.

Large counts of migrants include about 30 in one bush at Frensham on 19th August 1962 and 30+ in a small hedge at Papercourt Gravel Pits on 31st July 1975.

Movements and longevity. European recoveries of Surrey-ringed birds have been made in France (two), Portugal (four) and Spain (two). There are two African recoveries, both from Morocco. One was ringed at Thorpe on 27th July 1974 and recovered at Tinerhir on 20th April 1976. The other, ringed at Queen Mary Reservoir on 6th July 1995, had a longer journey and was recovered 2,288 km south at Anif on 8th August 1997. Whitethroat wintering grounds are further south. A Whitethroat ringed at West Byfleet on 26th May 1923 and recovered over six years and four months later in Portugal on 4th October 1929 remains the longest-lived on file.

Dartford Warbler   *Sylvia undata*

Locally common breeding resident

Breeds from Iberia and North Africa east to Italy and north to southern England. Dartford Warblers were first recorded in Britain by John Latham, who told Thomas Pennant of a pair shot at Bexley Heath, near Dartford in Kent on 10th April 1773 (Montagu). The bird is on the northern edge of its range in Britain and, being a resident species and a warbler, is much affected by the severity of the winters and especially by the duration of snow cover on the heaths. The *Historical Atlas* suggests that Dartford Warblers were common in southwest England in 1776 at least until the severe winter of that year. Snow features in the historical record as early as 1796, when Montagu recorded a colony at Falmouth, Cornwall which was not seen after a heavy fall of snow on 24th December and in the following year. Dartford Warblers bred from Cornwall to Kent at times during the 19th century (*Historical Atlas*). Loss of heathland has cut down the British range. Dartford Warblers were practically exterminated in Britain by the 1939/40 winter and again by the winter of 1962/63 (Fisher, 1966). There were an estimated 3,208 territories in England and Wales in 2006 (*BTO News 270*).

Early Surrey history. It seems likely that, in spite of the much greater extent of heathland in more distant times, any Dartford Warblers that there were in Surrey would have been eradicated by winters as savage as those in, for example, 1654 and 1658. They may have been lost or severely reduced in Surrey in 1776, three years after their discovery in Britain when, as mentioned, the winter was exceptionally cold and many birds of other species died. Recolonisation after an interval would be consistent with more recent observed behaviour.

The recorded history of the Dartford Warbler in Surrey begins with a note of several shot on a common near Wandsworth in the winter of 1783, where they were last seen in November 1881. The specimens were passed on to the Leverian Museum (Montagu).

19th century. Any surviving birds would probably not have got through the winter of 1813/14. There appear to be no further records until the 1830s. Blyth (1833) said that he had once or twice observed Dartford Warblers in the lavender fields at Mitcham and that a few pairs bred on Wimbledon Common. Yarrell (1845) mentioned a Dartford Warbler *shot on Wimbledon Common, where the nest and three young birds have been obtained* around 1830. He included an engraving of a nest obtained from Roehampton in May 1838 *after watching the birds for some hours each day for a fortnight*. Dartford Warblers were common around Elstead, Godalming, Hydons Ball and Munstead in the 1840s, when Newman recorded *the tops of the furze quite alive with these birds*. Meyer (1842) had seen Dartfords at Burwood Common, St George's Hill, Wimbledon and other places. A clutch was taken near Frensham in June 1860. The population must have been at a high level in the 1860s, when Phillip Crowley built up the bulk of his collection of 60 or 70 clutches from around Farnham. Dartford Warblers remained common at Wimbledon until the 1870s but came under heavy pressure from collectors. Gould, in his 1862-73 work on British birds said that *all the commons south of London, from Blackheath* [Kent, presumably] *and Wimbledon to the coast, were formerly tenanted by this little bird; but the increase in the number of collectors has, I fear, greatly thinned them in all districts near the metropolis; it is still, however, very abundant in many parts of Surrey and Hampshire* (Hudson, 1915). Hudson went on to say that Gould was shown birds and supplied with specimens, by a man named Smithers, a bird-stuffer from Churt, who was at the time collecting Dartford Warblers and their eggs, for the trade and for many private persons, on the open heath and gorse-grown country that lies between Farnham and Haslemere. He recounted a conversation with a heath-cutter on Milford Common, who told him [in about 1912] that about 35 years earlier, in the 1870s, Dartford Warblers had been very common in the area, but that, after Smithers offered a shilling for every clutch of eggs brought to him by the boys in the villages, the bird soon became rare, so much so that he had not seen one for a very long time. This is at about the time when Nightingale eggs cost a shilling for five. Dartford Warblers were on Leith Hill around 1876 (Thomas, 2001).

Localities given by other 19th century writers include Ashtead Common (seen by Bucknill), Bagshot (before 1900), Barnes Common, Chilworth (nest in the 1880s), Croydon, Epsom Common (nest about 1875, one in November 1892), near Farnham (might be Frensham, before 1854), Frensham Little Pond (1891), Hindhead, Hurtwood Common (nest in 1877), Kew Gardens (bred before 1880, *BRP* for 1949), Leith Hill (1870, 1873 and 1876), Oxted (June 1892), Reigate (nest 1890), Reigate Heath (two nests in the 1880s, extinct in 1900), Thursley Common (1892), and Walton Heath (extinct in 1900). A few birds hung on at Wimbledon Common into the 1890s.

The bird was evidently scarce again by 1900. Hudson knew that they had been common in Newman's time but had only managed to see one in Dorset (Hudson, 1921). Contemporary writers tended to blame collectors for the decline of the Dartford Warbler after the 1860s, but they said little about the weather. Temperature charts give another clue about why the population should have crashed in the late 19th century. There were two exceptionally cold January/February periods around 1880 and another, even colder, in 1896. Even the winter of 1856 was not as cold as these. We know from experience in the 20th century that the Dartford Warbler population can take many years to recover from a population crash. At the very least, these cold winters must have added considerably to the pressure from the bird-catchers and the Dartford Warblers had all but gone by the end of the 19th century.

1900-1950. A revival in the early 1900s found one near Colley Hill in 1904 and six near Hindhead on 28th August 1906. A nest was found at Churt in 1906 (Boorman). Further records were of a bird at Limpsfield and about 20 pairs around Thursley in 1908, a nest on Putney Heath in 1910 and birds on Wimbledon Common from 1910 to 1913 (Glegg, 1938). After a continued slow recovery, there were probably good numbers in 1915, to judge from a rather poignant note in the LNHS Ornithological Section report for 1917 which says that *several birds were disturbed during military manoeuvres in Surrey, on many occasions during the autumn of 1915 by the late Capt. C. S. Meares*. The winter of 1917 all but wiped out the Surrey Dartford Warblers. Bunyard did not find any at all until 22nd April 1922 and found none breeding in 1922 or 1923.

Recovery again proceeded slowly but Gosnell obtained a clutch at Frensham in 1932 and, by 1933, Venables could report 39 pairs on about 1,000 acres of west Surrey heathland (Venables, 1934). Pairs were scattered very unevenly over the site and Venables thought it could have held more, and that numbers were held back by hard winters, heath fires and egg collectors. The site was close to his home at Tilford, so it might have included Hankley Common. A fuller census of the western heaths and commons was carried out by L. S. V. Venables and Hugh Thompson in 1933 (HNHS, 1955; Raynsford, 1963). The census found 80-90 pairs but the sites surveyed are not known and might have included commons outside Surrey. Dartfords bred on Chobham Common from 1929 to 1934 (Parr). There were twelve pairs in less than a square mile of northwest Surrey in 1935. A few birds were in the Putney Heath/Wimbledon area in 1935-38 and on Epsom Common in the autumns of 1937 and 1938 and a pair bred on Wimbledon Common in 1936. At Walton Heath, eight pairs in 1938 marked a local peak. Numbers in the southwest fell back in 1936 and fell further in 1938 after fires and a cold winter. Even so, one common in southwest Surrey held ten pairs in 1938. Numbers fell again after a cold period and heavy snow in December 1938. In 1939 there were a few birds on Headley and Walton Heaths but the cold winters of the 1940s had a devastating effect on the Surrey Dartford Warbler population and no breeding records have been located for the years 1940-52.

Since 1950. A few birds were seen at one of the old sites in 1953 and by 1958 there were seven or eight pairs at one site in southwest Surrey and two others were occupied. An egg collector found Dartford Warblers at Thursley in 1960 (Cole and Trobe). The Surrey population is known to have been wiped out by the severe winter of 1960/61 even before the harsher winter of 1962/63. Most, if not all, of the damage was done by five inches of snow in January 1961 and a heavy snowfall on 13th December of the same year. Dartford Warblers did not breed in the county again until 1969, when food-carrying was observed at a locality north of the Hog's Back, probably on the Pirbright Commons. One or two pairs held on in the area and in 1974 a pair bred on Hankley Common. In 1976 the range extended to Frensham and Thursley Commons and by 1977 the population had risen to 16 or 18 pairs. The rising trend peaked at up to 51 pairs at four sites in 1981 but was halted by the severe 1981-82 winter and in 1982 there were not more than 22 pairs and these were at only two sites. Recovery was fairly rapid, with up to 75 pairs in nine areas by 1985 but was checked by a very severe February in 1986 and a severe winter in 1986-87, which brought numbers down to not more than 12 pairs in two areas in 1987. Despite this setback, there were 85 pairs at 11 sites during the early summer of 1990, but a later heath fire at the main site destroyed the habitat of about 50 pairs. Only nine pairs at three sites were reported in the following year. There was again a swift recovery to 274 territories in 1995 but a further cold winter cut numbers back to 155 territories in 1996. The reduction at the Pirbright Commons in 2000 was due to habitat destruction by a fire in the previous August. The table shows how numbers on the western heaths built up from 1994 to 2000. As with some other heathland species, these figures owe much to counts organised, and for some sites carried out, by J. M. Clark.

Territories 1994-2006

	1994	1995	1996	1997	1998	1999	2000	2001	2002	2003	2004	2005	2006
Bagshot Heath/Lightwater	6	3	4	3	7	9	7	12	9	13	12	14	17
Brentmoor Heath/Turf Hill	2	1	2	3	5	10	6	10	8	12	12	16	6
Brookwood Heath/ Pirbright Common	0	0	0	1	3	8	5	9	6	6	1	4	3
Chobham Common North	20	35	5	*10*	23	34				26	23	29	36
Chobham Common South			9		50	56				44	47	59	46
Sunningdale Golf Course					4	8				20	21	21	12
Wentworth Nature Reserve											1	3	3
Crooksbury Common	0	4	1	3	3	7	6	4	6	9	5	6	5
Frensham Common	12	18	6	6	14	21	30	31	26	32	37	41	24
Hankley Common	36	57	22	30	58	89	98	77	80	88	96	94	53
Hindhead Common North	0	1	0	0	1	3	1	3	3	3	3	5	4
Hindhead Common South	1	2	1	1	3	4	4	4	4	4	4	2	5
Horsell Common					8	13	14	15	15	17	20	17	3
Mare Hill	0	0	0	0	0	0	2	1	1	3	7	3	5
Olddean Common	0	1	0	4	4	12	11	12	10	20	8	10	11
Pirbright Common/ Ash Ranges	34	71	72	112	145	212	161	174	165	253	*169*	224	122
Sheet's Heath					1	3	2	3	2	2	2	3	3
Stanford and Cobbetthill Commons						3	6	4	2	4	5	5	4
Thursley/Ockley/ Elstead Commons	36	60	26	30	49	*42*	*27*	60	47	58	74	42	32
West End Common/ Pirbright Ranges	4	16	*5*	20	33	*24*	*41*	114	*80*	23	23	20	26
Whitmoor Common									3	7	8	2	5
Witley Common	0	1	0	0	2	5	9	4	4	9	22	20	4
Other places	3	4	2	0	1	4	13	16	16	13	8	20	11
Total counted	**154**	**274**	**155**	**223**	**414**	**567**	**443**	**553**	**487**	**666**	**609**	**653**	**458**

Italic – incomplete count

The table excludes a small number of other breeding areas east of Guildford. Heathland restoration in the Hurtwood at Winterfold enabled Dartford Warblers to colonise the area in the late 1998.

Since 2000. With the absence of really severe winters, the underlying upward trend has continued, with more than half of the territories on the military lands at Bisley and Pirbright. In 2002, after allowing for uncounted sites and those away from the western heaths, there were 595 territories in Surrey. This was 31% of an estimated UK total of 1,925 spread across nine counties (Ogilvie *et al.*, 2002). Numbers rose to a new record of 666 territories in 2003 (253 at Pirbright alone) and there were estimated to be at least 653 in 2005. Ockham Common, where Dartford Warblers had not bred since at least the 1960s, was occupied in 2006 after scrub removal by the Surrey Wildlife Trust.

There are no full censuses before the late 20th century, but we may hazard a guess at the maximum population size up to the early years of the 19th century by reference to the population high of 666 territories in 2003, at a time when heathland cover was less than ten per cent of its extent in 1800. These figures suggest that in a very good year the population may have been at least 6,000 pairs, though in a bad one it might have been zero.

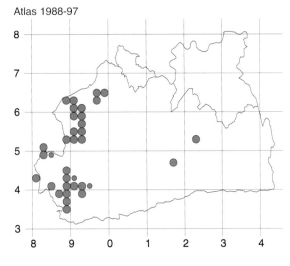

Atlas 1988-97

Movements. While most Dartford Warblers remain in their breeding areas all year round, a few move to other areas after the breeding season, enabling the recolonisation of lost breeding sites to take place. These movements tend to be somewhat random, and probably involve mainly juveniles. One on Wimbledon Common on 26th October 1935 (a good year for the species) is an example, as are others in Richmond Park from December 1937 to February 1938 and in several winters from 1999/2000, at Beddington Sewage Farm in January 2000, at Nonsuch Park on dates from November 2001 to January 2002, at South Norwood Country Park in December 2001 and at Hersham Sewage Farm/Gravel Pit in November 2005. In Spelthorne, there were single birds at Staines Reservoirs on 8th October 1978 and 18th October 1997, at Upper Halliford in November 1995 and at Staines Moor in October 2002 (*LNHSB*).

The new colonists after 20th century crashes are thought to have come from such wanderers and from residual populations further south and west in Britain, rather than from continental Europe. One killed and partly eaten by a cat at Castlenau Mansions, Barnes, on 1st November 1957 gives a longer-distance example of these movements. It had been ringed 110 km southwest, in the New Forest, as a juvenile on 1st June of the same year (*BTO News* 77). There is other evidence of movement between sites in Hampshire and Surrey. One colour-ringed at Frensham on 30th June 1985 was found at Fawley on 11th August of the same year. A male from a 1989 north Hampshire nest was found breeding at a Surrey site in April 1990 (Clark, 1993).

Longevity. The longest lived of the recovered birds had been ringed at the nest on Pirbright Commons in 1997 and was found there two years and six months later in 1999 (*Pirbright Conservation Group Report*).

Subalpine Warbler

One bird

Sylvia cantillans

Breeds in southern Europe and North Africa, moving south in winter.

Surrey. A male probably of the western race *S. c. albistriata*, was found at Lonsdale Road Reservoir on 21st April 2003 (R. J. Arnfield, J. Gordon, *BB, 97:607*) and seen by a number of other people. It remained at the site until dusk, when it flew to roost in shrubbery on the other side of Lonsdale Road and was not seen again.

Sardinian Warbler

One bird

Sylvia melanocephala

Breeds in countries around the Mediterranean. There is a partial migration to more southern parts of Africa. Records have been mostly from east coast counties and the Scillies, with most of them relating to males.

Surrey. An adult female trapped by D. J. Montier and Mary Waller while ringing at Berrylands Sewage Works on 2nd June 1992 (*BB, 86:515*), was the first found inland in Britain. It was doubly unusual in being a female. A photograph of the bird appears in the Surrey and London Bird Reports for 1992 and there is an account of the finding in Montier (1993).

Pallas's Warbler (Pallas's Leaf warbler)

Two birds

Phylloscopus proregulus

This is another autumn migrant which is associated with anticyclonic weather conditions. The breeding range runs from Siberia to China, most birds wintering further south. Vagrants are drifted west to reach Europe. From 1958 to 1985, all the British records were from late September to the end of November. The great majority were in eastern and southern coastal counties.

Surrey. The Surrey dates are typical. A male at Wandsworth Common on 29th October 1985 was found at 10.20 am. It sang and fed in a hawthorn for 15 minutes and then flew to nearby weeping willows where it could not be refound (A. Greensmith *et al.*, *BB, 79:574, LBR* for 1986:179). One visited S. Abbott's garden at Windlesham on 18th October 1989 (*BB, 84:494*). It was with Goldcrests. Surrey was the only inland county in the southeast to record Pallas's Warblers from 1958 to 1985, though there were a few inland occurrences further north.

Yellow-browed Warbler

Eight birds, none in Spelthorne.

Phylloscopus inornatus

Breeds in northern forests from Russia east across Siberia. The winter range and pattern of occurrence in Britain are similar to those of Pallas's Warbler, with the addition of a few British birds in winter and spring. Inland records are rather more frequent, in the southeast and elsewhere.

Surrey. Four of the birds have been in gardens:

1930: Sutton, one was seen and heard by F. W. Frohawk in his garden on 10th October (*BB, 24:159*).

1960: Reigate, one in a garden on 28th September (*BB, 54:193*).

1986: Reigate, another in a garden on 29th September.

1988: Wimbledon Common, one at the north end on 25th October, part of a national invasion. It was found at 10.10 am and remained until 11.20 am.

1990: Rowhill Copse, one on 6th November (*HSBBR* 1996/97), the year of a national influx.

1991: Stoneleigh. The only bird not to have been seen in the autumn was found in a garden on 17th February. It remained in the area until 2nd March and was photographed. The photographs, taken by David Eagle in whose garden the bird appeared, show a considerable similarity to Hume's Leaf Warbler *P. humei*, especially in the barely visible second wing bar, but the bird had a rather pale bill and was not considered to be Hume's by the BBRC.

1994: Stoke Water Meadows, one on 22nd October.

2006: River Blackwater at Hawley Meadows, one present from December 2006 to March 2007 (*Birding World*) spent much of its time in Hampshire. It was, however sometimes seen on the Surrey side of the border, for example on 30th December and in mid January. It was heard calling and was often seen in a patch of Dogwood and ivy-clad trees on the Surrey side (K. B. Wills *et al.*).

Wood Warbler   *Phylloscopus sibilatrix*

Locally common summer visitor, breeding annually

Breeds from Europe east to central Siberia, wintering in west and central Africa. Most foreign recoveries are on a southeast route through Italy (*MA*). There have been small range changes but overall the population seems to have been stable in Europe. In Britain, there was a small increase in numbers between the 1968-72 and 1988-91 BTO Atlases but more recently they have halved. Wood Warblers have a preference for woods with a sparse understorey, kept open by stock grazing or by a heavy leaf fall and this has probably been responsible for part of the national change in range.

Surrey. Beech woods provide the main habitat in Surrey, typically with a sparse understorey of bilberry, bramble, fern or holly. Suitable woods occur along the North Downs and the greensand hills from Limpsfield east through Dorking south and west to Haslemere. Changing woodland management has been among the reasons for falling population levels in Surrey. Breeding numbers are difficult to assess, because some singing males remain unmated and others become polygamous, singing from different areas to attract extra mates (Marchant *et al.*, 1990).

Early Surrey history. Wood Warblers were not uncommon around Tooting in the 1830s (Blyth, in Bucknill). Meyer (1842) knew them as summer visitors to St George's Hill. The Holmesdale Natural History Club Museum has a nest collected at Reigate in 1874. Hamilton (1881) listed them for the Wimbledon Common/Putney Heath area. Localities mentioned by Bucknill included Ashtead Park, Betchworth Park, Chobham, Churt, Dulwich, Ewell, Godalming, Headley, Mickleham, Red Hill (Redhill? about 1880), Richmond Park (1871), and Shirley. None of these places hold any Wood Warblers now, illustrating the early retreat from the London area. Bucknill also wrote of 'numerous other places' which he did not detail. Wood Warblers were no longer regular in Kew Gardens after 1899 (*BRP* 1949). Bucknill mentioned Churt (about 1893) and Frensham, still active well into the 20th century.

1900 to 1969. Wood Warblers bred in Dulwich Wood from 1900 to 1905 (Power) and on Wimbledon Common in 1902 (*Zool.*, 1902:313). A nest was found at South Park in 1905 (G. T. Winter). Song was heard at Brook on 21st April 1906. Eggs were collected at Oxshott in 1904 and at Woking in 1921-23 (Maitland and Turnbull). Wood Warblers were in Beulah Hill woods [Beaulieu Heights Wood], Norwood in 1930 and 1932. Beadell said there was usually a pair in Halliloo Wood, two pairs in Slynes Oak and a pair in Slynes Road. In Richmond Park, where there were a few pairs in the early 1900s (Mouritz, 1905), Collenette thought there were up to three pairs from 1925-37 and they were still breeding there in the 1950s (*BLA*). Wood Warblers were local in beech woods around the Farleigh district up to 1950 (Pounds). They were still breeding on Putney Heath and Wimbledon Common in the 1950s (*BLA*). These, too, are all lost breeding localities.

Other sites in the 1930s and 1940s include Addington Hills, Arbrook Common, Ashtead (seen),

Devil's Punch Bowl – beech glade. The deep shelter of these beeches provides a home for Redstarts, Wood Warblers, Firecrests and Spotted Flycatchers.

John Davis

Bookham Common (1946), Box Hill (1936, 1938), Carshalton (heard), Chessington (bred), Colley Hill, Combe Wood (presumably Coombe Wood, Wimbledon, bred 1936), Croham Hurst (1946), Dulwich Wood (1938), Effingham (1943), Epsom Common (1938, 1946), Esher (bred), Headley (seen), Horley (increasing 1945), Hydestile (plentiful 1945), Kingswood (five pairs 1937, eight pairs 1946), Limpsfield (bred 1934, 1936-37, 1939, present 1946, none in 1940), Old Malden (1938), Oxshott Heath (1946), Sheen (1946), Shirley/Shirley Hills (1938, 1946), Smallfield (12th May 1942, 1943), Tadworth (song), Walton Heath (1946) and Wimbledon Common. One at Staines Reservoirs on 24th April 1936 is the first record that has been located for Spelthorne.

In the 1950s, Wood Warblers were also breeding in the Hammer Pond area and at Munstead, Puttenham Heath, Tilford and Truxford (CNHS, 1959) and in the Shirley Hills (*BLA*). In the 1960s, they bred at Arbrook, Ashtead, Bookham and Oxshott commons and there were up to ten pairs on Hydon's Ball. P. G. Davis was able to ring up to 60 Wood Warblers each year around Haslemere (not all in Surrey) from 1962 to 1966 (Parr).

Since the 1960s. There has since been a further contraction of range. Wood Warblers were noted in the Surrey part of the LNHS area by Palmer (1988) and confirmed by the 1988-97 SBC Atlas survey, but the number of tetrads holding Wood Warblers in the LNHS area was only 16, compared with 35 in the 1968-72 survey. There were occasional records from Vann Lake from 1968 to 1994 (Blaker Log). During the period 1970 to 2000, Wood Warblers were present in the breeding season during at least one year at 70 places. The places, with their final year of presence, were: Abinger (1983), Addington Hills (1993), Arbrook Common (1994), Ash Green (1999), Ashhurst Roughs (1971), Ashtead Common/Woods (1997), Banstead Downs/Heath/Wood (1992), Bisley (1986), Bookham Common (1996), Box Hill (1970), Bricksbury Hill (1990), Brookwood Cemetery (1989), Chiddingfold (1973), Chipstead Valley (1974), Chobham (1978), Churt (1971), Crooksbury Common (1974), Cutt Mill (1990), Dorking (1979), East Horsley (1978), Englefield Green (1975), Epsom Common (1995), Esher (West End Common, 1994), Fairmile Common (1988), Farley Heath (1972), Frensham (1999), Grayswood (1982), Hackhurst Downs (1971), Ham Common/Lands (1992), Hambledon (1989), Hammer Ponds (1984), Hankley Common (1987), Haslemere (1999), Headley Heath (1987), Hindhead (2000), Holmbury (2000), Hydon Heath (1989), Keffolds (1982), Kingswood (1987), Leith Hill (1993), Lightwater/Bagshot (1994), Limpsfield/Chart (1998), Littleworth Common (1984), Lyne (1973), Margery (1986), Netley Heath (1975), Norbury Park (1970), Nower Wood (1983), Olddean Common (1987), Oxshott Heath (1990), Pebble Combe Hill (1970), Pirbright (1973), Ranmore (1996), Reigate Heath/Priory (1981), Richmond Park (1996), Rodborough Common (1984), Rowhill Copse (1971), Selsdon Wood (1971), South Marden (1995), Thursley/Ockley Commons (1989), Tilburstow Hill (1983), Virginia Water (1991), Walton Heath (1980), Wimbledon Common (1998), Winkworth (1973), Winterfold (2000), Wisley Common (1974), Witley Common (1993), Woldingham (1986) and Wormley (1989). Some of these birds were probably passage migrants. The only territorial birds recorded since 2000 have been at Frensham, Hindhead, Holmbury, Hurtwood and Winterfold.

Wood Warblers are occasionally seen at non-breeding sites. Examples are Barn Elms (1981),

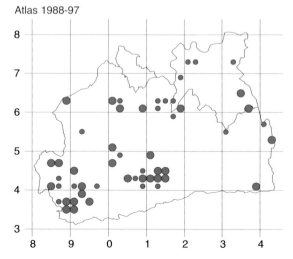

Atlas 1988-97

Barwell Court Manor (1992), Battersea Park (1980s), Betchworth (1978), Brooklands (1966), Caterham (1982), Clapham Common (1966, 1987), Croham Hurst (1977), Crystal Palace (1977), Dulwich Woods (at least four years), East Molesey (1995), Effingham (1988), Farnham (1980s), Godstone (1971), Holmethorpe (at least three years), Lambeth Reservoir (1992), Molesey Heath (1997), Morden Hall Park (1996), Putney Heath (1989), Ravensbury Park (1991), Unstead Sewage Farm, Whitmoor Common (1988). There have been a few in Battersea Park *e.g.* on 7th May 1967. One was trapped at Queen Mary Reservoir on 13th August 1977. One was singing in St Mary's churchyard, Staines on 25th April 1986 and there were single birds at Queen Mary Gravel Pits on 3rd August 1991 and 26th July 1997.

Population size. The 1984 BTO Wood Warbler survey included fairly full coverage in Surrey and was summarised by Herber (1985). A maximum of 93 singing males were mapped, including a few outside the vice-county boundary. The Surrey population was estimated at 80. Thirty-nine tetrads with suitable habitat were not covered and no results are given for most of Greater London, where very little suitable habitat exists. Only 13 10 km squares were found to hold any birds, compared with 20 in the 1968-72 BTO Atlas, the lost territories being in SU96, TQ03, TQ05, TQ24, TQ27, TQ34 and TQ36. Wood Warblers were rarely picked up in the Common Birds Census. A few were found in the Breeding Birds Survey, which offered an estimated average county population of eight adult birds from 1994 to 2004. This rather dark estimate is probably too low, but only 11 Wood Warbler territories were reported to the Surrey Bird Club in 2000 and five in 2001, compared with 20 in 1994.

Calendar. Bucknill said that Wood Warblers usually arrived at the end of April. This is a few days later than in the 1990s. Power gave an average arrival date (first song) of 12th May for 1900-09 at Dulwich. The average arrival date in the London area south of the Thames from 1929 to 1939 was 25th April. Spring passage extends well into May. Early and late dates are:

Early

8th April 1949	Beacon Hill, Hindhead (Clark, 1984)
10th April 1955	Leith Hill
10th April 1955	Upper Warlingham
10th April 1992	Capel
11th April 1976	Putney Heath
12th April 1945	Haslemere (HNHS)

Late

19th September 1978	Burgh Heath
24th September 1985	Battersea Park
25th September 1973	West Horsley
26th September 1995	Battersea Park
5th October 1947	Headley

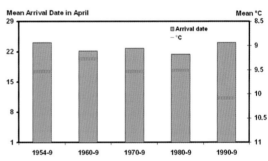

The chart shows that arrival dates have barely changed since the 1950s. A falling population size may have offset the temperature changes.

Movements and longevity. A nestling ringed at Haslemere on 6th July 1967 was recovered 1,159 km southeast at San Marcello, Italy on 29th August of the same year. Another nestling, ringed at Holly Hatch, in the New Forest on 5th June 1990, was recovered at Hindhead on 5th June 1993. A Wood Warbler trapped at Marley Common, Sussex on 9th June 1988 was recovered six km north and nearly seven years later at Hindhead on 2nd June 1995, a national as well as a Surrey longevity record.

Chiffchaff (Common Chiffchaff)   *Phylloscopus collybita*

Common summer visitor breeding annually, a few winter

Breeds from Europe east to Siberia, wintering in western Europe and West Africa east to northern India. The British range extended in the 19th century. Chiffchaffs breeding in Britain are of the race *P. c. collybita*, which also breeds elsewhere in northern Europe. They winter south to West Africa. The British winter population includes immigrants from other parts of Europe. It may include birds breeding in Britain as well, but no British-ringed nestlings have been recovered in the UK in winter to prove this (*Migration Atlas*). The *New Atlas* put the British population at 640,000 territories in 1988-91. Numbers have been stable or rising over the past 30 years.

Early Surrey history. Chiffchaffs seem to have been fairly common in Surrey for many years. They were listed by Newman for the Godalming district in 1849 and were breeding at Wimbledon Common around 1881. They were apparently rather local in the Staines area (Kerr, 1908). A consistent comment has been that they were less common than Willow Warblers and with a preference for taller trees.

1900 to 1969. Chiffchaffs were scarcer than Willow Warblers in Richmond Park (Mouritz, 1905), they bred at Tooting Graveney Common up to 1905 (*BLA*) and they were uncommon in the Dulwich area around 1910, though two or three pairs did breed (Power). Over the next 50 years, the status did not change much in the London suburbs. Chiffchaffs were present in the breeding season at Camberwell, Dulwich and Peckham in 1945 and at Wimbledon Common in the early 1950s (*BLA*). They were breeding at Kew Gardens and from 1951 at Richmond Park (*BRP*). Away from the London area, there were nine territories on Bookham Common in 1943, far fewer than those of the abundant Willow Warbler. They summered at Vann Lake in every year from 1964.

Since 1970. Chiffchaffs continued to summer at Vann Lake every year up to 1985 but were less frequent after that date (Blaker Log). A comparison of the 1968-72 LNHS and 1988-97 SBC Atlas surveys shows a small fall in the number of London area tetrads where the species was present, from 83% to 78%. The Common Birds Census, based on a small and declining sample, showed a strong and significant increase in territories from 1970 to 2000, reaching 17 per square km by the end of the period. For woodland alone, the estimated number rose from 5 to 38 per square km over the same period. Overall numbers may still be increasing.

Territory counts. On Ashtead Common there were 20 territories in 1990 and 18 territories in 2002, with a previous maximum back to 1970 of only ten. A 0.39 square km census area on Bookham Common held seven territories in 1997 but the number rose steadily to 27 in 2003 (Alan Prowse, *Surrey Bird Club Newsletter* No. 66). At Frensham, numbers have remained stable at around ten pairs since at least 1993. One or two pairs bred at Shepperton in the early 1980s but Chiffchaffs were more conspicuous as passage migrants (*Shepperton Bird Reports*). The Surrey Docks attracted occasional migrants in the 1970s and 80s. They probably bred in 1996, with two pairs in 1997 (Hewlett).

Population size. The unadjusted 1994-2004 Breeding Birds Survey grosses up to a breeding season population of 3,000-4,000 adults. The Common Birds Census grosses up to a figure which is definitely far too high. If Surrey held a proportionate share of the UK population as given by the *New Atlas*, the population would be nearer to 4,600 pairs, or just over two per square km, which feels a bit high but may be a closer estimate.

Calendar. Bucknill said that Chiffchaffs usually arrived on about the 26th March but thought a few stayed in mild winters. Power's earliest date for the Dulwich area was 23rd March. The average arrival date in the London area south of the Thames from 1929 to 1939 was 23rd March. Migrants may now be arriving earlier. Since the 1970s, the *Surrey Bird Report* has often put the arrival date at non-wintering sites in the first half of March and it was as early as 4th March in 1997. There was one at Walton-on-Thames on 1st February 1948. Autumn song is often heard. Power heard song up to 8th October, not an unusually late date for modern Surrey.

Overwintering. Chiffchaffs were known to overwinter occasionally, from as early as 1833/34 at Wimbledon. One was shot at East Molesey on 23rd December 1890. Winter records became regular from the 1960s and have come mainly from wetland sites including Beddington Sewage Farm (1959, 1963 etc), Dorking Sewage Farm (1969), Lonsdale Road Reservoirs (1955), Old Malden (1969), Ripley Sewage Farm (1970), Surbiton (1971), Thorpe (1970) and Worcester Park Sewage Farm (1968, 1971). There were nine at Unstead Sewage Farm on 29th December 2000. In Spelthorne, there was one at Perry Oaks on 27th December 1957 and three or four were there from 26th November 1960 to February 1961. There were winter records from the Shepperton area in November-December 1984 and January 1986 (*Shepperton Bird Reports*) and five were at Shepperton Gravel Pits on 13th December 1997. Winter song is occasionally heard, as at South Norwood Lake on 15th December 1954 and at Holmethorpe on 13th December 1989. Most, if not all, of the wintering birds are of thought to be of continental origin but many of them look similar to *P. c. collybita* or are not assigned to race by the observers.

Large counts of migrants include 43 at Barn Elms London Wetland Centre on 20th Sptember 2003, 50 on an allotment at Epsom, on 6th-8th August 1929, 40 at Unstead Sewage Farm on 30th August 1997 and 40 at the same place on 17th August 2000. Two hundred are said to have passed through in two hours at Silvermere on 27th March 1955, including about 30 in one party (*SBR*, H. Dickinson). No further details about this exceptional record, which is not in the *LBR*, have been located. It was included without comment by Parr. G. R. Geen ringed 838 at Queen Mary Gravel Pits in the 60 days from 22nd August to 20th October over the years 1970-86 (Geen, 1988). The Hersham Ringing Group trapped 171 there in 1989. Maximum site counts in recent years have usually been fewer than these but Chiffchaffs are still conspicuous passage migrants and they sometimes appear in Inner London. One was found at Southbank on 4th October 1983.

Movements and longevity. Three recoveries of Surrey-ringed birds have been made in Portugal and two in Spain. African recoveries have been one each from Algeria and Morocco and two from wintering grounds in Senegal. One of the Sengalese birds had been ringed at Capel on 9th September 1990 and was recovered 4,117 km south at the Parc National Oiseaux du Djoudj on 10th December 1992. The other was ringed at Buckland on 13th September 1986 and recovered 4,129 km south at Mare de Gainthe, Djoudj, Fleuve on 8th March 1989. A Chiffchaff ringed at Queen Mary Reservoir on 28th November 1998 was recovered over four years and ten months later, at Farlington, Hampshire on 26th October 2003.

Plumage variations. One trapped at Leatherhead on 24th January 1960 was a very pale individual of an undetermined northern race, 'nearer to *Phylloscopus collybita fulvescens* than to *P. collybita abietinus*'. One at Chessington on 25th May 1996 had a yellow crown and nape and lacked an eye stripe (*LBR*).

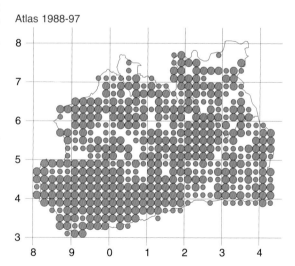

Atlas 1988-97

Scandinavian Chiffchaff

Phylloscopus collybita abietinus

Breeds in Finland and Scandinavia east to the Urals and occurs on passage in Britain (MA)

None have been proved for Surrey by having been ringed in the breeding area and trapped in

Surrey. Birds with characteristics of the race are these:

Trapped

1959:   Beddington Sewage Farm, one trapped on 3rd January and retrapped at Elmers End on 5th April. It had an almost complete body moult, 'the description suggesting *abietinus*'. (*LBR*, *BLA*).

Spelthorne: Queen Mary Reservoir, has been trapped (Geen, no dates given).

Sight records

1948:   Walton Heath, Howard Bentham saw and heard one on 25th April (*BB, 42:23-24*).

1955:   Tadworth, Howard Bentham reported one from his garden on September 9th (SBC archive, *SBR*).

1987:   Frimley Gravel Pits, birds believed to be of this race on 7th November and 2nd December.

1994:   Holmethorpe Sand Pits, one on 1st January to 6th March.
        Beddington Sewage Farm, two in early December.

1995:   Beddington Sewage Farm, single birds on 23rd March and 3rd December.

1998:   Stoke Lake, one on 21st November.
        Old Woking Sewage Farm, one on 29th November.

1999:   Old Woking Sewage Farm, one from 10th January to 17th March.
        Beddington Sewage Farm, one on 1st December.

2000:   Beddington Sewage Farm, one on 2nd January.
        Horton Country Park, one on 19th November.

Siberian Chiffchaff   *Phylloscopus collybita tristis*

Breeds in Siberia and occurs in Britain (*MA*).

Surrey. None have been proved for Surrey by having been ringed in the breeding area and trapped in Surrey. Birds reported as having characteristics of the race are these:

Trapped

1976:   Hersham Sewage Farm, one on 12th December.

1981:   Witley Common, one on 14th November (Lawn, *The birds of Witley Common*, 1981).

1982:   Witley Common, one on 27th November.

1989:   Berrylands Sewage Works, one on 5th November.

1991:   Witley Common, one on 5th December.

1995:   Beddington Sewage Farm, single birds on 3rd January and 7th February.
        Other(s) trapped and ringed there on 19th November.

1998:   Beddington Sewage Farm, one on 20th December.

Spelthorne: Queen Mary Reservoir, has been trapped (Geen, no dates given).

Others

1949:   Churt. Notes on a bird seen and heard at Churt in September 1949 and in 1950 and probably of this race are given in *British Birds* (*BB, 44:94*).

1986:   Ham Lands, one on 10th November.

1987:   Battersea Park, single birds on 26th, 29th and 30th October (*LBR*).

1989:   Berrylands Sewage Works, one on 11th November.

1990:   Battersea Park, one on 28th October.

1990:   South Norwood Country Park, one on dates from 25th November to 29th December.

1991:   South Norwood Country Park, one on 18th February.
        South Norwood Country Park, one on 11th November.

1992:   Holmethorpe Sand Pits, one from 1st January to 12th February (to 6th March *BHSP*).
        South Norwood Country Park, one on 28th February.
        Stoke Lake, Guildford, one singing on 21st -28th March (Gates, 1992).
1993:   Sydenham Hill Estate, one on 12th December.
        Chertsey Meads, one on 25th October.
1994:   Stoke Lake, one heard singing on 3rd-5th March.
1995:   Stoke Lake, one on 18th-26th March.
        Frimley Gravel Pits, one singing on 2nd April.
        South Norwood Country Park, two on 16th-18th November.
1996:   Walton Reservoirs, one singing from 19th March to 8th April.
1997:   Beddington Sewage Farm, one on 2nd-10th April.
1998:   Stoke Lake, one on 16th March.
        Unstead Sewage Farm, one on 24th and 27th November.
        Beddington Sewage Farm, one on 20th December.
1999:   Unstead Sewage Farm, one on 1st-16th January.
        Stoke Lake, one on 9th-13th March.
        Walton Reservoirs, one on 21st March.
        Beddington Sewage Farm, one on 27th November.
2001:   Walton Reservoir, one singing on 16th April.
        Barn Elms, one from 25th November to 6th December.
2002:   Stoke Lake, single birds on 16th January and 23rd March.
2003:   Beddington Sewage Farm, one on 21st December.

The chart suggests November and March passage.

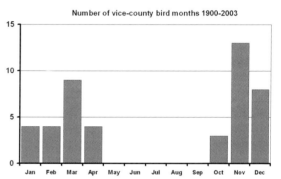

Number of vice-county bird months 1900-2003

Willow Warbler   *Phylloscopus trochilus*

Common summer visitor, breeding annually

Breeds across northern Europe and Asia and winters in Africa from south of the Sahara to the Cape. The nominate race *P. t. trochilus* breeds in western Europe north to southern Sweden and east to Poland and Romania. No British-ringed nestlings (*P. t. trochilus*) have been recovered in the UK in winter (*MA*). In Britain as elsewhere, the early stages of reafforestation have provided habitat improvement. The British population seems to have been stable from at least 1800 up to the 1970s but has since fallen by around 60% (*BTO News 269*). The *New Atlas* put the British population at 2,300,000 territories in 1988-91 but it is now lower. Deer browsing and reduced woodland management may have caused a deterioration in habitat (Fuller *et al.*, 2005).

Early Surrey history. Newman listed Willow Warblers for the Godalming district in 1849. Hamilton (1881) listed them for the Wimbledon Common/Putney Heath area. Sites near London at the end of the 19th century included Battersea and Richmond Park (Bucknill). They also bred in Dulwich Wood and on Mitcham and Tooting Commons (Power, 1910) and appear to have been common in rural Surrey.

Since 1900. Eggs were collected at Send from 1903 to 1920, at Woking in 1915 and at Frensham in the 1930s. In the Staines area, Willow Warblers were in every copse in spring (Kerr, 1906). Willow

Warblers remained common through most of the 20th century, assisted by the growth of birch scrub on Surrey commons. Places where they have been mentioned as being numerous include Banstead and Epsom (1934), Chobham Common (28 territories in 1982), Frensham Common (39 territories in 2000), Headley Heath (71 singing in 1985), Netley Heath (31 singing on 31st May 1970) and Westend Common/Bisley Ranges (63 pairs in 2001). In Spelthorne, Willow Warblers bred at Queen Mary Reservoir in the 1970s and 80s and at Shepperton in the 1980s with two or three pairs at the Littleton Lane lakes (*Shepp. BRs*). Willow Warblers were much scarcer than Chiffchaffs in Spelthorne in the 2003 BTO Spring Migration Watch.

Population Trends. Willow Warblers summered at Vann Lake every year from 1964 to 1990 but were recorded less frequently after that date (Blaker Log). There has been a substantial fall in numbers since the 1980s at some sites. A comparison of the 1968-72 LNHS and 1988-97 SBC Atlas surveys for the 231 tetrads of northeast Surrey shows a noticeable fall in the number of tetrads where the species was present, from 83% to 70%. The Common Birds Census showed an overall drop from 20 territories per square km in 1971 to 11 in 2000. For woodland alone the drop was from 57 to 28 per square km. These figures are close to the national trend.

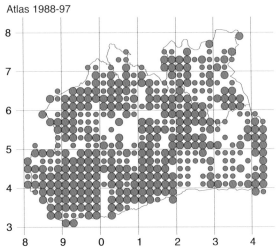
Atlas 1988-97

Breeding behaviour. A nest with seven young was found at Brooklands in 1972. One with four young was found in heather about a foot above ground at Slyfield Green in 1972. Notes about bigamous behaviour have appeared in *British Birds* (*BB, 71:503, 72:130, 76:413*). Song by a female, resembling first attempts of young birds in late summer, was given in response to tape in 1981. Song is sometimes heard in October.

Population Size. The 1994-2004 Breeding Birds Survey suggests a minimum breeding season population of 1,000-2,000 adults, lowest at the end of the period. If Surrey had held a proportionate share of the UK population as given by the *New Atlas* in 1988-91, the population would have been nearer to 17,000 territories, or eight per square km, before the recent national crash, which has been reflected in Surrey.

Other territory counts. There were 14 territories on Arbrook Common in 1964, only two in 2000 and none in 2004. At Ashtead Common there were 30 in 1990 but only 15 in 2002. On Bookham Common, which had 36 territories in 0.39 square km census area as late as 1997, the population fell to five territories in 2002 and six in 2003, a reverse of the Chiffchaff trend at the same site (Alan Prowse, *Surrey Bird Club Newsletter* No.66). Numbers held up at Frensham Common, where there were 40 to 46 territories from 1995 to 2001, 42 in 2004 and 40 in 2005. The Surrey Docks attracted migrants in 1975-77, June 1987, June 1988 and April-June 1989. There were five to ten pairs in 1990, three to five pairs bred in 1991, two territories in 1997, one in 1998 and 1999. There were 63 singing males at West End Common/Pirbright Ranges in 2001. At Wimbledon and Putney Heath, where there had been 119 pairs in 1982 (Wills and Kettle, 1997), numbers had collapsed to eight by 2005.

Calendar. Bucknill said that Willow Warblers usually arrived in the first week of April. This is about ten days later than in the 1990s. Power (1910) gave an average date for first song of 16th April (earliest 7th April) for the Dulwich district. The average arrival date in the London area south of the Thames from 1929 to 1939 was 30th March. The arrival chart shows that more recent arrival dates show no significant response to changing temperatures.

Early and late dates are:

Early

19th February 1967	New Haw, seen and heard
3rd March 1965	Earlswood Sewage Farm
4th March 1982	Papercourt Gravel Pits
15th March 1981	Frensham

Late

29th October 1977	Witley Common
30th October 1988	Ham Lands
11th November 1931	Sutton (F. W. Frohawk)
24th November 1940	Staines Moor

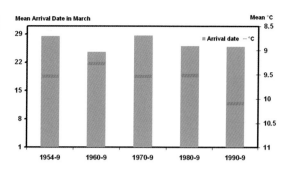

Large counts of migrants include 70+ at Bethlem Hospital, Croydon, on 16th April 1970 after an overnight fall and about 40 at Netley Heath on 10th April 1974, also after a fall.

Movements and longevity. Recoveries in continental Europe have come from France (three), Portugal (three) and Spain (three). The furthest travelled was one ringed at Barn Elms London Wetland Centre on 16th September 2003 and recovered three weeks later and 1,631 km south, at Setubal, Baixo Alentejo, Portugal on 6th October. A Willow Warbler colour-ringed at Witley Common on 24th April 1976 was seen there again over six years and two months later, on 28th June 1982, showing a good age and site fidelity.

Northern Willow Warbler   *Phylloscopus trochilus acredula*
One bird

Breeds in Norway, northern Sweden and elsewhere east of the range of *P. t. trochilus*, intergrading with other races further east.

One with characteristics of the race was trapped at Capel on 22nd August 1993 by W. Attridge.

Goldcrest   *Regulus regulus*
Common breeding resident

Has a scattered breeding distribution from northern Europe to Japan and south to central Asia. Resident over much of its range, but the more northern populations migrate, creating an autumn influx into the British Isles and other parts of western Europe. Those breeding in Britain are mostly sedentary. None have been found to winter abroad. Many winter immigrants come from Scandinavia and the near Continent. An increase in the British Isles was first noticed in the 1870s and continued through much of the 20th century. The main factor seems to have been the spread of conifer plantations. The *New Atlas* put the British population at 560,000 territories in 1988-91. Goldcrests use a widespread and unprotected habitat (Bird Study 226:4, 9). Goldcrests are vulnerable to hard winters but numbers recover quickly.

Early Surrey history. Goldcrests were listed as resident in the *Letters of Rusticus* (Newman, 1849). Hamilton (1881) listed them for the Wimbledon Common/Putney Heath area. Bucknill described them as somewhat rare as breeding birds in the Metropolitan area but widespread in rural localities. He said they were frequently seen in winter and cited winter records from Dulwich, Wandsworth and Wimbledon. In the Staines area, Goldcrests were found in winter and early spring but were not known to breed (Kerr, 1906).

1900 to 1970. Power (1910) said that Goldcrests were not uncommon in large gardens at Clapham Park and Balham, before they were built over, but he had only seen three in the Dulwich area in the previous ten years. There was one at Tadworth on 21st October 1923. Eggs were collected at Woking in 1928 and at Hindhead in 1932. Goldcrests were mainly winter visitors to Richmond Park, not known to breed, up to the 1930s. *Birds of the Royal Parks* contains no definite breeding records for Richmond Park up to 1970 (or indeed to 1977). Beadell (1932) mentioned nests around Warlingham. Goldcrests bred at Limpsfield in 1934. At Kew Gardens they bred in 1938 but were not regular until the 1950s. They were only winter visitors to Bookham Common in the 1940s. In the Farleigh district, they remained uncommon as breeding birds up to 1950. As late as 1959 they were said to be commoner in winter than in the breeding season in southwest Surrey (CNHS). The London and Surrey bird reports were still detailing breeding records into the late 1960s but Goldcrests were clearly becoming more common. The *LBR* for 1969 mentions 26 Surrey breeding season localities. Goldcrests suffered badly in the hard winters of 1916/17 and 1962/63 (Parr).

Since 1970. The Winter Atlas found partial survey counts and estimates totalling 450 birds in 1981-84, more than the number of Wrens and Dunnocks. There was no change in the number of tetrads holding Goldcrests in the Surrey part of the London Area between the 1968-72 and 1988-97 Surrey Atlases. Common Birds Census numbers showed a significant overall reduction from 1970 to 2000 but with a wide margin of error. In the 1988-97 SBC Atlas survey, Goldcrests were found in 393 (68%) of the Surrey tetrads. Goldcrests bred at Battersea Park in 1985 (*SBR*) and between 1988 and 1993 (Hewlett). At Vann Lake, there were Goldcrests in every month from 1965 to 1995 (Blaker Log). There have been many reports of breeding in gardens since 1970.

Breeding behaviour. Nest sites include one in bracken and bramble three feet above ground in a deciduous wood 400 yards from conifers (1971) and in honeysuckle (Frensham 1973).

Population Size. Goldcrest numbers found in the new Breeding Birds Survey rank between Chiffchaff and Willow Warbler in frequency. The survey suggests a breeding season population of at least 2,700 adults and probably far more, given that this is a small and inconspicuous bird. The implied Common Birds Census estimate was, not surprisingly for such a small bird, almost twice as high. If Surrey held a proportionate share of the UK population as given by the *New Atlas*, the population would be nearer to 4,000 pairs, or two per square km, which may be a good estimate.

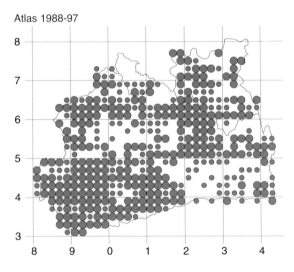

Atlas 1988-97

Territory counts. J. A. Little estimated that there were about 50 pairs on Hankley Common in 2002. There were 11 territories in 1.16 square km of farmland at Moor Park in 1980 (*HSBBR*). *Spelthorne*: breeding information is thin. There was one territory at Queen Mary Gravel Pits in 1991. Goldcrests were regular in winter in the Shepperton area but there were no summer territories in 1983, 1984, 1986 and 1992. One pair bred there in 1985 and in 2003 Goldcrests were present in the breeding season up to at least 16th June.

Large counts. Autumn migration to Britain is reflected in the relatively high counts obtained in October and November. Counts of up to 30 are often recorded. Some of the larger ones are:

near Albury: 80, 20th October 1981

Barn Elms: 50, 17th November 2002

Blackheath: 120, 12th November 1975

Capel area: 85, November 1992

Chessington and Oxshott: 50+, 21st November 1968

Esher and Oxshott: 30+, 22nd November 1975

Frensham: *c.*55, 12th December 1981; 100, 18th September 1995; 76, 29th September 1997

Headley Heath: 40+, 26th November 1968

Thursley: *c.*50, 24th January 1981

Vann Lake: 60+, 8th February 1991

Witley Common: 50+, 13th February 1982 (43 in one flock)

Spelthorne: At Queen Mary Gravel Pits there were 40 on 22nd and 30th October 1983 and other dates. There were 150 bird days at the pits in autumn 1985, only six in autumn 1986 but 25 on 7th November 1987 and 45 on 3rd November 1990.

Movements and longevity. There are two foreign ringing recoveries. A Goldcrest ringed in Belgium on 4th November 1994 and recovered nine days later in Staines is very likely to have hatched abroad. The other, a Goldcrest ringed at Ewhurst on 23rd October 1982 and recovered in Belgium on 23rd January 1983, is of less obvious origin. A Goldcrest ringed at Haslemere on 4th November 1976 and recovered 513 km northwest on the Copeland Islands, County Down on 18th April 1977 made the longest journey on record. A Goldcrest ringed at Virginia Water on 4th April 1976 was recovered there over three years later, on 16th April 1979 and is the longest-lived for which details are held.

Firecrest *Regulus ignicapilla*

Scarce breeder, passage migrant and winter visitor

Breeds in southern and central Europe, wintering within the breeding range. Northern birds, including at least some from southern England, are migratory. The breeding range in Europe has extended north and west since the 1920s. There were no definite British breeding records before 1962, when fledged young were found in the New Forest, Hampshire. Since then there has been a widespread colonisation of southern England. The *Migration Atlas* gives evidence of the arrival of Continental birds from early September. Birds from further north and east winter in or pass through southern Britain. No Firecrests ringed as young in Britain and no adults ringed in Britain in June or July have been recovered anywhere.

Early Surrey history. Little information is available about Firecrests in Surrey before 1900. Gurney (1889) said that they had been obtained in all southern counties but did not specifically mention Surrey. Bucknill knew of no definite records. Kerr (1906) knew of none for the Staines district.

1900 to 1959. There were at least 25 reports of migrants from 1905 to 1959. One was 'obtained' on Wimbledon Common on 31st December 1905 (Parr). Howard Bentham reported one at Tadworth on 21st October 1923 (*BB, 17:165*) and there was one at Caterham on 5th January 1926 (Pounds). There was another on Wimbledon Common on 28th March of that year and one at Farleigh in early 1927. One was at Thursley on 6th February 1934, an unusual date for southwest Surrey. In March 1935, there was one at Selsdon Wood (Pounds) and another was displaying in a Surrey garden on 13th April 1935 (*BB*, *29:27-28*). There were single birds at Mickleham on 15th February 1941 and on Epsom Common on 25th December 1941 and on 5th December 1942. One fed in hawthorn bushes at Titsey on 13th October 1946. Wimbledon Common held one in 1950 (*BLA*) and there was another in March 1955. There was one at Chipstead on 14th January 1951. Two were on Thursley Common on 24th October 1954. Three at Beddington Sewage Farm in November 1956 made for an unusual multiple sighting. In the same year there were others at Dulwich, Richmond Park and Selsdon, where there was also one in 1958. There were two with about 40 Goldcrests at Selsdon on 30th March 1958 and one was with Goldcrests at Weybridge on 14th November 1959.

Since the 1950s. In the 1960s there were about 15 records of migrants. Places included Addington (1969), Barnes (1968), Beddington Sewage Farm (1961), Chessington (1969), Ewell (1969), Ewhurst (1961, 1969), Godalming (1966), Haslemere (December 1960), Westhumble (February 1968), and Wimbledon Common (1968). Firecrests have been seen much more often in the past 35 years.

Breeding. An increasing number of Firecrests are now found in the breeding season. These are thought to be summer visitors, not overwintering birds. Proof of breeding was first obtained in 1983, when at least 11 and possibly 16 singing males were located in the Haslemere/Hindhead area. At least five were paired and pairs bred successfully at three sites (Kirkpatrick, 1983). A male and at least two young were seen near a nest at Haslemere on 30th July 1983. The Haslemere area has been well monitored by P. A. Hollow (née Kirkpatrick) over many years and she has provided some very helpful notes. The local breeding birds tend to arrive with the Chiffchaffs in March. Birds, usually probable family parties, remain around the local breeding sites from July to early September but can be elusive and are then more easily located by call. This may account for the very small number of July or August records from other parts Surrey. There was an upsurge of breeding season records from the later 1980s but very few were reported from 1990 to 1993. Typically, Firecrests breed south of the M25. Large, mature gardens and mixed woodland with a holly and ivy understorey are favoured by breeding and territorial birds, which are most easily located by their song. Firecrests have been found at various places along the North Downs and on the Greensand woods to the south of them, including Brook, Grayswood, Hindhead, Hurtwood, Netley Heath, Sanderstead, Shere, South Norwood, Wimbledon Common, Winterfold and Wormley.

Song seasons. Song may be heard as early as March and even in January (Croham Hurst 1987).As with Chiffchaffs, there is a short period of song in early September, after which the breeding birds are thought to leave.

Migrants since 1970. Birds thought to be non-breeding migrants have been seen since 1970 at Addington, Ash Ranges, Bagshot, Barn Elms, Beddington, Camberley, Cannizaro Park, Carshalton, Croydon, Burgh Heath, East Horsley, Epsom, Ewell, Fairoaks, Farnham, Fetcham, Frensham, Friday Street, Frimley, Godstone, Ham Lands, Haslemere, Holmbury Hill, Hydestile, Hydon's Ball, Kew Gardens, Kingston, Leith Hill, Limpsfield Chart, Merton, New Malden, Ockley Common, Richmond Park, South Norwood, Stoke Lake, Thorpe, Thursley, West Ewell, Wimbledon Common, Winkworth, Witley Common and Witley Park. Firecrests have been seen in Spelthorne but they have not definitely bred there. Reports include

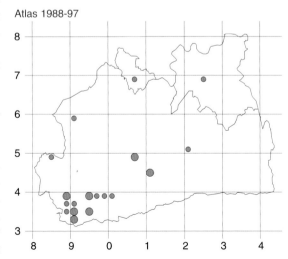

Atlas 1988-97

Queen Mary Gravel Pits: females on 12th May and 2nd June 1979 (*LBR* for 1980), three on 20th November 1982, one on 3rd November 1984, one in November and December 1985, one on 3rd December 1988, one on 8th December 1990, one on 13th April 1991; *Queen Mary Reservoir*: one on 28th December 1970, one in October-November 1972, one on 21st June 1975; *Staines Moor*: one on 15th December 1984; *Stanwell Moor*: one on 17th November 1997, one on 18th March 1999, also one on 25th March 2005 (*LNHSB*) and *Sunbury*: one on 27th January 1971.

Movements. The pattern of records since 1970 suggests a strong spring passage and arrival peaking in April and continuing into May. A weaker return passage, possibly of immigrants from northern Europe, may begin as early as August (South Norwood Lake, 28th August 1999) and it peaks in November.

A few Firecrests winter, many of them north of the A25/A31. We do not know the winter quarters of birds seen in the breeding season. They may go abroad, or to north Surrey or other parts of Britain. Nor do we know where the wintering birds have come from. The only ringing recovery located, of a first-year bird ringed in the Netherlands on 27th September 1990 and recovered 72 days later at Queen Mary Reservoir, 266 km away, on 8th December suggests a continental origin, at least for some. This is similar to the national position.

Calendar. The table illustrates the spring and autumn passage and the wintering birds.

Bird months 1970-2001 (excludes birds holding territory)

	Jan	Feb	Mar	Apr	May	Jun	Jul	Aug	Sep	Oct	Nov	Dec	Total
Vice-county	36	36	47	55	14	0	0	3	22	42	59	39	**353**

Large counts. Beaulieu Heights Wood has been an especially favoured locality, with up to six in November 1996 and other winter counts of three to five in the 1990s. The 1996 counts coincided with a national influx.

Spotted Flycatcher *Muscicapa striata*
Moderately common summer visitor, breeding annually

Breeds in Europe and North Africa east to Siberia and winters in Africa from south of the Sahara to the Cape. Most ringing recoveries are from France or Spain in August and September. Some continental birds pass through Britain (*MA*). Little change in the British or European range from 1800 to the late 20th century is on record but, in Britain at least, density is thinner. British numbers have fallen by 86% since 1967 (M. Raven, *Bird Watching July 2007*). Problems in the winter range and, in the UK, deer browsing and less woodland management, have been suggested as contributing to the decline (Fuller *et al.*, 2005). BTO research shows that a decrease in the first-year survival rates, perhaps due to food supply problems, could provide part of the explanation.

Early Surrey history. Gilbert White wrote of 'flycatchers' with young in South Lambeth on 20th June 1786, not a great distance from Archbishop's Park, Lambeth, where a pair of Spotted Flycatchers bred over 200 years later in 1992. Spotted Flycatchers had been seen in the Godalming area by 1849 (Newman). They were breeding at Norwood (Aldridge) and Wimbledon (Hamilton) around 1881. Bucknill described them as common summer visitors, breeding near Dulwich and at Richmond Park and similar places but they were declining in the Brixton/Dulwich area by 1910 (Power).

1900 to 1970s. Breeding was evidently widespread up to 1970. Boorman collected eggs at Clandon (1902), Cobham (1903), Ockham (1907, 1909, 1912) and Ripley (1904). Spotted Flycatchers were common in the Staines district, nesting in willows (Kerr, 1906). Gosnell obtained a clutch of eggs at Churt in May 1932. Spotted Flycatchers bred at Sutton in 1934 and were well distributed around Farleigh. Four or five pairs were thought to have bred at Richmond Park in 1938. Pairs were seen annually on Bookham Common in the 1940s, with fourteen nests in 1943. Fledged young were seen in the garden of Lambeth Palace in 1950. There was regular breeding at Ham House, Kew Gardens and Richmond Park from 1951 to at least 1976 (*BRP*).

The declining trend. An apparent decline was reported as early as 1965, though the number of reported breeding sites rose back to 21 in 1968 and rose further in later years. In 1970, there were four pairs in Kew Gardens ('a reduction of previous years') and five in Morden Hall Park (*Surrey Bird Reports*). There were many reports of Spotted Flycatchers becoming scarcer in the 1970s. Of the 231 tetrads in northeast Surrey, 75% were found to hold territories in the 1968-72 Surrey Atlas survey but only 46% in the 1988-97 Surrey Atlas. The fall continued through the 1990s, illustrated by the number of pairs reported in the LNHS part of Surrey, excluding Inner London, which dropped from 11 in 1987 to an average of three in 1996-98. At Vann Lake, Spotted Flycatchers summered every year from 1964 to 1989,

then in 1992 only (Blaker Log). The Surrey Bird Club received reports from 62 sites (including those in the LNHS area) in 1985 but only 28 in 2000. Only one Spotted Flycatcher territory has been found in Surrey Common Birds Censuses since 1982. In Spelthorne, Spotted Flycatchers were recorded at Queen Mary Gravel Pits in 1983, which was 'a poor year' at the site.

Selected territory counts and breeding since 1980. Inner London breeding sites include Burgess Park, where a juvenile was seen on 4th June 1988. In Spelthorne, adults were feeding young at Shepperton Studios and Laleham Park in 1985. Barwell Court Farm (Chessington), Baynards, Blindley Heath, Bookham Common, Capel, Chobham, Churt,

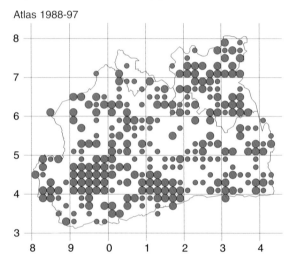

Atlas 1988-97

Enton, Hydestile, Morden Hall Park, Richmond Park, Royal Common, Thursley, Titsey, Unstead Sewage Farm, Wandsworth Common and Winterfold are among the places where territorial birds have been reported after 2000. They were breeding in Richmond Park up to 2004 (*The Birds of Richmond Park 1995-2004*). At Frensham Ponds, the number of pairs fell from seven to three from 1996 to 2001 but rose back to six from 2003 to 2005.

Breeding behaviour. A pair bred under the eaves of a house at Ash Vale for the eighth year running in 1974. A pair raised two broods in a coconut shell at Thorpe in 1974 and it was used again in 1976. Eggs laid in a coconut shell at Wormley in 1983 were deserted when a Cuckoo also laid eggs in it. Spotted Flycatchers sometimes nest very late. Recently fledged young were seen at Godstone on 29th August 1920, (Bentham, *BB*, *14:132*). Eggs were hatched at Purley on 1st September 1973 but the outcome was not known. A recently dead fledgling was found at Milford on 4th October 1960.

Population size. The 1988-97 SBC Atlas survey found Spotted Flycatchers in 282 tetrads (49% of the total). The 1994-2004 Breeding Birds Survey suggests a breeding season population of around 200 adults but the margin of error is probably large. The number of sites reported as having Spotted Flycatchers in the breeding season from 1996 to 2001 averaged only 18 but this is from casual records only. If Surrey held a proportionate share of the British population as given by the *New Atlas*, the population would be nearer to 900 territories, or 0.4 per square km. It is unlikely that there are as many as this now, but it provides an upper bound.

Calendar. Spotted Flycatchers arrived in the middle or third week of May in the Norwood district in the 1880s, (Aldridge). The average arrival date in the London area south of the Thames from 1929 to

1939 was 6th May. The chart shows that average arrival dates were earlier than this from the 1960s to the 1990s. There has been no obvious connection between arrival dates and temperature, perhaps because of the sharply declining trend.

More recent extreme dates are:

Early

10th April 1970	Frensham Great Pond
11th April 1988	Kew Gardens
19th April 1964	Wandsworth/Clapham Commons
20th April 1968	Godstone
20th April 1982	Kew Gardens

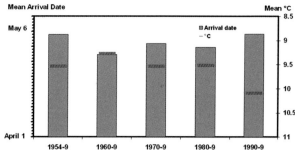

Late

8th October 1992	Beddington Sewage Farm	13th October 1985	Barn Elms Reservoirs
8th October 1995	Thursley Common	30th October 1988	Beddington Sewage Farm
10th October 1984	Barn Elms Reservoirs		

Earliest and latest dates at Queen Mary Reservoir up to 1988 were 11th May 1974 and 25th September 1976 (Geen).

Large counts. In earlier days, quite large numbers were seen on passage, including a party of 35 at Tadworth in September 1944 (*LBR*) and 53 in an hour at Tattenham Corner, Epsom Downs on 28th August 1956. A count of 37 in Farnham Park on 29th August 1987 was an exceptional number for more recent years.

Movements and longevity. A Spotted Flycatcher ringed at Kingswood on 18th June 1947 was recovered about 1,400 km southwest at Provenca-a-Nova, Portugal in October 1949. It might have travelled the furthest, the only rival being one ringed at Kempton Park on 12th August 1967 and recovered in Spain, 1,694 km southwest, on 23rd October 1967 but this one might not have been in Surrey. There are four other recoveries from Portugal and Spain. One ringed at Addington on 27th August 1961 and recovered at Wembley on 9th May 1964, over two years and eight months later had the greatest known longevity.

Plumage variations. Pure white birds were found near Balham in 1878 and at Reigate before 1900 (Bucknill).

Red-breasted Flycatcher   *Ficedula parva*
Seven birds

Breeds from Scandinavia east to Siberia and winters from India to southeast Asia. Like Yellow-browed Warblers, they are mainly autumn migrants to Britain, typically arriving on the east and south coasts in September or October. Records from inland counties are unusual, and included only Buckinghamshire (spring) and Nottinghamshire and Surrey (autumn) from 1958 to 1985.

Surrey. Two of the Surrey records are in November, perhaps reflecting the time it takes for coastal migrants to disperse inland:

1954:	Ockham, one on 10th June.
1954:	Eashing, a female on 25th May, notes in the *SBR*.
1955:	Beddington Sewage Farm, one on dates from 31st August to 16th September, notes in the *LBR*.
1958:	Banstead, Derek McCulloch (*Uncle Mac* for those with long broadcasting memories) watched one in his garden for 20 minutes on 18th August.
1973:	The Chantries, Guildford, one on 20th May.
1989:	Kew Gardens, one in a conifer on 5th November, watched for five to ten minutes.
1998:	Beaulieu Heights Wood, a first-winter bird on 5th-7th November, photograph in the *SBR*.

Pied Flycatcher
Ficedula hypoleuca

Scarce passage migrant, bred before 1900

Breeds from Britain, Spain and North Africa through northern Europe to central Siberia and winters in West Africa. Most foreign recoveries of British-ringed birds are from France, Spain or North Africa. Autumn migrants from Scandinavia and eastern Europe pass through Britain (*MA*). Pied Flycatchers might have been common in British woodlands 4,500 years ago (Thomas, 1999, no evidence given). They were rare in Britain during the first half of the 19th century. The population subsequently increased in Britain and some other parts of Europe but British numbers have recently declined in some areas.

Early Surrey history. Graves mentioned a nest from which seven young were fledged at Peckham in 1812. The same tree, which was on the edge of a pond, held the nests of a Spotted Flycatcher and a Wryneck. Blyth, in 1834, said he possessed two nests taken near Tooting, each of which held three eggs (Bucknill). There have been no further Surrey breeding reports. There are six other records in Bucknill. A Pied Flycatcher was shot near Godalming in about 1822 (Kidd, 1837 in Bucknill). The Charterhouse Collection contains two, of uncertain origin. One of them might be the bird that was shot in Witley Park in the middle of May, 1836 and seen by Bucknill at Charterhouse. Single birds were seen at Richmond Park on 29th May 1889, at Enton Pond on 29th April 1891 and near Virginia Water (in or out of Surrey?) on 10th May of the same year. There was one at Wimbledon many years before 1895.

Trend since 1900. Few were seen until the 1940s. From then until 1970 numbers averaged about three a year. Numbers rose further, to a total of 72 in the 1970s, 95 in the 1980s and 94 in the 1990s.

Calendar. Parr reported that about a third of the records up to 1970 were in April-May and two-thirds in August-September. The table shows that this balance has been broadly maintained in subsequent years.

Bird months 1970-2001

	Jan	Feb	Mar	Apr	May	Jun	Jul	Aug	Sep	Oct	Nov	Dec	Total
Vice-county	0	0	0	67	25	0	2	109	71	2	0	1	**277**
Spelthorne	0	0	0	0	1	0	0	3	2	0	0	0	**6**

Spring migrants occasionally linger. In 1948 a male sang in Windsor Great Park daily from 9th May to 13th June. A pair apparently held territory in Dulwich Wood in 1961. The male was seen on 11th April and was joined by a female the following day. The male was last seen on 9th June but the female was present until at least 15th July. There was no evidence of breeding. An autumn migrant in Dulwich Park stayed for 13 days, from 2nd-14th September 1993. Early and late dates are:

Early		Late	
1st April 1994	Frensham	4th October 1951	South Norwood
5th April 1995	Bletchingley	7th October 1999	Beddington Sewage Farm
6th April 1999	Croham Hurst	4th November 1956	Dulwich Wood
7th April 1990	Mickleham	6th December 1970	Barn Elms

Large counts. There were five birds in the vice-county on 27th August 1954 – at Addington, Richmond Park, South Norwood, and two at Barn Elms. Mitcham Common held four on 15th August 1983.

Movements and longevity. Two ringing recoveries have been located. A nestling ringed at Dipton, Northumberland on 6th June 1988 was found freshly dead at Chaldon on 20th August 1988, 425 km south. A nestling ringed in the Netherlands on 9th June 2000 was found dead at Dulwich, 466 km west, on 3rd August of the same year.

Plumage variations. There was an albinistic bird at Merrow in 1945.

Detailed records since 1900. *1900 to 1969*. Pied Flycatchers were at Bramley on 14th April 1906 (*Zool., 1906*) but there were no more, apparently, until one was found at Purley on 6th May 1922. Later birds up to 1970 were at Addington (1954, 1959-60), Addiscombe (1961), Banstead (1948, 1950-51, 1962), Barn Elms (1951-54, 1956, 1965), Barnes (Ranelagh Park, 1955), Battersea Park (1949, 1958, 1966), Beddington Sewage Farm (1931, 1952, 1954-58, 1966), Carshalton (1955), Caterham (1966), Cheam (1955), Chessington (1960), Churt (1957), Clapham Common (1949, 1962, 1964, 1966), Croham Hurst (1969), Crystal Palace Park (1958), Curley Hill (21st August 1966, Camberley Natural History Society), Dulwich (1952, 1955-56, 1959, 1964, 1969), Earlsfield (1963), East Molesey (1963-64, 1967), Epsom (1948, 1956, 1958, 1965), Esher Common (1967), Ewell (1967), Ewhurst (1963), Farnham (1964), Forest Hill (1956), Frensham (1952, 1957 and 1969), Godalming (1962), Godstone (1967-68), Green Street (1959), Ham (1950, 1952, 1955), Hersham Sewage Farm (1958), Island Barn Reservoir (1958), Kew Gardens (1953, 1961, 1965), Leatherhead (1953), Littleworth Common (22nd April 1947), Lonsdale Road Reservoir (1950), Lower Kingswood (1955), Milford (1968), Mitcham Common (19th June 1939, 1954), Morden (1956), Norbury Park (1970), Palewell Common (1969), Peckham (1951), Petersham Park (1927), Putney Heath (1969), Pyrford (1954), Ranmore (1961), Richmond Park (1927, 1929, 1934, 1935, 1940, 1951, 1954-56, 1959, 1961, 1968), Sanderstead (1956, 1960), Sheen Common (1954), Shirley (1953, 1955), South Croydon (1967), South Norwood (1943, 1951, 1954, 1958), Streatham Common (1950, 1958), Tadworth (1943-44, 1964), Tattenham Corner (1956), Thursley (1934), Tooting Bec Common (1966), Tulse Hill (1955), Wandsworth Common (1964), Wimbledon Common/Woods (1926, 1934, 1938, 1943, 1961), and Woodmansterne (1950). One at Staines Moor on 24th August 1952 is the earliest record that has been located for Spelthorne. There was one at Stanwell in September 1956.

1970 to 2000, Pied Flycatchers have been seen at Addlestone (1986, 1997), Arbrook Common (1985), Badshot Lea (1988), Banstead (1973-4). Barn Elms (1970, 1974, 1983, 1990, 1992, 1998), Barnes (1992, 1997), the Basingstoke Canal (1984), Battersea Park (1985-91, 1995, 1997), Beddington Sewage Farm (1971, 1973, 1979, 1982, 1988, 1992-93, 1995, 1997-98), Belair Park (1977), Berrylands (1984-85, 1995), Bletchingley (1984, 1995), Bricksbury Hill (1991), Burgh Heath (1983), Camberley (2000), Chessington (1970), Chiddingfold (1986), Chipstead (1977), Chobham (1984), Clandon Park (1978), Clapham Common (1987), Claygate (1983), Cleygate Common (1972), Cranleigh (1977), Croham Hurst (1999), Croydon (1971, 1973, 1995), Crystal Palace (1995), Dulwich (1971, 1977, 1991-94, 1999-2000), East Sheen (1977), Effingham (1974, 1985), Elstead Common (1976), Epsom (1974, 1978, 1980), Ewell (1991), Farnham (1983, 1987, 1990, 2000), Forked Pond (1977), Frensham (1976, 1978, 1989, 1991, 1994), Gatton Park (1976), Guildford (1974, 1976, 1989, 1992, 1996), Ham (1970, 1983, 1986, 1990), Headley (1982-83, 1986, 1988), Horley (1989), Holmethorpe (1983, 1993, 1995), Horton Country Park (1991), Kew Gardens (1975 (*BRP*), 1983-84), Lambeth Palace Gardens (1984), Limpsfield (1987, 1996-98), Lonsdale Road Reservoir (1985, 1996, 1998), Margery (1991), Merstham (1986), Mickleham (1990), Milford (1985), Mitcham (1983, 1985), Molesey Heath (1996), Moorhouse (2000), Morden (1996, 1998-2000), New Malden (1976, 1981), Norbury Park (1970), Nork Park (1991), Old Coulsdon (1976), Park Downs (1989), Peckham (1994), 'Perrotts Wood' (Perrotts Farm? 1977), Polesden Lacey (1996), Pyrford (1977), Reigate/Redhill (1973, 1975-77, 1987), Richmond (1972, 1974-76, 1983, 1985, 1989, 1995), Riddlesdown (1996), Rowhills Copse (1988), Seale (1985), Seears Park (1983), Shalford (1983), Shirley Heath (1977), South Norwood (1995), Stoke D'Abernon (1986), Streatham (1976), Surbiton (1972-73, 1975-77, 1980), Tadworth (1976, 1978, 1984), Thorpe (1992), Thursley (1978, 1983, 1990, 1995), Tilhill (1985-86), Unstead Sewage Farm (1996, 1998-99), Vachery (1990), Walton Heath (1982, 1984), West End Common (1984), Wimbledon (1989, 1992, 1994), Wimbledon Common/Putney Heath (1973, 1978, 1984, 1988, 1991, 1999, 2001), Winkworth (1986), Wisley (1970, 1979,1985), Witley Common (1979), Woking (1973, 1985), Woodmansterne (1985, 1988), Worplesdon (1973) and Wrecclesham (1983, 1998). *Spelthorne*: Available records since 1970 are from Queen Mary (28th August and 23rd September 1976, 15th August 1984, 4th May 1985 and 4th August 1987), Staines Moor (2nd September 1994) and Staines Reservoir (one on 23rd September 1976).

Records since 2000 have come from Addington Hills, Beddington (2003), Farthing Down (*Bird Watching*), Guildford (2001), Hankley Common (2001), Hindhead (2001, 2003), Hurst Green, Kingswood, Lonsdale Road Reservoir (2003), Oxted (2002), Pyrford, Thursley, Wandle Road Nature Reserve (2002), Weybridge (2003), Wimbledon Common (2001) and Winterfold (2001). These were in April, August or September. In Spelthorne, there were two at Staines Reservoirs on 21st September 2005 (*LNHSB*).

Bearded Tit   *Panurus biarmicus*
Scarce winter visitor, bred before 1900

The main stronghold lies in Asia, but there are scattered colonies across Europe to southeast England. Bearded Tits are dispersive rather than migratory over most of their European range. In the 18th century there was far more suitable habitat across Britain, and they may have had an extensive distribution. Land drainage and the clearing of river banks had driven the British range back to East Anglia by the last quarter of the 20th century. Numbers are currently fairly stable.

Early Surrey history. Bearded Tits were breeding in Surrey, along the Thames at least, two hundred years ago. Meyer wrote that in 1800 they bred all the way up the Thames Valley from the Essex Marshes to Oxford. Possibly they bred at unrecorded sites elsewhere, though reedbeds along the Mole and the Wey may never have been extensive enough to support them. Specific 19th century references are interesting but tantalising. Graves (1811-21) said he had killed one by the Surrey Canal at Sydenham Common. Long shot a pair at Cutt Mill Pond on 24th October 1825, a typical date for winter arrivals. Blyth (1837) recorded one that he thought might have been an escape. Newman (1849) mentions two or three at Catshall (Catteshall, Godalming) and a pair at Ockford Pond, presumably the Godalming area ponds mentioned by Yarrell. Waring Kidd obtained a specimen from Elstead. There were five at Milford on 16th August 1894 (Bucknill, 1902). One in the Charterhouse Collection was from Godalming (*SALEC*), but it is not now held there.

1900 to 1959. There were several 'probable' and hearsay reports of Bearded Tits in reedbeds along the Wey between Guildford and Pyrford from 1936 to 1946 (*SEBR* for 1946). The only certain and dated bird was one seen on 6th June 1946 at a range of six feet at Tannery House, Send.

Calendar since 1960. The rest of the reports began after irruptions from East Anglia in the early 1960s. The table shows that by far the largest number have been in October, with smaller numbers until April and occasional birds in June.

Bird months 1960-2004

	Jan	Feb	Mar	Apr	May	Jun	Jul	Aug	Sep	Oct	Nov	Dec	Total
Vice-county	10	10	7	14	0	2	0	0	0	84	38	19	**184**
Spelthorne	1	1	0	0	0	0	0	0	0	8	1	1	**12**

Where found from 1960:

1960:* Perry Oaks Sewage Farm, a male from 26th November to at least 19th February 1961 (*BB*, *54:189, to 20th in LBR*) was part of an irruption from East Anglia that brought the first records to the London area.

1964: Frensham Little Pond, two on 25th October.

1965: Lower Pen Pond, Richmond Park, one on 6th November.

1970: Frensham Little Pond, one on 18th October.

1971:* Perry Oaks Sewage Farm, seven on 17th October and one on the 20th.

1971: Beddington Sewage Farm, three males and a female on 23rd-24th October.
Frensham Great Pond, one on 26th October.

1972: Beddington Sewage Farm, two on 15th October.
Holmethorpe Sand Pits, 11 on 15th October.
Frensham Little Pond, one on 1st November, six later in the month (6th or 12th).
Hedgecourt, four on 4th and one on 30th November, two on 7th December.
Richmond Park, five on 11th November.
Broadwater, a male and a female on 9th December.

1973:* 'Staines Gravel Pit', eight on 3rd January.

1973: Frensham Great Pond, two on 11th November.
Frensham Little Pond, four on 24th November and 9th December. Up to six, including three males, were there on 16th-17th December and five on 26th and 29th December. Five on 4th January 1974. Others, including at least four males and two females, were seen there until 23rd March 1974.
Unstead Sewage Farm, a female trapped on 2nd December.

1974: Unstead Sewage Farm, a male and a female trapped on 17th February.
Pen Ponds, Richmond Park, ten on 6th April, nine on 7th April and four on 13th April.
Beddington Sewage Farm, six on 14th October.
Frensham Little Pond, two on 23rd December (Clark, 1984).

1975: Pen Ponds, Richmond Park, nine on 19th October.

1979: Frensham Little Pond, two on 9th February and 8th April.
Beddington Sewage Farm, two on 21st October.

1982: Beddington Sewage Farm, two on 16th October.
Frensham Little Pond, a male, a female and a juvenile on 14th-16th November.

1985:* Queen Mary Gravel Pits, one on 17th October.

1985: Frensham Little Pond, one or two on 3rd November, a male on 17th November.
Frimley Gravel Pits, a male on 7th December.

1986: Buckland Sand Pits, six flew over on 11th October.

1987: Frensham Great Pond, two on 21st October.
Frimley Gravel Pits, one on 28th October.

1988: Frensham Little Pond, a male on 14th February.

1991: Frensham Ponds, a male and a female from 18th March to 10th April.

1992: Frensham Little Pond, two on 23rd June.
Beddington Sewage Farm, eight on 17th October.

Frensham Great Pond, a male on 9th November moved to the Little Pond around 20th November and remained to 15th March 1993.

1993:   Beddington Sewage Farm, two males from 26th October to 11th November.
        South Norwood Country Park, up to six from 1st November to 11th January 1994, apparently in the Kent half of the park. Two stayed until 9th March.

1994:   South Norwood Country Park, a male from 16th November to 19th January 1995.

1995:   Banstead Heath, nine flew northwest on 28th October.

1996:   South Norwood Country Park, two on 24th October.
        Frensham Little Pond, five on 26th-28th October.
        Walton Reservoirs, two on 24th October, one on 17th December.

1997:   Frensham Little Pond, a pair from 24th January to 6th March.

1998:   Stoke Lake, three males and four females on 7th October.

1999:   Stoke Lake, a female on 26th October.

2003:   Beddington Sewage farm, one on 18th October and 9th November.

2004:   Frensham Great Pond, at least one heard on 16th October.

*Spelthorne

Movements and longevity. Six recoveries, all showing movements within the southeast, have been located and are shown in the table.

Ringed				Recovered			Distance
Kent		13th July	1985	Queen Mary Reservoir	17th October	1985	82 km
Sussex	Young	25th May	1996	Lambeth Reservoir	17th December	1996	
Stoke, Guildford	Adult	7th October	1998	Icklesham, Sussex	18th October	1998	94 km*
Sussex	Young	25th May	1996	Walton Reservoirs	17th December	1996	

*three birds

Long-tailed Tit   *Aegithalos caudatus*
Common breeding resident

Breeds across Europe and Asia. Resident and dispersive over most of its range. Some Norwegian birds move south in winter. The race breeding in Britain and Ireland is *A. c. rosaceus*. These birds tend to move west after the breeding season. None has been recovered abroad. A few immigrants reach Britain, mainly after population explosions in the Netherlands (*MA*). No marked population trends were on record until the 1970s, but numbers have since increased substantially, perhaps because of fewer hard winters.

Early Surrey history. Newman saw a party searching an elm for insects in a sandy lane leading to Eashing on 14th February 1835. Long-tailed Tits were uncommon in the late 19th century, mainly found in country districts. Eggs were collected at Gatwick in 1897. Long-tailed Tits were quite common at Wimbledon. In other parts of the London area they were more numerous in autumn and winter, as attested by Aldridge, who also said they had been scarce in the Norwood District in the 1880s.

Breeding since 1900. Eggs collected by Boorman at Bramley (Selhurst Common, 1902), Ripley (1907) and Send (1909) are in the Haslemere Museum. Long-tailed Tits were increasing but not numerous in the Staines area (Kerr, 1906). Mouritz (1905) saw family parties in Richmond Park, especially in winter. Power (1910) wrote of them as appearing in gardens of the Dulwich area during October and November with occasional local spring and summer records. Eggs were collected at Chobham and Woking in the 1920s. Long-tailed Tits were still mainly occasional visitors to Richmond Park in the 1930s and did not breed there regularly until the 1950s and not at Kew Gardens until the 1960s. Long-tailed Tits bred at Vann Lake in 1966 and were present throughout the year for the next 30 years (Blaker

Log). They are occasionally seen in the Surrey part of central London, *e.g.* five over Archbishop's Park, Lambeth in 1965. A pair bred at Battersea Park in 1985, apparently the first for the Surrey part of Inner London and they bred there again in 1986. At least one pair bred at the Surrey Docks in 1997. There were three territories in 1998 and two in 1999. At Bookham Common there were 20 territories in 1997, five in 1998, and seven in 2002. Morden Hall Park held ten pairs in 1998. Wimbledon Common had 23 pairs in 1983, 27 in 1984, 26 in 1985, 33 in 1986, 50 in 1997 and 41 in 2000. An average of 28 vice-county breeding sites was reported annually from 1994 to 2001, not many for such a common bird, but enough to show that its gregarious and confiding habits have a more than usual charm. In Spelthorne, four or five pairs bred at Queen Mary Reservoir in the 1980s (Geen).

Breeding behaviour. Examples of early nest building have come from Haslemere (19th February 1943 in Parr), Wimbledon Common (nest-building on 20th February 1983), Crastock (started on 22nd February 1971, not quite finished on 4th April) and Epsom Common (young in the nest on 25th March 1980). Sites include bamboo (Hambledon, 1981) and 55 feet above ground in a birch (Box Hill, 1971). Some of the larger birds whose feathers have been used are Mallard, Mute Swan, Tawny Owl (Frensham 1974).

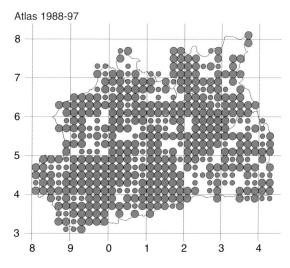

Atlas 1988-97

Trend since 1970. Of the 231 tetrads in northeast Surrey, 60% were found to hold territories in the 1968-72 Atlas survey and 78% in the 1988-97 Atlas, a substantial increase. The Common Birds Census shows a very significant increase, perhaps by a factor of seven, from 1970 to 2000. This is from a small sample and not very accurate but in the same direction as the national results. Milder winters are likely to have contributed to any growth.

Population size. Long-tailed Tits are badly affected by hard winters and numbers crashed after the winters of 1916/17, 1946/47 and 1962/63 (Parr). The Winter Atlas found partial survey counts and estimates totalling 596 birds in 1981-84, almost as many as the number of Great Tits. The Common Bird Census implies a county population of around 15,000 territories for the end of the period, but with an over-representation of woodland it looks too high. It is much higher than the average of around 3,000 adults implied by the Breeding Birds Survey. If Surrey held a proportionate share of the British population as given by the *New Atlas*, the population would be nearer to 1,500 territories, or 0.74 per square km, consistent with the Breeding Birds Survey but probably on the low side for recent years.

Large counts

Alderstead Common: *c.*200 in severe weather, 8th February 1939

Beaulieu Heights Wood: 70, 20th September 1998

Blackheath: 160+, 9th September 1975

Frensham Common: 110, 3rd March 1973

Freshfields, Croydon: 70, 6th July 1998

Holmethorpe Sand Pits: 75, 28th September 1993

Queen Mary Reservoir: a roost of 100+, November 1975

Queen Mary Gravel Pits: 50, 26th October 1985

Ranmore Common: *c.*60, 15th February 1971

Richmond Park: seventeen, 27th January 1935

South Norwood Lake: 70, 28th March 1999

Southwark: one, 28th October 1979

Thursley: 60, 11th August 1991

Walton South (Queen Elizabeth II) Reservoir: 50 northwest, 26th November 1960

In spite of the growth in numbers, the largest single counts in recent years are 60 at Morden Hall Park in December 2001 and about 70 by the Hogsmill in October 2003, not as large as the biggest counts of the past.

Movements and longevity. Most movements are local but a bird ringed at Purse Candle, Dorset on 8th February 1975 was recovered 160 km northeast at Banstead on 20th December 1975. A Long-tailed Tit ringed at Merrow on 28th December 1986 and found dead in Guildford over seven years and two months later, on 26th March 1994 is the greatest longevity located. Surrey Bird Reports since 1977 have included a longevity of eight years. This relates to a bird ringed at Queen Mary Reservoir by the Hersham Ringing Group (per Richard Denyer) but no further details have been traced.

Northern Long-tailed Tit · Aegithalos caudatus caudatus

No certain records

Breeds in northern Europe from Scandinavia east to Russia. Has been found in Britain. Two other races, from Siberia and Japan, also have white heads. The three together form the *caudatus* group.

Surrey. J. H. Gurney told Bucknill of a white-headed bird of this race that was shot near Reigate in 1896. The record is not included in *The Handbook* or in the BOU's 1971 list. A white-headed bird paired with a normal bird was seen by H. E. Pounds at Chelsham in April 1954. The Editors of British Birds thought that this was probably a pale-headed bird of the British race *A. c. rosaceus* (*BB*, 48:92).

Blue Tit · Cyanistes caeruleus (Parus caeruleus)

Abundant breeding resident

Resident in Europe, except the far north, and in North Africa and the Middle East, with irruptive movements from the centre and north of its range. The race breeding in the British Isles, where numbers have increased since 1970, is *P. c. obscurus*. The continental race *P. c. caeruleus* sometimes reaches Britain in autumn, notably in 1957.

Early Surrey history. References to this common breeding bird are rather sparse for the earlier years. Blue Tits were listed for the Godalming district by Newman and they were thought to breed commonly in the vice-county from 1875 to 1900 by the authors of the *Historical Atlas*. Blue Tits were widely distributed on Wimbledon Common in the 1880s (Hamilton) and eggs were collected at Charterhouse in 1894 (Maitland and Turnbull).

Since 1900. Blue Tits were numerous around Staines at the beginning of the 20th century (Kerr, 1906). Power (1910) said that they were numerous in Dulwich Wood, moving into gardens in the winter and that they had bred at least twice in gardens in Brixton. Boorman collected eggs at Clandon Common, Horsley and Send between 1902 and 1909. Other eggs were collected at Woking in 1915. There are long runs of breeding records at Kew Gardens and Richmond Park from the 1940s to 1976 (*BRP*). Blue Tits have been breeding in Battersea Park since at least the 1950s (*BLA*). They bred in 1966 and 1967 and 25 pairs raised 100 young there in 1989. Blue Tits were the third commonest species in 19 Common Birds Census areas in the 1960s, sometimes over one pair per two acres (Parr). The Winter Atlas found partial survey counts and estimates totalling 1,595 birds in 1981-84, making them the commonest of the tits.

Trend since 1970. The Common Birds Census shows a 260% trend increase from 1970 to 2000, peaking at an average of 66 territories per square km. This may look high but there has definitely been a growth in range. Of the 231 tetrads in northeast Surrey, 97% were found to hold territories in the 1968-

72 Atlas survey and 97% in the 1988-97 Surrey Atlas.

Population size. The county population implied by the grossed-up Common Birds Census is about 130,000 territories and compares with an estimate of 30,000 adults derived from grossing up the Breeding Birds Census figures. It is probably too high. If Surrey held a proportionate share of the UK population as given by the *New Atlas*, the population would be nearer to 24,000 territories, or twelve per square km, which provides another reference point, but there is much uncertainty about the number in Surrey.

Territory counts. Recent territory counts include 29 at Ashtead Common in 2002, ten at Beddington Sewage Farm in 2001 falling to eight in 2003, 20 at Cannon Hill Common in 2001 and 15 at Morden Hall Park in 2001. About 30 pairs bred at Queen Mary Gravel Pits in 1990. At least six pairs bred in nest boxes along the River Ash in 1984 and at least three pairs bred at the Littleton Lakes in 1986.

Atlas 1988-97

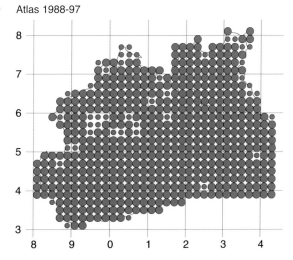

Large counts

Banstead Wood: 90, January 2002

Barnes Common: 132, January 2000

Blackheath: Up to 250, 9th September 1975 (see Coal Tit)

Earlswood: 600 were ringed in a garden in 1965

Epsom Downs: 80+, January 2001

Farnham Park: 100, December 1998

Frensham area: 200, 3rd August 1980

Frensham Great Pond: *c.*150, 10th August 1981; 150-200 juveniles, 20th June 1982; 175, 9th August 1987

Frensham Little Pond: 60+, January 2003

Hankley Common: A tight flock of at least 150 in heather and a small Scots Pine, 7th December 1980

Oxshott: 200, 30th November 1963 (Parr)

South Croydon: 80, June 2002

Streatham: Over 150 caught during four ringing sessions at a bird table in the first two months of 1986

Streatham Common: 120, early 1988

Witley Common: *c.*150+ together, 13th August 1977

Over 115,000 Blue Tits have been ringed in Surrey, more than of any other species and 16% of the total of all of them.

Food and Behaviour. Blue Tits are frequent visitors to nut and fat feeders in gardens. They were attacking cardboard milk bottle tops in Worcester Park in about 1932. An analysis of the 1957 irruption by Cramp (1960) for the London area mentioned its association with an increase in the opening of milk bottles and attacks on putty and paper by Blue Tits in Surrey. Up to 30 Blue Tits fed on hop waste at Tilhill Nurseries in late 1977.

Movements and longevity. At least seven Blue Tits have been recovered over 100 km from where they were ringed. One ringed at Leigh on 12th September 1955 and recovered 189 km north, in Cambridgeshire on 28th March 1990 had moved the furthest inland. There is one overseas recovery, see Continental Blue Tit below. A Blue Tit ringed at Mitcham Common on 16th June 1985 and recovered over ten years later at Rose Green, Sussex on 12th July 1995 was by far the oldest to be recovered.

Plumage variations. Orange-tinted birds at West Humble in the 1960s were thought to have been coloured by something in their diet (Parr). There was a yellow Blue Tit at Bookham Common in 1972. An almost completely yellow (flavistic) Blue Tit was seen at Weybridge from August to April 1969, after which it moulted to almost pure white (CO). Another similar bird visited a garden at Caterham from late June to September 1999 (Peter A. Hammersley). It was seen again in December, by which time the head, wings and tail had moulted to a white plumage, indicating that lack of blue pigment was the cause of the abnormal colouration. Photographs are in *British Birds* (*BB, 95:195*) and in the *Surrey Bird Report* for 1999. A white Blue Tit with blue centre to the crown was trapped at Weybridge in August 1969. An albino was reported from Bookham in 1976. One on which all normally yellow parts were pearly grey was recorded at Virginia Water in 1970.

Birds with bill deformities are occasionally seen, as at Fetcham in 1978 (25 mm upper mandible). One with a down-curved upper mandible three times the length of the normal lower mandible fed at a Guildford nut-feeder in January 1992 (photo in *SBR*, for more on this type of deformity see *BB, 84: 511-12*).

Continental Blue Tit   *Cyanistes caeruleus caeruleus* (*Parus caeruleus caeruleus*)
Blue Tits of a larger, brighter-plumaged migratory race have been seen at east coast observatories but remarkably few movements to or from Britain have been confirmed by ringing (MA).

Surrey. A Blue Tit that had been ringed at Windlesham on 24th November 1996 was recovered 292 km east, at St Laurens, Belgium, on 12th March 1997. The dates are consistent with this bird having been an immigrant of the race *C. c. caeruleus*, but no confirmatory notes are on file. Birds showing characteristics of the continental race have been trapped at West Humble (23rd August 1969) and Weybridge (26th December 1969).

Great Tit   *Parus major*
Common breeding resident
Resident from Europe east to Japan and south to India and southeast Asia. The Great Tits breeding in Britain and Ireland are of the race *P. m. newtoni*. They normally move only short distances. Continental birds of the race *P. m. major* sometimes make large irruptive movements and have reached Britain, as in the autumns of 1957 and 1959. Remains dating back half a million years have been found in Essex (Harrison, 1988). The *Historical Atlas* says that in the 19th century Great Tits were as numerous as the Blue Tit in deciduous woods. The British range has been extending in the north and west for many years and numbers increased nationally by around 50% in the last 30 years of the 20th century.

Early Surrey history. Great Tits were listed for the Godalming District by Newman. They were less common than Blue Tits in the Norwood District (Aldridge) and widely distributed on Wimbledon Common (Hamilton) in the 1880s. They were fairly common near London in orchards and market gardens at Barnes, Putney and similar places (Bucknill) but not as numerous, over the county as a whole at least, as Blue Tits. Kerr (1906) said they were resident, visiting gardens in winter, in the Staines area.

Breeding since 1900. Great Tits were common breeding birds throughout the 20th century. Boorman collected eggs at Send from 1902-1910. In 1910, Great Tits were as common as Blue Tits in Dulwich Woods, moving into gardens after the breeding season (Power). They were the seventh commonest Common Birds Census species in 1960s with, for example, 11-19 pairs in 40 acres of Bookham Woodland (Parr, Griffin 1970). Great Tits bred at Battersea Park and Lambeth Palace in 1967. In Spelthorne, at least four pairs bred at the Littleton Lakes in 1986 and counts of up to 19 were made in the 2003 BTO Spring Migration Watch.

Trend and population size. The Common Birds Census shows a 130% increase from 1970 to 2000. Of the 231 tetrads in northeast Surrey, 93% were found to hold territories in the 1968-72 Atlas survey and 94% in the 1988-97 Atlas, a small extension of range.

Population size. The Common Birds Census implies a county total of about 80,000 territories, but may not be representative because of the dwindling sample size. It compares with 14,000 adults derived from the Breeding Birds Survey. If Surrey held a proportionate share of the British population as given by the *New Atlas*, the population would be nearer to 12,000 territories, or six per square km.

Territory counts at individual sites in recent years have been broadly stable. They include 19 at Ashtead Common in 2001, 19 at Beddington Sewage Farm in 2001 rising to 23 in 2004, 30 at Bookham Common in 2002 (77 per square km), ten at Cannon Hill Common in 2001, 30+ at Hankley Common in 2002 and 25 at Morden Hall Park in 2001. There were 16 territories at the Surrey Docks in 1999.

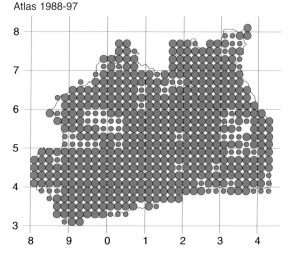

Atlas 1988-97

Blue Tit/Great Tit comparisons. A comparison with counts for Blue Tits at Ashtead, Beddington, Cannon Hill and Morden Hall in 2001 showed the two species to be about equally common in aggregate, as Power found for Dulwich at the beginning of the century. In the 1980s, Great Tits were commoner than the Blue Tits in the Shepperton area (*Shepp. BR*) but only about half as numerous as Blue Tits at Queen Mary (Geen). The Winter Atlas found partial survey counts and estimates totalling 746 birds in 1981-84, one for every two Blue Tits. In the Breeding Birds Survey for 1996-2004, Blue Tits outnumbered Great Tits by over two to one, which is a good current estimate. Over 49,000 Great Tits have been ringed in Surrey, the third commonest of all species to be ringed.

Breeding behaviour. A pair nested in a large drum partially filled with sand at Ashtead in 1970. The nest was 18 inches in diameter. A nest containing 12 eggs was found in a beehive in 1979. An adult helped two Blue Tits to feed their young at Ashtead in 1991. Breeding success varies greatly. Two pairs raised a total of 16 young at Old Compton Lane, Farnham in 1995, but at the same site in 1996, two nest box pairs fledged only four young from 25 eggs laid.

Large counts include about 50 at Cranleigh on 19th January 1964 (Parr) and 200 at Fairoak Lane, Oxshott on 30th November 1963. The largest counts in recent years have been 50 at Banstead Wood in January 2002, 52 at Barnes Common in January 2000, 55 at Epsom Downs in January 2001 and 50 at Wimbledon Common in July 2002.

Movements and longevity. An early ringing recovery, of a bird ringed as a nestling at Limpsfield on 19th June 1910 and recovered there on 29th October of the same year set a pattern for these typically resident birds. Great Tits ringed at Kempton Park in September 1969 (recovered there on 21st May 1977) and on 7th November 1971 (recovered at Hampton on 13th January 1979) might not have been in Surrey. There is one overseas recovery, probably of the continental race, see below. The greatest inland distance was covered by a Great Tit ringed at Egham on 22nd January 1994 and recovered 287 km northeast at Beccles, Suffolk on 19th May 1997. The oldest definitely Surrey bird seems to be one ringed at Virginia Water on 26th November 1966 and recovered there over six years and two months later, on 21st January 1973.

Plumage variations. Melanistic Great Tits have been recorded rather often in Surrey. The incidence has been local, but more frequent than in other counties. There is an early reference in a note by Bryan L. Sage, which tells of 'a bird with the entire head and neck black in the area of Oxshott, Surrey from 24th December 1945 to 1957' (*BB, 52:131*). Donald Parr and Christopher M. Perrins saw a Great Tit with black cheeks and the remainder of the plumage grey-black with the underparts nearly all black, fading to greyish on the flanks, at Hersham Sewage Farm in the winter of 1955-56. This, from subsequent records, appears to be the juvenile plumage. The bird was last seen holding territory in April. On 26th May 1957, in the same place, a normally-coloured female was seen with a brood of nine young, of which eight were similar to the 1956 bird (*BB, 52:131*). One of the young was photographed and the picture

Juvenile　　　　　　　　*Photo J. J. Wheatley*

appears in Sage (1962). Melanistic birds were reported from Ashtead, Esher, Hersham Sewage Farm, Long Ditton, Oxshott, Surbiton and Woking during the period 1954-59.

Since that date there have been many other reports from the same restricted part of Surrey and a few elsewhere, including one at Ashtead from February to April 1962, Esher (December 1965) and one at Worcester Park Sewage Farm on 20th December 1964. Others were at Addlestone (1979, paired with a normal female), Ashtead (1968, 1972), Chertsey (1978-81, a melanistic male bred with a normally-coloured female, raising at least two black-headed young in 1980), Chobham (1993 one seen to feed an identical young bird in summer), Claygate (1970), Epsom (16th December 1977 to 3rd February 1978, 20th December 1978, 1991), Ewell (1973, 1981), Hinchley Wood (1972), Leatherhead (1968), Lightwater (1999), New Haw (1989), Nonsuch Park (1975), Ottershaw (1975), Pyrford (1998), Ravensbury Park (1983), West Byfleet (1974, 1975), Weybridge (1970), Windlesham (1995), Woking (1988-92, 1994, two sites in 1998). These appear to be adult birds.

The adult birds always have black cheeks and reduced white in the wings and tail. Under-parts are often yellow with a very heavy black stripe. The 1977 Epsom bird was seen in January. It had the entire head, breast and belly black and lacked blue in the body and wing plumage, possibly a first winter bird with a delayed moult. No other definite juveniles were reported until 2001, when two almost uniformly greenish black juveniles, one still with a yellowish gape, appeared in the Chobham garden of Mrs B. Wallace. One of them was seen and photographed by J. J. Wheatley on 12th July and was of the melanistic form seen at Hersham, being almost completely greenish black. As the season progressed, they were seen to moult into black-headed adults of the usual melanistic type. The markings became more pronounced and by 28th August they had completely black heads and grey-green underparts with a black stripe. Young melanistic birds were seen there again in 2002 and 2003. In 2003, a melanistic adult was seen feeding a normal juvenile on 27th May and this or another melanistic bird was seen feeding two juveniles of a uniformly greenish colour in June. There are a few other recent records.

John Sage has provided a useful illustrated summary of the history of the melanistic birds up to the early 1990s (Sage, 1993). A comparison of his findings with more recent developments is made in the map. It shows that there has been a shift westwards in the distribution of melanism, which remains restricted to a small part of Surrey.

Adult　　　　　　　　*Photo J. Gates*

James (1996) says of Sussex only that 'such birds have been regularly recorded across the county'. Clark and Eyre (1993) make no reference to melanism in Hampshire. Swash (1996) mentions a leucistic bird in Berkshire and implies that melanism may occur there. In view of the apparently local nature of the occurrences, a national enquiry was launched by the Surrey Bird Club in 2001. A picture of a melanistic bird, with a request for information about local records, was sent to all 91 listed British Recorders. Among the 73 replies received, there were only four reporting melanistic birds. The birds reported were one on Anglesey from October 1988 to December 1991, one in Cumbria in 1983, one in Merseyside and Wirral in 1997 and several in Sussex. Thanks are due to all those helping with this enquiry. More recently there have been reports from Berkshire and it seems possible that the form has occurred on other dates and in other counties.

Atlas 1988-97

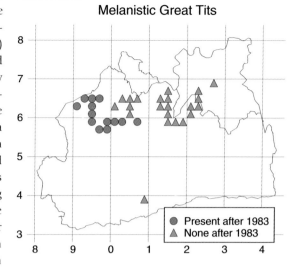

Melanistic Great Tits

Present after 1983
None after 1983

Three xanthic (yellow) birds were seen at Hurst Green in 1999.

Continental Great Tit   *Parus major major*

Surrey. An adult ringed at Esher on 22nd October 1959 and recovered 632 km east in the East Frisian Islands on 9th April 1960 remains the only Surrey ringing recovery to involve another country and followed a national irruption in 1959. The bird was presumably of the continental race *P. m. major*, though this was not in the published information. The *Migration Atlas* shows several similar movements of British-ringed Great Tits up to the 1970s but not later.

Crested Tit   *Lophophanes cristatus* (*Parus cristatus*)

Three birds, last in 1945

Breeds from Spain north to Norway and across Europe to Russia, but in Britain a separate race, *P. s. scoticus*, is confined to central Scotland. Sedentary, but disperses after mild winters and possibly increasing. May have arrived with the pine trees after the last glaciation (Thomas, 1999, no evidence given). English records are rare and most birds are of uncertain origin. Of ten mentioned in *BWP*, two were of different continental races and eight were not racially identified. Any Crested Tit found in Surrey is likely to be from one of the continental races.

Surrey. H. L. Meyer saw a bird, apparently of this species, in a fir wood near Claremont House during a rough gale from the northwest in the autumn of 1839 (Meyer, 1842, in *Zool., 1890:211*). One was killed at Hampton Lodge (*SALEC*, no date given). There was one in trees on marshy ground near Godstone on 10th April 1945. *The Handbook* mentioned the race *P. c. cristatus*, the Northern Crested Tit, as having been recorded in Surrey but put it in square brackets because no specimen was examined. Possibly the reference is to Meyer's bird.

Coal Tit

Locally common breeding resident

Periparus ater (*Parus ater*)

Breeds from Europe east to Siberia and Japan, a short-distance migrant in the north and east of its range but elsewhere mainly sedentary. The British race *P. a. britannicus* is endemic to Britain and replaced by *P. a. hibernicus* in Ireland. Movements of *britannicus* are mainly local. The *Migration Atlas* shows no overseas recoveries. Continental birds of the race *ater* sometimes reach Britain. Populations have increased in a number of European countries, including Britain, with the spread of conifer plantations. The *Historical Atlas* mentions a substantial increase in the 19th century as conifer plantations extended, an increase which continued through the first half of the 20th century as new conifer plantations were established. Numbers increased by about a quarter from 1970 to 2001 and are probably still increasing.

Early Surrey history. Coal Tits were in the Godalming district in 1849 (Newman) but they were uncommon breeders in the vice-county from 1875 to 1900 (*Historical Atlas*). They were widely distributed on Wimbledon Common in the 1880s (Hamilton). Bucknill described them as considerably rarer than Great or Blue Tits (as they are now away from fir woods). He mentioned them breeding at Dulwich, and Norwood but neither he nor Aldridge made any reference to an association with conifers. Coal Tits were rather common around Godalming (*SALEC*).

Breeding since 1900. Coal Tits bred at South Park in 1905 (T. G. Winter). They were at one time rare in Richmond Park (Mouritz, 1905) and were still mainly winter visitors in the 1930s, but they were breeding regularly there and at Kew Gardens by the 1950s. The Boorman egg collection includes specimens from Ockham (1910) and Send (1920). Power, writing in 1910, described them as much scarcer than Blue Tits, with a fondness for conifers, breeding sparingly in Sydenham but rare from there across to Brixton in the winter months. Eggs were collected at Shackleford in 1923 (Maitland and Turnbull). Four Coal Tits, including two juveniles, were seen in Battersea Park in June 1971. Later breeding records there include four pairs in 1988.

Although generally described as common breeding birds, Coal Tits were found in only 385 tetrads (67%) in the 1988-97 SBC Atlas survey. They were scarcest in the London area and in southeast Surrey, probably because of their close association with pine woods. Four Coal Tits at Beddington Sewage Farm on 4th May 1992 were the first there for 13 years. Coal Tits often come to gardens, especially those with conifers. The Croydon RSPB Group found that, in a 2003 survey of over 100 gardens, the monthly percentage visited varied from 50 (June) to 69 (October and December). Their distribution is very like that of the Goldcrest, which has a similar habitat preference. The newly restructured Barn Elms London Wetland Centre held a territory in 2002. Coal Tits were only occasional in the Shepperton area in the 1980s. A few were found at Queen Mary Reservoir pumping station in the autumn of 2005 (BTO).

Nesting. Coal Tits are not confined to nesting in tree cavities. A pair bred in a hole in a wall at Betchworth in 1981.

Trends. In contrast to national experience, the Common Birds Census shows a huge drop in Surrey numbers from 1970 to 2000 - perhaps 80% for the core woodland population although there may have been a change in the proportion of coniferous woodland. Of the 231 tetrads in northeast Surrey, 78% were found to hold territories in the 1968-72 Atlas survey but only 61% in the 1988-97 Atlas, perhaps a better measure of the decline. The difference may partly reflect coverage but there are several other pointers to a decline in the last 20-30 years. The Winter Atlas found partial survey counts and estimates totalling 348 birds in 1981-84, one for every 4.6 Blue Tits. Coal Tits were found in an annual average of only 39% of Breeding Birds Survey 1 km squares in 1994-2001 compared with 99% for Blue Tits. This is not directly comparable with the tetrad figure but is consistent with a decline. More relevant may be the largest counts on record, which date from the 1960s and 70s, two of them in 1975, a year in which there was an invasion of Continental Coal Tits on St Agnes, Scilly (Gantlett, 1991 in the *Migration Atlas*) and exceptional numbers of Coal Tits were recorded in Surrey.

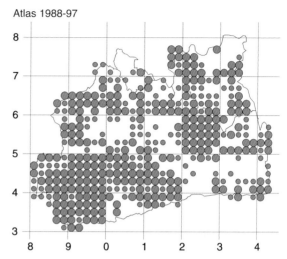

Atlas 1988-97

Population size. The 1994-2004 Breeding Birds Survey suggests a breeding season population of at least 2,000 adults. This is probably on the low side. If Surrey held a proportionate share of the British population as given by the *New Atlas*, the population would be nearer to 4,400 territories, or two per square km, highest in pine woods, which may be a closer estimate.

Territory counts. At Wimbledon Common and Putney Heath, limited surveys produced up to 48 territories in the mid 1980s. There were only 15-20 in the mid 1990s but there has since been a recovery, with 43 singing males in 2005. Battersea Park, which seems to have been colonised in the 1970s, had up to four pairs in the 1980s but Coal Tits bred only sporadically in the 1990s.

Large counts. The largest counts are over 30 years old:

Battersea Park: 50-60, 30th October 1954
Blackheath: *c*.250 on 9th September 1975
Cleygate Common: *c*.150, 23rd January 1966

Pirbright Common: 140, 31st December 1965
Thursley: *c*.100 on 28th September 1975

Bunyard saw a flock of about 30 at Shirley and found this so unusual that he thought they might have been immigrants. The largest recent count is of 22 on Frensham Common in 2001.

Movements and longevity. Movements are mainly local. An early example of one ringed at Limpsfield on 14th January 1911 and recovered there thirteen months later was typical. One ringed at Hornchurch, Essex, on 29th November 1975 and recovered 55 km west at Egham on 13th March 1976 travelled the furthest, apart from a Dutch bird thought to be *P. a. ater* and detailed below. The longest-lived Coal Tit for which details are available was ringed at Caterham on 21st November 1977 and recovered there over seven years and a month later, on 19th January 1985. Details of a longevity of seven years and five months, which has appeared in Surrey Bird Reports, have not been located.

Continental Coal Tit
Periparus ater ater (*Parus ater ater*)

Three birds

Breeds from continental Europe east to central Asia. An infrequent visitor to Britain.

Surrey. One ringed at Dungeness on 18th September 1993 and recovered at Woldingham on 1st November 1993 was judged (at Dungeness) to be of this race. A Coal Tit trapped at Windlesham on 19th February 1995 showed good *P. a. ater* characteristics. During the invasion year of 1996, a bird ringed at Castricum, in the Netherlands on 30th September was killed by a cat at Woking, 310 km west, on 1st November - only the second Dutch-ringed Coal Tit to be recovered in Britain. It had hatched in 1996 and was presumably of this race.

Willow Tit
Poecile montanus (*Parus montanus*)

Rare breeding resident

The British Willow Tit was initially separated as a British race of the Marsh Tit or the Black-capped Chickadee (*BB*, 1:23) and later recognised as a separate species. Willow Tits have a continuous breeding range from Britain and eastern France east to Siberia and Japan. Mostly resident, but irruptive in the northern part of the range. Not much was known about their British range before the preparation of a national survey in 1937 (Witherby and Nicholson, 1937). Willow Tits have been in decline since about 1970, falling over 80% by the end of the 20th century. As with Marsh Tits, deer browsing and less woodland management have been suggested as contributing to the decline (Fuller *et al.*, 2005). Movements are mainly local. No recorded movements involve foreign countries (*MA*).

Early Surrey history. The first Surrey records were from Leith Hill and Reigate (Alexander, 1910). An egg collected at Ockham by Boorman (not examined) is dated 5th May 1910. A nest was found in a rotten tree stump at Brockham on 27th May 1914 and another was found at Godstone in 1919. A pair bred in the lower Colne Valley in 1929 and 1930, possibly in Spelthorne.

Breeding from 1931 to 1944. Witherby provided the first description of a nest being built in Britain, the nest being on his bird reserve at Gracious Pond, Chobham in the spring of 1933 (Witherby, 1934). Willow Tits bred on Epsom Common in 1933. They were quite common on the edges of the greensand commons around Haslemere in the early 1930s (*SEBR* 1934). The 1937 survey found that Willow Tits were fairly frequent in wealden and greensand areas, especially in the Farnham-Haslemere area, where they might have been commoner than Marsh Tits. Records were fairly numerous at all times of the year along the North Downs immediately south of Croydon and also in the Epsom-Dorking district. Willow Tits were breeding at only one or two places between the North Downs and the Thames. A pair nested in a rotten branch in a holly bush near Godalming in 1938, 1941 and 1942 (*SEBR* for 1945).

Breeding from 1945 to 1980. Willow Tits became commoner than Marsh Tits south of Horley in the ten years to 1955 and, for the county as a whole, the Surrey Bird Club was receiving more breeding records for Willow Tits than for Marsh Tits in the 1960s. In 1969 there were breeding reports from ten areas and birds were seen during the breeding season in nine others (Parr).

Places where breeding was reported included Ashtead Forest (1967, 1969), Banstead Wood (1967-69), near Bisley (1971), Bookham Common (1945, 1947, 1961), Burgh Heath (1968-69), Coldharbour (1954, 1971), Epsom Common (1952), Farleigh (1962), Frensham (1956,1964, 1971, three pairs bred in 1972 and at least one in 1975), Haslemere (1954), Headley (1962, 1968), Kenley (1968-69), Littleworth Common (1969), Long Ditton (1967), Prince's Coverts (1966, 1969, 1971), Riddlesdown (1968), Royal Common (1954), Selsdon (1959), Walton Heath (1966), Warlingham (1955), Wey Manor Farm (1971), Winkworth (1954), and Worplesdon (1971). W. R. Ingram found 24 breeding pairs and 12 nests in surveys of Wimbledon Common and the area within five km of Oxshott Station in 1978.

In Spelthorne, there was a Willow Tit at Spout Wood, Stanwell in 1954 and a pair feeding young there in July 1955 (*LBR*).

Where else found to 1980. Willow Tits were identified at Addington (1954), Arbrook Common (1967, 1969), Bagmoor Common (five pairs 1971), Banstead (1954, 1956, 1959, 1961, 1966), Bookham Common (from 1940), Brooklands (1967), Byfleet (1959), Caterham (1958), Chelsham (Holt Wood, 1967), Chipstead (1957), Effingham (1946), Epsom Common (1954-55, 1957), Esher Common (1949), Farleigh (1953-54, 1959), Farthing Down (1966), Gatton Park (1959, 1961-62, 1969), Headley Heath (1959, 1961), Henley Park (1947), Kingswood (1961), Limpsfield (1946), Little Heath Woods (1963), Merstham (1969), Mitcham Watermeads (1949), Old Coulsdon (1955), Old Malden (1968-69), Oxshott (1946, 1963, 1968), Purley (1952), Oxted (1954), Richmond Park (1955 (*BRP*), 1958 (SBC archive)), Ripley (1958), Sanderstead (1951, 1954, 1962), Selsdon (nest hole excavated, abandoned 1944, 1949, 1952, 1954-56, 1958, 1961, 1966), Shirley (1961), Smallfield (1946), South Norwood (1953), Tadworth (1949, 1958-59, 1961-62), Tilford (1954), Vann Lake (resident 1969-76), Walton Heath (1956, 1959), West Weybridge (1949), River Wey at Godalming (1954), Wimbledon Common (1949, 1955, 1968, 1969), Woldingham (1962, 1967) and Worms Heath (1956). They probably bred at many of these places. Courtship feeding was seen at Coulsdon in 1946 (*BB, 39:245*).

Trend since 1970. There was a 10% decline in the number of 10 km squares occupied nationally between the 1968-72 and 1988-91 BTO Atlases. Numbers in Surrey fell further than this. Of the 231 tetrads in northeast Surrey, 32% held territories in the 1968-72 Atlas but only 9% in the 1988-97 Surrey Atlas. No breeding has been proved since 1997, when three pairs bred at Normandy. No Willow Tits have been found in Common Birds Censuses since 1987 but the new Breeding Birds Survey has registered a few up to 2004. Definite records for March to July from 2000 onwards have come from Bookham Common, Bricksbury Hill, Busbridge, Chiddingfold, and Headley Heath. Reports for other months have come from Coulsdon Common, Ewhurst, Hedgecourt, Moorhouse (November and December), Oxted (October) and Wimbledon Common (January). Willow Tits were fairly regular at Queen Mary Reservoir outside the breeding season until 1977, after which they were only found on 11th August 1984 (Geen).

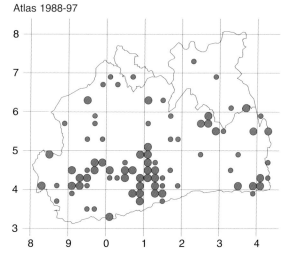

Atlas 1988-97

Willow Tits are now difficult birds to find in the county. The reasons for the decline are not too clear. Geoff Burton (*Kent Ornithological Society Newsletter* 442) thought that the drying out of breeding sites might be a factor in Kent. S. P. Peters has noted that Willow Tits outnumbered Marsh Tits at Frensham Ponds in the 1970s and 1980s but that the birds occupied the same areas. Willow Tits held out longest in the Outlet Pond/Wey valley area, which dried out less than around the Little Pond. Lack of rotten trees may have been a factor (pers. comm.). The twelve nests found by W. R. Ingram in 1978 were all in rotten wood, six in birch, four in willow, one in crab apple and one in an old oak fence post (*LBR*).

Movements and longevity. One ringed at Chobham Common on 26th July 1987 was recovered ten kilometres northeast in Berkshire on 19th September of the same year. The greatest known longevity was shown by a Willow Tit ringed at Caterham on 8th December 1977 and recovered at the same place over eight years later, on 4th January 1986.

Marsh Tit

Poecile palustris (*Parus palustris*)

Moderately common breeding resident

Resident in Europe, with a geographically separated population in Asia. Some northern birds move south within the breeding range in winter. Two races are found in the British Isles, *palustris* in the north and *dresseri* in the south. Both are sedentary. No recorded movements involve foreign countries (*MA*). Not separated from the Willow Tit until 1898, but apparently the joint British population was stable in the 19th century, as was that of the Marsh Tit until the 1960s. There has been a significant national decline since the 1970s (*Bird Study* 226:9). Numbers dropped by over 50%, but may now have levelled out. Deer browsing and less woodland management have been suggested as contributing to the decline (Fuller *et al.*, 2005).

Early Surrey history. Marsh/Willow Tits were in the Godalming area before 1849. The current Surrey population may be below the level of 1900, when Bucknill described the Marsh/Willow Tits as a *tolerably common resident in the county, somewhat more local in its distribution than any of the preceding four species* [Long-tailed, Coal, Blue and Great Tits]. They were not uncommon near Dulwich, and were the commonest tit in winter at Godalming. They were the commonest tit near Lingfield and plentiful in the Thames Valley but they were the least common tit near Epsom. Marsh Tits were uncommon in the Staines district, with no definite references to the area (Kerr, 1906). Bucknill had often seen parties of over 20 when shooting near Chertsey, so they were evidently much commoner then than they are now.

1900 to 1969. Boorman collected eggs at Ockham in 1910. Marsh Tits were occasional in the Dulwich area by 1910, and breeding was uncertain (Power) but they were breeding there in 1946 (*BLA*). At least one was seen in Battersea Park in February 1921 (Macpherson, 1929) and they were mainly winter visi-

tors to Richmond Park in the 1930s, though they occasionally bred there, as they did in Kew Gardens, up to 1938. Breeding season records came from Addington (1931), Chiddingfold (1936) and Selsdon (1931). Breeding sites mentioned by Parr included Cutt Mill, Headley and Hydon Heath and occasionally Dulwich and Kew. Marsh Tits were breeding residents at Vann Lake in the 1960s. They are still there but became less common in the 1990s (Blaker Log).

Trend since 1970. The national decline since the 1970s has also been experienced in Surrey. The largest counts are from the 1970s and 80s. The Common Birds Census, where woodland is over-represented, suggests a reduc-

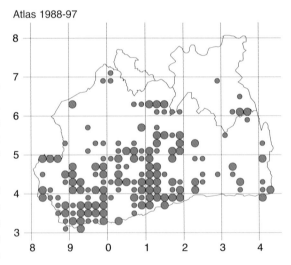

Atlas 1988-97

tion of about 40% from 1970 to 2000. Of the 231 tetrads in northeast Surrey, 37% held territories in the 1968-72 Atlas survey but only 11% in the 1988-97 Atlas, a similar measure of the decline. There have been no published breeding records from Spelthorne since at least 1970.

The number of sites reported has remained stable in recent years, consistent with a levelling out.

Breeding and non-breeding sites reported 1996 to 2001

Year	1996	1997	1998	1999	2000	2001
Vice-county	40	37	41	37	38	43

Population size. The Common Birds Census implies an end-period total of about 1,900 territories. This compares with only 240 adults from the grossed-up Breeding Birds Survey. If Surrey held a proportionate share of the British population as given by the *New Atlas*, the population would be nearer to 430 territories, or 0.2 per square km, which may be a closer estimate. Marsh Tits are still fairly common in open deciduous woodland for most of the year and, mainly outside the breeding season, they visit garden feeders.

Where found since 1970. Since 1970, reports have come from Abinger, Banstead Wood, Barnes, Baynards, Berrylands, Blatchford Down, Bletchingley, Bookham Common (16 territories in 2003), Busbridge, Chelsham, Chilworth, Colley Hill, Coulsdon Common, Cranleigh, Croydon, Cutt Mill, Eashing, Egham, Elstead, Englefield Green, Enton Ponds, Epsom, Esher, Ewhurst, Farleigh, Farnham, Foyle Riding, Frensham Great Pond (two pairs in 2001), Frensham Outlet Pond, Friday Street, Godalming, Grayswood, Hackhurst Downs/Netley Heath (fifteen to twenty pairs in 1974), Headley, Hedgecourt, Hindhead, Holmbury Hill, Horsley, Itchingwood Common, Jordans Wood, Leith Hill, Limpsfield, Lingfield (two pairs in 2001), Mickleham Downs, Milford, Moorhouse, Newlands Corner, New Malden, Nower Wood, Polesden Lacey, Purley, Ranmore Common, Riddlesdown, Sanderstead, Selsdon Wood, Shere, South Norwood, Staffhurst Wood, Thursley, Titsey, Tugley Wood, Unstead, Vann Lake, Warlingham, White Downs, Willinghurst, Woldingham and Wrecclesham. In Spelthorne, Geen listed a few at Queen Mary Reservoir in October 1978 and single birds were found in August 1979, February-March 1982, July-August 1982 and June 1984.

Large counts. Ten is a big count for recent years. The largest counts are all over 20 years old:

Banstead Heath: 30+, 10th October 1982

Barnet Wood, West Horsley: 20, 15th December 1973

Headley Heath: 20+, 6th March 1980; 30+, 2nd February 1985

Walton Heath: over 30, 11th October 1983

Movements and longevity. Most ringing recoveries have been local, including three of the longest lived birds. The BTO has supplied distances travelled of two, six, seven and 13 kilometres for Surrey. The oldest was ringed at Epsom Downs on 12th October 1980 and found nearby, freshly dead, over nine years later on 12th February 1990. Another was ringed at Godstone on 16th April 1972 and found there freshly dead on 28th January 1980. A third was ringed in its first year at Caterham on 10th August 1987 and retrapped there on 21st January 1994.

Nuthatch (Wood Nuthatch) *Sitta europaea*
Common breeding resident

Resident from Europe to India, Japan and southeast Asia. Limited dispersal, occasionally irruptive. A sedentary species with no British ringing recoveries involving other countries (*MA*). The British range extended north and west during the 19th century. National breeding numbers are thought to have more than doubled since 1970.

Early Surrey history. Nuthatches are typically birds of wooded rural areas and they come readily to gardens. They were breeding in the Godalming district before 1849. Bucknill mentions them as joining sparrows and other birds on lawns and has an observation of one feeding on a sunflower. Hamilton (1881) wrote that he wedged nuts into a tree in his Putney garden to attract Nuthatches. The birds would no doubt have been regular visitors to peanut feeders, had these existed at the time.

Since 1900. Nuthatches were quite common in woods around Staines (Kerr, 1906) and rather numerous in Richmond Park (Mouritz, 1905). Power, by contrast, said they were rare in the Dulwich area in 1910. He knew of no nests since 1901, and said that Nuthatches deserted Brockwell Park after it was opened to the public. Eggs were collected at Ockham from 1905 to 1910, at Chobham in 1920 and at Compton in 1924. In 1934 they were scarce around Epsom but common at Limpsfield, where there were eight pairs in 1936. Nuthatches bred in Richmond Park and Kew Gardens in almost every year from

1938 to 1976 (*BRP*). There were a few on Bookham Common in the 1940s. A pair nested on Streatham Common in 1950 and 1952 and they were still nesting at Dulwich around this time. The Winter Atlas found partial survey counts and estimates totalling 137 birds in 1981-84, compared with 90 Treecreepers.

A breeding density of one pair per ten acres (25 per square km) in 40 acres of Eastern Wood on Bookham Common (Parr) was similar to that in other woodland. Nuthatches were resident at Vann Lake from 1964 to 1986 and from 1993 to 1996 (Blaker Log). Inner London records include one in Battersea Park on 18th July 1985, one on 14th February 1989 and one on 22nd September 1997. There were a few in the Shepperton area in 1983-86 and they bred along the River Ash in 1984.

Trend since 1970. The Common Birds Census shows an estimated reduction of about 40% from 1970 to 2000. This is contrary to the national trend and may be partly due to a changing mix of habitat in the sample. It is supported, though, by information from some sites with a long history of coverage, particularly Arbrook Common, which had a peak of up to six territories in the 1980s but was down to one by 2000. Of the 231 tetrads in northeast Surrey, 67% were found to hold territories in the 1968-72 Atlas survey but only 60% in the 1988-97 Atlas, another indicator of a decline.

Population size. The Common Birds Census trend implies about 5,000 territories at the end of the period, which compares with a grossed up total from the Breeding Birds Survey of about 2,200 adult birds. If Surrey held a proportionate share of the British population as given by the *New Atlas*, and allowing for the fact that Nuthatches were absent from much of northern Britain, the population would be nearer to 1,800 territories, or 0.9 per square km.

Recent territory counts. Good numbers can still be found in some areas, for example about ten territories around Hankley Common in 2002, eight territories at Nower Wood in 2003 and 23 territories on Wimbledon Common/Putney Heath in that year (*The Birds of Wimbledon Common and Putney Heath 2004*). At Frensham, a total of seven territories in 1995 increased to ten in 2005.

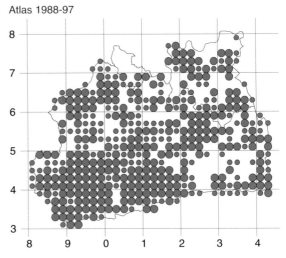

Atlas 1988-97

Breeding behaviour. Nuthatches will use nest boxes. Benson (1888) recorded a nest in a sandbank at Catteshall Manor. Belsey (2002) found one using tarmac to reduce the size of the entrance to its nest hole, which was in a tree on a Surrey golf course.

Large counts. Nuthatches are rarely seen in large numbers. Fifteen at the Devil's Punch Bowl on 27th December 1997 would be a good count for most woodland areas in Surrey.

Movements and longevity. The maximum movement located was made by a Nuthatch ringed at Nower Wood on 7th June 1979 and recovered 11 kilometres away at Horley on 26th August 1982. A Nuthatch ringed at Westhumble on 20th August 1966 was recovered there over six years and four months later, on 25th December 1972, the longest life for which details are available. Surrey Bird Reports since 1977 have given a longevity record of six years eight months but no further details have been located.

Behaviour. Nuthatches can cling to brickwork (Banstead, 1980). Nuthatches are not usually active at night but, at Shere in 1990, one stunned itself by flying into a kitchen window after dark when the lights were on.

Treecreeper (Eurasian Treecreeper)

Certhia familiaris

Moderately common breeding resident

Resident from Europe east to Central Asia and Japan and in North and Central America. Treecreepers have become scarcer in Britain over the past 30 years or so. British birds are sedentary with no ringing recoveries involving other countries (*MA*). The north and east European race, *C. f. familiaris*, is a partial migrant but usually moves no further southwest than the Netherlands. *The Handbook* lists four British records of it, all from Scotland. There are none in *BWP* but *MA* mentions a few sight records.

Early Surrey records are thin but they suggest that Treecreepers were well distributed for most of the period up to the 1950s. Hamilton (1881) mentioned a pair on Putney Heath. Bucknill described Treecreepers as fairly abundant and mentioned Dulwich, Putney Heath and Richmond Park as examples of sites near London. They were not quite as numerous as Nuthatches in Richmond Park (Mouritz, 1905), where there were four to seven pairs in the 1930s (Collenette).

Since 1900. Boorman collected eggs at Ripley (1902) and Cobham (Painshill 1904). Kerr (1906) found Treecreepers to be fairly common in the Staines area but they were uncommon around Dulwich (Power, 1910). Pounds found them well distributed around Farleigh up to the 1950s. Treecreepers bred at Englefield Green and Headley in 1934 and in the Wey Valley below Charterhouse before 1959. They were breeding in the London suburbs at Dulwich, Streatham, Tooting Bec and Wimbledon in the 1950s. Treecreepers commonly bred at Kew Gardens and Richmond Park from about 1948 to 1976 (*BRP*). There was one at Battersea Park in June 1967, one on 14th February 1985, several from August 1987 to April 1988, one on 5th September 1989 and one on 27th December 1999. Treecreepers were resident at Vann Lake from 1964 to 1996 (Blaker Log). They were present in 12 out of 19 Common Birds Census areas in the 1960s. There were seven pairs in Richmond Park in 1969 and five in 25 acres of damp woodland in Stoke Park (Parr). Treecreepers were sometimes recorded at Clapham Common and other Inner London localities outside the breeding season (Parr). The Winter Atlas found partial survey counts and estimates totalling 90 birds in 1981-84, far fewer than the three commonest tits with which it often associates in winter.

Breeding behaviour. Eric Parker found a nest made of 6,695 birch and pine fragments in his garden at Hambledon (Parker, 1947). Thin strands of rope were used in a nest at Knaphill in 1975. Treecreepers sometimes nest in buildings, as at Farnham (behind weather boards on a shed, 1978), Longcross (behind asbestos cladding on a farm building, 1978), Shere (Silent Pool boathouse, 1984) and Woking (in the eaves of a cottage, 1978).

Trend since 1970. The Common Birds Census suggests an increase in the number of territories from 1970 to 2000, amounting to 70% in the core woodland habitat. This seems at variance with the national trend and may not be very reliable. It is based on quite a small sample. Of the 231 tetrads in northeast Surrey, 63% were found to hold territories in the 1968-72 Atlas survey but only 45 % in the 1988-97 Atlas, perhaps a better measure of the decline. Treecreepers were scarce residents in the Shepperton area in 1983-86. Geen wrote that one or two pairs bred at Queen Mary Reservoir in the 1980s.

Population size. The end-period population level estimated from the Common Birds

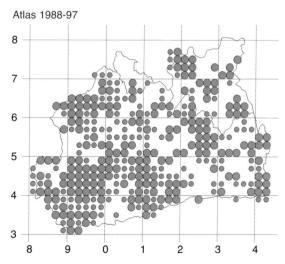

Atlas 1988-97

Census results is 5,000 territories and compares with an estimate of 600 adults which can be derived by grossing up the Breeding Birds Survey and which is likely to be biased downwards for such an inconspicuous bird. If Surrey held a proportionate share of the British population as given by the *New Atlas*, the population would be at least 1,400 territories, which may be a better estimate.

Territory counts. Numbers remained stable at Arbrook Common and fell slightly at Eastern Wood on Bookham Common from the 1960s to 2000. Dulwich Wood held six pairs in 1994. There were twelve territories at Frensham Ponds in 1995 and ten there in 2000. The largest populations recorded are both recent - an estimated 30 to 50 pairs at Bookham Common in 1999 (A. J. Prowse) and at least 30 territories on Wimbledon Common and Putney Heath in 2005 (*The Birds of Wimbledon Common and Putney Heath 2005*).

Large counts. A flock of 15 at Holy Cross Hospital, Haslemere on 4th March 1977, many singing, was of remarkable size for a bird which is usually seen as a handful of birds at most. Larger numbers may be scattered in small groups over a wider area. Thirty were ringed at Capel in August 1993.

Movements and longevity. One ringed at Stroud, Gloucestershire on 13th July 1978 and recovered 118 kilometres east, at Farnham on 7th October 1978 made the largest known movement. A Treecreeper ringed at Bullswater Common on 24th December 1987 and recovered there over six years later on 22nd January 1994 had the greatest longevity located. Surrey Bird Reports since 1977 have given a longevity record of six years nine months, but no details have been traced.

Golden Oriole (Eurasian Golden Oriole)   *Oriolus oriolus*

Scarce summer visitor

Breeds across Europe and east to Mongolia. Some breed in Africa and most European birds winter there. Golden Orioles have bred irregularly in Britain, most often in East Anglia.

Early Surrey history. A rich, fluty call, from an oak wood in May, is typically the first sign of this southern overshoot species for the fortunate finder in Surrey. Bucknill mentioned 19 records of which the first, a young male killed at Aldershot in 1824, might not have been in Surrey. The second was seen in 1833 near Godalming. A pair shot near Oxenford Bridge, Peper Harow in the spring of 1850 (*SALEC*) are in the Charterhouse Collection. In 1854, Waring Kidd had a male fly over his head *when riding in a gig by Ockford Pond, on the 10th of April, and looking for swallows* - a nice way to see one and a very early date (*Zool., 1854:4329*).

Breeding. Golden Orioles have bred successfully in Surrey at least once. A brood of four left the nest safely in 1930, (*BB, 24:226*), possibly at Godstone. A pair may have bred at Bellagio in the four years up to 1890 (*Zool., 1890:144*). Eggs were laid in a nest on Farleigh Common in 1963 but the nest was robbed (A. S. Turner in Parr).

Migrants. The number of migrants found has increased since 1970, after the colder 1960s. The table also shows a dip in the 1940s, which may be connected with the war or the colder winters of the period. The last confirmed record up to 2003 was in 2000.

Golden Orioles by decade 1900-2003

	1900s	1910s	1920s	1930s	1940s	1950s	1960s	1970s	1980s	1990s	2000s	Total
Vice-county	0	1	0	5	3	4	2	9	11	12	1	**48**
Spelthorne	0	0		0	0	0	0	0	1	0	0	**1**

Calendar. More than half of the reports have been in May:

Dated bird months 1824 to 2003(includes five before 1900, excludes undated breeding 1963)

	Jan	Feb	Mar	Apr	May	Jun	Jul	Aug	Sep	Oct	Nov	Dec	Total
Vice-county	0	0	0	7	30	8	3	1	3	0	0	0	**52**
Spelthorne	0	0	0	0	1	0	0	0	0	0	0	0	**1**

Extreme dates are:

Early

10th April 1854   Godalming
11th April 1935   Wimbledon Common
12th April 1955   Runfold
17th April 1934   Mitcham
19th April 1911   Farnham

Late

16th August 1988   Hevers Pond, Bletchingley
1st September 1990   Enton Golf Course
6th September 1986   Moat Pond
Mid September 1940   Guildford

Details of occurrences:

1824:   Aldershot, one, not Surrey?

1833:   near Godalming, one shot.

1844:   Burwood Common, one heard prior to 1844.
Burwood Common, a male seen later but still prior to 1844.

1850:   Peper Harrow, a pair shot at Oxenford Bridge, in the Charterhouse Collection.

1854:   Godalming, a male at Ockford Pond on 10th April.

1861:   Witley Park, one shot.

1870:   Redhill, High Trees, a male was shot on 22nd April in an influx year.
Gatton Woods, a pair.

1871:   Surrey, one in summer. Nesting?

1880:   Chiddingfold, one shot in summer.

1887:   Leatherhead, one seen in April.

1890:   near Redhill, one shot.

1891:   Bellagio, a pair present in the four years to this date. Thought to have bred.

1891:   Catteshall, two stayed for a few days in early spring.

1892:   Bellagio, one found dead.

1893:   Witley, a young bird sent for preservation.

1896:   Holmbury Hill, one on 24th May.

1899:   Addington, one on 9th June.

1911:   Farnham, a male on 19th April.

1930:   Godstone area, a pair bred.

1934:   near Mitcham, one on 17th April.
Kew Gardens (*Birds in London*, HMSO 1950).

1935:   Wimbledon Common, a female on 11th April (*LBR* for 1940).

1936:   Chiddingfold/Hambledon, a pair in May.

1940:   Wimbledon Common, a female on 11th May.
Guildford, one in a garden, mid September (Eric Parker).

1946:   Wimbledon Common, one on 22nd June.

1955:   Runfold, one on 12th-13th April.
Wimbledon Common, one, 20th May and 18th June.

1956:   Watermeads, Morden, an immature male, on 21st June.

1963:   near Farleigh Common, a pair laid eggs.

1969:   Banstead Downs, a male on 13th May.

1971:   Walton Reservoirs, a female on 8th May.
Selsdon Wood, a male heard on 8th June.

1972:   Avalon Fruit Farm, a male on 2nd-3rd June (Clark, 1984).

1975:   Newlands Corner, one on 14th June.
Vann Hill, one on 25th June.

1976:   Richmond Park, a male on 26th May.
Wormley, one heard on 4th July (*HSBBR*).

1978: Purley, a male at a bird table on 11th May and a second, paler bird present.

1979: Dockenfield, a male on 5th July.

1983: Chobham, one in Gracious Pond Road on 9th May.
Dulwich, a male heard in Peckarmans Wood on 30th May.

1984: Wimbledon Common, a male heard at Queens Mere on 4th May.

1986: Moat Pond, an immature or female bird on 6th September.

1987: Banstead Woods, a male seen on 9th May.
Nonsuch Park, a male on 16th May.

1987:* Queen Mary Reservoir, a singing male on 25th May.

1987: East Horsley, two on 30th May.

1988: Chessington, Castle Hill, heard on 21st May.
Richmond Park, one at Pen Ponds on 24th May.
Bletchingley, an immature bird at Hevers Pond on 16th August.

1989: Forest Green, a male singing on 2nd May.
Oxted, one in the first week of May (*LBR*).

1990: Enton Golf Course, a male heard on 1st September.

1991: Epsom, a female or immature bird on 6th July.

1992: Richmond Park, a male on 4th May.
Richmond Park, a male on 20th-25th May.
Frensham, a male on 20th May.
Dulwich Woods, one on 30th May.

1993: Richmond Park, a male on 26th May.

1994: Frensham Manor, one on 21st-22nd May.
Beddington SF, a female or immature bird on 26th-27th May.

1995: Battersea Park, a male on 20th May.

1996: Devil's Punch Bowl, a male on 12th May.

1998: Sanderstead, one singing on 4th May.

2000: Thursley Common, a male on 5th May.

* Spelthorne

HNHS 1980 contains references to singing birds at Hindhead and Thursley in 1971, not included above.

Isabelline Shrike   *Lanius isabellinus*

One bird

Separated from the Red-backed Shrike in 1978. Breeds from Iran east to Mongolia and winters south to Asia and Africa. In the British Isles, records are mainly from eastern and southwestern coastal counties of England. Most are from August to November. From 1950 to 1993 there was only one from an inland county, Huntingdonshire in 1978. The race *Lanius i. isabellinus*, known as the Daurian Isabelline Shrike, breeds in Northeast Africa, Northwest India and Turkestan.

Surrey. A long-dead male Daurian Shrike was brought into a house in Lambert Road, Richmond on 21st March 1994 (S. Ellison, J. Evans, *BB, 88:543*). Photographs taken by Peter Gasson are in the London and Surrey Bird Reports. The specimen was sent to the Natural History Museum at Tring, where the initial racial identification was made. It was at first thought to be *L. a. phoenicuroides* but was later given as *isabellinus* in *BB, 100:93*.

Red-backed Shrike   *Lanius collurio*

Scarce passage migrant, no longer breeds

Breeds from Europe to western Siberia and winters in Africa south of the Equator. Arrives in Europe in late April and leaves in August. Red-backed Shrikes are declining across Europe. In Britain, numbers have been falling since at least the middle of the 19th century. More intensive farmland management, stimulated by the Common Agricultural Policy, is partly to blame for the decline but since some sites have not changed very obviously over the past 50 years, and the national decline went on for at least 150 years, there must be other factors at work. These do not seem well understood.

Surrey. The preferred habitats in Surrey of these once common Shrikes were relatively unintensively-managed farmland and, to a lesser extent, young conifer plantations. They were also found in scrubby places, such as those along the south slope of the North Downs in Surrey. Such places are relatively rich in the large insects, such as bees, beetles and grasshoppers, on which they typically feed.

Early Surrey history. On 23rd May 1787, Gilbert White recorded a pair nesting on his brother Thomas's property in South Lambeth. A bird was seen on his brother Benjamin's property, also in South Lambeth, on 6th June 1788. H. L. Long said that in the 1820s they were known from the Devil's Punch Bowl and Whitmore Bottom. They were listed without comment for the Godalming district in Newman (1849). There was one at Wray Park in 1863 (Holmesdale Natural History Club). An adult female caught in a snow storm near Churt on 3rd December 1869 is the only fully dated record given by Bucknill. The Charterhouse Collection includes a specimen said to have come from Godalming. Hamilton (1881) wrote that they nested on both Putney Heath and Wimbledon Common. Power recorded one in his Brixton garden on 1st August 1894, eating the bees on the hollyhocks. Another there was doing the same thing on 25th September 1897. He saw a Red-backed Shrike on 24th May 1897 at Tooting Common and one on 22nd May 1898 in Dulwich Park.

Bucknill gives a hint of a decline in Surrey in describing its status as somewhat common, nesting in the London area at Barnes Common and Dulwich and that *it formerly appears to have been fairly common close to the metropolis*. He found Red-Backed Shrikes nesting near Dorking, Epsom, Godalming, Leatherhead and Reigate though, and had notes of them breeding in almost every part of the county. Overall, they seem to have been common on bushy places and heaths up to 1900.

1900 to 1960. In the opening decade of the 20th century, Red-backed Shrikes were still widely distributed, reported as present at Barnes Common, Dulwich, Epsom Common, Leatherhead, Oxted, Putney, Ranmore Common (very numerous, 1906), Reigate Hill (nest 1905), Thursley (1906) and Wimbledon. Kerr mentioned nests containing seven eggs in the Staines district. Red-backed Shrikes were occasional in Richmond Park (Mouritz) where they later bred irregularly from 1927 to 1933 (Collenette). The Boorman egg collection at the Haslemere Museum contains eggs from Newlands Corner (1908, 1910), Ockham (1904, 1910) and Send (1902, 1903, 1905, 1925). Red-backed Shrikes were reported from Caterham and Oxted in May 1911 and they bred at Norwood in 1913. By this date they were again said to be decreasing nationally and in Surrey (Vaughan, 1913). They bred at Headley in 1917 and Bookham Common in 1920 (*BB, 37*:155). A nest with five young in the vice-county on 3rd May 1926 was the earliest nest at the time.

Cherry Kearton had Red-backed Shrikes breeding just outside his garden at Kenley in the 1930s. Pairs bred at many other places, including Addington (1928), Addlestone (1935), Ashtead (1935-36, two or three pairs 1938), Banks/Bookham Commons (one pair 1933-34, three pairs 1942-43, probably others), Banstead (1933-34), Bramley (1944), Burgh Heath (1933), Chiddingfold (1936), Chobham Common (1960), Claremont (eggs collected 1925), Colley Hill (1935), Copthorne district (two pairs 1943, possibly not in Surrey), Croydon (about 1922-23, 1946), Epsom Common (1936), Epsom Downs (1934-35), Fairchildes (1947), Farleigh (1925, 1932, 1936), Ham (one pair, 1933 and 1934, 1937, 1939), Haslemere (1934), Hindhead (1954), Kenley Common (1939), Leatherhead (seven pairs 1961), Limpsfield (1934-36, 1939), Milford/Witley (1950s to 1960), Mitcham (four pairs 1938, five pairs 1939), Nore Hill (1944), Smallfield (1944), Tadworth (ten pairs 1946), Walton Heath (1935, several pairs 1938), Wimbledon Common (1935), Royal Wimbledon Golf Course (one pair 1938), Woking (eggs collected 1919) and Worms Heath (1936). They bred on practically all the commons in the Surrey part of the London area and all along the North Downs west to Dorking in 1937 (*LBR*) but were scarce and local in southeast Surrey.

In the Haslemere district, Red-backed Shrikes were scarcer in the 1930s than in the 1920s. Bentham found nests and young at Tadworth, Walton Downs and Walton Heath in many of the years from 1922 to 1962. Red-backed Shrikes were present at Smithwood Common before 1941 (Watson). Two nests were collected from a pair at Ranmore in 1965 but the birds bred on a third attempt. In Spelthorne there were three pairs at Staines Reservoirs in 1934, where pairs bred in 1935 and 1946.

In spite of the decline, the population was at a healthy level in the middle of the century. Pairs bred as far into London as Dulwich (1949), Wandsworth (1950) and Putney Vale (1947-51). Four pairs were present on Mitcham Common in 1954. They last bred at Mitcham in 1956, when they also bred on Wimbledon Common (Parr). Further out, there were still eight pairs on Ashtead Common after building development and the wartime ploughing up of commons, but further habitat loss reduced these to two in 1949. Overall there were 27 pairs in the Surrey part of the London area in 1952 (*BLA*) and the total county population must have been at least 50 pairs. A pair was found at Lloyd Park on 4th May 1958.

1960 to 1976. There was a steep decline in the 1960s, when the number of territorial pairs fell from 17-19 in 1961-64 to three, one at Caterham and two at Normandy, in 1970. There were two pairs at Thursley in 1969. A pair raised young in the northwest of the county in 1971 and breeding attempts continued at Caterham for several years. The last successful breeding was at Caterham in 1973. In 1976, for the first time since 1900, there were no county records at all.

More recent migrants. Subsequent sightings, of single birds except where shown, were at Artington, (30th November to 1st December 2002); Barn Elms (15th May 2004); Bletchingley (17th-24th September 1988); Chobham Common (16th-17th June 1991, 15th May to 15th June 1992); Denbies, Dorking (18th-23rd May 1990); Fairoaks (12th-13th September 2001); Farthing Down (5th July 1995); Frensham (4th June 1978, 20th August 1994); Headley Heath (14th May 1982); Horton Country Park (1st October 1995); Olddean Common (3rd July 1998); Pewley Down (31st May 1992); South Norwood Country Park (28th August to 9th September 1995); Trevereux (14th July 2002) and Windlesham (22nd June 1994, dead). In Spelthorne, Red-backed Shrikes were seen at Perry Oaks Sewage Farm in September 1970, Queen Mary Reservoir on 23rd May 1988 and Staines Moor on 28th-29th September 2003 and 10th-16th September 2005 (*LNHSB*).

Calendar. Bucknill said that Red-backed Shrikes usually arrived about the end of April or early May, sometimes leaving as late as October. The average arrival date in the London area south of the Thames from 1929 to 1939 was 7th May. Early and late dates are:

Early		Late	
3rd April 1948	on a Surrey heath	29th September 1974	Walton Heath
20th April 1924	Addington (Pounds)	1st October 1995	Horton Country Park
		1st December 2002	juvenile, Artington from 30th November
		3rd December 1869	near Churt

Large counts. A spring fall of about 24 at Sutton on 20th May 1933 (*LBR* for 1937) is the largest located count of adults.

Food. Prey items lardered in Surrey include: Dung beetle, Bumble bee, Wren, Blue Tit, Redpoll, Common Shrew and lizard. Others caught include Reed Bunting, House Mouse and Pygmy Shrew.

Movements and longevity. There is a remarkable overseas recovery, of a young bird ringed at Guildford on 6th July 1958 and recovered 2,720 kilometres southeast on the island of Kos, Greece, on 25th September 1958. A young Red-backed Shrike ringed at Witley Common on 6th July 1957 and recovered there over eleven months later on 3rd July 1958 is the meagre longevity record. It might be the untraced longevity record of one year that has appeared in Surrey Bird Reports since 1977.

Behaviour. Jordan (1896) said that a Red-backed Shrike made a most interesting pet.

Lesser Grey Shrike

Lanius minor

At least three, including one from Spelthorne

A southern shrike that breeds from France east to central Asia and winters in Africa. Records are most frequent in May and June and there is a smaller autumn peak in September. Most come from eastern coastal counties. There are several inland county records in the spring.

Surrey. Jordan (1896) mentioned a pair in his neighbourhood (Dorking) in late June, 1886: . . . .*they were far too cautious to let anyone get near them to shoot; and as the spot they pitched on for a couple of days was a worked-out chalk pit, on private property, they did not come to grief.* No further details are available. There are three dated occurrences:

1956: Banstead Downs, one on 21st May (W. P. Izzard, *LBR*).

1957:* Perry Oaks Sewage Farm, one on 6th October 1957 might have been within the Spelthorne boundary. Notes are in the *LBR* for 1957.

1973: Peperham, Haslemere, an immature female was found dying on 18th November by H. E. Cook (D. Parr, *BB*, 67:335, Haslemere). It later died and the skin was sent first to the BBRC and then to the Edward Grey Institute (*HSBBR*). Attempts to locate the skin have been unsuccessful. Surrey was the only inland county with an autumn record from 1958 to 2001.

*Spelthorne

Great Grey Shrike

Lanius excubitor

Scarce winter visitor

Breeds in Europe, Asia, northern Africa, Arabia and India. In the north of their range European birds winter further south in Europe, while northern Asian birds winter further south as far as northeast Africa. Those wintering in Britain are likely to be from Norway (*MA*). Great Grey Shrikes have declined in the west of their range.

Early Surrey history. The first fully dated Surrey record is of one shot from the top of a tall elm tree at Frensham in 1835 (James Lewcock in Newman, 1849). Other early records are from Ash (Newman, 1849), Elstead (one shot in December 1843), Ember Court (a pair in late autumn of 1837, staying for at least three weeks), Painshill Park (autumn of 1840), Redhill Common (near Hampton Lodge, one shot on 4th February 1837) and Tooting (one shot in 1834 and another nearby in 1835). Spicer (1854) knew of a bird in the Farnham district, possibly one of those already mentioned.

The next was not until 1862, when a Great Grey Shrike was shot at Dulwich. One was caught at Buckland around 1875 and records then became rather more frequent. One was caught near Reigate on 21st November 1877 and there were others in about February, 1880 (Godstone), November, 1880 (near

Cranleigh), 18th November 1882 (Croham Hurst), 21st October 1887 (Walton Heath), 29th and 30th November 1888 (Witley), 8th December 1891 (Chelsham), 30th October 1892 (Walton Heath), 1895 (Epsom Downs), 1896 (near Clandon), 1897 (Walton Heath) and 1899 (Oxshott). These are all from Bucknill, with a month correction for 1880. A specimen from Haslemere (*SALEC*) which was in the Charterhouse Museum, where Bucknill saw it, could not be located in 2001. The Museum held one from Brecon.

None of these records relates to the western Surrey heaths where the birds are now typically found. Indeed, apart from a note of one shot on 30th January, 1915 there is little evidence that the western heaths were known as wintering sites even in the early 20th century. Bentham's diary notes for the period only relate to Hedgecourt (October 1912), and Walton Heath (November 1912 and December 1922). There was a Great Grey Shrike at Thursley on 7th February 1935 (*SEBR*) and possibly the same bird hawking from a power line and pylon in 'southwest Surrey' on 17th and 24th February 1935 (*BB, 28:352*). Another was seen at Oxted on 18th March 1936. There is no reference, in these early records, to the habitat currently preferred, which is for heathland with wet areas and scattered trees, living and dead, from which the birds make swooping downward sallies for their prey, typically large insects, small mammals and lizards on the ground. Then, as now, the shrikes were probably elusive, ranging over wide areas when wintering. The winter habitat in Surrey is very similar to the breeding season habitat in, for example, Finland. The wintering shrikes are almost always solitary birds.

The number of bird months remained low until the 1950s when they rose sharply and peaked in the 1970s. Since then, numbers have fallen back and present indications are that there will have been fewer in the first decade of the 21st century than for many years. This does not fit too well with temperature changes but does suggest that recent warmer winters may have contributed to the recent decline.

Bird months by decade

	1900s	1910s	1920s	1930s	1940s	1950s	1960s	1970s	1980s	1990s	2000-01	Total
Vice-county	0	5	4	20	17	76	82	240	109	122	12	687

The most consistent places for Great Grey Shrikes have been Frensham (97 bird months), Pirbright Commons/Ash Ranges (69 bird months) and Thursley/Ockley/Elstead Commons (189 bird months).

Old locations. There are many places where the most recent reports date back to the 1970s or earlier. These, with their bird months if more than one, include Addington (16, latest 1959), Ashtead Common (two, latest 1975), Barnes Common (1947), Bisley Ranges (two, latest 1967), Blackheath (two in 1975), Bookham Common (four, latest 1967), Brook (four, latest 1960), Burgh Heath (1945), Caterham (four in 1966), Charlwood (one in 1963), Chipstead (one in 1949), Chitty's Common (1956), Cranleigh (1950), Croydon (1959), Enton (two, latest 1962), Epsom Common/Downs/Sewage Farm (seven, latest 1975), Ewhurst (1964), Farleigh (three in 1977), Farnham (1975), Farthing Down (1976), Frimley Gravel Pits (five, latest 1973), Gomshall (1976), Grayswood (1960), Guildford (two, 1964), Ham Common (11, latest 1956), Headley Heath (seven, 1975), Hedgecourt (1912), Hindhead (1954), Holmethorpe/Merstham (five, latest 1976), Kew Gardens (1976), Leatherhead (two, latest 1962), Limpsfield (1970), Milford/Witley (five, latest 1967), Old Coulsdon (1956), Oxted (1936), Palmers Green [Cross?] (1944), Papercourt Gravel Pits (four, latest 1975), Richmond Park (14, latest 1974), Ripley Sewage Farm (1979), Rushmoor (1976), Sanderstead (1955), Seale (1973), Walton Gravel Pits/Reservoirs (three, latest 1958), Walton Heath/Walton-on-the-Hill (24, latest 1971), the Wey near Godalming (eight, latest 1975), Wimbledon Common (seven, latest 1971) and Winterfold (1977). This list is noteworthy for the many localities in northeast Surrey that are no longer visited by Great Grey Shrikes.

Where found after the 1970s. Places where birds have been reported after 1979, with the bird months since 1900 if more than one, include Banstead (nine, last 1981), Beddington (25, latest 1993), Beddington/Mitcham Common (24, latest 1991), Bricksbury Hill (12, latest 1983), Chobham Common

(16, latest 1994), Churt Common (four, latest 1995), Crooksbury Common (two in 1982), Effingham (two, latest 1983), Hankley (17, latest 1994), Olddean Common/Wishmoor Bottom (27, 2000), Puttenham (two, latest 1982), Queen Elizabeth II Reservoir (1998), South Norwood (seven, 1991), south of Reigate (1981), Unstead Sewage Farm (1987), West End Common (six, 1999), Witley Common/Park (12, latest 1982) and Wrecclesham (1982).

Great Grey Shrikes reappeared at Ash Ranges/Pirbright Common from 2001 to 2004, Chobham Common in 2002-03, Frensham Common in 2003-4 and Thursley Common from 2001 to 2004, single birds seen in all cases though several may have been present in the county as a whole.

Few records have been published for Spelthorne but those available include one trapped at Queen Mary Reservoir on 12th February 1977 and another seen at Staines Moor on 9th April 2000.

Calendar. Great Grey Shrikes normally begin to arrive in October and have left by the end of May. The bird month table shows a spring peak in March and an autumn peak in November, showing that Surrey sees passage migrants as well as winter residents.

Bird months 1900 to 2001

	Jan	Feb	Mar	Apr	May	Jun	Jul	Aug	Sep	Oct	Nov	Dec	Total
Vice-county	88	96	114	80	4	2	0	0	1	81	113	108	687
Spelthorne	0	1	0	1	0	0	0	0	0	0	0	0	2

Extreme dates are:

Arrival		**Departure**	
18th September 1973	Pirbright	13th June 1920	Ham Common
4th October 1972	Cleygate Common	30th June 1957	Witley Common
4th October 1974	Walton Heath		
5th October 1975	Papercourt Gravel Pits		
5th October 1987	Thursley Common		

An injured bird remained on Thursley Common until 22nd May in 1994. It may have died rather than moving on.

Woodchat Shrike   *Lanius senator*
Thirteen birds

Another southern shrike, breeding from France east to the Ukraine and Iran and wintering in Africa. Numbers have fallen substantially in the north and west of the breeding range. Most British birds are seen in eastern and southern coastal counties but many inland counties have also recorded them. May is the peak month, with a broader and lower autumn peak in August and September.

Surrey. The Charterhouse Museum had a specimen which was said to have been shot at Milford (*SALEC*). It may be the one currently in the Museum and said to be of unknown origin. Neither was mentioned in Aplin (1892). All but two of the dated Surrey records fall in April or May.

1842: Guildford. H. L. Meyer saw one perched on an oak tree between Hatchlands and Guildford some time before 1842. He used it as a model for plate 44 of his book. (Meyer, 1842 in Aplin, 1892).

1853: Esher. A female was shot at Winterdown, on 7th May and later stuffed (Bucknill, 1902).

1888: Ham. There is a reference in Bucknill to one having been seen some time before 1888, without any details. This too may have been unknown to Aplin.

1951: Bookham Common, one on 26th-27th May (A. R. F. Hills and E. Giles, *BB, 45:258*).

1953: Richmond Park, an immature bird from 13th April to 5th May (A. Crutchley *et al.*, *BB, 46:305*).

1960: Addington, a male on 13th May (*BB, 54:194*).

1970: Oxshott, one on 8th June in the observer's garden (*BB, 64:365*).

1971: Fetcham Downs, one on 10th July (A. G. Channer, D. Parr, Miss M. Portlock *et al., BB, 65:546*).

1973: East Ewell, one found dead on 11th May (Mr and Mrs Panting *et al., BB, 67:336*).

1977: between Godstone and Crowhurst, an adult on 29th May (S. A. Robinson *et al., BB, 71:523*).

1986: A first-summer male at Moorhouse 8th October 1986 (E. Fell, *BB, 80:563*). Killed by the observer's car.

1999: Thursley Common, first-summer male on 22nd-24th May.

2005: Richmond Park, one on 12th June (Photograph, *Bird Watching*, August 2005).

Jay (Eurasian Jay)   *Garrulus glandarius*
Common breeding resident

Breeds in North Africa, Europe east to Japan and southern Asia. Currently stable or increasing in Britain. Irruptive in the north and east of its range, otherwise resident. British Jays, which are of the race *G. g. rufitergum*, are sedentary. *BWP* says that Jays are reluctant to cross the sea, but that, in some years, continental birds of the north and central European race *G. g. glandarius* reach Britain. A bird ringed in Kent in October 1955 and recovered in the Netherlands is the only British-ringed Jay to be recovered abroad and no foreign-ringed birds have been recovered in Britain. The firmest evidence of foreign origin comes from the Jays found to have characteristics of the Continental race *G. g. glandarius*, such as one shot in 1983 and several ringed in 1993 (*Migration Atlas*). In southeast England, Common Birds Census results showed an increase of 66% on farmland and a drop of 4% in woodland between 1964 and 1993 (Gregory and Marchant, 1995).

Early Surrey history. A bone from a Jay dated not later than 1650 was found at Oatlands Palace (Cohen). The number of Jays in Surrey probably fell during the 19th century but there is little direct evidence on the point. The Jay was included for the Godalming district by Newman. Kearton (1899) said of the Jay that '*we have a few pairs on the Surrey hills*' but that it was not common anywhere except in Devon and parts of Essex. Bucknill thought that Jays were still fairly abundant in 1900 and that, although they were persecuted by gamekeepers, they bred at Dulwich, Richmond Park, Box Hill and Leith Hill. Jays bred freely at Norwood (Aldridge) and, because of shooting, more sparingly at Wimbledon (Hamilton) in the 1880s.

Since 1900. During the 20th century, Jays have been helped by the spread of forestry and a reduction in persecution by gamekeepers. Jays were numerous in the wooded parts of the Staines district (Kerr, 1906).

Gamekeeper activity in Richmond Park ceased in 1904 and Collenette (1937) estimated that the number of breeding pairs increased from none to fifteen or sixteen pairs as a result. Boorman collected eggs at Shamley [Green] in 1902 and Cobham in 1903. A nest was found at Newdigate in 1905 (G. T. Winter). Power (1910) thought that three or four pairs bred in Dulwich Wood, much reduced in number compared with earlier years. Gamekeepers used to trap them with a Blackbird or Song Thrush's nest and eggs surrounded by snares. Jays are still found at Bucknill's sites and have become more common in subsequent years, losing some of their shyness and visiting gardens more often. They were widely distributed by 1935 (Parr) and continued to increase at least until the 1960s. Jays nested in Battersea Park in 1947 and 1967 and were still there in the 1988-97 SBC Atlas period. At Vann Lake, Jays were recorded in every month of every year from 1964 to 1996 (Blaker Log). They bred at Burgess Park in 1996 and Kennington Park in 1998. Bookham Common had 25-50 pairs in 1999 and there were nine pairs at Horton Country Park in March 2003.

Jays bred in the Shepperton area in 1982-86 (usually one pair) and were present in the breeding season there in 2003 (BTO Migration Watch).

Trend since 1970. The Common Birds Census showed a significant overall increase of at least 70% from 1970 to 2000. Of the 231 tetrads in northeast Surrey, 88% were found to hold territories in the 1968-72 Atlas survey and only 83% in the 1988-97 Atlas, suggesting that, at least locally, there may have been a decline.

Population size. The Winter Atlas found partial survey counts and estimates totalling 286 birds in 1981-84, compared with 750 Magpies. There is a wide range in the population estimates. The Common Birds Census implied a Surrey total of about 18,000 territories at the end of the period, about nine per square km. This may be a bit high and compares with an estimate grossed up from the Breeding Birds Survey of about 3,200 adults. If Surrey held a proportionate share of the British population as given by the *New Atlas*, the population would be nearer to 1,200 territories, or 0.6 per square km, which may be a bit low given the above-average amount of woodland in Surrey.

Large counts. The largest counts come from the 1950s:

near Chelsham: 43 at Birchwood, 29th September 1918 (Bentham in Pounds)

Dulwich Wood: a flock of 63, 24th November 1957

Epsom Common: 16, 29th September 2001 included ten flying south

Frensham: 56, 3rd October 1977

Holmethorpe Sand Pits: 15, 25th November 2004 (S. W. Gale).

Kew Gardens: 20+, 18th October 1992, 30th October 1998 and 10th October 2002

Wandsworth Common: 50-60, November 1965

near Wisley: 94 moving north and northwest, 11th October 1959

Spring gatherings of boisterous or displaying birds involved 16 birds near Frensham on 5th April 1981, 25+ near Whitmoor Pond on 9th April 1982 and 32 at Headley Heath on 20th April 1985.

Movements. Increases and movements are often noticed in the autumn and put down to possible migration. Nationally important movements occurred in every decade from the 1900s to the 1980s (John and Roskell) and unusual Surrey observations have sometimes coincided with them. Two Jays seen on a factory chimney between New Cross and Bermondsey on 3rd October 1911 provided an early example. In 1918, when there was an influx of continental birds in Norfolk (*BB, 29:213*), Bentham saw 'a great number' at Vachery Pond on 27th August and 43 at Caterham Rifle Range on 29th September (SBC archive). Increases noted by Boyd (Boyd 1946 in John and Roskell) for Cheshire in October 1931 and October 1941 (but not in 1937) match increases and movements noted by Bentham (SBC archive), as did an autumn 1947 influx of continental birds into Kent. During an exceptionally large influx in 1957, up to 32 Jays were seen moving WNW over Dulwich and there was a flock of 63 in Dulwich Wood on 24th November. A total of 94 moved north and northwest across Wisley Common on 11th October 1959. Movements observed in October 1961 seem to have been confined to the London area. There were 50-60 on Wandsworth Common on 5th November 1965 and five at the Surrey Docks on 18th October 1975. At Frensham, a maximum of 56 were found on 3rd October 1977. There was a major influx in 1983 (John and Roskell, 1985). It was extensively reported in Surrey, with 12-43 Jays seen at many localities from 25th

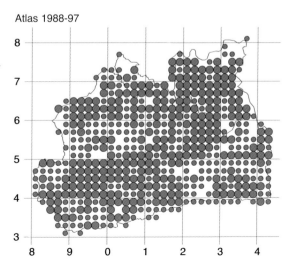

Atlas 1988-97

September to the end of October. Most of these birds were flying east or south but there were two westward movements of note.

In 1988 a total of 55 were counted at Frensham on 16th October and there were large October counts elsewhere in Surrey. A smaller influx in 1993 produced an autumn increase in Surrey. If these movements involve European birds they may be associated with acorn crop failures (*BWP*) but there is no Surrey ringing evidence to confirm that foreign birds or countries are involved. The increase in autumn numbers often commented on by Surrey observers may usually represent only local movements, rather than immigration.

An adult ringed at Headley Heath in July 1983 and presumably British born was found dead, 108 kilometres west, in Wiltshire in March 1984. A juvenile ringed at Ewhurst in October 1983 might have been a continental immigrant. It was found dead 284 kilometres west in Cornwall, also in March 1984.

Longevity. The longest-lived Surrey Jay had a known age of over fourteen years and four months. It was ringed at Tadworth on 17th August 1963 and recovered at Merstham on 4th January 1978.

Plumage variations. A leucistic bird was seen at Seale on 6th October 1984. A pale, grey individual near Richmond on 12th December 1986 might have been of the continental race.

Magpie (Black-billed Magpie) *Pica pica*

Common breeding resident

Resident in Europe, Asia, North Africa, Saudi Arabia and North America. Movements are very limited. The *Migration Atlas* shows no ringing recoveries involving other countries. In 19th century Britain, Magpies were among the birds most heavily persecuted by gamekeepers but they have since increased, partly due to a relaxation of gamekeeping, and are now commonly found in towns. Numbers doubled from 1970 but have now levelled off. The population has increased in some other European countries. In southeast England, Common Birds Census results showed an increase of 298% on farmland and 426% in woodland between 1964 and 1993 (Gregory and Marchant, 1995).

Early Surrey history. There were 16th century remains at Little Pickle, Bletchingley (Poulton *et al.*). Two Magpie bones dated not later than 1650 were found at Oatlands Palace (Cohen). William Cobbett's diary for 7th August 1823, records that he used to take the nests of Magpies at Crooksbury Hill in earlier years (*Rural Rides*). They were considered rare at Tooting as early as the 1830s. Jesse suggested they were common in Richmond Park at this time. Meyer (1842) found them *tolerably plentiful* in some wooded districts and they were said to breed, but not to be very common, in the Godalming district in 1849. They were uncommon in game-preserving districts, where *you might see no more than a pair in a twelve-mile walk* (Jordan, 1892).

Other references to breeding came from Ashtead Oaks, Dulwich (1894 and 1895), Haslemere (about 1880), Newton Wood (Epsom), Royal Common (being exterminated rapidly), Sidlow (1900), Upper Warlingham (1900), Wandsworth (1889), Wimbledon (1870 and very scarce in 1881) and Witley and Woking (1882). Even so, the population fell so much that, in 1900, Bucknill was able to describe the species as very much rarer than the Jay and, in his own words *you can go for a whole day through the woods in Surrey and not see or hear a single Magpie*. He contrasted this with their relative abundance in the north of Oxfordshire. Hudson (1898) watched Jays at Streatham but was surprised to see a Magpie there.

1900 to 1969. Magpies were sparsely distributed in the Staines area (Kerr, 1906). Mouritz reported two nests at Oxshott in 1901, a nest at Crowhurst in 1906 and recent nests at Wisley and Virginia Water but thought Magpies to be among Surrey's rarest breeding birds. Magpies bred at Newdigate in 1905 (G. T. Winter). They were well established at Crowhurst by 1911 but not at Chelsham (Pounds, 1952). Power (1910) only gave two records, both in April, one from Tooting Bec and the other from Sydenham.

Bentham saw 11 on 6th March 1910, which he thought most unusual for Surrey (Parr). Macpherson (1929) gave an undated reference to Battersea Park.

A reduction in gamekeeping during the 1914-18 war enabled Magpies to increase their numbers, though they appear to have remained uncommon until at least 1935. They were only scarce winter visitors to Richmond Park until the early 1930s (Collenette). The London Natural History Society published individual breeding records until at least 1934 (Ewell). A reduction in persecution during the 1939-45 war enabled further advances to be made. Breeding resumed at Richmond Park by 1948. Magpies were absent from Bookham, Effingham and Fetcham in 1939 but frequent by 1951 (Douglas). None bred in Kew Gardens before 1963 (*BRP*). By the 1960s there were occasional records from the Surrey part of Inner London, *e.g.* one flew over Battersea Park in a snowstorm on 1st February 1963. In Spelthorne, eight to ten pairs bred at Queen Mary Reservoir in the 1980s (Geen).

Since 1970. The Common Birds Census showed an increase of 300% from 1970 to 2000. This may overstate the growth but there is no doubt that Magpies have been increasing. The Common Birds Census for Ashtead Common shows a particularly large growth - the number of territories rose from one in the early 1970s to 11 in 2001. Of the 231 tetrads in northeast Surrey, 87% were found to hold territories in the 1968-72 Atlas survey and 97% in the 1988-97 Atlas, a substantial extension of range. Magpies penetrated further into the Surrey part of Inner London, where there were 16 territories in 1988. They bred at Southwark Park in 1979, at Battersea Park in 1987, at the Surrey Docks in 1990 and at Burgess Park, in 1992. Today, Magpies are commonly found in urban areas and may be seen, for example, in shrubs and trees around Bankside Power Station (now Tate Modern) in Southwark.

There were flocks of up to 27 in the Shepperton area in 1982-86 and 30 were seen at Staines Moor in March and November 2000.

Population size. The Winter Atlas found partial survey counts and estimates totalling 750 birds in 1981-84, more than double the number of Jays. The Common Birds Census grosses up to a county total of 32,000 territories by the end of the period. The latter compares with an estimated 14,000 adults derived from Breeding Birds Survey, perhaps the best minimum estimate. If Surrey held a proportionate share of the British population as given by the *New Atlas*, the population would be nearer to 4,300 territories, or two per square km, which looks a good deal too low, not allowing for the growth since the *New Atlas* or for the population density in the southeast of England.

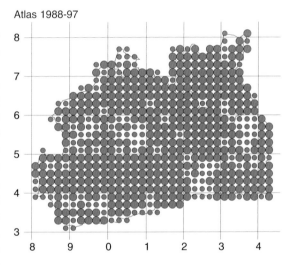

Atlas 1988-97

Breeding behaviour. Some nests are started very early. Nest material was being carried at Capel Woods on 30th December 1990 and Haslemere on 28th January 1980.

Large counts and roosts. The largest gathering of which Bucknill was aware was 21, seen many years previously at Newdigate. The largest known roost up to 1939 known to Parr was 50-60 at Eashing. About 80 were counted on one acre of Farleigh in December 1950 (*LBR*) but no more than 40 from then to 1970 (Parr). Roosts of much larger size have since been found, including two, each of over 120 birds and only six miles apart, at Papercourt and Stoke Lake in early 1992. About 300 roosted at Farthing Down on 1st January 1999 and 250 roosted on 13th January 2002 and 28th December 2003.

Other roost counts include:

near Caterham School: 63, 25th November 1982

Chessington: *c.*50 flying to roost, 19th February 1978

near Elstead: 60, March 1973

Ham Lands: 62, 18th January 1990

Mitcham Common Golf Course: 50-70, 1987

Papercourt Gravel Pits: 177+, 16th February 1992

Stoke, Guildford: 208+, 23rd January 1993

Roosts have been in hawthorns (Caterham 1982, Chessington 1978), oaks (West Horsley 1974) and willow scrub (Papercourt 1992)

Large counts not described as roosts include:

Devilsden Woods: 200+, 9th January 1993

East Wyke Farm, Normandy: *c.*100 on 300 acres (1.2 square km), 27th December 1974

Frimley Gravel Pits: 123, 25th November 1995

Merrist Wood: 191, 12th January 1995

Spring gatherings. Parties of 25-42 at Ham Lands, St Martha's Hill/Waterloo Pond, Smallfield and Thorpe Water Park are on record as 'spring gatherings'.

Food. Magpies notoriously rob nests, particularly of small birds. Prey items include a young Starling (Banstead 1984). Milk bottles were knocked over and opened, after which the milk was drunk, at Shottermill County School in 1989.

Movements and longevity. The largest movement on file is only 5 kilometres, made by a Magpie ringed at Lightwater on 1st August 1982 and recovered at Chobham on 5th February 1990. A Magpie ringed at Kempton Park on 29th August 1987 and recovered at Hampton on 27th April 1999 is given as the county longevity record in the Surrey Bird Report but might not have been in Spelthorne. No such doubt exists about one ringed at Holmwood on 6th November 1983 and recovered, over ten years and eight months later and a kilometre away, at South Holmwood on 23rd July 1994.

Plumage variations. There was a leucistic bird at South Norwood Country Park in 1993.

Nutcracker (Spotted Nutcracker)   *Nucifraga caryocatactes*

About twelve vice-county records

Nutcrackers breed in the northern pine forests from Scandinavia to northeast Asia and the mountains of central and southern Europe. They are normally resident but there are irruptions in years when a year of an abundant crop of the favoured food, which is the seed of Arolla Pine, *Pinus cembra*, is followed by one in which the crop is poor, driving birds out in search of food (Dymond *et al.* 1989). These irruptions usually reach the British Isles from August to December, with a few through to February. Most are found in the southern and eastern coastal counties of England and Wales, particularly Kent, Norfolk and Suffolk. The last invasion year was 1968, when at least 315 were reported. The Thick-billed race, *C. c. caryocatactes*, has very rarely been identified in Britain and never in Surrey. Of the others, one has been identified as of the Slender-billed race *N. c. macrorhynchus* and the others have not been assigned to a race.

Surrey. One was seen in Peper Harow Park by Samuel Haines (Kidd, 1837). Dated Surrey records are on typical dates. The records up to 1905 were not recognised by the BOU in their 1883 and 1915 lists:

1839:   Elstead, the Charterhouse Collection had a specimen that had been shot by John Woods, of Elstead, in 1839 (*SALEC*, and presumably shot locally but not so stated). It is no longer there.

1847:   Clandon. A labourer shot another on the roof of his cottage on Clandon Common in the autumn (*Zool.*, 1850:2914).

1849:   Guildford, Kidd saw one 'near Guildford' some time between 1837 and 1849 (*Letters of Rusticus*). This could have been one of the previous two birds.

1865:   Dulwich, Power was shown one that was said to have been obtained at Dulwich Meadows around 1865 by 'Mr Parsloe, a Brixton bird-stuffer'.

1957:   Frensham, one on 31st August (HNHS 1968, Clark 1984).

Frensham, one on 12th November supported by notes, in the *SBR*.

1968:   South Croydon, one seen five times from 24th August to 7th September (*BB, 63:372, SBR* and *LBR* also give 8th August).

1968:   Headley, one seen on 10th, 22nd and 26th September (*BB 63:372*, Leatherhead).

1975:   Seale, one visited a bird table several times a day from 10th-12th October (Mr and Mrs N. V. Leathes, *BB, 70:448*).

Slender-billed Nutcracker   *Nucifraga caryocatactes macrorhynchus*

Surrey. The BOU list of 1915 (BOU 1915) says that a Slender-billed Nutcracker was found in Surrey as part of an influx in 1911. It has not been possible to locate the source of this, which is not in accounts of the influx given in the BOC Bulletin (BOC 1913) and British Birds (Ticehurst, 1911) or in the 1911-14 indexes of British Birds. The BOU list does not mention one shot at Addington Park, Croydon on 13th October 1913 and identified as Slender-billed by T. A. Coward (*Zool.*, 1914:75, Coward 1914) and it is tempting to wonder if the BOU and Coward records relate to the same bird. The skin of the Croydon bird was examined by Bentham (Pounds, 1952) and is currently in storage in the Manchester Museum, accession number B.12164. It was donated by Ferris Neave in 1917.

Chough (Red-billed Chough)   *Pyrrhocorax pyrrhocorax*

Two probable vagrants

Resident on cliffs in Ireland and Wales and in the mountains of northwest Africa, Ethiopia, southern Europe and Central Asia. Numbers have declined in the northwest of the range and in the Alps. In Britain, Choughs are largely resident although some birds move long distances within the British Isles (*MA*). Numbers fell from around 550 pairs in 1800 to a low of less than 20 in 1940, since when there has been a small recovery (Owen, 1988).

Surrey. The first Surrey record, of one killed on Mitcham Common in or before 1836 comes from a period when Choughs were far more common and widely distributed in Britain than they are today. They were then breeding, for example, in Hampshire and Kent. The record found its way into the works of Blyth and other 19th century ornithologists.

Bucknill mentions two Chough specimens in the Charterhouse Museum. One was an escape. The other was shot at St Catherine's Hill, Guildford on an unspecified date and was acquired by W. Stafford (*SALEC*). It is presumably the bird with a normal bill and legs which was still at Charterhouse in 2001. One at Northbrook, near Godalming, was mentioned by Stafford in private notes but not supported by a specimen. A fifth bird, in Balham a few months before 1893, was published by Swann (1893) and considered a probable escape by Swann himself, Fitter (1949) and other writers.

Reviewing the 19th century records, Bucknill thought that *it is by no means unlikely that none . . . . are really wild birds. On the other hand, there is no evidence to show that this is the case . . . .* and Parr agreed. The 1836 record satisfied ornithologists of the day and looks good, circumstantially. The others seem most likely to be escapes.

An apparently wild Chough joined a pinioned captive in an open-topped cage in a Surrey garden early in the 20th century (Parker, 1929).

Chough skins were at one time in demand for the adornment of ladies' hats (Jefferies, 1948).

Jackdaw (Eurasian Jackdaw)

Corvus monedula

Common breeding resident

Breeds in Europe, North Africa and western Asia. Northern populations are migratory but almost all winter within the breeding range. British Jackdaws are of the race *spermologus* and mainly sedentary. Jackdaws from the near parts of the Continent and Scandinavia reach Britain. They have included, rarely, individuals resembling the eastern European race *soemmerringii*. Some British birds leave for Ireland in the autumn at about the time that continental birds are arriving on the east coast. The number breeding in Britain has probably increased since the 1939-45 war and in spite of a small drop between the 1968-72 and 1988-91 BTO Atlases they increased markedly from 1970 to 2005. In southeast England, though, Common Birds Census results showed a drop of 34% on farmland and 62% in woodland between 1964 and 1993 (Gregory and Marchant, 1995).

Early Surrey history. Jackdaw remains from the Roman period were found on the King William IV site at Ewell (Orton, 1997). Remains found at Guildford Castle were dated to about 1230-1268 with others up to about 1400. Other remains have been found at two sites in Southwark - Bermondsey Abbey (dated at 1480-1600) and Chaucer House (1500-1700). Thirty-three bones found at Oatlands Palace were dated not later than 1650 (Cohen). Jackdaws bred in great numbers in a chalk pit on Katherine Hill [St Catherine's], Guildford (*Letters of Rusticus* in Yarrell (1845)). They were common in the Norwood district in the 1880s (Aldridge). There were 90 in Richmond Park in 1898.

Since 1900. Jackdaws were common in the Spelthorne area (Kerr, 1906) and they were evidently widely distributed elsewhere. Eggs collected by Boorman at Newark Priory (1903, 1907) and Send (1907, 1908) are in the Haslemere Museum. Thirty or forty pairs bred in Brockwell Park before it was opened to the public but by 1910 they were rarely seen in the Brixton/Dulwich/Sydenham area in the summer (Power). They were also scarce in Inner London, but one flew east at the Surrey Docks on 20th February 1979, and there were a few non-breeding birds in Battersea Park from 1985. Jackdaws have yet to penetrate the most densely populated part of Greater London, breeding no further in than Raynes Park and Richmond Park. Jackdaws were recorded in every month of every year from 1964 to 1996 at Vann Lake (Blaker Log).

Trend since 1970. Of the 231 tetrads in northeast Surrey, 57% were found to hold territories in the 1968-72 Atlas survey but only 51% in the 1988-97 Atlas, flagging a decline. The Common Birds Census showed a significant increase but recorded very few Jackdaws in most years and is probably not a reliable indicator of the trend on its own. Jackdaws were uncommon, but increasing winter visitors to the Shepperton area from 1982 to 1986, mostly seen flying over in autumn and with a high count of about 80 on 19th October 1986.

Population size. The Common Birds Census indicated a county total of about 5,000 territories. The Breeding Birds Survey suggested a county total of about 17,000 adults. If Surrey held a proportionate share of the British breeding population as given by the *New Atlas*, the population would be nearer to 2,800 territories, or about 1.4 per square km, which feels a bit low for a county as heavily wooded as Surrey. The Winter Atlas found partial survey counts and estimates totalling 6,804 birds in 1981-84, suggesting a minimum size for winter population:

Winter Atlas maximum counts from 1981 to 1984 for each 10 km square

Square	84	93	94	95	96	03	04	05	06	07	14	15	16
Count	600	250	450	150	50	184	24	30	300	3,952	50	70	65

Square	24	25	26	27	34	35	36	37	Total				
Count	71	100	62	*221*	150	*15*	*10*	0	6,804				

Basic field counts from observers except for any in italics, which are adjusted figures from the BTO.

The large total of 3,952 in TQ07 may have come from the inclusion of a refuse tip at Wraysbury Gravel Pits, where counts of 2,000 birds were made in two different years in the period (*LBR*). The inclusion of this site, which is outside the vice-county, could not be confirmed. Nor could the coverage of large refuse tips that are within the vice-county.

Nests. Jackdaws are well known for nesting, often colonially in tree holes and old chimneys, and they often nest in quarries. Among the quarries they have used are Epsom, Riddlesdown (40 pairs in 1985) and Whyteleafe (*BLA*). They also have nested in sand pits at Limpsfield (Parr). A dead Blackcap found in a nest at Leatherhead in 1952 was thought to have been used as nest material (G. Douglas).

Large counts. Jackdaws may feed in large groups, often with Rooks and sometimes on tips and landfills. Large gatherings not described as roosts or roost flights include these:

Beddington Sewage Farm: 600, 29th December 2002

Beechfield Tip, Holmethorpe: 950, 19th July 1984

Betchworth Park, Old Park Wood: 400+, 10th November 1989

Bowlhead Green: *c.*300 with Rooks, 4th February 1979

Busbridge: 1,200, 15th December 1992

Cranleigh: 3,000, 14th March 1998

Headley Heath: 500+, 19th January 1981

Holmethorpe Sand Pits: 600, 5th December 2001

Horton Country Park: 600, 26th December 1989

Hunterwood Farm, Cranleigh: 600, 7th February 1999

Longcross rubbish tip: 600, 3rd February 1985

Newdigate: *c.*200, 12th December 1987

Papercourt landfill: 500, 19th July 1992

Richmond Park: over 600 in 1948 and 1949

Runfold: 500 at Princess Royal Sand Pits, 22nd December 2001

South Park, Godstone: 600, 9th January 2000

Stakescorner, Artington: 1,000, 8th January 2000

Wrecclesham rubbish tip: 500, 21st June 1986

Roosts and roost flights. Jackdaws make noisy roost flights, often with Rooks. There was a mixed roost (over 60% Jackdaws) of about 5,000 at Gatton in February 1947 (Parr). About 5,000 roosted at Oak Park, Sanderstead on 29th September 1956 and 14th October 1956. Up to 1,000 roosted at East Clandon from October to December 1974. There was a roost of at least 1,300 at Gatwick Airport on 16th July 1986. On 12th December none remained. Some 4,560 flew to roost at Capel in 1993. At Hurst Green, at least 1,350 roosted on 19th August 2000. At Tuesley Farm, Milford 1,000 flew to roost in December 2000. Flights to a large roost at Loseley Park have been regularly seen over Unstead Sewage Farm. Counts of over 3,000 were made in the Decembers of 1997 to 1999 and November 2000. There were 2,350 on 22nd February 2000 and 2,800 on 30th December 2001. At Hersham Gravel Pit, 2,400 flew to roost on 4th January 2002.

Movements and longevity. Autumn movements, such as twenty northwest over Dulwich on 3rd November 1994, and winter flocks are sometimes thought to include immigrants (Bentham, of Tadworth in the 1920s, various records in *BLA*, comments in Parr, *LBR* for 1994, *Migration Atlas*), but the continued absence of ringing recoveries involving birds ringed abroad must leave this as speculation. There is one overseas recovery, of a young Jackdaw ringed at Guildford on 15th March 1975 and recovered, 402 kilometres east, later in the year at Utrecht, Netherlands on 30th

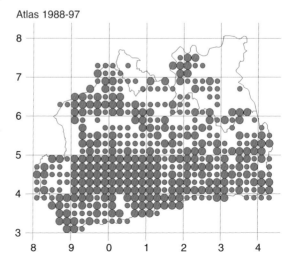

Atlas 1988-97

Denbies Hillside. In the 1960s this area supported Red-backed Shrikes and Cirl Buntings, both now lost to Surrey as breeding species. There has been little obvious change to the habitat.

John Davis

May. A young bird ringed at Capel on 26th May 1979 and recovered there over 15 years and eleven months later, on 30th April 1995, shows the great age that corvids can reach.

Plumage variations. Bucknill mentioned that birds with some white feathering were often seen. This may be so, but they are not often reported. There was a pied bird at Barnes on 25th November 1906.

Rook *Corvus frugilegus*
Locally common breeding resident

Breeds across Europe and Asia. Northern and eastern birds are migratory, wintering in more southerly regions of the same continents. Rooks ringed in eastern Europe and Scandinavia have reached Britain (*MA*). Many migrants from the Baltic and the Netherlands winter in eastern Britain. The British range extended during the 18th and early 19th century, with the creation of more habitat as a result of the enclosure movement and an increase in arable land. The increase continued into the 20th century.

Surrey. Rooks are familiar birds in rural areas, breeding colonially in tall trees and feeding mainly on arable land. Like other farmland birds, they have been under pressure with the expansion of suburban London and with changes in farming methods which have reduced their available food supply. They often associate with Jackdaws. There have been several comprehensive surveys of the numbers of nests. The first, carried out in the 1940s, covered only northeast Surrey and found 1,702 nests. Numbers found in later, countywide, surveys were 2,508 nests in 1975 and 2,295 nests in 1996.

Early history. Salmon (1736) commented on the abundance of crows at Crowhurst. They might, one could suppose, have been Rooks. In Richmond Park, Rooks nested at Sheen Gate in 1852 and moved to Spankers Hill by 1883. They nested at Bishops Lodge, 1894; southwest of Robin Hood gate in 1894. Rooks nested opposite Dulwich College and at Streatham (Aldridge) in the 1880s. A rookery in Brockwell Park was one of the biggest in or near London before the park was opened to the public in 1891. Nests declined to 35 in 1896 and about ten in 1898 (Hudson). Hamilton (1881) mentioned rookeries at Wimbledon and Putney Hill. A small rookery in Peckham Park in 1895-96 was abandoned (Hudson). One near Streatham Common Station had about 30 nests in 1897.

1900 to 1929. The Bishops Lodge rookery was deserted by 1903 and Spankers Hill was deserted by about 1905. There was a rookery at Brocklehurst Wood, Redhill in 1905 (Holmesdale Natural History Club). Other rookeries of the period include Milford: Rooks building in March 1906; Oxted: Rooks building in March 1906; Ham Gate: deserted in 1925; Tandridge: sitting in April 1906; Marden Park: an enormous rookery years ago (Beadell, 1932); Woldingham: a large rookery before the bombing school was established in the Great War. Rooks nested at Herne Hill until 1919 and Wandsworth until about 1924 (*BLA*). There were rookeries of various sizes all over the Staines district not later than 1906 (Kerr).

1930 to 1965. Rooks were still nesting at Dulwich until about 1930 (*BLA*). A Rook census covering England was carried out in the 1930s. No results for what was then Surrey have been located but Glegg

(1935) gives four Spelthorne rookeries: 150 nests at Kempton Park Race Course on 13th April 1930, 17 nests in elms near Staines Common on 15th March 1931, four or five nests at Sunbury Court in 1931 and twelve nests near Staines railway station on 22nd January 1933. At about this time, Fairchildes had 'quite a good little rookery' (Beadell, 1932) and later there were 112 nests in 1939 and 135 in 1946 (Pounds, 1952).

The BTO carried out a survey of rookeries in England, Scotland and Wales between 1944 and 1946 for the Ministry of Agriculture. In the 231 tetrads of northeast Surrey there were 1,702 nests in 68 rookeries (Fitter *et al.*, 1946). Further survey work in 1946 revealed another Surrey rookery of unstated size. The Surrey rookeries were concentrated 'around Godstone, with an inlier in the neighbourhood of Farleigh', with none in a zone six to ten miles from the centre of London (Ashby *et al.*, 1947). The Croydon Natural History and Scientific Society (CNHSS) published a map showing the BTO results for a 35 km x 35 km square which included their rectangular recording area of about 27 km x 23 km centred on Purley/Caterham (Newton, 1948). Some 2,500 breeding pairs were found in 77 rookeries, of which 17 rookeries were not in Surrey and about eight were in Surrey outside the northeast. The residue of 52 rookeries, plus a further eight rookeries near Leatherhead and one at Kingston come to 61, seven fewer than the Fitter account for northeast Surrey but broadly consistent with it, as they should be since the Fitter and CNHSS sets of figures came from the same BTO source. There were also 35 rookeries inside Surrey but outside the northeast area. They were in the eastern half of TQ14 (five), TQ24 (sixteen), TQ34 (eleven) and TQ44 (three). No results for the rest of the BTO Surrey survey have been located, leaving Fitter's 1,702 nests in northeast Surrey plus the 35 other rookeries from Newton as the only substantive regional counts for the period.

Surveys from 1966 to 1984. The Surrey Bird Club carried out surveys in 1973 and 1974 in preparation for another BTO census in 1975. These were organised by Gillian Craw (Craw, 1974). Coverage was not complete but a total of 1,648 nests were found in 100 rookeries in 1973 and 1,631 nests in 80 rookeries in 1974. Three more rookeries were seen but uncounted in 1973 and five in 1974. The 1975 survey for the LNHS part of Surrey produced 389 nests in 24 rookeries (Sage and Cornelius, 1977). An analysis of BTO information for the remainder of the county produced 2,508 nests in 133 rookeries. The BTO's Surrey result of 2,495 nests at 133 rookeries (Sage and Vernon, 1978) could not be separately identified.

The BTO organised a further sample census of 482 10 km national grid squares in 1980. Four of the squares were in Surrey. The Surrey information shows a fall of over 50% between the two surveys, much more than in the 100 km squares SU or TQ or in Great Britain as a whole. Results published by the BTO (*BTO News* 113, Sage and Whittington 1985) were summarised by 100 km national grid squares. Estimated percentage changes for squares including Surrey compared with the Surrey and national results are shown in the Table. The Surrey results were very much worse than those in surrounding areas.

Area	Nests			Rookeries		
	1975	1980	% change	1975	1980	% change
Surrey sample	265	118	-55	18	9	-50
100 km square SU			-10			-12
100 km square TQ			-7			-15
Great Britain			+6.8			-7.7

The Winter Atlas found partial survey counts and estimates totalling 3,801 birds in 1981-84, suggesting a minimum size for winter population. Given the nest counts, the true size is likely to have been a good deal higher.

The 1996 Survey and after. The BTO organised a further sample survey of rookeries which was carried out in 1996. This was expanded to a full census of nests by the local societies. The total number of nests found in the vice-county was 2,295 in 107 rookeries. None were found in Spelthorne. With one exception, all known rookeries were checked in 1996. The exception is Titsey Park, which had 47 nests in 1994. The rookery was overlooked in 1996 but a survey by N. J. Donnithorne in 1997 found 79 nests there, in groups at TQ402554 (Pitchfont Lodge), TQ403547 (Barton Shaw) and TQ408552 (Titsey Hill). Rookeries at Cranleigh Rectory (TQ03 tetrads U and P) and West Horsley (TQ083526) were noted but not counted. Available information about rookery sizes in subsequent years is very incomplete. The larger figures were:

Compton: 42 nests in 2001 (65 nests in 1990)
Bookham: 18 nests in 2002, 16 in 2003
Horley Railway Station: 13 nests in 2000

Polesden Lacey: 27 nests in 2003
Titsey Estate: 43 nests in 2002
Titsey Park: 61 nests in 2000

Nest sites. The trees used by Rooks for nest sites are analysed in the table, which shows comparative information for 1973 and 1996 (Surrey) and 1975 (England). Identification problems were greater for trees than for Rooks and in both years over 30% of the trees were not specifically identified, usually because the nests were in mixed woodland. Percentages, which are of nests in each kind of tree, are shown excluding and including unidentified trees.

Nests Analysed by Host Tree

Tree	Number Surrey 1973	Number Surrey 1996	% of identified trees Surrey 1973	% of identified trees Surrey 1996	% of all trees Surrey 1973	% of all trees Surrey 1996	% of all trees England 1975
Ash	2	220	0.2	14.7	0.1	9.6	9.9
Beech	239	130	26.7	8.7	14.5	5.7	18.4
Elm	157	3	17.6	0.2	9.5	0.1	27.9
False Acacia	0	9	0.0	0.6	0.0	0.4	
Holly	0	4	0.0	0.3	0.0	0.2	
Holm Oak	10	0	1.1	0.0	0.6	0.0	
Horse Chestnut	21	30	2.3	2.0	1.3	1.3	
Oak	269	734	30.1	48.9	16.4	32.0	12.4
Plane	2	2	0.2	0.1	0.1	0.1	
Sweet Chestnut	0	8	0.0	0.5	0.0	0.3	
Sycamore	26	95	2.9	6.3	1.6	4.1	11.2
Willow	0	6	0.0	0.4	0.0	0.3	
Pine	168	252	18.8	16.8	10.2	11.0	11.1
Yew	0	8	0.0	0.5	0.0	0.3	
Total identified	*894*	*1,501*	*100*	*100*			
Conifers	9	0			0.5	0.0	2.4
Deciduous	653	192			39.7	8.4	6.7
Unknown	89	602			5.4	26.2	
Total nests	*1,645*	*2,295*			*100*	*100*	*100*

The main conclusion to be drawn from the tree table seems to be that Rooks use the available trees, those that are high enough and near enough to feeding grounds. In 1973, Surrey Rooks made noticeably more use of Beech and Oak and less use of Ash and Elm, than Rooks were using in England as a whole. Elms, which held nearly 18% of the nests in 1973, are no longer significant host trees in Surrey after the ravages of Dutch Elm disease. Ash and Oak have become more important. Scots Pines hold many nests in West Surrey, where they are often the dominant tree, but are used less elsewhere.

Altitude is not an important factor in the choice of rookery site. Newton (1948) mentions that only three of the 77 rookeries in the CNHSS area were at an altitude of more than 550 feet and that others showed a marked tendency to be situated in valleys. The altitudinal distribution of the 1996 rookeries has not been analysed in detail, but most of the higher ground in Surrey is in the area of the North Downs or the sandy hills immediately to the south. Much of this is wooded, with little arable farmland. Where, as along the Hog's Back, there are large open areas of arable land with adjacent trees, there are substantial rookeries. The rookery at Puttenham is one of the largest in Surrey. Low-lying ground in the southeast of the county is mainly arable farmland and has many rookeries. It is not obvious why large rookeries on farmland at altitudes of under 100 metres (330 feet) in the Horsley/Wisley area have been abandoned.

The size distribution of Surrey rookeries is shown in the table. Most rookeries hold less than 30 nests. Fewer small rookeries were found in 1996:

Number of Rookeries

Nests	1-5	6-10	11-20	21-30	31-40	41-50	51-60	61-70	71-80	81-90	91-100	101-110	111-120	Total
1975	34	30	28	15	17	0	0	4	1	2	1	1		**133**
1996	18	29	25	14	5	5	3	2	2	1	1	1	1	**107**

Life length of individual rookeries. Rookeries can last more than twenty years, some much longer. A table summarises the information which is available about the 1996 rookeries, in the thirty-one cases where the date of foundation was given or estimated. Several others, of unknown age, were active in both 1975 and 1996 and were therefore at least twenty-two seasons old. The great gale of 1987 probably destroyed some rookeries but the effect cannot be quantified.

Age of Rookeries in Existence in 1996

Square	Place	Grid reference	Founded	Life in seasons
TQ34	Furze Wood, South Park	TQ348487	1896	101
TQ45	Ship Hill, Tatsfield	TQ414567	1929	68
TQ34	Jarretts, Blindley Heath	TQ349467	1966	31
TQ34	Shipley Bridge	TQ301402	1968	29
TQ44	The Beacon, Dormansland	TQ402414	1970	27
TQ34	Lanesmead, Blindley Heath	TQ361460	1972	25
SU84	Wrecclesham	SU827452	1973	24
SU84	Hankley Common North	SU893429	1973	24
SU94	Compton Village	SU957469	1973	24
SU94	near Compton	SU970463	1973	24
TQ03	Upper House, Hascombe	TQ005397	1973	24
TQ03	Slythhurst, Ewhurst	TQ088393	1973	24
TQ03	Tolt Copse, Ellens Green	TQ095353	1973	24
SU93	Tugley Farm	SU966339	1975	22
TQ05	West Horsley	TQ083526	1975	22
TQ34	Byers Lane, South Godstone	TQ356465	1975	22
TQ34	Pine Crest, Woodcock Hill	TQ369407	1976	21
TQ35	Nutfield Cemetery	TQ300505	1976	21
TQ44	Moor Lane, Dormansland	TQ409432	1976	21
TQ34	Kiln Heath, Newhouse Farm	TQ314405	1977	20
TQ34	Arden Wood	TQ390457	1987	10
TQ34	Littlehaven, Blindley Heath	TQ353461	1992	5
TQ34	Park Farm, Woodcock Hill	TQ367407	1993	4
TQ34	Ridge Green Close, South Nutfield	TQ303485	1995	2
SU93	Sandhills	SU935383	1996	2

Square	Place	Grid reference	Founded	Life in seasons
SU93	Ramsnest	SU949330	1996	2
SU93	Redlands Farm	SU952330	1996	2
TQ04	Hazel Brow	TQ090462	1996	2
TQ04	Hazel Brow	TQ091464	1996	2
TQ04	Hazel Brow	TQ092461	1996	2
TQ45	Shaw Road, Tatsfield	TQ414575	1996	2

Note: Foundation dates for the pre-1975 rookeries are approximate.

Longer term trend. There seems little doubt that the Rook population was once much larger than it is now. For the one substantial measure of population change since the 1930s we may turn to a census of 32 square miles in northeast Surrey carried out by P. A. D. Hollom in 1931. This area, bounded by approximate co-ordinates SU975610, SU975675, TQ100675 and TQ100610, contained 421 nests in ten rookeries. The same area held 193 nests in six rookeries in 1996. The northeast Surrey count of 1,702 nests in the 1940s also suggests a much larger county population than that found in later surveys. Of the 231 tetrads in this area, 26% were found to hold territories in the 1968-72 Atlas survey but only 16% in the 1988-97 Atlas, showing the extent of the withdrawal from the London suburbs. Numbers remained more stable in the rest of Surrey but there was an overall fall between the 1975 and 1996 BTO county surveys. A few Rooks nest in Spelthorne, where there were three nests at Queen Mary Reservoir in 1994. Rooks were uncommon winter visitors to the Shepperton area in 1983-86 and were apparently still scarce in 2003.

More comprehensive survey information is not available. The table assembles and interpolates what there is. The increase from the 1930s to 1945/46 is put at 20% in all areas, following the results for England in the 1945/46 survey. The decrease from the 1945/46 survey to 1975 outside the LNHS area is assumed to have been 44.6%, the figure for England shown by the 1975 Survey.

Atlas 1988-97

Nest Numbers

	1930s	1945/46	1975	1996
Northeast	1,418*	1,702	371	253
Rest of Surrey	3,215*	3,857*	2,137	2,042
All Surrey	4,633*	5,559*	2,508	2,295

*estimate

Rookeries

	1930s	1945/46	1975	1996
Northeast	n/a	68	27	14
Rest of Surrey	n/a	n/a	106	93
All Surrey	n/a	n/a	133	107

Average Rookery Size (nests)

	1930s	1945/46	1975	1996
Northeast	n/a	25.0	13.7	18.1
Rest of Surrey	n/a	n/a	20.2	22.0
All Surrey	n/a	n/a	18.9	21.4
England	n/a	n/a	24.4	n/a

n/a – Not available

Large counts: 3,500 corvids (90% Rooks) roosted at Marden Park, Woldingham on 16th December 1911. A roost at Frensham Little Pond held 4,000 birds in 1936 (*SEBR*) and 3,000 Rooks and Jackdaws (HNHS, 1955) at around this time. The trees at Frensham were felled in the 1939-45 war. They are back now, but not the Rooks. A roost of Rooks and Jackdaws at Gatton from 1889 or earlier to 1949 held about 5,000 birds in February 1947 (*BLA*). At least 1,000 were on newly ploughed land at Milford on 7th August 1986. About 2,000 were on flooded fields at Wrecclesham on 26th December 1990.

Movements. There is one overseas recovery, of an adult ringed at Bookham on 11th March 1962 and found freshly dead 185 kilometres ESE at Setques, northern France, on about 15th July 1962. The furthest recorded inland movement is only 42 kilometres (26 miles), made by a Rook ringed at Ewhurst on 29th June 1949 and recovered at Chichester on 18th December 1952. Goldsmith's *Animated Nature* (1774) gives an account of how, in the reign of Queen Anne (1702-14), Sir Edward Northey had a bough holding a nest with two young Rooks in it cut from one of his trees at Woodcote Park, Epsom and used it to start a new colony in Temple Gardens, London (Bucknill). This story does not appear in at least one later edition. It is a good story, widely doubted.

Longevity. Rooks can be long-lived. Parr mentioned one ringed at Ewhurst in July 1949 and recovered at Ockley in September 1963, still the greatest known longevity for Surrey.

Behaviour. Rooks will visit a bird table or bird bath (Godalming 1970, Elstead 2007) or a nut-feeder (Capel 1990). Once a rarity at Beddington Sewage Farm, landfill operations are now attracting Rooks, with 22 on 29th December 1999.

Plumage variations. Bucknill described a number of Rooks with a few white feathers. Albinos were (and still are) rare. Power saw a white-winged bird on Mitcham Common in 1892. One with white patches on its primaries was at Frensham on 26th August 1906.

Carrion/Hooded Crow   *Corvus corone/cornix*
Not distinguished in archaeological records

Surrey. The remains of four 'Carrion Crows' have been found at archaeological excavations in Southwark. One in a pit at the Arcadia Buildings site was dated from Roman Britain as was another from a well in Union Passage, dated at 250-300 AD. Orton (1997) mentions remains from the Roman period being found on the King William IV site at Ewell. Of three Carrion Crows found at Merton Priory, one was dated at 1150-1200 and two at 1230-1350 AD. Other remains were found in ditches at Bermondsey Abbey (1480-1600) and Fastolf's Palace and Rosary (1600-1650). Presumably none of these finds, the publication dates of which pre-date the split of the species, can reliably be assigned to *corone* or *cornix*.

Carrion Crow   *Corvus corone*
Common breeding resident

Crows are resident across Europe and Asia with a few stations elsewhere. No British recoveries involving foreign countries are mentioned in the *Migration Atlas*. The *corone* group of races includes *C. c. corone*, which breeds from the British Isles south to Iberia and east to central Europe, with stations in Iran and the Nile Valley and Asian races which are separated from *corone* by the range of the Hooded Crow. It has been suggested that the separation of the populations may have been brought about by climate changes in the last Ice Age. In 19th century Britain, Carrion Crows were heavily persecuted by gamekeepers in many parts of the country. In southeast England, Common Birds Census results showed an increase of 153% on farmland and 186% in woodland between 1964 and 1993 (Gregory and Marchant, 1995). Numbers breeding in the UK may have increased by as much as 80% since 1970.

Early Surrey history. Carrion Crows are long-established residents in Surrey. On 7th March 1658, John Evelyn wrote of *crows' feet being frozen to their prey during the severest winter that any man alive has known*. He later mentioned the killing of crows in the Wotton area. As elaborated below, Carrion Crows joined Hooded Crows in pillaging cabbage crops in the Godalming area during the severe winter of

1813/14. William Cobbett's diary for 7th August 1823, records that he used to take the nests of crows as well as Magpies at Crooksbury Hill in earlier years (*Rural Rides*). Only a few bred near Tooting early in the 1830s (Blyth). Carrion Crows nested at Wintershall, near Guildford, in the first week of January, 1843. A decline seems to have occurred in the 19th century, possibly due to persecution. They were said to be less common than they used to be around Godalming in 1849. In spite of the decline, large numbers were found in Richmond Park in 1860, where they later bred and they bred at Dulwich in 1893

(Bucknill). Hamilton (1881) wrote that they had occurred on Wimbledon Common (not, as quoted by Bucknill, that they bred there). Jordan (1896) wrote that he had only seen three in the previous nine years and these were flying from the downs to *some dreary moors on the tops of distant hills*. Bucknill described Carrion Crows in 1900 as partial residents and much less abundant than in former years. He knew of pairs that had bred in Battersea Park and, in 1893, near Dulwich. He was informed that they could still be seen at Elstead, Ockley and Thursley Commons, where they had 'recently' been found nesting. Crows fed then, as now, on exposed mud along the Thames. Some from Kew and Richmond fed in the London parks (Hudson, 1898).

Recovery since 1900. The fortunes of the Carrion Crows have changed a good deal since 1900. Breeding was attempted at Walton-on-Thames in 1904 (Boorman egg collection) and there were a few in Richmond Park (Mouritz, 1905). At about this time, two or three pairs were breeding around Dulwich (Power, 1910). An increase in numbers was noted during the 1914-18 war. Bunyard thought numbers had been cut back after it but there were 25 at Barnes on 22nd March 1931 and 48 at Richmond Park on 24th March 1936. Kerr regarded the bird as rare in the Staines area in 1906 but there were sixteen at Staines Reservoirs on 27th July 1930. In the same year, Glegg counted twenty between Hammersmith and Richmond on 16th February.

There was another surge forward during the war of 1939-45 and Carrion Crows became common in parks and gardens. The expansion has contin-ued. In 1950, four pairs nested at the Battersea Park site mentioned by Bucknill. One wintering at County Hall in 1942 signalled an entry to the Surrey part of central London, where they now breed commonly in suitable sites along the Thames.

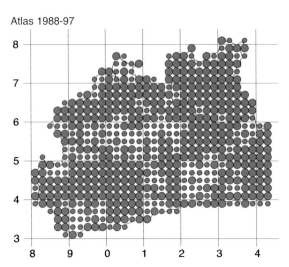

Atlas 1988-97

Breeding behaviour. A pair were nest-building at Cobham on 20th December 1996. Carrion Crows use a variety of postures in courtship and the defence of territory. Peter Carney saw the 'Bristle-head display' given many times from February to June 2001 by one of a pair in Peckham Rye Park and caught the action well in his drawing.

Trend since 1970. Of the 231 tetrads in

northeast Surrey, 94% were found to hold territories in the 1968-72 Atlas survey and 99.6% in the 1988-97 Atlas, showing how common Carrion Crows had become. The Common Birds Census suggested an increase of nearly 300% from 1970 to 2000.

Population size. The Winter Atlas found partial survey counts and estimates totalling 3,518 birds in 1981-84, suggesting a minimum size for winter population. The true population must have been a good deal higher:

Winter Atlas maximum counts from 1981 to 1984 for each 10 km square

Square	84	93	94	95	96	03	04	05	06	07	14	15	16	24
Count	50	55	30	152	9	46	25	25	260	*619*	11	68	45	100

Square	25	26	27	34	35	36	37	**Total**
Count	1,000	418	198	42	70	78	217	**3,518**

Basic field counts from observers except for any in italics, which are adjusted figures from the BTO.

The Common Birds Census suggests about 27,000 territories at the end of the period. The comparable Breeding Birds Survey estimate of 29,000 adults adds support to this. If Surrey held a proportionate share of the British population as given by the *New Atlas*, the population would be nearer to 5,700 territories, or 2.8 per square km, which feels a bit low.

Territory counts. The number of territories on Barwell Court Farm, Chessington rose from five or less in the late 1970s to fourteen in 2002. Large numbers now breed in the London Parks, with up to nine pairs in Battersea and Burgess Parks (Hewlett). There were 15 territories at Morden Hall Park in 2001. Carrion Crows were widely reported in Spelthorne during the 2003 BTO Spring Migration Watch, with counts of up to 37.

Large counts. Flocks as large as 160 were found in Richmond Park in 1950 (*BLA*). Gatherings of at least 200 birds have become more frequent in the last twenty years. They are usually at rubbish tips or sewage farms but have also been seen at other places, including Barn Elms, Battersea Park, Nunhead Cemetery, Peckham Rye Park and the Thames foreshore at Wandsworth. Some of the larger counts are:

Beddington Sewage Farm: 515, 2nd September 1999 (*BBR*); 762 on 24th July 2002

Betchworth: 250+ on stubble, 7th February 1987

Esher Sewage Farm: 400, 2nd May 2000

Hersham Gravel Pit: 250, 19th February 2000

Holmethorpe rubbish tip: 1,000, December 1981

Horton Country Park: 350, 19th January 2000

Island Barn Reservoir: 500, 24th July 1996

Pirbright Common: 120, 3rd November 1985

South Park, South Godstone: 300, 9th January 2000

Tuesley Farm, Milford: 500, 28th August 2000 and in the autumn of 2001

Unstead Sewage Farm: 262, 4th February 2000

Wimbledon Common: 1,000-1,500 flying to roost in January 1986; pre-roost gathering of *c.*1,000, 6th February 2002

Spelthorne

Laleham Farm fields: flocks of up to 250 in the winter of 1982/83.

Roosts do not feature much in the records but one near Woodmansterne held about 175 Carrion Crows at the end of 1946. Parr mentioned about 700 flying to roost at Carshalton in January 1963 and at Motspur Park, at least 230 were roosting on 27th January 1969. By far the largest roost has been at Wimbledon Common, where there were about 400 on 19th December 1964 (Parr). The roost held an estimated 1,000 or more birds on 9th November 1974 and at least 1,500 in 1979. An estimated 1,500-2,000 birds were in the vicinity of the roost at dusk on 4th January 1981 (B.A. Marsh). Some 800 roosted at Holmethorpe Sand Pits on 17th February 1993 and again in 1994 and 1995. At Nunhead Cemetery, 200 roosted in early 1998.

Movements and longevity. The furthest movement located is of only five kilometres, made by a 'Crow species' ringed at Worplesdon on 18th May 2001 and recovered at Normandy in the following month (BTO), doubtless a Carrion Crow. Surrey Bird Reports since 1989 have mentioned a longevity record of nine years and seven months. The BTO has advised of a *Corvus corone/cornix* ringed at Callow Hill, Egham on 17th October 1975 (before Carrion and Hooded Crows were separated as species) and found dead at Wraysbury on 6th June 1985. This is probably the bird.

Plumage variations. Carrion Crows not infrequently have white or partially white secondaries, showing as a white bar along the upper wing.

Hooded Crow   *Corvus cornix*

Rare winter visitor

The *cornix* group of races includes C. *c. cornix*, which breeds in Ireland, Scotland and other regions to the north and east of the range of the C. *c. corone* and other races in the Mediterranean region and the Balkans. There is an overlap range where both groups breed and hybridisation occurs, *e.g.* County Dublin (*BB, 36:143*). Although subject to the 19th century persecution suffered by the Carrion Crow, there has not been the same 20th century recovery. The British range has contracted northwards, possibly for climatic reasons. Hooded Crows were regular winter immigrants from continental Europe to southern Britain at the beginning of the 19th century (Montagu). Kearton and Bentham (1925) said that they arrived in great numbers on the east coast of Britain in autumn, which is certainly not the case today. The *Migration Atlas* mentions the recovery of Hooded Crows ringed in Scandinavia prior to 1951 and in Denmark in 1986 as an indication of the source of the British immigrants and adds that Scandinavian Hooded Crows are not moving so far in winter, possibly due to climate change.

Early Surrey history. Hooded Crows were at one time abundant round London (Graves, 1811-21) and common in the Wey valley during severe winters in the early part of the 19th century. They arrived from the north in October and November and stayed until March and were bold feeders. In the winter of 1813/14, which was extremely severe and one of those years when the Thames froze, they joined with Carrion Crows and Woodpigeons to come into gardens. As the authors of *Letters of Rusticus* put it, *so severely did they punish the whole of the cabbage and broccoli tribe that we got nothing at all from the stumps when the warm weather ought to have set them sprouting.* Modern gardeners will know the feeling. Spicer (1854) knew them in the Farnham district. Hamilton (1881) listed them for Wimbledon Common. Bucknill gives a few other records. They were occasional near Hampton Lodge, Puttenham in the 1820s and were thought to have been shot on Mitcham Common before 1836 and near Farnham prior to 1845. They had been found at East Molesey (1880), Epsom (1885), near Lingfield (1894), Merrow (1890), Walton Heath (1893), and Wimbledon (in most winters to 1895). There are undated reports for Banstead, Chobham Common, Frensham, Gatton and Headley. Bucknill regarded them as uncommon, most frequent in hard weather. Power recorded birds flying over the Dulwich area on 5th November 1880, 11th October 1890 and three on 27th October 1893.

1900 to 1939. Numbers seem to have held up well until the 1930s. There were single birds at Sidlow in December 1901 and by the riverside at Battersea Park on 30th January 1902. In Richmond Park there were single birds on 14th October 1902 and 12th March 1905 and two were there on 26th November (Mouritz). In 1906, there were birds at Godstone (21st January), Titsey Park (January, 1st April, two on 15th October), and Hedgecourt (13th October). Birds at Virginia Water in January and March 1907 (Kerr) might not have been in Surrey. Seven flew over Power's Brixton garden on 29th October 1909. One at Chelsham on 1st May 1919 was the first known May record apart from a bird found a few days dead at Vachery on 30th May 1906. The largest count which has been located is in Beadell (1932), who gave an undated maximum of sixty at Beddlestead Farm. Beadell gave the actual date, 22nd February 1920, to Pounds, who published it in *The Birds of Farleigh and District*. Hooded Crows were, at this time, usually seen on the more isolated parts of the Downs. Beadell also saw twenty at Warlingham on 20th February 1921 (*BLA*). In 1925 there was one on Wimbledon Common on 20th February and one at Barnes on 29th October. Later Richmond Park birds include one on 9th January 1927, three in January and one on 18th October 1933, one on 2nd February 1936 and on 10th-18th February 1937. Two Hooded Crows were on the Thames at Barnes from 3rd March to mid April, 1929 and Hooded Crows were 'often' seen at low tide on mud flats by Chelsea Reach in 1937.

1940 to 1980. As the table shows, a decline was evident from the 1940s. Places where Hooded Crows were found from 1940 to 1970 include: Addington (1952, 1953), Ashtead/Headley (1952), Barn Elms (1949, 1954, 1972), Beddington Sewage Farm (1945, 1947-48, 1953, 1962-63, 1967, 1972, 1976), Beddlestead Park (1947), Borough Farm (Milford, 1957), Brooklands (1960), Carshalton (1953-54), Chelsham (1962), Chipstead (1946), Epsom Sewage Farm (1953), Ewell (1949), Farleigh (1953), Frensham (1949, 1972), Godstone (1952, 1976), Guildford Sewage Farm (1967), Ham Common/Gravel Pits (1948, 1954, 1956), Haslemere (1949), Herne Hill (1962), Island Barn Reservoir (1976), Kew Gardens (1951), Lyne (1976), Mitcham Common (1949), Molesey rubbish tip (1961), Pyrford (1942), Ranmore (Bradley Farm, 1963), Richmond Park (1948, 1953-54, 1976), Ripley Sewage Farm (1972), Seale Sand Pits/rubbish tip (1976, 1978), South Norwood (1953-54), Walton-on-Thames (1972), Walton-on-the-Hill (1974), Wey Manor Farm (1963), Wimbledon (1946) and Wimbledon Common (1957, 1975-76). In Spelthorne there were Hooded Crows at Charlton Gravel Pits (1961) and at Perry Oaks Sewage Farm (1956, 1975).

Where seen since 1980. There was a collapse in the 1980s. Single Hooded Crows were seen at Beddington Sewage Farm on 10th April 1985, Bradley Farm, Ranmore in mid December 1985 and Stanwell Moor rubbish tip on 7th-8th May 1988. The last bird was seen over Thursley village on 11th December 1996. The decline of the Hooded Crows in Britain has come at a time when Carrion Crows were increasing. The changes might possibly be connected with climatic factors as well as reflecting reduced persecution of Carrion Crows.

Bird months by decade

	1900s	1910s	1920s	1930s	1940s	1950s	1960s	1970s	1980s	1990s	Total
Vice-county	21	7	94	49	30	30	17	20	2	1	**271**
Spelthorne	0	0	0	10	0	1	1	3	1	0	**16**

Calendar. Hooded Crows were always winter visitors but they occasionally lingered into May or June. There are none on record from July to September. The February peak in the monthly totals is due to two big counts in the 1920s.

Bird months since 1900

	Jan	Feb	Mar	Apr	May	Jun	Jul	Aug	Sep	Oct	Nov	Dec	Total
Vice-county	37	116	36	11	3	1	0	0	0	30	15	22	**271**
Spelthorne	2	3	3	0	1	0	0	0	0	1	4	2	**16**

There are several records for May including Chelsham on 1st May 1919 and one to three at Beddington Sewage Farm from 2nd November 1934 to 2nd May 1935. The one at Stanwell Moor Rubbish Tip on 8th May 1988 was the first, and latest, located May record anywhere in Surrey since 1935. The single June bird was near Frensham in June 1949 (HNHS 1955). Long-stayers include two on the Thames from Chiswick to Barnes, from 8th March to 14th April 1929 and two from 19th February to 4th March 1931 (Glegg).

Raven (Common Raven) *Corvus corax*

Lost breeding species, five vice-county records 1900 to 1990, now more frequent

Resident, with an extensive breeding range across Europe, North Africa, Asia and North America. The *Migration Atlas* shows no recoveries involving foreign countries. At the beginning of the 19th century, Ravens bred in virtually every British county and they often nested in trees. The reasons for the subsequent decline are not completely clear. The *Historical Atlas* mentions persecution by gamekeepers and egg collectors and the pet trade. It is possible that competition from Carrion Crows, another tree-nesting corvid, and one which has greatly increased, has been a factor in the Raven's decline. Carrion Crows, however, were heavily persecuted during the 19th century (see Jordan above), so this may not have been a significant factor. Bucknill wrote that they bred regularly up to about 1844 in Petworth Park, only seven miles (ten kilometres) into Sussex and later at Parham Park. He quoted Butler (1896-8) for hearsay evidence of a pair nesting near the Surrey border in Kent in 1885. Ravens are currently spreading east across Britain and breeding numbers have increased substantially since 1994. They bred successfully on the Sussex coast in the years 2001-03 (*Sussex Bird Report* for 2003), in Buckinghamshire in 2003, a county first for modern times (*BTO News 2004*) and on a pylon in Hampshire in 2004, also a modern county first (J. M. Clark, pers. comm.). They have recently been wintering in Hertfordshire (M. Ilett, pers. comm.).

Early Surrey history. Excavations in Southwark have produced the remains of seven Ravens dated to Roman Britain. They were from 104 Borough High Street (140-200 AD), 179 Borough High Street (150-170 AD), Winchester Palace (two, 250-400 AD), 4 St Thomas Street (270-400 AD), 15-23 Southwark Street and Courage's Brewery. Remains from the Roman period were also found on the King William IV site at Ewell (Orton, 1997). One from Winchester Palace, Southwark, was dated at 950-1150 and another from the Courage's Brewery site was probably medieval. In the 18th century, London Ravens flew as far as twenty miles to forage (Glegg, 1938) and would probably have visited rural Surrey. They could be told from country Ravens by their dulled or dusty plumage, the result of feeding in dust and ash heaps (Hudson, 1898). Ravens may have bred in Surrey in the 18th and early 19th centuries but the documented evidence is thin. Shrubb says that regular breeding ended in Surrey at some time between 1810 and 1819 but gives no details.

Newman (1849) included the Raven in a list of resident natives nesting in the Godalming district but gave no details. This is a pity since other records in the paper include a few from places well outside Surrey. Bentham, in Pounds (1952), gave an undated breeding record for Marden Park and said that Ravens bred in the Caterham valley around 1837. Bucknill mentions undated Surrey skins from Chiddingfold, Peper Harow and Shere in collections and a pair wintering at Penge in 1885/86. Jordan (1892) mentioned Ravens on the greensand hills in the distant past. In a later book (Jordan, 1896) he claimed to know of the last pair that nested in Surrey in his boyhood, but gave no place or date. He thought they had moved to Sussex and that they or others nested there in 1850 and 1852. Phillip Crowley's collection contained an egg said to have come from Churt in 1862 (Bucknill, 1901). The *Historical Atlas* appears to be correct in saying that the Raven was extinct as a Surrey breeding species by 1875.

The eight subsequent records are mostly in spring and autumn. Power saw and heard one fly over near Balham on 9th January 1894. Bucknill gave two other records, of an apparently wild bird seen in a field near Egham on 21st April 1895 and a pair seen daily in winter over a garden in Penge during 1895-96. One at Stoke D'Abernon on 23rd May 1896 (*Epsom College Natural History Society Report* No. 8) is mentioned in Bucknill (*Zool.*, 1901).

1900 to 2000. The later records, all in late summer or autumn, are these: one seen and heard flying over Esher on 12th September 1909, one at Frensham on 16th November 1956, one flew over Guildford on 2nd October 1977 and called and one flew over Bermondsey on 28th October 1984, mobbed by Blackheaded Gulls. There were two reports in 1990, one of a bird flying south over Wallington on 20th July and the other of one that flew north over Beddington Sewage Farm on 20th August, mobbed by Carrion Crows.

New colonisation? With the extension of the British range, vagrant Ravens are now being seen in outer Surrey and they might begin to breed again, perhaps in an old quarry or on a pylon, before too long. One was soaring over Chilworth on 27th February 2004. Another flew over Frensham Great Pond on 15th May 2005 (*Bird Watching*). A pair were seen mating at a pylon in southeast Surrey in 2005 but the birds moved out of the county without nesting (Richard Lowe, pers. comm.). There were a

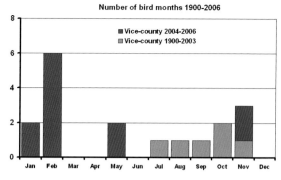

number of sightings in 2006. The chart shows that, whereas the earlier records since 1900 have been from July to November, all but one of the recent ones have been from January to May, spanning the Raven breeding season. This strongly suggests that we are now seeing birds that are prospecting as a prelude to breeding.

Starling (Common Starling) — *Sturnus vulgaris*

Common breeding resident

The original home of our Starlings was in Asia. They are now native breeding birds of Europe and Asia and have been introduced into North America, South Africa, and Australasia, with a range now covering almost thirty per cent of the earth's land area (Feare, 1984). Starlings were in Britain 600,000 years ago (Harrison, 1988) and were probably driven out by subsequent glaciation. Recolonisation became possible when ice sheets and tundra gave way to temperate grasslands. The range has been expanding westwards. Starlings were probably uncommon in most of Britain for some hundreds of years before 1800, though the existence of island forms in Scotland suggests that they might at some time before that have been more common and then lost ground. The British range and the breeding population increased during the 19th century. British Starlings are largely resident. Birds from Norway, Sweden, Finland, northern Poland and other parts of eastern Europe winter in Britain.

A national survey carried out in the 1960s showed that urban Starling winter roosts, which were first recorded in 1845, increased continuously in size and number until 1965, when approximately 400,000 birds were roosting on masonry at 13 places in central urban areas of Britain (Potts, 1967). Most birds were thought to be of British rather than continental origin, a conclusion supported by ringing evidence in *BLA*. Numbers have been in decline since the 1970s and breeding numbers have fallen by over 60%. Changes in grassland management over the past forty years have played a significant part in this decline. There has been a five per cent decrease in the area of permanent pasture in Britain since 1965 (Department for Environment, Food and Rural Affairs, 2004) and the invertebrate content of grasslands has been reduced by modern farming methods (Shrubb).

Early Surrey history. Starlings were breeding residents in the Godalming district in the 1830s. Numbers in Surrey increased considerably in the late 19th and early 20th centuries. As late as 1875, a report of Starlings nesting in Richmond Park was thought to be worth publishing in *The Field*, but they were common there by 1905 (Mouritz). They were much increased, building nests 'almost everywhere' in Wimbledon (Hamilton) and nesting in the Norwood district (Aldridge) by 1885. Hudson (1898) wrote of them gathering to roost at Battersea Park in July and August evenings. Bucknill reported them as abundant and increasing in 1900, having adapted well to life in the expanding suburbs. Birdcatchers of the period would use nets baited with bread or decoy birds and sell the Starlings for around fourpence (two new pence) each. In September 1898, a Peregrine was caught in starling nets at Mickleham while diving at decoys. Captured Starlings were released from traps as shooting targets, as were House Sparrows.

Breeding since 1900. Breeding numbers continued to increase, in Surrey and elsewhere, during the first half of the 20th century. Starlings bred commonly in the Staines district, where Kerr saw 'countless thousands' going to roost on an evening in the autumn of 1904. Starlings nested around Ripley in 1903 and Send in 1908 (Boorman). They bred commonly in buildings and woods around Dulwich in 1910 and were conspicuous visible migrants in October (Power). Inner London breeding places include Lambeth Palace in 1950 (*BLA*) and 1971 (*LBR*) and County Hall in 1974.

A decline became apparent after the 1960s. Spring censuses in Battersea Park showed a fall from 276 birds in 1964 to 99 in 1975, 92 in 1980 and 33 in 1991 (Nicholson, 1995). The number of immigrants also fell, reflecting decreases in other parts of the range. Of the 231 tetrads in northeast Surrey, 230 were found to hold territories in the 1968-72 Atlas survey and only slightly fewer, 227, in the 1988-97 Atlas. The Common Birds Census suggests a fall of about 50 % in the number of breeding pairs from 1970 to 2000. Most other evidence also suggests a decline. The most telling indication of the decline is given by the history of large counts and roosts.

Large counts. Starlings often collect in large numbers at feeding places which may be some distance from where they have bred. Most sewage farms support feeding flocks and numbers at them have sometimes been large. Wintering numbers at Beddington Sewage Farm and the adjoining Mitcham Common and Waddon Marsh were estimated at 5,000-10,000 (Fitter, 1940). There were about 5,000 at Wanborough Wood in the spring of 1966. Some 20,000 Starlings were seen at Earlswood on 23rd March 1979. Some 2,000 at Beddington on 7th July 2002 and about 2,500 at Seale rubbish tip on 10th January 2003 were large for a recent count. There were 200 at Staines Moor in February and November 2000.

Roosts. Starling roosts and fly-lines were discussed briefly in an introductory chapter. Birds often collect at gathering-places before flying to the main roost site. Typically they travel up to five miles to a roost and longer distances have been found. One ringed at Richmond in October 1948 was recovered at the Trafalgar Square roost in November 1949 (*LBR*). Birds at a single feeding place may use several different roosts. For example, Beddington Sewage Farm birds were found at Selsdon, Carshalton, Cheam Warren and Ruxley Corner roosts in the 1930s. Roost sites are mainly used from the late summer into the winter. They may be abandoned after a few years. Fly-lines may pass over one roost to get to another. A locality may be crossed by fly-lines going in different directions as, for example, at Guildford, where birds moving northeast and south were identified (Wheatley, 1972).

Potts, in his national analysis, says nothing specific about Surrey, but underlying trends, including the rise in Starling population, are reflected in Surrey information. The roosts generally build up in late summer, when they are probably made up mainly of birds that have bred in Surrey. The 1960s saw the Surrey roosts reach their maximum size. The largest on record held an estimated 600,000 birds at Ockham in December 1962. There were some 250,000 in an autumn roost south of Reigate, where the roost was reputed to have been present for thirty years, and other large roosts were in this part of Surrey. Some build up in the winter and presumably include immigrant birds. Two parties each of 20,000 Starlings were seen at Earlswood on 23rd March 1980 and were presumably related to a local roost. In subsequent years the roosting numbers have fallen very substantially and by the end of the period roosts of more than a few thousand birds were rare. The rise and fall can be roughly tracked by collected roost counts.

The rise, 1900-45. Early roost references include: *Albert Bridge*: a few on iron towers in 1926; *Battersea Park*: in 1896-97 this was the most important London roost. It was in use from June to October. In 1926 it was used as a gathering place only; *Box Hill*: a roost at the foot of Box Hill in 1939; *Cheam Warren*: a roost in 15-20 foot Elms at the old game-preserve of Nonsuch Palace was used regularly in autumns from 1924-35 intermittently up to at least 1940. In 1934 there were at least 10,000 birds in gathering-places up to a mile away from the roost. The main source of the birds was Epsom Sewage Farm (5,000-

6,000 birds on 24th July 1937), a place which itself had earlier held a roost. Others came from Beddington Sewage Farm, Coulsdon and Wallington. The roost site was later abandoned and the birds may have moved to Carshalton Beeches; *Chelsham*: flocks of thousands at Lunghurst firs, Chelsham around 1927 (Beadell); *Carshalton Beeches*: a roost in thorn bushes near St Mary's Hospital held an estimated 10,000 birds in February 1941; *East Horsley*: roost at Longhurst Road from at least 1932-40. Fly-lines in the direction of this roost came mainly from the north and west, from up to 13 miles away (Morden); *Epsom Sewage Farm*: a very large roost in 1929, apparently deserted by 1933; *Guy's Hospital*: a few hundred in 1932-33; *Jayes Park, Ockley*: first recorded in 1922. By 1933 it was drawing birds through the Mole Gap at Mickleham, eight miles away. In September 1940 an estimated 18,000 flew in the direction of the roost from Fetcham, ten miles away; *Merstham*: an autumn roost at the A23/Station Road junction for at least twenty years up to 1932; *Southwark Cathedral*: there were 60-70 in trees in April 1939. The roost was still in use in 1945; *Southwark Park*: 300-400 roosting in trees in December 1932. The roost was still in use in 1945; *Staines Reservoir*: about 60 birds roosted in the reeds of a pond southwest of the reservoir in July 1932.

The peak, 1946-90. Roosts of 1,000 or more birds include: *Ash Vale*: active from 1975, 4,000 in July 1979 and June 1981; *Badshot Lea*: 1,000 on 12th September 1979; *Banstead Downs*: a roost held 100,000 Starlings on 27th February 1973 and 120,000 on 20th February 1975, the last of the six-figure reports; *Bookham Common*: 2,000 on 11th February 1979; *Clandon Common*: 15,000 on 28th August, 1967; *Earlswood*: 10,000 on 12th February 1989; *Frensham Great Pond*: summer/autumn roost in *Phragmites* reeds, with 3,500 on 13th August 1976, 2,000 a year later and 5,000 in November 1980, 3,000 on 28th September 1981, 3,000 in July 1982, 5,000 in August 1983, about 800 in 1986, at least 1,000 in 1987, 1,600 in 1988, 5,000-6,000 in October 1989, 4,500 in July 1990; *Frensham Little Pond*: several thousand in 1979, 300 in 1988; *Frimley Gravel Pits*: 2,000 in the summer of 1979, 3,000 in August 1981; *Hedgecourt Lake*: at least 1,000 on 3rd June 1990; *Hersham Gravel Pit*: 13,000 on 13th August 1989; *Holmethorpe Sand Pits*: 2,000 on 21st September 1984, 2,500 in hawthorns on 6th August 1987; *Leigh*: 100,000 on 23rd October 1965; *Merrow Roughs*: 1,000 in December 1971; *Molesey Gravel Pit/Heath*: about 10,000 in September 1987; *Ockham*: 600,000 on 16th December 1962; *Papercourt Gravel Pits*: at least 2000 in the summer of 1983, up to 2,000 in willow scrub in 1984; south of *Reigate*: 250,000 on September 1967; *Ripley*: at least 2,000 in trees on 31st March 1972; *Wandsworth*: King George's Park held 7,000-8,200 birds in October 1982 but was deserted by December, up to 2,000 in 1985; *West Horsley*: 5,000-6,000 on 21st March 1972, 5,000 in December 1973, 3,000 in early 1974; *Wimbledon Common*: 1,500-2,000 near a roost at dusk on 4th January 1981, only 200 there on 25th January; *Wrecclesham*: at least 6,000 in trees near the floods on 13th July 1983.

The fall, 1991-2005. Roosts of 500 or more include: *Apps Court Farm Sand Pits*: 1,000 in June 1992; *Barn Elms*: 2,500 flew east to roost on 7th December 2001, about 60 roosted in a reedbed; *Beddington Sewage Farm*: 3,000 on 2nd September 1996, 2,000 in June 1997; *East Molesey*: 1,000 roosting in Green Lane on 11th September 1995; *Esher Sewage Farm*: 1,000 roosting on 13th November 2001; *Frensham Great Pond*: 2,000 in December 1994, 1,000 in December 1995, 600 in November 1998, 1,200 in October 2000; *Gatwick*: 1,000 at the Hilton Hotel on 18th August 1996; *Guildford*: 7,000 on power cables at dusk in August 1992, 2,500 roosted in the town centre on 14th August 1996, 1,500 at the bus station in August 1997; *Hedgecourt Lake*: 600 in January 2000; *Holmethorpe Sand Pits*: at least 2,500 in trees in July 1991, 5,000 in October 1994 and August 1995, 10,000 on 13th July 1997 (BHSP), 900 in 1998; *Kingston-upon-Thames*: 4,000 roosted in the town centre on 3rd December 1994, 4,000 there in 1995, 2,000 at Kingston Cemetery in May 1997 and 1,000 there in May 1998; *Molesey*: 1,000 on 30th September 1995; *Molesey Gravel Pit/Heath*: 2,000 in 1994, 5,000 in July 1995; *New Malden*: 1,000 in September 1995 and August 1996; *Papercourt Gravel Pits*: 1,000 in bushes on 14th August 1991, 1,200 in 1994, 1,000 in reeds in October 2001, gone by the end of November; *Putney*: 1,200 roosted in December

1996; *Stoke Water Meadows*: 1,000 on 26th September 1998; *Unstead Sewage Farm*: 1,000 on 8th September 1996; *Walton Reservoirs (drained Lambeth basins)*: 10,000 present at dusk on 28th June 1996, half flew north to roost elsewhere. About 2,500 roosted in May 1997, 5,000 in November 1999; *Winkworth Arboretum*: 1,000 on 27th November 1994. In 2001, the largest reported figure was a roost of 2,000 at Frensham in December. Some 2,560 flew west at Barn Elms London Wetland Centre on 15th November 2002.

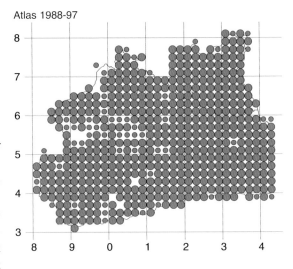

Atlas 1988-97

In Spelthorne, roost flights of up to 5,000 were seen over the Shepperton area in 1983-86 and Starlings bred there but more recent numbers have been lower. There were about 1,500 at Staines Moor on 7th February 1997 but only 200 at Staines Moor on 3rd February 2000. Counts of up to 100 were made in Spelthorne during the 2003 BTO Spring Migration Watch.

Population size. The Winter Atlas found partial survey counts and estimates totalling 14,488 birds in 1981-84, suggesting a minimum size for winter population:

Winter Atlas maximum counts from 1981 to 1984 for each 10 km square

Square	84	93	94	95	96	03	04	05	06	07	14	15	16
Count	500	175	434	200	18	500	130	200	1,000	568	200	3,000	600

Square	24	25	26	27	34	35	36	37	**Total**
Count	1,000	950	*2,002*	*522*	917	600	*354*	*618*	**14,488**

Basic field counts from observers except for any in italics, which are adjusted figures from the BTO.

Breeding season population estimates also suggest a higher winter population. The end-period figure of 12,000 territories implied by the Common Birds Census compares surprisingly well with an estimate of 62,000 adults derived from the Breeding Birds Survey. If Surrey held a proportionate share of the British population as given by the *New Atlas*, the breeding population would be nearer to 8,000 territories, or four per square km, perhaps on the low side.

Territory counts. Arbrook Common is a place where numbers have fallen, from up to 12 territories in the later 1970s to a maximum of four in the 1990s. Eastern Wood, on Bookham Common, had at least five nesting pairs in 1963 and up to 12 territories in the 1970s. By 2006, Starlings were not breeding anywhere on the common (*LN*). There are no recent counts but Starlings were still breeding in 1998. Kingston Cemetery had nine territories in 1973 but none by 1978. Brick spaces left in the walls of the London Wetland Centre at Barn Elms attracted six breeding pairs in 2005.

Nesting. Starlings have nested successfully as late as November if the weather is mild *e.g.* at Camberley in 1953 (*BB, 48:126*). One was seen to take nest material into a hole at Addlestone on 2nd November 1984.

Song. Bird song mimicked in Surrey includes that of Green Sandpiper, Golden Oriole and Cetti's Warbler.

Food. Starlings are common at garden bird feeders, taking almost anything on offer, though they seem less keen on grain and seeds. Starlings were seen eating rosechafer grubs from a two or three acre lawn at Oatlands before 1870 (*Zool., 1870:2027*) - typical behaviour for a grassland feeder. They are often seen on playing fields and lawns.

Movements. In the 1960s and 70s there were widespread reports of movements, sometimes of thousands of birds, thought to be migrants. They have been in October and November, when birds from the Baltic and other parts of northwest Europe move into Britain. The largest numbers that have been located are of 3,000 flying west at Worcester Park on 5th November 1969 and 3,000 flying west at Thames Ditton on 28th October 1972. The huge winter roosts that built up at the time give this some support. The reports have been less frequent in recent years. Foreign ringing recoveries peaked in the 1960s and 70s. In the years up to 1959 there were only four, from East Prussia, Estonia, France and the old USSR, together with a Polish-ringed bird recovered in Surrey. There were twenty foreign recoveries of Starlings ringed in Surrey from 1960 to 1979. They came from Belgium, (three), the Republic of Ireland (two), France (two), Germany (six), the Netherlands (two), Poland (one), Latvia (one) and the old USSR (three). Three Starlings ringed in Belgium were recovered in Surrey in the same period. Only nine of those ringed in Surrey during the next 25 years have so far been recovered abroad, from Belgium (three), Finland (one), France (one), the Netherlands (two) and the old USSR (two) and there have been only four more recoveries of Starlings ringed abroad. Taking the period as a whole, there were 14 recoveries of birds ringed in Surrey in October to March and recovered in the breeding season in Belgium, France, Germany, the Netherlands, Poland or the old USSR and five recoveries of birds ringed in Surrey in the breeding season and recovered in Belgium, France and the Republic of Ireland in the winter, showing both winter immigration from the east and the emigration of breeding birds from Surrey. The general picture is consistent with the roost figures. There are fewer immigrants and fewer breeding birds than there were in the 1960s.

Longevity. The longest-lived Starling for which details are available was ringed as a first-year bird at Hersham Sewage Farm on 25th July 1965 and found dead over 27 years and two months later, at nearby West Molesey on 23rd October 1992, a remarkable age for a passerine of any species. The most distant recovery was of a Starling ringed at Shirley on 14th January 1973 and recovered about 2,665 kilometres east near Yaroslavl, old USSR on May 21st of that year.

Plumage variations. Albino and 'wholly white' birds are reported from time to time. Bucknill mentioned one from Surbiton which was presented to the 'National Collection' in 1875 and he had himself seen a live bird on sale in Guildford. There was one at Hersham Sewage Farm in 1960 and others at Peaslake (1964), in the Reigate roost (1967), Charlwood (1971), Beddington Sewage Farm (1974 and 1992), Hersham Sewage Farm (1975), Queen Elizabeth II Reservoir (two in 1980), New Haw (1980 and 1982), Ockham (two in 1983), Old Coulsdon (1992), Woodmansterne (1993). Partially white birds include one at Walton [Walton-on Thames presumed] in 1970. Bucknill heard of a buff-coloured bird near Dorking. There was a similar bird at Epsom in 1993 and 1994. A Starling with an upper mandible twice the length of the normal lower mandible was seen at Farncombe in 1976 and 1977.

Rose-coloured Starling (Rosy Starling) *Sturnus roseus*

About twelve, including one from Spelthorne

Breeds from the Balkans east to Central Asia, normally wintering south to India but with westward irruptive movements in summer. The first British record is in Edwards (1743-51). It is undated. Edwards said that the stuffed bird could be seen in a Chelsea coffee house, where he had drawn it for his book and that *it was shot at Norwood near London*. Immigrants arrive most often from June to October and this is when they are usually seen in eastern and southern counties. Arrivals in other months are generally seen in the south.

Surrey. Most, where dated, fall into the main arrival period and have been seen in gardens. All are of single birds. Bucknill mentioned the Edwards record, which might have referred to the Norwood which is in Surrey, (but see Other Published Records). He gave four others.

1845:   Ditton Marsh, a female shot in May (Bucknill, 1902).

1849:   Busbridge near Godalming, one shot in a garden while feeding on berries (*SALEC*), presumed to be after 1849 since it was not mentioned by Newman. It was subsequently acquired for the Charterhouse Collection, where it could still be seen in 2001.

1857:   Dorking, one shot (Holmesdale Natural History Club).

1861:   Thames Ditton, one shot in July and preserved by Chalwin, a Molesey taxidermist (Bucknill).

1961:*   Sunbury-on-Thames, one on 9th-12th August after a SSW gale.

1971:   Surrey Docks, one on 11th August (*BB, 65:346-47*, Bermondsey).

1972:   Virginia Water, one in a garden on 31st July (Mr and Mrs P. A. M. Bishop, P. Bishop, *BB, 66:351*).

1987:   Christmas Pie, Normandy, an adult in winter plumage from 17th October (after the great gale) to 6th January 1988. Mr and Mrs D. R. Tier reported it to SBC on 4th November (J. M. Clark, Mr and Mrs J. R. Romaine, Mr and Mrs D. R. Tier *et al., BB, 81:588* with photograph, *BB, 82:554*).

1996:   Bookham, one in a garden on 23rd-25th September, associating with Starlings (Mrs F. Prince, *BB, 90:505*).

1997:   Battersea Power Station, one on 15th August (B. Mist, *BB, 92:602*).

2001:   New Malden, a juvenile on 6th October (D. Millington, *BB, 95:518*).

2002:   West Horsley, one on 8th July in the year of a national spring influx (T. Harris).

Spelthorne

House Sparrow   *Passer domesticus*
Locally common breeding resident

A native resident of Europe, North Africa and much of Asia with an introduced range covering many other parts of the world. Mostly sedentary though a few birds ringed in Britain have been recovered on the near Continent (*MA*). Numbers in England had increased substantially before 1800 and continued to rise during the 19th century. They fell sharply in the 1920s, following the replacement of the horse by the internal combustion engine. Farmland House Sparrows have declined since the 1970s due to changes in farming practice. There has been a massive decline in the urban population (Summers-Smith, 2003). National numbers have stabilised since 1994 (*BTO News 266*) but the decline has continued in south-east England.

Early Surrey history. Gilbert White saw House Sparrows building nests in South Lambeth on 27th February 1779. Newman listed them for the Godalming district. House Sparrows were abundant at all times and seasons in the Norwood district (Aldridge) and 'pretty numerous' on Wimbledon Common

(Hamilton) during the 1880s. Richard Jefferies' earlier quoted observation in the late 19th century that *Sparrows crowd every hedge and field, their numbers are incredible* shows just how common they must have been at this time. Bucknill described House Sparrows as abundant residents that formed huge flocks in autumn and frequented stubble fields. They were often unpopular because of the damage they did to crops. Sparrow Clubs were formed in many parishes to destroy the birds (Jordan, 1894). Bucknill wrote that the parish might pay a bounty for each dozen eggs found. Many were also trapped by birdcatchers, either for shooting from traps (see also the Starling) or for millinery purposes. The wings would be cut off, dyed, and used to decorate hats and bonnets. The birds were caught with clap nets by day and with bat-fowling nets at night. Sparrows were cooked for the farmhouse table in a variety of ways. Beadell collected up to fifty eggs at a time on Bugg Hill Farm, when he worked there. He gave then to the cat. Boorman had eggs from Send in his collection. Hudson (1898) had a more sensitive view of the urban Sparrow: *In London there are no grain-growers and market gardeners, consequently there is no tiresome sparrow question, and no sparrow-clubs to vex the tender-hearted. These sparrows were not to be thought about in relation to agriculture, but were simply little birds, too often, in many a weary mile, in many an unlovely district, the only representatives of the avian class, flying to and fro, chirping and chirruping from dawn to dark.*

1900 to 1990. For a while, agricultural practice and the use of horse transport in towns provided conditions that favoured House Sparrows but with the loss of the horses things began to change. Numbers remained strong in more rural areas such as Richmond Park, where there was a winter roost of several thousand in Rhododendrons in the 1930s. The increased area of cornfields in the Chelsham area after 1939 drew large flocks to feed on the ripening ears. Large roosts were still being found on the North Downs up to 1960. Population densities in town areas were high. There were five birds per acre (1,200 per square km) in Battersea Park in the springs of 1945 and 1950 and four birds per acre (990 per square km) in Lambeth during the 1950 breeding season (*BLA*). From then on there was a striking decline at Battersea Park. Nicholson counted 1,058 House Sparrows in the spring of 1950, falling to 541 in 1964, 448 in 1975, 198 in 1980 and 92 in 1991 (Nicholson, 1995). Forty-six pairs raised about 150 young at Battersea Park in 1989. The 600 acres of Beddington Sewage Farm held an average of 70 pairs of House Sparrows (similar to the number of Tree Sparrow pairs) in 1954 and 1955, an average of 1.1 pairs per ten acres (29 per square km).

Trend since 1970. In spite of the decline, House Sparrows remained widely distributed throughout the period, at least in urban areas. The 1988-94 LNHS Atlas showed House Sparrows to be present in every Surrey tetrad but one at some time in the period, a net increase of three on the results from the 1968-72 LNHS Atlas survey. The percentage of homes reporting the presence of House Sparrows in a survey of London Boroughs carried out between 18th June and 19th July 2002 was: Lambeth 61.5-72.5, Southwark 61.5-72.5, Wandsworth 50.5-61.5, Croydon 61.5-72.5, Kingston 72.5-83.5, Merton 72.5-83.5, Richmond 61.5-72.5 and Sutton 72.5-83.5 (RSPB 2002). The sample was selected by the observers, making estimates of total numbers unreliable, but it showed House Sparrows to be well distributed in the suburbs. The Common Birds Census showed a significant increase from 1970 to 2000 but was based on a thin and changing sample and was probably not representative of the change in numbers.

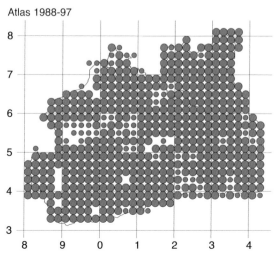

Atlas 1988-97

The decline was more obvious in rural areas and some urban areas also experienced losses. House Sparrows were recorded at Vann Lake in every month from 1964 to 1988 but very infrequently in later years (Blaker Log). RSPB garden surveys at Croydon showed a decline from a presence in 91% of gardens in 1995 to 70% in 2000 and 61% in 2003. Some areas show recent stability. There were 22 nests at Park Farm, Chessington in 1993, 19 in 1994, 16 in 1995, 15 in 1996, 19 in 1997, 13 in 1998, nine in 1999 and 21 in 2000. In Spelthorne, House Sparrows were common breeding residents in residential and commercial areas of Shepperton in the 1980s. They were widely reported, with counts of up to thirty, in the 2003 BTO Spring Migration Watch. The largest flocks reported to the Surrey Bird Club for 2001 were ninety in a Farnham garden in December and fifty at South Norwood Country Park in August - good figures compared with the previous few years. A hundred and twenty roosting on the Slyfield Industrial Estate at Guildford in October 2003 (J. Gates) was large by modern standards.

The decline of the House Sparrows has taken many people by surprise and seems not well understood. Power (1910) mentioned their destruction of flowers in South London gardens, a habit common in the 1960s, when they would wantonly destroy the spring crocuses in gardens, especially the yellow ones, and black cotton would have to be deployed to keep them off. In these same gardens now, they are often only rare visitors. Many factors have been blamed, mostly based on the tidying up of buildings (reducing nest sites), farmland and streets (reducing food), along with radiation from mobile phones and the decline of the horse. In Croydon, habitat change was thought to have been a factor. Sparrows were lost from several gardens after roofing or guttering work was carried out. At Oxted in 1999 House Sparrows were holding on where older houses allowed access for nesting. Another factor in the decline must have been the loss of stubble fields for winter foraging.

Nest sites. About a third of the participants in the RSPB survey of London mentioned above reported nesting in homes and parks, most often in bushes, shrubs and hedges (38% of nests) and roof spaces (36%).

Population size. An estimate based on the Common Birds Census gives a level of 16,000 territories at the end of the period which is surprisingly close to an estimate of 36,000 adults based on the Breeding Birds Survey. If Surrey held a proportionate share of the British population as given by the *New Atlas*, the population would be nearer to 26,000 territories, or 12.7 per square km, which is higher than either of these, but based on a period when the decline was not so advanced. The Winter Atlas found partial survey counts and estimates totalling 3,263 birds in 1981-84, suggesting a minimum size for winter population, well under the likely size, being a sample, but the only broadly-based estimate count for the period.

Large flocks and roosts. There have been no counts in excess of 10,000 since the 1960s and none over 1,000 since the 1980s apart from the aggregate in the Winter Atlas.

Flocks:

Beddington Sewage Farm: *c.*300, 8th September 1974; 400, 11th July 1980 and August-November 1982

Holmethorpe Sand Pits: up to 500 were reported in the 1960s *e.g.* 500 on stubble, 4th September 1966

Lyne Old Sewage Farm: 400, 11th September and 3rd October 1970

Papercourt Gravel Pits: *c.*1,000, October-December 1972

Richmond Park: 2,710, 21st January 1936

Surrey Docks: *c.*700, October 1975; 140, 31st March 1998

Tolworth: *c.*600, October 1974; 700, October 1975

Unstead Sewage Farm: Up to 200 in winter before 1960 (CNHS)

Wimbledon: 550; 27th December 1988

Roosts:

Banstead Downs: several thousand, December 1950;

18,000 counted into roost on Banstead Downs, 22nd November 1960, total number not counted

near Croydon: 10,000 roosting in autumn in the 1950s (Summers-Smith, 1956), the birds travelling up to three miles

Farthing Down: separate winter roosts of *c.*500 and *c.*300 in 1974

Frimley Gravel Pits: *c.*200, 17th December 1971

Milford: 1,000, 1st September 1973

Mitcham: 150 in town centre, 6th October 1984

Mitcham Common: 5,000 roosted in the winter months of 1953 and from July 1955 (*LBR*); 6,000+ in 1958

Mortlake: 210 in London Planes, 4th February 1981; *c.*270 in the trees, 3rd February 1982; *c.*700, 2nd February 1983

Motspur Park: several thousand, December 1950

Richmond Park: 2,710, 21st January 1936 (Collenette)

South Norwood Country Park: 200+ in trees, November-December 1983; 120+, 4th February 1984

outside Southwark Cathedral: 1,200 in London Planes, February 1937 (*BLA*).

Stoke Lake: 381 left a Blackthorn roost, 31st October 1995; 284 left, 2nd March 1996.

Tooting: *c.*2,200 in trees at St George's Hospital, 29th October 1982

West Horsley: *c.*500 roosting in hedges and a barn, 1974

Food. House Sparrows are basically grain feeders but they have been known to take a variety of other foods:

Farnham Sewage Farm: 200+ feeding on weeds, 27th October 1976

Godstone: 30+ on arable land, 21st August 1982

Holmethorpe Sand Pits: *c.*400, 4th August 1985; 500+ feeding in stubble, 4th September 1966

Milford: *c.*100 destroyed *c.*2,000 lettuce seedlings in a glass-house in October 1975

New Addington: 200-300 on wheat, 14th August 1975

Riddlesdown: *c.*300 on stubble, 19th October 1976

Sanderstead: 300+ feeding in standing corn, 1st September 1973

West Horsley: *c.*800 feeding on grain, 16th March 1974

William Curtis Ecological Park, Bermondsey: up to 50 stripped 100 square metres of barley in two days in 1978

Movements and longevity. Few House Sparrows move very far, but one ringed at Aston Abbotts, Buckinghamshire on 21st March 1987 was recovered 68 kilometres southeast, at Ewell on 12th March 1990. Homing experiments have shown that House Sparrows, although non-migratory, can navigate over short distances. A House Sparrow trapped at Virginia Water in 1949 and released three miles away got back safely. Of 21 birds caught at Richmond and released eight miles away, nine were released individually and four of them returned. The others were released in groups of five and seven and none of them returned (Summers-Smith, 1956).

The very large number of House Sparrows ringed at Beddington Sewage Farm have yielded three recoveries, from the Pilgrims Way near Dartford, Fulham Gas Works and Sutton (J. P. Allan, *Surrey Birders*).

House Sparrows can be surprisingly long-lived. One ringed as an adult at Little Bookham on 23rd October 1965 was recovered at the same place nine years and six months later, on 23rd April 1975. Birds infected with Salmonellosis were found at Sanderstead in the four years to 1968 and in 1970 and with *Salmonella typhimurium* at Oxted in 1971.

Plumage variations. House Sparrows sometimes have the odd white feather in their plumage and leucistic birds are reported from time to time. Power saw a pure white one in Dulwich Park in 1903. There were other albinos at Albury and Limpsfield 1934 and at Old Coulsdon in 1971. A leucistic bird was seen at Badshot Lea in 1980. The lower mandible of a male visiting a bird table at Epsom in December 1972 was over an inch (2.5 cm) in length. It was able to feed by scooping sideways.

Behaviour. House Sparrows sometimes get into the London Underground. One was found 120 feet below ground level on a platform at London Bridge on 5th November 1990 and one was caught on a train at Vauxhall on 21st June 1991.

Tree Sparrow (Eurasian Tree Sparrow)

Passer montanus

Uncommon breeding resident

Breeds across Europe and Asia to Japan. In the eastern part of the range, where House Sparrows are absent, Tree Sparrows replace them as the common sparrows in towns. The British range appears to have been expanding out from the Midlands and eastern counties in the 19th century, but it was still an uncommon Surrey breeding species in 1900, better known as a winter visitor. The British population remained stable until the 1930s and then went into decline. A large expansion of numbers and range began around 1958. The 1968-72 BTO Atlas was prepared at a time when the British population was close to the maximum. Numbers have fallen by at least 90% since the 1970s, taking Tree Sparrows back to a degree of rarity which, in Surrey, may be greater than it was in Bucknill's time. British Tree Sparrows are mostly sedentary, though prior to 1981 a few birds ringed in Britain were recovered on the near Continent and continental-ringed birds have been found in Britain (*MA*).

Early Surrey history. In the first half of the 19th century, Tree Sparrows were somewhat scarce as residents, but more numerous in winter, at Claremont (Meyer), Godalming (Newman) and Tooting (Blyth). There was an enormous winter influx, with Bramblings, at Tilford in 1843 (*Zool., 1843:188* in Bucknill) and there was an abundance in some years at Churt. Bucknill only detailed three breeding sites: a colony of about twenty pairs in willows near Epsom until 1895, a record of nesting at Woking in 1899 and an old record of nesting at Wimbledon. They were fairly frequent autumn visitors to the Dulwich area up to 1895 but then scarce (Power).

1900 to 1949. Tree Sparrows were irregular in Richmond Park around 1900. A pair bred there in 1905 (Mouritz, 1905) but by the 1930s Collenette could describe them as common summer residents and they bred there annually up to at least 1976. A pair bred near a waterworks in the Redhill area in 1905 (G. T. Winter). Boorman collected eggs at Ockham (1908) and Send (1907, 1918). Beadell (1932) described them as rare in the Warlingham district, where they remained uncommon into the 1950s (Pounds). There was a small colony at Tadworth in 1934. The colony at Beddington, where the Tree Sparrow bred in 1912, 1914 and 1929-34 was the largest in Surrey at the time, as it still is. It held 240 birds on 3rd March 1935. Other breeding places in the period were at Ham (1949), Mitcham (1946), Richmond (1936, 1948-49) and Walton-on-Thames (1948, 1949). Flocks included 120 at Ham Gravel Pits on 22nd November 1942. In Spelthorne, Kerr found several nests in the sides of a haystack at Staines in 1906. By 1935 many were nesting in the area and flocks of over fifty were being seen at the reservoirs at the end of July.

1950 to 1970. There were 11 pairs at Beddington Sewage Farm in 1950 and 44 nests in 1951. In 1952 there were 51 pairs on the sewage farm and 15 more in the nearby Beddington Park. There were 40-50 pairs in 1953 and 78 pairs in 1955, with a flock of about 300 birds in March. Mitcham held two pairs in 1953. Tree Sparrows nested on and around Guildford Sewage Farm from 1953 or earlier, with about 30 birds resident in 1956 and a winter flock of around 100. Tree Sparrows also bred at Elmers End Sewage Farm, Ham Gravel Pit (1951) and in other places further from central London (*BLA*) including Walton Gravel Pits in the 1950s. Up to five pairs bred at Unstead Sewage Farm in the 1950s, where up to 30 (12th January 1955) would winter. They bred irregularly up to at least 1976 at Ham House. Breeding pairs were predominantly found in the north of the county. None came from the southwestern heaths and few from the farmlands in the southeast. In Spelthorne, in 1955, 87 nests were located in an area between Perry Oaks and Stanwell Moor.

A 1960-61 survey found 70 pairs at Beddington, 44-54 in the Addlestone/Weybridge area, 26 at Walton-on-Thames and 38 at other places in the London area (Sage, 1963). The survey did not cover Spelthorne or Epsom Sewage Farm. Away from Beddington, the 1960s were a high water mark for Tree Sparrows in Surrey, in terms of both breeding and wintering numbers. Tree Sparrows did not breed in the Haslemere district up to 1967, where they were rare winter visitors, only seen at Thursley until the 1950s and then were wintering more widely by 1967. There were up to 700 at Addington in November 1961, the largest count on record. At Guildford Sewage Farm, numbers in 1960 peaked at 400-500 on 22nd January (*SBR*) and the same number were at Unstead Sewage Farm in 1968. Smaller winter flocks, of up to 200 birds, could be found elsewhere in the 1960s (Parr) and in southwest Surrey in the 1970s (HNHS, 1980). There were 250 at Holmethorpe on 25th February 1962. Other large counts are tabulated below.

Breeding after 1970. Of the 231 tetrads in northeast Surrey, 55% were found to hold territories in the 1968-72 Atlas survey but only 10% in the 1988-97 Atlas, a good measure of the decline. A pair bred in a nest box at Brook in 1972. Others nested at Vann Lake in 1971 and 1972. There was a small colony at Godstone water works in 1978 and birds were present in the breeding season at Povey Cross in 1985. A colony at Holmethorpe was nesting in old Sand Martin holes in the 1970s and 80s. Tree Sparrows last bred there in 1992 (*BHSP*). There were 25 pairs at Hedgecourt in 1979 and 1980 and a few pairs at Itchingwood Common in 1992. Falling numbers became noticeable in the early 1980s, both in winter flocks and breeding pairs. At East Horsley, where there had been 20-30 breeding pairs and winter flocks of up to 400 birds in 1975, the Tree Sparrow was reduced to a rare winter visitor by 1981. There were about 150 at West Hill, Elstead on 28th February 1976. No Tree Sparrow territories were recorded in the Common Birds Census after 1983 but the Winter Atlas found partial survey counts and estimates totalling 587 birds in 1981-84, suggesting a minimum size for winter population. Tree Sparrows were found in twenty of the twenty-one 10 km squares surveyed.

Beddington Sewage Farm has long been the premier Surrey and London locality for Tree Sparrows. In 1987 there were winter flocks of up to 300 but the breeding population was down to 15-20 pairs. Until this time they had been breeding in holes in hedges, trees and dykes and available nest sites were being reduced by structural changes on the sewage farm. A far-sighted initiative by Simon Aspinall and others resulted in a hundred nest boxes being set up there in March 1992 and these soon became the location of a healthy and increasing resident population. Several papers in the *Beddington Farm Bird Report* and elsewhere describe the Nest Box project, which now has about 200 boxes. Supplementary feeding was begun in 1998. In the year 2001, a total of 165 nesting attempts were made in the boxes, hatching a minimum of 593 young (Netherwood *et al.*, 2003). Over 800 fledglings were ringed in 2006 (N. Gardner in *LNHSB*).

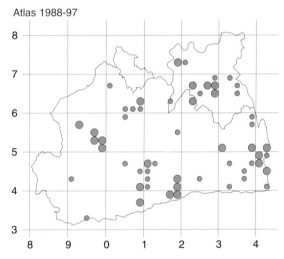

Atlas 1988-97

The Beddington colony, which is thought to be second only to one at Rutland Water in size, has an uncertain future because of continued development activity.

Tree Sparrows, away from Beddington Sewage Farm, have become extremely scarce and there have been no further breeding records since a pair bred at Oxted in 1994 and no significant winter flocks. Tree Sparrows fared similarly in Spelthorne. In 1982, 25 pairs bred at Queen Mary Gravel Pits. Rather fewer bred in the following year and by 1988 they had almost gone. There were two pairs at Perry Oaks Sewage Farm in 1987 and up to 25 in May and June 1989. Three or four pairs bred in 1991 and there were three pairs from 1993 to 1995 and two in 1996. They were present in the 1997 and 1998 breeding seasons but none bred in 1999. At Staines Moor there were two pairs in 1989. A few records came from Shepperton Gravel Pits up to 1986 but they have probably not bred in the Shepperton area since. Four at Perry Oaks Sewage Farm on 25th March 2000 did not apparently breed.

As typical farmland birds, Tree Sparrows may have been favoured by agricultural changes in the 19th century, but they have been hard hit by the late 20th century changes in agricultural methods, notably in the management of arable land in winter, that have hit other farmland birds (Shrubb).

Nesting. Oaks and willows were found to be the commonest London area nest sites by Sage, with about 6% in concrete structures and machinery. In 1976 a pair bred in old gravel extraction machinery at Ash Vale Gravel Pits and in 1978 a pair bred in a hole in the roof of a concrete hut at North Camp Gravel Pits (*HSBBR*). Garden nest boxes have been used in rural areas. At Beddington, where the original population used holes in trees and banks, virtually all the birds are now using nest boxes.

Large counts. At one time large winter flocks could be found across the county on farmland and at sewage farms. Now only the Beddington flock remains:

Beddington Sewage Farm: 400, January/February 1972; 350, January 1993

Berrylands: 250 on waste ground, 11th February 1973; *c*.300, January 1974; 150+ on wasteland, 5th January 1975; 100, 1983 and 1984

Dorking: *c*.200, 27th January 1962

Elmers End Sewage Farm: 150-200 October/November 1934 and November 1935; 60+, 3rd March 1980.

Elstead: *c*.150 at West Hill, 28th February 1976; 200+ at Red House Farm, 12th March 1977; 100 at Red House Farm, 23rd January 1983

Farleigh: *c*.200, 19th February 1972

Foxwarren Park: *c*.140, 13th August 1961

Guildford Sewage Farm: *c*.350, 2nd February 1968

Holmethorpe: 250, 25th February 1962; 155, 18th December 1972; 200, 5th January 1973, *c*.150 in March 1976 and December 1977; the last three figure flock was 100 on 24th February 1985 (*BHSP*) with smaller numbers until the late 1990s

Leatherhead Sewage Farm: *c*.200 on ploughed land, 5th November 1944

Lower Ashtead: *c*.300, 15th January 1977

Lyne Old Sewage Farm: 300, 18th October 1970

Ockham: 200 in a Brussels Sprouts field, 24th November 1973

Papercourt Gravel Pits: up to 500 from October-December 1972, 250+ on 26th January 1975

Ripley Sewage Farm: *c*.250, February 1974, falling to *c*.50 by mid April

Send Gravel Pits: 300, December 1968

Surbiton Cemetery: *c*.150, 14th February 1976

Unstead Sewage Farm: 400-500, March/April 1968; *c*.250, 11th February 1962; *c*.150, 4th March 1973

Walton Reservoirs: 150, 21st November 1976

Wimbledon Common: 100-120, 21st December 1976

Worcester Park Sewage Farm: 80, 20th February 1971

Spelthorne

Perry Oaks: over 100 July 1952, 1953; *c*.300, 10th December 1960; only four, 25th March 2000

Staines Moor: *c*.150, 10th March 1939

Roosts include 200 at Queen Mary Reservoir on 15th December 1973 (Geen) and about 50 in hawthorn at Walton Reservoirs in October-December 1970.

Movements and longevity. The big flocks used to be in the winter but their summer locations were not known. Breeding numbers at the flock sites were much lower but there are no foreign ringing recoveries and few from elsewhere in the UK. A Tree Sparrow ringed at Redhill on 15th December 1961 was recovered 171 kilometres north, near Bourne, Lincolnshire on 11th May 1962. There is at least one other movement of over 100 kilometres. A Tree Sparrow ringed at Stoke D'Abernon on 11th January 1970 was recovered over five years and three months later at Cobham, on 5th May 1975. Surrey Bird Reports since 1977 have mentioned a longevity record of five years four months, which probably refers to this bird.

Behaviour. A Tree Sparrow in a Langshott garden in 1994 consistently fed juvenile House Sparrows.

Chaffinch
Common breeding resident

Fringilla coelebs

Breeds across Europe to western Siberia and in North Africa. Numbers and range have been relatively stable in Britain and the number has increased in recent years. Northern and eastern birds are migratory, wintering within or a little south of the breeding range. The females begin to migrate in autumn before the males (*BWP* in *Migration Atlas*). British breeding birds rarely move far but they are joined by immigrants from continental Europe northeast to the Baltic (*MA*).

Early Surrey history. Gilbert White heard Chaffinch song in South Lambeth on 19th February 1782. Chaffinches were listed for the Godalming district by Newman (1849) and, overall, they seem to have been fairly common in the 19th century. They were breeding in the Norwood district in the 1880s, with song from the end of January (Aldridge), were quite numerous on Wimbledon Common (Hamilton) and they were common in Richmond Park (Mouritz, 1905).

1900 to 1970. Power described Chaffinches as by no means plentiful in South London in 1909 but Boorman collected many eggs at Clandon Common, Ockham, Ripley and Send from 1902 to 1910. Eggs were collected at Shackleford in 1923 and at Frensham and Hindhead in the 1930s. There were some extremely large flocks, for example at least 1,000 at Warlingham in 1913. Specific information for the subsequent period up to the 1960s is rather sparse, but they appear to have remained common over the period with, for example, 100 at Unstead Sewage Farm on 26th January 1956 (CNHS, 1959) and at least 500 at Nonsuch Park in 1969. There were also large movements, with some of the highest recorded figures in 1968.

Trend since 1970. As with some other passerines, trend indicators are a little contradictory. The Common Birds Census shows a significant increase of about 60% from 1970 to 2000. Of the 231 tetrads in northeast Surrey, 93% were found to hold territories in the 1968-72 Atlas survey but only 88% in the 1988-97 Atlas, a small contraction of range. Some Common Birds Census sites show little change but at Ashtead Common there were 21 territories in 2002 compared with one in the early 1980s. Chaffinches have not bred on Cannon Hill Common since 1980 and they no longer breed in Morden Hall Park. The large counts detailed below suggest a decline in the number wintering (which includes immigrants). The last count as high as 1,000 was in 1988.

Population size. The Winter Atlas found partial survey counts and estimates totalling 2,682 birds in 1981-84, which probably included immigrants. It is obviously too low as a total but suggests that there were nearly seven Chaffinches for each Brambling, a more interesting result. An estimated 49,000 territories (24 per square km) at the end of the period derived from the Common Birds Census compares with a figure of 20,000 adults derived from Breeding Birds Survey. If Surrey held a proportionate share of the British population as given by the *New Atlas*, the population would be nearer to 39,000 territories, or 19 per square km, which may be a closer estimate. Chaffinches remain widely distributed. They were present in 546 of the 575 tetrads in the 1988-97 Surrey Atlas, including all of those away from the London area.

Territory counts. Numbers have been fairly stable at Frensham, with 45 singing males in 1982, 38 in 1992, 57 in 1993, 37 in 1994, 40 in 1995, 55 in 1996, 55 in 1997, 40 in 1998,

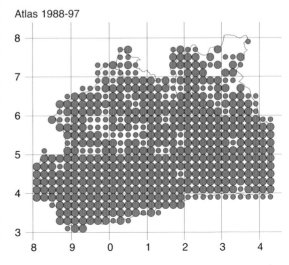

Atlas 1988-97

and 44 in 1999 on an incomplete, but consistent survey. A full survey by S. P. Peters in 2004 found 89 territories. At Wimbledon Common there were 47 territories in 1986 and 41 in 1995. There were nineteen territories at Moor Park and eight territories at Hyde Copse, Churt in 1980. Up to eight pairs bred at Littleton Lakes (Spelthorne) in 1986. A pair bred at Battersea Park in 1988. Unstead Sewage Farm held 25 pairs in 1998. With about 90 pairs, the Chaffinch was the commonest breeding bird on Hankley Common in 2002 (J. A. Little). The Plains area of Bookham Common had 30 territories in 2002, a population density of 77 per square km (A. D. Prowse).

Song. Chaffinch song is sometimes heard in winter. One was heard at West Horsley on 30th November 1973, one at Haslemere on 27th December 1973 and one at Wormley on 22nd January 1980.

Large counts. Winter flocks of up to 200 birds have been widely reported. Many of the birds in these flocks would have been of local origin but some would have been immigrants. The largest flocks, and all those of over 300 since 1970 are these:

Elstead: 1,000+ at Red House Farm, 23rd December 1988 and dates to 23rd February 1989

Frensham: 300 +, October/November 1978

Guildford: 500 with Bramblings, 4th January 1971

Hersham: 300-400, 4th December 1991

Merrist Wood College: 500, 27th February 1993

Nonsuch Park: 500+ including only 40 males, 21st March 1969

near Polesden Lacey: 400, 20th February 1983

Tilhill: up to 400, November 1979; 600, January 1980. These large flocks were attracted by stacks of spent hops.

Virginia Water: 1,000, 29th December 1976

Walton Heath: 300+, 11th November 1977

Warlingham: 1,000+ at Halliloo Farm, March 1913

West Horsley: over 300, 12th January 1974

There were roosts of up to 500 at Queen Mary Reservoir in the 1970s, (*e.g.* on 12th December 1973) but many fewer by 1988 (Geen).

Movements. Power described Chaffinches as plentiful autumn migrants in South London. Movement was especially noticeable from 7th October to 5th November 1902, when he saw many thousands pass over his Brixton garden and thought he missed nine-tenths of those that passed. They remain conspicuous autumn migrants, flying low on sunny mornings in October and November. Typically they move in small parties, totalling a hundred or two on a good day. The movements are probably broad-fronted, so that site counts are indicative of much larger numbers on the move. The 2,550 that flew WNW over Dulwich on dates from 26th September to 5th November 1957 and westward movements at Worcester Park in October 1968 that peaked at 1,100 on the 15th, point to tens and perhaps even hundreds of thousands of Chaffinches passing through Surrey. In October 1981, counts of about 300 over Wandsworth in five and a half hours on the 21st and at least 200 flying over Beddington Sewage Farm in two and a half hours on the 24th were larger than most, as were the 537 flying west in two and three quarter hours at the Surrey Docks on 14th October 1997. The Surrey Docks saw fairly large movements in 1998, with 691 west on 15th October and 423 mostly west between 0650 and 1030 hrs on 6th November. Some 960 flew west over Barn Elms on 11th November 2001.

Chaffinches have been recovered abroad from Belgium (five), the Republic of Ireland (one), France (two), Germany (six), the Netherlands (three), Norway (nine), Spain (one) and Sweden (six). There have been Surrey recoveries of birds ringed in Belgium (three), Denmark (one), the Netherlands (two), Norway (one), Sweden (one) and the old USSR (two). None of the foreign recoveries is of a bird ringed in Surrey in the breeding season, supporting the suggestion in the *Migration Atlas* that British breeding birds rarely move far. May-July recoveries of Surrey-ringed birds have come from Norway and Sweden, consistent with winter immigration from Scandinavia. The two recoveries of birds ringed in the old USSR both relate to ringing at Kaliningrad in October. A Chaffinch ringed at Chessington on 1st February 1958 was recovered about 1,550 kilometres northeast, at Steinkjer, Norway in May of the same year. A flock of 300 males at Leatherhead Downs on 28th December 1986 and another of at least fifty females at Walton Downs on 23rd March 1979 support the *Migration Atlas* suggestion that males and females tend to migrate at different times.

Longevity. A Chaffinch ringed at Caterham on 8th January 1970 and recovered there over ten years and three months later, on 26th April 1980 is the longest-lived on file.

Plumage variations. Bond's collection included one from Staines that had the head, neck and part of the breast and wings white (*Zool.*, 1889). Bucknill had seen white and buff specimens. There was a leucistic bird at Beddington Sewage Farm in November and December 1999.

Brambling   *Fringilla montifringilla*
Moderately common winter visitor

Breeds from Norway east through northern Siberia and has occasionally bred in Scotland. Almost all Bramblings winter south of the breeding range, from Britain, central and southern Europe east to Japan. Bramblings ringed in Britain in winter have been recovered south to southern France in subsequent winters and northeast to Scandinavia and Finland in the breeding season (*MA*).

Early Surrey history. Bramblings were irregular winter visitors to Godalming and other parts of Surrey in the 1830s. Large numbers appeared in 1835 and in the cold winter of 1836. 'Immense' flocks appeared near Farnham during the winter of 1842/43. The winters of 1863/64 and 1871/72 brought in large numbers and many were seen in 1892 and 1893. Places mentioned by Bucknill include Banstead, Caterham, Chobham, Cobham, Dorking, Eashing, East Molesey, Epsom, Gatton, Guildford, Headley, Mickleham, Thursley, Windlesham, Witley and Wotton. They were regular autumn migrants over Power's Brixton garden until Brixton and Herne Hill became connected by continuous bricks and mortar (Power, 1910).

1900 to 1993. There were further big arrivals in Surrey during the winters of 1905/06, 1919, 1920/21 and 1922/23 with, for example, about 150 at Titsey on 11th February 1906. Bentham saw about eight at Titsey on 17th April 1910. There were exceptional numbers at Warlingham in 1929. In Spelthorne, there were two near Staines Reservoirs on 12th January 1908 (Kerr). Large counts from the 1930s include 300 at Tadworth on 9th March 1930, about 360 at Beddington Sewage Farm on 22nd March 1931, flocks of 100 in Richmond Park in the winter of 1934/35 and about 400 at Hedgecourt in 1935. Unusual numbers were present in the London area in early 1950, though in the Surrey part of it, the largest flock was 50, at Beddington Sewage Farm. In February 1953 there were 200-300 at Epsom. In 1956 there were 250 with Chaffinches at Unstead Sewage Farm on 26th January and at least 300 at Perry Oaks Sewage Farm in March. Beddington Sewage Farm held large numbers in the 1970s with about 500 on 8th March 1970, about 1,000 on 1st March 1974 and at least 500 on 2nd March 1979. Old Woking also had many Bramblings in early 1979. At Queen Mary Reservoir there were about 150 on 28th February 1965 (Geen) and at least 100 on 29th December 1973. The Winter Atlas found partial survey counts and estimates totalling 406 birds in 1981-84. None were found in four of the 21 10 km squares surveyed.

Since 1994. As the table shows, Brambling numbers have fallen sharply since 1994, a possible consequence of milder winters:

Vice-county monthly totals reported

Year	Jan	Feb	Mar	Apr	May	Jun	Jul	Aug	Sep	Oct	Nov	Dec	Total
1994	297	605	263	295						54	123	19	**1,656**
1995	156	66	91	114	1					85	20	85	**618**
1996	37	16	63	23	1				1	36	26	31	**234**
1997	275	16	40	186						163	26	169	**875**

1998	284	364	486	120	1					86	54	40	**1,435**
1999	303	21	262	13				1		37	19	34	**690**
2000	31	97	139	138						19	23	4	**451**
2001	2	6	3	4						22	54	61	**152**
Total	**1,385**	**1,191**	**1,347**	**893**	**3**	**0**	**0**	**1**	**1**	**502**	**345**	**443**	**6,111**

Bramblings have been occasional visitors to Battersea Park and the Surrey Docks.

Calendar. One in Dulwich Wood on 9th May 1909 was Power's latest spring record for the area (Power, 1910). The average arrival date in the London area south of the Thames from 1929 to 1939 was 15th October. More recently the average arrival dates have been earlier. Average final departure dates have been getting later.

Average	1970s	1980s	1990s
Arrival	5th October	5th October	8th October
Departure	25th April	26th April	28th April

Early and late dates are:

Arrivals		Departures	
5th-15th August 1984	Dorking, in a garden	11th May 1996	Winterfold
17th-18th August 1999	Lightwater, a female	15th May 1995	Dulwich Park
7th September 1953	Chase, Haslemere	24th May 1960	Wisley
26th September 1992	Capel	12th June 1938	Wimbledon Common

Breeding. A hen Brambling, apparently mated to a cock Chaffinch, was seen on a nest in Battersea Park in June 1967. The nest was later disturbed (Miss M. C. L. Christopher). The Brambling, which had a blue ring on its leg, was presumably an escape.

Large counts. The largest counts date back to the 1970s and earlier:

Beddington Sewage Farm: *c*.1,000, 1st March 1974

Camberley: *c*.1,000 in Royal Military Academy woods, January 1954

Chipstead: 600-800, 14th March 1959

Epsom Downs: *c*.400, 16th-17th March 1957

Hedgecourt: *c*.400 in nearby fields, 9th February 1935

Hersham Sewage Farm: *c*.400, 14th February 1960

Norbury Park: 400, 20th February 1994; 500 at nearby Westhumble, 25th February 1994

Old Woking: 300-500, 27th January 1979.

Tilhill Nurseries: 300-500, January 1980

Warlingham: thousands under beeches at Slynes Road, spring 1929

Roosts. There are very few records of roosts. Thirty or more roosted with Lesser Redpolls in Rhododendrons at Effingham on 29th December 1973.

Food. Bramblings are particularly associated with beech woods, where large numbers may be found in some winters. They also feed on cones in pine trees and many fed on the piles of spent hops at Tilhill Nursery in the 1970s and 80s. Bramblings have been seen feeding on Mountain Ash berries at Frensham. Five took cherry blossom buds at Haslemere in 1991. One fed on peanuts in a suspended nut basket at Addiscombe on 4th March 1972 (*BB*, 65:445), apparently the first time this behaviour had been reported in Britain. Since then, they have become frequent winter visitors to some gardens, generally feeding on sunflower seeds and grain.

Movements. The tabulated monthly totals show some evidence of passage migration in October and March and larger arrivals in January. Bramblings are often scarce in November and December. Spring passage is generally in February and March. Bentham saw 300 Bramblings flying northeast at Tadworth on 9th March 1930 (Parr). One that was ringed at Bullswater Common on 2nd January 1997 and recovered over three years and three months later, 1,886 kilometres northeast at Riihikallio, Finland on 20th April 2000, is the furthest travelled among the recovered birds. There are other foreign recoveries from

Belgium (two), Denmark (one), France (one) and Norway (two). Single birds from Belgium and the Netherlands have been recovered in Surrey. A Brambling ringed at Albury in March 1999, was controlled at Hilborough, Norfolk, in the following two winters.

Longevity. A Brambling that was ringed in Finland on 8th May 1976 and recovered over three years and seven months later at Frensham on 1st January 1980 showed the greatest longevity.

Serin (European Serin)   *Serinus serinus*

Three vice-county birds

Serins breed from the Baltic south to North Africa and east to Turkey. A few have bred in southern Britain. Most winter in southern Europe. They have appeared in Britain in all months of the year, with peaks in April and November. Most records, particularly in autumn, are from southern coastal counties.

Surrey. The three are all in the early part of the year:

1985:   Streatham, a male was seen briefly in a garden on 10th February (F. W. Lockwood).
          Thursley Common, one flew over on 24th April (S. Abbott).

1986:   Barn Elms Reservoirs, a singing male on 2nd June, watched from 18.55 to 19.20 hrs (R. B. Hastings).

Greenfinch (European Greenfinch)   *Carduelis chloris*

Common breeding resident

A native resident of Europe, western Russia, North Africa and the Middle East, introduced in South America and Australasia. There has been an increase in parts of the western range. Northern birds move southwest in winter, within the breeding range and no further south than North Africa. Birds from north-west Europe reach Britain. Some of the Greenfinches present in Britain in the breeding season move to Ireland or continental Europe. Most foreign-ringed arrivals are from Norway. Movements in both directions are occasional rather than annual (*MA*). The British population probably increased in the 19th century with the spread of arable farming and was still growing in the last thirty years of the 20th.

Early Surrey history. Greenfinches were in the Godalming District by 1849 (Newman). They bred in Battersea Park in 1879 or earlier (*Zool., 1879:284*) but were basically farmland birds. They were uncommon in the Norwood district during the 1880s (Aldridge), 'pretty numerous' on Wimbledon Common (Hamilton, 1881), numerous in Richmond Park (Mouritz, 1905) and common in the Staines area (Kerr, 1906).

After 1900. Eggs collected by Boorman at Selhurst Common (Bramley, 1902) and Send (1902, 1904, 1909) are in the Haslemere Museum. They were breeding sparingly in South London in 1910 (Power). Numbers increased during the 20th century when Greenfinches moved further into towns and gardens, where they are now common, especially where conifers such as *Cupressus* have been planted. Eggs were collected at Bookham, Fetcham and Hindhead in the 1930s. A nest was found in Battersea Park in 1950, where there was successful breeding in 1959, reflecting the more general increase. Greenfinches have bred at the Surrey Docks from at least 1974. Up to five pairs nested near Battersea Power Station in 1985 and, in 1987, twenty pairs raised at least twenty young there. Greenfinches can now be found in small central London shrubberies such as those in Jubilee Gardens, at Southbank.

In Spelthorne, many Greenfinches used to feed on waste ground by Queen Mary Reservoir before the gravel pits were dug. A few pairs bred around the reservoir in the 1980s (Geen). They were fairly common as breeding residents in the Shepperton area in 1983-86, with flocks of up to 60. Three pairs bred at the Littleton Lakes in 1986. The biggest Spelthorne count in the 2003 BTO Spring Migration Watch was of 12 on Stanwell Moor in March.

Trend since 1970. The Common Birds Census showed a decline after 1970 but has changes in the habitat mix and may not be very reliable. Of the 231 tetrads in northeast Surrey, 96% were found to hold territories in the 1968-72 Atlas survey and were only slightly down, at 94%, in the 1988-97 Atlas, perhaps a better measure. In addition to colonising the Inner London area, breeding numbers appear to be up at Bookham Common. On the negative side though, the biggest counts date back to the 1980s and earlier.

Population size. A county total of 3,000 territories at the end of the period implied by the Common Birds Census seems low compared with an estimated 9,300 adults derived from Breeding Birds Survey. If Surrey held a proportionate share of the British breeding population as given by the *New Atlas*, the population would be nearer to 3,800 territories, or 1.9 per square km, possibly also low for a southern county. Greenfinches were found in 536 of the 575 Surrey tetrads in the 1988-97 Surrey Atlas survey.

The Winter Atlas found partial survey counts and estimates totalling 1,199 birds in 1981-84, similar to the number of Siskins and about two-thirds of the number of Blue Tits. They were found in all 21 squares surveyed. Greenfinches are second only to the Blue Tits in the number ringed in Surrey, nearly 60,000 or 8.5% of the total. Local numbers can be hard to gauge. Over 500 different individuals were trapped in a Dorking garden from January-March 1980, even though the largest number seen at any one time was 15, feeding on peanuts (C. J. Forss). The Croydon RSPB Group recorded Greenfinches in a range of 30% (August) to 65% (December) of the surveyed gardens each month in 2003.

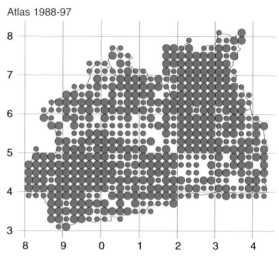

Atlas 1988-97

Song. Full song may start as early as January in mild weather (*e.g.* Riddlesdown 1984).

Large counts. All the counts of 1,000 or more are earlier than 1981:

Beddington Sewage Farm: 1,000+, 2nd October 1977; 800, 18th September 1980; 500+, 16th April 1981

Elstead: 2,000 at Red House Farm, 18th January 1976

Epsom Sewage Farm: *c*.400, 9th September 1955 and 27th September 1956

Esher Sewage Farm: *c*.500, 30th November 1957

Farnham Sewage Farm: 500, 1st September 1969

Frensham Little Pond, on hop piles: 600-1,000 March 1971; 400+, 28th January 1972; 400, November 1972; 400, December 1975; 500, 22nd December 1976; 1,000, 20th October 1979 and January 1980

Frensham Outlet Pond: 400, 3rd-10th December 1977

Hersham Sewage Farm: 300-400, October 1972

Lyne Sewage Farm: 500, 31st August 1969; 400, 6th September 1970

Papercourt Gravel Pits: *c*.400, December 1972; 600, 8th December 1974

Ranmore: *c*.1,000, 18th February 1969

Ripley Sewage Farm: 500, 28th September 1975

Tilhill Nursery: 1,000, 20th October 1979 and January 1980

Unstead Sewage Farm: 1,000, 24th December 1961; *c*.600, September and October 1970

Spelthorne

Staines Reservoir: 800 on the drained and over-grown north basin, 22nd October 1983

Wraysbury Reservoir: 1,000, 21st January 1967

Roosts and roost flights. The largest count dates back to 1968:

Bourne Hall Lake: 120 to roost, 12th November 2003

Claremont: 160 at Claremont Landscape Gardens, 31st December 1998/1st January 1999

Croham Hurst: *c*.40, 20th April 1986

East Clandon: *c*.100 in Hawthorns, 22nd February 1974

Pirbright Common: 200+ roosting with Fieldfares and Redwings, 8th December 1991

Richmond Park: *c*.220, 21st February 1982

Walton Reservoirs: *c*.1,200 flew to a local roost, 4th February 1968

Food. Spent hops *Humulus lupulus* at Tilhill Nursery often attracted hundreds of Greenfinches outside the breeding season in the 1970s and 80s. There were about 1,000 at the site on 20th October 1979 and in late January 1980. Cotoneaster berries were eaten during a cold spell in 1981. Other seeds noted have been Bur-Marigold, Oil Seed Rape, *Persicaria* seed, Sorrel seed and Yew berries.

Movements and longevity. Autumn movements are sometimes observed (Capel 1992, Rowledge 1980, Surrey Docks 1997). One ringed at Appleby on 3rd June 1970 and found dying 395 kilometres south, at Limpsfield on 11th April 1971, was the furthest travelled. Greenfinches breeding in Surrey normally make only local movements. There are three winter ringing recoveries of Surrey-ringed adults from France and two (one of a post-juvenile) from Belgium. One ringed in France in February was recovered in Sanderstead in March of the following year.

A Greenfinch ringed at Ormesby, Cleveland on 31st January 1987 and recovered over 11 years and three months later at Ripley, on 25th May 1998, provided a new Surrey and national longevity record. Deaths from *Salmonella typhimurium* were recorded in the five years to 1969.

Plumage variations. Bronze and reddish tinted Greenfinches were seen in a garden at Brockham from 1966 to 1967. There were copper-tinted birds at Westhumble in 1969 and 1971 and males with orange plumage at Lyne, Thorpe and Weybridge in 1970 and Banstead in 1996. Males with abnormal orange plumage were thought to have fed on food rich in carotene (Washington and Harrison, 1969). Leucistic birds were seen at Tilhill Nursery in 1980 and 1982. One with a white head was seen at Wonersh. A bright yellow (xanthic) bird was seen at Staines Moor in May 1988.

Goldfinch (European Goldfinch) *Carduelis carduelis*
Common breeding resident

Breeds from Europe and North Africa east to Central Asia, with introduced populations in the Americas and Australasia. Winters almost wholly within the breeding range. Some of the Goldfinches present in Britain in the breeding season winter on the continent, mainly in western France and Iberia. Evidence for immigration from Scandinavia is thin (*MA*). Goldfinches would have benefited from the spread of farmland in the Stone Age. Many western European birds, including most of those breeding in Britain, move southwest and high ground is vacated. Some of the birds that leave Europe reach Britain, where the largely resident population is increasing.

Early Surrey history. Goldfinches were in the Godalming district by 1849. They were popular cage-birds in 19th century Britain and the activities of birdcatchers were at least partly responsible for their increasing scarcity up to 1900. They were only spring and autumn migrants to Wimbledon in 1881 and rare in the Norwood district by 1885, when 46 were entered for a local cage bird show. Good singers changed hands for £5 each at East End pub competitions (Aldridge). The persecution was vigorous in Surrey and by the end of the century they had become uncommon as breeding birds, though well known as autumn and winter visitors. Kerr had heard of one at Staines but had not seen one there. Twenty or thirty was a good flock in the Dorking area (Jordan, 1892). Bucknill knew of recent breeding at Cheam, Churt, Epsom, Godalming, Godstone, Gatton, Headley, Leatherhead, Reigate and a few other localities, with winter observations from Dulwich, Norwood, and Wimbledon. Autumn and winter flocks of up to forty birds were to be found with the Siskins and Redpolls frequenting alders in the Mole and Wey valleys.

Since 1900. The 20th century saw an increase in numbers following the enforcement of the Wild Birds Protection Acts of 1880 and 1881. Mouritz (1905) only had one record, in 1903, for Richmond Park but counted fifteen at Ripley on 19th March 1905. Boorman collected eggs at Send in 1905 and 1913. Macpherson (1929) gave an undated reference to Battersea Park. The increase was probably assisted by the spread of thistles during the agricultural depression of the early 20th century and by the rising popularity of bird feeders in gardens. A flock of 36 on Staines Moor on 3rd October 1932 was part of the general increase, as was a flock of 150 on Epsom Common in September 1938. There were a few in Battersea Park in October 1942 and Goldfinches bred there in 1949, 1950, 1985-90 and no doubt many of the years between. They have been breeding freely in parkland areas such as Kew Gardens since at least the 1950s. A pair bred at the Surrey Docks in 1971, 1973-77, 1980, 1987, 1990, and 1997 and Goldfinches have often been present in the breeding season in other years. They have bred at least intermittently on Bookham Common since the 1940s, with four or more territories in 2004.

In Spelthorne, there were 200+ at Queen Mary Reservoir on 24th September 1977. Goldfinches were fairly common in the Shepperton area in 1983-86, with a few pairs breeding and flocks of up to 35. There were about 100 at Queen Mary Gravel Pits on 1st October 1983, 75 at Staines Reservoirs on 29th September 1994 and 105 at Staines Moor on 3rd September 1995. The largest count in the 2003 BTO Spring Migration Watch was of 12 on Stanwell Moor in March.

Trend since 1970. The Common Birds Census shows no significant change in numbers from 1970 to 2000 and it is possible that losses in woodland have been offset by new colonisations in other habitats. Two other things suggest a decline, though. Of the 231 tetrads in northeast Surrey, 89% were found to hold territories in the 1968-72 Atlas survey but only 80% in the 1988-97 Atlas. Also, as with some other finches, the largest counts (500 or more) date back to 1980 or earlier. Large counts are typically in August or September and are probably of local breeding birds rather than immigrants.

Population size. The implied population level of about 4,500 territories compares with an estimate of 4,000 adult birds derived from the Breeding Birds Survey. If Surrey held a proportionate share of the British breeding population as given by the *New Atlas*, the population would be nearer to 1,600 territories, or 0.8 per

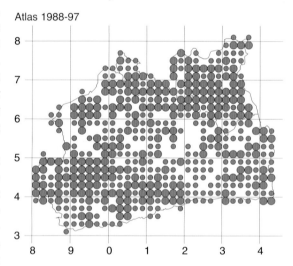

Atlas 1988-97

square km, which feels low for a southern county. The Winter Atlas found partial survey counts and estimates totalling 982 birds in 1981-84, more than the 751 Redpolls but less than the 1,199 Linnets.

Large counts. The last count of 500 or more birds was in 1980:

Addington: 250, August 1961

Banstead/Walton Heath: *c.*300, 12th September 1973

Beddington Sewage Farm: 650, 8th September 1980

Beddlestead Valley: 200 before 1932 (Beadell)

Cannon Hill Common: *c.*200, 3rd September 1990

Effingham: about 300 feeding on thistle seed, 24th September 1972; 400, 5th May 1973

Epsom/Walton Downs: 500+, 19th September 1975

Farleigh Downs: 250, 4th September 1967

Farnham: about 120 at Moor Park, 1st May 1978

Farthing Down: 225, 21st August 1976

Fieldcommon: about 300, 16th August 1977

Hersham Sewage Farm: *c*.400, 7th October 1961

Island Barn Reservoir: 200+, 15th September 1974

Langshott: 163 were ringed in a garden in 1996

Norbury Park: *c*.200, 10th December 1971

Papercourt Gravel Pits: 500+, 17th December 1972

Park Downs: 200, 6th October 1971

Sanderstead: 200, September 1961

South Norwood Country Park: *c*.200, October 1990

Surrey Docks: *c*.250, September 1974; 300, 15th September 1980

Thursley: 200, 27th April 1964

Tilhill Nursery: up to 200 feeding on spent hops in 1972; 200, 17th March 1983

Walton Heath: 300+, 13th October 1974

Movements. Goldfinches are noticeable daytime visible migrants in October and November. A Goldfinch ringed at Ewhurst on 13th August 1964 was recovered over two years and eight months later, at Irun, Spain on 23rd April 1967. Foreign recoveries have come from Belgium (four), France (eleven), and Spain (fourteen). None of the birds was ringed in the breeding season (April to July) and all were recovered from October to April, so they could have been passage migrants from further north. A Goldfinch ringed at Effingham on 17th August 1980 and recovered 1,731 kilometres south, at Algeciras, Spain on 25th November 1980 had travelled the furthest.

Longevity. The longest-lived Goldfinch located was ringed at Horley on 16th October 1996 and found freshly dead at Minster, Kent over four years and a month later, on 15th December 2000. Surrey Bird Reports since 1977 have given a record of three years six months, without details but this was equalled by a Goldfinch ringed at Stoke on 19th May 2001 and recovered nearby at Burpham on 27th November 2004 (per Richard A. Denyer).

Siskin (Eurasian Siskin) *Carduelis spinus*
Common winter visitor, breeding annually

Breeds across Europe and northern Asia. Most Siskins are migratory though the more southern breeding birds, including those in Britain, may remain closer to their breeding grounds in winter. Birds breeding in more northern locations winter in western Europe, North Africa and the Middle East. Those in the east winter further south in Asia. In western Europe, including Britain, the population has increased with the spread of conifer plantations, and for other reasons less well understood. In Britain, where there is a large winter influx of Siskins, breeding numbers are thought to have fallen a little since 1994 (*BTO News 266*). Siskins remain in their breeding areas throughout the year if food is available but most have left the conifer forests by early August and return from February onwards. Eggs may be laid by mid March if the cone crop is good. Scottish birds migrate south to join immigrants from Norway and the Baltic countries in winter (*MA*). Some Siskins move further south, as far as North Africa.

Early Surrey history. Kidd (1849) said that Siskins were very numerous in winter in riverside alders at Catteshall. Yarrell knew them as seen more or less frequently in Surrey from Michaelmas to April. The year 1880 brought many Siskins to Surrey. Siskins appeared near Witley in large numbers in some winters, particularly in 1884, 1885 and 1886. Power had only one record for the Dulwich area, of two flying west over his Brixton garden on 1st November 1892. Siskins were numerous in Surrey in 1893. Numbers may even so have been lower than today. A note in the *Zoologist* for 1894 suggests that a flock of 35 was noteworthy. Siskins were distinctly rare in the Staines district, with no definite Spelthorne records in Kerr (1906).

The *Historical Atlas* says that Siskins bred regularly in Surrey from 1836, probably as escaped cage birds, but this may overstate the position somewhat. The records that have been located relate to five nests. The first three instances are quoted by Bucknill from Meyer. One at St Anne's Hill (St Ann's Hill, Chertsey) raised young in a gorse bush in 1836 and another, in the same year, raised young in a whitethorn bush bordering the Thames. Two other nests were built in gorse near Combe Wood (presumably Coombe Wood, Wimbledon) some years later. The eggs were taken and hatched under Canaries to prove identification. These nest sites are unusual for a bird which, today at least, nests rather high in larch or pine. Blyth knew of a Siskin in 'nestling' plumage taken near Tooting in 1838 and believed to have been hatched locally. A nest with four eggs was collected at Capel in the third week of May, 1894.

Breeding seasons since 1900. Summer sightings include a Siskin singing at Weybridge in May and June 1924 (*BLA*) and a pair at Weybridge Heath in the late summer of 1970. There were summer sightings at Banstead in July 1969 and at Woking in July-August 1974. July records might, in the light of subsequent experience, relate to early migrants and cannot normally be taken as evidence of breeding in Surrey. A family party of at least three birds was seen at Ash Vale Station on 2nd July 1976, where a singing male had been present in June 1974. These were almost certainly local birds. One or two were at Frensham in May-June 1977 but there were no definite records of Surrey breeding until adults were seen carrying food at Beacon Hill in 1978. In the same year, four pairs bred, with unknown success, on or over the Surrey border at Bricksbury Hill (*HSBBR*). Siskins were reported to have nested at Thursley in 1980.

Parties of Siskins seen in July may include young birds which have not bred in the area where they were seen, and perhaps not in Surrey at all. Juveniles and family parties were seen at five places, including Lightwater Country Park in July 1985. These were thought to have been immigrants since they were the first seen since 18th March and there was a national influx in July followed by the appearance of 76 at Thursley Common on 11th August. There was circumstantial evidence of breeding from Dorking (1981), Tilhill (1986) and Frensham in (1988 and 1989). A nest at Winkworth in 1989 was predated. Summer records in 1991 may have been related to a July influx at coastal observatories. Family parties at Capel, West Horsley and Wisley in late July and Olddean Common on 1st August were of unknown origin. A family party of five near Moat Pond on 26th June 1992 were thought to have bred locally, as were family

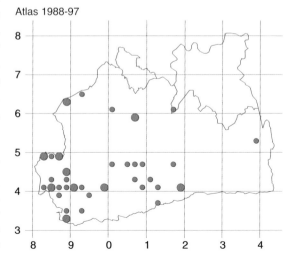

Atlas 1988-97

parties at Bricksbury Hill and Frensham Little Pond in 1993. Siskins bred again at Thursley in 1994 but a family party at Pyrford in August 1994 were probably early migrants. Later breeding records came from Botany Bay (1995), Chilworth (1997-98, a juvenile in July 2005), Crooksbury Common (three pairs 1998), the Devil's Punch Bowl (1997), Elstead (two pairs near Copse Edge in 1998, one pair 1999, juvenile 2000, family party 2005), Farnham (family party April 2003), Frensham (1995, 1997, three young at the Little Pond on 2nd June 2001, female with four young on 13th June 2004), Haslemere (1995), Kiln Platt (1997), Milford (1996), Olddean Common (one pair in 1996, 1998), The Sands (1996), Thursley/Ockley Commons (1995-98, 2000). Birds were seen in the breeding season at several other localities. Some would probably have been missed altogether.

It now seems that a few wintering Siskins linger to breed early in some years, so that fledged young may be seen as early as April, for example at a garden feeder at Elstead in 2005. This matches the national note that they may remain in their wintering areas if the cone crop is good and may lay eggs in March. These early breeding birds move away from gardens in May. Where they are during the summer is not known.

The Atlas map covers breeding evidence including recently fledged young but it may overstate the extent of nesting in Surrey. Only three occupied nests have been reported since 1900 – those at Thursley (1980) and Winkworth (robbed, 1989) and one at Pirbright Common in 2004. The latter, found by Jeremy Gates, required a fifty foot climb up a Scots Pine to obtain evidence of fledging, in the form of droppings round the edge of a nest on which a female had previously been seen sitting. No Siskin territories have ever been found in Common Birds Censuses.

Calendar. The average arrival date in the London area south of the Thames from 1929 to 1939 was 25th October. Winter numbers peak in December. There were late birds at Queen Mary Reservoir on 3rd May 1975 and Queen Mary Gravel Pits on 1st May 1989. An early migrant appeared at King George VI Reservoir on 10th July 1994. A strange summer occurrence of up to 100 Siskins, mostly juveniles, in an Elstead garden in July 1995 (M. R. Pankhurst) was probably an early arrival of immigrants.

Vice-county approximate monthly totals 1983-2001

Year	Jan	Feb	Mar	Apr	May	Jun	Jul	Aug	Sep	Oct	Nov	Dec	Total
1983	106	259	113							72	149	291	**990**
1984	450	440	180	130						40	100	160	**1,500**
1985	85	120	95						130	520	575	1,675	**3,200**
1986	1,100	1,000	470	270						150	30	125	**3,145**
1987	92	188	64	260	1		1	1		20	35	35	**697**
1988	160	50	25	5					40	130	70	350	**830**
1989	450	300	340	80						10	265	800	**2,245**
1990	650	260	180							70	300	400	**1,860**
1991	600	550	420	390					210	250	250	340	**3,010**
1992	480	560	405	160				2	45	100	200	575	**2,527**
1993	560	420	280	30		1			50	650	820	920	**3,731**
1994	933	405	180	216	5	2	2	5	98	190	483	520	**3,039**
1995	921	294	187	31	15	12	144	19	6	33	242	204	**2,108**
1996	243	269	53	41	16	11	15	0	253	298	566	678	**2,443**
1997	788	477	1,154	259	4	41	34	3	1,156	714	1,050	1,316	**6,996**
1998	1,553	647	555	107	45	15	5	2	16	127	181	237	**3,490**
1999	394	291	172	27	7	2	2	0	200	141	156	1,807	**3,199**
2000	904	734	1,138	196	15	33	15	0	9	180	247	485	**3,956**
2001	326	249	139	110	6	4	0	3	263	389	356	328	**2,173**
Total	**10,795**	**7,513**	**6,150**	**2,312**	**114**	**120**	**218**	**35**	**2,477**	**4,084**	**6,075**	**11,246**	**51,139**

Spring song is sometimes heard in February (*e.g.* Bookham Common, 17th February 1998) and often heard in March and April, before the winter visitors depart. Song late in the year includes Silvermere on 20th October 1973 (20 in full song) and Woking on 28th November 1983, in a garden.

Large counts. Some 80 at Frensham on 8th December 1936 made up a large party for the period, as did 70-100 in Richmond Park on 5th March 1937. The biggest count dates back to the 1970s:

Esher Common: 500, 22nd March 2000
Olddean Common: 500+, 22nd February 1976
Thursley Common: an estimated 2,000 roosting, 18th January 1976 (R. M. Fry in Clark, 1984)
Wey Navigation near Wisley: *c.*1,000, 7th December 1985
Wisley Common: 450, 24th March 1963

Food. Niger seed (*Guizotia abyssinica*), peanuts and sunflower hearts can attract large numbers. The first British records of Siskins feeding regularly in gardens came from a garden in Guildford in the second week of March 1963, at the end of the severest winter since 1900 (Spencer and Gush, 1973). Siskins soon became known as garden birds and a count of 137 in a small Weybridge garden in March 1969 (Parr) would still be a good one today. Reports from gardens in the northern half of Surrey became widespread in the early 1970s. D. C. Bailey ringed 297 in his Byfleet garden between 17th February and 31st March 1974. G. H. Gush ringed 451 in his Weybridge garden in 1970 (*LBR*).

Movements. Visible migration is not often noted but 52 Siskins flew northeast at Walton-on-Thames on 25th March 1971 at 0750 hrs. Over 32,000 Siskins have been ringed in Surrey, the fifth commonest of the species ringed. The furthest travelled was ringed at Lightwater on 29th January 1978 and recovered 2,426 kilometres east, at Vologda, old USSR on 4th May 1978. A Siskin that was ringed at Walton-on-Thames in April 1974 and recovered at Beauly, Inverness, 715 kilometres NNW, in April 1975 was an early indication that Scottish Siskins winter in Surrey. Since then there have been many more and the links with breeding areas abroad have also been established more clearly. The table below analyses 151 recoveries of Siskins ringed in Surrey and recovered outside England and 68 Siskins ringed outside England and recovered in Surrey. The month relates to when each bird was ringed or recovered outside England.

Siskin Recoveries: Months when ringed or recovered outside England

	Jan	Feb	Mar	Apr	May	Jun	Jul	Aug	Sep	Oct	Nov	Dec	Total
Scotland		2	6	10	2	4	2					1	**27**
Belgium	3	9	8	9	2					23	2	1	**57**
Channel Isles										1	1		**2**
Czechoslovakia											1		**1**
Denmark			1	4	1			1					**7**
Estonia									2				**2**
Finland			1	1	2	3		1	1				**9**
France											1	1	**2**
Germany	5	3	3	7						4	3	2	**27**
Italy			1						1	1	4	1	**8**
Lithuania										1			**1**
Luxemburg										1			**1**
Morocco												1	**1**
Netherlands	1	3	1	5					1	4	3		**18**
Norway		2	6	3	2	5	4	2	2				**26**
Poland										1			**1**
Portugal		1									2		**3**
Spain		2	1								1		**4**
Sweden				4	1			2					**7**

	Jan	Feb	Mar	Apr	May	Jun	Jul	Aug	Sep	Oct	Nov	Dec	Total
Switzerland		1								1			**2**
old USSR				1	2	1			3	5			**12**
Wales						1							**1**
Total	**9**	**21**	**24**	**47**	**13**	**11**	**7**	**8**	**10**	**44**	**18**	**7**	**219**

The table shows that at the distant (outside England) end of their journey most of these birds were not trapped in the breeding season, counting this as May to July. Scotland, Norway and to a less extent Finland are the only areas clearly relating to a breeding season population. So the ringing information is best at indicating migration routes and hot spots. At this point it must be said that Siskins are much easier to catch when away from their nest sites. The Moroccan recovery, of a Siskin ringed at Ottershaw on 22nd March 1987, is a surprising outlier.

Migrant Siskins are not often seen in the Surrey part of Inner London but there were winter records (November to March) from Battersea Park in 1985 and 1987, the Surrey Docks in 1987, 1989-91, 1997-98 and there were others from the Surrey Docks in April 1991 and October 1998. A few flew south at Bankside Reach in 1996 and in Battersea Park on dates from August to October 1997. Siskins have been seen in the Spelthorne district since at least 1931, when there was a single bird at Queen Mary Reservoir on 23rd April. There were two at Staines Reservoirs on 26th February 1935. The biggest count at Queen Mary Reservoir up to 1988 was 25 on 13th March 1971 (Geen). Other significant flocks include 44 at Shepperton Gravel Pits on 7th January 1994. There were flocks of up to 14 or so in the Shepperton area in 1983-86. The Winter Atlas found partial survey counts and estimates totalling 1,289 birds in 1981-84.

Longevity. A Siskin ringed at Virginia Water on 12th March 1967 and recovered there over six years and eleven months later, on 17th February 1974 is the longest-lived bird on file.

Linnet (Common Linnet)   *Carduelis cannabina*

Locally common breeding resident

Breeds from Europe to Central Asia and in North Africa. Northern birds move south in winter, some as far as Egypt. Some of the Linnets present in Britain in the breeding season winter south to Gibraltar. A very small number of Scandinavian breeding birds have been found in Britain (*MA*).

British records date back to the end of the last glaciation. Linnets would have benefited from Stone Age forest clearances and the spread of farmland. Breeding numbers in Britain fell in the late 19th century because of loss of habitat during the agricultural depression. It stabilised and may have improved with the appearance of scrubby edges along roadsides and scrub encroachment on the commons, but went into a further decline as a result of agricultural changes in the late 20th century, falling by around 50% in the last thirty years. Declines have been recorded in other European countries, following the intensification of agriculture. Once known as the Greater Redpole - see Lesser Redpoll.

Early Surrey records. Linnets had been recorded in the Godalming area by 1849 and were 'pretty numerous' on Wimbledon Common in 1881 (Hamilton). Bucknill described Linnets as common residents *frequenting the furze-covered commons of the county and breeding rather freely both there and in gardens*. He knew them to be fairly abundant near London on Streatham, Wimbledon and other commons. This is not a bad summary of their present status, except that they now rarely breed in gardens. Power had one on the roof of his Brixton aviary for a few days in the springs of 1896 to 1901 but knew of no definite local breeding and none was mentioned by Aldridge for the Norwood district.

1900 to 1970s. Eggs collected at Send from 1902 to 1910 by Boorman are in the Haslemere Museum. Linnets bred at Colley Hill in 1905 (G. T. Winter). A nest with eggs was found on Walton Heath in 1906.

For Spelthorne, Kerr (1906) stated that their increase at Staines was remarkable. *Ten years previously there was only one spot where the bird could be found, now every bush and hedge contains a nest.* Linnets were only winter visitors to Richmond Park at this time (Mouritz) but began breeding in 1924 (Collenette). A pair were feeding young on the fairly late date of 16th August on Holmwood Common in 1916. Linnets bred on Wandsworth Common in the 1920s (*BLA*). Gosnell collected eggs at Cutt Mill and Frensham in the 1930s. They bred on Bookham Common in the 1940s and 50s and in Kew Gardens from 1953 to at least 1976. The Surrey Bird Reports covering 1945 to 1962 gave no breeding season information beyond describing them as common residents, but in 1963 there was an estimate of 30-50 pairs for the Dorking area and a note that one or two observers had mentioned declines. The next reference was to eight successful nests in one and a half acres at Thorpe in 1967, evidently a local colony since this is equivalent to a very high 1,300 per square km of the same habitat type.

Trend since 1970. The Common Birds Census shows a huge decline, down by over 90% from 1970 to 2000. At the beginning of the period most of the Census territories were on heath and commonland, which were poorly represented in the later years of the census, so the decline is probably exaggerated. Of the 231 tetrads in northeast Surrey, 82% were found to hold territories in the 1968-72 Atlas survey but only 63% in the 1988-97 Atlas, perhaps a better measure of the decline. The counts of 1,000 or more up to 1986 but not since, confirm that numbers are down.

Population size. The Winter Atlas found partial survey counts and estimates totalling 1,199 birds in 1981-84, almost as many as for Siskins, and with presence in 17 of the 21 10 km squares surveyed. An end-period population estimate of about 1,100 territories derived from the Common Birds Census compares well with an estimate of 2,200 adults derived from 1994-2004 Breeding Birds Survey. If Surrey held a proportionate share of the British breeding population as given by the *New Atlas*, the population would be nearer to 3,800 territories, or 1.8 per square km. Autumn song may be heard, *e.g.* at Frensham on 28th September 1975.

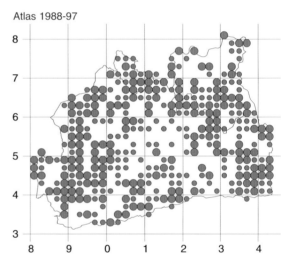

Atlas 1988-97

There were flocks of up to 150 in the Shepperton area in 1983-86 and a few pairs bred. Three pairs bred at Perry Oaks Sewage Farm in 1996. Fifty were found at Staines Moor on 6th October 2000 but the largest Spelthorne count in the 2003 BTO Spring Migration Watch was of thirty there on 1st March.

Territory counts. The Common Birds Census area on Ashtead Common, which held twelve territories in 1968 and up to seven in the 1970s, did not have more than three from 1989 to 1999. Linnets bred at the Surrey Docks in 1971. They were commonly seen in the breeding season at Vann Lake from 1964 to 1978, but rarely after that date (Blaker Log). At Limpsfield Chart, where Linnets bred commonly in 1938, all in gorse, there were none in 1999. Even so, heathlands and commons remain a stronghold. There were 42 territories on Pirbright Common/Ash Ranges in 2000 and in 2001 there were 26 pairs on Hankley Common and 19 on Thursley/Ockley/Elstead Commons. In 2003, three areas of golf course at Walton Heath held a total of about 20 pairs and West End Common, Esher held about 35.

Large counts. The largest counts date back to 1986 and earlier:

near Box Hill: 1,200, 30th December 1979
Clapham Common: *c.*400, 3rd March 1965
Hog's Back: *c.*400 in stubble, 17th February 1969

Leigh/Godstone: 700 on 17th April 1933 (Bentham)
Molesey Heath: *c.*1,000, 16th February 1986

Papercourt Gravel Pits: 500+, 15th October and 17th December 1972; 500+, 20th October 1974

Surrey Docks: 500+, 13th February 1978

Tuesley Farm, Milford: 400, 9th October 2003 (Eric Soden)

West Horsley: *c*.600, 2nd February 1974

Winkworth: *c*.500, 31st December 1972

Roosts. The largest roost is from 1971:

Ash Vale Gravel Pits: 150, 13th December 1979

Capel: flock of 30+ throughout June 1992

East Clandon: *c*.150 in hawthorns, 22nd February 1974

Elstead: up to 190 roosting in Elms, April 1973 (D. M. Parker)

Frensham Great Pond: *c*.300 roosting in gorse, January/February 1961

Gatwick: *c*.60 roosting at Brockley Wood, 14th September 2003 (J. R. Havers)

Holmbury Hill: 145 roosting, 3rd January 1999

Mitcham Common: *c*.50 roosting in dense elder,

near Worms Heath: flocks of thousands at times on stubbles (Beadell, 1932).

Spelthorne

Staines Reservoirs: 500-1,000, 10th February 1977; 500 on the overgrown north basin, 1983; 500 on the drained north basin, October 1997

December 1983; *c*.90 roosted, 11th January 1984

Winkworth: 100+ roosted, 16th December 1973; 100+, 17th November 1974

Witley Common: 150+ roosted, 18th February 1979; *c*.75, 21st December 1980; *c*.30 maximum each end of 1982

Spelthorne

Queen Mary Reservoir: *c*.1,000 birds roosted on 31st January 1971. Numbers were much lower by 1988.

Food. Linnets have been seen feeding on Chickweed (Sidlow 1974), Corn stubble (Riddlesdown 1977) spent Hops (Tilhill Nurseries), Linseed (=Flax, Hurst Green 1994), Oilseed rape (Holmethorpe August 1995) and they will take a variety of other small seeds. They will come to garden feeders for niger seed.

Movements. There is a small spring passage in March and April and a larger return passage from September to November. Winter cold weather movements also occur:

Barn Elms: 42 southwest, 1st November 2000

Beddington Sewage Farm: 45 north, 7th April 1995 and 25 north on the next day

Capel: 80 south, 26th September 1992

Surbiton Cemetery: 25 northwest, 4th April 1973

Thursley/Ockley Commons: very big southerly passage all day, 10th October 1976; 45 south, 30th September 1984

Worcester Park: SSW movements, 23rd September to early November 1969

The origin of the migrant birds is not certain. There are foreign recoveries from Belgium (one), France (nine) and Spain (two). Only one of these, which had been ringed at Queen Mary Gravel Pits on 22nd June 1974 and recovered 1,440 kilometres south at Puertollano, Spain on 15th October 1974, was ringed in the breeding season. This bird, which might not have been in Surrey, provides the most convincing evidence that some Surrey Linnets emigrate in winter. The others were mainly ringed from August into winter and could have been passage migrants from further north or east. The furthest-travelled of them was ringed at Kempton Park, also possibly not in Surrey, on 1st August 1970 and recovered 1,664 kilometres south, later in the year at Malaga, Spain on 18th October. Linnets from the north of England are known from ringing to pass through Surrey on passage.

Longevity. The oldest known Linnet was ringed at Guildford on 23rd December 1973 and recovered over three years and five months later, in Derbyshire on 28th May 1977.

Plumage variations. Bucknill knew of pied and buff varieties. A Linnet with a white head, breast and scapulars was seen at Worcester Park in 1967. There was an albino at Kemishford (Smart's Heath) in 1972.

Twite   *Carduelis flavirostris*

Declining winter visitor, 26 records 1900 to 2004 including five from Spelthorne

Breeds in northern Britain and Norway with a separate population in upland areas from the Caucasus to Central Asia. British birds winter mainly on the coast. Those in Norway winter further south in northern and eastern Europe. Others are mainly altitudinal migrants. The British population is thought to have been stable in the 19th century but since then there has been a decline.

Early Surrey history. Twites were more common in Surrey during the first half of the 19th century and perhaps later. Writers in the 1830s described them as regular in winter in the neighbourhood of Tooting and that they were now and then shot on Munstead Heath. They were sometimes found near Godalming (*SALEC*). Birdcatchers told Bucknill that some had been taken on Banstead Downs in 1895 and that a few were captured every winter with Linnets. Power had a small party over his Brixton garden on 25th October 1893. There are no Spelthorne records in Glegg.

Since 1900. One said to be on Clapham Common on 1st January 1918 was not adequately documented (*BLA*) and 'some' at Haslemere in December 1919 might not have been in Surrey. Later records are:

1933:   Thursley, one in February (HNHS 1955).
1946:   Barn Elms Reservoirs, two on 28th October, feeding on dandelion heads.
1948:* Staines Moor, two on 29th September (*LBR*) appear to be the first for the area.
1953:* Staines Reservoirs, four on 2nd and 23rd February (*LBR*).
1955:* King George VI Reservoir, one on 6th November.
1956:   Epsom Sewage Farm, two on 10th-11th March.
1959:   Epsom, one on 15th February, with Linnets on a refuse tip.
        Richmond, at least one on 25th October in a flock of about 100 Linnets.
1960:* Queen Mary Reservoir, one on 5th November.
1960:   Farleigh, four on 29th December.
1963:   Godalming, two on 4th January.
1965:   Riddlesdown, a male on 27th March.
1968:   Frensham Great Pond, one on 16th March.
1969:   Barn Elms Reservoirs, one on 28th October.
1978:   Barn Elms Reservoirs, one on 23rd October.
1981:   Barn Elms Reservoirs, one on dates from 17th September to 23rd December.
        West Horsley, a female or immature bird on 13th October.
1986:   Barn Elms Reservoirs, two on 27th and 28th October.
        Barn Elms Reservoirs, one on 16th November, a different bird.
1990:   Barn Elms Reservoirs, at least one on 24th October, among a Meadow Pipit flock.
1991:   Beddington Sewage Farm, one on 29th October.
1994:   South Norwood Country Park, one on 9th December, seen on dates to 18th February 1995.
1999:* Perry Oaks Sewage Farm, one on 20th February.
1999:   Hersham, a first-winter bird on 21st, 27th and 28th November and on 2nd and 27th December at the gravel pit and on 27th and 28th November at the sewage farm. It was seen again on 10th and 31st March 2000.
2000:   Barn Elms WWT, one on November 11th.
2004:   Berrylands Sewage Works, one flew over, calling on 26th January.

*Spelthorne

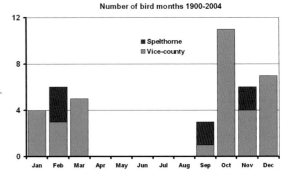

Number of bird months 1900-2004

■ Spelthorne
▨ Vice-county

Calendar. The 37 bird months derived from these records show a peak in October.

Mealy (Common) **and Lesser Redpolls** *Carduelis flammea/cabaret*

The Mealy/Lesser Redpoll group has recently been split into two species by the BOU. One is *C. flammea*, comprising the Mealy Redpoll, *C. f. flammea*, which breeds in northern parts of Europe, Asia and America, the Greenland, or Greater Redpoll, *C. f. rostrata* and the Icelandic Redpoll *C. f. islandica* (once lumped with the Greenland Redpoll). *C. flammea* is now called the Common Redpoll by the BOU, an unhelpful name in a British context. The other species is the monotypic *C. cabaret*, breeding in Britain (eighty per cent of the population), Switzerland and parts of northwest and central Europe. This is called the Lesser Redpoll by the BOU. The split is not a new idea but the undoing of an earlier 20th century lumping, see for example Kearton and Bentham (1925). Most redpolls move further south in Europe, Asia and North America in winter. Many European Redpolls migrate, some wintering in France and the Low Countries. There is a north-south movement within the UK.

Mealy Redpoll (race of Common Redpoll) *Carduelis flammea*
(*Carduelis flammea flammea*)

Scarce winter visitor

A few of the redpolls passing through Britain on passage are of the race *C. f. flammea*, the Mealy Redpoll, which breeds in northern Europe. Birds of this race that had been ringed in Scandinavia have been recovered in Britain (*MA*).

Surrey. All Surrey 'Mealy Redpoll' records are included here and assumed to be *C. f. flammea*, though it is possible that these may include unrecognised members of other races. There has been an increased attention to the accurate identification of Mealy Redpolls since they were split off as a separate species. Earlier records were often accepted somewhat more casually.

Early Surrey history. About half a dozen were taken near Croydon in the winter of 1833 and a few at Tooting in the winter of 1835 (Blyth). There was a record from Wimbledon in 1895 or earlier and Bucknill (1900) knew of birds trapped at Cobham and Leigh.

1900 to 1980. Beadell wrote of a flock of 'hundreds' near Holt Wood, Chelsham in May 1915 that stayed for a fortnight. It was included in Parr but is not in *BLA*, possibly because the number and the date are both unusual, suggesting a possible error. There were some at Frensham, on 2nd February 1932 and on 5th February and 10th November 1936. H. Bentham described one at Tadworth on 6th April 1941 (*LBR* for 1941). Others, mostly sight observations of single birds, were at Runfold (January 1953), Leatherhead (February 1961), Shirley Hills (February 1962), Elmers End Sewage Farm (March 1962), Headley Heath (1962), Guildford (January and February 1966), Holmethorpe (November 1966), Inval (April 1967), Vann Lake (1966 and 1975, Blaker Log), Woking (October 1970), Brooklands (November 1972), Frensham (January 1975 and 1976), Knaphill and Witley Common (February 1976), Godstone and Thursley Common (March 1978) and there was one at King George VI Reservoir on 14th February 1960. One caught and ringed at Holmethorpe on 12th November 1966 had a wing measurement of 77 mm, consistent with it being of the longer-winged Mealy rather than the shorter-winged Lesser Redpoll.

Since 1980. Reports since 1980 have been in January and March 1984 (Frensham), March 1985 (Pirbright Commons), February 1986 (Molesey Heath and Barnes Common), March 1986 (Battersea Park), April 1986 (Old Coulsdon), March 1990 (Thursley Common), January 1991 (Egham), January 1992 (Frensham), March 1992 (Capel), January to March 1995 (Addlestone), December 1995 (Thursley Common), November 1997 (Chertsey Meads, three), December 1997 (Seale rubbish tip, two), January and February 1998 (Rushett Farm (three, several), January 1999 (Compton and Papercourt Gravel Pits). There were three on 7th November 2001 at Pyrford and up to five in February 2002 in a garden at New Malden (at least one photographed). Single birds were seen at Barn Elms on 20th November 2003 and at Frensham on 11th January 2005.

One was trapped at Stoke Lake on 28th January 1995 and one was trapped at Englefield Green on 15th December 2001.

Lesser Redpoll
Carduelis cabaret (*Carduelis [flammea] cabaret*)

Common winter visitor breeding annually but declining

Lesser Redpole is an old name going back at least to Montagu, when the Linnet was known as the Greater Redpole. The redpoll's breeding range (presumably *cabaret*) extended somewhat in Britain during the 19th and early 20th century. Redpolls lost ground in the 1920s and expanded again in the 1950s. The number breeding in Britain has fallen by around 90% since the 1970s. There is a strong spring and autumn passage through Britain.

Early Surrey history. Even by 1900, Lesser Redpolls were still rare breeders in Surrey. Bucknill could only cite thirteen possible instances. A redpoll was trapped near Claremont in June 1846, suggesting local breeding. Redpolls were said to have bred regularly in the Withy Bed, a damp spot by Catteshall Mill, Godalming some years prior to 1872 (Newman, *Zool.*, *1872:3235*). A young bird caught near Guildford on 1st August 1885 was seen by H. A. McPherson (*Zool.*, *1886:299*). They apparently had some value as cagebirds at the time. Aldridge (1885) bought one for twopence when he was a boy. Contrary to what is in Bucknill, McPherson did not write that it undoubtedly bred. Birds were seen in Dulwich Wood in May 1894, June 1895 and July 1896. Nests with eggs or young were found in a willow near Reigate on 20th May 1886; near Cobham on 7th June 1890 (*The Field* in Bucknill); at Addlestone on 19th May 1894; near Epsom on the following day, at Weybridge on 20th May 1894; in Combe Woods (presumably Coombe Wood, Wimbledon) on 30th May 1897; at Lingfield in 1897 (*Zoologist*), near Headley in 1897 and 1898 and on Wimbledon Common in 1899 (Bucknill 1900, 1901 and 1902), 1902 (*Zool.*, *1902:313*) and 1908 (*BB*, *2:91*).

1900 to 1950. In Surrey, where breeding Lesser Redpolls became considerably more common during the 20th century, important factors were probably the spread of forestry plantations and birch encroachment on the commons. The Boorman egg collection includes the species, collected at Cobham in 1903. The earliest breeding record which has been located for Spelthorne also relates to 1903. Mouritz saw a few in Richmond Park during the autumn and winter of 1905. Power (1910) thought they had bred occasionally at Sydenham but they were better known in the area as spring and autumn migrants. Other nesting and breeding localities up to 1950 included Carshalton (family party 1949), Caterham (1917), Cobham (1948), Kingswood (six nests 1914, 1927, 1929), Limpsfield (1912, 1913, 1915, 1935, 1946, 1949), Oxted (1908), Reigate Heath (1934), Richmond Park (before 1921), Roehampton (1939), Selsdon (1945), Sheen Common (1939), South Croydon (1947-48), Sutton (1934), Tadworth (1925, 1928, 1930, 1938-39, 1943, 1945), Upper Warlingham (1914), Waddon (1932), Walton Heath (1934, 1942), Wandsworth Common (family party in 1948, 1949), Wimbledon Common (1902, 1908, 1931, 1934, 1935, 1939) and Worms Heath (1929). They were breeding freely in the Surrey part of the London area by 1936. Winter flocks of over twenty were uncommon during this period but there were 150-200 on Wimbledon Common in February 1939.

1950 to 1970s. In the Surrey part of the London area, Lesser Redpolls were breeding or present in the breeding season at Ashtead, Banstead Heath (*LBR* for 1957), Burgh Heath (*LBR* for 1958), Cheam (*LBR* for 1957), Chipstead (1959), Kew Gardens (1975), Oxshott (1958-1959), Oxted, Tadworth (*LBR*), Walton Heath (*LBR* for 1957) and Wimbledon Common in the 1950s (*BLA*) but they were still not breeding on the southwest Surrey commons (CNHS, 1959). The Lesser Redpoll population probably peaked in the 1960s and remained fairly high in the 1970s. There were at least 32 pairs in the Burgh Heath/Tadworth/Headley Heath area in 1961, 10-12 pairs on Walton Heath in 1964 and 10-12 pairs on

Hankley Common in 1977. The number of pairs on 96 acres of grass and scrub on Bookham Common reached six in 1969. The *LBR* for 1967 details 15 breeding season localities for the Surrey part of the London area. During this period a few Lesser Redpolls held territory in urban areas.

Trend since 1970. A measure of the decline is given, for the 231 tetrads of northeast Surrey, by comparing the number of occupied tetrads found in the 1968-72 LNHS and 1988-97 SBC Atlas surveys. This shows a drop from 33% to 22% between the two. There has since been a further withdrawal. For example, Palmer (1987) mentions Nunhead Cemetery and Sydenham Hill Wood as being occupied in 1985-87. By 2000 they were not. No Lesser Redpoll territories have been recorded in the Common Birds Census since 1986, mainly because of the poorer coverage of heathland localities. The Winter Atlas found partial survey counts and estimates totalling 751 birds in 1981-84, a fraction of the likely total. They would probably have been mainly immigrant birds, as they are now and wintering numbers also seem to have fallen. There have been no counts of 1,000 or more since the 1970s.

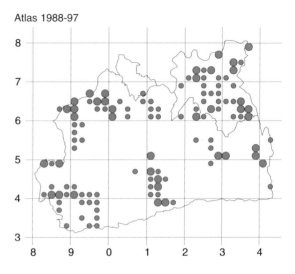

Atlas 1988-97

Breeding Population size. The Breeding Birds Survey suggests a breeding season population of only about 200 adults. Even this might be high. Recent indications of presence in May or June are only to hand from Ash Ranges (2000), Barn Elms (2002), Frensham Common (2002, 2003), Limpsfield Chart (2000), Pirbright Common (2001), a garden in Purley (2002), Puttenham Common (2003), Richmond Park (2002), Thursley Common (2002), over a garden in Walton-on-Thames (2001), Wimbledon Common (migrant flock on 30th May 2001) and Winterfold (2001). Surveys of the western heaths since 1994 have found no more than two pairs on Frensham Common, Horsell Common, Olddean Common, Pirbright Common/Ash Ranges, Puttenham Common, Thursley/Ockley/Elstead Commons or West End Common/Pirbright Ranges and none elsewhere.

Nest sites. Lesser Redpolls breed mainly on heathland and in open birch woodland. Parr mentions nesting in large gardens. There was a failed attempt in a garden at East Molesey in 1967, a pair bred in a garden at Parkside, Wimbledon in 1979 and a pair nested in a Hurst Green garden in 1982 and 1983. Late fledging dates include 14th August and 12th September in 1972.

Calendar. Migrant Lesser Redpolls normally begin to arrive in September and most leave by the end of April. They are mainly found on alder and birch in winter but later move to pines and then to flowering sallows in April and they forage in weedy fields. They will take niger seed at garden feeders.

Vice-county approximate monthly totals 1998- 2001

	Jan	Feb	Mar	Apr	May	Jun	Jul	Aug	Sep	Oct	Nov	Dec	Total
1998	431	359	372	366	92	20	2	0	12	83	60	39	**1,836**
1999	152	20	146	260	2	0	0	0	26	160	250	312	**1,328**
2000	282	147	362	585	48	2	1	4	3	164	58	60	**1,716**
2001	236	48	34	175	4	1	0	0	2	129	349	207	**1,185**

Source: Surrey Bird Reports

Large counts. By far the largest counts and estimates date back to the 1970s:

Ashtead Woods: 425+, 2nd January 1970

Chobham Common: 219 were ringed at a small waterhole in November 1981, 600 present on 19th January 1992

Epsom Common: 400-500, 5th December 1969

Limpsfield Chart: *c.*200 roosted in conifers, 15th December 1974

Olddean Common: 500, 14th April 1992

Red House Farm, Elstead: 500, February/March 1989

Sheen Common: 400, 28th February 1970

St George's Hill: 6,000, March 1970

Thursley/Ockley Commons: estimated 2,000, 25th March 1976; 500 in April 1992; several 400+ counts

Wimbledon Common: 800-1,000, 30th January 1966

Spelthorne

Queen Mary Reservoir: 50+, 29th December 1971; in the 1980s the largest flock published was of 17 on 20th March 1986

Movements. Spring passage is often evident in the Surrey records, with especially large numbers passing through the county from late March to late April in some years, for example about 300 at Hankley Common on 21st April 1981. At Banstead and Walton Heaths, parties totalling about 500 arrived from the southeast on 20th April 1973. Up to 6,000 were recorded at St George's Hill, Weybridge in March 1970 (G. H. Gush), apparently the largest figure for the county from 1900 to 1970 (Parr, 1972). A total of 2,000 was estimated by R. M. Fry at Thursley Common on 25th March 1976 (Clark, 1984 and pers. comm.) and is the second largest figure known. There have been no counts of comparable size in more recent years.

Lesser Redpolls ringed at Chobham Common in the 1981/82 winter were recovered at Warrington and Lichfield in the following year, illustrating the north-south movement within Britain. In the 1995/96 winter, when western Europe received a massive irruption of Redpolls from Scandinavia and northern Russia in December and January (Riddington *et al.*, 2000) flocks built up on Thursley Common from late October, to peak at 420 on 20th November, with 400 there on 20th January. These numbers, higher than in other winters of the period, suggest that Surrey shared in the irruption.

The five foreign ringing recoveries below are all of birds wintering in, or passing through, Surrey and found in continental Europe in the autumn. There are three other similar recoveries of Haslemere area birds. The dates are consistent with all of them being birds breeding in other parts of the British Isles, but some of the other migrants in Surrey might be *C. cabaret* of continental origin moving further south or north.

Ringed	**Date**		**Recovered**		**Date**	
Haslemere	17th January	1965	Wassenaar	Netherlands	11th November	1965
Haslemere	13th March	1965	Goussainville	France	26th October	1966
Haslemere	15th October	1970	Satory	France	19th November	1970
Westhumble	4th October	1970	Louhans	France	17th October	1973
Chobham Common	8th December	1979	Koksijde	Belgium	20th October	1983

A Lesser Redpoll ringed at Tayside on 24th June 1990 and recovered 599 kilometres south, at Windlesham on 19th February 1992, had travelled the furthest.

Longevity. A Lesser Redpoll ringed at Chobham Common on 8th December 1979 and recovered over three years and ten months later, in Belgium on 20th October 1983, is the most long-lived on file.

Arctic Redpoll

Carduelis hornemanni

One bird

An arctic and subarctic breeding species which disperses irregularly southwards in winter. British records have been most frequent in March and December, though there have been occurrences in other months. From 1958 to 1985 they were exclusively in coastal counties and mostly on the east coast but there have since been a few in inland counties. There was a national influx of Arctic Redpolls in the winter of 1990/91.

Surrey. A first-winter bird reported from Godstone Sand Pits on 10th-11th March 1991 was part of the national movement of that year (R. J. and S. J. Aspinall, R. P. Bosanquet *et al.*, *BB*, *86:526*). A 1986 record from Molesey Heath was not accepted by the BBRC but the decision was not published (BBRC 28th July 2002, pers. comm.).

Two-barred Crossbill

Loxia leucoptera

Seven records, including at least four birds shot before 1900.

This slightly smaller relative of the Crossbill has a Eurasian race *L. l. bifasciata* with a breeding season distribution which stretches from Scandinavia east to Amurland. The North American race is *L. l. leucoptera*. Both races are vagrants to Britain. Movements of *bifasciata* are irruptive and dispersive rather than migratory and, as with the Nutcracker, depend mainly on the conifer seed crop. Also, as with Nutcrackers, most of the birds that arrive in Britain do so from July to March, with a few from April to June. There is an east coast bias to the arrivals but birds have been found in most inland counties. The current BOU British List gives the first birds as being from an influx in 1845/46 (*Ibis January 2007 p. 149*). Another took place in the autumn of 1889, when many birds were seen from Yorkshire to Surrey (Saunders, 1899).

Surrey. In Bucknill's day the Charterhouse Collection held a specimen shot by J. P. Stafford on Munstead Heath many years previously (*SALEC*), but this was no longer in the collection in 2001.

1849: Unstead. One of the early British records is of a male shot in 'Unsted Wood' sometime before 1849 that passed into the possession of H. Nicholson of Waverley Abbey (J. D. Salmon in Newman, 1849). Newman said it was of the Eurasian race *bifasciata*.

1876: East Molesey, one near East Molesey at the beginning of February (Mitford, 1876), described as a White-winged Crossbill. The notes suggest it was *bifasciata*.

1889: Godalming, two were killed close to Charterhouse school, at Frith Hill on 28th November (*Zool. 1890:17-18*).

The same *Zoologist* note, by H. Benson, said that *The Field*, 30th November 1889 contained a report of a flock of White-winged Crossbills near Croydon.

The 1897 Two-barred Crossbill   Photo Jeremy Adams

1897: near Godalming, one was said to have been shot while among a flock of Crossbills many years before 1897. Bucknill said that this bird passed into the collection of a Mr Munroe, from which it was bought by William Borrer. The Booth Museum Catalogue for 1927 says that its specimen, apparently the same bird, came from Borrer's collection and that Borrer was given it by Mr W.

W. Reeves of Tunbridge Wells, so there is a little confusion about the chain of ownership. The 1927 catalogue puts it in case 464. This case could not be located by the staff when the Museum was visited in January 2005 but a male Two-barred Crossbill found in a case of Parrot Crossbills is probably the bird.

1948:   Vice-county, two males and two females were at an undisclosed place on 11th-12th March (*BB, 42:119-20*).

1966:   Frensham Little Pond, a male at Frensham Little Pond from 22nd September to 20th October (D. Carr, Dr S. G. Kent and H. W. Rudd, *BB, 60:331*).

Crossbill (Common Crossbill)   *Loxia curvirostra*

Moderately common winter visitor, irregular breeding species

Resident in suitable areas across Europe, Asia and North America, and locally in northwest Africa. Irruptive and dispersive. There are large fluctuations in population levels. In England, Crossbills bred occasionally during the 19th century and breeding was more frequently recorded in the 20th. The *Migration Atlas* notes that most European recoveries are of birds ringed on migration rather than in the nest and that they show onward movements farther south and west. Ringing provides little evidence about the origin of immigrants.

Early Surrey history. Crossbills were first recorded in Surrey by Graves, who mentioned several in a large fir plantation near Leith Hill in 1807. They appeared at Puttenham and Tooting in the winter of 1835/36, and there were a few at Tooting in the summer of 1836, following an irruption in 1835. Long (1839) contains a lengthy account of breeding in Holt Forest, just over the Surrey border in Hampshire, in 1839, which is summarised in Newman's edition of Montagu, in Yarrell and in Bucknill. Crossbills had been resident in the area for several years. An irruption in 1868 brought further birds to Cobham and Reigate. Birds were still at Foxwarren Park, Cobham in February 1869. Flocks were seen in Gatton Park on Christmas Day, 1873 and near Guildford and Haslemere in about 1880. There were rather more records after 1880 including six Crossbills shot at Ripley in 1883, a few in the Dulwich and Godalming areas in 1895/96, four over Dulwich Park on 4th September 1898, one there on 15th August 1899, several found near Shere and many at Lingfield in the winter of 1898/99 (a few of the Lingfield birds staying until May) and four across Dulwich Park Lake on 10th September 1900. Aldridge (1885) gave an undated record for Norwood. It 'no doubt' nested sometimes in the Bagshot and Witley districts (*BB, 1:247*).

The Field for 12th November 1898 reported on a Surrey nest but did not give the locality (in Bucknill). Crossbills may also have nested near Shere 'in the past season' (Bucknill, 1900), presumably meaning 1899. There are no confirmed 19th century breeding records for Surrey, though the 1898 account seems an advance on the *Probable* status conferred by Witherby (*BB, 4:332-334*), which referred to 1899 only. The *Historical Atlas* does not mention the 1898 record.

1900 to 1914. Breeding definitely took place in 1910, after a national irruption in the previous year. The sequence of events was typical of the way that breeding was subsequently associated with irruptions. The 1909 irruption into Britain began in late June. It was detected near Godalming, Reigate and Tilford in July, at Leith Hill, Limpsfield, Oxted and Witley in August, at Leatherhead and Purley in September, Hampton Court in October, Frensham and Walton-on-Thames in November, Addington and Shirley in

December (*BB*, 4). Flocks of up to 150 (at Woodmansterne, *BLA*) were reported in these movements. Crossbills began to desert southeast Surrey in January and most left the conifer woods of west Surrey in March, though a few continued to be seen after the breeding season. Notes by Lynes, Tutt and Russell in *British Birds* (*BB*, 3:404-06) describe eight nesting attempts early in 1910. These were: a nest in a railway cutting near Witley Station; six nests, of which at least one progressed to egg-laying at a place within fifteen miles of London; nest-building on Shere Heath. A ninth nest, with four eggs, was found near Aldershot on 28th April (*Brit. Birds*, 4:187). Crossbills also nested at Walton Heath (*BLA*) and Weybridge (*LN* for 1924). Song was heard at other places.

The final records for early 1910 were of a party over Dormans [Dormans Park presumably] on 2nd April (H. H. Farwig, *BB*, 4:22), and then one at Lingfield on 24th April, one at Oxted on 22nd May, a party of four near Woldingham on 26th June and two at Limpsfield on 17th July (Howard Bentham, *BB*, 4:53, 83). The June and July birds, along with two at Frensham and six at Millbridge seen by Bentham on 11th September, may have been 1910 immigrants. A few were seen at Croydon in the following spring. Crossbills nested at Walton Heath in 1914 (*BLA*).

1915 to 1949. There were no other breeding records until 1926, when five pairs were found, after a small east Surrey influx in the previous year. Breeding took place again in 1927 (three pairs, *BB*, 20:271, *BB*, 24:156). There was a substantial influx in 1929, followed by breeding in 1930 (up to four pairs, *BB*, 25:22-23) and eight to ten pairs bred in 1931 (*BB*, 25:163). There was a major invasion in 1935, with many records from late June until June of the following year, with flocks and aggregations of a hundred or more birds at Hambledon and Reigate Heath and smaller numbers at many other places. Crossbills were seen in Richmond Park for the first time. In 1936 one nest was found in Kew Gardens and another at Thursley and birds attempted or succeeded in breeding elsewhere. The *SEBR* reported that up to four pairs nested in the 'Western Weald', possibly including Surrey, in 1938 and a pair nested at Thursley in 1939 (HNHS, 1955). A pair raised five young near Woking in 1940. A major invasion in 1942 does not seem to have affected Surrey but a pair were seen nestbuilding at Reigate Heath in 1943. Four at Banstead on 25th January 1944 were part of a small national influx.

1950 to 1969. A substantial national invasion in 1953 produced six to eight birds in Surrey on 5th June (*BB*, 49:291) and July records from Banstead Heath (twenty), Barn Elms (six), Hambledon (large party), Pewley Down (twelve), Tadworth (six), Tilford/Hankley (up to twenty), and Weybridge (twelve). Others were seen at Farnham, Frensham, Haslemere, Kenley, Kingswood, Richmond Park, Shirley, South Norwood, Thursley, Wimbledon and Wrecclesham later in the year. A family party seen at Leith Hill in June 1955 may have bred locally (D. Parr).

Another invasion began in early July 1956, mostly in west Surrey. There were parties of up to fifty in the county until May 1957 and breeding was suspected. Some of the birds lingered and, perhaps joined by further arrivals, five pairs bred in 1960, with possible breeding pairs in eight further localities. A pair bred at Hindhead in 1961. There was a substantial invasion in 1962. It peaked in the first week of August, when a total of over 150 birds was seen at fifteen localities, about half of the birds being in Larches. Flocks of up to sixty Crossbills appeared at Oxshott in late spring of 1963. At least one pair of Crossbills raised young at Frensham.

A substantial invasion occurred in 1966, reaching a peak of 772 birds in July, including a flock of 107 on Wisley Common. Crossbills bred at Frensham, Kew Gardens and Ottershaw in the following year, when there was a smaller influx, and at St George's Hill, Weybridge in 1968.

Since 1970. Crossbills may have bred at Beacon Hill in 1971 and 1972. No breeding was proved from 1970-76. Flocks of up to 24 were seen in west Surrey from mid 1972. One pair was thought to have bred in 1977 but the next significant influx was not until 1979. A pair were seen with five juveniles at The Sands in May 1980. There was a similar influx in 1983 and again this was followed by breeding. A pair with two juveniles were seen at Linkside, Hindhead in the spring of 1984. The Winter Atlas found partial survey counts and estimates totalling 13 birds in three 10 km squares in 1981-84. Crossbills bred in 1986-87, but were not proved to breed from 1988 to 1990.

After several years of small arrivals there was a substantial invasion in mid 1990. It began on 8th May, when a Crossbill was found on Olddean Common. There were reports totalling over 400 birds, from at least 36 localities, in the months June to December, the peak being in October. The largest individual counts were at least 28 at Hackhurst Downs and 25-30 at Thursley Common, both in October. Large numbers remained in the county and were joined by others in the following year. Some 200 were found at Hascombe Hill on 23rd January 1991 and the reported flock totals for the year came to 1,250. Singing males were reported from at least seven places and breeding may have taken place at some of them but firm proof is lacking. Juveniles were found at Churt Common, the Devil's Punch Bowl, Frensham, Tilhill Nurseries and Thursley Common from early June, but at about the time further immigrants were being logged at coastal observatories, so they may not have bred locally. Six, thought to be a family party, were seen at Mountain Wood, Effingham on 22nd March 1992 and in April of that year song and display were seen at Olddean and Thursley Commons. Single pairs bred at Frensham and Thursley in 1994 and territorial birds were seen at Pirbright Common, Tilhill Nurseries and Wishmoor Bottom. Of flocks totalling 837 in 1994, only ten at Banstead and 14 at Holmethorpe were larger than nine and not in south or west Surrey. A pair bred at Thursley in 1995.

1997 was a record year, with some of the largest flocks ever recorded in Surrey. Only seven birds were reported up to the end of May but there were 332 in June and a peak of 800, from 44 places, in July. Monthly flock totals remained above 150 to the end of the year and for 1997 as a whole they came to over 2,700. Among the bigger flocks were 200 at Netley Heath on 28th June and 400 at Hindhead Golf Course on 27th September. Many lingered into May 1998. Single pairs bred at Chobham, Crooksbury, Horsell and Thursley commons and at Winterfold. None bred in 1999 but, after a small influx in the second half of the year, nine pairs bred at seven localities in 2000 – two each at Pirbright and Thursley Commons and single pairs at Crooksbury and Frensham Commons, Limpsfield Chart, Mytchett Place and Olddean Common. There was a displaying pair at Walton Heath.

A pair held territory at Bourne Woods in 2001 but could not be monitored because of Foot and Mouth Disease access restrictions. A family party was at Thursley/Ockley Common on 24th April. There was an influx of up to seventy birds from July to August 2001 and Crossbills bred again at Thursley in 2002, 2003 and 2004. There was a significant influx in early 2003, singing males being heard into May and a pair bred at Crooksbury Common. Two pairs bred at Frensham in 2004.

The few published records for Spelthorne include one at Queen Mary Reservoir on 23rd September 1966 and two over Staines Reservoirs on 28th August 1994.

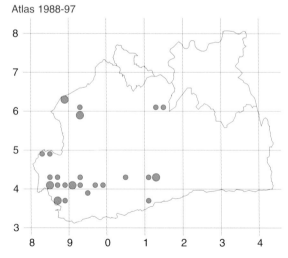

Atlas 1988-97

Food. Food taken is mainly pine and larch seed but includes woolly aphid and Mountain Ash *Sorbus aria* berries (Parr).

Calendar. Immigrant Crossbills may arrive as early as June and there have been big arrivals in July. They will normally linger into the following year, reinforcing the residents if there are any, and often nesting very early in the season. The peak in March suggests a spring passage:

Vice-county bird months 1994-2001

	Jan	Feb	Mar	Apr	May	Jun	Jul	Aug	Sep	Oct	Nov	Dec	Total
1994	58	45	250	120	235	44	8	11	11	23	32		**837**
1995	3	4	37	10	0	1	3	0	0	2	2	0	**62**
1996	0	2	2	1	0	2	0	5	2	32	0	2	**48**
1997	0	1	0	1	5	332	800	259	589	299	279	153	**2,718**
1998	165	237	327	116	309	15	2	0	4	6	0	0	**1,181**
1999	0	0	2	0	4	1	14	83	64	68	38	23	**297**
2000	36	35	54	66	69	19	5	0	0	1	3	2	**290**
2001	2	4	0	11	3	30	21	10	0	6	5	9	**101**
Total	**264**	**328**	**672**	**325**	**625**	**444**	**853**	**368**	**670**	**437**	**359**	**189**	**5,534**

Large counts

Hascombe Hill: 200, 23rd January 1991

Hindhead Golf Course: 400, 27th September 1997

Holloways Heath: 123, 2nd July 1997

Netley Heath: 200, 28th June 1997

Thursley Common: 128, 30th March 1994 (four flocks northwest)

Wisley Common: a flock of 107, 17th July 1966

Parrot Crossbill   *Loxia pytyopsittacus*

Three birds, none Spelthorne

Another crossbill subject to irruptive rather than migratory movements. Parrot Crossbills breed from Scandinavia east to the Urals and have bred in Britain. Arrivals are mainly in October and November, with a much smaller peak in January and February. From 1958 to 1985, Parrot Crossbills were found in only three inland counties, Berkshire, Derbyshire and Surrey, the remainder of the birds being in eastern coastal counties from Shetland to Suffolk.

Surrey. The three available records are rather lacking in detail or corroboration by other observers. The first is of one killed at Tooting in the winter of 1831. A cat stole and ate the corpse before Blyth could see it but he accepted a description and the record was published in *The Field Naturalist* vol. i, pp. 130 and 354 (Bucknill). The second is of a young female shot among Common Crossbills in the summer of 1868 (*Zool., 1868:1376*) and identified on unquoted bill and other measurements. The third, better documented, is of a female trapped near Wisley by K. D. Edwards on 15th May 1963, identified by quoted measurements and the call on release (Davis, 1964). The most convincing measure in this paper is the 14.5 mm bill depth, well out of range for a Crossbill *L. curvirostra*. The wing length (103 mm) and the bill length (20 mm) are both within the range found for female Crossbills in Summers *et al.* (1996) although outside the range given in Svensson (1992). The tail length was given as 63 mm, outside the range given for a sample of twenty by Svensson.

The Wisley record has been listed by Parr and others. In view of its importance, it has been carefully researched. The bird in question was one of two Parrot Crossbills ringed in 1963 (Davis). The BTO has confirmed that both were reported, but only one is shown in the Ringing Report for 1963 (Spencer, 1964), which the BTO say must have been an error (pers. comm.). Parrot Crossbills were not considered by the BBRC until 1978, when records for 1958-77 were considered retrospectively (Dymond *et al.* 1989) and the Wisley bird was published as an accepted record in 1984 (*BB, 77:557*). When approached, the BBRC were not able to locate the underlying documentation that led to this decision. The record has not appeared in the London or Surrey Bird Reports, probably because it was overlooked. The bird was among a large Crossbill flock for which there were a number of observers. As far as can be determined from records and additional enquiries, no observer other than the ringer reported a Parrot Crossbill. This was in a period well before the advent of the mobile phone, so it would have been less easy to alert others. The additional claim in Parr that there were probably three other Parrot Crossbills present from 23rd April to 15th May 1963 is apparently connected with sight records of possible birds in the original paper, which also mentions a possible nest. The nest record was not accepted as being of a Parrot Crossbill by Davis because the identity of the nestbuilders was not confirmed, a judgement which has been followed by later writers.

Common Rosefinch *Carpodacus erythrinus*

Four birds, including two from Spelthorne

Many might prefer the less prosaic name of Scarlet Rosefinch for this attractive bird, which has a discontinuous breeding range from France and Germany to Scandinavia and east to China, and which winters from India eastwards. There are a few winter sightings from Britain. The range expanded during the 20th century and a few pairs have bred in Britain in recent years. British records show a pronounced spring peak in May and June and a larger autumn peak in September and October. The distribution is predominantly northern, concentrated on coastal counties from Shetland south to Yorkshire. Berkshire, Middlesex and Hertfordshire were the only inland counties with records during the period 1958 to 1985.

Surrey. One was trapped at the Kempton Park ringing site on the exceptionally early date of 6th February 1971 and it remained there until the 28th. The bird's age and sex do not appear to have been published. The net in which the rosefinch was caught was placed on the edge of the marsh in the small wood immediately southeast of Red House reservoir (*Hersham Ringing Group Report No. 2*). Since the Spelthorne boundary passes through this wood, the net might not have been in Spelthorne. Given the length of stay, though, and the fact that the ringing hut was in Spelthorne, it seems reasonable to include the record. The bird was the first for Spelthorne and the second for Middlesex, the first Middlesex bird being at Hampstead in 1870 (Glegg). There was a female or immature bird at Perry Oaks Sewage Farm on 8th October 1995, another borderline locality.

The first record for the vice-county was of a summer-plumaged adult male in full song found by S. J. Aspinall at Beddington Sewage Farm on 13th July 1995. A male was seen at Walton Heath on 16th June 1996 (A. D. Prowse).

Bullfinch (Common Bullfinch) *Pyrrhula pyrrhula*

Common breeding resident

Breeds across the temperate parts of Europe and Asia. Mostly resident but some northern birds migrate to regions within the breeding range or further south, including central Spain and Asia Minor. There has been some expansion in the north and west of its range, but not recently. Numbers in Britain declined during the 19th century, mainly in the north and west. They increased in the early 20th century, slowly at first after the enforcement of the Wild Birds Protection Acts, and then faster with the spread of new forestry plantations. The increase continued until the 1960s, after which there was a renewed decline of over 50%, most obvious in the north and west and on farmland, but also apparent elsewhere. Deer browsing and less woodland management have been suggested as contributing to the decline (Fuller *et al.*, 2005). Few British movements exceed twenty kilometres. There are several recoveries in or from the near Continent and sight records suggest that Northern Bullfinches *P. p. pyrrhula* reach Britain in most years (*MA*).

Early Surrey history. Newman's reference to one shot by Kidd at Eashing around 1835 is an early record. There is no evidence of a 19th century decline in the county. Bucknill makes no reference to bird catchers, though they certainly operated in the London area. Jefferies (1885) gave a price of eight or nine shillings a dozen for cock birds. There is a 19th century record from Battersea Park (Hamilton, 1879). Bullfinches nested at Streatham and Beaulieu Heights in the 1880s (Aldridge). A nest was found at Gatwick in 1899. Bucknill described Bullfinches as common residents and found sixteen nests in an afternoon near Epsom, in Ashtead Woods and on the common - a feat not likely to have been carried out very often in later years. They were quite plentiful in the Staines district (Kerr, 1906).

1900 to 1940. Power knew of a nest in Dulwich Wood in 1901 but Bullfinches were becoming scarce. They bred at South Park in 1905 (G. T. Winter). Boorman collected eggs at Clandon, Ockham and Ripley from 1902-10. Mouritz (1905) had no personal records for Richmond Park, where they were only occasional visitors, but he knew them from Kew Gardens. They began nesting in Richmond Park some time after 1925 (Collenette). Eggs were collected at Woking in 1922 and at Bookham in 1937.

Mid 20th century. Bullfinches were described as moderately abundant on Bookham Common in the 1940s (Carrington *et al.*, 1944). In the 1950s, they were breeding at Dulwich (*BLA*). A number of references suggest that Bullfinches were a good deal commoner in the middle decades of the 20th century than they are now. Eric Parker mentioned a 'plague year' when he let his gardener shoot 66 from January to the spring in his Hambledon garden (Parker, 1947). A roost at Weybridge held 38 on 20th December 1958. Large numbers were reported in the county in 1961 and 1963 and winter flocks of twenty or more were common (Parr, also the Common Birds Census). Fifty roosted at Frensham on 10th December 1967. The largest count known for Surrey is about 84 at Lyne Sewage Farm on 25th November 1967 (Parr). There were about 50 near Queen Mary Reservoir on 4th December 1965. The Surrey population may therefore have broadly followed the 20th century changes found elsewhere in Britain.

Trend since 1970. The Common Birds Census shows a significant decline from 1970 to 2000. Of the 231 tetrads in northeast Surrey, 80% were found to hold territories in the 1968-72 Atlas survey but only 67% in the 1988-97 Atlas, a similar measure of the decline. The absence of any large counts in recent years also suggests that breeding numbers are down. The experience at individual places varies noticeably. Arbrook Common had up to four territories in the 1970s but at most one (in 1994) from 1984 to 1999. They continued to breed in Richmond Park until at least 1975 but were only occasional visitors from 1995 to 2004 (*The Birds of Richmond Park 1995-2004*). They were resident at Vann Lake from 1964 to 1996 (Blaker Log). In Inner London, Bullfinches bred at the Surrey Docks in 1980 and at Battersea Park in 1987-90 and 1995. A count of twenty at Epsom Common on 20th January 2001 was unusual for recent times. Bullfinches are often elusive.

Nesting. Bullfinches are normally solitary nesters but a colony of five pairs reared 28 young in a hawthorn copse at Walton Reservoirs in 1967. Two pairs nested in honeysuckle on a house at Worplesdon in 1973. A clutch of four unmarked white eggs was found at Betchworth in 1989.

Population size. The Winter Atlas found partial survey counts and estimates totalling 214 birds in 1981-84, almost the same as the number of Yellowhammers. Birds were found in twenty of the twenty-one 10 km squares surveyed. An end-period estimate of about 3,000 territories can be derived from the Common Birds Census. A total of about 1,100 adults can be derived from Breeding Birds Survey. If Surrey held a proportionate share of the British breeding population as given by the *New Atlas*, the

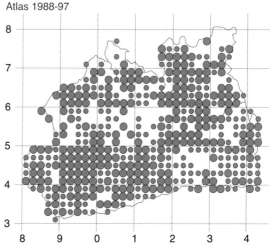

Atlas 1988-97

population would be nearer to 1,400 territories, or 0.7 per square km, which is in the same general range. Bullfinches have done well on Bookham Common, where there were thirteen territories in the Plains area in 2002 (A. D. Prowse). The Croydon RSPB Group's 2003 survey found them in no more than 10% of its gardens in any month. At Frensham there were twelve territories in 1995 and then eight or nine from 1996 to 2005. There were a few in the Shepperton area in 1983-86, not proved to breed (*Shepp. BR*) though Geen thought up to six pairs might have done so around Queen Mary Reservoir in the 1980s.

Large vice-county counts from 1970. There have been no counts to match the largest of those before 1970:

Ash Vale Gravel Pits: 20, 31st December 1976

Beddington Sewage Farm: 18, 14th November 1971

Capel: 24+, 23rd November 1991; 25+ on 15th September 1992; 36 together at Aldhurst Farm in February 1993 or 1994

Epsom Downs: 20, 20th January 2001

Farnham Park: 19, 27th December 1995

Frensham: 19, 16th August 1993 (not a flock)

Ham Lands: 18 in one flock, 15th December 1994

Horton Country Park: flock of 21, 2nd February 1986

Kingswood, Englefield Green: 20, 24th January 1998

Mitcham Common: 31 ringed in July-October 1984

Ockley Common: 19, 28th January 1981

Old Lyne Sewage Farm: 45, 3rd August 1970

Pirbright Common (Tunnel/Spur Hill): 50, 20th January 1978

Tadworth area: 30, 1973

Thursley Common: *c*.40, 3rd January 1972

Witley Common: 35+ including juveniles, 10th September 1977; 40, 31st October 1983

Woodham: 20, 20th December 1973

Elstead   *Photo J. J. Wheatley*

Food. Examples of the seeds and berries taken include 18 feeding on Chickweed *Stellaria media* at Lyne Old Sewage Farm (1971); Dandelion seeds (Horley, 1987); Delphinium seeds (Epsom, 1983); about twenty eating hips and haws at Merrow Downs (1972); Honeysuckle berries (Ewell, 1973); Rowan and *Cotoneaster horizontalis* at Chertsey (1973) and Raspberries and Sow Thistle seeds (Fetcham, 1980). A pair fed on niger seed daily at Elstead for several weeks in July/August 2005.

Movements and longevity. One or two have been seen on autumn movement watches, *e.g.* at Lightwater in 1984. Recoveries have links with Cambridgeshire, Kent and Sussex. The furthest recorded distance is for a Bullfinch ringed at Kingswood, Englefield Green on 18th November 1973 and recovered 117 kilometres northeast, at Cheveley, Cambridgeshire, on 12th March 1976. A Bullfinch ringed at TQ0468 (Laleham Burway area) on 30th November 1970 was found freshly dead there over six years and five months later, on 12th May 1977 and had the longest longevity located.

Hawfinch
Scarce breeding resident

Coccothraustes coccothraustes

Breeds in Europe and Asia from Britain to Japan and Kamchatka and in North Africa. Many northern European birds winter south to the Mediterranean. Most Asian birds winter south of the breeding range, in southeast Asia. Some movements of British birds are comparatively long and others confirm links with the Continent (*MA*). Hawfinches were only known as winter visitors to Britain in the 18th century. The first British breeding records came in the early 19th century. Hawfinches were breeding in a number of localities by the 1830s and breeding was widespread by 1900. Colonisation of the west and north of Britain continued until the 1960s. A decline was apparent across the whole British range by the time of the 1988-91 BTO Atlas. Increased predation by Grey Squirrels has been suggested as contributing to it (Fuller *et al.*, 2005).

Early Surrey history. The first record is of a flock feeding on Mountain Ash berries near Albury Park (Graves, 1811-21, vol. ii, about 1816). Meyer knew of one shot near Esher. The first breeding records are from Tooting Common in 1833 (Blyth, in Bucknill) and Roehampton (Jesse, undated, in Yarrell). By 1837, Newman could describe them as extremely common at Godalming and they were included in his 1849 list as breeding residents, though without any specific breeding references. Salmon mentioned a pair nesting in a garden at Peper Harow in 1848. The nest was destroyed by a cat (Salmon, 1849). The Holmesdale Natural History Club Museum has a nest taken at Godstone Mill in 1877. Hamilton (1881) had a Hawfinch in his garden in 1870 but no other Wimbledon records. The spread continued through Surrey, though its rapidity might have been exaggerated by the increased intensity of observation. Hawfinches nested in Wray Park around 1880 (Crossfield), were common around Godalming in the 1880s (*SALEC*), nested at Haslemere, on the Hog's Back and at Sutton Place (Guildford) in about 1880 and were common around Dorking by the 1890s. Many young birds were shot taking peas from gardens (Jordan, 1894). At the end of the century Bucknill could say that there were *very many records of both nest and birds from almost every part of the county.*

The peak years, 1900 to the 1970s. Eggs collected by Boorman at Bramley (1913), Clandon Common (1903), Ockham (1907) and Ripley (1902, 1903) are in the Haslemere Museum. At Vann Lake, Hawfinches were recorded in spring in 1966-67, 1971-73 and 1984 only (Blaker Log). The table shows many breeding localities for the years 1901 to 1975. In Spelthorne, Hawfinches bred at Stanwell in 1931 (*LN* for 1934). There was a pair in Spout Wood in May 1963.

The decline since 1970. Of the 231 tetrads in northeast Surrey, 9% were found to hold territories in the 1968-72 Atlas survey but only 1% in the 1988-97 Atlas. Over the whole county, Hawfinches were found in only 17 of the 575 tetrads in the 1988-97 Atlas. The only birds picked up by the Common Birds Census were at Bookham Common in 1996 and 1997. The Winter Atlas found partial survey counts and estimates totalling seven birds in 1981-84, Hawfinches being present in only four of the 21 ten km squares surveyed. No Hawfinches were found in the 1994-2004 Breeding Birds Survey. Langston *et al.* (2002) put the Surrey decline in the twenty years to 1995/99 at 57-75%.

By the end of the 20th century they were rarer in Surrey, both as breeding birds and as winter visitors, than they were 100 years or so

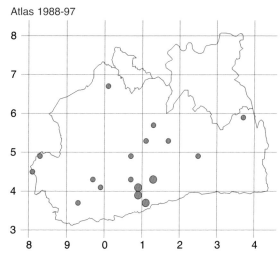

Atlas 1988-97

earlier, as is shown by comparisons for the specific breeding places mentioned in Bucknill and later sources:

Places with strong evidence of Hawfinches breeding, 1800-2000

Place	1800-1900	1901-1975	1976-2000
Addlestone		1929	
Ashtead	1890 or later	1938	
Banstead area	undated	1930, 1958, 1974 nest built	
Betchworth		1977	
Box Hill/Juniper Top		1968, 1970	
Burgh Heath		1958	
Capel			1996
Caterham		Before 1934	
Chelsham		Before 1934, 1945, 1958	
Chertsey		1971	
Chiddingfold			1981
Chipstead		Before 1934, 1939, 1942-43, 1945-46, 1951, 1958-59	
Chobham			1977
Claygate area	before 1842		
Coulsdon Common			1976
near Dorking	1894 or earlier		
Dulwich	1894	1949, 1951-53	
East Horsley		1971	1983, 1991, present most years
Effingham Forest		1975	
Elstead			1978
Englefield Green		1954	
Epsom and Ewell	1890 or later	1932	
Fairmile Common			1987
Farleigh		1935, 1946	
Farnham		1950s (Mountfort)	
Fetcham		1940	
Godalming	Before 1849	1971	
Godstone	1877	Before 1934	
Grayswood		1970	
Guildford		1944-45	
Hascombe	Regular		
Haslemere	1880	1934	
Headley		1939	
Hog's Back	1880		
Hurst Green			1991
Hydon Heath		1944	
Kenley		1947	
Kew Gardens		1940, most years 1949-75	1976
Leatherhead	1890 or later		

Leith Hill area	1887 or earlier		
Limpsfield		1937, 1939, 1946, 1949	
Lingfield	1894		
Marden Park		Before 1934	
Mortlake	1898		
Netley Heath			1983
Newton Wood	1890 or later		
Nonsuch Park		1933	
Nore Hill		Before 1935	
Peper Harow	1848		
Purley		1936, 1950	
Putney Heath		1946, 1950s	
Reigate	Regular	1963, 1966, 1975	1976-78, 1983, 1985, 1992
Richmond Park	1836, 1890s	1930s, most years 1949-66	
Roehampton	1835 or earlier	1949	
Sanderstead		1958	
Selsdon Wood		1946, 1963	
Shere		1974	
Streatham Common	1899	1949	
Sutton Place	1880		
Tadworth		Before 1934, 1943	
Tandridge		Before 1934	
Tooting Common	1833	1949-50	
Walton-on-the-Hill		Before 1934	
West Horsley			1981
West Humble		1966, 1967	
White Down, Ranmore			1977
Wimbledon Common	1890s	1932 (one pair), 1943, 1946, 1953, 1955	
Wisley RHS Gardens		1970	
Witley	Regular		
Woldingham		1970	

Nest sites include:

40 feet up Birch (Netley Heath 1983)

35 feet up Horse Chestnut (Reigate Priory 1983)

55 feet up Hornbeam (Reigate Priory 1976)

25 feet up Sycamore (Reigate Priory 1976)

Non-breeding and winter locations. Hawfinches were seen in Battersea Park on 25th April 1986 (one) and 30th August 1986 (three). A male was seen at St Mary's churchyard, Staines on 21st April 1986. While some Hawfinches remain within their breeding areas during the winter, others venture further afield, appearing in such places as Epsom and Thursley Commons and Island Barn Reservoir (these three in 2001). Birds have been found feeding around Blackthorn bushes on Bookham Common, apparently on sloes, and also on hawthorn and hogweed, in the early months of the year. There were ten on 2nd February 2004 (A. D. Prowse). It is presumed that they are from the dwindling colony in Great Ridings Wood (East Horsley), a short distance to the northwest which, with Bookham Common, has been the source of most of the recent records. Two were heard calling at Ranmore Common, an old Hawfinch locality (no definite breeding records), on 31st March 2003.

Large counts. The largest counts date back to the 1970s or earlier:

Bookham Common: *c*.30, 28th December 1969

Earlswood: *c*.100, February 1966; *c*.40, 30th March 1974

East Horsley area: 58, 11th April 1974

Haslemere Museum: 50, 5th April 1938; 20-30, 19th February 1942

Holmwood Common: flocks of 150 and 100, 21st March 1919 (H. Bentham)

Leatherhead: 'hundreds', 20th February 1927

Mickleham Downs: 40-50, 2nd and 15th April 1938

Nore Hill: flock of about 50 (Beadell, 1932)

Richmond Park: 30, 13th March 1936

near Thursley: *c*.50, 5th April 1938

Roosts. At Harestone Valley, Caterham, up to twelve roosted in ivy from 7th March 1978, four to six roosted in ivy on 20th January 1980 and three on 28th January 1981.

Food. Hawfinches are very much associated with Hornbeams. Other food reported as being taken includes wild Cherries (Chiddingfold 1981); Hawthorn (Fetcham 1982, Reigate 1992); Holly berries (Haslemere 1977); Rose hips (1981); Sycamore seeds (Shamley Green 1977) and Yew berries (Park Downs 1983).

Movements and longevity. An adult Hawfinch ringed at Sittingbourne, Kent, on 6th June 1982 was recovered at Effingham, five years and two months later and 76 kilometres west, on 14th August 1987.

Lapland Bunting (Lapland Longspur)   *Calcarius lapponicus*

Scarce double passage migrant, 23 records to 2001, including three from Spelthorne

Circumpolar distribution, breeding in tundras. European birds are mainly in Norway. Present in Britain during the last glaciation and may then have bred. Most British records come from the east coast and are of autumn migrants and wintering birds from Scandinavia. Inland occurrences are uncommon. Has bred in Scotland.

Surrey. Bucknill mentioned one in the Charterhouse Collection that had been killed from a flock of Skylarks at Mousehill in severe weather on an unknown date (*SALEC*). This bird is no longer in the collection. Dated occurrences, which peak in October, are:

1830:   Battersea Fields, a female was shot near the Red House, in the winter by Frederick Bond (*Zool., 1889:418*).

1869:   London area, one captured alive a few miles south of London in October (*Zool., 1870:2061*) was presumably in Surrey.

1895:   Wimbledon Common, two in the severe February weather (Bucknill).

1957:   Wimbledon Common, one on 3rd November, notes in the *LBR* for 1957.

1958:   Beddington Sewage Farm, one on 5th April, notes in the *LBR*. The *SBR* includes one on 18th April also, but the notes have not been seen.

1958:*   Staines Reservoirs, one on 13th April (*LBR*).

1973:   Beddington Sewage Farm, one on 25th October.

1976:*   Queen Mary Reservoir, one on 18th September.

1981:   Barn Elms Reservoir, one on 5th October, calling.

1983:   Beddington Sewage Farm, one on 29th October.

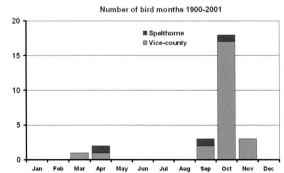

1983: Beddington Sewage Farm, one on 7th November, the 29th October bird?

1987: Barn Elms Reservoir, one flushed, calling, on 7th November.

1988: Ottershaw, one flushed on 26th March, notes in the *SBR*.

1989: Beddington Sewage Farm, one heard and seen while flying over on 3rd October.

1990: Beddington Sewage Farm, five west on 6th October (8th in the *SBR*, 6th in the *LBR*.). Beddington Sewage Farm, one flew over on 22nd October.

1992: Beddington Sewage Farm, two northwest, a third ten minutes later on 8th October.

1994: Barn Elms Reservoirs, one flew over, going west and calling, on 27th September.

1995:* King George VI Reservoir, one on 7th-9th October.

1997: Barn Elms Reservoirs, one flew over, calling, on 28th September. Beddington Sewage Farm, two flew northwest, calling, on 24th October and one was seen in flight there on the 25th.

2000: South Norwood Country Park, one west on 1st October.

2001: Queen Elizabeth II Reservoir, one flew over on 14th October.

*Spelthorne

Snow Bunting   *Plectrophenax nivalis*

Scarce winter visitor, nearly 100 records since 1900 and a few earlier.

The most northerly breeding land bird, found in circumpolar arctic and subarctic regions, including Scotland. Most winter south of the breeding range south to central Europe, central Asia and the USA. Snow Buntings were present in Britain during the last glaciation and probably bred. They have bred in Scotland since at least 1887. The breeding range has probably not changed much since, though numbers may have done. In pre-1900 Britain the wintering birds were hunted as a table delicacy and later the breeding birds were sought for their nests and eggs. Winter visitors to Britain probably come mainly from Greenland and Iceland rather than Scandinavia. The *Migration Atlas* shows Iceland as the main breeding area for birds reaching Scotland but casts little light on the origin of birds in southeast England.

Early Surrey history. A severe spring in 1830 brought the first known birds to Surrey (Meyer). One was shot at Hale some time before 1849. Specimens seen by Bucknill in the Charterhouse Collection may have come from Surrey but the only specimen held there in 2001 was said to have come from Inverness. One was shot at West Molesey in December 1880, one was shot at Epsom in 1889 and four or five were seen on a heap of manure at Morden in 1893 during the hard weather, presumably the great frost of that year (Bucknill). There are undated 19th century records from Egham, Milford and Mousehill.

Since 1900. One was found at Cranleigh on 26th January 1902 (*The Field*, vol. 99). In Spelthorne, five were at Staines Reservoirs on 20th November 1929 (Eton College Natural History Society in *The London Naturalist* for 1930). The table shows that there were only four more bird months in the first half of the 20th century. Single birds at Dulwich in November 1951 and 1952 were the first for the Surrey part of the London area since 1900. There was a male at Queen Mary Reservoir on 2nd March 1958. Snow Buntings were at one time fairly regular late autumn migrants there, including three on 27th October 1962 but there were none from 1968 to 1988 (Geen). No less then 79 of the 133 bird months since 1900 were in the 1950s and 60s, peaking in the coldest decade. Numbers have since tailed off and there have been no Snow Buntings at Staines Reservoirs, once a premier locality, since 1991.

Bird months by decade since 1900

	1900s	1910s	1920s	1930s	1940s	1950s	1960s	1970s	1980s	1990s	2000-02	Total
Vice-county	1	0	0	0	1	18	22	7	5	10	3	**67**
Spelthorne	0	0	5	1	2	19	20	5	10	4	0	**66**

Where found. Places with the largest number of bird months are Barn Elms (22), Beddington Sewage Farm (10) and, in Spelthorne, Staines Reservoirs (32) and Queen Mary Reservoir (13). Other places where Snow Buntings have been seen, with their bird months if more than three, are Box Hill, Chobham Common, Cranleigh, Dulwich Common, Elmers End Sewage Farm, Ewell, Ewhurst, Frensham, Gibbet Hill, Hersham, Holmethorpe, Island Barn Reservoir, Kingswood (five), Limpsfield Chart, Molesey Heath, Queen Elizabeth II Reservoir (six), Thursley/Ockley Commons, Walton Reservoirs (five) and, in Spelthorne, King George VI Reservoirs (nine), Perry Oaks Sewage Farm (nine) and Wraysbury Reservoir.

Since 2002, Snow Buntings have been seen at Barn Elms (four on 9th November 2005), Milford (Tuesley Farm, 16th November 2003) and Walton Reservoirs (6th November 2004). Five flying over Kingswood on 16th January 1956 was an unusually large number.

Calendar. By far the most Snow Buntings have been seen in November:

Bird months 1900 to 2002

	Jan	Feb	Mar	Apr	May	Jun	Jul	Aug	Sep	Oct	Nov	Dec	Total
Vice-county	9	2	1	1	0	0	0	0	0	16	27	11	**67**
Spelthorne	4	2	3	1	0	0	0	0	0	5	36	15	**66**

Among the early and late birds, one at Ewhurst on 14th April 1944 followed L. G. Weller's tractor for several hours while he was ploughing and one flew over Beddington Sewage Farm on 10th October 1992. There was one at Staines Reservoirs on 3rd October 1975.

Pine Bunting   *Emberiza leucocephalos*
One bird

Breeds from the Urals to Siberia and China, wintering mainly in the Indian subcontinent and China. Of about 36 records to 2001, 18 were in Orkney or Shetland. Most were from October to January.

Surrey. A female was found dead on a roadside at Ewhurst by J. J. and L. G. Weller on 29th January 1989 (*BB, 83:490*). The corpse was next to a field containing a large, mixed bunting flock. The skin has been retained by the Surrey Bird Club. Photographs appear in the *Surrey Bird Report* for 1991. The first record for Britain from an inland county and only the second anywhere for January.

Yellowhammer   *Emberiza citrinella*
Locally common breeding resident

Breeds from Europe east to central Asia with an introduced population in New Zealand. Northern and eastern birds migrate, wintering in Europe south to the Mediterranean, Asia Minor and central Asia. Others make more local movements. Most British Yellowhammers are sedentary. The few recoveries involving other countries may all have been of continental migrants (*MA*). The earliest remains found in Britain date back to the last glaciation. Yellowhammers probably benefited from the spread of heathland and they were common and widely distributed throughout the 19th and 20th centuries up to the 1970s. They were, for example, often seen at Vann Lake at the end of this period (Blaker Log). Since then, there has been a national decline of around 50% which has been attributed mainly to changes in farming practice, particularly the loss of winter stubble fields.

Early Surrey history. Yellowhammers were listed for the Godalming District in 1849 (Newman). They bred abundantly in the vice-county from 1875 to 1900 according to the *Historical Atlas*. The Holmesdale Natural History Club Museum has a nest taken at Wray Common in 1874. Eggs were collected at Charterhouse in 1894. Then, as now, Yellowhammers seem to have been scarce in the Surrey part of the London area. They still bred at Wandsworth Common (Hudson, 1898) but Aldridge said they were not common in Norwood. Power described them as irregular and not breeding in the Dulwich area from 1874 to 1900. Hamilton (1881) described Yellowhammers as 'common enough' on Wimbledon Common.

Since 1900. Bucknill described Yellowhammers as common residents and the commonest buntings in Surrey. The latter, at least, was still true, at least until recently, but the large winter flocks also mentioned by him, and found up to the 1970s, are no longer present. In Richmond Park numbers increased from around 1905 until the 1930s, when three to five pairs bred and flocks of up to twenty were present in winter (Collenette). Eggs were collected at Frensham in 1935. Limpsfield Common held a few pairs in 1937-40. Breeding continued there until at least 1976 but there were none in 1999. In the Surrey part of the London area during the 1950s, Yellowhammers bred at Epsom Downs, Park Downs, Wimbledon Common (*BLA*) and many other places. At one time Yellowhammers were common in the Staines district from April to September. A newly fledged bird was seen in 1907 or 1908 (Kerr). There were five pairs at Queen Mary Reservoir in 1971 but they last bred in 1979 (Geen). There were only two published records in the Shepperton area from 1983 to 1986 - four with Corn Buntings in 1984 and one at Laleham Lakes on 8th January 1986. Occurrences in the Surrey part of Inner London are rare but there were occasional winter records from the Surrey Docks in the 1970s and there was one at Battersea Park on 20th January 1987. There was early song at Woking Sewage Farm on 8th February 1981.

Measures of the trend since 1970. The Common Birds Census shows a significant decline of at least 60% from 1970 to 2000. Of the 231 tetrads in northeast Surrey, 58% were found to hold territories in the 1968-72 Atlas survey but only 37% in the 1988-97 Atlas.

Large flocks of Yellowhammers could sometimes be found up to the 1980s but more recent counts have been smaller. Places experiencing a decline include the Common Birds Census area at Ashtead Common, which had five territories in 1970 but then fewer up to 1998 when there were again five, but none by 2001. There were none on Pirbright Common/Ash Ranges from 1998 to 2004, a place that held 18 territories in 1978. Territory counts on the main western heaths suggest the decline has bottomed out, with stable numbers since 1995.

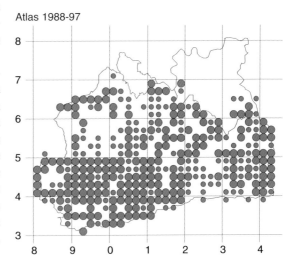

Atlas 1988-97

Territory counts on the main western heaths

	1995	1996	1997	1998	1999	2000	2001	2002	2003	2004
Crooksbury Common	8	6	6	9	4	5	2			
Frensham Common	11	11	12	13	13	10	12	12	12	13
Hankley Common	7	10	10	10	10	14	14	11	10	2
Hindhead Commons	3	1	3	2	3	2	1	1	1	1
Mare Hill			1	3	3	3	4	4	3	6
Puttenham Common	9*	6*	29	29	32	32	24	26	27	23
Thursley/Ockley/										
Elstead Commons	16	18	18	13	7	3*	6	7	5	13
Witley Common	3	2	4	5	6	8	6	5	6	4
Total	57	54	83	84	78	77	69	66	64	62

*From counts organised by John Clark. * incomplete count*

Population size. The Winter Atlas found partial survey counts and estimates totalling 239 birds in 1981-84, similar to the Bullfinches but fewer than the Reed Buntings. They were present in all 21 of the 10 km squares surveyed. A current population estimate of about 4,000 territories can be derived from the Common Birds Census but this was based on only a small sample towards the end of the period. It compares with an estimate of 1,500 adult birds based on the Breeding Birds Survey and with reported counts from individual localities, which averaged about 130 territories from 1994 to 2001. If Surrey held a proportionate share of the British breeding population as given for 1988-91 by the *New Atlas*, the population would be nearer to 9,000 territories, or about four per square km which, like the Common Birds Census, feels a bit high.

Large counts. Most of the largest counts date back to the 1980s or earlier, but there was an exceptional number at Tongham in 1997:

Ash: 70 at East Wyke Farm, 16th February 1970
Ashtead Downs: *c.*100, 29th December 1970
Beddington Sewage Farm: *c.*100, 31st January 1971
Capel: 75 feeding among sheep, 30th December 1994
Chilworth: 60, 18th February 1995
Ewhurst: 200+ in fields early in 1989
Holmethorpe Sand Pits: 75, 15th February 1979
Palewell Fields: 80, March 1970
Send Water Meadows: *c.*60, 10th March 1974
Thorpe: 135, 7th March 1970

Tongham Gravel Pit: 125, 28th January 1997
Walton-on-the-Hill: 80, 26th December 1972
Warlingham: 60 at Court Farm, 2nd February 1998
West Horsley: *c.*70 feeding in a hayrick, 24th February 1973
Woodlands Park, Leatherhead: 60+, 28th February 1972
Spelthorne
Queen Mary Reservoir: 41, 20th January 1973 (Geen's largest count)

Roosts. The larger roost counts also date back many years:

Ash Vale: 250 in a single oak in February/March 1973
Epsom Common: 15 to roost on 1st February 2001
Horley: flock of 35 in a cold spell, December 1935

Limpsfield Chart: about 50 on 13th December 1974
Margery: ten in a privet hedge on 27th December 1986
Papercourt Gravel Pits: 50+ on 19th January 1975

Feeding flocks. In Surrey, most Yellowhammers leave the commons in winter. They used to move to farmland where there was a better winter food supply. Counts of at least 30 in cropped sweetcorn at Beddlestead on 20th January 2002, at least 60 in stubble at Dippenhall on 30th December 2001, 20-50 on stubble at Limpsfield Chart in December 2001, 50 on stubble at Norbury Park on 25th January 2000 and about 33 on stubble at Riddlesdown on 8th January 2000 show the importance of winter food supply and the vulnerability of Yellowhammers to changing farming practice, in this case the autumn ploughing of stubbles.

Movements and longevity. The furthest known movement is 38 kilometres (24 miles), made by a Yellowhammer ringed at Frensham on 12th September 1965 and recovered over two years and four months later at Wickham, Hampshire. There are no foreign ringing recoveries. A Yellowhammer ringed near Newdigate on 25th August 1980 and recovered over three years and seven months later at Holmwood is the longest-lived for which details are available. Surrey Bird Reports since 1977 have included a longevity record of five years eight months but no details have been found.

Plumage variations. Bucknill mentioned a specimen from Farnham that had a few white feathers in the wings and tail.

Cirl Bunting

Emberiza cirlus

Rare, no longer breeds

Resident in Mediterranean countries including north-west Africa. Southern Britain is the most northerly part of its breeding range. Montagu found Cirl Buntings feeding on ploughed fields with finches in Devon during 1800. They remained there during the severe winter of that year, an early indication of the importance to the species of arable land. It was only known from the southwestern counties in the early 19th century.

The British population of Cirl Buntings began to decline in the 1930s and collapsed in the 1960s. The reasons for the decline seem to be complex, and as much to do with subtle changes in the general environment and climate as with changes in farming practice, though their dependence on winter stubble fields has been established as critical. The 1982 survey showed that typical nest sites were on southerly-facing slopes and most often associated with Elm or Hawthorn. The survey did not find that competition with Yellowhammers was detrimental to Cirl Buntings.

Early Surrey history. The first Surrey reference which has been located is by Blyth, who stated that Cirl Buntings were *occasionally taken in the nets during the winter months* near Tooting (Blyth, 1836). Local breeding in Surrey was established by Meyer (1846). Yarrell (1845) said that the species had been found near Godalming, probably using Newman, who described Cirl Buntings as occasional visitors to the Godalming area, as his source. The Holmesdale Natural History Club was given a locally taken specimen in 1861. Harting (1866) said that one had been observed and shot at Peckham. A Cirl Bunting was seen near Reigate in 1870 by J. A. Crosfield, who found a nest with young in a Juniper bush at Reigate Hill on 8th June 1871. Cirl Buntings bred nearby in 1872 and 1874. A nest with eggs was collected for the Holmesdale Natural History Club near Reigate Hill on 25th June 1877 and is still in the Club Museum. Cirl Buntings bred at Gatton in 1873 and at Croydon in 1878. Reports of breeding then became more frequent, coming from Godalming (1887 and 1889), Reigate Heath (1887), Betchworth, Reigate and Wimbledon Common (1890), Epsom, Gomshall and Wray Common (1892), Mickleham (1894), Abinger (1897) and Combe Wood (presumably Coombe Wood, Wimbledon, 1898). Bucknill had more information than this, and included only a summary to illustrate the range.

1900 to 1972. Pairs bred at Banstead in 1900 and at Epsom and Weybridge in 1905 (*BLA*). Males were found at Frensham in 1909 and Tilford in 1912. Bunyard found a nest in 1919. There were two pairs at Tadworth in 1922 and birds were present up to 1925 (*LN* for 1932). Males were seen at Richmond Park in 1927 and 1937 (Collenette) and in 1940. There was a pair at Sutton in November 1930, a singing male was there on 27th May 1933 and others were present up to 1935. At Oxshott Heath, there were three on 30th December 1934. There were males at Farnham on 20th April 1936, and Epsom Downs in 1940. A pair was at Bookham Common in 1940, one was singing at Betchworth in 1945, 1946 and 1950 and one was at Tongham in 1947. Cirl Buntings nested at Chipstead in 1942-44 and at Betchworth in 1947 (*LBR*). A pair bred at Chaldon in 1949 (*LBR*). Cirl Buntings bred along the Hog's Back from 1954-69 and they bred at Puttenham in the 1960s. A nest with four eggs was found in an Elm hedge at Wisley in 1959.

Cirl Buntings have also been recorded at Beddington Sewage Farm (1954), Betchworth (1957),

Chipstead (1960), Cobham (1956), Effingham (1961), Enton (4th June 1961), Godstone (1961-62), Guildford Sewage Farm (1960, 1969), Haslemere (1945), Headley (1969), Juniper Top (1970), Merrow Downs (1969, 1971), Mickleham (1954), Newlands Corner (1966), Oxted (1954), Papercourt (1956), Pebble Combe (Headley, present in 1969), Prince's Coverts (7th April 1966), Ranmore (1965-66), Richmond Park (1940s), Seale (1966, 1968, 1969, 1970, 1972), Shirley (1962), Thursley (28th July 1957), Whitmoor Common (1956) and Wimbledon Common (1965-67) and probably bred at some of these places. One at Staines Reservoirs on 15th October 1949 (*LBR*) appears to be the first recorded for the district.

After 1972. The national preference for southerly facing slopes with Elm or Hawthorn was shared by Cirl Buntings in Surrey, right down to their final years. The few records from 1973 are almost all from the North Downs between Dorking and Guildford. A pair were at Dorking on 1st April 1973. A male was singing on Merrow Downs on 17th May 1973. A pair were at Pewley Down on 16th April 1975 and in the following year there were up to three males from 20th March to 10th July 1976. One of them had frequent territorial disputes with a Yellowhammer. A pair were present there on 27th November 1976. Cirl Buntings were present at three sites around St Luke's Hospital and Pewley Down from 29th January to 28th August 1977. One held a pair and a male. A pair were feeding young on 28th August and an unpaired male had territorial disputes with a male Yellowhammer. A pair raised three young at the south end of Thursley Common, near Thursley Village, in 1977 (Clark, 1984). Back at Pewley Down a male was seen in March and May 1978. A pair were seen on 28th June and the cock displayed against a male Yellowhammer. A male was seen and heard at Pewley Down on dates from 13th April to 7th July 1979 and one was there on 26th-29th May 1980. P. Gasson saw a male on six dates from April to June. Interaction between a male Cirl Bunting and female Yellowhammer was seen on Pewley Down in 1980 (J R Mullins in *BB, 77:26, SBR*). A male was calling near the old mill at Banstead Heath on 6th July 1980 (not Walton Heath as in *LBR*). Apparently unmated males were seen at Pewley Down in 1981 and again during the BTO Cirl Bunting Survey of 1982, when a second male was seen chasing a cock Yellowhammer – the only birds that the Survey found in Surrey. Formal nil returns were obtained from past breeding sites at Banstead Heath, Compton, Effingham, Juniper Top, Merrow Down, Pebble Combe, Puttenham, Ranmore Common, and Seale and there was no reason to believe that birds were present elsewhere. Since then, the only Cirl Buntings found have been a pair at Frensham Common on 4th April 1986 and a male seen and heard briefly there on 3rd May 1993.

Song has been recorded as late as 4th October (Betchworth, 1957).

Ortolan Bunting   *Emberiza hortulana*
Passage migrant, at least twelve records, none from Spelthorne

Breeds from Iberia to Scandinavia and east to Mongolia, wintering in Africa and Saudi Arabia. British records show a strong bias towards eastern and southern coastal counties with well-marked spring and autumn peaks, the latter being larger.

Surrey. A male seen in the Charterhouse Collection by Bucknill was said to have been shot in Godalming (*SALEC*). It is no longer in the collection. Live Ortolans were brought to England for food from 1837 onwards (Bucknill) so escape is a possibility to consider for this bird. Later Surrey dates are typical:

1947:   Chelsham, a male at Nore Hill dew pond on 23rd August was the first for the London area (*LBR*).

1955:   Epsom Sewage Farm, an immature bird in stubble on 1st October, notes in the *LBR*.

1958:   Epsom Sewage Farm, a male and a female or immature bird on 3rd-10th May, birds not seen together, notes in the *LBR*.

1972:   Beddington Sewage Farm, one on 22nd August, watched for forty minutes.

1985:   Barn Elms Reservoirs, a probable male on 23rd May.

1993:   Richmond Park, a male near Pen Ponds on 7th-9th May.

1994:   Beddington Sewage Farm, one southwest, calling, on 9th October.

1995:   Beddington Sewage Farm, a first-winter bird on 13th September.

1999:   Barn Elms Reservoirs, a male on 6th May.

        Beddington Sewage Farm, a male on 11th June.

2000:   Queen Elizabeth II Reservoir, a male on 3rd and 4th May.

2004:   Beddington Sewage Farm, one on 27th August.

Berkshire and Surrey were the only inland counties to record the species from 1958 to 1985.

Rustic Bunting   *Emberiza rustica*

One bird

Another eastern bunting, breeding from Scandinavia to eastern Asia and wintering from Central Asia eastwards. Nearly all the British records have been from Orkney, Shetland and eastern coastal counties and in May, September or October.

Surrey. The one record is remarkable for its early date as well as for being inland. There was a male at Beddington Sewage Farm from 9th February to 13th March 1993. It was found by J. S. Walshe (A. Greensmith, J. S. Walshe *et al.*, *BB, 88:554*).

Little Bunting   *Emberiza pusilla*

Spring passage migrant, eight records including two from Spelthorne

Breeds from Scandinavia to Siberia, further north than the Rustic Bunting, and wintering from Central Asia southwards. Most British birds arrive from September to November, the others, from 1958 to 1985, being spread thinly from December through to May. The east coast bias to the records is apparent, but less obvious, and there have been a number of inland records, all in southeast England.

Surrey. The eight records are:

1956:   Beddington Sewage Farm, as originally published, two were found on 31st March. They were joined by a third bird on 3rd April and the last bird left on 21st April. Notes are in *British Birds* (*BB, 50:206-07*). A BBRC review (*BB, 99:460-64*) has concluded that only one of these is now acceptable, from March 31st to April 3rd.

1956:* Staines Reservoirs, two on the causeway on 7th April.

1965:* Perry Oaks Sewage Farm, one from 2nd to 19th May (D. M. Putman, M. J. Rogers, *BB, 60:335*; J. B. Cox, D. M. Putman, M. J. Rogers, *BB, 61:361*).

1986:   Pirbright Common, one flushed on 25th April (J. R. Mullins, *BB, 80:567*).

1991:   Milford, one at 2 Busdens Close on 13th- 27th April (Dr E. F. J. Garcia, S. Abbott, J. J. Wheatley *et al.*, *BB, 88:551*, photograph plate 217). This bird was featured in the *British Birds Monthly Marathon* competition with a photograph (*BB, 93:53* and *BB, 93:157*).

1992:   Frensham Little Pond, one on 14th-17th April, singing sporadically (S. P. Peters *et al.*, *BB, 86:534*).

1993:   Beddington Sewage Farm, one from 12th February to 17th April (S. J. Aspinall, Beddington Farm Bird Group *et al.*, *BB, 88:554*).

1995:   Thursley Common, one singing on 15th April.

Spelthorne

There were eight bird months in April, two in March and one each in February and May.

Thursley and Ockley Commons. This site has been renowned throughout the 20th century for its breeding and wintering heathland birds, including the Hen Harrier, Hobby, Woodlark, Stonechat, Dartford Warbler, Great Grey Shrike and Crossbill. Many migrant raptors pass through.

John Davis

John Pewin '98

Reed Bunting
Locally common breeding resident

Emberiza schoeniclus

Breeds across Europe and Asia. Northern birds are migratory but those in Europe mostly make only local movements. British Reed Buntings are mainly sedentary but some disperse to milder areas after breeding. A few Scandinavian and Finnish birds have been found to winter in Britain (*MA*).

The British population remained stable during the 19th century and up to the 1950s, when it began to increase in many areas. It probably peaked in the 1970s, offsetting the more or less continuous loss of wetland habitat by moving into dryer areas. A subsequent decline of around 50% is most plausibly linked to the changes in farming practice that have affected other seed-eating passerines, but also reflecting some bad winters, notably those of 1961/62, 1962/63, 1978/79 and 1981/82 (Marchant *et al.*, 1990). There has been a partial recovery since 1994 (BTO).

Early Surrey history. There is an intriguing reference to Reed Buntings *in Arundinetis prope Kingstoniam* (in reeds near Kingston) in Christopher Merrett's *Pinax*, published in 1666 (Bucknill, *BB, 2:153*). Reed Buntings had been found in the Godalming area by 1849 (Newman). In the late 19th century they were common breeding residents in the wetter habitats of Surrey, including places like Wimbledon Common (a pair in 1874, Hamilton) and Crystal Palace Lakes (occasional, Aldridge). They were known to nest a considerable distance from any water and they would winter with flocks of sparrows and finches on stubbles and in rickyards. Bucknill mentioned breeding on the Mole, Thames, Wandle and Wey, on the Ashtead, Epsom, Mitcham and Wandsworth commons and at Churt, Godalming, Godstone, Farnham, Reigate, Shere and Woking.

1900 to 1970. Reed Buntings were breeding residents and numerous passage migrants in the Staines area (Kerr, 1906). Mouritz did not see any Reed Buntings in Richmond Park before 1905, when a pair bred. Four or five pairs bred there annually in the 1930s (Collenette). Limpsfield had six pairs in 1934. There were eight pairs at Elmers End Sewage Farm in 1935. Reed Buntings bred on Bookham Common in 1940 and at Guildford Sewage Farm (about six pairs) in 1945. There were about twenty pairs in the Wey Valley between Guildford and Shalford in 1964 and the same number at Guildford in 1970 (Parr) but they were only winter visitors to Vann Lake at this time (Blaker Log). There were four pairs on 44 acres of clay commonland at Ashtead in 1968 and 1969 (Parr).

Since 1970. Common Birds Censuses from 1970 to 2000 show a decline of over 80% but may not be representative of the countywide picture. Of the 231 tetrads in northeast Surrey, 39% were found to hold territories in the 1968-72 Atlas survey but only 30% in the 1988-97 Atlas, perhaps a better measure of the decline.

Winter numbers held up well into the 1980s. The Winter Atlas found partial survey counts and estimates totalling 362 birds in 1981-84, suggesting a rather larger size for the winter population. From 1994 to 2001, observers reported an average of 164 territories at an average of 31 places, which is five per place. At the three main heathlands, territory counts have been falling since at least 1994:

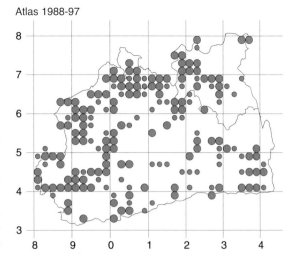

Territories on the main heaths 1994-2004

	1994	1995	1996	1997	1998	1999	2000	2001	2002	2003	2004
Frensham Ponds and Common	30	34	30	26	24	26	22	20	19	19	17
Pirbright Common/ Ash Ranges	28	15	7*	17	11*	20	28	9*	15	6*	9*
Thursley/Ockley/ Elstead Commons	12	9	8	6	4	3	6	8	7	3	9

* incomplete count

At Wimbledon Common and Putney Heath a population of up to 18 pairs in the 1980s was lost by the late 1990s but recovered to five pairs by 2003. To some extent the losses have been offset, at least temporarily, by changes elsewhere. A pair that bred at the Surrey Docks in 1973 were the first recorded to do so anywhere in Inner London. At Beddington Sewage Farm, where breeding numbers peaked in the 1970s and then declined before stabilising from about 1984, a renewed high of 30 territories in 1996 was followed by a collapse to two in 2004. Habitat changes offer only a partial explanation (Coleman, 2003). Reed Buntings are still breeding in Richmond Park and they now breed in the extensive new reedbeds at the Barn Elms London Wetland Centre, with 21 pairs in 2002 and 20 in 2005.

Three or four pairs were breeding at Queen Mary Gravel Pits in the 1980s, where they were often absent from November to February (Geen). Up to six pairs bred at Sheepwalk East in 1983-86. There were 46 Reed Buntings at Queen Mary Reservoir on 5th February 1983 and 20 at Staines Reservoirs on 12th October 1996. Perry Oaks Sewage Farm held three pairs in 1999 and one in 2000. Up to eight birds were found on Staines Moor in the 2003 BTO Spring Migration watch.

Nests and nest sites. Reed Buntings were breeding on dry habitats at Oxshott, Wisley and elsewhere in the 1960s (Parr). Their use of dry habitats nationally is analysed by Bell (*BB*, *62:209-218*). They were reported during the breeding season in dry habitats at Netley Heath (low scrub, 1974), Riddlesdown (1999), St Martha's Hill (heather and bracken, 1973) and West Horsley (dry farmland, 1974). In none of these cases was breeding claimed, but it was proved at Chobham Common (young fledged in *Calluna*, 1975), where it had completely replaced the Yellowhammer by 1977. Nests at Send Water meadows were destroyed by mowing in 1973.

Population size. The Common Birds Censuses suggest about 900 territories at the end of the 20th century. This may be too high but an estimate of less than 100 adults grossed up from the Breeding Birds Survey is clearly too low given the average of 164 territories being reported directly by observers. If Surrey held a proportionate share of the British breeding population as given by the *New Atlas*, the population would be nearer to 1,600 territories, or 0.8 per square km. This feels a bit high for a county without really extensive reedbeds.

Large counts. Winter counts of 200 or more Reed Buntings were made at Beddington Sewage Farm, Hindhead, Ockley Common and other places up to the 1980s but recent numbers have generally been lower:

Ash Ranges: 100+, 25th February 1977

Beddington Sewage Farm: *c.*400, 24th February 1974 and 24th March 1974; 250, 15th February 1986

Burpham: *c.*75, 20th February 1969

Bricksbury Hill: 100, 21st January 1981

Chobham: *c.*100 feeding on grass in snow, December 1981

Chobham Common: 200+ on burnt ground, mid January 1992

Elstead Common: 250, 5th and 7th January 1974

Ewhurst: 200+, early 1989

Ockley Common: 500-600, 18th-19th January 1985; 300+, 8th February 1986

Papercourt Gravel Pits: *c.*70, 25th February 1973, 70+ on 17th August 1975

Pirbright Common: *c.*100, 19th December 1981 and 19th January 1987

Ripley Sewage Farm: *c.*100, 17th February 1979

Roosts. Some of the large counts above were probably at roosts. Those reported as roosts include:

Ash Vale Gravel Pits: 50 in *Phragmites* on 24th October 1976

Buckland Sand Pits: 11, 21st October 1984

Capel: roost of 40 at Old Stores Meadow in 2001

Chessington, pond near Jubilee Wood: 41 to roost, 8th November 2001

Frensham Great Pond: *c.*20 in *Phragmites*, 25th October 1983

Frensham Little Pond: 20+, 7th November 1980

Horton Country Park: 20, 7th February 2001

Papercourt Gravel Pits: 100+, 19th January 1975

Stoke Water Meadows: 25, 10th January 1998

Movements. Parr speculated that the increased numbers in autumn may represent immigrants. Occasional observations of passage, such as a south to southwest movement at Thursley Common all day on 10th October 1976 and morning of 17th, and ten east at Frensham Common on 21st October 1979, would be consistent with this, as are winter ringing recoveries in Surrey of Reed Buntings ringed in Norway in September 1979 and the Netherlands in October 1994. Seventy-five on re-seeded land at Frensham Great Pond on 16th March 1977 were thought to be migrants. A possible Surrey emigrant was one hatched at an unknown location in 1992, ringed in France on 30th October 1992 and recovered at Mitcham Common on 2nd May 1993.

There are single recoveries of birds ringed in September or October in France, the Netherlands and Norway.

Reed Buntings sometimes come to gardens and bird tables in winter. In gardens at St Helier, Carshalton, 24 were trapped in February 1984. Seven came to a Guildford bird table in early 1992 and five were feeding in my Elstead garden in early 2007.

Longevity. A Reed Bunting that had been ringed at Stoke Lake in January 1997 was seen there over eight years and two months later, on 5th April 2005 (J. Gates).

Plumage variations. A white bird with dark primaries was seen at Ripley in 1970.

Corn Bunting

Emberiza calandra (*Miliaria calandra*)

Lost breeding resident, winter visitor

Breeds from Britain south to North Africa and east to Central Asia. Britain is at the northwest edge of the range. The only British ringing recovery to involve another country is of a bird recovered in France (*MA*). The British range expanded from the late 18th century with the increase in arable land that was a result of the Enclosure movement and may have peaked between 1850 and 1900, when Corn Buntings began to be affected by a decline in cereal farmland. The decline continued more or less unabated until the 1940s, when a recovery began, but the decline resumed, falling 90% from the 1970s to the end of the century.

Early Surrey history. The Surrey population has probably followed a similar trend. Newman included the 'Common Bunting', as it was sometimes called, in his 1849 list of 57 breeding residents of the country around Godalming without further comment. Hamilton (1881) described it as 'common enough' on Wimbledon Common. There was a record from near Addington prior to 1900 (*LN* for 1929).

1900 to 1929. Bucknill, writing in 1900, describes Corn Buntings as 'resident . . . although not very abundant' and 'tolerably plentiful both on the commons and high fallows throughout the county'. He gives some specific records, including a combination of personal observation and marksmanship:

Mr Booth has found it nesting near Wimbledon, Mr Teesdale near Mitcham and Mr Felton at Surbiton. I have shot it in winter in a garden at Epsom, feeding on bread put out for sparrows, and have found it nesting on Epsom and Ashtead Commons. I have also seen and heard it on the very top of the Hogsback, at Frensham, at Thursley, Godalming, Dorking, Caterham, Weybridge, and on top of Box Hill. I have notes of its occurrence from correspondents in all parts of the county

The only one of these places from which there have been recent records is the Hog's Back, where birds were regularly seen around Wanborough until at least 1990. Birds at Earlsfield (February 1908, November 1907) and Wandsworth Common (March 1904, February 1908), in *BLA* were probably not breeding. Mouritz (1905) had seen at least one Corn Bunting once at Ham Common but gave no date. Dixon (1909) says:

I can record this species from the Wembley and Horsenden Districts [neither in Surrey], from Wimbledon and Richmond, from Croydon, Epsom, the Crays and Epping [Crays and Epping are not in Surrey], in all of which it nests sparingly. It has been recorded as a nesting species from Mitcham and Surbiton. I have no records from urban parks …

Wimbledon is a refinding of Bucknill's site. Richmond is a new site found by Dixon. Croydon is an unsourced site. Mitcham and Surbiton are quoted from Bucknill. Power (1910) said that Wallington was the site nearest to Dulwich. Harting, in a 1910 lecture, said that Corn Buntings were not seen in the Weybridge area. Many bred on farm fields around Purley, Waddon and Wallington from 1900 to 1914, before they were built over (*LN* for 1933). One was singing at Chelsham on 16th February 1919 (LNHS 1919). Other localities from this period are Addington: one singing near a clover field on 23rd April 1904 and another heard at the same spot on 7th and 13th May (Pounds); Nutfield Marsh: 1904; near Tandridge: 1906; Walton Heath: one on 12th July 1913; Chelsham: one in song at the Church on 21st March 1915, a pair remained in the locality for two years (Beadell), one singing on 16th February 1919 (Pounds); Banstead: near the station in the summer of 1918 (*LN* for 1929); near Titsey Wood: one on 11th July 1920, 'A rare bird in these parts'. Also one (the same?) in a tares field close to Worms Heath (Pounds); near Banstead Heath: one on 15th May 1926; Wanborough: 1927; Weybridge: 1929. Rev. W. A. Shaw's 1921 *List of the Birds of Haslemere and District* says: 'Mentioned for the district in the lists of Roger J. Hutchinson and H. Watkins. Rare in this part of Surrey'. In 1906, Kerr wrote that Corn Buntings were resident and breeding in the Staines area. One was singing there on 20th April 1922 and again in 1923 and May 1925.

Here and elsewhere in this account, it should be borne in mind that some Corn Buntings are polygynous (several females sharing one male). Counts of singing males may therefore underestimate the number of breeding females. References to 'pairs' are mostly taken from Bird Reports and may in some cases have been based on counts of singing males only.

1930 to 1970. Coverage was probably better over the next twenty years or so, but the picture is of a very locally distributed bird. The Pounds (1952) list for Farleigh and District says:

At the present day the Corn Bunting is unaccountably scarce in this north-eastern corner of Surrey. Whether this state of affairs has always persisted is a matter which must remain open to speculation, although fifty years ago, the bird was described as "tolerably plentiful both on the commons and high fallows throughout the county" [he is quoting Bucknill here]. Be this as it may, one thing seems fairly certain and that is an odd pair or two occasionally nest within the area, more especially, I suspect, upon the higher portions of our chalk downs. ... This species was noticed at Chelsham Common on May 12, 1943.

The Pounds account suggests considerable scarcity in northeast Surrey even before 1940. There was one singing at Limpsfield in 1953. The rather fewer reports elsewhere for the 1930s and 40s include Molesey: 1930 (one pair), 1931 and 1932; Esher/Walton-on-Thames: 1932, 1933; Addlestone: one singing, 1932; Beddington Sewage Farm: 1933, 1934; Cuddington: a pair summered in 1934; Ewell Downs: a small colony in the 1930s, (also two singing males in the spring of 1952) (*BLA*), probably five or six pairs in 1935; Banstead: two pairs nesting on 18th May 1935; Worms Heath: '*On 24th May 1939, I examined a nest containing four eggs below a thin hedge bordering on a cornfield not far from Worms Heath, and have also seen eggs that were procured two years previously at another locality over a mile distant*' (Pounds).

There were seven in the Staines area on 10th August 1930 and two pairs, no nest found, in 1933. Glegg (1935) named Staines Moor and reservoirs as being the main area for Middlesex, where they were still present in 1936 and May 1937, they bred in 1939, four were singing in 1940, they were present 1942 and they bred in the Stanwell district in 1949. The King George VI Reservoir (filled in 1947) was built on Corn Bunting habitat. At Perry Oaks, there were up to five pairs in 1950, they bred nearby in 1955 and there were three singing males in 1958. There was a roost of about thirty on Staines Moor in March 1959.

Small colonies existed at Chertsey, Thorpe, Wanborough (seven to possibly thirteen singing males from 1963 to 1970) and Compton in the 1960s. Breeding season records came from Addlestone (1964), Ash Green (pair present in 1964), Beddington Sewage Farm (1956, 1966), Burgh Heath (1969), Chessington (1966, 1969), Clandon Downs (1970), Effingham (1964), Ewell (1969), Godstone (1964), Guildford, Ottershaw (1970), Papercourt (1969), Richmond Park (1956), Shalford (1970), Stoke D'Abernon (1969), Thorpe (1966, 1968), Walton Gravel Pits (1950, 1952-53, 1955-57), Walton Reservoirs (1968) and Wey Manor Farm (1969). There were occasional winter and passage records from Hersham Gravel Pit, Holmethorpe Sand Pits and Barn Elms Reservoir but there were no roosts there. One was found at Frensham on 4th February 1968. In Spelthorne, a pair summered on Staines Moor in 1960 and Perry Oaks held single pairs in 1965 and 1967.

Since 1970. Regular breeding ended in the 1970s although a few pairs hung on into the next decade. At Wanborough, the most consistent site with records going back to at least 1927 (Raynsford), Corn Buntings were present in the 1971 breeding season. They bred from 1973 to 1975. There were four singing males in

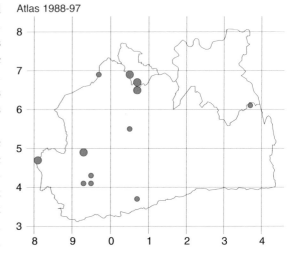

Atlas 1988-97

1976, one in 1977 and three or four singing in 1978 of which two bred. One was singing in 1981-82 and in 1985. The decline was well established in the 1980s. More recently, wire fences were removed to enlarge the fields and the birds have gone. There were single-figure breeding colonies at Chertsey and Thorpe in the 1970s (three pairs were breeding at Thorpe in 1971). Corn Buntings were present in the breeding season at 17 localities in 1974. These included three singing males at Witley in June, where breeding was not established. A pair bred at Badshot Lea in 1977, as did a pair at Runfold in 1978.

Others were present in the breeding season at Banstead Heath (August 1971), Effingham (1971), Ottershaw (five singing in 1971), Send (1971), Shackleford (June 1986) and Woldingham (1971). In 1987 there were three to five singing males between Christmas Pie and the A31 (presumably the Wanborough birds) and two at Shackleford (*HSBBR*). Around forty roosted at Queen Mary Reservoir in 1971. In the Shepperton area there were four singing males in 1984 and at least four in 1986, sites being at Laleham Farm, Littleton Lane West, Sheepwalk East and Staines Road Farm. All breeding had ceased in Middlesex by 1997 (Hewlett). Wandering birds were found at Thursley Common (December 1975, 10th November 1979), Tilhill Nurseries (20th April 1979), Papercourt Gravel Pits and Titsey (1985), fields by Milford Station (1989) and fields north of the Send service station on the A3 (1990). At Holmethorpe Sand Pits there were several on 17th April 1979 and one was there on 21st November 1991. Thirty flew northeast at first light on 30th September 1995 and may have roosted there. A winter flock of up to four birds was present in 1996-98 (*BHSP*).

The national Corn Bunting Survey of 1992/93 covered 17 winter tetrads and 19 summer tetrads in Surrey. A single wintering bird was found with Skylarks and one was found singing in the breeding season (Evans, 1993). Two at the A3/Milford interchange on 23rd July 1994 might have been breeding. A pair at Riddlesdown in July 1998 apparently did not breed. The only more recent reports to hand are of one in South Norwood Country Park on 7th January 2000, one at Fetcham Mill Pond on 26th-27th March 2001, up to three at Riddlesdown in January/February 2002 and one at Send on 1st February 2004.

Summary. The general history seems clear. The older writers thought Corn Buntings were moderately common, at least on cornfields and downland. By the 1930s the bird was being described as rare or scarce. Some large (up to ten pair) colonies were found in the 1960s, at least one of which goes back to 1927. It is not certain, from the evidence, that these colonies were as large before the 1939-45 war - there seem to be no counts of more than two or three pairs from that period.

There was a subsequent crash, possibly connected with changes in land management. London area sites in Surrey are mainly unsuitable for Corn Buntings now, because of building development. Sites at Chertsey were lost to motorway construction. Outer Surrey downland sites have changed with the decline of grazing and greater recreational use. The cessation of downland grazing and a reduction in winter stubbles are among the critical factors. Old-style cornfields with wire fences and the occasional shrub or rank weed patch on the fence line are on the decline. Some of the Wanborough land still looks suitable, as do some fields south of the Hog's Back at Compton, but wire fences have been lost at Wanborough and both places have been abandoned by Corn Buntings.

The fall in breeding population does not seem to be quite matched by a fall in roosts.

Breeding success. Infertile eggs were common in nests at Thorpe in 1971. One of three nests at Thorpe in 1973 was washed out by heavy rain.

Large counts are mostly associated with roosts. The biggest known counts come from the 1970s:

Beddington Sewage Farm: 45+, 31st January 1971

Hamm Moor, Weybridge: 150 roosting, 22nd January 1970; 80 roosting, 31st January 1971

Papercourt Gravel Pits: 80 roosting, 19th January 1975

Riddlesdown: 30, 26th December 1964

South Norwood Country Park: 50 roosting, 7th March 1991

Walton Reservoirs: *c*.60 on snow, 13th December 1981

Wey at Weybridge: *c*.45, 23rd February 1979

Roosting sites have often been at sewage farms and gravel pits. Beddington and South Norwood were both exposed sites with large areas of coarse weeds and grass and patches of bullrush. The largest winter roost recorded was of about 150 birds in sallow and reeds at Hamm Moor, Weybridge. Known roosts in 1958-91 were at Beddington Sewage Farm with up to 25 birds in most years (*e.g.* 19 from March to May in 1960) and at South Norwood Country Park with up to 30 in most years.

Movements and longevity. The origin of the wintering birds does not seem to have been determined, apart from one ringed as an adult at Weybridge on 21st January 1979 and recovered as a road casualty at Rainham, Kent on 7th June 1986, over seven years four months later and 74 kilometres away. This is the one that has travelled furthest, rivalled only by a young bird ringed at Thorpe on 24th June 1968 and recovered 52 kilometres away at Hertford on 10th January 1970. It has also created a Surrey and national longevity record.

The Surrey List by Region and Month

Regional analysis: OS = Outer Surrey   GL = Greater London   Sp = Spelthorne   VC = Vice-county
AC = Administrative Surrey   All = Whole area

Bird	OS	GL	Sp	VC	AC	All	Bird	OS	GL	Sp	VC	AC	All
Mute Swan	x	x	x	x	x	x	Black Grouse	x			x	x	x
Bewick's Swan	x	x	x	x	x	x	Red-legged Partridge	x	x	x	x	x	x
Whooper Swan	x	x	x	x	x	x	Grey Partridge	x	x	x	x	x	x
Bean Goose	x	x	x	x	x	x	Quail	x	x	x	x	x	x
Pink-footed Goose	x	x	x	x	x	x	Pheasant	x	x	x	x	x	x
White-fronted Goose	x	x	x	x	x	x	Golden Pheasant	x			x	x	x
Greylag Goose	x	x	x	x	x	x	Red-throated Diver	x	x	x	x	x	x
Canada Goose	x	x	x	x	x	x	Black-throated Diver	x	x	x	x	x	x
Barnacle Goose	x	x		x	x	x	Great Northern Diver	x	x	x	x	x	x
Brent Goose	x	x	x	x	x	x	Pied-billed Grebe	x	x		x	x	x
Egyptian Goose	x	x	x	x	x	x	Little Grebe	x	x	x	x	x	x
Ruddy Shelduck	x	x	x	x	x	x	Great Crested Grebe	x	x	x	x	x	x
Shelduck	x	x	x	x	x	x	Red-necked Grebe	x	x	x	x	x	x
Mandarin	x	x	x	x	x	x	Slavonian Grebe	x	x	x	x	x	x
Wigeon	x	x	x	x	x	x	Black-necked Grebe	x	x	x	x	x	x
American Wigeon		x		x		x	Fulmar	x	x	x	x	x	x
Gadwall	x	x	x	x	x	x	Manx Shearwater	x	x	x	x	x	x
Teal	x	x	x	x	x	x	Balearic Shearwater	x			x	x	x
Green-winged Teal		x	x	x	x	x	Storm Petrel	x	x	x	x	x	x
Mallard	x	x	x	x	x	x	Leach's Petrel	x	x	x	x	x	x
Pintail	x	x	x	x	x	x	Gannet	x	x	x	x	x	x
Garganey	x	x	x	x	x	x	Cormorant	x	x	x	x	x	x
Blue-winged Teal	x	x		x	x	x	Shag	x	x	x	x	x	x
Shoveler	x	x	x	x	x	x	Bittern	x	x	x	x	x	x
Red-crested Pochard	x	x	x	x	x	x	Little Bittern	x	x		x	x	x
Pochard	x	x	x	x	x	x	Night Heron	x	x		x	x	x
Ring-necked Duck	x	x	x	x	x	x	Squacco Heron	x			x	x	x
Ferruginous Duck	x	x	x	x	x	x	Cattle Egret		x		x		x
Tufted Duck	x	x	x	x	x	x	Little Egret	x	x	x	x	x	x
Scaup	x	x	x	x	x	x	Great White Egret	x		x	x	x	x
Eider	x	x	x	x	x	x	Grey Heron	x	x	x	x	x	x
Long-tailed Duck	x	x	x	x	x	x	Purple Heron	x	x	x	x	x	x
Common Scoter	x	x	x	x	x	x	Black Stork	x	x		x	x	x
Velvet Scoter	x	x	x	x	x	x	White Stork	x	x	x	x	x	x
Goldeneye	x	x	x	x	x	x	Glossy Ibis	x			x	x	x
Smew	x	x	x	x	x	x	Spoonbill	x	x	x	x	x	x
Red-breasted Merganser	x	x	x	x	x	x	Honey Buzzard	x	x	x	x	x	x
Goosander	x	x	x	x	x	x	Black Kite	x	x	x	x	x	x
Ruddy Duck	x	x	x	x	x	x	Red Kite	x	x	x	x	x	x

Bird	OS	GL	Sp	VC	AC	All
White-tailed Eagle	x		x	x	x	x
Marsh Harrier	x	x	x	x	x	x
Hen Harrier	x	x	x	x	x	x
Montagu's Harrier	x	x	x	x	x	x
Goshawk	x	x	x	x	x	x
Sparrowhawk	x	x	x	x	x	x
Buzzard	x	x	x	x	x	x
Rough-legged Buzzard	x	x	x	x	x	x
Golden Eagle	x			x	x	x
Osprey	x	x	x	x	x	x
Kestrel	x	x	x	x	x	x
Red-footed Falcon	x	x		x	x	x
Merlin	x	x	x	x	x	x
Hobby	x	x	x	x	x	x
Gyrfalcon		x	x	x	x	x
Peregrine	x	x	x	x	x	x
Water Rail	x	x	x	x	x	x
Spotted Crake	x	x	x	x	x	x
Little Crake	x	x		x	x	x
Baillon's Crake	x	x		x	x	x
Corncrake	x	x	x	x	x	x
Moorhen	x	x	x	x	x	x
Coot	x	x	x	x	x	x
Crane	x			x	x	x
Little Bustard	x			x	x	x
Oystercatcher	x	x	x	x	x	x
Black-winged Stilt	x	x	x	x	x	x
Avocet	x	x	x	x	x	x
Stone Curlew	x	x	`	x	x	x
Collared Practincole	x		x	x	x	x
Little Ringed Plover	x	x	x	x	x	x
Ringed Plover	x	x	x	x	x	x
Killdeer		x		x		x
Kentish Plover	x		x	x	x	x
Dotterel	OS	GL	Sp	VC	AC	All
American Golden Plover		x			x	x
Pacific Golden Plover	x			x	x	x
Golden Plover	x	x	x	x	x	x
Grey Plover	x	x	x	x	x	x
Lapwing	x	x	x	x	x	x
Knot	x	x	x	x	x	x
Sanderling	x	x	x	x	x	x
Little Stint	x	x	x	x	x	x
Temminck's Stint	x	x	x	x	x	x
White-rumped Sandpiper	x		x	x	x	x
Baird's Sandpiper			x		x	x
Pectoral Sandpiper	x	x	x	x	x	x
Sharp-tailed Sandpiper			x		x	x
Curlew Sandpiper	x	x	x	x	x	x
Purple Sandpiper	x	x	x	x	x	x
Dunlin	x	x	x	x	x	x
Buff-breasted Sandpiper			x		x	x
Ruff	x	x	x	x	x	x
Jack Snipe	x	x	x	x	x	x
Snipe	x	x	x	x	x	x
Great Snipe	x			x	x	x
Long-billed Dowitcher			x		x	x
Woodcock	x	x	x	x	x	x
Black-tailed Godwit	x	x	x	x	x	x
Bar-tailed Godwit	x	x	x	x	x	x
Whimbrel	x	x	x	x	x	x
Curlew	x	x	x	x	x	x
Spotted Redshank	x	x	x	x	x	x
Redshank	x	x	x	x	x	x
Marsh Sandpiper	x			x	x	x
Greenshank	x	x	x	x	x	x
Lesser Yellowlegs		x	x	x	x	x
Solitary Sandpiper			x		x	x
Green Sandpiper	x	x	x	x	x	x
Wood Sandpiper	x	x	x	x	x	x
Common Sandpiper	x	x	x	x	x	x
Spotted Sandpiper			x		x	x
Turnstone	x	x	x	x	x	x
Wilson's Phalarope			x		x	x
Red-necked Phalarope	x		x	x	x	x
Grey Phalarope	x	x	x	x	x	x
Pomarine Skua	x	x	x	x	x	x
Arctic Skua	x	x	x	x	x	x
Long-tailed Skua	x	x	x	x	x	x
Great Skua	x	x	x	x	x	x
Mediterranean Gull	x	x	x	x	x	x
Little Gull	x	x	x	x	x	x
Sabine's Gull	x	x	x	x	x	x
Bonaparte's Gull			x		x	x
Black-headed Gull	x	x	x	x	x	x
Ring-billed Gull	x	x	x	x	x	x
Common Gull	x	x	x	x	x	x
Lesser Black-backed Gull	x	x	x	x	x	x
Yellow-legged Gull	x	x	x	x	x	x
Herring Gull	x	x	x	x	x	x
Iceland Gull	x	x	x	x	x	x
Glaucous Gull	x	x	x	x	x	x
Great Black-backed Gull	x	x	x	x	x	x

Bird	OS	GL	Sp	VC	AC	All	Bird	OS	GL	Sp	VC	AC	All
Kittiwake	x	x	x	x	x	x	Crested Lark		x		x		x
Sooty Tern			x		x	x	Woodlark	x	x	x	x	x	x
Little Tern	x	x	x	x	x	x	Skylark	x	x	x	x	x	x
Gull-billed Tern		x		x		x	Shore Lark	x	x	x	x	x	x
Caspian Tern	x		x	x	x	x	Sand Martin	x	x	x	x	x	x
Whiskered Tern			x		x	x	Swallow	x	x	x	x	x	x
Black Tern	x	x	x	x	x	x	House Martin	x	x	x	x	x	x
White-winged							Red-rumped Swallow	x	x	x	x	x	x
Black Tern	x	x	x	x	x	x	Richard's Pipit		x	x	x	x	x
Sandwich Tern	x	x	x	x	x	x	Tawny Pipit	x	x	x	x	x	x
Common Tern	x	x	x	x	x	x	Tree Pipit	x	x	x	x	x	x
Roseate Tern	x	x	x	x	x	x	Meadow Pipit	x	x	x	x	x	x
Arctic Tern	x	x	x	x	x	x	Red-throated Pipit		x	x	x	x	x
Guillemot	x	x	x	x	x	x	Rock Pipit	x	x	x	x	x	x
Razorbill	x	x	x	x	x	x	Water Pipit	x	x	x	x	x	x
Black Guillemot	x	x		x		x	Yellow Wagtail	x	x	x	x	x	x
Little Auk	x	x	x	x	x	x	Citrine Wagtail		x		x		x
Puffin	x	x	x	x	x	x	Grey Wagtail	x	x	x	x	x	x
Pallas's Sandgrouse	x	x	x	x	x	x	Pied/White Wagtail	x	x	x	x	x	x
Feral Rock Dove	x	x	x	x	x	x	Waxwing	x	x	x	x	x	x
Stock Dove	x	x	x	x	x	x	Dipper	x		x	x	x	x
Woodpigeon	x	x	x	x	x	x	Wren	x	x	x	x	x	x
Collared Dove	x	x	x	x	x	x	Dunnock	x	x	x	x	x	x
Turtle Dove	x	x	x	x	x	x	Alpine Accentor	x	x		x	x	x
Ring-necked Parakeet	x	x	x	x	x	x	Robin	x	x	x	x	x	x
Cuckoo	x	x	x	x	x	x	Nightingale	x	x	x	x	x	x
Yellow-billed Cuckoo	x			x	x	x	Bluethroat	x	x		x	x	x
Barn Owl	x	x	x	x	x	x	Black Redstart	x	x	x	x	x	x
Little Owl	x	x	x	x	x	x	Redstart	x	x	x	x	x	x
Tawny Owl	x	x	x	x	x	x	Whinchat	x	x	x	x	x	x
Long-eared Owl	x	x	x	x	x	x	Stonechat	x	x	x	x	x	x
Short-eared Owl	x	x	x	x	x	x	Wheatear	x	x	x	x	x	x
Nightjar	x	x	x	x	x	x	Desert Wheatear		x		x		x
Common Nighthawk		x		x		x	Siberian Thrush	x			x	x	x
Swift	x	x	x	x	x	x	Ring Ouzel	x	x	x	x	x	x
Alpine Swift	x	x	x	x	x	x	Blackbird	x	x	x	x	x	x
Kingfisher	x	x	x	x	x	x	Fieldfare	x	x	x	x	x	x
Bee-eater	x	x	x	x	x	x	Song Thrush	x	x	x	x	x	x
Roller	x		x	x	x	x	Redwing	x	x	x	x	x	x
Hoopoe	x	x	x	x	x	x	Mistle Thrush	x	x	x	x	x	x
Wryneck	x	x	x	x	x	x	American Robin	x	x		x	x	x
Green Woodpecker	x	x	x	x	x	x	Cetti's Warbler	x	x	x	x	x	x
Great Spotted							Grasshopper Warbler	x	x	x	x	x	x
Woodpecker	x	x	x	x	x	x	Aquatic Warbler	x	x		x	x	x
Lesser Spotted							Sedge Warbler	x	x	x	x	x	x
Woodpecker	x	x	x	x	x	x	Marsh Warbler	x	x		x	x	x
Short-toed Lark		x	x	x	x	x	Reed Warbler	x	x	x	x	x	x

Bird	OS	GL	Sp	VC	AC	All	Bird	OS	GL	Sp	VC	AC	All
Great Reed Warbler	x			x	x	x	Nutcracker	x	x		x	x	x
Icterine Warbler	x	x	x	x	x	x	Chough		x		x		x
Melodious Warbler	x	x		x	x	x	Jackdaw	x	x	x	x	x	x
Blackcap	x	x	x	x	x	x	Rook	x	x	x	x	x	x
Garden Warbler		x	x	x	x	x	Carrion Crow	x			x	x	x
Barred Warbler		x		x		x	Hooded Crow	x	x	x	x	x	x
Lesser Whitethroat	x	x	x	x	x	x	Raven	x	x		x	x	x
Whitethroat	x	x	x	x	x	x	Starling	x	x	x	x	x	x
Dartford Warbler	x	x	x	x	x	x	Rose-coloured Starling	x	x	x	x	x	x
Subalpine Warbler		x		x		x	House Sparrow	x	x	x	x	x	x
Sardinian Warbler		x		x		x	Tree Sparrow	x	x	x	x	x	x
Pallas's Warbler	x	x		x	x	x	Chaffinch	x	x	x	x	x	x
Yellow-browed Warbler	x	x		x	x	x	Brambling	x	x	x	x	x	x
Wood Warbler	x	x	x	x	x	x	Serin	x	x		x	x	x
Chiffchaff	x	x	x	x	x	x	Greenfinch	x	x	x	x	x	x
Willow Warbler	x	x	x	x	x	x	Goldfinch	x	x	x	x	x	x
Goldcrest	x	x	x	x	x	x	Siskin	x	x	x	x	x	x
Firecrest	x	x	x	x	x	x	Linnet	x	x	x	x	x	x
Spotted Flycatcher	x	x	x	x	x	x	Twite	x	x	x	x	x	x
Red-breasted Flycatcher	x	x		x	x	x	Mealy Redpoll	x	x		x	x	x
Pied Flycatcher	x	x	x	x	x	x	Lesser Redpoll	x	x	x	x	x	x
Bearded Tit	x	x	x	x	x	x	Arctic Redpoll	x			x	x	x
Long-tailed Tit	x	x	x	x	x	x	Two-barred Crossbill	x			x	x	x
Blue Tit	x	x	x	x	x	x	Crossbill	x	x	x	x	x	x
Great Tit	x	x	x	x	x	x	Parrot Crossbill	x	x		x	x	x
Crested Tit	x	x		x	x	x	Common Rosefinch	x	x	x	x	x	x
Coal Tit	x	x	x	x	x	x	Bullfinch	x	x	x	x	x	x
Willow Tit	x	x	x	x	x	x	Hawfinch	x	x	x	x	x	x
Marsh Tit	x	x	x	x	x	x	Lapland Bunting	x	x	x	x	x	x
Nuthatch	x	x	x	x	x	x	Snow Bunting	x	x	x	x	x	x
Treecreeper	x	x	x	x	x	x	Pine Bunting	x			x	x	x
Golden Oriole	x	x	x	x	x	x	Yellowhammer	x	x	x	x	x	x
Isabelline Shrike		x		x		x	Cirl Bunting	x	x	x	x	x	x
Red-backed Shrike	x	x	x	x	x	x	Ortolan Bunting	x	x		x	x	x
Lesser Grey Shrike	OS		Sp	VC	AC	x	Rustic Bunting		x		x		x
Great Grey Shrike	x	x	x	x	x	x	Little Bunting	x	x	x	x	x	x
Woodchat Shrike	x	x		x	x	x	Reed Bunting	x	x	x	x	x	x
Jay	x	x	x	x	x	x	Corn Bunting	x	x	x	x	x	x
Magpie	x	x	x	x	x	x	Total number recorded	307	303	278	331	323	339

Number of Birds seen in the vice-county each month, from dated records. An analysis for 1900-1973 is compared with the whole period. The peak month for 1900-1973 was April, with 204 different species. Over the whole period the peak month was October, with 248.

	Jan	Feb	Mar	Apr	May	Jun	Jul	Aug	Sep	Oct	Nov	Dec
1900-1973	162	161	176	204	197	173	171	190	196	198	172	165
All years	197	200	216	240	238	214	202	224	234	248	219	204

Hybrids

The identification of hybrids is often difficult and generally based on the appearance of characteristics of two species in one individual. It has not been possible for the Surrey Bird Club to check the reports below other than to say that they are thought to come from reliable sources. They are presented for interest but should be treated with a measure of caution. Unless otherwise indicated, hybrids are listed without regard to the sex of the parents, i.e. birds reported as Pochard x Tufted Duck and Tufted Duck x Pochard are all listed as Pochard x Tufted Duck. The sex of the hybrid is given if it is given in a published report. The best documented identification features are those for waterfowl, particularly Gilham and Gilham (1996), various papers in London Bird Reports which deal with *Aythya* hybrids, such as Osborne (1972), and other papers such as Randler (2001).

Geese

Lesser White-fronted Goose x Bar-headed Goose. Found at Barn Elms in 1998 and at Kew Gardens, where there were three full-winged birds on 2nd December 2000.

Greylag Goose varieties. White farmyard geese of the greylag type, and cross-breeds between these and normally coloured birds are quite often seen. At one time they were commoner than the pure form. Now they are not.

Greylag Goose (normal and farmyard types) x Canada Goose. One at Wrecclesham in December 1982 (*HSBBR*). Widely reported since 1993, reflecting the increase in both parent species.

Canada Goose x Bar-headed Goose. Barn Elms Reservoirs in 1993.

Canada Goose x Barnacle Goose. One at Cutt Mill on 24th October 1972 (*HSBBR*) and two at Kew Gardens in 1985.

Canada Goose x Lesser White-fronted Goose. Barn Elms Reservoirs in 1993.

Canada Goose x Snow Goose. Barn Elms and Lonsdale Road Reservoirs in 1993.

Brent Goose x Snow Goose. One at Shepperton Gravel Pits from 1984 to1986 (*Shepp. BR*).

Shelducks

Ruddy/Cape/Paradise Shelduck. Many recent reports for this confusing group of species and hybrids, which are dealt with in the *Escapes, Introductions and Birds of Unknown Origin* section.

Shelduck x Mallard. An escaped male Shelduck mated with a female Mallard and raised seven young at Frensham in 1978.

Anas varieties and related intergeneric forms

Mallard Domestic forms including Aylesbury, Cayuga, Indian Runner (bred at Vann Lake in 1967, 1968 and 1978), Khaki Campbell and White Call Ducks are seen from time to time. East Indian Black Ducks bred at Vann Lake in 1967, 1968 and 1978 (Blaker log).

'American Wigeon type'. Reported from Old Woking Sewage Farm in 1994, Stoke Lake in 1993 and 1996 and Thorpe Lea in 1998.

Chiloe Wigeon (*Anas sibilatix*) **x Mallard**. One at Esher in 1999.

Mallard x Red-crested Pochard. Single birds at Frimley Gravel Pits from 1996 to 1999 and Frensham in 2004.

Mallard x Rosy-billed Pochard (*Netta peposaca*). One on the Thames at Kew in 1986.

Mallard x Shoveler. One at Barn Elms in 2002.

Pintail x Mallard. Single birds at Holmethorpe in 1995-96 and Old Woking in 1996.

Red-crested Pochard x Pintail. One at Beddington in 1996.

Shoveler x Blue-winged Teal. One at Barn Elms London Wetland Centre in 2002.

Wigeon x Chiloe Wigeon. Single birds at Barn Elms London Wetland Centre in 2000 and 2001.

Wigeon x Gadwall. A male was at Walton Reservoirs in 1986 and a bird was at Barn Elms in 2001.

Wigeon x Mallard. One was seen at Staines Reservoirs each summer from 1985 to 1993 and 1995 to 1997, sometimes seen elsewhere. The wintering site was apparently not located.

Wigeon x Pintail. Single males were at Frensham in 1996 and Staines Reservoirs in 1987.

Wigeon x Shoveler. One at Barn Elms London Wetland Centre in 2001.

Aythya hybrids and intergeneric forms

These are mostly seen in the London area, where they probably originate from local parks and collections. They often resemble particular members of the genus. The appearance of hybrids resembling the Lesser Scaup in the late 1950s led to a national controversy which was finally resolved by Perrins (1962). One of these birds was at Barn Elms from 8th-12th February 1958 and at Richmond Park on the 16th (Recent Reports: *BB, 51:131*). Other examples follow, using Osborne's nomenclature. They are a selection.

Ferruginous Duck x Pochard ('Ferruginous type', Paget's Pochard). Single birds were at Barn Elms in 1983, Beddington Sewage Farm and Frimley Gravel Pits in 1987, Lonsdale Road in 1980-81 and Walton Reservoirs in January 1963.

Ferruginous Duck x Tufted Duck ('Baer's Pochard type'). One at Thorpe Water Park in 2000.

Pochard female x Tufted Duck male ('Lesser Scaup type'). Reports from Barn Elms in 1960, 1967, 1968 and 2002, Frensham Little Pond, Hammer Pond and Moat Pond in 1997, Painshill Park in 2001, Staines Reservoirs in 1994 and the Walton area reservoirs in 1999, 2000 and 2003.

Pochard x Tufted Duck (unsexed). Reports from Beddington Sewage Farm in 1986, 1993 and 1994, Enton in 1963 (a male), Frensham in 1976, King George VI Reservoir in 2000, Papercourt Gravel Pits in 1976, Queen Mary Reservoir in 1982, South Norwood in 1988, 1990 and 1992-95, Staines Reservoirs in 1986, 1988 and 1995 (males), Stoke Lake in 1992, the Thames at Kew in 1994 and Wraysbury Reservoir in 2000.

Pochard x Pintail. One reported from Gatton in 1964-65.

'Redhead type'. Burgess Park in 2000.

Ring-necked Duck x Tufted Duck. There were three reports of males in 1987, one on the Thames at Ham on 12th January, a male at Barn Elms Reservoir on 30th December, and one at Staines Reservoirs on 25th April where there was also one on 9th April 1988. A male at Kew Green from 24th April to 1st May 1992 has been described in detail, with photographs, by Gasson and Lawrence (1993). There were two males at Beddington Sewage Farm in 1993 and a bird was seen at Barn Elms London Wetland Centre in 2002.

Scaup x Tufted Duck ('Scaup type'). There was a female at Barn Elms Rerservoirs in 1975. A male was at Frensham Great Pond in April/May 1976 (*HSBBR*). Other birds were at South Norwood in 1991 and Staines Reservoirs in 1980. A male was seen at Walton Reservoirs in 1992.

Tufted Duck x Ring-necked Duck. Barn Elms in 1993, 1994 and 2002, Staines Reservoirs in 1988 and Wandsworth in 2002.

Tufted Duck x Rosy-billed Pochard (*Netta peposaca*). A Tufted Duck with features of the Rosy-billed Pochard was at Barn Elms Reservoirs on 28th January 1984.

Other ducks

Hooded Merganser x Goldeneye. One at Staines Reservoirs in May 2000 and May 2001.

Game birds

Black Grouse male x Pheasant female. One was shot near Frimley Ridges on 26th October 1854 (Bucknill).

Pheasant x Chicken (Domestic Fowl). Three were shot near Woking in December 1883 (Bucknill).

Pheasant male x Golden Pheasant female. Three mid 19th century specimens mentioned by Bucknill.

Golden Pheasant x Lady Amherst's Pheasant. Two males were at Kew Gardens on 23rd July 1993.

Others

African Spoonbill (*Platalea alba*) **x Spoonbill**. Two escaped from Birdworld, just outside the Surrey border at Farnham, in the summer of 1988 (*Birding World* 2, p.74). They might have been the two unidentified Spoonbills seen over Kenley on 31st July of that year. There was an unidentified Spoonbill species or hybrid at Beddington Sewage Farm on 4th May 1988.

Glaucous Gull x Herring Gull. Two apparent hybrids at Wraysbury Reservoir in 1986, one at Beddington and Staines in 1996 and one at Thorpe in 1990.

Swallow x House Martin. Apparent hybrids at Beddington Sewage Farm on 27th September 1993 and at Enton on 27th June 2000.

Carrion Crow x Hooded Crow. One at Frensham on 15th October 1972 and one in Peckham Rye Park from 15th October 1999 to 17th March 2000.

Greenfinch x Goldfinch. A male and two female supposed wild hybrids of this parentage were captured at Hackbridge in November 1887. The male was exhibited at the Crystal Palace show in 1890 (MacPherson, 1890). There was one at Chertsey Meads in 1997. One was trapped, ringed and photographed by Derek Washington at Langshott on 2nd December of the same year. A photograph appears in the Surrey Bird Report for 1997.

Goldfinch x Canary (*Serinus canarius*?). Hersham in

Carrion Crow x Hooded Crow hybrid, Peckham

1986.

Escapes, Introductions and Birds of Unknown Origin

Possible or probable escapes which are an essential part of the narrative are covered in the main text. Notes are given below for the more interesting of the other occurrences. These will be only a fraction of the likely total, many being unreported. Identifications are normally those given by the observer. They have not been vetted except to weed out obvious errors.

Birds of species that have occurred in the wild in Britain but were not in the wild when in Surrey.

Bewick's Swan *Cygnus columbianus*

One at Hurst Park in April 1990, with Mute Swans. One at Beddington Sewage Farm, 3rd May 1993.

Whooper Swan *Cygnus cygnus*

Quite common in wildfowl collections and pinioned birds have bred (though not in Surrey). Two at Frensham on 23rd and 30th April 1967 seem likely to have been escapes in view of the dates, although 1967 was an influx year. One at Betchworth from 5th October to 26th December 1971 was thought to be an escape. There were two in the Surrey section of Virginia Water in 1995 and other sightings were made there in later years. One at Barn Elms from 1993 to at least 2003 was originally in Ravenscourt Park. Other places since 1978 include Beddington Sewage Farm, Brockwell Park, Holmethorpe, Hurst Green, Island Barn Reservoir, Leigh Place, Lightwater, Lonsdale Road Reservoir, Oxted and Wrecclesham.

Bean Goose *Anser fabalis*

Two at Addlestone on 23rd May 1984 and two *A. f. rossicus* (Tundra Bean Goose) at Holmethorpe on 28th March 1997. A large Pink-footed Goose type at Beddington Sewage Farm from 1989 to 1993 was possibly a form of *rossicus*.

Pink-footed Goose *Anser brachyrhynchus*

Single birds have frequently been reported from the Earlswood/Gatton/Holmethorpe area since the first at Earlswood lakes in 1967. There have been others at Badshot Lea, Barn Elms, Battersea Park, Beddington Sewage Farm, Chertsey Meads, Enton, Fetcham Mill Pond, Godstone, Kew Gardens, Kingston, Seale and South Norwood Lake since 1969.

White-fronted Goose *Anser albifrons*

Single and long-staying birds like the one that wintered at Frensham with Canada Geese in 1972/73 seem at best to be feral. So do a few, usually single birds, at Barn Elms Reservoirs (1993-94, 1998), Beddington Sewage Farm (1993), Gatton (1975), Holmethorpe Sand Pits (1993, 1995, 1997), Lonsdale Road Reservoir (1993-94), New Lines [Lyne?] Pond (1979), Papercourt Gravel Pits (1971), South Norwood (1997), Thorpe (1975), Thursley Common (1983, 1997), Walton Reservoirs (1993) and Walton-on-Thames (1997) and in Spelthorne at Queen Mary Reservoir (1986), Shepperton Gravel Pits (1986) and Staines Reservoirs (1988).

Lesser White-fronted Goose *Anser erythropus*

Breeds from northern Scandinavia to Siberia, wintering mainly in southern Russia. Most British records are from the Yare valley in Norfolk and from the Wildfowl and Wetlands Trust Reserve at Slimbridge in Gloucestershire. Escapes are found in Surrey from time to time. Single birds, except where indicated, were at Barn Elms (1993-95, 1998-99), Effingham Fish Ponds (1980), Kew Gardens (two in 1998), Lonsdale Road Reservoir (1994-95), Papercourt (1980, 1986), Stoke Lake (1995), the Surrey Docks (1995, 1998) and the Thames near Hammersmith Bridge (1988).

Snow Goose *Anser caerulescens*

Breeds ferally in north Hampshire but has not done so in Surrey, although there are many Surrey records, usually of one or two with Canada Geese. Early reports included single blue-phase birds at Enton on dates from 1961 to 1965, at Chobham Common in 1965 and at Send in 1967. A white-phase bird was at Enton in 1963 and 1965. Both phases are mentioned from time to time. Other places from 1975 include Ash Vale Gravel Pits, Ashtead Common, Battersea Park, Beddington Sewage Farm, Boldermere, Bookham Common, Buckland, Capel, Effingham Fish Ponds, Enton, Frensham, Frillinghurst, Frimley Gravel Pits, Gatton, Godalming, Godstone, Holmethorpe/Nutfield, Hurst Green, Lightwater, Molesey Gravel Pit, New Haw, Newark Priory, Ockham Park, Old Woking, Outwood Swan Cemetery, Papercourt Gravel Pits, Pyrford, Queen Elizabeth II Reservoir, Reigate Priory, Runnymede, South Norwood Country Park, Stoke Lake, Thames Ditton, the Thames (Richmond-Teddington, Sunbury Lock), Thorpe, Tooting Bec Common, Vann Lake, Walton Bridge, Walton Reservoirs, Weybridge, Windlesham and Wrecclesham. In Spelthorne they have been reported since 1982 from King George VI Reservoir, Queen Mary Gravel Pits, Shepperton Gravel Pits (1982, 1985, 1986) and Staines Reservoirs. Five white-phase birds at Papercourt and Ripley in 1986 were presumed to be the five of unspecified phase at Effingham, Ockham Park and Wisley in the same year.

Brent Goose *Branta bernicla*

All presumed to be dark-bellied, though often not stated. A pair were at Frensham on 23rd April 1923. One was at Barn Elms Reservoirs on 11th April 1935. One flushed at Beddington on 19th March 1942 might have been wild. One at Frensham for about three weeks from 22nd March 1953 was rather tame. One in Richmond Park and at Walton Reservoirs on 23rd January 1966 was thought to be a possible escape by Parr. Another visited Barn Elms, Kew Gardens and Richmond Park in the summer of 1984. One at Barn Elms Reservoirs and Barn Elms Park from 27th January 1987 to 5th February 1987. This bird may have been the sole source of records from Barn Elms, Battersea Park, Beddington Sewage Farm, Kew Gardens, Lonsdale Road Reservoir and Walton Reservoirs until at least December 1994. It was absent during the summer. One was at King George VI Reservoir on 13th August 1995. One was with Canada Geese at Shepperton Gravel Pits on 14th September 1985.

Red-breasted Goose *Branta ruficollis*

Single birds at Gatton in February 1970 and at Walton-on-the-Hill in early 1972.

Ruddy Shelduck *Tadorna ferruginea*

One reported at Wallington on 12th-19th January 1929 (*BLA*) was presumably the one that Bentham saw at Beddington Sewage Farm on these dates (SBC archive). Another was at Brooklands Sewage Farm in April 1939. There was one at Guildford Sewage Farm on 23rd May 1945. Introduced birds killed young Pochards and Tufted Ducks at Battersea Park in 1956 (*BRP*). One or two were in the Walton-on-Thames area in late 1962. Later records came from Barn Elms (1968, 1972, 1973, 1981, 1984 and 1986), Beddington Sewage Farm (1982), Brockwell Park (1983), Carshalton (1983), Ewell (pinioned pair 1972), Frensham (1977), Hedgecourt (1984), Island Barn Reservoir/Hersham (1968, 1973), Kew (1979, 1984-86), Papercourt (1977), Richmond Park (1972), Walton Reservoirs (1973), Wandsworth (1982-83, 1986) and in Spelthorne from Staines Reservoirs (1964, 1997) and Wraysbury Reservoir (1998, 2000).

Shelduck *Tadorna tadorna*

Reports have come from Battersea Park (1999, possibly one of the full-winged feral birds in St James's Park), Frensham (1976-79, from a collection at Fernhurst), Kew Gardens (1993, pinioned but able to fly), Lonsdale Road Reservoirs (1958), Obelisk Pond (1972) and Putney Bridge (1971).

Wigeon *Anas penelope*

A tame bird in Kew Gardens on 6th January 1989.

American Wigeon *Anas americana*

One at the Surrey Docks on 4th June 1975. A pair at the same site on 5th September and one on five dates in the period 9th-15th September 1975 were also thought to be possible escapes (*BB, 69:330-31*).

Pintail   *Anas acuta*

Twelve were hatched from a pinioned pair at Enton Mill Pond in 1907 (Mouritz). Reported from Beddington Sewage Farm (1997, a colour-ringed bird in 1999), Carshalton area (1964 and 1983), Holmethorpe (1979), Kew (1989, 1990), Lightwater Country Park (December 1984 to January 1985), Richmond Park (1994, 1996), South Norwood Country Park (1989), Teddington Lock (1988), the Thames at Westminster (1978), Unstead Sewage Farm (1990), Walton Reservoirs (1993), Wimbledon Common (1997) and Woking (1989). There have been two very long stayers, a male at Cutt Mill (November 1992 to May 1999) and a female at Frensham (October 1991 to December 1998).

Garganey   *Anas querquedula*

A tame bird at Barn Elms from September to November, 1961 and one on the Thames there in May and June 1962.

Ferruginous Duck   *Aythya nyroca*

A pair at Barn Elms Reservoir on 17th July 1938 were thought to have come from St James's Park, see main text. One at Barn Elms Reservoir from 9th to at least 21st June 1971 is thought to have been an escape in view of the date. One at Gatton on 24th January 1971 (no details, *LBR*). A bird first seen at Lonsdale Road Reservoir on 2nd November 1980 and subsequently seen at the same reservoir on 3rd January and 9th July 1981, and at Barn Elms Reservoir from 11th February to 2nd March, on 17th-20th May and on 9th November 1981 was originally published as a Ferruginous Duck, then judged to be a hybrid but was finally reinstated, as a probable escape in view of the odd dates (*LBR* for 1980, 1981, 1982 and 1992). One at Brockwell Park in 1989 was thought to have been an escape.

Scaup   *Aythya marila*

One at Holmethorpe on 22nd July 1989. One at Beddington, Berrylands and South Norwood in 2001.

Goldeneye species   *Bucephala species*

An unidentified immature goldeneye was at Queen Mary Reservoir in September and October 1971, (per BOU). It was seen by H. W. Evans on 26th October.

Barrow's Goldeneye   *Bucephala islandica*

There was an unringed bird at Queen Mary Reservoir from 10th September to October 1972. At the time, Barrow's Goldeneye was not on the British list and this one was thought to be of uncertain origin. In 1990 the BOU said that the record was under review (*Ibis 133:222*) but no conclusions from this review have so far been published. It is understood that the identification of the bird was not in doubt but that there was disagreement among observers on its age and sex. One wing was longer than the other, which was reported as uneven moult but might have been because of a clipped wing. The BOU concluded that the bird was an escape. Barrow's Goldeneye was commonly bred in captivity at the time and many water-fowl breeders did not use rings. There was a subsequent record of a wild bird in Ayrshire in November and December 1979.

Red Grouse   *Lagopus lagopus*

Salmon (1736) wrote of 'Red-game' at Hindhead, thought by Bucknill to mean Red Grouse and to be based on wrong information. Graves wrote that the Red Grouse had been turned out in Surrey not later than 1821 but that they did not breed. Seventeen were released on Bagshot Heath in 1829 and others were released on Chobham Common.

Black Grouse   *Tetrao tetrix*

A blackcock found at Runnymede on 17th December 1954 is thought to have been an escape.

Quail   *Coturnix coturnix*

There have been several attempts at introduction, discussed above in the main list. Power saw one fly over his Brixton garden on 16th June 1906 and thought it had escaped from one of the London Markets. One at Epsom Common on 25th August 1988 was very tame and only a few miles from a Quail farm.

Golden Pheasant   *Chrysolophus pictus*

Since Golden Pheasants are commonly kept and raised in captivity, the possibility that any birds seen are escapes or releases must be regarded as high, but feral birds do breed in Hampshire and Sussex. One flushed by foxhounds from gorse on Winterfold Hill on 10th March 1906 (Mouritz) was an early probable escape. Later probable escapes are:

1976:   Arbrook Common, a male from 18th June to 15th January 1977.

1980:   Fetcham, feathers in a garden in April.

1985:   Churt, an immature bird feeding on fat, seeds and apples in a garden on 22nd February.

1992:   Hydestile, a male from 19th March to 10th April.

          London SW15, an immature male in a garden on 11th April.

1993:   Hydestile, a male on 16th March.

1995:   Wimbledon Common, occasional sightings in the summer.

1997:   Guildford, one found dead on 17th May.

At Kew Gardens there were two or three in April 1990, up to four from January to April 1993, two males (one distinctly tame) on 26th September 1999, five in a Kew Gardens Collection in 2001 and a male in Kew Gardens Road in 2002.

Lady Amherst's Pheasant   *Chrysolophus amherstiae*

A small British breeding population of this handsome resident of mountain forests in Burma and China has been established in the Woburn area. Attempts to establish it in Surrey have not been successful. A number were reared from eggs and released in Richmond Park in 1928-29 and 24 full-winged birds were released there in 1931-32. Collenette (1937) wrote that they were still present in small numbers in the larger plantations, where they could be heard crowing, but that he had not known them to breed, or even seen a hen bird. There was a male at Sutton Place, Guildford on 7th August 1981 and a male at Kew Gardens in 1993. One was seen at Haslemere in 1993.

Night Heron   *Nycticorax nycticorax*

A Night Heron in Battersea Park in November and December 1967 and an adult bird at Berrylands in 1966-67 proved to have escaped from London Zoo (J, Gale, S. Greenwood *BB, 60:313, BB, 61:334*).

Cattle Egret   *Bubulcus ibis*

Alfred Ezra released five full-winged birds of the eastern race *B. i. coromandus* at Foxwarren Park, Cobham in April 1930 and lost two of them. One, which had starved to death, was subsequently found at Godalming. The other was seen in Devonshire in June 1930 (*BB, 24:85*). One visited a garden at New Addington on 1st July 1995. Notes and a video were obtained, showing that the bird was of the western race *B. i. ibis*. This or another was seen flying east at Walton Reservoirs on 15th August. The British Birds Rarities Committee felt obliged to assume that a series of records in the London/Home Counties during the summer months related to one, possibly two, escaped birds, one certainly being of the eastern race *coromandus*. While this judgement is not beyond dispute, both records have been excluded from the main list. A third bird in 1995, at Ockley, was photographed and was of the eastern race.

White Stork   *Ciconia ciconia*

1974:   One at North Camp Gravel Pits, on the Surrey/Hampshire border, on 21st June was not accepted as a wild bird by the BBRC (*BB, 68:336*).

1975:   One that escaped from Chessington Zoo early in 1975 (*BB, 55:568*) was presumably the bird seen flying near the zoo on 29th June.

1978:   One flew over Croydon on 6th August.

1979:   One at Cobham on 25th February.

1982:   One at Guildford on 31st December was also not accepted as a wild bird (*BB, 76:528*), and might have come from a collection near the A3 at Cobham, where another was seen earlier in the year (*SBR* for 1982).

1990:   One flying towards Egham town centre on 10th August. One in the Cranleigh Hotel area of Cranleigh on 21st-23rd September was also seen at Weybridge on the 23rd. A photograph of this bird, which was unringed, is in the *Surrey Bird Report* for 1990. Two White Storks which had escaped from Whipsnade were roving southern England at about the time of these two records.

2000, 2001: One seen at Chertsey Meads, Thorpe, Cobham and Byfleet on dates from July 2000 to January 2001 was seen to be carrying a leg ring on the latter date and was presumed to be the escaped bird seen at various other places in southern England. A colour- ringed bird reported near Charlton Gravel Pits on 30th December 2000 (Birdguides) was probably the same.

2002:   One at Warlingham on 22nd May.

2005:   One at South Nutfield on 2nd July (J. Potts, *BB, 98:449 Recent Reports*). One flew over Redhill on 2nd July (*Bird Watching*). One flew over Papercourt on 3rd July (*Bird Watching*). All three were the same bird?

Goshawk   *Accipiter gentilis*

One at Kew Gardens on 29th and 30th September 1960 was carrying a bell, as was one at Wisley on 24th February 1961. One at Beddington Sewage Farm in 1969. One at Olddean Common on 19th August 1980 allowed close approach and may have been an escape (*HSBBR*). One seen at Capel in 1990 had been present for some years. Single birds were at South Norwood Country Park on 21st November 1993 and Beddington Sewage Farm on 13th-30th November 1998.

Buzzard   *Buteo buteo*

Birds at Forest Hill in July 1976, Thornton Heath in 1982, Chobham in 1985 and South Norwood Country Park in 1991 were probably escapes.

Merlin   *Falco columbarius*

Beddington Sewage Farm 1969.

Peregrine   *Falco peregrinus*

A trained bird with a bell attached to it was killed near Horsley in 1889 (Bucknill). One wearing jesses at Kew Gardens in April 1979. One at Staines Reservoirs on 6th December 1987 (falconers were seen flying Peregrines without jesses in January 1988). One at Thursley Common on 29 September 1993 was suspected of wearing jesses. One with jesses flew over London SW18 on 21st November 1993.

Crane   *Grus grus*

One came into roost at dusk at Frensham Little Pond on 1st-7th October 1961. The record is included in square brackets by the British Birds Rarities Committee (*BB, 55:571*), indicating a likely escape. The *Surrey Bird Report* for 1961 suggested that the bird had escaped from a private zoo in Tilford.

Oystercatcher   *Haematopus ostralegus*

One that escaped from Crystal Palace Zoo was seen nearby in August 1983.

Herring Gull   *Larus argentatus*

A captive pair built a nest at Epsom in 1901. Three eggs were laid, from which one was hatched, but no young were fledged (Bucknill, 1902).

Barn Owl   *Tyto alba*

One with jesses at Mitcham Common in December 1989, a 'bedraggled and tame' bird at Berrylands Station on 5th June 1993.

American Robin   *Turdus migratorius*

One in Richmond Park in May 1912 (Collenette).

Chough   *Pyrrhocorax pyrrhocorax*

One, an old bird knocked over with a stone at Balham a few months prior to 1893, was thought to be an escape (Swann, 1893). One with a twisted lower mandible and the lower part of the leg missing was shot among rooks at Effingham on 27th December 1894 and was probably the bird with these characteristics that had escaped from captivity at Windlesham at about this time. The specimen was at one time in the Charterhouse Collection. Choughs at Woldingham in the early 1950s (Parr), at Sutton on 3rd May 1961 (SBC archive) and at Horsell in 2001 (SBC archive) are likely to have been escapes.

Hooded Crow *Corvus cornix*

One at Capel from 16th July to 19th October 1987 often perched on television aerials.

Raven *Corvus corax*

One at Weybridge in August 1963 was an escaped pet. There was a tame bird at Headley Heath on 1st-18th August 1973 (*SBR* for 1974). Single birds flying north over Ashtead Common on 29th October 1997 and north over Leatherhead Station on 20th December 1997 might possibly have been wild birds.

Exotic birds with a story

Ostrich *Struthio camelus*

Breeds in Africa. Ostriches on a farm at Horsell are said to have sometimes escaped from their enclosures with at least one reaching an adjacent main road. No dates but before 2002.

Emu *Dromaius novaehollandiae*

Breeds in Australia. A pair were acclimatised at Brockham by William Bennet in 1860. They later bred, raising young successfully. In 1863, eighteen eggs were laid between 2nd January and 20th March (*Zool., 1863:8312, 8494*). One of the Emus was given to the Holmesdale Museum after its death but is no longer held there. An escaped Emu was reported from Rushmoor in 2000.

White Pelican *Pelecanus onocrotalus*

Has a scattered breeding distribution from the Balkans to Central Asia, and in Africa. European birds winter in Africa. Some British records may be of vagrants, though this has yet to be proved. The single vice-county bird was seen by R. B. Hastings at Barn Elms Reservoir, Greater London, from 22nd to 24th May 1973 (*BB, 74:492*). Three adults were at Staines Reservoirs on 18th April 1971 (A. V. Moon, *BB, 90:518; 91:515* and *LBR for 1996*). Two adults at Wraysbury Reservoir on 10th November 1972 were probably the two at Kempton Park Reservoirs (Greater London) on the 11th and Dungeness (Kent) on the 11th and 12th. There were two adults at Wraysbury Reservoir on 10th November 1993 (C. D. R. Heard, *BB, 87:566*). Three adults flew to Staines Reservoirs from the west on 18th April 1996 and drifted off east. They may have been the birds at Breydon Water (Norfolk) in August and September. All five records were thought to be unproven as wild *onocrotalus* by the British Birds Rarities Committee. No British records so far have adequately excluded the possibility of American White Pelican *P. erythrorhynchos* (*BB, 90:518*).

Sacred Ibis *Threskiornis aethiopicus*

Feral birds have been breeding in France and the Netherlands. Unringed birds are becoming more frequent in Surrey.

Flamingo species *Phoenicopterus species*

A flamingo that had escaped from captivity at Windsor took up residence on the Pen Ponds, Richmond Park from 9th December 1932 to mid January 1933. It was popular with visitors but harried by the resident Swans, and escaped capture even though a reward was offered (Collenette, 1937). An unidentified flamingo flew over East Molesey in 1965 and another was seen at Effingham on 2nd January 1974. There was a Chilean Flamingo *P. chilensis* at Walton Reservoirs in 1970.

Greater Flamingo *Phoenicopterus roseus*

There are breeding populations from southern Europe east to India and in Africa. British records may refer to vagrants but this has yet to be proved. One was seen at Frensham in 1909 by O. H. Latter and Howard Bentham (Shaw, 1921) and was probably the bird referred to in the Daily Telegraph of 29th March 1968. This bird was designated *P. roseus* by Shaw (1921), the name then excluding the Caribbean Flamingo *P. ruber* (BOU 1915). The two were subsequently lumped but were split again by the BOU in 2002.

Black Swan *Cygnus atratus*

Breeds in Australia. Bucknill gave references to several that had been shot. Places from which Black

Swans have been reported away from collections in the first half of the 20th century include Fetcham Mill Pond (1937) and the Thames. Numbers on the Thames fell during the 1939-45 war and as a result of the hard winter of 1947 (*LBR* for 1989). Fitter (1949) said a few had been on the Thames in London for at least 20 years and that they had been caught in swan-upping but he gave no specifically Surrey localities or breeding records. There were still two in the herd of the Vintners Company in 1957 (Fitter, 1959). Single birds were seen on the Thames at Walton-on-Thames in 1972 and Sunbury in 1973.

Places where Black Swans have been recorded since 1978 include Badshot Lea (1979, *HSBBR*), Barn Elms, Barnes, Barwell Court Farm, Battersea Park, Beddington Sewage Farm, Claremont Lake, Cranleigh, Earlswood, Effingham Fish Ponds, Enton, Frensham Great and Little Ponds, Frimley, Godstone (1996, 1997, 1998), Ham Lands, Hedgecourt (1991), Holmethorpe Sand Pits, Kew, Kingston, Leatherhead, Lonsdale Road Reservoir, Molesey, Mytchett Lake (1985, *HSBBR*), Papercourt, Queen Elizabeth II Reservoir, Richmond, South Norwood Country Park, the Surrey Docks, Thorpe, Thursley Common, Unstead Sewage Farm, Walton-on-Thames (including local reservoirs) and in Spelthorne at Sheepwalk east (1984), Staines Moor (1987, 2001), Staines Reservoirs (1998) and Wraysbury Reservoir (2000). Most of these places are in the London area. Records from southeast England are uncommon.
Thorpe Water Park, with three in June 1998, was one of only nine British sites with at least three Black Swans in the 1998-99 Wetland Bird Survey counts and higher counts have been recorded. Most of the Thorpe birds are pinioned.

Young Black Swans breeding outside Surrey, in St James's Park (*LBR* for 1989) may disperse into the county. There are a few Surrey breeding records: Battersea Park (1992), Claremont Lake (1998 and 1999, pinioned, one cygnet in 2000) and at Kew Gardens (five cygnets in 1964).

Black-necked Swan   *Cygnus melanocoryphus*
Breeds in South America. Single birds at Barn Elms Reservoirs in 1963, Thorpe Water Park in 1981 and Kingston in 2002.

Swan Goose   *Anser cygnoides*
Bred at Godstone and Norwood in 1967. A pair that had three young at Effingham Ponds on 25th June 1974 had recently been introduced and presumably bred after their introduction. One flew into Outwood Swan Sanctuary with Canada Geese in 2004. In Spelthorne, there was one at Stanwell Moor in 1998.

Eastern Greylag Goose   *Anser anser rubirostris*
Breeds in Eastern Europe and Asia. Not proved to have occurred in Britain as a wild bird although birds that resemble it have been seen (*BB, 99:623*). A ringed bird on the Thames at Hammersmith on 3rd March 1963 had a bill of a 'delicate but definite pink' (*LBR, SBR*) and might have been of this race. Birds with characteristics of the pink-billed *rubirostris* were reported in 1978 from Clandon Park and Sutton Place (Guildford). None of these can be taken as proved and wild, but they might be escapes.

Bar-headed Goose   *Anser indicus*
Breeds in Asia. Escaped and feral birds occasionally breed in Britain. Surrey records go back to at least 1965, when one was seen at Barn Elms Reservoirs. There were others at Barn Elms in 2000, Broadwater in 1970, at the Gatton/Holmethorpe area in 1972, at Gatton and Godstone in 1973 and at Frensham Great Pond in 1979. It is now one of the most commonly reported non-native species. Other places at which they have been seen, often with Canada Geese, include Barn Elms, Battersea Park, Beddington Sewage Farm, Boldermere, Buckland Sand Pits, Burgess Park, Chertsey Meads, Clapham Common, Cranleigh, Dulwich Park, Frensham Great Pond (1979 *HSBBR*), Frimley Gravel Pits, Ham Lands, Hersham, Kew Gardens (sixteen, of which seven were full-winged, in 1993, at least 20 in 2004), Lyne, Island Barn Reservoir, Molesey, Papercourt Gravel Pits, Richmond Park, Rushett Farm, South Norwood Country Park and Lake, the Surrey Docks, Sydenham, Thorpe Water Park, Thursley Common, Vachery, Walton Reservoirs, West End Common (Esher) and in Spelthorne from King George VI Reservoir,

Queen Mary Gravel Pits and Reservoir, Shepperton Gravel Pits, Staines Moor, Staines Reservoirs and Wraysbury Reservoir.

Bar-headed Geese have bred in north Hampshire. The first reported breeding record for Surrey was from Kew Gardens, where a pair raised five young in 1992. There were at least six pairs and three broods in 1998.

Emperor Goose   *Chen canagica*

Breeds in Alaska and Siberia. Up to three in most years since 1987. Localities include Barn Elms, Beddington Sewage Farm, Claremont Lake, Frensham Little Pond, Island Barn Reservoir, Kew Gardens, Papercourt Gravel Pits (three in 1992), Queen Elizabeth II Reservoir, South Norwood Lake, Stoke Lake, Sunbury Lock and Walton Reservoirs.

Cackling Canada Goose   *Branta canadensis minima*

Breeds in North America. Not proved to have occurred in Britain as a wild bird although birds that resemble it have been seen (*BB, 99:623*). One at Frensham in March and Frimley Gravel Pits in May and June 1985 (*HSBBR*), two at Beddington Sewage Farm on 22nd August to 22nd September 1986 (*Beddington Bird Report* for 1992) and one at Badshot Lea on 5th October 1986.

Shelduck species and hybrids   *Tadorna spp.*

The identification of species and hybrids has been a particular problem with Australian, Cape, Paradise and similar shelduck species. Following the 1995 influx, some of the birds at Queen Elizabeth II Reservoir in 1996 were thought to be hybrids with Ruddy or Paradise Shelducks. A male Paradise x Australian Shelduck was reported at Claremont in 1997, with unspecified hybrids at Walton Reservoirs. A South African Shelduck and Paradise Shelduck pair bred at Queen Elizabeth II Reservoir in 1997, raising four young and in the following year a pair of hybrid adults were present there with four chicks. In 1998 there was a hybrid Paradise x South African (or Australian?) Shelduck at Claremont but there were no breeding reports. Hybrids continued to be seen in 1999.

South African Shelducks have been rather variously reported. A pair of Paradise type shelducks that bred at Claremont in 2000 closely resembled the Paradise species but the male had a narrow grey crown stripe and the female had whitish patches on the cheek, suggesting that there might have been South African somewhere in their parentage. They raised three young. A pair of the Paradise or South African type at Walton Reservoirs on dates in the years 1998-2002 and at West End Common in 2001 and 2002 may have been from Claremont, as might one seen at Epsom in 2000. In Spelthorne, there were South African Shelducks at King George VI and Staines Reservoirs in 1997. Mead mentions a pair with four juveniles in Surrey in 1997, which would be the first breeding as wild if they had nested unconfined (*BB, 92: 176-82, 472-76*). A South African Shelduck at Epsom and a Paradise Shelduck family at Claremont in 2000 (*LBR*) were in the *SBR* as Cape/Paradise Shelduck *T. cana/variegata*.

South African (Cape) Shelduck   *Tadorna cana*

South African Shelducks and possibly at least one *Tadorna* hybrid were released from Kew Gardens on the outbreak of war in 1939. One of the birds moved to Barnes Common where it later found a mate and raised a brood in 1946. In the same year, two were seen in Richmond Park. The original bird was found dead in 1982. (*BLA*, 1st edition). The next report located is of a Cape Shelduck at Barn Elms in 1981. There were several reports from Holmethorpe Sand Pits in 1984 and one from Queen Elizabeth II Reservoir in 1985.

The current run of reports began with a female at Queen Elizabeth II Reservoir on 19th February 1995 and single females at Beddington Sewage Farm, South Norwood Country Park and Thorpe Water Park on 16th March and many records of up to nine in the Walton-on-Thames area from April into 1996, with smaller numbers up to at least 1999. A pair were seen at Stoke Lake on 11th October 1996 and others were there in 1997. The birds were thought to have come from a private collection in Greater London north of the Thames. There was one at King George VI Reservoir in December 1995. Some or all of these may have been hybrids.

Australian Shelduck   *Tadorna tadornoides*

Breeds in Australia. Single birds at Beddington Sewage Farm in 1984, Walton Reservoirs in 1985 and 1989 and at Island Barn Reservoir in 1990 and in Spelthorne one paired with a Shelduck (*T. tadorna*) at Sheepwalk East in early 1984, no offspring being recorded.

Paradise Shelduck   *Tadorna variegata*

Breeds in New Zealand. One at Barn Elms Reservoirs in 1965, a female at Walton Reservoirs in March and April 1991, one at Walton-on-Thames in July 1994, one at Frensham in 1995. One was found during a King George VI Reservoir wildfowl count in 1997. Subsequent records, and perhaps one or two of the earlier ones, have an element of doubt about them. These include one or two at Chertsey Meads, Claremont, Epsom Common, Papercourt Gravel Pits in 1996, at Queen Elizabeth II Reservoir in 1997, at Claremont and West End Common (Esher) in 1998 and 1999 and one at Hersham in 1999.

Muscovy Duck   *Cairina moschata*

Breeds in Central and South America. Little has come to light about the early Surrey history. Breeding has been recorded at Papercourt Gravel Pits (female with 13 young in 1970), Godstone Pond (pair with four young in 1972), Guildford (11 ducklings at Millmead in 1976) and Clapham (adult and juvenile on 6th September 1998). They bred in Surrey in 1996 and/or 1997 (*BB, 92:176-82, 472-76*).

Other places where they have been seen include: Albury, Barnes Pond, Barn Elms WWT, Battersea Park, Beddington Sewage Farm, Britten's Pond (Guildford), Central Pond (Wandsworth), Chilworth, Clapham, Claremont, Dorking (Mill Pond and Milton Court, 1976), Effingham Fish Ponds, Enton, Epsom Common, Ewell Court Lake, Frensham, Godstone (also 1977), Guildford Sewage Farm (1974), Holmethorpe, Horley, Kew Gardens, Langshott, Longside Lake, Lonsdale Road Reservoir, Outwood Swan Sanctuary, Pirbright village pond, Reigate Priory, Richmond, Shamley Green, Shottermill Ponds, Stamford Green Pond (Epsom), South Norwood Lake, the Surrey Docks, Thames Ditton, Wandsworth Common, Wimbledon Common, Windlesham and Woking, all 1990 or later unless otherwise indicated. There was an unsuccessful introduction at Shepperton Gravel Pits (Poole End Lake) in 1985 and a Muscovy was seen on the Thames at Staines in 1999.

Large counts include eight at Frensham on 3rd December 1990. About 30 on the water meadows at Burpham in January 1998 were from a wildlife farm. One feeding on a bird table at Langshott in 1999 and 2000 was acting as native Muscovy Ducks do in the West Indies.

Ringed Teal   *Callonetta leucophrys*

Breeds in South America. A pair at Fetcham in 1985. Bred at Capel, raising two young, around 1987, seen in most years since.

Wood Duck   *Aix sponsa*

Also known as the Carolina Duck and Summer Duck and is the North American counterpart of the other member of its genus, the Mandarin. It has been frequently kept in collections and is said to breed readily in captivity. Full-winged birds apparently roamed much of Devonshire, where they were widely kept, at the end of the 19th century (D'Urban and Matthew, 1892). A pair shot near Dorking two or three years prior to 1835 *apparently in a wild state* (Bucknill) seems to be the first reference to full-winged British birds. In spite of their early success, Wood Ducks have yet to establish a significant feral population in Surrey or elsewhere in Britain. This is surprising, given the success of the Mandarins. Lever (1977) suggests that it may be due to a lower duckling survival rate than that of the Mandarin. The fledging period lasts for ten weeks, compared with six to eight weeks for the Mandarin, making Wood Duck young more vulnerable to predators. It may also be that the Mandarin, with which it competes for the same habitat, is the dominant bird. Recorded occurrences since 1900 have been at Norbury Park (May 1959), Guildford Sewage Farm (1967), the River Wandle at Hackbridge (October 1969), the Surrey/Berkshire border (several pairs, 1969) and then, from 1970, at Albury (1985-86), Ash Vale Gravel Pits (1987), Badshot Lea (1999), Barnes Pond (1993), Beddington Sewage Farm (1993), Betchworth (1978-79),

Broadwater (1991-92), Busbridge (1977, 1992, 1998), Carshalton (1987), Chobham (1978), Claremont (1995-96, collection), Coxhill Green (1991), Cutt Mill (1970-71, nine in 1972, 1973-74, 1976, 1979, 1988-90, 1992, 1994-98), Dorking (1997, 1999-2000), Enton (1980, 2002), Farnham (2001), Frensham (1985-86, 1991-92, 1996, 1998-99), Godalming (Lammas Lands 1978), Godstone (1993 including three pinioned, 1996), Goldsworth Park Lake (1991-92), Guildford (1985, 1991), Haslemere (1994), Holmethorpe (1985), Kew Gardens (1998), Leatherhead (1999, 2001-02), North Holmwood (1985), Nower Wood (1996), Pyrford Lock (1977), Shottermill (1991-92), South Norwood Lake (1988), Stoke Water Meadows (1991), the Surrey Docks (1975, after an introduction at Southwark Park, 1998-2000), the Thames at Ham (1986), Thorpe Water Park (1976 after the introduction of pinioned birds, 1984, 1992-95), Thursley (1995 Moat Pond), Tongham Gravel Pit (1999-2002), Vachery (1988), (Virginia Water (1972-73, 1976-77, 1982-83), West Byfleet (1991, 1994), Woking (1992 Basingstoke Canal) and Wrecclesham Floods (1984).

There have been several breeding attempts. At Vann Lake in 1968, young from another area appeared after a failed local breeding attempt (Blaker Log). A pair with three young were seen at Cutt Mill on 18th May 1975. The ducklings were believed to have been lost to predators later. A pair nested unsuccessfully at Sunbury Lock in 1987 (Hewlett).

Chiloe Wigeon — *Anas sibilatrix*

Breeds in South America. Many reports. One at Clapham Common and Barn Elms Reservoirs in 1962. Recorded in 1970, 1973, 1974, 1976, 1978, 1979, 1984, 1985 and almost every year since 1988. No more than two at any one time. Places include Beddington Sewage Farm, Reigate Priory, Unstead and Walton Reservoirs. Staines Reservoirs in 1997.

White-cheeked Pintail (Bahama Pintail) — *Anas bahamensis*

Breeds in the West Indies and South America. Recorded at Queen Elizabeth II Reservoir in 1973 and Papercourt Gravel Pits and Ripley Sewage Farm in 1974, then in most years since 1983, no more than two at any one time. Others were at Frensham Little Pond in 1985, Frimley Gravel Pits in 1996 and King George VI Reservoir (Spelthorne) in 1995.

Cinnamon Teal — *Anas cyanoptera*

Breeds in the Americas. Several seen at Frensham Little Pond in many of the years from 1989 to 2002, usually in the spring but sometimes also in the July-October period. Also recorded from Beddington Sewage Farm and Staines Reservoirs in the 1990s.

Marbled Teal — *Marmaronetta angustirostris*

A mainly resident duck which breeds around the Mediterranean east to Pakistan. There are no definite British records of wild birds. There was one at Staines Reservoirs (Spelthorne) in September 1984 (*Rare Birds, 7:37*). One at Barn Elms Reservoirs on 3rd-30th August 1991 (R. B. Hastings *et al.*) was thought by the British Birds Rarities Committee to be a bird of uncertain origin (per C. Lamsdell, *BB, 88:555, SBR*). Another at Perry Oaks Sewage Farm (Spelthorne) from 15th May to 7th June 1998 (C. Lamsdell) might have crossed the old Spelthorne boundary (*BB, 92:607*).

Hooded Merganser — *Mergus cucullatus*

Breeds in North America, wintering south to Mexico. Hooded Mergansers are very rare winter migrants to the British Isles but they are often kept in wildfowl collections. One was killed at Elstead prior to 1885 (*SALEC*). A full-winged female on the River Wey at Guildford from 8th November 1971 to 27th April 1972 was thought to have escaped from a collection near Winchester (*BB, 65:90*). A pinioned drake was at Weston Trout Lake and the Tillingbourne at Gomshall from the spring of 1988 to at least February 1989.

Swallow-tailed Kite — *Elanoides forficatus*

Resident in wetlands of the southern USA and winters south to Paraguay. A reference to one shot in Farnham Park in the summer of 1855 (*Zool., 1856:5042*) has no supporting details. Intriguingly, the BOU List of 1915 mentions one at Farnham in 1833 but not the 1855 bird. Given that on the same page of the

Zoologist, another record for the same species, Wensleydale in 1805, is dated 1854, the BOU date of 1833 may be the correct one. One shot 'many years ago' by Chiddingfold Pond is mentioned in Walpole-Bond (1938), with the additional note that *it is perhaps still in the Swan Inn, Haslemere*. An immaculate specimen, fitting Bond's description of a *resplendent creature in black and white* is currently in the Haslemere Museum. There is no doubt about the identification but the provenance of the Chiddingfold bird has long been regarded as uncertain, *e.g. BB, 4:93*. The Haslemere Natural History Society at one time met in premises adjacent to the Swan Inn, so it may be the one shot at Chiddingfold. As Evans (1994), who mentions neither of the Surrey birds, and Naylor (1996), who mentions only the Farnham bird, both point out, there are several 18th and 19th century records and claims for the species, three from Yorkshire.

Lanner Falcon   *Falco biarmicus*
Breeds in Southern Europe and in Africa. At least four since 1994.

Wild Turkey   *Meleagris gallopavo*
Thousands of Turkeys were introduced into Richmond Park during the reign of King George I. The birds attracted poachers and a keeper named Lucas was recruited, on account of his skill in fighting with the quarter-staff, to guard them. There were frequent fights between the poachers and the keepers. The Turkeys were hunted with dogs and would take refuge in trees where George II, for one, would shoot them. Eventually the poachers began to get the upper hand and George III, early in his reign, restored peace by ordering the extirpation of the Turkeys (Collenette, 1937). These events would have taken place at some time within the period 1714-1800.

Bobwhite   *Colinus virginianus*
Breeds in the Americas. Numerous attempts have been made to introduce this species, known also as the Virginian Colin and the American Partridge to 19th century writers, into the British Isles, the first probably being before 1813 in Ireland. Populations have sometimes survived for a few years but all have eventually died out. Prince Albert put some down near Windsor in or around 1840 and several were found in Surrey shortly after. Two were shot in pea stubble near Egham in September 1844 and a covey of seven or eight were seen nearby in the following month. Two of the birds were shot. A boy killed a male with a stone between Weybridge and Chertsey in April 1845 and a male was shot near Chelsham Court, Godstone in the October of the same year. Bucknill mentions others from the same period in Meyer. An introduction made by S. Gill near Godalming persisted for a few years and provided at least one for Stafford's collection (*SALEC*). A few were released at Milford in 1962 but were not seen after April of that year until one was seen there in January 1965. There was one at Claygate in 1972.

Chukar   *Alectoris chukar*
A native of Greece and other countries east to Central Asia, widely introduced by sporting interests in the 1980s. The Chukars were often tame and have sometimes been seen in large numbers where introduced. There were occasional breeding records from residential areas, the best documented being of some very tame birds that nested in gardens at Elmbridge, Cranleigh in 1992-95. The release of Chukars after 1992 was made illegal and there have been no reports of them since 1996.

Ogridge   *Alectoris rufa x chukar*
The introduction of the hybrid was first reported in 1975, from the Ripley area. As with the Chukar, their release after 1992 was made illegal and there have been no recent reports of them.

Silver Pheasant   *Lophura nycthermera*
Breeds in Asia. Five were released in Richmond Park in 1929. They disappeared after a short period (Collenette). Silver Pheasants were seen at Kew Gardens in 1993 and at Epsom Common in 1994.

Indian Peafowl   *Pavo cristatus*
Breeds in India. In 1999 a pair near Barn Elms London Wetland Centre raised three young which occasionally ventured onto the reserve. Peafowl were seen in the Barn Elms Playing fields/Anglers Pond area until April 2000, when they were removed (*London Wetland Centre Bird and Natural History Report 2000*).

Crowned-Crane species   *Balearica species*

Breeds in Africa. The African Crowned Crane was recently split into two species, the Black Crowned-Crane *Balearica pavonina* and the Grey Crowned-Crane *B. regulorum*. Birds were seen in the Guildford area in 1969, Cobham in 1979 and Pirbright Common in 1981 (roosted on 18th October, *HSBBR*). There were two at Hersham and Thorpe and one at Worcester Park in 1985, possibly escapes from Chessington Zoo and another fed on grain at a private lake in Chiddingfold in 1989. None of these records distinguish between the two species.

At Laleham Farm (Spelthorne) and nearby areas there were two in the winter of 1985/86, apparently the Hersham birds and said to have escaped from Chessington Zoo (*Shepp. BR*). Belsey (2002) includes a photograph of a pair, probably these two and possibly of the *gibbericeps* race of the Grey Crowned-Crane *Balearica regulorum*, on farmland at Laleham in winter. This pair was also seen by H. W. Evans on 13th November 1985. A single bird flew over the area on 26th January 1986. One on the A3 near Cobham on 6th November 2006 caused the road to be closed until it was captured for return to its owner (*Staines Guardian*, 16th November 2006 with photo).

Demoiselle Crane   *Anthropoides virgo*

Breeds in Southern Europe, Africa and Asia. One in 1960 at Carshalton on 31st March and Beddington on 10th April (*BB, 53:239*). One at Ripley on 30th October 1976.

Grey-winged Trumpeter   *Psophia crepitans*

Breeds in South America. Montagu included an entertaining account of a 'Golden-breasted Trumpeter *Psophia crepitans*' that frequented a Surrey farmyard and fed on scraps of meat. On one occasion it followed a pack of hounds that ran through the yard and kept up with them for three miles. Later, after it was captured, Lord Derby tried, unsuccessfully, to find out who owned the bird. He then offered it for sale and it died on a journey to Lancashire.

Purple Swamphen (Purple Gallinule)   *Porphyrio porphyrio*

A southern European breeding species. The one Surrey record, of a bird at Bury Lake, Dorking, from September 1894 to February 1895 (*Zool., 1896:475*), was thought by Bucknill to be a possible escape and was not mentioned in the 1915 BOU List.

Grey-headed Gull   *Larus cirrocephalus*

One at Beddington Sewage Farm in 2001 and May 2002, race (South African or South American) not determined. There are photographs in the *Beddington Farm Bird Report* for 2001.

Passenger Pigeon   *Ectopistes migratorius*

Extinct. Bred in North America. Meyer, as quoted in Glegg, stated that two males and a female were seen in the woods of Littleton Common (later known as Ashford Common). It was said that they *alighted and gave the observers, who were familiar with the species, time to note the lengthened tails and the colour of the plumage* and that the call resembled that of a Pheasant. This would have been not later than 1850. The birds were presumably not of wild origin. Yarrell recorded three occurrences in Britain, one of which he thought was wild. Writing half a century later, Saunders mentioned five British occurrences, all of which he thought were escapes and added that, from 1830, many had been released in Britain. Neither author mentioned Littleton Common. One in the Charterhouse Collection was bought at the Leadenhall Market (*SALEC*).

Cockatoo and Parrot species   *Cacatuidae/Psittacacidae*

Charles Buxton, a Member of Parliament, tried to acclimatise a variety of species at Foxwarren Park, Cobham in the 1860s (*Zool., 1868:1395-1401*). Species included African, Amazonian, Carolina and Honduras Parrots, Leadbeater's and White Cockatoos, Bengal and Rosella Parakeets (Buxton's names). The birds were free-flying and some left the estate: *One of the large cockatoos deserted my place in Surrey, and was continually seen associating with a flock of rooks some miles away, but at length returned. On one occasion a flock of our parrots flew to a place named Brooke, full twenty-five miles away, and eleven were shot by a gamekeeper who naturally thought he had secured a wonderful prize* ... Presumably they bred for a while, but the colony eventually died out.

Cockatiel   *Nymphicus hollandicus*

Breeds in Australia. Many colour varieties have been developed by breeders. Pure white ones were seen at Wallington and Shepperton in 1985. Escaped birds are seen in most years.

Budgerigar   *Melopsittacus undulatus*

Breeds in Australia. Introduced to the Scillies in 1969 but the colony is now extinct (Butler, 2002). One flew very low over Kennington Oval during a cricket match on 11th August 1876 (Power). Seen at Barn Elms and Kew Gardens in 1986. Over 20 subsequent records and no doubt many unrecorded.

Alexandrine Parakeet   *Psittacula eupatria*

Breeds in Asia and India. Has nested in Kent (hybrid pair) and Merseyside (Butler, 2002). Recorded in Surrey in 1989. Feathers found at Thursley Common in July 1993. There were single birds at Hersham in 2000 and at Barn Elms, Esher, Hersham and Queen Elizabeth II Reservoir in subsequent years.

Blue-crowned Parakeet   *Aratinga acuticaudata*

Breeds in South America. Nested in Kent in 2001 (Butley, 2002) and has been seen in Surrey.

Monk Parakeet   *Myiopsitta monachus*

The natural range is in South America. Monk Parakeets first bred in Britain at Whipsnade in the 1930s (Hewlett). There are small feral populations in several European countries, including one at Borehamwood, Hertfordshire to 2001 at least, and extinct colonies in Cheshire and Devon (Butler, 2002). A pair built a nest at Lonsdale Road Reservoir, Barnes in 1996 and 1997 (*SBR*). Two were seen again in the area in 1998-99 (*SBR*), and one in 2002. There were up to two at Barn Elms in 2000 and 2002 and there were reports from Beddington Sewage Farm in 2002 and 2003. No young have been seen.

Sunbird species   *Nectariniidae*

A female or immature bird flying round a garden at Tadworth in late February 1988 was later found dead.

Eagle Owl   *Bubo bubo*

A number of reports of this spectacular bird, which in much colder times was probably a resident and has recently bred again in northern Britain, the origin of the stock being uncertain. A significant proportion of the Surrey reports turn out to be stone or plastic birds on roofs or pylons. Lack of movement, even if watched for some time, is a good field character for these.

Zebra Finch   *Taeniopygia guttata*

Breeds in Australia. Recorded from time to time since 1984.

Chestnut Munia   *Lonchura atricapilla*

Breeds in Asia and India. Said to have nested at or near Haslemere (Restall, 1996). It is understood that the site was a reed-fringed pond on the Godalming side of Haslemere and that the date was probably 1960 or 1961.

Canary   *Serinus canaria*

Breeds in the Canary Isles. Common in captivity. Reported from time to time. Power saw one in Brixton during August, 1877. Two others perched on his Brixton aviary.

Red-headed Bunting   *Emberiza bruniceps*

Breeds in Asia. Evans (1994) mentions a male 'of suspect origin' at Pirbright Common on 3rd May 1990. The British Birds Rarities Committee, for whom this is not a proven wild bird, has apparently not considered the record.

Other exotics

Well over 50 other escaped species have been reported. Waterfowl and parrots are the most frequent groups, together with a variety of finches and other small cagebirds. Raptors include Bald Eagle *Haliaeetus leucocephalus*, Harris' Hawk *Parabuteo unicinctus*, Red-tailed Hawk *Buteo jamaicensis* and Saker Falcon *Falco cherrug*.

Other Published Records

This section lists a selection of records which have been published but which for one reason or another are not fully acceptable for the purposes of this book. It does not include the many records published as unacceptable by the British Birds Rarities Committee but it does include a few interesting records from just outside the border. The intention is to remove doubts about whether these have been overlooked.

Unidentified Geese
A party of 100-120 flew over County Hall, Lambeth on 30th January 1984, possibly Brent Geese (*LBR*).

Grey Geese   *Anser species*
Wild grey geese rarely land to feed in Surrey and flying birds are sometimes not seen well enough for specific identification. Single birds and those (other than Greylags) seen in the breeding season are unlikely to be wild. Skeins of 100 or more unidentified grey geese from November to March have been seen *e.g.* at East Horsley (about 100, 18th March 1956) and Leatherhead (about 100, 30th December 1962) and there are records of smaller numbers elsewhere. Most are probably White-fronts. A party of about 25 that flew northeast over Queen Mary Reservoir on 4th January 1997 were thought by the observer to be Pink-footed Geese, the wintering population of which has increased in East Anglia (*LBR*).

Bean Goose   *Anser fabalis*
An undated reference in the *SBR* for 1964 was an error.

Pink-footed Goose   *Anser brachyrhynchus*
One with Mute Swans at Sheen Bridge in November and December 1954 (*SBR* for 1953 and 1955). A tame bird at Beddington Sewage Farm in February 1958. Single birds at Earlswood Lakes on 26th January 1961, Fetcham Mill Pond on 15th April 1961 and Holmethorpe in 1995. One at Holmethorpe in January 1980 (*LBR*) may have been wild.

Black Brant   *Branta bernicla nigricans*
A Brent Goose ringed as an adult in Alaska on 13th July 1965 was reported to have been recovered in the Caterham area on or about 15th January 1977 (*Ringing Report 2002, p.259*). Upon enquiry through the BTO, it transpired that the bird was a Black Brant that had been bought for a wildfowl collection just over the county border at Edenbridge, in Kent. The owner removed the ring because it was getting a sharp edge and reported the number to the US authorities, who supplied the ringing details. These were passed on to the BTO. It is not known how the bird came to be in captivity or how it got from Alaska to the UK. It was never in Surrey.

Red-breasted Goose   *Branta ruficollis*
Harting mentioned one shot near London (not necessarily in Middlesex), at the beginning of the severe frost of 1776, a record due to J. Latham according to Montagu. The specimen was taken to the museum at Newcastle, where Bewick saw it and used it as a model for an engraving in his *British Birds* and where Harting saw it in May 1863 (Harting, 1866). The bird is not mentioned by Bucknill but has an interesting provenance and just might have come from the Thames or the Spelthorne district. There is a photograph of it in Palmer (2000).

Black Duck   *Anas rubripes*
One at King George VI Reservoir on 8th-15th November 1964 (Recent Reports, *BB, 58:31*) is no longer accepted (*BB, 58:312*).

Scaup   *Aythya marila*
Richmond Park, 27th March 1904. See Collenette (1937).

Red-breasted Merganser   *Mergus serrator*

Twenty-five, including three males, at Frensham Little Pond 13th January 1939. This record has appeared in the HNHS Lists and in Parr. It may well be correct but in the absence of such an exceptional number in Surrey before or since, there seems a possibility of confusion with Goosander, at least for some of the females. Time has not, unfortunately, preserved enough information to say.

Great Northern Diver   *Gavia immer*

A Diver at Pen Ponds, Richmond Park from 16th October to 3rd November 1965 was published as a Great Northern in the London and Surrey Bird Reports. B. A. Marsh has kindly supplied a copy of a recently-located photograph that he took of the bird and has corrected the identification to a Black-throated Diver.

Red-necked Grebe   *Podiceps grisegena*

Source for one at Barn Elms in 1913 (Parr) could not be located. Possible confusion with one at Highgate Ponds in 1913 (*BLA*).

Black-necked Grebe   *Podiceps nigricollis*

A reference to the two or three pairs of Eared Grebes present for many seasons at Forked Pond in Newman (1849) were thought to refer to the Great Crested Grebe by Bucknill, whose view seems rather plausible.

Wilson's Petrel   *Oceanites oceanicus*

Stafford's collection included two said to have been killed after storms at 'Pease Marsh' (Peasmarsh), Godalming and two others killed nearby a few days later (*SALEC*). None are in the present Charterhouse Collection. Bucknill thought that the birds were correctly identified. It seems possible that Stafford was misled as regards their origin. The record was not accepted for the UK (*BB, 2:369-70*).

Night Heron   *Nycticorax nycticorax*

Aldridge (1885) gave a brief note of five flying over his Norwood garden on an evening in 1885. *Their legs seemed shorter, the wings smaller and the body thicker and the colour … was much darker* [than the Grey Heron]. He later heard of others being shot and thought that these were members of the same flock. Bucknill was uncertain about the record. At this distance in time, when another flock of five has yet to be seen in the county, prudence suggests that we should share the uncertainty. An adult at Richmond 23rd May 1980, accepted for Surrey and Greater London (*BB, 74:457*), proved on investigation to have been only on the north side of the Thames.

Purple Heron   *Ardea purpurea*

One shot in Middlesex, near London in 1722 (Harting, Glegg) was probably not in Spelthorne. One reported from Beddington Sewage Farm on 14th May 1989 (*Beddington Bird Report*) did not appear in the London or Surrey Bird Reports.

White Stork   *Ciconia ciconia*

One reported at Sheen on 17th June 2000 (*LBR*) was not included in the *SBR*.

Glossy Ibis   *Plegadis falcinellus*

Birds flying over Fairmile Common nine or ten years before 1847 were originally thought to be Curlews and later judged to be this species by their flight (Meyer and Morris in Bucknill). A preliminary report of a flock of 14 over Addlestone Moor (Addlestonemoor) on 25th May 2007 (*Birding World, 245:179*) had not been checked at the time of writing but may prove to be valid.

Honey Buzzard   *Pernis apivorus*

Box Hill, autumn of 1953 (no other details, *SBR* for 1954). Ashtead, 5th September 1954 (*SBR* 1954 and 1955). A buzzard probably of this species flew over Witley Common on 11th August 1979.

Black Kite   *Milvus migrans*

A record of one over Box Hill on 9th September 1977 was published in the Surrey Bird Report but not accepted by the British Birds Rarities Committee. The original papers have been reviewed.

Red Kite   *Milvus milvus*

One recorded over Haslemere on 20th February 1987 (*HSBBR*) was regarded as a probable by the Surrey Bird Club.

White-tailed Eagle   *Haliaeetus albicilla*

Bucknill mentions one shot near Farnham on an unknown date and reported to Stafford by a Mr Allden, of Ash. There is no definite evidence that this bird was in Surrey. Another Bucknill record, of one shot at Rapley Lake on 23rd December, 1887, was definitely in Berkshire if the site is correct. Bentham (1969) mentions a Rough-legged Buzzard shot in Titsey Wood in 1888 or 1889 and wrongly identified as a White-tailed Eagle.

Montagu's Harrier   *Circus pygargus*

One at Grayshott in July 1922 and a subsequent pair there may not have been in Surrey

Rough-legged Buzzard   *Buteo lagopus*

The source of Bentham's foregoing Titsey Wood record has not been located, either as a Rough-legged Buzzard or as a White-tailed Eagle. A possible Rough-legged Buzzard at Thursley Common on 3rd November 1974 (*SBR*) is listed without qualification in the *HSBBR*.

Osprey   *Pandion haliaetus*

One reported to a newspaper as fishing in Richmond Park on 5th January 1913 (Collenette, 1937) has not been taken up in *BLA*, Parr (1972) or Hudson (1973), presumably because of the secondhand nature of the report and the unusual date. No new information is available, but there have been other January records in Britain, before and since.

Red-footed Falcon   *Falco vespertinus*

One reported from Staines Reservoirs on 8th May 2001 (*LNHSB*) has not appeared in the *London Bird Report*.

Merlin   *Falco columbarius*

Inval, 27th December 1970; Seale, 7th February 1973 (in *HSBBR* but not accepted by the Surrey Bird Club).

Peregrine   *Falco peregrinus*

A report that a pair raised one young at the disused and gutted Battersea Power Station in 2000 (Hewlett) might not refer to Surrey since the actual nest site was not, on information available to the Surrey Bird Club, located.

Spotted Crake   *Porzana porzana*

One killed at Crondall in the winter of 1828/29 (Bucknill) would have been in Hampshire. Another shot on Headley Heath in 1884 (Bucknill) would appear to be the one mentioned by Shaw (1921) as being on the Headley Heath in Sussex, not the one near Leatherhead. Reports from Frimley Gravel Pits in 1972 and 1973 (*HSBBR*) were not included in the *SBR* or in Clark (1984).

Little Crake   *Porzana parva*

One in the collection of Mr Plasted of Chelsea had been shot on the banks of the Thames nearby in around 1812 (Montagu). It might, given Plasted's address, have been on the northern bank and hence not in the vice-county or Spelthorne.

Coot   *Fulica atra*

An albino at Chipstead Lake in 1986 (*LBR*) should presumably have been listed under Kent, not Surrey.

Black-winged Stilt   *Himantopus himantopus*

A letter from Frederick Holme to Edward Hearle Rodd stated that *An itinerant bird-stuffer named Burls … told me that in December 1832, he saw a specimen of the long-legged plover at Frensham Pond, but could not get at it; at the same time there were some specimens of the Egyptian spur-winged plover, one of which was shot (Zool., 1856:5041).* As Bucknill concluded, the second part of the text tends to throw doubt on the first, though the Spur-winged Plover *Vanellus spinosus* (if that is what was meant) has since occurred as an escape.

Little Ringed Plover *Charadrius dubius*

The first British breeding records were in 1938, when a pair bred at Tring and in 1944 when two pairs bred at Tring and one pair bred at Ashford in Middlesex (*BB, 38:102-11*). The *British Birds* account includes detailed notes by E. O. Höhn in which the site is given as *a group of three gravel pits in the Ashford district of Middlesex* on *a broad-based peninsular which projects into the waters of the pit*. The site is not further identified in *London Bird Reports* of the period, but there is a map of the Feltham area gravel pits in Keywood and Melluish (1952), from which it is clear that the only group of three pits which was even partly in Spelthorne lay to the east of the B3003 (Clockhouse Lane), on the northern outskirts of Ashford. Only the eastern pit then had a peninsular, and this pit is not within the current Spelthorne boundary. The total water area of these pits was then 30 acres, rather less than the half a square mile estimated for the largest pit in *British Birds*.

Kentish Plover *Charadrius alexandrinus*

A record of one at Ewhurst Green on 8th October 1960 (Recent Reports, *BB, 53:535*) appeared in the Surrey Bird Report and in Parr but was not accepted by the British Birds Rarities Committee (*BB, 54:200*). The original papers have been reviewed by the SBC.

Dotterel *Charadrius morinellus*

One reported by P. G. Davis from Frensham Common on 2nd May 1973 (Kirkpatrick and Davis, 1980; Clark, 1984) was seen very briefly when flushed by two dogs and the documentation was not considered fully acceptable by the Surrey Bird Club. Given the date and the note in Clark (1993) that 58 of 64 birds recorded in spring from Hampshire in the years 1934-91 occurred between 3rd and 6th May (though none as early as the 2nd), the circumstantial evidence looks rather strong. On the other hand, it would be the only record for Surrey since the 1850s apart from two at Staines, and the only one in spring.

Temminck's Stint *Calidris temminckii*

One at Epsom Sewage Farm in 1954 (*SBR* for 1954 and 1955).

Sharp-tailed Sandpiper *Calidris acuminata*

A report of one at Staines Reservoirs on 8th September 1966 (*BB, 60:319*) was withdrawn in a later review (*BB, 73:334*).

Snipe *Gallinago gallinago*

Beddington Sewage Farm: 600 on 1st April 1983 (*SBR*) should be 60 as in the *LBR*.

Great Snipe *Gallinago media*

The report of one killed at Lingfield in late June, 1861 (*The Field* 12th July 1861:17 *per* Birdguide), seemed suspect to Bucknill in view of the date. Two shooters were said to have flushed one at Mitcham a few years before 1900. They shot at it but missed (Bucknill). Stafford had a specimen that had been shot between Guildford and Godalming in 1850 (*SALEC*). Bucknill doubted the identifications of the specimens held by Charterhouse in his day. There were none in the Charterhouse Collection in 2001. Reports from Beddington and Perry Oaks sewage farms in 1965 were not acceptable (*BB, 59:302*).

Bar-tailed Godwit *Limosa lapponica*

One seen in the Charterhouse Collection by Bucknill had been obtained from 'the Cranleigh carrier, a man named Elliott' in the early spring of 1840, but it is not clear that the bird itself was found in Surrey. It is no longer at Charterhouse.

Whimbrel *Numenius phaeopus*

Five at Epsom Sewage Farm in November 1954 (*SBR* for 1953 and 1955).

Curlew *Numenius arquata*

One at Sickle Mill, Haslemere in 1880 (Bucknill, 1902), presumed to be in Sickle Mill Road, would be just outside the county border.

Common Sandpiper *Actitis hypoleucos*

One at Sickle mill pond, Haslemere (Bucknill, 1902), presumed to be in Sickle Mill Road, would be just outside the county border.

Phalarope species   *Phalaropus species*

One in west Surrey on 25th September 1940 (*SEBR*) was not specifically identified.

Red-necked Phalarope   *Phalaropus lobatus*

Glegg put one of his own records, a bird at Staines Reservoirs on 28th September 1930, in doubt because of doubts expressed by other observers.

Grey Phalarope   *Phalaropus fulicarius*

Epsom Sewage Farm 20th-25th October 1955 (*LBR*, secondhand report, observer not known).

Arctic Skua   *Stercorarius parasiticus*

One found exhausted on Headley Heath in October 1891 (Bucknill) is listed for the Haslemere district by Shaw, so was presumably from the Headley Heath outside Surrey, not the one near Leatherhead.

Ring-billed Gull   *Larus delawarensis*

Wrecclesham Floods, 1st December 1987 (*HSBBR*). No details. Not sent to the British Birds Rarities Committee?

Siberian (Heuglin's) Gull   *Larus fuscus heuglini*

Not yet on the British List. A gull possibly of this form was reported from Seale/Tongham in 1995 (*HSBBR*).

Glaucous-winged Gull   *Larus glaucesens*

Not on the British list at the time of writing, but a bird described from Beddington Sewage Farm on 18th April 2007 (Allan, 2007) would be a worthy addition for Surrey.

Great Black-backed Gull   *Larus marinus*

An immature bird at Frensham on 2nd June 1906 (Mouritz) was on an unusual date for a bird that was far from common in Surrey at the time.

Kittiwake   *Rissa tridactyla*

When gulls first began to appear on the Thames the identifications were sometimes confused. Glegg considered that records of many Kittiwakes on the Thames in January and February 1895 might have been examples. The same might go for some other records of the period.

Caspian Tern   *Hydroprogne caspia*

One reported from Frimley Gravel Pits in 1987 (*HSBBR*) was put to the British Birds Rarities Committee but not accepted (*BB, 81:595*).

Whiskered Tern   *Chlidonias hybrida*

Two identified as Whiskered Terns in the Stafford Collection (*SALEC*) were actually Black Terns (Bucknill).

Roseate Tern   *Sterna dougallii*

A tern at Barn Elms Reservoir on April 28th, 1921 (Countryside, June 1921) had a rich pink colour on its breast but not enough other details were available to confirm it (Parr, *BLA*).

Guillemot   *Uria aalge*

One at Sickle Mill Pond, Haslemere, presumed to be in Sickle Mill Road, after a severe storm in 1869 (Bucknill, 1902), would be just outside the county border.

Razorbill   *Alca torda*

A Guillemot on 8th October 1955 was wrongly duplicated among the Razorbill records in Wheatley (1986).

Feral Rock Dove   *Columba livia*

Some 4,000 flying west at Holmethorpe Sand Pits in 1999 were owned by pigeon-fanciers (*BHSP*).

Woodpigeon   *Columba palumbus*

Thorpe, 14th October 1967, 7000-8,000 (*SBR*) is a misprint. The number was 700-800.

Hawk Owl   *Surnia ulula*

An owl seen in a tree at Walton Reservoirs on 27th December 1926 was considered a probable Hawk Owl (*BB, 20:226*).

Bee-eater *Merops apiaster*

One heard over Littleworth Cross on 30th May 1997 was mentioned in the *HSBBR* and the *SBC Newsletter*.

Hoopoe *Upupa epops*

A Hoopoe shot at Norwood (Edwards, 1743-51) might have been at the Norwood in Middlesex.

Black Woodpecker *Dryocopus martius*

A bird that breeds across Europe and east to China, with no accepted British records. Two Surrey claims are discussed in Bucknill and four in *Birds, Discovery and Conservation (Snow, 1992)* p.138 *et seq.* Full details in R. S. R. Fitter, *Bull. BOC* 1959. Details are pieced together below.

1. George Montagu wrote that *we have heard that another was shot in the winter of 1805, on the trunk of an old willow tree in Battersea Fields.* This has been mentioned by many later authors. With such limited information, the report is unsatisfactory. The specimen, if there was one, seems to have been lost.

2. A Mr. McIntosh wrote of the supposed nesting of the species at Claremont, the communication being published in *The Naturalist*, vol. i., 1850, pp.20-21 (Bucknill). The same pair was said to have bred in the same spot, a hole in a wall for three successive years. This or another specimen was said to have been preserved in an inn at Esher (*q. v.* vol. vii, p. 91). The record, though frequently quoted since that date, has always been regarded as a mistake (Bucknill).

3. A sight record, description unsatisfactory only in a minor detail, which might well have been due to observational error (red on the head not seen). In *BOC Bulletin* for 1959 and Snow (1992).

4. A melanistic Green Woodpecker suspect, Frensham 1982, not accepted by British Birds Rarities Committee.

Shore Lark *Eremophila alpestris*

There is no available supporting information about six on Wimbledon Common on 4th April 1911 and two on the 26th and 30th (*Countryside* 1911, p.236).

Crag Martin (Eurasion Crag Martin) *Ptyonopnigne rupestris*

The BBRC is considering a report of one at Tice's meadow on 22nd October 2006 at the time of writing.

Richard's Pipit *Anthus richardii*

One at Staines Reservoirs on 12th April 1958 (*BB, 51:207*) no longer accepted (*BB, 53:430*).

Olive-backed Pipit *Anthus hodgsoni*

One reported at Thursley on 25th October 1978 was published with the caveat that it had not yet been accepted by the British Birds Rarities Committee (HNHS 1980) and was apparently not sent to them (BBRC pers. comm.).

Tree Pipit *Anthus trivialis*

A record of Tree Pipits at Mitcham Common on 19th March 1933 (*BB, 26:364*) was later withdrawn by the observer.

Rock/Water Pipit *Anthus petrosus/spinoletta*

The Rock and Water Pipits had not been split in Bucknill's time and the few records that he and others before him gave are not, as he himself admitted, fully persuasive. Blyth (1836) did not give a definite Surrey record and might have meant Meadow Pipits. One was shot at Tilford (James Lewcock in Newman, 1849). One which was in the Charterhouse Collection in Bucknill's time was shot by William Stafford at Eashing on an unknown date and is not in the collection now.

Yellow Wagtail *Motacilla flava*

A male watched a few feet outside a window 'near Haslemere' on 15th December 1953 might not have been in Surrey. No other details are available.

Blue-headed Wagtail *Motacilla flava flava*

Several by the River Wey near Guildford in May and June 1874 (*Zool., 1874:4118*) were called Yellow Wagtails M. *flava*, an ambiguity which might have indicated either race with the nomenclature of the time (Bucknill).

White Wagtail   *Motacilla alba alba*

One in Richmond Park on 17th April 1905 (Mouritz, 1905) was not seen by Mouritz himself and was omitted by Collenette.

Bluethroat   *Luscinia svecica*

A report of one on 17th June 1904 (*Zool.* 104, p.263, *BB, 1:55*) was probably an error (*BLA*).

Redwing   *Turdus iliacus*

Edward Blyth wrote of a nest with three eggs found in a gooseberry bush near Godalming in the early 1830s. For various reasons discussed by Bucknill, the record is not acceptable. Bucknill also dismissed a report of nesting in Croydon.

Marsh Warbler   *Acrocephalus palustris*

Richmond Park, 24th April to 8th May 1906 (*BB, 1:84 in square brackets indicating doubt*, Mouritz 1907, Parr 1972). Early arrival date, no song or calls heard. Shaw (1921) gives undated records of a nest that he himself found, and a bird that he saw on passage. Even if acceptable, neither was specifically in the Surrey part of the Haslemere district. A nest with four eggs was found near Bookham in the lower part of a bramble bush surrounded by rushes and coarse grass (*SEBR* 1934). Parr was not clear if the record had been fully authenticated.

Great Reed Warbler   *Acrocephalus arundinaceus*

An account of a nest supposed to have been found at Dorking some time before 1867 was published in several places but subsequently discredited. Bucknill gives details.

Greenish Warbler   *Phylloscopus trochiloides*

A bird reported at Perry Oaks Sewage Farm from at least 1st January to 26th February 1961(*BB, 55:579*, *LBR* for 1985) might have been in the Spelthorne part of the area at some time. Acceptance was later withdrawn by the British Birds Rarities Committee (*BB, 78:437-51*).

Willow Warbler   *Phylloscopus trochilus*

One reported from Wisley on 26th February 1985 was later thought not to have been fully identified (*SBR* for 1985, 1986).

Red-breasted Flycatcher   *Ficedula parva*

One at Elstead Common on 7th October 1972 (HNHS, 1980; Clark, 1984) was later withdrawn by the observer.

Crested Tit   *Lophophanes cristatus*

Bucknill mentions a pair in the Charthouse Collection, one of which may have been shot at Hampton Lodge, Puttenham, by H. L. Long. Neither Long nor Stafford was thought to have mentioned the bird in their notes and the specimen is no longer in the Charterhouse Collection. One at Croydon on 24th April 1904 was only rated as a probable (*BB, 16:161*).

Golden Oriole   *Oriolus oriolus*

One shot at Aldershot in April 1824 was said to be in Hampshire by Yarrell (1845), although Bucknill included it. Bucknill also mentioned a young male in Richmond Park on 25th April 1892. Collenette followed this up for his study of Richmond Park, published in 1937, and found that the observer, who saw the bird at the age of 12, was on reflection inclined to think it had been a Green Woodpecker. Insufficient details are available about Golden Orioles said to have been heard at Hindhead and Thursley (*HSBBR* 1971 and HNHS 1980) but not included in Clark (1984).

The Surrey Bird Report for 1954 says that the Golden Oriole 'has occurred in winter' without giving examples. No winter records have been traced.

Great Grey Shrike   *Lanius excubitor*

One at Headley Heath on 8th and 15th July 1956 (*Surrey Bird Report* for 1956) is probably satisfactory but no details have been located and it is not in the *London Bird Report*. Ockham Common 27th March 1962 (*SBR*) should have read Ockley Common, an archival correction by D. Parr.

Nutcracker *Nucifraga caryocatactes*

One at Kew Green on 6th July 1936 was thought to be an escape in view of the date (*BB, 30:93*). Records from Dulwich on 14th April 1905, Frensham Vale in June 1948 and Banstead on 16th December 1968 were regarded by Parr as being unsubstantiated.

Russian Jackdaw *Corvus monedula soemmerringii*

Not yet on the British list but it has occurred in France. The BOU is waiting for British ringing evidence of origin supported by correct plumage. A bird with a very pale nape similar to that of the race was reported from Beddington Sewage Farm in 2000 (*LBR*).

Rose-coloured Starling *Sturnus roseus*

The first bird of this species to be found in the British Isles is described and illustrated by Edwards (1743-51). The bird was shot at Norwood, near London, in 1742. Unfortunately there are two Norwoods in the London area, one in south London and the other in Middlesex (not in Spelthorne though) and we do not know which one was meant. The record has been included by authors from both counties. One later writer was confident that this was a Surrey bird but gave no evidence to support the claim. No one else has been able to solve the riddle, so we have to include it here as a good bird of uncertain provenance.

Brambling *Fringilla montifringilla*

An account in Meyer of a pair breeding in a Surrey garden in May 1843, after a large influx, was not regarded as wholly satisfactory by Bucknill and is not included in *The Handbook* or in *BWP*, where the date of the first breeding record is given as 1920, in northern Scotland.

Twite *Carduelis flavirostris*

Eggs shown to Bucknill were said to have been taken from Weybridge on 24th June 1894. The claim does not seem to have been accepted, *e.g.* Surrey is not listed as a breeding county in BOU (1915).

Lapland Bunting *Calcarius lapponicus*

A male captured just on the Surrey border at Lewisham in 1867 (Bucknill) was quite clearly in Kent from the location given in *The Zoologist* for 1867, p.705. One at 'Poyle, near Staines' on 8th-14th April 1978 (*BB, 72:543*) was presumably not in Spelthorne, although shown under Surrey.

Black-headed Bunting *Emberiza melanocephala*

One at Guildford on 18th and 28th April 1960 (Recent Reports in *BB, 53:456*, not accepted *BB, 54:200*). An escape reported in the *SBR* for 1978 proved to be some type of Masked Weaver (*SBR* for 1979).

Abbreviations, Definitions and Additional Notes on Boundaries

Abbreviations

Books	Reference (see References and Bibliography)
1968-72 BTO Atlas	Sharrock (1976)
1968-72 LNHS Atlas	Montier (1977)
1988-91 BTO Atlas/New Atlas	Gibbons et al. (1993)
1988-94 London Atlas	Hewlett et al. (2002)
1988-97 SBC Atlas	Data published for the first time in this volume
BBWC	Breeding Birds of the Wider Countryside, BTO, JNCC 2000-2003
BLA	Birds of the London Area (London Natural History Society, 1964)
BRP	Birds of the Royal Parks (HMSO)
BWP	Birds of the Western Palearctic (Cramp. 1994)
EBCC atlas	Hagemeijer and Blair, 1997
Historical Atlas	Holloway, Simon (1996)
Migration Atlas (MA)	Wernham et al. (2002)
SALEC	Surrey Art Loan Exhibition Catalogue (1884)
Shaw	Shaw (1921)
The Handbook	Witherby et al. (1941)
Winter Atlas	Lack (1986)

Other Abbreviations

Abbreviations	Note
AR	from unpublished material in the Surrey Bird Club Archive
BB	British Birds.
BB, x:y	British Birds volume x page y
BBC	British Broadcasting Corporation
BBR	Beddington Bird Report, Beddington (Farm[lands]) Bird Report
BBS	Breeding Birds Survey
BHSP	The Birds of Holmethorpe Sand Pits (Gale)
BBRC	British Birds Rarities Committee (The national committee that adjudicates on rare bird records)
BTO	British Trust for Ornithology
BOC	British Ornithologists' Club
BOU	British Ornithologists' Union
CNHS	Charterhouse Natural History Society
CNHSS	Croydon Natural History and Scientific Society
ha	hectare(s)
HNHS	Haslemere Natural History Society
HSBBR	Hants/Surrey Border Bird Report
km	kilometre(s)
LBR	London Bird Report
LN	The London Naturalist

LNHS	London Natural History Society
LNHSB	London Natural History Society Ornithological Bulletin
Pers. comm.	Personal communication
Pullus	Nestling or chick not yet flying
RHS	Royal Horticultural Society
RRG	Runnymede Ringing Group
RSPB	Royal Society for the Protection of Birds
RSPCA	Royal Society for the Prevention of Cruelty to Animals
SBC	Surrey Bird Club
SBR	Surrey Bird Report
SCCMS	Stafford Collection Catalogue manuscript (in Charterhouse library).
SDBWS	Surbiton and District Bird Watching Society
SEBR	South-Eastern Bird Report
Shepp. BR	Shepperton Bird Report
SPN	Stafford's Private Notebook
SWT	Surrey Wildlife Trust
WeBS	Wetlands Bird Survey, organised by the Wildfowl and Wetlands Trust
Zool.	The Zoologist

Definitions

Australasia:	Australia, New Zealand and associated islands
10 km square	10 km x 10 km National Grid square
Sahel	A semi-arid region in West Africa on the southern edge of the Sahara Desert, which is a wintering area for many British summer visitors, such as Whitethroats.
Tetrad	2 km x 2 km National Grid square

Status

For rare birds, the number of records is given. For others, status notes given for each species are based on the following broad measures:

Migrants

Scarce: Normally fewer than five records in a year

Breeding birds

Uncommon: Occurs each year in small numbers

Locally common: Common in a specialised habitat, rare elsewhere

Common: Found in at least moderate numbers in most parts of the county

Numbers

1956/57	is used for winters. In the context of wildfowl counts it means the count year April 1956 to March 1957.
1956-57	means 1956 and 1957.
In tables	0 means visit made but no birds seen, n/a or a blank cell means no figure is available, n/c means no count made.
c.	*circa*, about. Large numbers are generally as reported by observers. Some put *c.*, others do not.
+	at least, *e.g.* 100+ means at least 100.

Some lists of places have bracketed numbers after place names, *e.g.* France (eight). These indicate the number at the place in the list. The absence of a bracketed number in such a list means that there was only one bird or record for the place.

Times, Weights and Measures

These have generally been put in as reported by observers, to avoid possible errors and anachronisms. Older terms in the text include old penny, (240 to the Pound) and ounce. A conversion to hectares or to square kilometres (100 hectares) is added for acreages.

Additional notes on boundaries

The boundary between the vice-counties of Surrey and Kent differs somewhat from the borough boundaries shown on current maps and is difficult to trace even with a street atlas. The most critical part to track is the section from the Surrey Docks through South London to South Norwood. A paper by Burton (1994) describes this section, with street maps. The boundary starts at the southern edge of South Dock TQ368790 to South Bermondsey Station, where it turns south to Goldsmith's Hal1 TQ355769, leaving Fordham Park in Kent. From there it zigzags southeast to TQ354740 on a line which puts Nunhead Cemetery and One Tree Hill (except for the southeast edge) in Surrey, but Brockley Station, Camberwell New Cemetery and Honor Oak Park in Kent. From here it continues southwest to the Sydenham Hill/Rock Hill road junction, putting the Horniman gardens in Surrey and leaving Sydenham Wells Park in Kent. The boundary then turns southwest across Crystal Palace Park from the end of Sydenham Hill to Penge West station, continuing on to a point just west of Kent House Station, where it then turns southwest to the Bromley/Croydon boundary in Marlow road at TQ348687, leaving Penge and at least part of Anerley in Surrey. At this point it turns southeast, to follow the pre-1994 Bromley/Croydon boundary across South Norwood Country Park, leaving the northwest portion of the park, including all the wetland, in Kent. On leaving the park at TQ356680, the boundary continues southwest to run across the Bethlem Royal Hospital site from TQ366674 to TQ373665, from where it continues south down the Bromley/Croydon boundary. Boundary changes made on 1st April 1994 put the whole of South Norwood Country Park into Croydon and the whole of the Bethlem Hospital into Bromley.

The district of Spelthorne, which includes Staines, King George VI and Wraysbury Reservoirs, lies north of the Thames and was not part of the Administrative county of Surrey until 1965. Administrative county boundaries

Field boundaries in east Surrey   *Photo D. J. Brassington*

are subject to frequent change and the Spelthorne boundary has itself been changed several times since 1965. The western third of Wraysbury Reservoir, which was in Berkshire, was transferred to Surrey in 1991. The reservoir is now wholly in Surrey (Statutory Instrument (1990) 264). Approximately a third of Heathrow Airport, including half of Perry Oaks Sewage Farm and half of Terminal 4, were transferred from Surrey to Hillingdon in 1994 and the airport is now wholly outside Surrey (Statutory Instrument (1993) 1342). Colne and Poyle were transferred from Surrey to Berkshire and Slough on 1st April 1995 (Statutory Instrument (1994) 330). Spelthorne is covered in this book so these changes are not completely without consequences. A 1977 Perry Oaks Sewage Farm Solitary Sandpiper record is the only one for any definition of Surrey. Records for Poyle Gravel Pits, the most significant of which is probably a Slavonian Grebe breeding attempt in 1948, are assumed to relate to the pits about a mile north of Poyle and outside any Spelthorne boundary.

References and Bibliography

BB = British Birds   LN = LN   LBR = London Bird Report   SBR = Surrey Bird Report   Zool. = The Zoologist

ADAMS, L. E. G. 1953a: Daily Mid-winter Movements of Black-headed Gulls at Guildford Sewage Farm. *SBR* for 1953:13.

ADAMS, L. E. G. 1953b: Daily Winter Movements of Starlings, Rooks and Jackdaws. *SBR* for 1953:13.

ALBIN, E. 1731: A Natural History of Birds. London. In Glegg (1935).

ALDERTON, R. E. 1977: Birds at the Surrey Commercial Docks, January 1973 to December 1975. *LBR* for 1975: 85-90.

ALDRIDGE, W. 1885: A Gossip on the Wild Birds of Norwood and Crystal Palace District. Burdett, Upper Norwood.

ALEXANDER, C. J. 1910: The Notes of the British Willow Tit. *BB*, 4:146-47.

ALEXANDER, H. G. 1914: A Report on the Land-rail Inquiry. *BB*, 8: 83-92.

ALLAN, J. 2007: The Glaucous-winged Gull in Surrey. Birding World 20 (4):151-151.

ANDREW, D. G., J. A. Nelder & Mary Hawkes: Siberian Thrush on the Isle of May: a new British Bird. *BB*, 48:21-25.

APLIN, O. V. 1892: The Status of the Woodchat, *Lanius rufus* in Great Britain. *Zool.*, 1892:849.

ARCHER, John, Bob Britton, Robert Burley, Tony Hare & Ian Yarham 1989: Nature Conservation in Southwark, Ecology Handbook 12. London Ecology Unit, London.

ARCHER, John & David Curson 1993: Nature Conservation in Richmond upon Thames, Ecology Handbook 21. London Ecology Unit, London.

ARIS, Ben P. 1991: Desert Wheatear at Barn Elms Reservoir – new to the London Area. *LBR* for 1989:136-137.

ARIS, Ernest 1925: In Retrospect. *LN* for 1924.

ASH, J. S., M. W. Ridley & N. Ridley 1956: On the Movements and Survival of Woopigeons and Stock Doves. *BB*, 49:298-305.

ASHBY C. B. 1948: The Effects of the Cold Spell of Early 1947 on Birds in the London Area. *LBR* for 1947:39-44.

ASHBY, C. B., Richard S. R. Fitter & E. R. Parrinder 1947: The Rookeries of the London Area. *LBR* for 1946:31-32.

ASPINALL, Simon, Mike Netherwood & Mick Cook 1991: The Tree Sparrow Nest-box Project at Beddington Sewage Farm 1992. *SBR* for 1991:76-78.

BAKER, Harry J. & H. C. Minchin 1938: Frensham Then and Now. Langham, Farnham. Revised and enlarged edition 1948.

BAKER, Helen 1985: The Status of the Canada Goose in the London Area. *LBR* for 1984: 111-136.

BAKER, Helen & Derek Coleman 2000: Status of the Canada Goose, the Greylag Goose and other naturalised geese in Greater London, 2000. *LBR* for 2000.

BAKER, Leslie 1972: Mortality among Wildfowl at Kew. *LBR* for 1971:84-85.

BARBER, Bruno (forthcoming): The Rose and the Globe: Playhouses of London.

BARLOW, I. Helen, Phyllis M. Bond, Peter G. Davis & Margaret M. Hutchinson 1968: A Review of the Birds of the Haslemere District. Haslemere Natural History Society, Haslemere.

BEADELL, Arthur 1932: Nature Notes of Warlingham and Chelsham. The Croydon Advertiser Ltd, Croydon.

BEAMES, Ian 1988: The BP Guide to Exploring Britain's Wildlife, David & Charles, Newton Abbott.

BECHER, H. 1905: Puffin on the Thames. *The Field*, vol. 106:607 in Glegg (1935).

BELSEY, Derek 1997: Seeing is Believing, Belsey, Shepperton

BELSEY, Derek (undated): More Seeing is Believing, Belsey, Shepperton.

BELSEY, Derek 2002: Birds Around Surrey, Belsey, Shepperton.

BELSEY, Derek 2006: Photographic Bird Memories, Belsey, Shepperton.

BENSON, Rev. Henry 1888: *Zool.*, 1888:309-310 in Bucknill.

BENTHAM, C. Howard & L. B. Mouritz 1908: The Breeding of the Hen Harrier and Hobby in Surrey in 1907. *BB*, 1:237-38.

BENTHAM, Howard 1954: Changes in the Status of some Surrey Birds. *SBR* for 1954:2-4.

BENTHAM, Howard 1959: Autumn Movements of Chiffchaffs and Willow Warblers. *SBR* for 1957:24-26.

BENTHAM, Howard 1961: Some Autumn Passage Movements on Epsom Downs. *SBR* for 1959:26-27.

BENTHAM, Howard 1967: A Bird-Watcher's Memories of Long Ago. *SBR* for 1965:36-38.

BENTHAM, Howard 1969: A Bird Watcher's Recollections of the Early Years of the Century – Part 1. *SBR* for 1967:44-47.

BENTHAM, Howard 1970: A Bird-Watcher's Recollections – Parts 2 & 3. *SBR* for 1968:49-52.

BESANT, Walter 1912: South London. Chatto & Windus, London.

BEVEN, Geoffrey 1947: Display of House Sparrow. *BB*, 40:308-310.

BEVEN, Geoffrey 1963: Nest of Willow Tit on Bookham Common. *LBR* for 1961:113.

BEVEN, Geoffrey 1965: The Food of Tawny Owls in London. *LBR* for 1964:56-72.

BEVEN, Geoffrey 1967: The Food of Tawny Owls in Surrey. *SBR* for 1966:32-38.

BEVEN, Geoffrey 1971: Variations of Bird Populations in Scrubland on Bookham Commons, in Relation to Habitat Changes, with Special Reference to Conservation Management. *SBR* for 1970:17-20.

BEVEN, Geoffrey 1980: Survey of Bookham Common: 38th Year. *LN* for 1979:60-65.

BIRDGUIDES 2001: The CD-ROM Guide to Rarer British Birds. Birdguides, Sheffield.

BIRKETT, John 1992: Birds of South Norwood Country Park. *LBR* for 1991:136-149.

BLAKER, George 1934: The Barn Owl in England and Wales. Royal Society for the Protection of Birds, London.

BLATHERWICK, Simon & Richard Bluer (forthcoming): The Medieval Great Houses of Southwark: The Rosary, Fastolf Place and Edward III's Residence at Rotherhithe.

BLOCKEY, Robert C. 1936: The Stork Experiment of 1936. *South-Eastern Bird Report* for 1936.

BLYTH, E. 1833: *Field Naturalist*, 1:309 in Bucknill.

BLYTH, E. 1836: On the species of birds observed during the last four years at Tooting, Surrey. Loudon's *Magazine of Natural History* pp.622-38 in Bucknill.

BOND, Phyllis M. 1937: Watching Wild Life. Longmans, Green & Co., London.

BOND, Phyllis 1955: A Revised List of the Birds of the Haslemere District. Haslemere Natural History Society, Haslemere.

BOOTH, Edward. Thomas & A. F. Griffith 1927: Catalogue of Cases of Birds in the Dyke Road Museum, Brighton, 5th Edition. Brighton Library, Brighton.

BORRER, William 1891: The Birds of Sussex. London. In Bucknill.

BOSWALL, Jeffery 1964: A Discography of Palearctic Sound Recordings. Supplement to *BB*, 57.

BOURNE, W. R. P. 1971: Visible and Radar Observations of Gulls in the Staines area; a correction. *LBR* for 1970, p.56.

BOURNE, W. R. P. 2003a: Fred Stubbs, Egrets, Brewes and Climatic Change. *BB*, 96:332-339.

BOURNE, W. R. P. 2003b: Birds and past Agriculture. *BB*, 96:462.

BOWLEY, Jonathan J. 1976: Spotted Crake. *SBR* for 1975:86.

BOYD, A. W. 1946: The Country Diary of a Cheshire Man. London. In John & Roskell.

BRAMWELL, D. 1976: Bird Remains from Medieval London. *LN* for 1975:15-20.

BRANDON, Peter 1998: A History of Surrey. Philimore, Chichester.

BRASSINGTON, David 2003: Site List for the Birds of Thursley Common. Published by the author.

BRAZELL, J. H. 1968: London Weather. HMSO, London.

BREWER, James Alexander 1856: A New Flora of the Neighbourhood of Reigate. In Bucknill, 1901. There is a list of 115 local birds, including Kite and Raven in an Appendix but without dates.

BRITISH BROADCASTING CORPORATION 2001: Website http://www.bbc.co.uk/beasts, November 30th, 2001.

BRITISH ORNITHOLOGISTS' CLUB 1913: The Nutcracker Nucifraga caryocatactes. *British Ornithologists' Club Bulletin*, 32:251.

BRITISH ORNITHOLOGISTS' UNION 1883: A List of British Birds. BOU, London.

BRITISH ORNITHOLOGISTS' UNION 1915: A List of British Birds. BOU, London.

BRITISH ORNITHOLOGISTS' UNION 1952: Check-List of the Birds of Britain and Ireland. Witherby, London.

BRITISH ORNITHOLOGISTS' UNION 1971: The Status of Birds in Britain and Ireland. Blackwell, London.

BRITISH TRUST FOR ORNITHOLOGY 1998: Nightingales: A celebration, CD and leaflet ISBN 0 903793 91 1. Thetford.

BRITISH TRUST FOR ORNITHOLOGY & Joint Nature Conservation Committee 2001-2003: Breeding Birds in the Wider Countryside.

BROWN, John W. 1996: Haslemere in 1839, compiled from Pigot's 1839 Directory of Surrey. Local History Reprints, Streatham.

BROWN, R. S. 1963: Carrion Crows attacking Starlings. *LBR* for 1961:112.

BROWNE, Stephen & Nicholas Aebischer 2003: Turtle Dove Declines. BTO News 245:8-9.

BUCKNILL, John A. 1900: The Birds of Surrey. R. H. Porter, London.

BUCKNILL, John A. 1901: Ornithological Notes from Surrey. *Zool.*,1901:247-254.

BUCKNILL, John A. 1902: Ornithological Notes from Surrey. *Zool.*,1902:223-231, 305-312.

BULLOCK, D. A. 1967: Siskin Weights. *SBR* for 1965:33-35.

BULLOCK, Richard 2002:Reservoir to Reserve – an historical perspective. *London Wetland Centre Bird and Natural History Report* for 2000:4-15.

BUNYARD, Percy F. 1924: Surrey Field Notes. *BB*, 17:198-205.

BURKHILL, H. J. 1928: Cuckoo taking Eggs. *LN* for 1927:20-21.

BURKHILL, H. J. 1931: Notes on the Coots of Fetcham Mill Pond. *LN* for 1931:61-62.

BURKHILL, Harold J. 1933: Notes on Coots. *BB*, 26:342-347.

BURKHILL, H. J. 1942: A Bigamous Mute Swan. *LBR* for 1942: 21.

BURTON, John F. 1995: Birds and Climate Change, Christopher Helm, London.

BURTON, Niall H. K., Andy J. Musgrove, Mark M. Rehfisch, Anna Sutcliffe & Ray Waters 2003: Numbers of Wintering Gulls in the United Kingdom, Channel Islands and Isle of Man: a review of the 1993 and previous Winter Gull Surveys. *BB*, 96:376-401.

BURTON, Rodney M. 1994: Watsonian vice-county boundaries in the London area. *LN* No. 73 for 1993.

BUTLER, A. G. See TEGETMEIER.

BUTLER, Chris 2002: Breeding parrots in Britain. *BB*, 95:345-348.

BUTLER, R. E. 1970: Looking into the Past. *LN* for 1970:7-13.

CAREW HOUSEHOLD BOOK. *Surrey Archaeological Collections* 31:7, 1918.

CARRINGTON, L. T., C. P. Castell & A. R. Wilton 1944: Some preliminary Notes on the Birds of Bookham Common. *LN* for 1943:23-29.

CARTER, Ian & Phil Grice, 2000: Studies of Re-established Red Kites in England. *BB*, 93:304-322.

CARTER, M. J. 1963: Additional Comments on Peakall (1962). *SBR* for 1961:27.

CHAMBERLAIN, D. E & H. Q. P. Crick, 1999: Population declines and reproductive performance of Skylarks *Alauda arvensis* in different regions and habitats of the United Kingdom. *Ibis (1999) 141*, 38-51.

CHANCE, Edgar. P. 1939: Buzzards in Surrey. South-Eastern Bird Report for 1939: 4-5.

CHANDLER, Richard 2003: Rose-ringed Parakeets – how long have they been around? *BB*, 96:407-408.

CHANNER, Alan G. 1971: Greenfinch Movements, *Hersham Ringing Group Report* No. 2 1969-1971:24-25.

CHAPPELL, John A. & Thelma M. 1988: The Heronries of Surrey, an historical review. *SBR* for 1988:48-68.

CHARTERHOUSE NATURAL HISTORY SOCIETY 1959: Birds, Butterflies and Moths of the Godalming District.

CHATFIELD, June 1987: F. W. Frohawk, his life and work. The Crowood Press, Ramsbury, Wiltshire.

CHATFIELD, June E. 1992: Gilbert White and his London Connections. *LN* for 1991.

CLARK, John M. 1984: Birds of the Hants/Surrey Border. Hobby Books, Aldershot.

CLARK, J. M. & Eyre J. A. (Ed.) 1993: Birds Of Hampshire. Hampshire Ornithological Society.

CLEMENTS, James F. 2000: Birds of the World: A Checklist, 5th Edition. Ibis Publishing Company, Vista.

CLEMENTS, Rob 2002: The Common Buzzard in Britain: a new population estimate. *BB*. 95:377-383.

CLENET, Dierdre, Bob Britton & Meg Game 1988: Nature Conservation in Croydon, Ecology Handbook 9. London Ecology Unit, London.

COBBETT, William 1830: Rural Rides. Penguin Classics Edition (1985).

COCKSEDGE, W. C. 1935: The Hundred of Brixton. *LN* for 1934:53-58.

COHEN, A. (undated): Report on the Bird Bones from Oatlands Palace. Typescript in Elmbridge Museum.

COLE, Andrew C. & William P. Trobe 2000: The Egg Collectors of Great Britain and Ireland. Peregrine Books, Otley.

COLEMAN, Derek A. 1985: The Coot Population at Waddon Ponds, 1980-1986. *SBR* for 1985:53-59.

COLEMAN, Derek A. 1991: The Water Birds of Gatton Park. *SBR* for 1991:63-75

COLEMAN, Derek A. 1995: Waterways Bird Survey of the River Wandle between 1983 and 1994. *LBR* for 1994:184-195.

COLEMAN, Derek & Brian Milne 1996: The History of the Green Sandpiper at Beddington. *Beddington Farm Bird Report* for 1996.

COLLENETTE, Cyril Leslie. 1937: A History of Richmond Park. Sidgwick & Jackson, republished by S. R. Publishers in 1971 with a new introduction by G. Turner.

COLLINS' ILLUSTRATED ATLAS OF LONDON (1854): See DYOS.

COLLYER, W. L. 1937: Pied Wagtail Roost in Richmond Park. *LBR* for 1937:28-29.

COOK, R. T. 1894: Razorbills at Rotherhithe, *The Naturalists Journal* 2:135 in Glegg (1935).

COPELAND, Peter, Boswall, Jeffery & Petts, Leonard 1988: Birdsongs on Old Records, a coarsegroove discography of Palearctic bird sound 1910-1958. British Library National Sound Archive Wildlife Section, London.

CORNELIUS, L. W. 1971: Yellow Wagtails Breeding in Inner London. *LBR* for 1970:92.

CORNELIUS, L. W. 1973: Salmonellosis in Surrey. *SBR* for 1972:76-78.

COWAN, Carrie 1992: A possible Mansion in Roman Southwark: Excavations at 15-23 Southwark Street, 1980-86. LAMAS Transaction 1992, Vol. 43.

COWAN, Carrie 2003: Urban development in northwest Roman Southwark: excavations 1974-90. MoLAS, London.

COWARD, T. A. 1914: Slender-billed Nutcracker in Surrey. *BB*, 7:301.

COX, J. B. 1964: Manx Sheawater at Staines. *LBR* for 1963:81.

CRAMP, Stanley 1960: The Irruption of Tits and other Species in the London Area, 1957-58. *LBR* for 1950:62-69.

CRAMP, Stanley (Chief Editor) 1994: Handbook of the Birds of Europe. The Birds of the Western Palearctic. Oxford University Press, Oxford.

CRAMP, S. & W. G. Teagle 1952: The Birds of Inner London, 1900-1950. *BB*, 45:433-456.

CRAMP, S. & W. G. Teagle 1955: A Comparative Study of the Birds of Two Stretches of the Thames in Inner London. 1951-1953, *LBR* for 1953:42-57.

CRAMP, S. & A. D. Tomlins 1966: The Birds of Inner London 1951-65. *BB*, 59:209-233.

CRAW, Gillian L. A. 1974: Rookery Census 1974. *Surrey Bird Club Quarterly Bulletin* 72:9-12.

CROCKER, Glenys & Alan 2000: Damnable Inventions. Surrey Industrial History Group, Guildford.

CROFT, S. 1942: Communal Display of Partridges. *LBR* for 1942:23.

CROSSFIELD, J. B. 1882: Ornithology in Wray Park. Unpublished in Holmesdale Natural History Club archive.

CURRIE, Ian 1996: Frosts, Freezes and Fairs. Frosted Earth, Coulsdon.

DALGLEISH, Gordon 1902: Rare Birds in Surrey. *Zool.*, 1902:32.

DALGLIESH, Gordon 1906: Ornithological Notes from Surrey. *Zool., 1906:114-5*.

DALLAS, John E. S. 928: Notes on the Woodlark. *LN* for 1927:18-19.

DAVIES, Andrew 1985: The British Mandarins – Outstripping the Ancestors? *BTO News* 136:12.

DAVIES, Andrew K. 1986: The Status and Distribution of the Mandarin *Aix galericulata* in Surrey. *SBR* for 1986:52-58.

DAVIS, Peter 1964: Crossbills in Britain and Ireland in 1963. *BB*, 57:477-501.

DAVIS, Peter G. 1975: Observations on the Nesting of some Heathland Birds. *SBR* 22 1974:56-63.

DAVISON, Mark & Ian Currie 1991: The Surrey Weather Book, 2nd edition. Frosted Earth, Coulsdon.

DAY, David 1989: Vanished Species. Gallery Books, New York.

DENNIS, M. K. 1990: Wintering Birds in the London Area. *LBR* for 1988:117-125.

DEPARTMENT FOR THE ENVIRONMENT, FOOD AND RURAL AFFAIRS 2004: Investigation of the Causes of the Decline of House Sparrow and Starling in Great Britain. www.defra.gov.uk.

DES FORGES, Charles Grahame & D. D. Harber 1963: A Guide to the Birds of Sussex. Oliver & Boyd, Edinburgh

DIXON, Charles 1909: The Bird-Life of London. William Heinemann, London.

DORMOR, I. G. R. 1995: A Short History of Thursley National Nature Reserve. Typescript.

DOUGLAS, Gordon 1951: Recent Changes in the Local Bird Population. *Proceedings of the Leatherhead and District Local History Society* Vol. 1 No. 5, 1951:15-16.

DOYLE, Jay 2000: Surrey's Landscape through the Millennia. *Nature Line*, Winter 1999-2000 and extended manuscript from the Surrey Wildlife Trust.

DRAKEFORD, Tony & Una Sutcliffe 2000: Wimbledon Common and Putney Heath. A Natural History, Wimbledon and Putney Commons Conservators.

DRESSER, Henry Eeles 1871-1881: History of the Birds of Europe.

DREWITT, John 1987: The Nature of Surrey. Barracuda Books Ltd, Buckingham.

DRUMMOND-MURRAY, James & Pete Thompson (forthcoming): Roman Southwark 4: The origins of the settlement: excavations on the Jubilee Line extension.

D'URBAN, W. S. M. & Rev. M. A. Matthew 1892: The Birds of Devon. R. H. Porter, London in Lever 1979 and the Historical Atlas.

DYMOND, J. N., Fraser, P. A. & S. J. M. Gantlett 1989: Rare Birds in Britain and Ireland. T. & A. D. Poyser, Waterhouses.

DYOS, H. J. (1973): COLLINS' ILLUSTRATED ATLAS OF LONDON (1854), Introduction and text. Leicester University Press, New York.

EARP, Michael J. 1991: The Origins of the Inner London Recording Area. *LBR* for 1989:138-140.

EDEN, Phillip 1995: Weatherwise. Macmillan, London.

EDWARDS, George 1743-51: Natural History of Uncommon Birds and of some other Rare and Undescribed Animals. London. In Bucknill (1900) and Lever (1997).

EDWARDS, George 1758-64: Gleanings of Natural History vol i, p.228. London. In Harting 1866.

ELLIOTT, David & June Elliott (undated): Birds of Wisley Edition Two, Birds of Wisley 1985, published from the Royal Horticultural Society's gardens at Wisley.

ELLIOTT, David, June Elliott & Chris Howkins 1988: Enjoying Wisley's Birds. Chris Howkins, 70 Grange Road, New Haw, Weybridge, Surrey KT15 3RH.

EVANS, Hugh 1993a: The Status of Breeding Nightjars in Surrey 1992. *SBR* for 1993:86-88.

EVANS, Hugh 1993b: The National Corn Bunting Surveys 1992/1993. *SBR* for 1993:89-90.

EVANS, Lee G. R. 1992: Rare Birds in Britain 1991 p.29. Published by the author.

EVANS, Lee G. R. 1994: Rare Birds in Britain 1800-1990. LGRE Publications Ltd, Amersham.

EVELYN, John 1966: The Diary of John Evelyn, edited by William Bray. Dent, London. Bray's first edition was published in 1818.

FEARE, Christopher 1984: The Starling. Oxford University Press, Oxford.

FISHER, James 1966: The Shell Bird Book. Ebury Press & Michael Joseph.

FITTER, Richard S. R.1940: Special Species for 1940. *LBR* for 1940:16-19.

FITTER, Richard S. R.1941: Report on the Effect of the Severe Winter of 1939-40 on Bird-life in the Area within 20 Miles of London. *BB*, 35:33-36.

FITTER, Richard. S. R.1942: The Starling roosts of the London area. *LN* for 1942:3-23.

FITTER, Richard. S. R.1943: Status of the Black-backed Gulls in the London Area. *BB*, 36:163-164.

FITTER, Richard. S. R.1949: London's Birds. Collins, London.

FITTER, Richard S. R. 1959: The Ark in Our Midst. Cited in the *LBR* for 1989.

FITTER, Richard S. R. 2000: The London Natural History Society in the 1930s and 1940s. *LN* for 2000.

FITTER, Richard S. R. & R. C. Homes 1939: Effects of the Severe Weather, December 17th-26th. *LBR* for 1938: 30-33.

FITTER, Richard S. R., E. R. Parrinder & C. B. Ashby 1946: The Rookery Census of the London Area. *LBR* for 1945: 22-23.

FITZERALD, F. R. 1888: Shoveller and Rough-legged Buzzard in Surrey. *Zool.*, 1888:352.

FLYNN, John 1998: Pied-billed Grebe at South Norwood Lake – New to the London Area. *LBR* for 1997:195-198.

FORSTER, E. 1999: The History of Witley, Milford and Surrounding Area.

FORSTER, Robert H. B. 1971: Conservation in Surrey with Special Reference to Birdlife. *SBR* for 1970:7-16.

FORSTER, Robert H. B. 1973: Atlas of Breeding Birds. *SBR* for 1972:9-18.

FORSTER, Robert H. B. 1975: Conservation Report. *SBR* for 1974:100.

FORSTER, Robert H. B. 1976: The B.T.O. Register of Ornithological Sites in Surrey. *SBR* for 1975:53-59.

FROHAWK, Frederick William 1891: Martins and Wasps Nests. *The Field*, 70:828 in Chatfield (1987).

FRY, Raymond & Edwin T. Welland 1962: Birds of Ockley and Surrounding Commons – 1962. *Surrey Bird Club Quarterly Bulletin*, 21 for March 1962:2-6.

FULLER, Erroll 1987: Extinct Birds. Rainbird Publishing Group, London.

FULLER, Robert J., David G. Noble, Ken W. Smith & Des Vanhinsbergh 2005: Recent Declines in Populations of Woodland Birds in Britain: a review of possible causes. *BB*, 98:116-143.

GALE, S. (undated): Checklist of the Birds of Holmethorpe 1960-2004.

GANTLETT, S, J. M. 1991: The Birds of the Isles of Scilly. In the *Migration Atlas*.

GANTLETT, Steve 2000: A Checklist of the Bird Forms of Britain and Ireland. *Birding World* for 2000:19-26.

GARCIA, Dr Ernest F. J. 1986: The B.T.O. Lapwing Survey in Surrey, 1987. *SBR* for 1986:59-60.

GARCIA, Dr Ernest F. J. 1990: Bee-eater *Merops apiaster* at Milford. *SBR* for 1990:62.

GARCIA, Dr Ernest F. J. 1991: Little Bunting *Emberiza pusilla* at Milford. *SBR* for 1991:62.

GASSON, P. & T. J. Lawrence 1993: Hybrid Male Ring-necked x Tufted Duck at Kew Green. *LBR* for 1992:180.

GATES, Jeremy 1992a: Siberian Chiffchaff at Stoke Water Meadows. *SBR* for 1992:71.

GATES, Jeremy 1992b: The Birds in a Guildford Tetrad. A Comparative Study Twenty Years Later. *SBR* for 1992:72-90.

GATES, Jeremy 1993: A Study of the Water Pipits occurring at Stoke Water Meadows 1990-1994. *SBR* for 1993:74-80.

GATES, Jeremy 1994: Marsh Sandpiper at Old Woking Sewage Farm. *SBR* for 1994:86.

GATES, Jeremy 1997: Red-rumped Swallow at Stoke Lake. *SBR* for 1997:107.

GEEN, Graham R. 1988: The Autumn Migration of Chiffchaffs at an Inland Site in South-east England. *Ringing & Migration* 9:65-67.

GEEN, Graham R. 1990: The Birds of Queen Mary 1925-1988. *Hersham Ringing Group Report* No. 6.

GEORGE, R. W. 1974: Birds at the Surrey Commercial Docks, April 1971 to December 1972. *LBR* for 1972:67-70.

GIBBONS, David Wingfield, James B. Reid & Robert A. Chapman 1993: The New Atlas of Breeding Birds in Britain and Ireland: 1988-1991. T. & A. D. Poyser Ltd, London.

GIBBS, A. 1963: The Bird Population of Rubbish Dumps. *LBR* for 1961:104-110.

GILBERT, Gillian 2000: The Status and Habitat of Spotted Crakes *Porzana porzana* in the UK in 1999. Royal Society for the Protection of Birds, Sandy.

GILHAM, Eric & Barry Gilham 1996: Hybrid Ducks. Gilham, Wallington.

GLEGG, William E. 1928: The Thames as a Bird-Migration Route. *LN* for 1928:3-15.

GLEGG, William E. 1929: The Birds of Middlesex Since 1866. *LN* for 1929:3-32.

GLEGG, William E. 1935: History of the Birds of Middlesex. H. F. & G. Witherby, London.

GLEGG, William E. 1938: Changes of Bird-Life in Relation to the Increase of London. *LBR* for 1938:34-44.

GLUE, David 2000: Bramblings and Bullfinches brighten late winter bird tables. *BTO News* 231:10-11.

GOODERS, John 1965: The Birds of Clapham and Wandsworth Commons. *LBR* for 1964:73-88.

GOODERS, John 1968: The Swift in Central London. *LBR* for 1967:93-98.

GOULD, John 1862-73: The Birds of Great Britain. London. In Bucknill.

GRANT, P. J. 1971: Birds at the Surrey Commercial Docks. *LBR* for 1970:87-91.

GRANT, Peter J. 1980: Field Identification of West Palearctic Gulls, Part 3, *BB*, 73:113-158.

GRANT, P. J., J. G. Harrison & K. Noble 1974: The Return of Birdlife to the Thames. *LBR* for 1972:61-64.

GRAVES, George 1811-21: British Ornithology, London. In Bucknill.

GREEN, J. F. 1893: Guillemots in the Thames. *The Field* 1893:528 in Glegg and Bucknill.

GREENSMITH, Alan J. 1987: Pallas's Warbler at Wandsworth Common – new to the London Area, *LBR* for 1986:179.

GREGORY, R. D. & J. H. Marchant 1995: Population trends of Jays, Magpies and Carrion Crows in the United Kingdom. Bird Study 43: 28-37.

GREGORY, Richard D, Nicholas I. Wilkinson, David G. Noble, James A. Robinson, Andrew F. Brown, Julian Hughes, Deborah Proctor, David W, Gibbons & Colin A. Galbraith 2002: The Population status of birds in the United Kingdom, Channel Islands and Isle of Man: an analysis of conservation concern 2002-2007. *BB*, 95:410-448.

GRIFFIN, David 1970: The Common Birds Census in Surrey. *SBR* for 1969:52-69.

GRIFFIN, David 1975: The Common Bird Census in Surrey 1970-1974. *SBR* for 1974:64-85.

GRIFFIN, David 1979: The Common Bird Census in Surrey 1975-1979. *SBR* for 1979:85-105.

GRIFFIN, David 1980: The Common Bird Census in Surrey 1975-1979 (Addendum). *SBR* for 1980.

GRIFFIN, David 1984: The Common Birds Census in Surrey, 1980-1984. *SBR* for 1984:53-64.

GRIFFIN, David 1989: The Common Birds Census in Surrey 1985-1989. *SBR* for 1989:55-63.

GRIFFIN, David 1990: The BTO Waterways Bird Survey 1975-1990. *SBR* for 1990:69-75.

GRIFFIN, David 1994: The Common Bird Census in Surrey 1990-1994. *SBR* for 1994:92-100.

GRIFFIN, David 1995: The BTO Waterways Bird Survey in Surrey 1994-1995. *SBR* for 1995:94-97.

GRIFFIN, David 1996: Addition to the BTO Waterways Bird Survey in Surrey 1991-1995. *SBR* for 1996:102.

GURNEY, J. H. 1889: The Status of the Fire-crest as a British Bird. *Zool.*, 1889:172-174 in Bucknill 1900.

GURNEY, J. H. 1921: Early Annals of Ornithology. Witherby, London, 1972. Reprint Minet, Chicheley. The note on James I keeping Cormorants and Ospreys is based on Harting's *Essays on Sport and Natural History*, p. 429.

GURNEY, Samuel 1854: Waterhen carrying her Young in her Feet. *Zool.*, 1854:4367.

HAGEMEIJER, Ward J. M. & Michael J. Blair 1997: The EBCC Atlas of European Breeding Birds. T. & A. D. Poyser, London.

HAIG, G. M. 1983: Wintering Baird's Sandpiper at Staines Reservoir. *LBR* for 1982:87-90.

HAIG, G. M. 1985: Ring-billed Gull at Staines Res., in November 1982. *LBR* for 1984: 139-140.

HAMILTON, E.1879: The Birds of London. *Zool.*, 1879:284.

HAMILTON, Edward 1881: The Avi-fauna of Wimbledon Common. *Zool.*, 1881:237-242.

HARDWICK, Mark & A. S. M. Self 1992: Rare Birds in the London Area. *LBR* for 1991:183-211.

HARMSWORTH, Cecil 1930: A Little Fishing Book. Cuala Press, Dublin.

HARRIS, Dave 1995: White-rumped Sandpiper at Walton Reservoirs. *SBR*. for 1995.

HARRIS, Dave 1997a: Red-footed Falcon in Surrey – 1997-98. *SBR* for 1997:108-109.

HARRIS, Dave 1997b: Squacco Heron at Walton Reservoirs. *SBR* for 1997:110-111.

HARRISON, C. J. O. 1961: Woodlark Population and Habitat. *LBR* for 1959:71-80.

HARRISON, C. J. O. & Cyril A. Walker, 1977: Birds of the British Lower Eocene. *Tertiary Research Special Paper* Number 3, The Tertiary Research Group, London.

HARRISON, C. J. O. 1979: Pleistocene Birds from Swanscombe, Kent. *LN* for 1978:6-8.

HARRISON, C. J. O. 1984: Rail-like Cursorial Birds of the British Lower Eocene, with Descriptions of Two new Species. *LN* for 1983:14-23.

HARRISON, Colin J. O. 1988: The History of the Birds of Britain. Collins, London.

HARRISON, J. G. 1945: Spring Migration in the Wey Valley. *South-Eastern Bird Report* for 1945:6.

HARRISON, Jeffery 1947: Bird Haunts in Surrey. The Guildford Sewage Farm. South-Eastern Bird Report, 1947:4-5.

HARRISON, T. H. & P. A. D. Hollom 1932: The Great Crested Grebe Enquiry, 1931. *BB*, 26:105, citing Alphonse Milne-Edwards, *Annales de Sciences Naturelles*, 1968 concerning fens near Cambridge.

HARTING, J. E. 1866: The Birds of Middlesex. John van Voorst, London. The account of the Red Kite by Clusius is given in the original latin on page 10. It was a note to his translation of the works of a French ornithologist, Pierre Belon. Lovegrove 1990 provides a gloss.

HARTING, J. E.1889: Memoir of the Late Frederick Bond. *Zool.*, 1889.

HARTLEY, P. H. Trahair 1933: Field Notes on the Little Grebe. *BB*, 27:82-86.

HARTLEY, P. H. Trahair 1937: The Sexual Display of the Little Grebe. *BB*, 30:266-275.

HASTINGS, Rupert B. 1985: Balearic Shearwater – new to the London Area. *LBR* for 1984:132-134.

HASTINGS, Rupert B. 1986: White-rumped Sandpiper at Perry Oaks Sewage Farm – new to the London Area. *LBR* for 1985:203-204.

HATTON, David H. 1982: Beddington Sewage Farm. Wader Survey February 1979 – February 1982. *SBR* for 1982:45-55.

HERBER, Keith J. 1971: Wing Length and Weights of Goldcrests. *Hersham Ringing Group Report* No. 2 1969-1971:14-16.

HERBER, Keith J. 1984: The BTO Ringed Plover and Little Ringed Plover Surveys in Surrey, 1984. *SBR* for 1984:65-68.

HERBER, Keith J. 1985: The BTO Wood Warbler Survey in Surrey, 1984. *SBR* for 1984:51-53.

HEWLET, Jan (Ed.), K. F. Betton & M. J. Earp 2002: The Breeding Birds of the London Area. London Natural History Society, London.

HEWSON, Chris & Juliet Vickery 2003: Yellow Wagtail Decline – collaborating to find the causes. *BTO News* 245:14-15.

HIBBARD, Shirley: *Intellectual Observer* 36:174 in Harting (1866).

HIBBERT-WARE, Alice 1938: Report of the Little Owl Food Inquiry 1936-37. Witherby, London for British Trust for Ornithology.

HICKLING, R. A. O. 1954: The wintering of Gulls in Britain. Bird Study, 1:129-148.

HICKLING, R. A. O. 1967: The Inland Wintering of Gulls in England, 1963. Bird Study, 14:104-113.

HICKLING, R. A. O. 1977: Inland Wintering of Gulls in England and Wales, 1973. *Bird Study* 24:79-88.

HILL, Dr John1752: History of Animals. London. In Bucknill.

HINDE, R. A. 1951: Further Report on the Inland Migration of Waders and Terns. *BB*, 44:329-346.

HNHS 1955 see BOND, 1955.

HNHS 1968 see BARLOW.

HNHS, 1980 see KIRKPATRICK, 1980.

HOLLEYMAN, R. A. (undated) *Shepperton Bird Reports* for September 1982-December 1983, 1984, 1985 and 1986. 339 Laleham Road, Shepperton.

HOLLOM, Phillip A. D. 1933: The Great Crested Grebe in the London Area. *LN* for 1932: 51-56.

HOLLOM, Phillip A. D. 1935: Brooklands Sewage Farm, Surrey, 1931-34. *BB*, 28:342-343.

HOLLOM, Phillip A. D. 1936: Report on the Great Crested Grebe Sample Count, 1935. *BB*, 30:138-158.

HOLLOM, Phillip A. D. 1937: Brooklands Sewage Farm, Surrey, 1936. *BB*, 30:346-347.

HOLLOM, Phillip A. D. 1937: Observations on the Courtship and Mating of the Smew. *BB*, 31:106-111.

HOLLOM, Phillip A. D. 1941: General Field-characteristics of Gulls *The Handbook of British Birds, Vol. V:149-53.*

HOLLOM, Phillip A. D. 1955: The Great Crested Grebe in Surrey. *SBR* for 1955:3-4.

HOLLOM, Phillip A. D. 1959: The Great Crested Grebe sample census 1946-55. *Bird Study* 6:1-7.

HOLLOWAY, Simon 1996: The Historical Atlas of Breeding Birds in Britain and Ireland: 1875-1900. T. & A. D. Poyser, London.

HOME, G. 1901: Epsom, its history and surroundings. Quoted in *Nonsuch Watch Newsletter* No. 29, June 1999.

HOMES, Richard C. 1942: Sex Ratios in Winter Duck Flocks. *BB*, 36:42-48.

HOMES, Richard C. 1955: Gull Roosts of the London Area. *LBR* for 1953:37-39.

HOMES, Richard C. 1957: Wildfowl and Wader Movements in the London Area in the Severe Weather of February, 1956. *LBR* for 1956:41-47.

HOMES, Richard C., B. L. Sage & R. Spencer 1960: Breeding Populations of Lapwings, Coot and Meadow Pipits. *LBR* for 1958:54-61.

HOPE, L. 1911: Puffin on the Thames. *The Field* 118:825 in Glegg (1935).

HORN, George 1846: Curious capture of the Goshawk. *Zool.*, 1846:1496.

HOWARD, Robert Mowbray undated: Records and Letters of the Family of the Longs of Longville, Jamaica and Hampton Lodge, Surrey (2 vols). Simpkin, Marshall, Hamilton, Kent & Co. Ltd, London.

HOWKINS, Christopher 1987: Hidden Surrey. Countryside Books, Newbury.

HUDSON, Robert 1973: Early and Late Dates for Summer Migrants. *British Trust for Ornithology Field Guide 15*, Tring.

HUDSON, Robert 1974: Feral Parakeets near London. *BB*, 67:33.

HUDSON, Robert 1974a: Parakeets in the London Area. *BB*, 67:167.

HUDSON, W. H.1898: Birds in London. Longmans, Green & Co., 1924 edition Dent, London.

HUDSON, W. H.1915: Birds and Man. Duckworth, London.

HUDSON, W. H.1921: British Birds. Longmans, Green & Co., London.

HUDSON, W. H.1923: Rare, Vanishing and Lost British Birds. J. M. Dent & Sons, London. In Shrubb 2003.

HUGHES, Baz, Jenny Bruce, Graham Ekins & Stuart Newson 2000: Movements and Distribution of Inland breeding Cormorants in England. English Nature Research Report No. 360, Peterborough.

HUTSON, A. M., John A. Burton & S. D. G. Stephens 1971): Some Preliminary Results of Swift Ringing at Beddington Sewage Farm, Surrey. *LBR* for 1971:81-87.

HUTSON, A. M. & John Gooders 1970: Possible Breeding of Spotted Crake in the London Area. *LBR* for 1969:86-88.

HUXLEY, J. S. 1947: Display of the Mute Swan. *BB*, 40:130-134.

JACKSON, A. A. 1973: Semi-detached London. George Allen & Unwin, London.

JAMES, P., Ed. 1996: Birds of Sussex. Sussex Ornithological Society.

JEFFERIES, Richard 1878: Decline of Partridge Shooting. *Pall Mall Gazette*, August 31st, 1878. In Jefferies, 1948.

JEFFERIES, Richard 1885: The Professional Bird-catcher. *St James's Gazette*, August 4th 1885. In Jefferies, 1948.

JEFFERIES, Richard 1886: Nightingales. *St James's Gazette*, April 1886. In Jefferies, 1948.

JEFFERIES, Richard 1948: Chronicles of the Hedges and other Essays, Edited by Samuel J. Looker, Phoenix House, London.

JESSE, Edward 1835-36: Gleanings in Natural History, 3 vols. London in Bucknill 1900, 1838 Edition in Yarrell 1845.

JOHN, A. W. G. & J. Roskell, 1985: Jay Movements in Autumn 1983. *BB*, 78: 611-637.

JONES, A. W. 1961: The Vegetation of South Norwood or Elmers End Sewage Works. *LN* for 1960:102-114.

JONES, Phillip 1992: Yellow-billed Cuckoo at Oxted – new to the London Area. *LBR* for 1991:214.

JORDAN, Denham ('A Son of the Marshes') 1892: On Surrey Hills. William Blackwood & Sons, London (Bean Goose p.21, Honey Buzzard and Rough-legged Buzzard p.102, Harrier and Black Grouse p.53, Stone Curlew p.68-9, Green Sandpiper p.10, Magpie p.289, Raven p.53, Goldfinch p.24, winter of 1890 p.283).

JORDAN, Denham ('A Son of the Marshes') 1893: With the Woodlanders *and* By the Tide, Ed. J. A. Owen. Blackwood, London (p.74 Woodlark).

JORDAN, Denham ('A Son of the Marshes') 1893a: Forest Tithes and other Studies. London. In Bucknill, 1900, (Herring Gull p.184).

JORDAN, Denham ('A Son of the Marshes') 1894: Within an Hour of London Town. William Blackwood & Sons, London, edited by J. A. Owen (Bewick's Swan p.232-3, Whooper Swan p.225, Black Grouse p.134, Water Rail p.135, Roseate Tern p.308, Razorbill p.235, Turtle Dove p.57, Kingfisher p.142, Mistle Thrush p.16, Sparrow Clubs p.59, Hawfinch p.72).

JORDAN, Denham ('A Son of the Marshes') 1895: The Wild-Fowl and Sea-Fowl of Great Britain. Chapman & Hall, London (Gadwall pp.230-231, Eider and Puffin p.246, Corncrake p.145, Common Sandpiper p.86-7).

JORDAN, Denham ('A Son of the Marshes') 1896: In the Green Leaf and the Sere. Kegan Paul, Trench, Trübner & Co., London (Cormorant p.178-9, Red-backed Shrike p.127, Lesser Grey Shrike p.130, Carrion Crow p.107, Raven p.27, p.274).

JOURDAIN, Rev. F. C. R. & Lieut. H. F. Witherby 1918: The Effect of the Winter of 1916-1917 on our Resident Birds. *BB*, 12:26-35.

KALAHAR, Martin 1999: The Current Status of the Buzzard in Sussex. *Sussex Bird Report* for 1998, pp.173-176.

KEARTON, Cherry: 1938: My Woodland Home. Jarrolds, London.

KEARTON, Richard 1909: Wild Nature's Ways. Cassell & Co., London.

KEARTON, Richard 1911: With Nature and a Camera. Popular Edition, Cassell & Co., London (1st Edn 1897).

KEARTON, Richard & Howard Bentham 1925: The Pocket Book of British Birds. Cassell & Company Ltd, London.

KEHOE, Chris 2006: Racial Assessment and Identification in Britain: a Report from the RIACT Committee. *Birding World* 19:619-645

KERR, Graham W. 1906: The Birds of the District of Staines. *Zool.*, 1906:230-234, 307-310, 386-389.

KERR, Graham W. 1907: Marsh Warbler Nesting in Surrey. *BB*, 1:186.

KERR, Graham W. 1908: The Birds of the District of Staines. *Zool.*, 1908:137-143.

KETTLE, Ronald H. 1983: Common Bird Census Results on a Woodland Plot on Wimbledon Common 1973-80. *LBR* for 1982.

KETTLE, Ronald H. (Ed.) 1987: British Bird Songs and Calls. Tape cassette, British Library of Wildlife Sounds, London.

KETTLE, Ronald H. (Ed.) 1989: More British Bird Sounds. Tape cassette, British Library of Wildlife Sounds, London.

KETTLE, Ronald H. 1998: The Bird Life of Cannon Hill Common, Merton. *LBR* for 1997:210-219.

KEYWOOD, K. P. 1936: Notes on A Pied Wagtail Roost. *LBR* for 1936:28-29.

KEYWOOD, K. P. & W. D. Melluish 1952: A Report of the Bird Population of Four Gravel Pits in the London Area, 1948 to 1951. *LBR* for 1952:43-72.

KIDD, Waring 1843: Enquiry respecting the Water-rail. *Zool.*, 1843:148-9.

KIDD, Waring *et al.* 1837: Some account of the Birds of Godalming. *Entomological Magazine* for 1837 in Bucknill (1900).

KIRKPATRICK, P. A. & Peter G. Davis 1980: The Birds of the Haslemere District. Haslemere Natural History Society, Haslemere.

KIRKPATRICK, P. A. 1983: Breeding Firecrests in Haslemere in 1983. *SBR* for 1983:44-48.

KNIPE, H. R. (Ed.) 1916: Tunbridge Wells and Neighbourhood. Felton, Tunbridge Wells.

KOCH, Ludwig 1955: Memoirs of a Birdman. Phoenix House Ltd, London.

LACK, David & R. M. Lockley, 1938: Skokholm Bird Observatory Homing Experiments. *BB*, 31:242-248.

LACK, Peter 1986: The Atlas of Wintering Birds in Britain and Ireland. T. & A. D. Poyser, Calton.

LANCASTER, M. B. 1995: Observations at a Diurnal Gull Gathering Site (DIGGS) – St Paul's School Playing Field, Addlestone, Surrey. *SBR* for 1995:89-93.

LANCASTER, M. B. 1998: Further Observations at a Diurnal Gull Gathering Site (DIGGS) at St Paul's School, Addlestone, Surrey. *SBR* for 1998:117-124.

LANGLEY, Graham 1998: Once upon a Time. *Birdwatch*, August 1998.

LANGSTON, Rowena, Richard Gregory & Roy Adams 2002: The Status of the Hawfinch in the UK 1975-1999. *BB*, 95:166-173.

LAWN, M. R. undated: The Birds of Witley Common 1981.

LAWN, M. R. 1984: Premigratory Dispersal of Juvenile Willow Warblers *Phylloscopus trochilus* in Southern England. *Ringing & Migration* 5:125-131.

LAXTON, R. G., T. H. Sparks & J. A. Newnham 1997: Spring Arrival Dates of Migrants in Sussex and Leicestershire (1966-1996). *Sussex Bird Report* for 1997: 183-196.

LEVER, Christopher 1977, 1979: The Naturalised Animals of the British Isles. Hutchinson & Co. Ltd, Paladin Edition 1979.

LEVER, Christopher 1987: Naturalised Birds of the World.

LEWIS, Victor C. 1965: Bird Song Recognition – An Aural Index, three sets of three EP records HMV 7EG 8923-25. HMV, London.

LEWIS, Victor C. 1970: Bird Sounds in Close-up, Volume Two, 12-inch 33.3 rpm disc, Marble Arch MAL1316. Pye Records, London.

LINDLEY A. (Undated): Surrey's Vanishing Wildlife. Surrey Wildlife Trust.

LISTER, M. D. 1938: An Account of the Lapwing Population on a Surrey Farm. *BB*, 32:260-271.

LONDON NATURAL HISTORY SOCIETY 1918: Report of the Committee of the Ornithological Section for 1918.

LONDON NATURAL HISTORY SOCIETY 1919: Report of the Ornithological Section for 1919.

LONDON NATURAL HISTORY SOCIETY 1957: The Birds of the London Area since 1900. Collins, London and Revised Edition 1964, Rupert Hart-Davis, London.

LONG, H. L. 1839: Notice of the Discovery of the Nest and Eggs of the Common Crossbill near Farnham, Surrey. *Charlesworth's Magazine of Natural History* 2:451. In Bucknill (1900).

LOUSLEY, Job Edward 1976: Flora of Surrey. David & Charles, London.

LOVEGROVE, Roger 1990: The Kite's Tale. Royal Society for the Protection of Birds, Sandy.

MABEY R. 1993: Whistling in the Dark. Sinclair-Stevenson, London.

MABEY R. 1997: The Book of Nightingales. Random House, London.

MACPHERSON, A. Holte 1929: A List of the Birds of Inner London. *BB*, 22:222-244.

MACPHERSON, A. H. 1890: *Zool.*, 1890:135-136 in Bucknill.

MAITLAND, Hubert & Ernest Raphael Turnbull (unpublished): Annals of Egg Collection. Manuscript held at Charterhouse.

MANNING, Rev. Owen & W. Bray, 1804-14: The History and Antiquities of the County of Surrey, 3 vols. London.

MANSER, G. E. 1944: Bird Notes of the Elmers End Sewage Farm, 1935-1938. *LBR* for 1944:23-28.

MARCHANT, John H., Robert Hudson, Steve M. Carter & Phil Whittington 1990: Population Trends in British Breeding Birds. British Trust for Ornithology, Tring.

MAROEVIC, Franco J. 1994: White-winged Black Tern at Barn Elms Reservoirs. *SBR* for 1994:87-88.

MARSHALL, Charles J. 1936: A History of the Old Villages of Cheam and Sutton. Cryer's Library, Cheam.

MASON, C. F. 1995: Long-term trends in the arrival dates of spring migrants. *Bird Study* 42, pp.182-189.

MASSEY, Michael 1979: Changes in Suburban Habitat and Wildlife Populations. *SBR* for 1979:79-84.

MAXWELL Donald 1924: Unknown Surrey. John Lane. The Bodley Head Ltd, London.

McNEIL, D. A. C. 1994: A Comparison between Bird Populations in two Cemeteries 100 Miles apart. *SBR* for 1994:89-91.

MEAD, Chris 1999: Old Mead's Almanack. *Bird Watching*, December 1999: 28-29.

MEAD, Chris 2000: The State of the Nation's Birds. Whittet Books, Stowmarket.

MEARNS, Barbara & Richard 1998: The Bird Collectors. Academic Press, London.

MERRETT, Christopher 1666: *Pinax Rerum Naturalium Brittanicarum, continens Vegetabilia, Animalia et Fossilia*. London.

MERTON, Ronald Keir 1965: The Wood Pigeon. Harper Collins, London.

MESSENBIRD, G. D. J. 1986: Killdeer at Beddington Sewage Farm – new to the London Area. *LBR* for 1985:202.

MEYER, H. L. 1842-50: Coloured Illustrations of British Birds and their Eggs, 7 vols. London.

MILNE, B. S. 1956: A Report on the Bird Population of Beddington Sewage Farm, 1954-55. *LBR* for 1955:39-54.

MILNE, B. S. 1959: Variation in a Population of Yellow Wagtails. *BB*, 52:281-295.

MILNE, Brian S., Ken Osborne and Derek Coleman 2000: Yellow Wagtails at Beddington. *Beddington Farmlands Bird Report* for 2000:33-40.

MITCHELL, Captain K. D. G. 1955: Aircraft Observations of Birds in Flight, *BB*, 49: 59-70.

MITCHELL, Captain Keith D. G. 1957: Further Aircraft Observations of Birds in Flight. *BB*, 50:291-302.

MITFORD, Robert 1876: Whitewinged Crossbill near London. *Zool.*, 1876:4835-4836.

MONK, J. F. 1956: The Wryneck, *SBR* for 1956:2-3.

MONTAGU, George 1802: Ornithological Dictionary and 1813 Supplement. 1866 edition by E. Newman, Swan, Soneenscheinn & Allan, London.

MONTIER, David 1968: A Survey of the Breeding Distribution of the Kestrel, Barn Owl and Tawny Owl in the London Area in 1967. *LBR* for 1967:81-92.

MONTIER, David J. (Ed.) 1977: Atlas of Breeding Birds of the London Area. Batsford, London.

MONTIER, D. J. 1993: Sardinian Warbler at Surbiton – New to the London Area. *LBR* for 1992:183.

MOON, A. V. 1984: The Occurrence of Pelagic Seabirds in the London Area. *LBR* for 1983:106-119.

MOON, A. V. 1987a: Wildfowl on King George VI and Staines Reservoirs during 1986. *LBR* for 1986:165-171.

MOON, A. V. 1987b: Wilson's Phalarope at Staines Reservoir – new to the London Area. *LBR* for 1986:177-178.

MOON, A. V. 1988: The Influx of Sabine's Gulls and other Seabirds in October 1987. *LBR* for 1987:121-132.

MOON. Andrew V. 1997: American Golden Plover at King George VI Reservoir – New to the London Area. *LBR* for 1995:164-167.

MOORMAN, R. F. 1961: Some Notes on the Geology of Sutton and District. *LN* for 1960:121-130.

MORRIS, F. O. (2nd edition): A History of British Birds, 6 vols. London. In Bucknill.

MOSS, Martin 1972: The Birdlife at Frimley Gravel Pits. *SBR* for 1971:71-76.

MOURITZ, L. Beresford 1905: Notes on the Ornithology of Richmond Park, Surrey. *Zool.*, 1905:147-151, 187-188, 349.

MOURITZ, L. Beresford 1907: Ornithological Observations in Surrey: 1906. *Zool.*, 1907:92-106.

MULLINS, John R. 1976: Tawny Pipit. *SBR* for 1975:85-86.

MULLINS, J. R. 1986: Little Bunting (*Emberiza pusilla*) at Pirbright Common. *SBR* for 1986:60-61.

MULLINS. W. H., H Kirke Swan & F. C. R. Jourdain 1920: A Geographical Bibliography of British Ornithology. Witherby & Co, London.

MURRAY, Ian 1977: Victorian and Edwardian Middlesex from Old Photographs. B. T. Batsford Ltd, London.

MUSGROVE, Andy, 2004: Little Egrets in the UK: an update. *WeBS News* 19:6-7.

NAU, B. S. 1961: Sand Martin Colonies in the London Area. *LBR* for 1960:69-81.

NAYLOR, Peter 1985: Collared Pratincole at Staines Reservoir – new to the London Area. *LBR* for 1984:135-136.

NAYLOR, K. A. 1996: A Reference Manual of Rare Birds in Great Britain and Ireland Vol. 1. Vol. 2 in 1998, Naylor, Nottingham.

NETHERWOOD, Mike, Mick Cook & Derek Coleman 2003: The Tree Sparrow Nest box Project at Beddington Farmlands. *Beddington Bird Report* for 2001: 46-47.

NEWMAN, Edward 1837: *Entomological Magazine* 4:270 Lesser Spotted Woodpecker. In Bucknill.

NEWMAN, Edward 1849: The Letters of Rusticus on the Natural History of Godalming. J. van Voorst, London.

NEWMAN, Errol 1974: Bird in a Guildford Tetrad – Pewley. *SBR* for 1973:53-73.

NEWTON, E. T. 1886: On the remains of a gigantic species of bird (*Gastornis klaasseni* n. sp.) from the Lower Eocene Beds near Croydon. *Trans. Zool. Soc. Lond.* 12, 5: 143-160. In Harrison & Walker, 1977.

NEWTON, R. G. 1948: Rook Survey by the Ornithological Section. *Proceedings of the Croydon Natural History and Scientific Society*, 1948.

NICHOLSON, E. M. 1926: Birds in the Haslemere Educational Museum. Haslemere Natural History Society.

NICHOLSON, E. M. (unpublished): Survey of London Starling roosts in 1932-33. Manuscript quoted in Fitter (1942).

NICHOLSON, E. M. 1995: Spring Bird Censuses of Battersea Park – 1950-1991. *LBR* for 1994:180-183.

NISBET, I. C. T. 1959: The Kites of Sixteenth Century London. *BB*, 52:239-240.

NORRIS, C. A. 1947: Report on the Distribution and Status of the Corn-Crake. *BB*, 40:226-244.

OGILVIE, Malcolm & the Rare Breeding Birds Panel 2002: Rare Breeding Birds in the United Kingdom in 2000. *BB*, 95:542-582.

OGLEY, Bob 1988: In the Wake of the Hurricane, National Edition. Froglets Publications Ltd, Brasted Chart.

OGSTON, Charles 1966: Inland Observation Points in Surrey, 1964. *SBR* for 1964:33-37.

OGSTON, Charles 1971: An Ageing Character for Dunnocks, *Hersham Ringing Group Report* No. 2: 26-36.

OLIVER, P. J. 1974: Little Gulls in the London Area. *LBR* for 1972:56-60.

OLIVER, P. J. 1975: Heronries in the London Area. *LBR* for 1973:73-77.

OLIVER, P. J. 1977: Great Crested Grebe Census, 1975. *LBR* for 1975:75-77.

OLIVER, P. J. 1978: Some Observations on Goldeneyes in West Middlesex. *LBR* for 1977:85-88.

OLIVER, P. J. 1982: The Decline of the Mute Swan in the London Area. *LBR* for 1981:87-91.

OLIVER, P. J. 1985: Tufted Ducks in the London Area. *LBR* for 1984:104-110.

OLIVER, P. J. 1992: The Decline of the Yellowhammer at Limpsfield. *SBR* for 1992:91-92.

OLIVER, P. J. 1994: Black-headed Gulls at Bankside. *LBR* for 1993:159-163.

OLIVER, P. J. 1998: Gulls and other Water Birds on the Thames in Inner London in Winter. *LBR* for 1997:220-224.

OLIVER, P. J. 1998a: Crossbills in the London Area, with particular reference to the 1997 invasion. *LBR* for 1997:221-231.

OLIVER, P. J. 2000: Limpsfield Common Revisited – the birds compared after six decades. *LN* for 2000.

OLIVER, P. J. 2003: Ornithological Records from Dulwich Woods, 1959-60, *LN* for 2003:135-6.

ORTON, Clive 1997: Excavations at the King William IV Site, Ewell, 1967-77. *Surrey Archaeological Collections* 84:89-122.

OSBORNE, Kenneth C. 1971: Water Pipits in the London Area. *LBR* for 1970:68-73.

OSBORNE, Kenneth C. 1972: The Need for Caution when identifying Scaup, Ferruginous Duck and other species in the Aythya genus. *LBR* for 1971:86-94.

OSBORNE, Kenneth C. 1997: The Breeding Birds of Inner London 1970-95. *LBR* for 1996: 190-210.

OWEN, D. A. L. 1988: Factors affecting the status of the Chough in England and Wales; 1780-1980 in E. Bignal & D. J. Curtis Eds. Choughs and Land-use in Europe, Proceedings of an International Workshop on the Conservation of the Chough, *Pyrrhocorax pyrrhocorax* in the E.C. 11th-14th November 1988. Scottish Chough Study Group, Tarbert, pp.72-80, cited in the *Historical Atlas*.

OWEN, Jane 2002: Battersea regains its former glories. *The Times*, November 2nd 2002 p.48.

PAINE, A. R. J. 1978: Black Tern Movement of Sept. 15th, 1974. *LBR* for 1977:.89-91.

PALMER, K. H. 1982: The Breeding Season Status of the Grey Wagtail in the London Area, 1979-81. *LBR* for 1981:106-122.

PALMER, K. H. 1988: A Survey of the Breeding Bird Species in major London Woodlands, 1985-87. *LBR* for 1987:142-69.

PALMER, Phillip 2000: First for Britain and Ireland 1600-1999. Arlequin Press, Chelmsford.

PARKER, Eric 1929: English Wild Life. Longmans, Green & Co.,London (Chough pp.90-91).

PARKER, Eric 1941: World of Birds. Longmans Green & Co., London.

PARKER, Eric 1947: Surrey. Robert Hale Ltd, London.

PARKER, Eric 1952: Surrey Naturalist. Robert Hale, London.

PARKER, Eric 1954: Surrey Gardens. Batsford, London.

PARKER, Eric 1987: The Song of the Nightingale. James Reeve, Hull.

PARMENTER, L. 1937: Notes on the Courtship and Mating of Smew and Goosander. *BB*, 31:151-152.

PARR, Donald 1963: Bird Life on a Sewage Disposal Works. *LBR* for 1962.

PARR, Donald 1965: Inland Observation Points in Surrey, 1963. *SBR* for 1963:37-40.

PARR, Donald 1969a: A Review of the Status of the Kestrel, Tawny Owl and Barn Owl in Surrey. *SBR* for 1967:35-40.

PARR, Donald 1969b: Weights of Blackbirds in Winter. *SBR* for 1967:41-43.

PARR, Donald 1970: Gull Flight Lines in Middlesex and Surrey in the Winter of 1968/69. *SBR* for 1968:36-42.

PARR, Donald (Ed.) 1972: Birds in Surrey, 1900-1970. Batsford, London.

PARR, Donald 1974: The Effect on Wildfowl of Sailing at Island Barn Reservoir. *SBR* for 1973:74-78.

PARR, Donald 1976: The Great Crested Grebe in Surrey. *SBR* for 1975.

PARRINDER, E. D. & E. R. Parrinder 1940: Arrival and Departure of Migrants, 1929-39: A Summary. *LBR* for 1939:30-32.

PARSLOW, J. L. F. 1967: Changes in Status among Breeding Birds in Britain and Ireland. *BB*, 60 (Hobby p.42, Barn Owl p.198).

PEACH, Will J., Rob A. Robinson & Kathryn A. Murrey (2004): Demographic and environmental causes of the decline of rural Song Thrushes *Turdus philomelos* in lowland Britain. *Ibis* for 2004: 50-59, 146 (Suppl. 2).

PEAKALL, D. B. 1962: The Post-War Status of the Red-backed Shrike in Surrey. *SBR* for 1960:30-32.

PEAL, R. E. F. 1968: The Distribution of the Wryneck in the British Isles 1964-1966. *Bird Study* 15:111-126.

PEMBERTON, John E. 1997: Who's Who in Ornithology. Buckingham Press Ltd, Maids Moreton.

PENNANT, Thomas 1766: British Zoology. Published by a Welsh Literary Society, later editions.

PERRINS, Christopher 1962: The "Lesser Scaup" problem. *BB*, 54:49-54.

PIGOT & Co. 1839: Royal National and Commercial Directory and Topography of the County of Surrey. London. In Brown (1996).

PITHON, Josephine A. & Calvin Dytham 1999: Breeding performance of Ring-necked Parakeets *Psittacula krameri* in small introduced populations in southeast England. *Bird Study* 46:342-347.

PITELKA, Frank A. 1961: Long-billed and Short-billed Dowitcher Specimens in the British Museum. *BB*, 54:340-342.

POTTS, G. R. 1967: Urban Starling Roosts in the British Isles, *Bird Study* 14:25-42.

POULTON, Rob forthcoming: Guildford Castle and Royal Palace, Archaeological Investigations, Vol. 1. Surrey County Archaeological Unit.

POULTON, Rob, 1988: The Lost Manor of Hextalls, Little Pickle, Bletchingley, Archaeological Investigations, with contributions by *J. Bourdillon, A. Bullock, A. Clark, S. Dyer, S. Hudson, P. Jones, M. Saaler, A. Tribe & D. Williams*. Surrey County Archaeological Unit.

POUNDS, Hubert E. 1952: Notes on the Birds of Farleigh and District and the North Downs Surrey. Witherby, London.

POUNDS, Hubert E. 1965: The Birds of Dulwich (Surrey) and its Neighbourhood. Pounds, Ringwood.

POWER, F. D. 1910: Ornithological Notes from a South London Suburb 1874-1909. Henry J. Glaisher, London.

PRESTT, Ian 1965: An Enquiry into the Recent Breeding Status of some of the Smaller Birds of Prey and Crows in Britain. *Bird Study* 12:196-221.

PRESTT, Ian & D. H. Mills 1966: A Census of Great Crested Grebes in Britain 1965. *Bird Study*, 13:163-203.

PROWSE, Alan 1999: Nightingales in Scrub at Bookham Common: their habitat and conservation. *SBR* for 1999:116-129.

PULLEN, A. E. 1977: A Farmland Habitat Study – Hurst Farm, Milford. *SBR* for 1976:66-78.

PYCRAFT, W. P. 1907: Sea Eagle in Surrey. *Knowledge*.

RANDLER, Christopher 2001: Field Identification of Hybrid Wildfowl – Geese, *Alula* 2:42-48.

RAYNSFORD, L. J. 1960: Dartford Warblers – 1960. *Surrey Bird Club Quarterly Bulletin* 16:1-4.

RAYNSFORD, L. J. 1961: A Short History of the Dartford Warbler in Surrey, *SBR* for 1961: 31-33.

REDFERN, Robin 2002: Greylag Goose nesting in oak tree. *BB*, 95:189.

RESTALL, Robin 1996: Munias and Mannikins. Pica Press, Mountfield.

REYNOLDS, C. M. 1979: The Heronries Census: 1972-77 population changes and a review. *Bird Study*, 26:7-12.

RIDDINGTON, R. S. C. Votier & J. Steele 2000: Influx of Redpolls in 1995/96. *BB*, 93:59-67.

ROBBINS, R. W. 1931: A Note on the Wryneck, *LN* for 1930: 132-133.

ROGER, Thierry & Alain Fosse 2001: Nidifications arboricole et rupestre du Martinet noir *Apus apus* en Maine-et Loire. *Crex*, 2001, 6:21-29.

ROWBERRY, E. C. 1934: Gulls in the London Area. *LN* for 1933: 48-58.

RSPB 2002: Where have all the sparrows gone? Survey report London, 2002. RSPB, Sandy.

RUSHEN, W. N. 1896, Notes on London Birds in 1895. *Nature Notes* 6:75. In Glegg.

SAGE, Bryan A.1960: The Spring Migration of the Common Gull through the London Area. *LBR* for 1958:69-74.

SAGE, Bryan L.1963: The Breeding Distribution of the Tree Sparrow. *LBR* for 1962:56-65.

SAGE, Bryan L.1970: The Winter Population of Gulls in the London Area. *LBR* for 1968:67-80.

SAGE, Bryan L. & L. W. Cornelius 1977: Rook Population of the London Area. *LBR* for 1975:66-73.

SAGE, Bryan L. & J. D. R. Vernon 1978: The 1975 National Survey of Rookeries. *Bird Study*, 25:64-86.

SAGE, Bryan L. & P. A. Whittington 1985: The 1980 Sample of Rookeries. *Bird Study*, 32:77-81.

SAGE, John A. 1976: The Nightjar in Surrey 1973-1975. *SBR* for 1975:60-65.

SAGE, John A. 1977: Heath Fires in Surrey, 1976. *SBR* for 1976:54-61.

SAGE, John A. 1982: Nightjars in Surrey, 1981. *SBR* for 1981:53-57.

SAGE, John A. 1993: The Occurrence of Melanism in the Surrey Great Tit Population. *SBR* for 1993:82-85

SALMON, J. D. 1849: in Newman 1849, p.152.

SALMON, Nathaniel 1736: Antiquities of Surrey collected from the most ancient records, with some account of the Present State and Natural History of the County. In Bucknill.

SAUNDERS, David 1991: Rare Birds of the British Isles. Patrick Stevens, Yeovil.

SAUNDERS, Howard 1899: Manual of British Birds, 2nd Edition. Gurney & Jackson, London.

SAVAGE, D. 1952: The Mandarin Duck. In Parr (1972).

SEELEY, D., M. Carlin & C. Phillpotts (forthcoming): Winchester Palace: excavations at the Southwark residence of the bishops of Winchester. MOLAS Monograph series.

SHARROCK, J. T. R. 1976: The Atlas of Breeding Birds in Britain and Ireland. British Trust for Ornithology, Tring.

SHAW, Rev. W. A. 1921: A List of the Birds of the Haslemere District. *Science Paper No. 7*, Haslemere Natural History Society, Haslemere.

SHAWYER, Colin R. 1987: The Barn Owl in the British Isles. The Hawk Trust, London.

SHERLOCK, R. L. 1960: British Regional Geology: London and the Thames Valley. HMSO, London.

SHRUBB, Michael 2003: Birds, Scythes and Combines. Cambridge University Press. See also Farming and birds: an historic perspective, *BB*, 96:158-177.

SITTERS, H. P., R. J. Fuller, R. A. Hoblyn, M. T. Wright, N. Cowie & C. G. R. Bowden 1996: The Woodlark *Lullula arborea* in Britain: population trends, distribution and habitat occupancy. *Bird Study*, 43:17-187.

SMITH, Rev. A. C. 1887: The Birds of Wiltshire. R. H. Porter, London. In the *Historical Atlas*.

SMITH, Robert 1971: A Study of Gulls at Worcester Park. *SBR* for 1970:66-74.

SNOW, David (Ed.) 1992: Birds, Discovery and Conservation. Helm Information Ltd, Mountfield.

SODEN, Eric 2002: The Golden Plover Flock at Tuesley Farm, Milford. *Surrey Bird Club Newsletter* 60:11-12.

SOUTH, R. 1966: Great Crested Grebes in Windsor Great Park, *The Middle-Thames Naturalist* for 1965.

SOUTH, Raymond 1977: Windsor Great Park and its Birds. *SBR* for 1976:62-65.

SOUTH, Raymond 1980: Royal Lake. Barracuda Books, Buckingham.

SOUTH, Raymond, John A. Chappell & Thelma M. Chappell 1979: A Royal Heronry. *SBR* for 1978:52-58.

SPARKS, Tim (1999): Phenology: past, present and future. Institute of Terrestrial Ecology *Newsletter* 157.

SPARKS, T. H. & P. D. Carey 1995: The Responses of Species to Climate over Two Centuries: an analysis of the Marsham Phenological Record, 1736-1947. *Journal of Ecology* (1995): 83:321-329.

SPENCER, Robert 1964: Report on Bird-ringing for 1963. *BB*, 57: 525-595.

SPENCER, Robert & Geoffrey H. Gush 1973: Siskins Feeding in Gardens. *BB*, 66:91-99.

SPICER, John W. G. 1854: Occurrence of the Little Bittern and other Rare Birds in Surrey. *Zool.*, 1854:4366-4367.

STAFFORD, J. 1962: Nightjar Enquiry, 1957-58. *Bird Study* 9:104-113.

STAINTON, Miss J. M. 1970: Coot in Flight at Barn Elms. *LBR* for 1968:96-102.

STANLEY, P. I., T. Brough, M. R. Fletcher, N. Horton & J. B. A. Rochard 1981: The origins of Herring Gulls wintering inland in south-east England. *Bird Study* 28:123-132.

STRANGEMAN, P. J. 1971: Birds of the River Thames at Westminster, 1968-1970. *LBR* for 1970:73-80.

STRANGEMAN, P. J. 1977: A Census of Breeding House Martins in the London Area. 1974. *LBR* for 1975:78-84.

STRANGEMAN, P. J. 1986: An Inner London Study of Birds of the River Thames at Westminster and Waterloo. *LBR* for 1985:170-186.

STRANGEMAN, P. J. 1988: The Status of the Cormorant in the London Area. *LBR* for 1987:173-94.

STRIDE, Robin 1997: Great White Egret at Vachery Pond. *SBR* for 1997.

STRIDE, Robin 1998: Red-footed Falcon at Winterfold Heath. *SBR* for 1998:115-116.

STRIDE, Robin 2000: Birds of the Isles of Surrey. Dayfive Publications, Cranleigh.

STUBBS, Frederick J. 1910: A Lost British Bird, *Zool.*, 15:150-156. In Bourne, 2003a.

SUCKLING, Roger L. 1997: Grey Herons in Surrey. *SBR* for 1997:120-138.

SUCKLING, Roger L. 1999: Grey Herons *Ardea cinerea* – Status and Conservation in Surrey. Typescript.

SUMMERS, Derek D. B. 1969: Common Birds in Surrey. *SBR* for 1967:31-35.

SUMMERS, R. W., D. C. Jardine, M. Marquiss & R. Proctor 1996: The Biometrics of Invading Common Crossbills *Loxia curvirostra* in Britain during 1990-1991. *Ringing & Migration* 17:1-10.

SUMMERS-SMITH, D. 1956: Movements of House Sparrows. *BB*, 49:465-488.

SUMMERS-SMITH, J. Denis 2003: The decline of the House Sparrow: a review. *BB*, 96: 439-446.

SURREY ART LOAN EXHIBITION CATALOGUE (SALEC) 1884, 2nd Edition Revised. Billing & Sons, Guildford.

SURREYBIRDERS: an Internet News Group.

SVENSSON, Lars 1992: Identification Guide to European Passerines, Fourth revised and enlarged edition. Stockholm, distributed by the British Trust for Ornithology, Thetford.

SWAN, Mike 1990: Redlegs, Hybrids and Other Funnies. *SBR* for 1990:67-68.

SWANN, H. K. 1893: The Birds of London. London.

SWANTON, E. W. 1947: A Country Museum. Educational Museum, Haslemere.

SWASH, Andy (Ed.), Standley, Peter, Bucknill, N. J. & Collins, Ian D. 1996: The Birds of Berkshire. The Berkshire Atlas Group, Reading.

SWAYNE, F. G. 1933: Birds of the Norwood District. *LN* for 1933:90-97.

SWINNERTON, Henry Hurd 1960: Fossils. New Naturalist series, Collins, London.

SWINNERTON, W. E. 1958: Fossil Birds. British Museum, London.

TATNER, Paul 1980: Magpies: a Question of Control. *SBR* for 1980:53-54.

TEGETMEIER, CORDEAUX, APLIN *et al.* 1896-98: *British Birds with their Nests and Eggs*. Passerines by Arthur Gardiner Butler.

THE VILLAGE LONDON ATLAS: the changing face of Greater London 1989. The Village Press Ltd, London

THOMAS, Adrian, 1999: Celebrate the Millennium. *Bird Watching* December 1999: 19-22.

THOMAS, Brian J. 2001: The Good Old Days. *RSPB East Surrey Group Newsletter* 29.

THORNTON, Richard 2000; A History of the Hampton Estate. http://www.elsteadvillage.org.uk/hampton.htm, possibly since removed.

TICEHURST, Norman F. 1911: Slender-billed Nutcrackers in Kent and Sussex. *BB*, 7:261-262.

TICEHURST, Norman F. 1926: On Swan-Marks (Part I). *BB*, 19:262-277.

TICEHURST, Norman F. 1924: The Early History of the Mute Swan in England. *BB*, 17:174-182.

TICEHURST, Norman F. 1928: The Office of Master of the Swans. *BB*, 22:74-84.

TICEHURST, Norman F. 1934: The Marks Used by Swan-owners of London and Middlesex. *LN* for 1933:67-84.

TICEHURST, Norman F. & Rev. F. C. R. Jourdain 1911: On the Distribution of the Nightingale during the Breeding Season in Great Britain. *BB*, 5:2-21.

TUCKER, B. W. 1943: Harry Forbes Witherby: A biographical sketch. *BB*, 37:162-174.

TURNER, William 1544: Avium Praecipuarum. Gymnicus, Cologne in Lovegrove 1990.

VAUGHAN, M. 1913: Report on the 1912 Inquiry. *BB*, 6:298-311.

VENABLES, L. S. V. 1934: Notes on Territory in the Dartford Warbler. *BB*, 28:58-63.

VENABLES, L. S. V. 1934a: Territory in the Great Crested Grebe. *BB*, 28:191-198.

VENABLES, L. S. V. & David Lack 1936: Further Notes on Territory in the Great Crested Grebe. *BB*, 30:60-69.

VENABLES, L. S. V. 1937: Bird Distribution on the Surrey Greensand Heaths: the avifaunal-botanical correlation. *Journal of Animal Ecology* 6:73-85.

VINICOMBE K. E. & A. J. H. Harrop 1999: Ruddy Shelducks in Britain and Ireland, 1986-94. *BB*, 92:225-255.

VINICOMBE, Keith 2000: Ruddy Shelducks in Britain and Ireland. (*BB, 93:149*).

WALKER, Ian D. 1983: Siskins in Surrey 1963-1983. *SBR* for 1983:49-54.

WALKER, Ian D. 1984: A Summary of Ringing Recoveries of Chaffinch, Brambling, Goldfinch, Linnet and Redpoll. *SBR* for 1984:68-78.

WALLIS, H. W. 1987: Icterine Warbler (*Hippolais icterina*) at Abinger. *SBR* for 1987:54.

WALPOLE-BOND, John 1938: A History of Sussex Birds. Witherby, London.

WASHINGTON, Derek 1978: Natural Foods in Winter, *SBR* for 1977:54-63.

WASHINGTON, Derek & C. J. O. Harrison 1969: Abnormal reddish plumage due to 'colour feeding' in wild Greenfinches. *Bird Study* 16:111-113.

WATSON, Bruce, Trevor Brigham and Tony Dyson 2001: London Bridge 2000 years of a river crossing. *MoLAS Monograph* 8.

WATSON, David: A Bird Artist in Scotland. H. F. & G. Witherby Ltd.

WATTS, Annabel 2004: An Artist's Surrey. Eden, Godalming.

WEBB, Nigel 1986: Heathlands. Collins, London.

WELLER, L. J. & J. J. Weller 1964: Ringing Sand Martins in Surrey. *SBR* for 1962.

WERNHAM, Chris, Mike Toms, John Marchant, Jacquie Clark, Gavin Siriwardena & Stephen Baillie 2002: The Migration Atlas. T. & A. D. Poyser. London.

WESTWOOD, N. J. 1961: The Pattern of Snipe Migration at Guildford Sewage Farm over Seven Years. *SBR* for 1959:22-26.

WESTWOOD, N. J. 1962: The Pattern of Wader Migration at Guildford Sewage Farm. *SBR* for 1960:24-29.

WESTWOOD, N. J. & G. Farr 1953: Notes on an Autumn Morning's Watch from a Hide on the Bank between Two Settling Beds at Guildford Sewage Farm. *SBR* for 1953:14

WHEATLEY, Jeffery J. 1972: Birds of a Guildford Tetrad – Boxgrove and Stoke. *SBR* for 1970:53-70.

WHEATLEY, Jeffery J. 1973a: Recent Carolina Duck Breeding Records in Surrey. *SBR* for 1972:64-65.

WHEATLEY, Jeffery J. 1973b: The Surrey Nightingale Population 1957-1971. *SBR* for 1972:66-72.

WHEATLEY, Jeffery J. 1974: A Calendar of Birds in Surrey. *SBR* for 1973:79-86.

WHEATLEY, Jeffery J. 1975: A Note on Great Northern Divers in Surrey. *SBR* for 1974:99.

WHEATLEY, Jeffery J. 1978a: A Revised Calendar of Birds in Surrey. *SBR* for 1977:64-70.

WHEATLEY, Jeffery J. 1978b: Long-eared Owls and Short-eared Owls in Surrey. *SBR* for 1978:61.

WHEATLEY, Jeffery J. 1980: Surrey Nightingales 1970-1980. *SBR* for 1980:46-52.

WHEATLEY, Jeffery J. 1986: Guillemots and Razorbills in Surrey. *SBR* for 1986:61-62.

WHEATLEY, Jeffery J. 1989: Birds Brought into Surrey by the Great Gale of October 1987. *SBR* for 1987:55-59.

WHEATLEY, Jeffery J. 1990: Bird Racing in Surrey. *SBR* for 1990:63-66.

WHEATLEY, Jeffery J. 1996: The 1996 Surrey Rook Census. *SBR* for 1996:103-119.

WHEATLEY, Jeffery J. 1997: The 1997 Woodlark Survey in Surrey. *SBR* for 1997:114-119.

WHITE, Gilbert 1789: The Natural History and Antiquities of Selbourne.

WHITE, Gilbert 1986, 1988, 1989: The Journals of Gilbert White, ed. Francesca Oak & Richard Mabey, 3. vols. Century, London.

WHITE, Monica 1972: Rooks in a Surrey Garden. *SBR* for 1971:77-81.

WIGHTMAN, J. S.1936: The Crossbill: Personal Observations during the Recent Invasion. *LBR* for 1936:26-28.

WILLS, D. L. & Ron H. Kettle 1997: The Birds of Wimbledon Common and Putney Heath. *LBR* for 1996:213-228.

WILSON, Andrew M., Juliet A. Vickery & Stephen J. Browne 2001: Numbers and Distribution of Northern Lapwings *Vanellus vanellus* breeding in England and Wales in 1998. *Bird Study* 48:2-17.

WILSON, Andy 2001: Countryside Survey 2000.*BTO News* 236, p.6-7.

WILSON, Andy 2001a: Nightingale Habitat Requirement Study. *BTO News* 234:6.

WILSON, David F. 1972: Dockers, The impact of industrial change. Fontana.

WILLUGHBY, Francis 1768: The Ornithology of Francis Willughby. London. 1972 facsimile edition of Paul P. B. Minet, Newport Pagnell.

WINTER, G. T. (unpublished): South Park 1905. Document in Holmesdale Natural History Club Museum.

WITHERBY, Harry F. 1911: The Crossbill as a British Bird. *BB*, 4:332-334.

WITHERBY, Harold F. 1934: The Willow-Tit's Method of Boring its Nesting-Hole. *BB*, 27:320-324.

WITHERBY H. F., Rev. F. C. R. Jourdain, Norman F. Ticehurst & Bernard W. Tucker 1941: The Handbook of British Birds, 5 vols. H.F. & G. Witherby Ltd, London. Checklist in Vol. 5.

WITHERBY, H. F. & E. M. Nicholson, 1937: On the Distribution and Status of the British Willow Tit. *BB*, 30:358-364.

WYCHERLEY, Julia & Richard Anstis 2001: Amphibians and Reptiles of Surrey. Surrey Wildlife Trust, Pirbright.

YAPP, Brunsdon 1981: Birds in Medieval Manuscripts. The British Library.

YARHAM, Ian, Dave Dawson, Martin Boyle & Rebecca Holliday 1998: Nature Conservation in Merton, Ecology Handbook 29. London Ecology Unit, London.

YARHAM, Ian, Michael Waite, Andrew Simpson & Niall Machin 1994: Nature Conservation in Lambeth, Ecology Handbook 26. London Ecology Unit, London.

YARHAM, Ian, Richard Barnes & Bob Britton 1993a: Nature Conservation in Sutton, Ecology Handbook 22. London Ecology Unit, London.

YARRELL, William 1825: *The Zoological Journal*, April 1825. In Harting 1866.

YARRELL, William E. 1826: Notice of the Occurrence of some rare British Birds. *The Zoological Journal*, 2: 24-27 in Glegg (1935). Harting (1866) refers to a note of the same bird by Yarrell in the same journal for April 1825.

YARRELL, William 1845: A History of British Birds, 3 vols. 2nd edition. John Van Voorst, London.

YULE, Brian (forthcoming): Roman Southwark 2: Roman Buildings on the Southwark waterfront: excavations at Winchester Palace, 1983-90, Part I.

Selected Site and Species Studies:

Single Species, Single Site

Mute Swan: Fetcham Mill Pond, Burkhill (1942); Cutt Mill, Huxley (1947).

Canada Goose: Shepperton, Holleyman (undated).

Mallard: Kew, Baker (1972).

Ring-necked Duck x Tufted Duck hybrid: Kew Green, Gasson & Lawrence (1993).

Goldeneye: Spelthorne, Oliver (1978).

Grey Partridge: Addington, Croft (1942).

Pied-billed Grebe: South Norwood, Flynn (1998).

Little Grebe: Fetcham Mill Pond, Hartley (1933, 1937).

Great Crested Grebe: Frensham, Venables (1934a), Venables & Lack (1936).

Manx Shearwater: Staines, Cox (1964).

Mediterranean (Balearic) Shearwater: Hastings (1985).

Squacco Heron: Walton Reservoirs, Harris (1997b).

Great White Egret: Vachery Pond, Stride (1997).

Grey Heron: Windsor Great Park, South *et al.* (1979).

Buzzard: Witley Park, Chance (1939), *SBR* for 1954.

Red-footed Falcon: Shamley Green, released Thursley, Harris (1997a); Winterfold Heath, Stride (1998).

Spotted Crake: Beddington, Hutson & Gooders (1970); Papercourt Gravel Pits, Bowley (1976).

Coot: Barn Elms, Stainton (1970): Fetcham Mill Pond, Burkhill (1931, 1933); Waddon Ponds, Coleman (1985).

Collared Pratincole: Staines Reservoir, Naylor (1985).

Killdeer: Beddington Sewage Farm, Messenbird (1986).

American Golden Plover: King George VI Reservoir, Moon (1997).

Lapwing: Farm at Epsom, Lister (1938).

White-rumped Sandpiper: Perry Oaks Sewage Farm, Hastings (1986); Walton Reservoirs, Harris (1995).

Baird's Sandpiper: Staines Reservoir, Haig (1983).

Snipe: Guildford Sewage Farm, Westwood (1961).

Marsh Sandpiper: Old Woking Sewage Farm, Gates (1994).

Green Sandpiper: Beddington Sewage Farm, Coleman and Milne (1996).

Wilson's Phalarope: Staines Reservoir, Moon (1987b).

Black-headed Gull: Bankside, Oliver (1994).

Ring-billed Gull: Staines Reservoir, Haig (1985).

Glaucous-winged Gull: Beddington, Allan 2007.

White-winged Black Tern: Barn Elms Reservoirs, Maroevic (1994).

Cuckoo: West End Common, Esher, Burkhill (1928).

Yellow-billed Cuckoo: Oxted, Jones (1992).

Tawny Owl: Morden, Beven (1965).

Swift: Beddington Sewage Farm, Hutson *et al.* (1971).

Bee-eater: Milford, Garcia (1990).

Wryneck: Limpsfield, Robbins (1930).

Red-rumped Swallow: Stoke Lake, Gates (1997).

Tawny Pipit: Claygate Common, Mullins (1976).

Water Pipit: Stoke Water Meadows, Gates (1993).

Pied Wagtail: Esher Common, Keywood (1936), Richmond Park, Collyer (1937).

Nightingale: Bookham Common, Prowse (1999).

Desert Wheatear: Barn Elms Reservoir, Aris (1991).

Blackbird: Walton-on-Thames, Parr (1969b).

Dartford Warbler: West Surrey, Venables (1934).

Sardinian Warbler: Surbiton, Montier (1993).

Pallas's Warbler: Wandsworth Common, Greensmith (1987).

Siberian Chiffchaff: Stoke Water Meadows, Gates (1992a).

Willow Warbler: Witley Common, Lawn (1984).

Firecrest: Haslemere, Kirkpatrick (1983).

Willow Tit: Bookham Common, Beven (1963).

Rook: Godalming, White (1972).

Carrion Crow: Mitcham, Brown (1963).

House Sparrow: Morden, Beven (1947).

Tree Sparrow: Beddington Sewage Farm, Aspinall *et al.* (1991.)

Siskin: Weybridge, Bullock (1967).

Yellowhammer: Limpsfield, Oliver (1992).

Little Bunting: Pirbright Common, Mullins (1986); Milford, Garcia, (1991)

Single Species, Multiple Sites

Wood Duck: Wheatley (1973a).

Mandarin: Davies (1986).

Great Northern Diver: Wheatley (1975).

Great Crested Grebe: Hollom (1933, 1955), Parr (1976).

Grey Heron: Chappell & Chappell (1988), Suckling (1997, 1999).

Lapwing: Garcia (1986).

Black Tern: Paine (1978).

Nightjar: Sage (1976), Sage (1981), Evans (1993a).

Wryneck: Monk (1956).

Woodlark: Dallas (1928), Wheatley (1997).

Sand Martin: Weller & Weller (1964).

Dunnock: Ogston (1971).

Nightingale: Wheatley (1973b), Wheatley (1980).

Icterine Warbler: Abinger, Wallis (1987).

Dartford Warbler: Raynsford (1963).

Wood Warbler: Herber (1985).

Goldcrest: Herber (1971).

Great Tit (Melanistic): Sage (1993).

Willow Tit: Witherby & Nicholson (1937).

Red-backed Shrike: Peakall (1962), Carter (1963).

Magpie: Tatner (1980).

Rook: Wheatley (1996).

Greenfinch: Channer (1971).

Siskin: Walker (1983).

Crossbill: Wightman (1936), Oliver (1998a).

Corn Bunting: Evans (1993b).

Multi-species Surveys of Single Sites

Addlestone: Gulls, Lancaster (1995), Lancaster (1998).

Battersea Park: Nicholson (1995).

Beddington Sewage Farm: Milne (1956), Hatton (1982).

Bookham Common: LN for 1943, 1946 and most years since, Carrington (1944), Beven (1971).

Brixton: Power (1910).

Brooklands Sewage Farm: Hollom (1935, 1937).

Cannon Hill Common, Merton: Kettle (1998).

Clapham and Wandsworth Commons: Gooders (1965).

Cranleigh area: Stride (2000).

Dulwich: Power (1910), Pounds (1965).

Dulwich Wood: Oliver (2003).

Epsom and Ewell: Massey (1979).

Epsom Downs: Bentham (1961).

Farleigh and District: Pounds (1952).

Frimley Gravel Pits: Moss (1972).

Gatton Park: Coleman (1991).

Guildford: Boxgrove and Stoke, Wheatley (1972), Gates (1992b).

Pewley, Newman (1974).

Guildford Sewage Farm: Harrison (1945 and 1947), Adams (1953a), Adams (1953b), Westwood & Farr (1953), Westwood (1962).

Hersham Sewage Farm: Parr (1963).

Holmethorpe Sand Pits: Gale (undated).

Hurst Farm, Milford: Pullen (1977).

Island Barn Reservoir: Parr (1974).

Kew: Wildfowl Mortality, Baker (1972).

King George VI and Staines Reservoirs: Wildfowl, Moon (1987).

Kingston Cemetery: McNeil (1994).

Limpsfield Common: LN for 1937, 1938, 1939, 1940 and 1941, Oliver (2000).

London Area: pelagic seabirds, Moon (1984).

Norwood/South Norwood Country Park/Elmers End Sewage Farm: Swayne (1933), Aldridge (1885), Manser (1944), Birkett (1992).

Queen Mary Reservoir: Geen (1990).

Reigate: Brewer (1856).

River Thames, Inner London: Cramp & Teagle (1955), Oliver (1998); *Westminster*, Strangeman (1971), *Westminster and Waterloo*, Strangeman (1986).

River Wandle: Coleman (1995).

Shepperton: Shepperton Bird Reports 1982-86 (Holleyman).

Surrey Commercial Docks: Grant (1971), George (1974), Alderton (1977).

Tadworth: Bentham (1959).

Thursley Common: Fry & Welland (1962), Brassington (2003).

Wimbledon Common: Kettle (1983).

Wimbledon Common and Putney Heath: Wills & Kettle (1997), Drakeford & Sutcliffe (2000).

Windsor Great Park: South (1977).

Wisley: Elliott *et al.* (1985 and 1988).

Witley Common: Lawn (undated).

Worcester Park: Gulls, Smith (1971).

Multi-species, Multiple sites

Atlas: Forster (1973).

Bird Racing: Wheatley (1990).

Calendar: Wheatley (1974), Wheatley (1978a).

Censuses: Parr (1969), Summers (1969), Griffin (1970, 1975, 1979, 1980, 1984, 1989, 1990, 1994, 1995, 1996, 2000).

Conservation and Nature Reserves: Forster (1971, 1975, 1976).

Finch recoveries: Walker (1984).

Guillemot and Razorbill: Wheatley (1986).

Gulls: Rowberry (1934), Parr (1970).

Heathland species: Davis (1975), Sage (1977).

Historical surveys: Bentham (1954), Bentham (1967), Bentham (1969), Bentham (1970).

Little Ringed Plover and Ringed Plover: Herber (1984).

Migration: Parr (1965), Ogston (1966).

Owls: Wheatley (1978b).

Partridges: Swan (1990).

Salmonellosis: Cornelius (1973).

Storm-driven birds: Moon (1988), Wheatley (1987).

Winter Food: Washington (1978).

Ringing

Beddington Ringing Station: LBRs for 1958-64.

Surrey (including Beddington): Surrey Bird Reports 1957-2001 (including parts of Middlesex inside and outside Spelthorne, from 1967 and parts of Berkshire, from 1977). Some London Bird Reports contain Surrey information, often highly summarised.

Northwest Surrey and Spelthorne: Hersham Ringing Group Reports, Runnymede Ringing Group Reports. *The Middle Thames Naturalist* includes a ringing report .

UK including Surrey: BTO annual Ringing Report, in *British Birds* and later in *Ringing and Migration*.

Papers on species: see Sand Martin, Blackbird, Finch and Siskin recoveries above.

Gazetteer:
including places mentioned in the text

† = Greater London
* = Spelthorne

Abbey Lake	TQ0368	
Abbot's Pond see Frensham Little Pond		
Abinger Common	TQ1145	
Abinger Hammer	TQ0947	
Abinger Roughs	TQ1047	
Addington	† TQ3764	
Addington Hills	† TQ3564	
Addington Park	† TQ3663	
Addiscombe	† TQ3466	
Addlestone	TQ0564	
Addlestonemoor	TQ0565	
Albert Bridge	† TQ2777	
Albury	TQ0547	
Albury Bottom	SU9764	
Albury Heath	TQ0646	
Albury Park	TQ0647	
Albury Warren	TQ0547	
Alderbrook	TQ0642	
Aldershot	SU8650	
Aldershot Camp Sewage Farm	SU8852	
Alderstead Farm	TQ2954	
Alderstead Heath	TQ3055	
Aldhurst Farm	TQ1840	
Alfold	TQ0334	
Anerley	† TQ3469	
Anstead Brook	SU9332	
Anstiebury	† TQ1544	
Apps Court Gravel Pit	† TQ1662	
Arbrook Common	† TQ1463	
Archbishop's Park	† TQ2476	
Arden Green Sewage Farm	TQ3845	
Arden Wood	TQ3945	
Artington	SU9947	
Ash Common	SU9052	
Ash Ranges	SU9052	
Ash Vale Gravel Pits	SU8853	
Ashford	* TQ0771	
Ashtead	† TQ1858	
Ashtead Common	TQ1759	

Axe Pond	SU8640	
Backside Common, Wood Street	SU9450	
Badshot Lea	SU8649	
Bagmoor Common	SU9242	
Bagshot	SU9063	
Bagshot Heath	SU9161	
Bank's Common	TQ1156	
Bankside Power Station	† TQ3280	
Bankside Reach	† TQ3280	
Banstead	† TQ2559	
Banstead Downs	† TQ2561	
Banstead Heath	† TQ2354	
Banstead Wood	† TQ2656	
Barfold Copse	SU9232	
Barn Elms	† TQ2277	
Barn Elms London Wetland Centre	† TQ2277	
Barn Elms Park	† TQ2276	
Barn Elms Reservoirs	† TQ2277	
Barnes	† TQ2276	
Barnes Common	† TQ2275	
Barnsthorns Wood	TQ0855	
Barossa Common	SU8761	
Barrow Green Sand Pit	TQ3752	
Barwell Court Farm, Chessington	† TQ1763	
Battersea	† TQ2676	
Battersea Fields	† TQ2877	
Battersea Park	† TQ2877	
Battersea Power Station	† TQ2777	
Bay Pond, Godstone	TQ3551	
Baynards Park	TQ0836	
Beacon Hill, Hindhead	SU8736	
Beare Green	TQ1743	
Beaulieu Heights Wood	† TQ3369	
Beddington Corner	† TQ2866	
Beddington Park	† TQ2965	
Beddington Sewage Farm	† TQ2966	
Beddlestead Valley	TQ3957	
Bedfont Lakes Country Park	† TQ0772	
Belair Park, Dulwich	† TQ3273	

Bellfields, Guildford	SU9951	
Belmont	† TQ2562	
Bermondsey	† TQ3479	
Berrylands Sewage Works	† TQ1968	
Bessborough Reservoir	TQ1268	
Betchworth	TQ2150	
Betchworth Park	TQ1849	
Beverley Brook, Richmond Park	† TQ2172	
Binscombe	SU9746	
Birchy Pond	SU9141	
Birtley Green	TQ0143	
Bisley Common	SU9458	
Bisley Ranges	SU9358	
Black Pond, Esher	TQ1262	
Blackberry Land Pond	TQ3941	
Blackfriars Bridge	† TQ3180	
Blackhatch Wood	TQ4039	
Blackheath	TQ0346	
Blackwater Wood	TQ4139	
Bletchingley	TQ3250	
Blindley Heath	TQ3546	
Bluegate Gravel Pit	† TQ2271	
Boldermere	TQ0758	
Bonsey's Farm	TQ0061	
Bookham Common	TQ1356	
Botany Bay	SU9834	
Botley's Park, Chertsey	TQ0264	
Boundstone	SU8344	
Bourne Hall Pond, Ewell	TQ2162	
Bourne Woods	SU8544	
Bower's Lock	TQ0152	
Bowlhead Green	SU9138	
Box Hill	TQ1951	
Bramley Sewage Farm	TQ0243	
Bransland Wood	TQ3248	
Brentford Ait	† TQ1877	
Brentmoor Heath	SU9361	
Bricksbury Hill	SU8349	
Brickworks Wood	TQ3944	
Britten's Pond	SU9953	
Brixton	† TQ3074	
Broadford Bridge	SU9946	
Broadford Marsh	SU9946	

Broadham Green, Oxted	TQ3851	Carshalton Park	† TQ2764	Cleygate Common	SU9153
Broadmead, Send	TQ0256	Carshalton Pond	† TQ2764	Clock Barn Farm	SU9741
Broadstreet Common	SU9550	Castle Bottom, Banstead	TQ2559	Cobbetthill Common	SU9445
Broadwater, Farncombe	SU9845	Caterham	TQ3355	Cobham	TQ1159
Brockham	TQ2049	Caterham Valley	TQ3456	Coldharbour	TQ1543
Brockley Wood	TQ2540	Catteshall, Godalming	SU9844	Coleford Bridge Rd, Frimley	SU8855
Brockwell Park	† TQ3174	Chaldon	TQ3155	Colley Hill	TQ2452
Brook	SU9338	Chantries, Guildford	TQ0048	Collier's Wood	† TQ2770
Brooklands	TQ0662	Charles Hill	SU8844	Colony Bog	SU9259
Brooklands Sewage Farm	TQ0662	Charlton Gravel Pits	* TQ0869	Combe Lane Farm	SU9437
Brookwood Cemetery	SU9556	Charlton Rubbish Dump	* TQ0869	Compton	SU9547
Brookwood Heath	SU9555	Charlwood	TQ2541	Coombe Hill Golf Course	† TQ2170
Broome Hall	TQ2150	Charterhouse	SU9645	Coombe Warren, Wimbledon	† TQ2070
Broome Park, Betchworth	TQ2150	Chase, Haslemere	SU9131	Coombe Wood, Wimbledon	† TQ2070
Brunswick Park	† TQ3376	Cheam	† TQ2363	Coopers Hill, Runnymede	SU9972
Buckland Sand Pits	TQ2251	Chelsea Reservoir, Walton	TQ1268	Copthorne	TQ3239
Bugg Hill Farm, Warlingham	TQ3557	Chelsham	TQ3858	Cosford Pond	SU9138
Bullswater Common	SU9554	Chelsham Court	TQ3758	Coulsdon	† TQ2959
Burgess Park	† TQ3377	Chertsey	TQ0466	Coulsdon Common	† TQ3257
Burgh Heath	TQ2259	Chertsey Bridge	TQ0466	County Hall, Southbank	† TQ3079
Burpham	TQ0152	Chertsey Gravel Pit/ Laleham Burway	TQ0468	Court Wood, Addington	† TQ3662
Burstow	TQ3144	Chertsey Lock	TQ0566	Cowey Sale	TQ0966
Burstow Sewage Farm	TQ3043	Chertsey Meads	TQ0666	Cranleigh	TQ0538
Burstow Stream, Horley	TQ2844	Chertsey Meads Sewage Farm	TQ0566	Cranleigh Sewage Farm	TQ0439
Burwood Park	TQ1064	Chertsey Weir	TQ0564	Crastock	SU9755
Bury Lake, Dorking	TQ1548	Chessington	† TQ1864	Crawley Sewage Farm	TQ2840
Busbridge	SU9742	Chiddingfold	SU9535	Croham Hurst	† TQ3363
Busbridge Lakes	SU9742	Childown	SU9964	Crooksbury Common	SU8945
Bushy Park	† TQ1669	Chilworth	TQ0247	Crooksbury Hill	SU8746
Butterhill	† TQ2865	Chilworth Ponds	TQ0247	Crossways Farm, Abinger	TQ1047
Byfleet	TQ0561	Chipstead	† TQ2758	Crowhurst	TQ3946
Caesar's Camp (Surrey)	SU8349	Chiswick Bridge	† TQ2076	Crownpits, Godalming	SU9743
Camberley	SU8760	Chiswick Eyot	TQ2277	Croydon	† TQ3265
Camberley Rubbish Tip	SU8659	Chobham Common	SU9864	Croydon Airport	† TQ3163
Camberley Sewage Farm	SU8659	Chobham Ridges	SU9059	Crystal Palace Park	† TQ3470
Camberwell Old Cemetery	† TQ3474	Christmas Pie, Normandy	SU9249	Cuckoo Hill	SU9361
Canada Water	† TQ3579	Churt	SU8538	Cuddington Golf Club	† TQ2461
Canfold	TQ0839	Clandon	TQ0452	Culmer, Witley	SU9439
Cannizaro Park	† TQ2370	Clandon Downs	TQ0550	Curley Hill	SU9161
Cannon Hill Common	† TQ2368	Clandon Park	TQ0451	Cutt Mill	SU9045
Canterbury Rew	SU9936	Clapham Common	† TQ2874	Deepcut	SU9056
Capel	TQ1740	Clapham Junction	† TQ2775	Denbies Vineyard	TQ1651
Carron Pond, Farnham Park	SU8348	Claremont	TQ1363	Derry's Wood, Wonersh	TQ0345
Carshalton Beeches	† TQ2763	Claremont Lake	TQ1363	Devil's Punch Bowl	SU8936
		Claygate	TQ1563		
		Claypit Wood	SU8241		

Devilsden Wood,
Coulsdon † TQ3056
Dippenhall SU8146
Ditton Field (=Ditton
Common?) † TQ1567
Ditton Hill † TQ1765
Ditton Marsh
(not marsh now). † TQ1465
Dockenfield SU8239
Donkey Town SU9360
Dorking TQ1648
Dorking Mill Pond TQ1649
Dorking Sewage Farm TQ1750
Dormans Park TQ3940
Dormansland TQ4042
Downside TQ1158
Dulwich † TQ3372
Dulwich Allotments † TQ3472
Dulwich Common/
Park/Lake † TQ3373
Dulwich Meadows – lost site,
Dulwich
Dulwich Mill Pond † TQ3373
Dulwich Park † TQ3373
Dulwich Wood † TQ3472
Dungates Farm TQ2250
Dungeon Hill TQ2759
Dunsfold TQ0036
Dunsfold Aerodrome TQ0236
Durfold Wood SU9832
Duxhurst TQ2345
Earlsfield † TQ2673
Earlswood Common TQ2748
Earlswood Lakes, Reigate TQ2748
Earlswood Sewage Farm SU2748
Eashing SU9443
Eashing Bridge SU9443
East Croydon † TQ3365
East Dulwich
(Dulwich?) † TQ3372
East Ewell TQ2362
East Horsley TQ0953
East Molesey TQ1467
East Sheen † TQ1974
East Wyke Farm,
Normandy SU9150
Effingham TQ1253
Effingham Common TQ1055
Effingham Fish Ponds TQ1155
Egham TQ0071
Egham Refuse Tip –
exact site unknown TQ0171

Ellens Green TQ1035
Elmbridge Leisure Centre TQ1067
Elmers End Sewage Farm – see
South Norwood Country Park
Elstead SU9043
Elstead Common SU8942
Embercourt = Imber Court?
Englefield Green SU9970
Enticknaps Copse SU9937
Enton SU9540
Enton Golf Course SU9640
Epsom TQ2060
Epsom Common TQ1960
Epsom Common Stew
Ponds TQ1860
Epsom Downs TQ2158
Epsom Race Course TQ2158
Epsom Rubbish Tip TQ2161
Epsom Sewage Farm TQ2161
Esher TQ1464
Esher Common TQ1362
Esher Rugby Club TQ1265
Esher Sewage Farm TQ1366
Eude Waters (Ewood) TQ2044
Ewell TQ2163
Ewell Court TQ2163
Ewhurst TQ0940
Ewhurst Green TQ0939
Fairchildes TQ3960
Fairmile Common TQ1261
Fairoaks Airport TQ0062
Farleigh TQ3660
Farley Heath TQ0545
Farnborough North
Camp Gravel Pits SU8853
Farncombe SU9745
Farnham SU8443
Farnham Park SU8448
Farnham Sewage Farm SU8548
Farthing Down TQ2958
Felbridge TQ3639
Felcourt Lake TQ3842
Felix Lane Gravel Pit * TQ0967
Ferris Meadow Gravel Pit – see
Ferry Lane
Ferry Lane Gravel Pits * TQ0766
Fetcham TQ1455
Fetcham Downs TQ1554
Fetcham Mill Pond TQ1860
Fickleshole TQ3960
Fieldcommon Gravel Pit TQ1267

Fisherlane Wood SU9832
Fleet Lake TQ0368
Flutters Hill, Chobham SU9965
Folly Bog SU9261
Forked Pond, Thursley SU9141
Fort Belvedere SU9768
Foxwarren Park,
Cobham TQ0759
Freelands – see Frylands Wood
Frensham SU8441
Frensham Common SU8540
Frensham Great Pond SU8440
Frensham Little Pond SU8641
Frensham Manor SU8340
Frensham Outlet Pond SU8340
Frensham Vale SU8443
Friday Street TQ1245
Frimley SU8858
Frimley Gravel Pits SU8856
Frimley Green SU8856
Frillinghurst SU9334
Frith Hill, Godalming SU9744
Frylands Wood TQ3761
Furze Farm, Bisley SU9359
Furzefield Wood TQ0634
Gatton Bottom TQ2753
Gatton Lake TQ2752
Gatton Park TQ2752
Gatwick Airport TQ2741
Gibbet Hill SU8935
Gatwick Water Works TQ2742
Glebe Water, Godstone TQ3551
Godalming Sewage Farm – see
Unstead
Godalming Wharf SU9744
Godstone TQ3551
Godstone Reserve TQ3452
Godstone Sand Pits TQ3451
Goldsworth Park Lake SU9858
Gomshall TQ0847
Gracious Pond SU9863
Grand Surrey Canal – see Surrey
Docks
Gravelly Hill TQ3353
Grayshott SU8735
Grayswood SU9134
Great Ridings Wood/
Plantation TQ1054
Guildford SU9849
Guildford Castle SU9949
Guildford Refuse Tip TQ0050

Guildford Sewage Farm TQ0050
Hackbridge † TQ2865
Hackhurst Downs TQ1048
Hale SU8448
Halliford Mere * TQ0766
Halliloo Wood/
  Plantation TQ3657
Ham Common † TQ1871
Ham Gravel Pit(s) † TQ1672
Ham House † TQ1772
Ham Lands † TQ1672
Hambledon SU9638
Hamm Moor, Weybridge TQ0684
Hammer Pond, Thursley SU9140
Hammersmith Bridge † TQ2278
Hampton (Tree) Nursery SU8945
Hamsey Green † TQ3559
Hankley Common SU8841
Happy Valley, Farthing
  Down TQ3057
Hascombe Camp/Hill TQ0038
Haslemere SU8934
Hatches Pit, Frimley SU8856
Hatchlands TQ0652
Hatherop Road Playing
  Fields † TQ1270
Hays Wharf † TQ3380
Headley TQ2054
Headley Heath TQ2053
Heathrow/Airport † TQ0775
Hedgecourt TQ3540
Henley Park Lake SU9353
Henley Wood, Chelsham TQ3758
Herne Hill † TQ3274
Hersham TQ1163
Hersham Gravel Pit TQ1266
Hersham Sewage Farm TQ1265
Highcombe Bottom SU8937
Highfield SU8938
Highstreet Green SU9835
Hinchley Wood TQ1565
Hindhead SU8835
Hindhead Commons SU8936
Hindhead Golf Course SU8637
Hoebridge, Old Woking TQ0257
Hog's Back SU9348
Hogsmill Sewage Farm see
  Berrylands
Holloways Heath SU9939
Holmbury Hill TQ1043
Holmbury St Mary TQ1044

Holmethorpe Sand Pits TQ2951
Holmwood Common TQ1745
Holmwood Sewage
  Works TQ1646
Holt Wood, Chelsham TQ3759
Honor Oak † TQ3574
Hook † TQ1864
Hook Allotments † TQ1764
Hookwood TQ2542
Hooley TQ2856
Horley TQ2943
Horley Sewage Farm TQ2643
Horns Hill TQ1559
Horsell TQ1061
Horsell Common TQ1061
Horsley TQ0954
Horton Country Park TQ1962
Hurst Gate Lake SU9542
Hurst Green TQ3951
Hurst Park TQ1469
Hurtmore SU9445
Hurtwood TQ1044
Hydestile SU9740
Hydon Heath SU9739
Hydons Ball SU9739
Hythe SU0271
Imber Court TQ1466
Inval, Haslemere SU8934
Isabella Plantation † TQ1971
Island Barn Reservoir TQ1467
Isleworth Ait † TQ1675
Itchingwood Common TQ4150
Jacobswell, Guildford SU9953
Jayes Park TQ1440
Jordan's Wood TQ2039
Jubilee Gardens † TQ3180
Juniper Top, Box Hill TQ1852
Kemishford, Smart's
  Heath SU9855
Kempton Park * TQ1169
Kempton Reservoirs † TQ1170
Kenley † TQ3259
Kennington Oval † TQ3077
Kettlebury Hill SU8840
Kew † TQ1877
Kew Gardens † TQ1876
Kew Green † TQ1877
Kiln Platt, Shere TQ0744
King George VI
  Reservoir * TQ0473
King George's Park † TQ2574

King's Mere, Wimbledon
  Common † TQ2373
Kings Ridge, Frensham SU8540
Kingston † TQ1869
Kingston Hill † TQ1970
Kingswood TQ0071
Kingswood Warren TQ2455
Knaphill SU9658
Knight (Knights)
  Reservoir TQ1167
Knott Park TQ1459
Lake House, Ockley TQ1539
Lakeside, Ash SU8956
Laleham * TQ0568
Laleham Burway TQ0467
Laleham Park * TQ0568
Laleham Rubbish Dump – see
  Thorpe
Lambeth Bridge † TQ3078
Lambeth Palace † TQ3079
Lambeth Reservoir,
  Walton TQ1268
Lammas Lands,
  Godalming SU9744
Langham Ponds,
  Runnymede TQ0072
Langshott, Horley TQ2944
Lea Park – see Witley Park
Leatherhead TQ1658
Leatherhead Rubbish
  Dump TQ1457
Leatherhead Sewage
  Works TQ1457
Leigh Mill/Place TQ3950
Leith Hill TQ1444
Lewisham † TQ3873
Lightwater Country Park SU9162
Limpsfield TQ4053
Limpsfield Chart TQ4452
Lingfield TQ3844
Little Bookham TQ1256
Littleton Lane Gravel
  Pits/Lakes * TQ0667
Littleton Reservoir – see Queen
  Mary
Littleworth Common TQ1565
Littleworth Cross SU8945
Lloyd Park † TQ3465
London Bridge † TQ3280
London Wetland Centre – see
  Barn Elms

Long Ditton † TQ1766
Long Valley, Hampshire SU8352
Longside Lake TQ0168
Lonsdale Road
   Reservoir † TQ2177
Loseley Park SU9747
Lower Halliford * TQ0866
Lower Kingswood † TQ2553
Lower Pyrford TQ0359
Lowfield Heath TQ2640
Lucas Green SU9359
Lumberline TQ3957
Lyne TQ0166
Lyne Sewage Farm TQ0167
Manor Lake, Thorpe TQ0368
Mare Hill, Witley SU9340
Margery TQ2552
Martyr's Green TQ0957
Mayford SU9956
Meath Green Sewage Farm – see
   Horley
Mercers Farm TQ3051
Mercers Lake TQ2918
Merrist Wood Agricultural
   College SU9653
Merrow TQ0250
Merrow Common,
   Guildford TQ0251
Merrow Downs TQ0450
Merstham Sewage Works TQ3052
Merton † TQ2669
Merton Park
Mickleham TQ1753
Milford SU9442
Milford Common SU9341
Milford Station SU9541
Miller's Pond, Shirley † TQ3665
Milton Court, Dorking TQ1549
Mitcham † TQ2868
Mitcham Common † TQ2967
Mitcham Common
   Golf Course † TQ2867
Mitcham Gravel Pit(s) † TQ2967
Mizen's Farm, Horsell TQ0161
Moat Pond SU9041
Moated Farm TQ0563
Molesey TQ1368
Molesey Gravel Pit TQ1267
Molesey Heath TQ1367
Molesey Reservoirs – see Walton
Molesey Sewage Farm TQ1367

Moor Lane Nature
   Reserve TQ0272
Moor Park SU8645
Moorhouse TQ4353
Morden TQ2556
Morden Hall Park † TQ2668
Mortlake † TQ2075
Motspur Park † TQ2267
Mousehill Down SU9342
Mugswell TQ2654
Munstead Heath SU9842
Mytchett Gravel Pit SU8854
Mytchett Lake SU8954
Mytchett Place SU9055
Nanhurst TQ0338
Netherne TQ2956
Netley Heath TQ0849
New Addington † TQ3863
New Cross † TQ3676
New Haw TQ0563
New Malden † TQ2068
Newark Mill (now gone) TQ0457
Newark Priory TQ0457
Newchapel TQ3642
Newdigate TQ1942
Newhouse Farm, Kiln
   Heath TQ3140
Newlands Corner TQ0449
Newton Wood TQ1860
Nine Elms † TQ2977
Nonsuch Park † TQ2353
Norbury Park TQ1553
Nore Hill TQ3757
Nork Park TQ2359
Normandy SU9251
North Breache TQ1040
Norwood † TQ3270
Norwood Farm, Cobham TQ1159
Nower Wood TQ1954
Nunhead Cemetery † TQ3575
Nutfield TQ3050
Nutfield Marsh TQ3051
Nutfield Ridge TQ2950
Oaken Wood,
   Chiddingfold SU9933
Oatlands Park TQ0964
Oatlands, Walton-on-
   Thames TQ0964
Obelisk Pond SU9770
Ockford (Coppice),
   Godalming SU9543

Ockford Pond,
   Godalming SU9643
Ockham TQ0756
Ockham Common TQ0858
Ockley TQ1440
Ockley Common SU9141
Old Coulsdon † TQ3157
Old Deer Park,
   Richmond † TQ1775
Old Lyne Sewage Farm – see Lyne
Old Malden † TQ2066
Old Woking Sewage
   Farm TQ0357
Olddean Common SU8862
One Tree Hill, Honour
   Oak † TQ3574
Ottershaw TQ0264
Outwood TQ3145
Oxenford SU9343
Oxshott TQ1460
Oxshott Brickworks – probable
   site TQ1360
Oxshott Heath TQ1361
Oxted TQ3852
Oxted Mill TQ3951
Painshill Park TQ0960
Papercourt Gravel Pits TQ0356
Papercourt Lock TQ0259
Papercourt Marshes TQ0356
Papercourt Meadows TQ0356
Parish Field, Thursley SU9040
Park Downs, Banstead TQ2658
Park Farm, Banstead TQ2658
Park Farm, Chessington TQ1862
Peaslake TQ0844
Peasmarsh SU9946
Pebble Combe TQ2152
Peckham † TQ3476
Peckham Rye Park † TQ3475
Pen Ponds, Richmond
   Park † TQ1973
Penge † TQ3570
Penton Hook TQ0469
Peper Harow SU9344
Perrots Farm TQ2357
Perry Oaks Sewage
   Farm * TQ0575
Petersham Meadows † TQ1873
Pewley Down, Guildford TQ0048
Pickhurst SU9634
Pirbright Common SU9254

Pirbright Ranges	SU9260	Reigate	TQ2549	Seale Sand Pits	SU8947
Pirbright Village	SU9455	Reigate Heath	TQ2350	Secretts Garden Centre	SU9542
Pitch Hill	TQ0842	Reigate Hill	TQ2552	Seears Park, Cheam	† TQ2464
Pitchers Wood near		Reigate Priory	TQ2449	Seething Wells Filter	
Titsey	TQ3956	Richmond	† TQ1775	Beds	† TQ1766
Pitchfont Lodge	TQ4055	Richmond Green	† TQ1774	Selsdon	† TQ3562
Pockford Harbour	SU9836	Richmond Park	† TQ2073	Selsdon Wood	† TQ3661
Polesden Lacey	TQ1352	Rickford Common	TQ9754	Send	TQ0255
Pondover Pit	SU9653	Riddlesdown	TQ3260	Send Gravel Pits	TQ0255
Posterngate Trout Lake	TQ3649	Ripley	TQ0556	Send Grove	TQ0154
Postford Pond	TQ0347	Ripley Sewage Farm	TQ0457	Send Heath Ponds	TQ0256
Potters Lane Sand Pit	TQ0255	River Ember at East		Send Marsh	TQ0355
Povey Cross	TQ2642	Molesey	TQ1467	Send Water Meadows	TQ0356
Poynter's	TQ0958	Rivermead Island	TQ1168	Sendholme	TQ0154
Prest Wood	SU9837	Rodborough Common	SU9341	Shackleford	SU9345
Prey Heath	SU9855	Rodsall	SU9245	Shad Thames, Borough	† TQ3380
Prince George's Playing		Roehampton	† TQ2274	Shalford Common	TQ0046
Fields	† TQ2368	Rolls Meadows/Road	† TQ3478	Shamley Green	TQ0344
Prince's Coverts	TQ1661	Rookery Pond, Westcott	TQ1348	Shawfield	SU8850
Princes Lake	† TQ0772	Rotherhythe	† TQ3579	Sheen Bridge – see Chiswick	
Princess Royal Sand		Roundshaw Downs	† TQ3063	Bridge	
Pits, Runfold	SU8647	Rowhills Copse Nature		Sheen Common	† TQ1974
Pudmore	SU9041	Reserve	SU8549	Sheepleas, Horsley	TQ0851
Pudmore Pond	SU9041	Rowledge	SU8243	Sheepwalk Gravel	
Punch Bowl – see Devil's Punch		Royal Common, Elstead	SU9242	Pits/Lake	* TQ0667
Bowl		Royal Military Academy	SU8660	Sheerwater	TQ0260
Purley	† TQ3162	Royal Mills, Esher	TQ1365	Sheet's Heath,	
Putney	† TQ2375	Run Common	TQ0341	Brookwood	SU9457
Putney Bridge	† TQ2475	Runfold	SU8747	Shepperton	* TQ0867
Putney Heath	† TQ2373	Runfold Sand Pits	SU8747	Shere	TQ0747
Puttenden Manor	TQ4045	Runnymede	TQ0072	Shipley Bridge	TQ3040
Puttenham Common	SU9145	Rush Mere, Wimbledon		Shirley	† TQ3565
Pyrford Common	TQ0259	Common	† TQ2370	Shirley Hills – see Addington	
Pyrford Golf Course	TQ0559	Rushett Farm, Chessington		Hills	
Queen Elizabeth II			† TQ1760	Shoelands Farm	TQ9147
Reservoir	TQ1267	Rushmoor	SU8740	Shortfield	SU8442
Queen Mary Gravel Pits	* TQ0570	Russ Hill	TQ2340	Shortwood Common,	
Queen Mary Reservoir	* TQ0769	Salfords	TQ2846	Staines	* TQ0471
Queen's Mere, Wimbledon		Sanderstead	† TQ3461	Shrike Hill, Thursley	
Common	† TQ2272	Sanderstead Downs	† TQ3461	Common	SU9040
Rampingdown Copse	SU9436	Sanderstead Pond	† TQ3461	Sickle Mill Pond,	
Ranelagh Park – Barn Elms Park?		Sandhills, Brook	SU9338	Haslemere	SU9031
Ranmore Common	TQ1451	Sandown Park Race		Sidlow Bridge	TQ2547
Ravensbury Park	† TQ2668	Course	TQ1465	Sidney Wood	TQ0234
Ravenscourt Park	† TQ2279	Sands Golf Course	SU8846	Silent Pool, Shere	TQ0648
Raynes Park	† TQ2368	Savill Garden, Windsor Great		Silkmill Pond, Thursley	SU9140
Red House Reservoir	* TQ1170	Park	SU9770	Silvermere	TQ0860
Reddings Wood,		Scratch Wood,		Slyfield, Cobham	TQ1159
Tandridge	TQ3850	Woodmansterne	TQ2759	Slyfield, Guildford	SU9952
Redhill	TQ2850	Seale	SU8947	Slynes (Slines) Green	TQ3757
Redhill Aerodrome	TQ3047	Seale Rubbish Tip	SU8947	Smallfield	TQ3142

Smart's Heath, Worplesdon	SU9855	Sunbury Lock	TQ1168	Tongham Gravel Pit	SU8849
Smithwood Common	TQ0541	Sunningdale	SU9567	Tooting	† TQ2770
Snowdenham	TQ0044	Surbiton	† TQ1867	Tooting Graveney	† TQ2671
Snoxhall Playing Fields	TQ0238	Surrey Canal/Docks	† TQ3679	Tooting/Tooting Bec Common	† TQ2972
South Croydon	† TQ3263	Sutton	† TQ2564	Tower Bridge	† TQ3380
South Godstone	TQ3748	Sutton Green	TQ0054	Trevereux, Limpsfield	TQ4350
South Norwood Country Park	† TQ3568	Sutton Place, Guildford	TQ1359	Triggs Lock, Send	TQ0154
		Swaynesland	TQ4250	Truxford	SU8940
South Norwood Hill	† TQ3469	Sweetwater, Witley	SU9538	Tugley Wood	SU9833
South Norwood Lake	† TQ3469	Sydenham	† TQ3571	Tulse Hill	† TQ3173
South Norwood Sewage Works – see Country Park		Sydenham Common	† TQ3472	Turf Hill	SU9361
		Sydenham Hill	† TQ3372	Tythebarns Farm, Ripley	TQ0454
South Nutfield	TQ3049	Tadworth	TQ2356	Unstead Lock	SU9945
South Park	TQ3548	Tandridge	TQ3750	Unstead Sewage Farm	SU9945
Southwark	† TQ3180	Tankersford Common	SU8642	Unsted Wood	SU9944
Speynes Mere	TQ3053	Tate Modern	† TQ3180	Upper Halliford	* TQ0968
Spout Wood, Stanwell	* TQ0475	Tatsfield	TQ4157	Upper Norwood	† TQ3269
St Ann's Hill, Chertsey	TQ0367	Tattenham Corner	TQ2258	Vachery Pond	TQ0737
St Ann's Lake	TQ0268	Teddington Lock/Weir	† TQ1671	Vann Hill	SU9738
St Catherine's, Guildford	SU9948	Telegraph Hill, Claygate	TQ1564	Vann Lake	TQ1539
St George's Hill, Weybridge	TQ0862	Tenningshook Wood	TQ0945	Vauxhall	† TQ3078
		Thames Ditton	† TQ1667	Vauxhall Bridge	† TQ3078
St Martha's, Guildford	TQ0248	Thames Ditton Reservoirs	† TQ1767	Virginia Water	SU9968
St Saviour's Creek	† TQ3479			Virginia Water Lake	SU9768
St Thomas's Hospital	† TQ3079	The Borough	† TQ3279	Waddon	† TQ3065
Staffhurst Wood	TQ4148	The Devil's Jumps	SU8639	Waddon Ponds	† TQ3065
Staines Moor	* TQ0373	The Flashes, Churt	SU8640	Wallington	† TQ2964
Staines Reservoirs	* TQ0573	The Moors	TQ2951	Wallington Green	† TQ2962
Stamford Green Pond, Epsom	TQ1960	The Sands	SU8846	Wallis Wood	TQ1238
		Thornycroft, Stoke Park	TQ0051	Walsham Lock, Pyrford	TQ0557
Stanford Common	SU9454	Thorpe	TQ0268	Walton Bridge	TQ0966
Stanley Pool, Pirbright	SU9256	Thorpe Gravel Pits	TQ0468	Walton Downs	TQ2157
Stanners Hill	TQ0063	Thorpe Water Park	TQ0368	Walton Heath	TQ2354
Stanwell Moor	* TQ0474	Thunderfield Castle	TQ3042	Walton Reservoirs	TQ1268
Stanwell Moor Gravel Pits	* TQ0374	Thundry Meadows SWT Reserve	SU9844	Walton Rubbish Dump	TQ1067
				Walton-on-Thames	TQ1165
Stockbridge Pond	SU8742	Thursley Common	SU9040	Walton-on-Thames Sewage Farm	TQ1067
Stoke D'Abernon	TQ1358	Thursley Lake, Witley Park	SU9239		
Stoke Lake, Guildford	TQ0051			Walton-on-the- Hill	TQ2255
Stoke Park, Guildford	TQ0050	Thursley National Nature Reserve	SU9040	Wanborough	SU9348
Stoke Water Meadows, Guildford	TQ0051			Wandle Valley Nature Park	† TQ2671
		Thursley village	SU9039		
Stonehill	TQ0063	Tice's Meadow	SU8748	Wandle Valley Sewage Works – see Nature Park	
Stoneleigh	TQ2264	Tilburstow Hill	TQ3450		
Stow Coppice, Tandridge	TQ3749	Tilford	SU8743	Wandsworth Common	† TQ2774
Streatham	† TQ3071	Tilhill Nurseries	SU8641	Wandsworth Creek	† TQ2575
Streatham Common	† TQ3070	Tillingdown, Caterham	† TQ3455	Wandsworth Park	† TQ2475
Stringer's Common	SU9853	Titsey	TQ4055	Warlingham	TQ3558
Sugden Road	† TQ1766	Titsey Wood	TQ4254	Warren Barn Farm	† TQ3757
Sunbury	* TQ0068	Tolt Copse, Ellens Green	TQ0935	Warren Mere	SU9141
		Tolworth	† TQ1965	Waterloo Bridge	† TQ3080
		Tomlins Pond, Frimley	SU8858		

Waterloo Pond, Chilworth	White Hill Test Track SU9061	Wisley Sewage Farm TQ0559
TQ0448	Whitehill Roughets TQ3352	Wisley Village TQ0659
Watermeads, Mitcham † TQ2767	Whitgift Centre,	Witley Common SU9240
Waverley Abbey SU8645	Croydon † TQ3265	Witley Park SU9239
Weare Street TQ1639	Whitmoor Common SU8953	Woking TQ0058
Weatherhill TQ3043	Whitmoor Pond SU9954	Woldingham TQ3757
Wentworth SU9766	Whitmore Vale SU8636	Wonersh/Wonersh Park TQ0145
Wentworth Lake SU9767	Whyteleafe † TQ3358	Wood Street SU9551
West Byfleet TQ0460	Wick Pond, Windsor	Woodham, near Woking TQ0462
West End Common,	Great Park SU9869	Woodmansterne TQ2759
Esher TQ1263	Will Reeds, Thursley SU9040	Worcester Park † TQ2266
West Ewell TQ2163	Willinghurst TQ0543	Worcester Park Sewage
West Horsley TQ0753	Willinghurst Lake TQ0542	Farm † TQ2366
West Molesey TQ1368	Willow Park SU8851	Wormley SU9538
West Norwood † TQ3272	Wimbledon Common † TQ2472	Wormley Hill SU9538
Westcott TQ1448	Wimbledon Park Lake † TQ2472	Worms Heath TQ3757
Westend Common,	Windlesham SU9363	Worplesdon SU9653
Pirbright SU9260	Windsor Great Park SU9769	Wotton TQ1247
Westhumble TQ1651	Winkworth Arboretum SU9941	Wray Common TQ2650
Westminster Bridge † TQ3079	Winterdown Woods TQ1262	Wray Park (now built
Weybridge TQ0764	Winterfold TQ0643	over) TQ2651
Weybridge Sewage Farm – see	Winterfold Heath TQ0642	Wraysbury Reservoir * TQ0274
next	Wire Mill Lake TQ3641	Wrecclesham Floods SU8245
Weybridge Water Pollution	Wishmoor Bottom SU8762	Wrecclesham Sand Pits SU8144
Works TQ0663	Wisley Airfield TQ0757	Wyke Common SU9152
Whipley Manor TQ0240	Wisley Common TQ0758	Yagden Hill SU8842
White Downs TQ1249	Wisley RHS Gardens TQ0657	

Moat Pond   *John Reaney*

Index of Birds

Spelthorne

RESERVOIRS:
WRAYSBURY
STAINES
KING GEORGE VI

PERRY OAKS

QUEEN MARY
RESERVOIR

VIRGINIA WATER

THORPE

Shepperton

Chertsey

Addlestone

CHOBHAM
COMMON

OLDDEAN
COMMON

ESł
CO

Bisley

Horsell

Camberley

WISLEY
COMMON

PIRBRIGHT
RANGES

Woking

FRIMLEY GP

Pirbright

Send

PAPERCOURT GP

ASH RANGES

STOKE

Guildford

Puttenham

Abinger

Farnham

CUTT MILL

UNSTEAD

Wrecclesham

WINTERFOLD HEAT

Elstead

Godalming

FRENSHAM PONDS

Ewhurst

COMMONS:
HANKLEY
THURSLEY
OCKLEY
MILFORD

Witley

Cranleigh

VACHERY

HINDHEAD COMMON

Haslemere

5 km